W9-ANP-427

The Crowell Geography Series

GEORGE T. RENNER, Editor

OUTSIDE READINGS IN GEOGRAPHY

Outside Readings in GEOGRAPHY

FRED E. DOHRS
Assistant Professor of Geography
Wayne University

LAWRENCE M. SOMMERS
Professor of Geography and
Head of the Department of Geography
Michigan State University

DONALD R. PETTERSON
Assistant Professor of Geography
Northwestern University

New York · 1961
THOMAS Y. CROWELL COMPANY

Library of Congress Catalog Card Number 55-7300

FIRST PRINTING, JANUARY, 1955
SECOND PRINTING, JULY, 1955
THIRD PRINTING, FEBRUARY, 1958
FOURTH PRINTING, JULY, 1961
FIFTH PRINTING, JUNE, 1963

MANUFACTURED IN THE UNITED STATES OF AMERICA
BY THE VAIL-BALLOU PRESS, INC., BINGHAMTON, N.Y.

Editor's Foreword

DURING THE PAST few decades, the teaching of geography has been established in nearly all American colleges and universities. Instruction in this important field of knowledge is, therefore, now being done under widely differing conditions and for many different purposes. As a consequence, new types of educational instruments must be designed to meet these varied conditions and purposes.

Through this same period the literature of geography has increased from a few books and an occasional magazine article to a veritable flood of writings—scientific, educational, professional, semi-popular, and popular. Today, few if any persons can hope to keep abreast of this literary output—let alone to familiarize themselves with what has previously been published. The college student usually fails, therefore, to have any real contact with either the past or the current literature of geography. One much-needed new educational instrument in geography is a book of readings, which will make available under one cover a wide range of selections from this literature.

Accordingly, the editors have prepared this volume. It includes more than eighty separate writings from almost as many authors—American, Canadian, British, French, Indian, and Australian. These have been chosen in such manner as to render them useful in connection with several kinds of introductory courses. Each individual reading has been provided with headnote, footnote, and brief biographical information about the author. The readings are grouped into twelve chapters, each representing a major area of interest to geographers.

The aims of this volume are several:

1. To assemble some of the "classics" in geography that have appeared from time to time during the past few decades, and that would otherwise be lost to the average pupil.

2. To render available collateral materials that will complement various standard texts.

3. To enable students, where it is deemed desirable for them to do so, to approach the study of geography through synthesis of discrete materials rather than through more commonly used channels.

4. To enrich courses of instruction in geography by providing supplementary materials.

5. To provide the student indirect contact with many of the major contributors to geography and adjacent fields.

6. To stimulate the student to do further reading in the literature of geography.

7. To relieve the burden placed upon library facilities by the recent great increase in college enrollments.

The educational and cultural virtues of this volume stem primarily from the works of the original authors that have been incorporated into its contents, and secondarily from the efforts of the special editors who have selected, compiled, arranged, and annotated these materials so as to put them into useful educational form.

It is with considerable pleasure that the publisher presents this unique volume to the students and teachers of geography everywhere in America.

GEORGE T. RENNER, Editor
The Crowell Geography Series

Preface

In recent years a serious problem in respect to outside reading assignments has plagued college teachers, especially those who have large lower-division classes. Rapidly increasing enrollments coupled with inadequate financial support to maintain library facilities have made extensive use of the library for these readings difficult, if not impossible. As a further handicap in the case of geography, course offerings and, in consequence, the demand for supplementary reading materials have greatly increased since World War II.

We have prepared this book of readings to meet these developments. With it each student in an introductory geography course can enjoy the advantage of owning a volume of carefully selected readings that provides maximum coverage at a minimum cost.

In making our choices we kept one major objective before us. That was to provide a collection that complements the generalizations and concepts of the basic text through specific examples illustrating the exceptional as well as the typical. Our stress on this goal has provided a book that enhances student understanding, interest, and motivation.

Our primary criteria in the selection of articles were interest, information, and readability. This standard meant seeking articles with a high level of scholarship, yet with a vocabulary suited to the intended readers (some material originally written for professional geographers has been edited).

The readings are organized according to the systematic approach to introductory geography. Emphasis is given to both the physical and the human aspects of the subject. The great variety of articles, which reflects the range of sources from which they were drawn, gives the instructor the opportunity to select those readings that meet his particular needs. As indicated in the tables correlating the articles with the appropriate chapters in a number of standard texts, the book is adaptable for courses of varying length and intensity and for courses of a regional, economic, or political nature.

In order to provide reading material in the most useful and convenient form for students and teachers, the following features are included:

1. *Chapter introductions.* The brief introduction at the beginning of each chapter indicates the breadth and scope of the subject of that chapter and its place within the larger field of geography.

2. *Headnotes.* The short paragraph introducing each selection relates the material in the selection to the discussion in the basic text, to other selections in the chapter, and to the field of geography generally.

3. *Biographical notes.* The biographical note, which appears as part of the bibliographical footnote on the opening page of each selection, documents the scientific, scholarly, or other qualifications of the writer. Taken together these notes give some idea of the wealth and variety of experience the authors represent as a group.

4. *Correlation tables.* Suggestions for using the selections in the book with several leading recent textbooks in geography are included in correlation tables on pages xvii–xxii.

5. *Index.* The index for this volume has been prepared for convenience in locating specific topics that normally appear in standard introductory geography textbooks.

The editors gratefully acknowledge the cooperation of all authors and publishers whose works are reproduced in the book. Deep appreciation is due colleagues and others who gave valuable encouragement and suggestions. Finally, thanks are extended to Mrs. Janet Petterson and Mrs. Marjorie Sommers for assistance in various stages of the project.

F. E. D.
L. M. S.
D. R. P.

Contents

Figures

Bengtson and Van Royen
Fundamentals of Economic Geography, 3rd ed.
Prentice-Hall, 1950

Ch. nos.	*Related articles*
1	1–4, 56
2	10, 35, 73–78
3	18–27
4	10, 28, 30, 35–37, 43–49
5	9–11, 13–17
6	10, 36
7	10, 31, 38–40
8	10, 31, 38–40, 78
9	27, 33, 38, 42
10	11, 21, 38, 44
11	11, 16, 32, 38, 41, 54
12	9, 11, 34, 43, 68, 69
13	10, 14, 29, 33, 42–45
14	9–11, 14, 29, 33, 34, 42–45, 68, 69
15	30, 32, 34, 51
16	13, 22, 51
17	46–48, 76
18	49
19	37, 54
20	49, 56, 66
21	50, 52, 67
22	53
23	43, 44
24	50, 51
25	59
26	55, 59
27	50, 57, 61, 62, 64, 65, 75, 83, 84
28	60, 62, 63, 75
29	67, 68, 70–72
30	67, 73, 80, 83, 84

Davis
The Earth and Man
Macmillan, 1948

Ch. nos.	*Related articles*	*Ch. nos.*	*Related articles*
1	1–5	42	6–8
2	74	43	6
3	10, 74, 77	44	7
4	56	45	6
5	10, 35, 67, 73	46	—
6	10, 18, 28, 35, 43	47	6, 8
7	17, 18, 21, 22, 25	48	—
8	23, 30, 32	49	—
9	36, 38, 42, 49, 51, 54, 55	50	—
10	35–38, 45	51	12, 15
11	10, 11, 13	52	36
12	10, 11, 15	53	—
13	11, 14, 15		
14	9, 11, 15, 16		
15	9, 12, 14, 17		
16	35–37		
17	24, 44, 71		
18	43, 44		
19	43–45		
20	43–45		
21	24, 43, 44		
22	14, 18, 22, 24, 29, 38, 54		
23	20, 26, 27, 51, 55, 70		
24	49, 51, 53, 55		
25	19, 25, 46		
26	28, 30, 36, 42		
27	67, 79, 80		
28	10, 13, 38		
29	14, 27, 29, 38, 42		
30	10, 18, 38, 39, 42		
31	38, 79		
32	14, 36–38, 41, 45		
33	38, 40, 78		
34	30–32, 34, 39		
35	49–55		
36	46–48, 76		
37	67–69, 70–72		
38	57–69		
39	74–78		
40	73, 80, 82		
41	6		

Durand *World Geography* Holt, 1954	
Ch. nos.	*Related articles*
1	18–27
2	14, 22, 29, 37–39, 41, 79
3	—
4	41, 51, 78
5	27, 55, 78
6	20, 26, 27
7	9–17, 28–34, 35–42
8	39
9	10, 11, 38–40, 64
10	10, 16, 20, 31, 40, 64, 65, 78
11	10, 27, 33, 38, 45
12	33, 39, 40
13	9, 11, 12, 14, 16, 17, 24, 29, 32, 36, 83
14	21, 26, 28, 32, 38, 44
15	16, 41, 54
16	9, 30, 48, 76
17	9, 14, 24, 29, 36, 44, 60, 61, 62, 71, 77, 83, 84
18	29, 33, 36
19	30, 51, 69
20	26
21	13, 22, 47
22	49–55, 59–62
23	73–78
24	1–8, 79–84, Appendix

Finch and Trewartha *Elements of Geography* McGraw-Hill, 1949	
Ch. nos.	*Related articles*
1	1–5, Appendix
2	4–8
3	14
4	9, 11, 12, 16
5	9, 11–16
6	9, 11, 12, 14–16, 31
7	10, 11, 17, 30, 38–40
8	10, 27, 33, 38, 45
9	9, 33, 41, 54, 60–63, 76
10	14, 29, 34, 37, 43, 44, 83
11	10, 13, 22, 30, 38, 47, 48, 51, 79, 84
12	18–21, 25
13	18, 22–25
14	22, 24, 41
15	24, 41, 54
16	22, 76, 83
17	27, 33, 38, 45
18	22, 24, 54, 75
19	25, 55, 78
20	41, 51, 78
21	20, 26, 27
22	23, 24, 43–48
23	28–34, 36, 39, 42, 46–48
24	35–42
25	35–42
26	49, 52, 53, 60–62
27	49–51, 54, 55, 59–62
28	73–78
29	74–78
30	35–42
31	50, 56–66
32	67–72
33	79–84

Freeman and Raup *Essentials of Geography* McGraw-Hill, 1949	
Ch. nos.	*Related articles*
1	1–5, 82, Appendix
2	6–8
3	15
4	9, 11, 12, 14, 16
5	17, 48, 79
6	28–34, 36, 39, 42, 46–48
7	10, 11, 17, 30, 38–40
8	10, 27, 33, 38, 45
9	9, 11, 14, 21, 24, 26, 29, 32, 37, 38, 41, 44, 68, 79, 83, 84
10	10, 13, 22, 30, 38, 47, 48, 51, 79, 84
11	26, 30–34, 39–41
12	18–27
13	14, 22, 27, 29, 37–39, 41, 55 77, 79
14	20, 26, 27, 41, 51, 78
15	25, 46–48, 67
16	22, 24, 46–48, 75, 76, 81
17	23, 35–42
18	28, 35–42
19	49–55, 59, 60–62
20	24, 25, 43–48
21	50, 56–66
22	67–72
23	38, 73–78
24	73–78
25	79–84
26	19, 69, 82–84

Correlation with Representative Texts—*continued*

Huntington and Shaw, *Principles of Human Geography*, 6th ed. Wiley, 1951	
Ch. nos.	*Related articles*
1	1–5
2	—
3	10, 17, 19
4	6–8
5	10, 11, 17
6	9–17
7	18, 19, 20, 21, 70–72, 79
8	26, 27, 30, 32, 51
9	11, 15, 16, 17, 46–48, 67, 74–76, 80
10	43–45, 71
11	35–37
12	49–51
13	52, 53, 56, 61, 66
14	10, 13, 17
15	28, 33
16	10, 31, 38–40, 78
17	38–40, 65
18	10, 13, 33, 38, 42, 51
19	32, 38, 41
20	27, 33, 40, 43–45
21	9, 11, 12, 14, 15, 17, 34, 36, 37, 48, 50, 56, 60–63
22	14, 17, 20, 23, 42, 48
23	10, 13, 17, 30, 37, 48, 79
24	26, 64, 66, 79–81
25	79–81, 83, 84
26	56, 70, 72, 80, 84
27	38, 44, 57, 64, 69, 80, 83
28	38, 52, 60–63, 71, 76
29	27, 38, 42, 55, 65, 78, 79

James, *A Geography of Man* Ginn, 1949	
Ch. nos.	*Related articles*
1	1–3, 18, 73, 77, 82–84, Appendix
2	10, 27, 33, 38, 45
3	10, 11, 17, 30, 38–40, 64, 65, 78
4	21, 26, 28, 30, 33, 38, 42
5	30–35, 37, 41, 49–55, 57–64, 66, 68, 69, 70, 71, 74–76, 79, 83, 84
6	14, 29, 31, 36, 38, 41, 42
7	10, 30, 48, 51, 69
8	13, 22, 46–48, 84
9	20, 26, 27
10	49–84

Jones and Darkenwald, *Economic Geography*, 2nd ed. Macmillan, 1954	
Ch. nos.	*Related articles*
1	1–4, 56, Appendix
2	10, 13, 73–78
3	10, 13, 22, 38, 39
4	—
5	46–48, 76
6	30, 32, 38, 39
7	26, 30–34, 38, 39, 41, 84
8	—
9	13, 27, 38, 42
10	29, 36, 38, 42
11	10, 28, 30, 38, 39
12	39, 40
13	39, 41, 63
14	38, 78
15	26, 33, 38, 42
16	37
17	37
18	38
19	41, 42
20	41
21	49
22	55
23	37, 54, 58
24	59
25	50, 51, 61, 62, 84
26	52, 61, 84
27	53, 84
28	43, 44
29	56, 57, 64–66, 84
30	50, 60–62, 84
31	61, 62
32	—
33	58–61
34	60, 63, 65
35	37
36	70–73, 84
37	67–69

Kendall, Glendinning, and MacFadden *Introduction to Geography* Harcourt, Brace, 1951		Pearcy, Fifield and Associates *World Political Geography* Crowell, 1948		Renner, Durand, White, and Gibson *World Economic Geography* Crowell, 1951	
Ch. nos.	*Related articles*	*Ch. nos.*	*Related articles*	*Ch. nos.*	*Related articles*
1	1–5	1	1, 2, 80	1	1–4, Appendix
2	—	2	80, 81	2	35, 49, 73
3	6–8	3	79–81	3	37, 39, 56
4	18, 19	4	9, 35, 43, 44, 50, 57, 72, 80, 83	4	10, 11, 38–40, 64
5	9, 10, 12, 15, 17	5	64, 70, 80, 83	5	10, 16, 20, 31, 40, 64, 65, 78
6	11, 48	6	53, 79, 84	6	10, 27, 33, 38, 45
7	10, 11, 16, 17, 27, 33, 38–40, 45	7	60, 67, 73, 79	7	16, 41, 54
8	9, 13, 14, 15, 22, 24, 26, 27, 36, 37, 38, 41, 47, 51	8	22, 48, 50, 52, 63	8	21, 26, 28, 32, 38, 44
9	10, 35, 73	9	51, 55, 65, 67, 69	9	9, 30, 48, 76
10	18, 19	10	50, 60, 61, 62, 71	10	41, 83
11	20, 26, 27, 29, 38, 41, 51	11	60, 62, 71	11	30, 35, 51, 75, 83, 84
12	20–22, 24, 25	12	60, 62, 71	12	10, 28, 29, 37, 38, 45, 83–84
13	43, 44, 45, 46, 48	13	60, 71	13	13, 22, 47, 48
14	28, 33	14	38, 60	14	26, 30–34, 39–41
15	23, 35–37, 66	15	26, 60	15	46–48, 76
16	49, 52, 53	16	47, 60, 76	16	46–48, 67, 80
17	50, 51, 61, 62	17	60, 84	17	49
18	54, 55, 58, 61	18	60, 84	18	49, 52, 61
19	4	19	53, 60, 84	19	49, 53, 66
20	30, 73, 78, 79	20	79	20	49–51, 59
21	74–78	21	27, 38	21	50, 57, 60-62, 84
22	10, 56	22	38	22	51, 54, 55, 59
23	56, 61, 62, 63, 83, 84	23	17, 65, 78	23	50, 51, 58, 59
24	38–42	24	67, 73, 79	24	37, 54, 55
25	49–52, 55	25	38, 42	25	58–61
26	28, 30, 32, 34, 39, 41	26	79	26	49, 56, 57, 62, 63, 84
27	46, 47, 48	27	27, 38, 39	27	50, 57, 59–62, 84
28	67–69, 70–72	28	69, 79	28	58
29	1, 3, 82–84	29	38, 39, 46	29	60, 63, 65
30	2, 30, 79–83	30	39, 40	30	—
		31	40, 80	31	41
		32	30, 38, 39, 64	32	56, 57, 69, 73, 84
		33	42, 64	33	56, 67–69, 75
		34	64	34	74, 75
		35	79–81	35	71
		36	62, 67	36	70, 84
		37	73, 77, 78	37	67, 80
		38	70, 72, 79	38	73
		39	35, 46, 67, 73, 79–81	39	56, 67–69

Russell and Kniffen *Culture Worlds* Macmillan, 1951				Staats and Harding *Elements of World Geography,* 2nd ed. Van Nostrand, 1953	
Ch. nos.	*Related articles*	*Ch. nos.*	*Related articles*	*Ch. nos.*	*Related articles*
1	1–4	45	—	1	1–5
2	10, 13, 22, 51	46	39	2	6, 19
3	13, 22, 47	47	39	3	6–8
4	19, 70	48	—	4	—
5	11	49	—	5	10, 12
6	60	50	—	6	11, 15, 16
7	52	51	9, 11, 12, 14, 18, 21,	7	10, 17
8	63		28, 29, 43	8	10, 11, 13, 16, 17, 27,
9	76	52	84		33, 38–40, 45
10	60	53	22, 34, 44, 49, 51, 57,	9	9, 10, 11, 12, 14, 30,
11	38, 60		58, 59, 69, 75		33, 38, 41, 48
12	38	54	24, 37, 38, 44, 54, 68	10	10, 13, 22, 38, 51
13	61, 62, 71	55	14, 29, 33, 36, 38	11	14, 18, 19, 20, 21, 26,
14	79	56	16, 20, 30, 38, 39, 40,		29, 34
15	84		64	12	22, 27, 31, 51, 55
16	53, 84	57	31, 38, 39, 64, 70	13	28, 35–38, 45
17	53, 84			14	14, 29, 35, 36
18	—			15	49–55, 61, 66
19	60			16	22, 23, 24, 43
20	38, 60			17	43, 44, 70
21	38, 60			18	19, 46, 47
22	38, 60			19	69, 74, 76, 81
23	38, 60			20	2, 42, 56, 82
24	26, 38, 60				
25	38, 60				
26	62, 71				
27	10, 33				
28	27, 38				
29	27				
30	—				
31	—				
32	77, 79				
33	79				
34	—				
35	27				
36	27, 70				
37	—				
38	38, 39				
39	55				
40	11, 77, 79				
41	78				
42	65				
43	—				
44	—				

Correlation with Representative Texts—*concluded*

Strahler, *Physical Geography*, Wiley, 1951

Ch. nos.	*Related articles*
1	1–5, Appendix
2	6, 7
3	—
4	—
5	—
6	6, 7
7	6–8
8	18, 19
9	—
10	18, 22–24
11	22, 24, 54
12	22
13	22
14	—
15	27
16	22, 41, 54
17	18
18	—
19	20, 51
20	9, 11, 12, 14–16
21	9, 11, 12, 14–16, 31
22	9, 11, 12, 14, 16
23	—
24	10, 17, 20, 27, 31, 38, 40, 64, 65, 78
25	9, 11, 14, 21, 24, 26, 29, 32, 37, 38, 41, 44, 68, 77, 83, 84
26	10, 13, 22, 30, 38, 47, 48, 51, 79, 84
27	35–42
28	35–42

White and Renner, *Human Geography*, Appleton-Century-Crofts, 1948

Ch. nos.	*Related articles*
1	1–4
2	5–8
3	9–12, 15
4	10, 11, 30, 31, 38–40
5	10, 27, 33, 45
6	10, 17, 38, 40, 77
7	36, 38
8	21, 38
9	24, 32, 38, 41
10	33, 37
11	9, 15, 24, 34, 36, 37
12	9, 14, 36
13	9, 15, 17, 60
14	10, 13, 22, 51
15	10, 13, 47
16	28, 29, 30, 31
17	41, 48
18	—
19	18, 19
20	41, 42, 79
21	20, 26, 27
22	41
23	27, 51
24	35, 36, 37
25	35, 36, 37
26	49
27	54, 58
28	50, 51, 55, 59
29	52, 53, 61
30	43, 44, 45
31	44, 45
32	46–48
33	50, 56, 69, 79, 81, 83, 84
34	68, 74, 80, 82, 84
35	5, 6, 8
36	72, 76, 79–82
37	2, 57, 70, 75, 80, 81, 84
38	42, 73
39	73, 74, 77, 78, 84
40	1, 2, 3, 82
41	38, 82–84
42	38, 39, 45, 83, 84

OUTSIDE READINGS
IN
GEOGRAPHY

CHAPTER ONE

The Scope and Tools of Geography

GEOGRAPHY CONCERNS ITSELF with the earth, and, as the origin of the word indicates (*ge,* earth; *graphein,* to write), it has both a descriptive and analytical character. But geography connotes many things to many people, and among the writings of leading geographers, past and present, one finds the philosophy, the scope, the limits, and the approach of American geographical thinking.

Geography is best studied in the field, that is, where land, area, or region in its physical and cultural complex can be seen, felt, and understood directly. Man—students particularly—can hardly visit all of the earth, even in a lifetime. Tools are therefore necessary to bring the whole land—the landscape—into a "seeable" size, and thereby make the products of the geographer's field work available and understandable to one another and to all other men. Among the tools of geography, none is of greater importance than the map. It is the key to an understanding of space up on the earth's surface; its graphic portrayal of spatial distributions over the earth reveals to the trained observer many physical and cultural similarities and differences, and it suggests to him reasons why these exist. Comprehension of the significance of these similarities and differences leads to regional geographical understanding of small areas as well as of the world as a whole.

The geographer's philosophy and viewpoint, and a knowledge of the methodology and tools of geographical work, provide the bases for studying specific problems within the field of geography.

1. *The Circumference of Geography* *

Geography has been called the mother of sciences, and there is little doubt that geographers make use of materials and methods of nearly all other sciences, both physical and social. Fenneman, in this article and in the illustration, shows effectively not only the scope of geographical material, but also the relationship of geography to the many other fields from which it draws much of its materials. This scope indicates the unique field of the geographer and classifies geography as the "correlative" science.

It is a peculiarity of geography to be always discussing and debating its own content—as though a society were to be organized for the sole purpose of finding out what the organization was for. This is not said by way of criticism; indeed this very paper is a continuation of the same discussion. The situation is, however, unique and can scarcely fail to be remarked by on-lookers from other sciences, who have no such doubts as to what their subjects are about.

The basis of this constant concern is not greed but *fear*. Geography wages no aggressive wars and seems to covet no new territory. In certain quarters it bristles with defense; but it is mainly concerned with purging its own house rather than spreading its borders. To rule out "what is not geography" would seem from the discussions to be much more important than to find and claim geography where it has been passing under other names. The constant apprehension is that by admitting alien subjects we shall sooner or later be absorbed by a foreign power and lose our identity.

It is probably unnecessary to point out that this is purely an American attitude. Geography of the European brand has no such concern for its own purity or fear of being absorbed. Scholarly geographic treatises from Europe may contain long lists of botanical names, or geological descriptions, or chapters which might be transferred bodily to monographs on economics or history.

To many American geographers this would seem like betraying their cause and selling their birthright. There is an implied dread that if geography accepts the work and uses the language of other sciences, geography itself will be dismembered and its remains be divided among

* Reprinted from Nevin M. Fenneman, "The Circumference of Geography," *Annals of the Association of American Geographers,* Vol. 9 (1919), pp. 3–11. By permission.

The author (1866–1945) was one of the outstanding physiographers in American geography. His two major works, *Physiography of the Eastern United States* and *Physiography of the Western United States,* are standard classics of physiographic literature.

its competitors. It is worth while to consider this possibility, and a rough plan is here submitted for a partition of geography's domain.

Suppose geography were dead, what would be left?

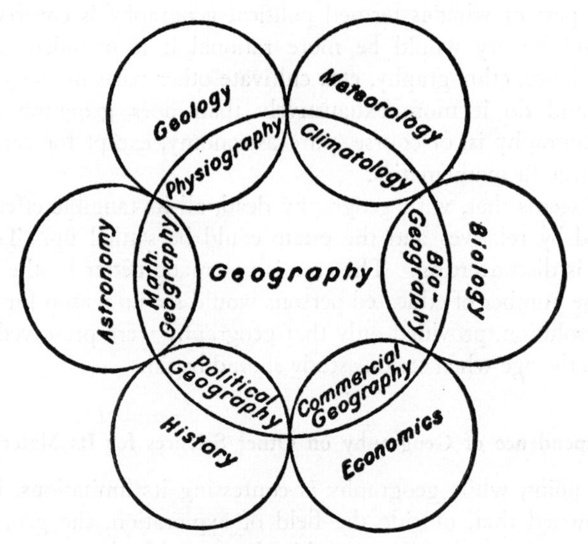

FIGURE I

This diagram expresses the fundamental conception that sciences overlap and that each one of the specialized phases of geography belongs equally to some other science. Such a diagram will be helpful if not construed too strictly. In a loose way the central residual part of the circle may represent regional geography.

Proposed Partition of Geography's Domain

Geology might easily take over topography, including its genetic treatment, which is physiography—in fact, has never given it up. So also botany has never relinquished plant geography and ecology. Zoölogy does not forget the distribution of animals. Agriculture is now so specialized and so firmly entrenched that crops and their distribution, and their relation to all manner of factors, are studied without concern for geography. Meteorology has official standing in all civilized countries and could take care of climatology if geography were bankrupt. Moreover, meteorology is commercially employed and so has the satisfaction of being good for something beside being merely good "to teach." So it is not afflicted with heart searchings regarding its own content. Mining is abundantly treated by geology and economics. The geographer only borrows from these, smooths out their details, and relates their results to something else. So economics deals with all other industries and with commerce, sometimes availing itself of the aid of chemistry and other sciences and always paying its respects to engineering.

A good part of what is termed political geography is covered also by history, and history would be more rational if it included still more. Political science, ethnography, etc., cultivate other parts of the geographical field and do it more exhaustively than does geography. Mathematical geography is, of course, pure astronomy, except for cartography, which is straight mathematics.

Thus it seems that, with geography dead, all its tangible effects would be claimed by relatives and the estate could be settled up. To say the least, this is disconcerting. The case is not made better by the reflection that a large number of educated persons would see no reason for objecting to such a solution, provided only that geography were preserved for children up to the age when serious study should begin.

Dependence of Geography on Other Sciences for Its Material

At this point, while geography is confessing its limitations, it may as well be owned that, outside the field of exploration, the geographer is mainly dependent on others for his data. Aside from mere location, direction, and distance, almost every fact that he employs belongs quite as much to some other science. In so far as that fact represents a class, the entire class of facts is much more apt to be known exhaustively by the other science than by geography. If the geographer speaks of soils, the agriculturist knows more; if he speaks of mines, the geologist knows more; if the reference be to manufacturing, the economist's knowledge is more thorough, or at least more exhaustive; if the subject is the people, the ethnographer, sociologist, or economist has first-hand knowledge, and the geographer is generally a borrower; and so through the list. With respect to all these data someone else is the original student, the "authority," and the geographer is merely "informed." How often is a geographer called in as an expert, and in what lines? This question is not intended to suggest a wholly negative answer, especially in view of the fact that three of our members are at present in Paris on the staff of the Peace Commission and nearly one-half of our members have been engaged in some expert capacity during the war. It does not follow, of course, that all these were engaged as geographers.

Concession has here been made freely because scholars outside of geography know these facts to be true, and there is nothing to be gained by claiming more than we can defend. If geography is not worth while despite these admissions, its business may as well be wound up.

Need of a Synthetic Areal Science

Reverting now to our former figure of speech, what has geography to say of its proposed demise, the division of its tangible effects and the settling of the estate? The obvious question arises: Would the decedent stay dead? If he were to come to life again, the situation would be embarrassing as between him and his relatives. Assuming that after his decease each of the branches named above as contributing to geography does its task well with respect to Russia, for instance, is there any likelihood that a craving would arise for a synthetic picture of the whole or a critical study of inter-relations? If so, who would satisfy this craving, and who could paint the picture, and what would be its value or standing among scholars?

To begin with, the first question answers itself. There is not one chance in a hundred that ten years would go by without a conscious craving, and an attempt to meet the craving, for a comprehensive view of the areal unit; and not one chance in a million that a century would elapse before such an interest would be the center of a new science. It matters no whit that all concrete data are already organized into other sciences, each more exhaustive and more critical with respect to its own data than the new science; it is absolutely certain that interest in the areal unit as such would clothe itself in appropriate form. It is the *areal relation*, after all, that makes geography.

To dwell on the kind of picture to be painted is not within our present purpose. In part it is a mere assembling of facts from diverse fields, facts joined together by the sole bond of a common locality. Whether we deride or apologize for this aggregation of facts, call it mere description, mere compilation, mere this or mere that (whatever it is, it is always "mere"), this humble task must still be performed before higher work is possible. Description bears the same relation to geography that narrative does to history. There can be no sound philosophy in either, based on faulty narrative or description.

But data thus assembled from diverse fields do not remain inert. They react on each other like chemicals to produce new compounds, that is, new truths. If the geographer knows less about soils and crops than the agriculturist, less of climate than the meteorologist, less of industry than the economist, less of society than the sociologist, he should still be supreme in this field of secondary compounds which cannot be formed by those who handle the data of one science only.

Value of "Scientific Trespass"

This point needs no elaboration here, but it is worth while recalling a passage from the presidential address of Dr. G. K. Gilbert before this association in this same city ten years ago. In explaining his choice of a subject, he announced himself as an advocate of the principle of "scientific trespass." "The specialist who forever stays at home and digs and delves within his private enclosure has all the advantages of intensive cultivation—except one; and the thing he misses is *cross-fertilization.* Trespass is one of the ways of securing cross-fertilization for his own crops, and of carrying cross-fertilization to the paddock he invades." Gilbert might have added that the geographer is, or should be, the great insect that carries pollen from field to field.

It is not intended here to concede that geography does not concern itself at all in the first-hand search for data. Geographers have, for example, done much for topography. Light on land forms has been by far the leading contribution of American geography (though it is a question whether anyone has contributed to this subject who was not first trained as a geologist).

Regional Geography the Core of the Science

Since geography *is to be,* it is quite right that physiography and climatology and the study of natural resources and even ecology should be of its family and bear its name, but the point here urged is that these are not the things which make geography *necessary* and *inevitable.* They may be necessary to it, but it is not necessary to them. All these might live with geography dead. All these and others belong to the regions of overlap, or ground common both to geography and to some other science, and, having two parents, would not be totally orphaned if one died; but the study of areas as before described belongs solely to geography and is, moreover, an only child. If these figures are somewhat mixed, it may be well to add in plain English that the one thing that is first, last, and always geography and nothing else, is the study of areas in their compositeness or complexity, that is *regional geography.*

It is not to be implied for one brief moment that physiography and the other branches named are not geography. They all become so when directed toward a geographic purpose. But without the touchstone of areal studies, there is nothing to make physiography other than geology, ecology other than botany, the study of natural resources other than economics.

There is, then, in geography this central core which is pure geography and nothing else, but there is much beyond this core which is none the less geography, though it belongs also to overlapping sciences. Here belong physiography and climatology, mathematical and commercial geography. Still, *the seeds are in the core, and the core is regional geography,* and this is why the subject propagates itself and maintains a separate existence. Without regional geography there is no reason why geography should be treated as a separate branch.

This emphasis on areal relations instead of on the "elements" which enter into such relations is, of course, not new. It comes to much the same thing in practice as Ritter's "home of man" or Davis's "physical element and human element" or this and that man's "responses" or Keltie's "science of distributions" or Hettner's *"dingliche Erfüllung der Erdräume"* (material filling of the earth's surface). Nor is it necessary, for the purpose here in hand, to point out that every element (topography, vegetation, climate, etc.) can be treated with reference to its distribution as well as with reference to its types. Such a treatment belongs to regional geography. It should, however, be noted that the study of the distribution of any one element by itself falls somewhat short of that *distinctive* geographic flavor which comes only when the various elements are studied in their inter-relations.

Cultivation of the Central Theme of Geography as a Safeguard Against Absorption by Other Sciences

Let us now go back to the fear above alluded to, that our subject is going to be swallowed by something else. Why this constant dread? The situation at once suggests that we live too much on our borders and not enough in the center. If we dwell mainly in systematic physiography, why should not geology claim us as a vassal? If we live largely in commercial geography, we are in similar danger from economics; and why should it not be so? We can go round the circle with the same logic. A narrowly political geography of boundaries and capitals never had any reason for a separate existence apart from history.

If we are concerned for our independent existence no amount of fortifying our border will take the place of developing our domain. What we need is more and better studies of regions in their entirety, their compositeness, their complexity, their inter-relations of physical, economic, racial, historic, and other factors. No other science can swallow that and live.

Unnecessary Discrimination Against Geologic Terms

An illustration of warring on the border instead of farming our domain is found in our curious boycott of terms from other sciences even when needed to make the truth clear. It is not permissible to say that the Cumberland Plateau is co-extensive with the strong "Carboniferous" rock (even where that is true) or that the High Plains (of Nebraska and Wyoming) end at the north with certain late "Tertiary" formations. It is permissible to say that the Cumberland Plateau is as broad as certain "resistant" rocks, but a term which would enable us to locate those rocks on the geologic map is taboo. True, the plateau border can be made out on very large-scale and awkward-to-handle topographic maps, but such maps at best are empirical, while the geologic map is interpretative. Since when has geography become so reactionary? Why must we secrete the geologic map as medieval priests secreted the Bible?

In the debates concerning this point there has been the most curious oversight of common usage. "Carboniferous" and its like are dubbed "geologic time names." Such they are indeed, sometimes, just as "Carboniferous" might be the name of a man or a horse or a brand of shoe polish—all as irrelevant as geologic time—but the term also designates a body of material (in this case a system of strata) and, more important still, on the geologic map it stands for an *area*. "Triassic" indeed connotes geologic time, but the same word designates certain areas on the geologic map of the eastern United States. "Portage" is not only a Devonian epoch but a belt on the geologic map of western New York, a belt that must be spoken of and cannot be designated with equal clearness under any other name. In this manner, much use is properly made of geologic terms, not because they are names of epochs but because they are names of areas that force themselves on our notice by certain peculiarities, thus leading to rational explanations. For three-fourths of the United States the geologic map is beyond comparison the one most valuable map for interpreting topographic contrasts between adjacent areas. Why must the words printed on it be classed as dangerous? The answer is: Geography is in danger of being swallowed, and self-preservation is nature's first law.

But "Cumberland Plateau" is a geographic term. How can the geologist say with impunity that the Carboniferous rocks are co-extensive with the Cumberland Plateau? Is not the danger mutual? Is his science not in danger of being swallowed by geography? The answer is: He is not afraid on that borderland where sciences overlap, because his own peculiar domain, which is not overlapped by geography or anything else, is too large and too well cultivated to admit of such fears. Our own safety lies in the same policy.

In our efforts toward self-preservation through purity, we have classed scientific terms as clean and unclean. The latter, such as Archean, Mesozoic, etc., cannot be touched without defilement. So we have built up a whole ceremonial by which we hope to be saved; but not so is salvation found. Its price to geography is no less than the diligent cultivating of its own peculiar field, the doing of something which the world needs and which no other science can do.

Animals have more than one way of evading the jaws of their competitors. The turtle is encased and puts up a good defense but is weak on the offensive. It is the same with the oyster. Others, like the squash bug, owe their safety to a peculiar flavor or odor. Still others specialize in modes of escape. But all such special provision belongs to the weak rather than to the strong. If geography will cultivate its own strength like the large mammals, it will not be necessary for it to encase itself like the oyster or cultivate the peculiar flavor of the squash bug to avoid being eaten.

In so far as there are frontiers between the sciences, let us have them ungarrisoned and let us have free trade. Let there be among sciences the same struggle for existence and law of survival that Darwin found among species. Then every field of study that answers to an intellectual need will have due recognition.

The Several Sciences Designated by Their Centers, Not by Their Circumferences

The subject announced for this brief address was "The Circumference of Geography." Presumably enough has been said to show that a science cannot be defined by its circumference. We may designate the center, and that should be enough. Everyone knows what botany is so long as we stay near the center, but where is its farthest limit? Far out in chemistry and medicine and geology, to say the least. And where is the limit of chemistry? Nowhere. Yet chemistry is not hard to define if it be designated by its center instead of by trying to draw its circumference. So the center of geography is the study of *areas,* generally, of course, in relation to man, for human habitation affords the most frequent utilitarian reason for such study and is also the center of the greatest intellectual interest; but the comprehensive study of an uninhabitable region would still be geography.

It is not only the right but the duty of every science to develop all parts of its domain, but it is none the less true of all, as of geography, that their right to separate existence depends on their cultivation of that part of their field which is not overlapped by others. Let there be no misunderstanding; there is no intention of assigning more dignity to one part of the field than to another or of asking any man to turn aside from that which interests him to something else. There is no more inherent worth in a center than in a border. But some of us have a philosophic interest in viewing relationships, and in asking why the whole range of knowledge has grouped itself around certain centers, and what it is that keeps those centers, which have received names, somewhat permanent, and what the advantage is in grouping knowledge around one center rather than another.

Moreover, all of us have a very practical interest in seeing that our own work should not suffer by isolation. We all want our own work to have the advantage of connections, and it is greatly to our interest that somebody should cultivate certain central fields even though most of us work on the borders. The logic of events, if no other logic, has brought together in this association a group of men of rather diverse interests. We are disposed to think that this is not a mere chance but that something fundamental underlies our union. Much that interests the individual does not concern the whole; but we feel more or less intelligently that there is profit in this intercourse and we want the relation to be closer. If there is a class of studies that will make our separate fields more important and more interesting to others and enable us to profit more by our association, we want to know what that class is and to encourage it.

Beside those who are, first and last, geographers, our association contains geologists, topographers, geodesists, meteorologists, ecologists, zoölogists, geophysicists, historians, and economists. The list is not intended to be complete. We have joined ourselves together evidently expecting to find a common interest. Where is the common ground on which such diversity can meet? Interest in places, areas, regions is the common bond.

This quasi-philosophical study of relationships is therefore important to those whose privilege it is to direct research or to organize education. If men in such position decide with eyes open that physiography and commercial geography and anthropogeography and the rest should not be merely geology, economics, ethnography, etc., they must act accordingly. The character of these subjects cannot be controlled by ceremonial law. The effective way is to set in the midst of them a great light, the light which comes alone from the comprehensive, rational, systematic study of regions.

2. *Geographical Interpretation* *

As is indicated in other selections, much of serious geographical work consists of scientific *and* intelligent interpretation of phenomena as they appear on the surface of the earth. Bowman, a leading political geographer as well as a most thorough field worker, stresses the importance of subjective interpretation in the field of geography. Although some people may contend that any observations subjectively interpreted cannot possibly be scientific, Bowman makes a convincing case for this personal element in geographical analysis.

By "geographical interpretation" I mean the interpretation of the elements of the environment by scientists who understand the origin and variability of those elements, the identification of crop and land-use achievements and possibilities which laboratory and field experimentation makes possible, and the play of related social processes which is involved in production and use by a rational society. Only in such an assemblage of interpreted facts, applied under agreed conditions by a dynamic society, can national policies avoid the hit-and-miss use that brings waste and destruction. Such an interpretation is old in concept but new in method. Thus the Inca rulers and their counselors were among the best empirical geographers the world has ever known. They recognized the broad regional differences of their severe environment, adapted crop levies to climatic possibilities, and even managed their forced migrations of settlers on the principle of acclimatization. They did not require the low-altitude man and the high-altitude man to change places. They learned the value of fallowing and of guano as a fertilizer. They experimented with new crops in likely situations. Their cosmography was feeble: they used the land and the sea without a systematic knowledge of the larger world outside. Their knowledge of landforms, hydraulics, and soil chemistry was empirical, whereas many of their social processes were experimental and rational. For us today the possibilities are greater than ever before, because of a diversified and powerful equipment of scientific principles, materials, and tools, and a scientific understanding of cause and effect in the play of forces only recently discovered.

. . . . .

* Isaiah Bowman, "Geographical Interpretation," from *Geographical Review,* Vol. 39, 1949, pp. 355–370; published by the American Geographical Society, New York.

The author (1878–1950) was a leader in both governmental and academic geography. He was Adviser to the United States Government at the Versailles Conference in 1919, and later, President of The Johns Hopkins University. His two most important books are *Geography in Relation to the Social Sciences,* and *The New World.*

What is the nature of geographical thinking? In part it is like all thinking; for although it may begin with accidental or systematic elements, or even the notional elements of reverie, it becomes *critical* in the end. This means that it sorts out importances and apparent relationships, answers the skepticisms that should arise in every trained mind, and searches relentlessly for cause-and-effect relations. Once we know what causes a thing, we can more rationally and quickly plan its control. Speed and sureness of control of agreed critical elements, such as public health, are more and more urgent as population density and complexity increase. Geographical thinking starts with an observation or an idea. All geographers recognize the indispensability of field observation. With his own specific training and a body of individual ideas every geographer is surprised on reaching what is to him new territory to find how much has gone unobserved and unrecorded. It may be a bit of local climatology that blazes with meaning, or a food source, or a social idea confirmed by centuries of experience in a specific environment. Questions begin. How much and where and why and what else *could be* are the whirling electrons of the curiosity atom in man? We single out *how much* for further comment.

Measurement, and if possible exact measurement, is one of the basic elements of most scientific research. In geography, maps are the commonest records of field measurements, reduced to conventional symbolism as a condition of comparative use. To the layman all maps look pretty much alike except as to color, but to the geographer original surveys, projection, scale, technique of construction, symbolism, and relative reliability are the first objects of study if the map is to be used as an instrument of interpretation. One of the conditions of Napoleon's military genius was its support by extraordinarily good maps. From a limited topographic point of view one would find the maps of his time still useful. He was a quick and skillful student of maps, and his geographical epigrams still have wide currency. He had what some would call today a "geopolitical" sense, but I dislike that pretentious word extremely and prefer the simple and customary phrase "geographical sense."

At one point Napoleon made a serious mistake in exercising his geographical sense. He had persuaded himself, perhaps by the brilliance of his victories and his almost uniform success whatever the terrain, that he could invade and conquer England. Like Hitler, he had to give up the scheme. He learned, as Hitler did, that even a narrow belt of water (it is little more than 20 miles wide at its narrowest) has a high strategic value. A narrow belt of salt water is a terrific obstacle, because one can neither wade through it nor improvise a bridge over it. One must counter its tidal vagaries and the caprice of wind and wave and cross it in full military panoply against resistance that has room for naval maneuver and fleets within call, as the captains of the Spanish Armada discovered. Hitler thought that his airplanes in our Air Age had overturned that centuries-old doctrine and diminished the value of the Channel so greatly that he could venture to ferry troops across it under an air umbrella. He thought that he could gain maneuverability in the air, knowing that he could not win it on the sea. Other factors also played upon the scene, such as the will of the British, the gallantry and self-sacrifice of the Royal Air Force, the overwhelming power of the British Navy to destroy the surface craft of an invading force, and the limited range of the mass of aircraft available at the time, which worked in favor of the island defenders. Skill and an inspiring tradition also had their place: "Whatever our shortcomings, we understood the sea affair very thoroughly." * Yet the basic factor in the whole invasion strategy was that narrow strip of water, the salt-water girdle of Britain. Once armed on the one side with modern industry and on the other side with a fleet commanded by superior sea-fighters, Britain was advantaged by its geography to a degree that has enabled it to remain if not inviolate at least independent.

Geographical elements of strategy about which a Napoleon may be mistaken are obviously not measurable by a laboratory balance or disposed of by a mathematical formula. Behind their employment must be human judgments about humans. No one can measure a geographical fact, however physical and concrete, and say: "There you are. Feed this precise fact into a calculating machine or a general-staff evaluation, and it will tell you what to do with a given military component or instrument at a designated moment of time." Always there must be something more than an array of facts and figures; there must be a judgment upon and about the humans who are involved, as to what they can do, or may do, or may be persuaded to do. And judgment lies in the realm of the imponderable. No man can claim to be infallible or purely "scientific" as he navigates around the misty headlands of human behavior. "In the greater matters of life the mind must fling itself forward beyond its data." †

Yet measurement is an essential precursor of most human judgments affecting either broad or parochial questions of policy, military or civilian. Many of the problems of land use, water use, forest use, resource use in general, can be solved only if we have fairly reliable measurements of their elements. Before we can determine the rate of forest cutting on a given tract of land, we must know the growth rate of trees throughout their life cycle. What to cut and when to cut it are questions that can be answered only after careful measurement and scientific understanding of

* Winston Churchill, *Their Finest Hour* (Houghton Mifflin, 1949), p. 314.

† John Buchan (Lord Tweedsmuir), *The Pilgrim's Way* (Houghton Mifflin, 1940), p. 209 (in commenting upon F. S. Oliver, M.P.).

the biology of the tree in relation to its geographical environment. Measurement offers a further advantage. If the imponderables of both good and bad human behavior limit the application of science in human society, it is also true that the area of the imponderables is narrowed by science. Scientific measurement reduces the scope of guesswork and sets narrower bounds to uncertainty. We all have to be reminded how wide is the sea where submarines may hide in wartime, while each new discovery in the field of matter and power and speed requires oceanographic remeasurement for the opposite reason. Ruler and protractor have now to be flexible, not rigid, and an index of flexibility is as important in geographical interpretation as a scale of miles.

From the standpoint of social application and use the world of intellect and materials is a vast interpenetrating complex of forces. We cannot carry all of it in our heads all the time or at any time. For some kinds of scientific discovery we must narrow the view in order to deepen the understanding through intensive concentration upon a given line of thought. Seen in this light, specialization is indispensable. The world has never known a thinker who was not exceptionally expert in some field. His expertness is his ticket of admission to the main tent. Once a discovery is made, one must then look at the framework or mosaic within which the newly acquired knowledge has its place, whether in science or life. Thus every scientist becomes in time a social instrument, in thought or at all events in effect. Through him forces are generated that impinge on life and may change life, here to its improvement, there to its loss.

Geography happens to be a science that is more largely and directly social than almost any other. That is why it has proved so useful to departments of history, international affairs, biology, government, and social structures and process. That is also why geography is a changing subject. How often we have heard otherwise intelligent men say, "The geography of the earth is *fixed,* but the history of the earth *changes.*" The contrast is invalid. The geography of the earth changes, and at times and places it changes profoundly. One could illustrate the fact from the climatic changes that have taken place since the time of the cave man, or the change that has come over man's earth through soil erosion and deforestation, some of it by natural processes, other parts by the influence of man.

But it is not on the physical side that geography changes most. The geographer is concerned with relationships as well as with the things related. The social evolution of human societies has been speeded by modern science and engineering and by the spread of technically equipped migrants over most of the habitable lands. A changing society has thus encountered in its pioneering advance a series of diversified environments, where the climate is too hot or too cold, or the land too wet or too dry. The pioneer fringe has been a laboratory, priceless to historian and geographer alike, in which young and experimental societies adapt themselves to new conditions and new cultural practices and techniques, with a minimum of city influence. However, in this century, to a higher degree than ever before, the pioneer depends upon crop experimentation to tell him how to counter the physical conditions of his marginal environment, and upon government to give him schools, community houses, telephones, library facilities, medical service, and highway or railway right from the start. He is aware of his marginal position as to crops and climate but equally aware of the power of his government to make up the chief environmental and social deficiencies. The modern pioneer asks government to assume many of the risks of his venture.

. . . . .

A man is not educated who lacks a sense of time and place. Where are we in time, where do we live? It was not given to thinking men to change the world overnight—it takes time to change even in small degree at one place. "Place" conditions and therefore limits endeavor whether the place is large or small. Emerson reminds us that we have not been invited to run the universe. Nor did we make the earth or the fullness and diversities thereof. All life on the earth has been unequal in its parts throughout time, from the beginning. Some streams of migration early and late moved into favorable sites, others into rigorous environments. Cultures arose as the mind of man conceived ideas, codes, language, tools, foods, adornments, and beliefs. Endless creative interplay between mind and matter ensued, between culture and environment, wherever men were free to choose, reject, or modify. When a new idea about the environment was adopted, it was as if the environment itself had been changed. What had been neglected was found to have use. Primitive man did not mine coal and start mills and factories. All this is a result of slow growth as progressive discovery and development changed both the meaning and use of the earth and changed them unevenly from place to place.

At no time in the world have things been equal, nor could anyone stop the processes of idea making, invention, and unequal distribution of benefits and make all societies alike in a world where men are still in general living close to their different environments. Some people have been advantaged by their environment, others have pursued the same low cultural pattern in the same forbidding sites over endless generations. The great force of literacy came upon the scene with revolutionary effects. Through it men learned about each other, so that all men are becoming more and more conscious of their condition. They are comparing themselves with others. This is as true of you and me as it is of native and plantation owner, the peasant grower of peanuts in the Gambia and the captain of the port through which the peanuts are transported on their way to the white man's market.

. . . . .

There is a core of geographical knowledge, some of it scientific, some of it systematically ordered and arranged, and much of it capable of assisting the scholar, the statesman, the manager of industry, to understand the earth better, which can mean to use it in a better way for mutual benefit. Today this can also mean the achievement of a humane "defense in depth," to resist the forces of Communism that derive their strength from degradation of manliness and character, from an exclusive materialism, from confusion among nations and societies, our own no less than those of dependent peoples, and from forms of slavery of thought and persons for which death is a welcome alternative to hundreds of millions of men and women who are still free to choose.

3. *The Nature of Geography* *

The essential duality of geography in its regional and systematic branches has often made geographical research and philosophy matters of considerable controversy. This selection, from a much longer book of the same name, summarizes most of the thinking regarding geographical dualism, and points out the concensus of opinion in the field.

Our examination of the great variety of different ideas that have been suggested for geography has repeatedly led us into sidetracks that proved to be blind alleys or routes leading outside of geography. No doubt also we have lingered at other points along the way to investigate in detail certain important problems within the field. It may be well therefore to summarize briefly the positive conclusions to which we have arrived concerning the nature of geography.

* Reprinted from Richard Hartshorne, "The Nature of Geography," *Annals of the Association of American Geographers,* Vol. 29, Nos. 3 and 4 (1939), Chap. XII. By permission.

The author (1899) is Professor and Chairman of Geography at the University of Wisconsin. His exhaustive study *The Nature of Geography* is the standard reference work on American geographical philosophy and thought. Numerous other publications are primarily in the field of political geography.

In its historical development geography has occupied a logically defensible position among the sciences as one of the chorographical studies, which, like the historical studies, attempt to consider not particular kinds of objects and phenomena in reality but actual sections of reality; which attempt to analyze and synthesize not processes of phenomena, but the associations of phenomena as related in sections of reality.

Whereas the historical studies consider temporal sections of reality, the chorographical studies consider spatial sections; geography, in particular, studies the spatial sections of the earth's surface, of the world. Geography is therefore true to its name; it studies the world, seeking to describe, and to interpret, the differences among its different parts, as seen at any one time, commonly the present time. This field it shares with no other branch of science; rather it brings together in this field parts of many other sciences. These parts, however, it does not merely add together in some convenient organization. The heterogeneous phenomena which these other sciences study by classes are not merely mixed together in terms of physical juxtaposition in the earth surface, but are causally interrelated in complex areal combinations. Geography must integrate the materials that other sciences study separately, in terms of the actual integrations which the heterogeneous phenomena form in different parts of the world. As Humboldt most effectively established, in practice as well as in theory, though any phenomenon studied in geography may at the same time be an object of study in some systematic field, geography is not an agglomeration of pieces of the systematic sciences: it integrates these phenomena according to its distinctive chorographic point of view.

Since geography cuts a section through all the systematic sciences, there is an intimate and mutual relation between it and each of those fields. On the one hand, geography takes from the systematic sciences all knowledge that it can effectively utilize in making its descriptions of phenomena and interpretations of their interrelations as accurate and certain as possible. This borrowed knowledge may include generic concepts or type classifications, developed in the systematic sciences; but, where these are found unsuitable for geographic purposes, geography must develop its own generic concepts and systems of classification.

In return, geography has contributed, and continues to contribute, much to the systematic sciences. In its naive examination of the interrelation of phenomena in the real world it discovers phenomena which the sophisticated academic view of the systematic sciences may not have observed, shows them to be worthy of study in themselves and thus adds to the field of the systematic studies. Further, geography constantly emphasizes one aspect of phenomena which is frequently lost sight of in the more theoretical approach of the systematic fields, namely, the geographic aspect. It serves, therefore, as a realistic critic whose function it is constantly to remind the systematic sciences that they cannot completely understand their phenomena by considering them only in terms of their common characteristics and processes. They must also note the differences in those phenomena that result from their actual location in different areas of the world. In order to interpret these differences correctly, and to interpret the resultant world distribution of their phenomena, the systematic sciences take from geography something of the particular techniques which its point of view has required it to develop—notably the techniques of maps and map interpretation.

. . . . .

It is a corollary of this proposition that, in the application of science to society, as Finch observes, the chorological science of geography can function directly, since many of the problems of society—notably those concerned with the most efficient organization of land use—are, in fact, regional problems. But that statement does not mean—and I assume that Finch did not intend it to mean—that the chorological point of view requires the justification of utility. On the contrary, whatever value geography has in relating science to the problems of society, merely confirms the fact that in pure science itself—the pursuit of knowledge for the sake of gaining more knowledge—there is need for a science that interprets the realities of areal differentiation of the world as they are found, not only in terms of the differences in certain things from place to place, but also in terms of the total combination of phenomena in each place, different from those at every other place.

Geography, like history, is so comprehensive in character, that the ideally complete geographer, like the ideally complete historian, would have to know all about science that has to do with the world, both of nature and of man. The converse of this proposition, however, is that every student of a systematic science is somewhat at home in some part of geography. Furthermore, both geography and history endeavor to describe and interpret actual sections of reality as they exist, and in these sections they observe phenomena by methods that, in a general way, are available to the common man. Consequently geography, like history, is a field apparently open for layman to enter. Whereas the study of history, other than current history, at least requires the degree of learning sufficient to utilize the records of the past, geography may be studied by any one who has the opportunity to travel and the ability to describe what he sees. Consequently, geography was in fact studied by laymen long before any organized subject of geography was constructed, and countless nonprofessional travelers since have contributed more or less useful data to its literature. This characteristic, likewise, it shares, for good or ill, with history.

In consequence, Richthofen has noted, "many have the delusion that geography is a field in which one can reap without sowing. Because a great part of that which the serious research students have won in it is easily understood, one thinks that he can work successfully in it without preparatory training, and can win laurels by the easy means of describing fleeting travel observations or by uncritical compilations. An endless flood of superficial literature, which, in spite of its deficiencies, may not be denied the service of popularization, has been able to obscure the judgment of a great part even of the educated public concerning the scientific content of geography. But, just as with history, the apparent ease with which a great part of the facts secured can readily be understood, stands in contrast to the difficulty of sound research." Allen Johnson, among many others, has discussed the importance of the same contrast in history.

Since the vulnerability of both geography and history to occasional trespass by wandering laymen is a result of the fundamental character of the field in each case, little would be gained by attempting to set up barbed wire fences in the form of erudite technical terms designed to bar trespass. Few geographers, presumably, will wish to have their subject strive for prestige by hiding its knowledge behind smoke-screens. On the contrary, in a subject in which the field includes vast areas that few professionals will have the opportunity to explore, the assistance of the interested amateur may heartily be welcomed. The sole provision that we might like to suggest is that the amateur, as in any activity of life, should recognize his need of securing as much knowledge and training from professionals as is possible for him, so that his efforts may produce results of greater accuracy and interest in themselves and of more lasting value for the science of geography.

Geography and history are alike in that they are integrating sciences concerned with studying the world. There is, therefore, a universal and mutual relation between them, even though their bases of integration are in a sense opposite—geography in terms of earth spaces, history in terms of periods of time. The interpretation of present geographic features requires some knowledge of their historical development; in this case history is the means to a geographic end. Likewise the interpretation of historical events requires some knowledge of their geographic background; in this case geography is the means to an historical end. Such combinations of the two opposite points of view are possible if the major emphasis is clearly and continuously maintained on one point of view. To combine them coordinately involves difficulties which, as yet at least, appear to be beyond the limitations of human thought. Possibly one approach to such a combination can be made in geography by the lantern-slide method of successive views of historical geographies of the same place. An attempt to develop a motion picture would produce a continuous variation with respect to both time and space which would, of course, represent reality in its completeness, but which appears to be beyond our capacity even to visualize, not to say, to interpret.

Though the point of view under which geography attempts to acquire knowledge of reality is distinct, the fundamental ideals which govern its pursuit of knowledge are the same as those of all parts of that total field of knowledge for which we have no other name than science.

Geography seeks to acquire a complete knowledge of the areal differentiation of the world, and therefore discriminates among the phenomena that vary in different parts of the world only in terms of their geographic significance—*i.e.,* their relation to the total differentiation of areas. Phenomena significant to areal differentiation have areal expression—not necessarily in terms of physical extent over the ground, but as a characteristic of an area of more or less definite extent. Consequently, in studying the interrelation of these phenomena, geography depends first and fundamentally on the comparison of maps depicting the areal expression of individual phenomena, or of interrelated phenomena. In terms of scientific techniques, geography is represented in the world of knowledge primarily by its techniques of map use.

There are no set rules for determining which phenomena are, in general, of geographic significance. That must be determined, in any particular case, on the basis of the direct importance of the phenomenon to areal differentiation, and of its indirect importance through its causal relation to other phenomena. In order to determine his findings as accurately as possible, the individual student, in any particular case, must depend upon those among the significant phenomena for which he is able to secure some sort of measured data. Non-measurable, but geographically significant, phenomena must be studied indirectly, by whatever measurable effects they have produced.

These general principles lead to no general exclusion of any kind of phenomena, nor of any aspect of the field. In any particular study in systematic geography or in any partial study of a region, particular kinds of phenomena may logically be excluded only if they are not significant to the interrelations of those that are being studied. Finally, the ideal of completeness requires geography to consider not only those features and relationships that can be expressed in generic concepts but a great number of features and relationships that are essentially unique.

In order to make its knowledge of interrelated phenomena as accurate and as certain as possible, geography considers all kinds of facts involved in such relations and utilizes all possible means of determining the facts, so that results obtained from one set of facts, or by one method of observation, may be checked by those secured from other facts or from other observations.

With the same ends in view, geography accepts the universal scientific standards of precise logical reasoning based on specifically defined, if not standardized, concepts. It seeks to organize its field so that scholarly procedures of investigation and presentation may make possible, not an accumulation of unrelated fragments of individual evidence, but rather the organic growth of repeatedly checked and constantly reproductive research.

In order that the vast detail of the knowledge of the world may be simplified, geography seeks to establish generalized pictures of combinations of dissimilar parts of areas that will nevertheless be as nearly correct as the limitations of a generalization permit, and to establish generic concepts of common characteristics of phenomena, or phenomenon-complexes that shall describe with certainty the common characteristics that these features actually possess. On the basis of such generic concepts, geography seeks to establish principles of relationships between the phenomena that are areally related in the same or different areas, in order that it may correctly interpret the interrelations of such phenomena in any particular area.

Finally, geography seeks to organize its knowledge of the world into inter-connected systems, in order that any particular fragment of knowledge may be related to all others that bear upon it. The areal differentiation of the world involves the integration, for all points on the earth's surface, of the resultant of many interrelated, but in part independent, variables. The simultaneous integration all over the world of the resultant of all these variables cannot be organized into a single system.

In systematic geography each particular element, or element-complex, that is geographically significant, is studied in terms of its relation to the total differentiation of areas, as it varies from place to place over the world, or any part of it. This is in no sense the complete study of that particular phenomenon, such as would be made in the appropriate systematic science, but the study of it solely in its geographic significance—namely in its own areal connections, and in the relations of its variations to those of other features that determine the character of areas. Although the study of any single earth feature is thus organized into a complete system in systematic geography, it is clear that at every point on the earth it is connected with the coordinate systems concerned with the other features.

In regional geography all the knowledge of the interrelations of all features at given places—obtained in part from the different systems of systematic geography—is integrated, in terms of the interrelations which those features have to each other, to provide the total geography of those places. The areal integration of an infinite number of place-integrations of factors varying somewhat independently in relation to place, is possible only by the arbitrary device of ignoring variations within small unit-areas so that these finite areal units, each arbitrarily distorted into a homogeneous unit, may be studied in their relations to each other as parts of larger areas. These larger areas are themselves but parts of still larger divisions—ultimately divisions of the world.

The problem of dividing the world, or any part of it, into subdivisions in which to focus the study of areas, is the most difficult problem of organization in regional geography. It is a task that involves a complete division of the world in a logical system, or systems, of division and subdivision, down to, ultimately, the approximately homogeneous units of areas. Difficult though the task may be, the principles of completeness and organization demand that geography seek the best possible solution.

One method of providing such an organization represents perhaps an intermediate step between systematic and regional geography. On the basis of any one element or element-complex—which latter may represent a great number and variety of closely related elements—we may construct a logical system of division and subdivision of the world according to types. Each of these systems of division determined on the basis of generic concepts of element-complexes, may be carried through by objective decisions based on measurement. Possibly as few as three such systems—each based on a cultural complex of many elements—may be adequate to provide outlines into which to organize most of our regional knowledge of the world. In each case, however, we are organizing separately different aspects of the geography of regions, we are not organizing the complete geography of regions.

A single system in which to organize the complete geography of the regions of the world must be based on the total character of areas, including their location as parts of larger units. Such a system of specific regions requires the consideration of all features significant in geography, some more significant in some areas, others in others. The determination of the divisions at any level involves, therefore, subjective judgment as to which features are more, which less, important in determining similarities and dissimilarities, and in determining the relative closeness of regional interrelations. At any level therefore, the regions are fragments of the land, so determined that we may most economically describe the character of each region,—that is, that in each region we will have a minimum number of different generalized descriptions of approximately similar units, each description involving the maximum number of nearly common characteristics and applicable to the maximum number of similar units.

Although all the fundamental ideals of science apply equally in all parts of geography, there are differences in the degree to which they can be attained in the different parts. These differences among the special divisions of geography—physical, economic, political, etc.—are differences in degree corresponding to the similar differences in degree to which the various systematic sciences are able to attain those ideals.

The greatest differences in character within geography are found between the two major methods of organizing geographic knowledge—systematic geography and regional geography—each of which includes its appropriate part of all the special fields. In addition to the difference in form of organization in the two parts, there is a radical difference in the extent to which knowledge may be expressed in universals, whether generic concepts or principles of relationships.

Systematic geography is organized in terms of particular phenomena of general geographic significance, each of which is studied in terms of the relations of its areal differentiation to that of the others. Its descriptive form is therefore similar to that of the systematic sciences. Like them, it seeks to establish generic concepts of the phenomena studied and universal principles of their relationships, but only in terms of significance to areal differentiation. No more than in the systematic sciences, however, can systematic geography hope to express all its knowledge in terms of universals; much must be expressed and studied as unique.

While there are no logical limitations to the development of generic concepts and principles in systematic geography, the nature of the phenomena and the relations between them that are studied in geography present many difficulties preventing the establishment of precise principles. These difficulties are of the same kind as are found, in differing degree, in all parts of science. In many of the systematic sciences, both natural and social, the degree of difficulty is as great, or greater, than in geography. In that field which is most nearly the counterpart of geography, namely history, the difficulties are in almost every case far greater. Systematic geography is therefore far more able to develop universals than is "systematic history." Nevertheless the degree of completeness, accuracy, and certainty, both of the principles established and of the facts known in regard to any particular situation, seldom permit definite predictions in geography. This characteristic, geography shares not only with history, but also with many other sciences, both natural and social.

Regional geography organizes the knowledge of all interrelated forms of areal differentiation in individual units of area, which it must organize into a system of division and subdivision of the total earth surface. Its form of description involves two steps. It must first express, by analysis and synthesis, the integration of all interrelated features at individual unit places, and must then express, by analysis and synthesis, the integration of all such unit places within a given area. In order to make this possible, it must distort reality to the extent of considering small but finite areas as homogeneous units which can be compared with each other and added together in areal patterns of larger units. These larger, likewise arbitrary units, are so determined as to make possible a minimum of generalized description of each unit "region," that will involve a minimum of inaccuracy and incompleteness.

Since the units with which it deals are neither real phenomena nor real units but, at any level of division, represent distortions of reality, regional geography itself cannot develop either generic concepts or principles of reality. For the interpretation of its findings it depends upon generic concepts and principles developed in systematic geography. Furthermore, by comparing different units of area that are in part similar, it can test and correct the universals developed in systematic geography.

The direct subject of regional geography is the uniquely varying character of the earth's surface—a single unit which can only be divided arbitrarily into parts that, at any level of division, are, like the temporal parts of history, unique in total character. Consequently the findings of regional geography, though they include interpretations of details, are in large part descriptive. The discovery, analysis and synthesis of the unique is not to be dismissed as "mere description"; on the contrary, it represents an essential function of science, and the only function that it can perform in studying the unique. To know and understand fully the character of the unique is to know it completely; no universals need be evolved, other than the general law of geography that all its areas are unique.

In the same way that science as a whole requires both the systematic fields that study particular kinds of phenomena and the integrating fields that study the ways in which those phenomena are actually related as they are found in reality, so geography requires both its systematic and its regional methods of study of phenomena and organization of knowledge. Systematic geography is essential to an understanding of the areal differences in each kind of phenomena and the principles governing their relations to each other. This alone, however, cannot provide a comprehension of the individual earth units, but rather divests them of the fullness of their color and life. To comprehend the full character of each area in comparison with others, we must examine the totality of related features as that is found in different units of area—*i.e.*, regional geography. Though each of these methods represents a different point of view, both are essential to the single purpose of geography and therefore are properly included in the unified field. Further, the two methods are intimately related and essential to each other. The ultimate purpose of geography, the study of areal differentiation of the world, is most clearly expressed in regional geography; only by constantly maintaining its relation to regional geography can systematic geography hold to the purpose of geography and not disappear into other sciences. On the other hand, regional geography in itself is sterile; without the continuous fertilization of generic concepts and principles from systematic geography, it could not advance to higher degrees of accuracy and certainty in interpretation of its findings.

4. Procedures in Investigating the Human Occupance of a Region *

Wellington "Duke" Jones, one of the ablest field workers in geography, prepared this article and check list for use in advanced research in human geography. Because of its purpose, perhaps, this selection shows not only the scope and breadth of phenomena to be considered by the geographer, but also the objectives of geographical field work.

In employing such a check list as is here presented one should remember certain inherent limitations of the list. In the first place, it is illustrative of the kinds of phenomena to be investigated, but it is not an all-inclusive catalogue. In the second place, no such generalized list can indicate for a particular region which phenomena are important and which are insignificant, since each region possesses a unique total association of phenomena giving it individuality. In the third place, the list cannot be employed as a precise guide to the order in which particular phenomena or groups of phenomena are to be investigated. In field investigation one sees what he can where and when he can. One asks questions of the inhabitants when he can and about what they happen to know. In the library this fortuitous order is even more marked. The geographical investigator using the library is perforce restricted to the materials there available. Library materials, whether in the form of maps, statistical data, printed words, or photographs, are the results of selection and sorting by

* Reprinted from Wellington D. Jones, "Procedures in Investigating the Human Occupance of a Region," *Annals of the Association of American Geographers,* Vol. 24 (1934), p. 93. By permission.

The author (1886) is Professor Emeritus of Geography at the University of Chicago. He has been a leader in field training, an expert on soils, and has had as students many of the leading geographers of today.

persons who were in most cases not geographers, and whose interests were very diverse. Furthermore, books and pamphlets in most libraries are widely scattered over the shelves according to a classification devised as though with malice aforethought to separate what deals with any particular region. In the fourth place, the arrangement of items in a check list should never be permitted to dim the investigator's recognition of areal and time associations, and of time sequences, of phenomena. Thus, fields of crops occupy the valley floor flats of alluvial soil, whereas forests clothe the steeply sloping valley sides. Corn in the field nearby is being husked on a crisp day in October, whereas the seed was planted in May in silt loam soils which had only a short time before dried out sufficiently to be plowed. The freight train in the distance moving towards the city carries coal, whereas the train moving away carries steel girders. The very high-class residential district under observation is composed of fine houses with spacious grounds, and lies along the ravine dissected and wooded lakeshore bluffs, well out from the heart of the great city; the low-class residential district of shabby apartment buildings closely crowded between warehouses and factories, lies well in towards the heart of the city. The worker in the library, even more than the investigator in the field, must exercise care not to overlook such areal and time associations and time sequences. In short, the limitations of a check list are numerous, and no list can do away with the necessity for the exercise of initiative and judgment on the part of the observer. The purpose of the list is, in so far as is feasible, to introduce system and orderliness into observation and other methods of acquiring data, and to guard against the omission of important categories of data. Specifically, the list herewith presented is designed to facilitate the collection of an adequate body of data for the understanding of human occupance of regions. The list obviously must be more or less altered to fit any other statement of objectives.

Check List for Analysis of Human Occupance of a Region

I. Inherent traits of characteristic individual operation units.
   A. Function (purpose served).
   B. Component parts and arrangement thereof.
   C. Forms, dimensions, materials, color of component parts.
   D. Fixity on a site or mobility.

II. Pattern of distribution and areal extent of operation units, of component elements of these units, of groups of units.
   A. Production units.
      1. Agriculture—farms, ranches, plantations, farmsteads, ranch cen-

ters, fields, pastures, crops, fences, wells, windmills, irrigation and drainage ditches, livestock, plows, harrows, wagons, other machinery and tools.

2. Forest exploitation—logging "outfits," forest areas being cut, camps, dams, logging roads, log piles, horses, implement equipment.
3. Fishing and hunting—fishing grounds, piers, fish sheds, boats, nets, hunting grounds, camps, lines of traps, pitfalls.
4. Mineral exploitation—mines, quarries, pits, shafts, tunnels, ore piles, spoil dumps, power houses, loading sheds, camps.
5. Manufacturing—manufacturing establishments, buildings, machinery, power plants, yards, piles of raw materials, waste piles, deposits of finished products, settling ponds, docks.
6. Groups of units—areal associations of similar production units (localities, districts, subregions); degree of regional homogeneity in farming, ranching, hunting, logging, mining, and manufacturing.

B. Transportation units.

1. Railways—steam and electric railway and street car lines, main and branch lines, switch tracks, terminals, stations, yards, repair shops, coaling sheds, water tanks, power houses, car barns, bridges, tunnels, cuts, fills, portions of line with low, medium and steep grades, control signals; numbers and kinds of freight and passenger trains, trolley cars, steam or electric locomotives, size and types of cars, number of cars in train.
2. Roads and trails—main and secondary roads and trails, streets, bridges, culverts, cuts, fills, portions of roads, trails, or streets with low, medium, and steep grades, parking areas, bus terminals; numbers and kinds of automobile trucks, busses, private cars, wagons and carts pulled by draft animals, pack animals, human carriers.
3. Waterways—river, lake, canal, coastal, and oceanic waterways, main and secondary lines, portions of lines with different depths, shallow places, dredged stretches, rapids, locks, harbors, docks, piers, other landing places, loading and unloading equipment at landing places, passenger and freight sheds; numbers and kinds of ships, boats, barges, and rafts of various types and sizes, moved by wind, steam, motor, man, or current.
4. Airways—landing fields, hangars, runways, passenger and freight sheds, other buildings, beacons; numbers and kinds of airplanes, dirigibles.

5. Pipe lines, electric power transmission lines—pipe lines for oil, water, gas, wire lines for electric power transmission, pumping stations, tanks, electric power substations.
6. Telephone, telegraph, radio lines—wire transmission lines, underground conduits, underwater cables, telephone exchanges, broadcasting and receiving plants.
7. Groups of units—regional, sub-regional, district, and locality systems of each major class of transportation lines, and of combinations thereof.

C. Commercial units.

1. Wholesale establishments—produce markets, main and branch wholesale houses.
2. Retail establishments—for sale of various commodities or groups of commodities: grocery stores, drug stores, department stores; for sale of various services: banks, lawyers' offices, laundries.
3. Storage establishments—warehouses, cold storage warehouses, grain elevators, coal, lumber, sand and gravel yards.
4. Groups of commercial establishments, by localities, districts, subregions.

D. Habitation units.

1. Kinds of structures devoted in whole or in part to habitation.

   Caves, tents, thatch huts, other types of simple structures of people with primitive or relatively low civilization, boats, log cabins, frame shacks, wood, brick, or stone cottages, bungalows, frame, brick, or stone houses of more than one story, apartment buildings of various types of construction and size.
2. Component elements of habitation—structures housing associated outbuildings, courtyards, gardens, other associated grounds, walls, fences, hedges, walks.
3. Groups of habitation units—areas of widely separated units, small groups of relatively spaced units (camps, hamlets, villages), residential districts in towns and cities (each district more or less homogeneous in kinds and spacing of buildings); degree of regional homogeneity in kinds and spacing of habitation units.

E. Recreation units.

1. Buildings devoted to indoor recreation.

   Theaters, dance halls, skating rinks, gymnasiums, other large structures for games or other spectacles.
2. Outdoor recreation areas of comparatively small extent, in most cases serving crowds, and in most instances much modified from a natural state.

   Playing grounds for athletic contests (baseball parks, athletic fields, golf courses), amusement parks, city parks, bathing beaches.

3. Extensive outdoor recreation areas.
   Districts visited for hunting, fishing, enjoyment of scenery; resort hotels, summer cottages; trails.

F. Government, education, religion, and other units.
   Legislative buildings, court houses, police stations, firehouses, army barracks; school units of various grades; churches.

G. Groupings of areally and functionally associated operation units of several kinds—regional, sub-regional, district, locality.

III. Construction, maintenance, and working of operational units.

A. Production units.

1. Agriculture—clearing land, constructing barns, houses, sheds, building and repairing fences, digging and cleaning out irrigation and drainage ditches, plowing, harrowing, seeding, transplanting, cultivating, irrigating, fertilizing, spraying, pruning, harvesting, feeding and otherwise handling livestock, preparing products for shipment.
2. Forest exploitation—estimating timber stands, establishing camps, building logging roads, building dams, clearing out streams for log drives, cutting trees, hauling logs, piling logs by streams or railways, driving logs down streams, loading logs onto railway cars.
3. Fishing and hunting—building piers, sheds, boats, repairing nets, going out to fishing grounds, setting and lifting nets, fishing with lines, trawls, and seines, cleaning, icing, salting, smoking fish; establishing camps, setting lines of traps, skinning animals, curing pelts.
4. Mineral exploitation—prospecting, opening mines, pits, quarries, and wells, working mines, preparing products shipment.
5. Manufacturing—preparation of land for factory site, construction of buildings, switches, docks, receipt of raw materials and fuel, transforming raw materials into finished products, disposal of wastes, packing and shipping finished products.

B. Transportation units.

1. Railways—preliminary location surveys, making cuts and fills, driving tunnels, building bridges, grading line, laying tracks, erecting stations, water tanks, coal sheds, and signals, repairing washouts, replacing rails and ties, painting bridges and buildings, removing snow; frequency of trains, speeds, stops, length of hauls, temporary interruptions in service, control systems.
2. Roads and trails—preliminary location surveys, making cuts and

fills, building bridges and culverts, grading and surfacing roads, cutting trails through forest or brush, marking roads and trails, removing snow from roads, dragging surface of roads after rains; frequency, speeds, stops, length of hauls of various kinds of conveyances, temporary interruptions to traffic.

3. Waterways—dredging or digging channels or basins to appropriate depths and widths, clearing out logs or other obstructions, constructing locks, docks, piers, breakwaters, freight and passenger sheds, dredging out sediment, breaking ice; rates of speed, length of runs, frequency of stops, interruptions to traffic.
4. Airways—preliminary surveys, construction and maintenance of landing fields, hangars, freight and passenger sheds, and beacons, fog dispersal at landing fields; rates of speed, length of runs, stops, interruptions to traffic.
5. Pipe lines, electric power transmission lines—preliminary surveys, digging ditches and laying pipe lines therein, erecting power transmission lines, building pumping plants and power stations, repairing lines; operating lines, interruptions to operation.
6. Telephone, telegraph, and radio—preliminary surveys, erecting lines and other plant, laying conduits, repairing lines and plant; operating, interruptions.

C. Commercial, D. Habitation, E. Recreation, F. Government, education, religion, and other units.

IV. Disposal of products or services of operation units and of groups of units.

A. Production units.

1. Output consumed or otherwise utilized by producers—kinds, qualities, quantities, time of year.
2. Output sold—locally, outside of locality but within region, to other regions.

B. Transportation units.

1. Commodities, passengers, messages carried by various units—kinds and amounts of commodities, numbers of passengers, amount of mail, number of telephone, telegraph, cable, and radio messages, periodic and aperiodic fluctuations thereof.
2. Areas served and transportation centers involved.
   a. Source and destination areas of commodities, passengers, and messages carried.
   b. Points at which goods or passengers are transferred from one line or mode of transportation to another.

C. Commercial units.

1. Commodities and services sold—kinds and amounts of com-

modities, kinds of services, numbers of people served, periodic and aperiodic fluctuations thereof.

2. Areas served and transportation connections therewith.
   a. Source areas of commodities sold or stored and of people served, and transportation therefrom.
   b. Market areas of commodities sold or stored, and transportation thereto.

D. Habitation units.
1. Quality (degree of luxury) of quarters afforded. A significant feature is upkeep of exterior of building and of grounds.
2. Size of quarters—for individuals, couples, small families, large families.
3. Population housing capacity per unit of ground area occupied by establishment.
4. Permanency of occupancy afforded—transient, seasonal, a few years, many years.

E. Recreation, and F. Other units.

V. Phenomena which account for present day (1) pattern of distribution, (2) areal extent, (3) operations involved in construction, maintenance, and working, (4) disposal of products or services, of operation units of a region.

A. Population of the region—distribution and characteristics.
1. Numbers.
2. Areal density.
3. Technological knowledge and skill.
4. Energy.
5. Social, economic, and political status and organization.
6. Plans, tastes, superstitions, and beliefs.

B. Natural features of the region—distribution and characteristics.
1. Land forms (surface configuration features).
2. Soils.
3. Surface water features.
4. Ground water.
5. Rocks and mineral deposits.
6. Natural vegetation.
7. Wild animal life.
8. Climate.

C. Connections and relations between operation units.

D. Past stages in human occupance of the region—pattern of distribution, areal extent, operations, disposal of products or services, of operation units.

E. Extra-regional connections and relations.

1. Transportation lines.
2. Commodity movements.
3. Population movements.
4. Political connections.

Analysis of Individual Operation Units

Field investigation of human occupance of a region consists in no small degree of the study of individual operation units, with subsequent generalizations about groups of units. Various kinds of individual operation units are indicated in the preceding check list, such as those (1) for production of commodities—farms, ranches, plantations, logging or fishing "outfits," mines, factories; (2) for transportation of commodities, passengers, messages, railway lines, bus lines, steamship lines, telephone lines; (3) for sale of commodities or services—banks, drug stores, wholesale grocery establishments, grain elevators; (4) for habitation—houses, apartment buildings; (5) for recreation—theaters, baseball parks, bathing beaches, golf clubs, hunting preserves, national parks; (6) for government—court houses, police stations, legislative buildings, military barracks; (7) for education—elementary schools, universities; (8) for religion—churches.

Each of these material works of man, which occupy area and which are functional (operation) units, can be analyzed according to the following scheme, which by repeating points taken from the preceding check list directs attention to (a) inherent traits or characteristics of the unit, which traits give individuality to the unit, make possible its recognition, and are significant in understanding its occupance of a particular site, and (b) phenomena which in association explain the characteristics of the unit and its occupance of a particular site.

1. Function—purpose served.
2. Forms, dimensions, materials, colors, arrangement of component parts.
3. Operations involved in construction, maintenance, working or using the unit.
4. Disposal of output of products or services.
5. Population involved in operation and in disposal of output.
6. Natural features of the site occupied.
7. External connections and relations involved in operations and in disposal of output (both within and without the region in which the unit under study is located).
8. Past stages in occupance of the site.
9. Future probable or desirable changes in the character of occupance of the site.

5. *Introductory Field Study* *

For the student at the introductory or "orientation" level of geography, some of its methods and many of its details may appear too complex, and erudite—or, for that matter, too simple. This article is designed to clarify many of the ideas and objectives of geographical study for both geographers and nongeographers. Field analysis of the details of diverse phenomena on the earth's surface will indicate their logical arrangement and distributions.

A preliminary taste of field study belongs at an early stage of orientation. A first question is: Why is this so? It is because in the field students confront directly the basic phenomena of geography. The empirical evidence is in the field. Answers are found to basic questions: What are we talking about in geography? What are we trying to undertsand? What phenomena do we perceive in geographic space? Along with this opportunity, unmatched in the classroom, field study does not preclude the devices available in the classroom, of saying anything in words and displaying maps and other materials that reach beyond the visible landscape.

A second major question is: What is to be studied at the orientation stage? In general, the appropriate object of study is the areal association, the complex pattern of things together in place. Geography deals essentially with things in place, as seen in the field and not as gathered in the classroom. Geography is an integrative subject first and last, dealing with things in association, not merely elements taken separately or items listed in inventory form.

Field study cannot include everything existing in a place. Geographers cannot give attention to totality without discrimination—to all molecules, all insects, all aspects of bird plumage, tree bark and surface irregularities—in microscopic detail, or even in large aggregation. Attention is focussed on a coherent group of things under an organizing theme. Following historic precedent, the theme chosen here concerns the areal pattern of occupance made by human endeavor in the earthly setting, the enterprise of people living and making a living in this place, directed by human will.

A specific need is for objective evidence of this human enterprise from

* Robert S. Platt, "Introductory Field Study," *Perspective in the Study of Geography*, Department of Geography, University of Chicago, 1951, pp. 12–15.

The author (1891) is Professor of Geography at the University of Chicago. He has done extensive field work in both North and South America and has been influential in developing field techniques and methodology. His *Latin America* is a collection of "microgeographical" studies.

a geographic viewpoint. For purposes of orientation such evidence is found at the outset most clearly observable in simple units of functional organization, particularly in basic rural units of productive enterprise, each comprising the areal pattern of activity of one man or a small group of people—a farm, for example.

In field study, consideration of such a unit may begin appropriately with its functions in the human enterprise: What is done here? What activities take place within the site? What active connections does it have with other areas? What system of operations for purposes of living and making a living is reflected in the visible pattern of buildings, roads, fields, and fences, stationary forms understandable in terms of a living pattern?

But consideration of functions is not enough. The pattern of forms and functions represents a complex system inherited from the past, not invented by the present operators to fulfill current needs in direct response to nature but developed by predecessors in a long sequence of historic cultural invention, brought here from far-off places of origin and applied to this place, possibly on foundations laid by an older system here before, and still being modified in the ecological contacts of life in this setting. The significance of the cultural heritage is to be recognized for Illinois as well as for China or Peru, including both concept of cultural origin, (of a pattern originating elsewhere in the past and spreading to this place) and the concept of sequent occupance (of this pattern succeeding a different previous pattern in this place).

Thus the object of study is recognized as a pattern of occupance, functionally organized and using an old system set down in a natural environment suitable enough for its continued operation. The natural environment has been mentioned but not emphasized. This now finally deserves close attention as no less important than preceding topics. It is left to the last for better understanding than seems possible under the theory of environmental influence, which emphasizes first the active role of nature as against other factors. In proper perspective, as providing the setting of functional organization and cultural development, the natural environment appears to have even more pervasive and universal importance. Every human activity is in a setting of natural environment, and so is every cultural system at every stage of development—not just occasional activities influenced by conspicuous environmental factors. At this point students are introduced to aspects of nature analytically categorized.

So much for the objects to be studied. A third major question is: What mode or means of field study is to be used? Obviously a primary means is by direct sense impressions, mostly by sight, observation.

Another means, by inquiry or interview, is needed almost as soon as observation. This tool for learning in the field has lagged behind observation and has been regarded as inferior. Perhaps this is due to the example set by geology, with which geography was until recently associated in the field, and in which inquiry is unimportant. In geography inquiry is important: The major objective is to understand occupance as an expression of human enterprise, and the best evidence on this is from the people engaged in the enterprise. Informants need not be big authorities but may be anybody engaged in the enterprise—a hired hand for example, just as, in observing the landscape, the student looks at any hill and not only at the biggest hills in sight. Moreover, the ideas of local people about their enterprise may be no less helpful than objective facts of occupance for purposes of understanding.

Inquiry need not depend on a formal questionnaire but involves conscious grasp of objectives, to find out: What is here and what goes on here? What is the system of operations and what are its internal and external connections? Where did it come from? What was here previously? What natural conditions does it enjoy or suffer from?

Field study also requires means for recording findings. The outstanding device is the map, which shows things in two or three dimensions, as they are wanted in geography, instead of in the one dimension of words (suitable enough for expressing a sequence of time). Another device is the photograph, also showing objects in two or three dimensions, but ordinarily more useful for showing individual features of the pattern than their space relations (except in the case of air photographs, which serve as a kind of map). Finally the device of field notes is indispensable, as an easy substitute and a necessary supplement to maps and pictures.

In connection with maps, pictures, and notes, certain useful devices have been invented. The device of analytical classification is so old and well known that it is occasionally mistaken for something inherent in objective reality and not recognized properly as a device of the human mind for dealing with a complex world. The student is already familiar with common categories (of buildings, crops, and livestock) and may proceed directly to systems of farming and types of land, soil, and climate.

A device more distinctively geographical is that of generalized areal uniformity, of choosing criteria on which areas are recognized as uniform or homogeneous and different from adjacent areas. Small unit areas visible in the landscape or large regions visible on a map may be recognized either on the basis of a single criterion (such as slope) or on multiple criteria expressed in such symbols as those of the fractional code.

Areal units of functional organization need to be clearly distinguished from those of uniformity, though allied with them and similarly useful.

Units of organization, already discussed as objects of study, are characterized by a pattern of lines of movement, boundaries of movement, and points of focus.

Conventions and devices for field study form an arbitrary framework which may be interposed between the student and the geographic landscape. Geographers differ as to whether students at the outset should be presented with explicit directions and a full set of categories or whether they should first confront the landscape and discover their own problems and need of categories.

A fourth and final question is: What ideas from the progress of geographic thought are helpful for field-study orientation? In answer it may be said that each stage has made a valid contribution. (1) The residual contribution of environmentalism is simple: There are relations between occupance and nature. (2) The contributions of the inventory stage are basic and substantial: Empirical data are needed and are gathered by means of various devices, particularly that of mapping unit areas based on uniformity in multiple categories. (3) Functional organization as a unifying concept remains of primary significance. (4) Cultural origin as a concept needed in interpretation completes the series to the present.

6. *A Greater Appreciation of Maps* *

The fundamental tool of the geographer is the map. An appreciation of the characteristics, uses, and limitations of maps is basic for any student of geography.

A fine map is in some respects like a fine Persian rug. It is the product of a vast amount of painstaking labor and is both a useful piece of equipment and an object of art. Just as the beauty of the rug depends upon ancient skills in dyeing, weaving, and the blending of colors, so the production of a fine map is the outgrowth of the even more specialized technical skills included in map drawing, engraving, and printing.

In one respect, at least, the rug and the map differ markedly. The rug, however perfect its design, records only ideals of artistic beauty or ideas of

* Vernor C. Finch, "A Greater Appreciation of Maps," *Business Education World,* Vol. 18, No. 4 (Dec. 1937), pp. 1–5.

The author (1883), Emeritus Professor of Geography, University of Wisconsin, has been a leader in geographic teaching and training. His work includes many publications such as *Elements of Geography* with G. T. Trewartha as co-author—long a leading standard university textbook.

an historical or mythological nature that have been evolved by the human mind and copied from time immemorial. The map, by its patterns of line and color, records facts, and these facts are the result of the most painful labors of scientists and explorers who for centuries have added their bits of information to the correction of the map of the world or to the enrichment of its variety of forms.

Mariners, land surveyors, mathematicians, topographers, geographers, geologists, statisticians, and many others have contributed either basic facts of map construction or new information with which to correct or amplify the ever-growing volume of facts capable of representation in map form.

For one who knows how to use them fully, maps hold treasures that may yield business profit, scientific interest, or literary adventure, according to his desires. There are so many different kinds of things that may be obtained from maps that a full appreciation of them comes only from a study of them and an understanding of some of their essential characteristics and structural differences. They constitute, in fact, a form of graphic art.

An appreciation of painting is arrived at through a study and appreciation of the schools of painting, their ideals and techniques, and one need not himself be a painter to understand and value paintings.

The same is true with maps. Some are rough and crude, as are some forms of painting. They are made to serve a temporary purpose. They may be, as they are intended to be, mere caricatures of the areas they represent. It is unfortunate, however, when one who needs a good map accepts such a caricature because he does not know that it is not a good map for his purpose.

How, then, can one know good maps from bad, maps that are suited to one's requirements from those that are unsuited? How may a teacher select wisely from the many maps offered by a publisher and thus expend his or her limited funds effectively in the equipment of the schoolroom?

To have this ability, the teacher must know something of the major classes or groups into which maps may be divided according to the purposes for which they are intended. He should know something of the possibilities of form, line, and symbolism that are available for selection by the cartographer who planned the map and made the original drawings for it. He should be able to judge also of the quality of the printing by which the reproduction of the drawings is made.

Classes of Maps

No simple classification of maps can be made that will cover all the essential groups based on difference in form and utility. It will perhaps be better to note several contrasting groups.

One possible subdivision is into groups that may be called, respectively, *desk maps* and *wall maps*. The latter, properly, are bold of feature and lacking in minute detail. They are intended to be read at a distance, particularly the length of an ordinary classroom. The desk map, on the other hand, lacks boldness of feature, and its surface may literally be filled with the site marks and names of natural and cultural features, such as mountains, rivers, and towns.

Viewed at close range, this kind of map yields much detailed information, but, since it was not constructed to be read at a distance, it is a mistake to mount such a map on sticks and hang it on the wall of a large room with the assumption that it will do as well as any other for instructional purposes. The schoolrooms of the United States, unfortunately, contain too many such mistakes.

Control of Necessary Distortions

It is perhaps not known to the average user of maps that no map can be made of a large area, such as a country, a continent, or the entire earth, which is an entirely correct representation in every respect. This is true because it is impossible to transfer any large part of the curved surface of a globe to a flat sheet of paper without distortion of some kind. It is no more possible than it would be to flatten part or all of a slit tennis ball without some stretching of the rubber.

In order to control the kind and the place of this necessary distortion, scientists have from time to time invented mathematical schemes for arranging the parallels and meridians of the globe in ways to suit different ends. These devices are called map projections, and they fall into two main classes.

In one of these, which may be called equivalent or *equal-area,* the grid of the map is so arranged that the area of any quadrilateral formed by two parallels and two meridians is to any other quadrilateral on the map as are the areas of the two earth quadrilaterals they represent. Such map projections clearly will be proper to use for purposes that require features to be represented in their proper *areal* relationships, such as data showing the distribution and relative densities of population, the production of agricultural crops, etc. Unfortunately, some parts of every equivalent projection show the features of the earth very distorted.

The class of projections called *conformal* corrects this defect to the extent that the shape of every small area of the map has nearly its true earth shape, although a large area, such as a continent, may not have its true shape at all.

It is particularly important that the user of maps, and especially the teacher, be aware of the kind and extent of the distortion present in a map.

The name of the map projection employed usually is printed in the legend of commercial maps, and some study of the matter will suffice to indicate the general nature of the distortion inherent in each of the commonly used forms.

In this respect, one of the most common offenses is the use of the Mercator's projection of the world as a means of introducing young children to the sizes and shapes of the continents. Mercator's is a conformal projection, and on it small features, such as peninsulas or small countries, have nearly their true shapes. However, the continents are shown in shapes considerably distorted, especially in high latitudes, and their areas are so far from comparable that the errors of comparative size inflicted upon the mind of the child are little short of tragic.

Physical Maps, Political Maps, Cartograms

Still another classification of maps groups them in accordance with the kinds of features shown upon them and the nature of the cartographic devices employed in representing them. From this point of view, one may recognize such groups as physical maps, political maps, and cartograms.

Physical maps attempt to create an impression of the surface relief of the land. The means employed are hachure work, or crayon shading, to simulate the effect of light and shadow upon a modeled surface; or the use of the contour line, with shades or tints of color to distinguish the contour intervals. In some famous wall maps, two or more of these devices are employed together with great skill. The maps that result are worthy of rating among the artistic masterpieces of their kind.

Political maps are too well known to require comment. It may be noted, however, that such maps differ greatly in effectiveness. By choice of color, means of its application, clarity of outline, and degree of detail, the cartographer and the map printer may work together in the production of a clear, well-modulated, and pleasing representation of the political subdivisions of a country or continent. Lack of attention on the part of either the cartographer or the printer, or both, may, on the other hand, result in the production of a map with boundaries that are indistinct and colors that overlap due to poor registry in the printing process.

The colors themselves may be muddy and indecisive or, by contrast, overbold and garish, resulting from an improper selection of inks or from crude patterns of line and stipple, the means by which color combinations are made to yield additional colors without additional impressions. In other words, some political maps are clear and pleasing in their effects while others obviously are indefinite as to their effects and shoddy in their construction.

Since the political type of map is, more than any other, used by teachers of history and civics and by other non-geographers who are not likely to have had training in the qualities of maps, it is especially desirable that such teachers give thought to these matters in selecting maps for classroom equipment.

The term "cartogram" usually refers to maps that show the areal distribution of a great variety of statistical values by means of an equally great variety of cartographic devices or symbols. There is such great diversity in the types and forms of cartograms that it is almost impossible to describe them briefly. Some of their forms, however, are well known.

Maps showing the distribution of the world's population are included in many atlases and textbooks. Commonly, the variations in degree of density are indicated by intensity gradations in patterns of shading or color. In the same class are those climatic maps that, by isotherms, isobars, isohyets, or other iso-lines, picture the distribution of temperatures, atmosopheric pressure, or precipitation.

Contour maps belong to this group also, the contour line being by definition a line on the land surface passing through all points in the area having the same elevation above sea level. Because of this mode of construction, by lines passing through points of equal value in any chosen terms, maps of this kind are often spoken of as "isarithmic" maps.

Another familiar form of the cartogram is that in which statistical values are represented by means of dots, circles, squares, or other devices whose numbers and total areas are directly proportional to the number or extent of the thing represented. By this means the number of people, number of live stock, or acres of crops are appropriately shown in a form whose meaning is almost self-evident, even to children.

Unfortunately, maps of this type, as well as isarithmic maps, are subject to both cartographic and statistical errors. The selection of an unfortunate dot scale, an inappropriate isarithmic interval, or the use of data only for large statistical enumeration districts may render such maps of little value. Their accuracy and value generally increase as the size of the enumeration district and the statistical unit of value are decreased. For example, a dot map showing the distribution of corn acreage in Wisconsin will be more accurate in detail if the statistics used apply to townships rather than to counties, and if the scale of the map permits each 10,000 acres of corn to be represented by ten dots rather than by one.

Cartograms of this type should, of course, be constructed only on base maps that are equal-area in projection. Also their value will be increased if they are made by one familiar with the conditions affecting the distribution of the things shown, not by one who places the dots in a purely mechanical manner within their respective areal subdivisions.

A Practical Scheme for Map Evaluation

The many kinds of maps just noted do not lend themselves readily to the application of any simple test of value. It may seem, therefore, that only a student of cartography may hope to pass with more than casual success upon their merits. It is so essential, however, that all who must use maps, especially teachers, should have some practical basis for separating the valuable from the worthless that the following scheme is suggested. It is presented with a full realization that its application may not prove easy or uniform and that its proper use may call for more knowledge about maps than the average teacher is likely to possess. Any scheme may be better than no scheme, however, particularly if it calls attention to some of the specific attributes of maps and thus in a measure creates a greater appreciation of their qualities and the details and purposes of their construction.

The scheme is in the nature of a score card, resembling those now commonly in use for judging corn, cattle, children, and many other things. The score card presumes accuracy of the facts shown in the map, for naturally the critic employing this scheme would, at best, have little opportunity or ability to verify the facts. It is analytical in nature and assigns arbitrary values to each of several recognizable features or qualities of maps in general.

A Score Card for Judging Maps Printed in Color

A. The Map Drawing — 70

1. Choice of map projection: Is it suitable to the area shown and to the purpose of the map? — 15
2. Legend: Is the map provided with legend, scale, and the lines of latitude and longitude by means of which it may be located and oriented? — 5
3. Execution of the shoreline or outline:
   a. Is the line clearly visible at the distance at which the map is intended to be read? — 6
   b. Does the map contain a reasonable amount of realistic shoreline detail? — 4
4. Execution of the representations on the map:
   a. Clearness: Are the drawing and lettering neat and clear? — 5
   b. Appropriateness: Is the symbolism used on the map appropriate to the subject of the map and the use for which it was intended? — 10
   c. Simplicity: Is the symbolism direct and simple, or does the number of things shown confuse the eye? — 10
   d. Effectiveness: Does the design of the map symbols make them effective at the distance at which they were intended to be distinguished? — 15

B. The Map Printing — 30

1. Registry: Do the several impressions register perfectly without gaps or overlaps? — 5
2. Color: Are the colors in good taste—that is, are they attractive and do they harmonize with each other? — 10

3. Ben Days: Are the devices of line (Ben Days) and stipple used in producing the color effects crude or refined? 5
4. Carrying quality: Do the colors carry effectively to the distance at which the map was intended to be read? 10

Total per cent 100

The author attributes no great exactness to the values assigned and would agree that another interested person might assign values considerably different without at all destroying the purpose of the scheme.

Learning, Artistry, Romance Represented in Maps

It must, of course, be recognized that there are bad maps as well as good ones, but it is hoped that the critical study necessary in selecting maps will not dull the teacher's appreciation of good maps. They are, indeed, the repositories of the geographical learning of the centuries. Pictured in the lines and symbols of any one of them is an amount of descriptive and locative information so great that many pages of carefully composed text would be required to express it, even if it could be stated in words.

In the patterns of line and blended color in a fine map, the experienced eye detects the artistry of the engraver's craft, skillfully executed and more complicated than an etching. Such a map is composed upon a grid of parallels and meridians that is itself a product of mathematical genius. Upon it are located the positions of streams, boundaries, towns, and a multitude of other features.

The discovery and the correct determination of their positions represent the work of generations of navigators, explorers, and surveyors, and the names of many of these men of gallant exploits are commemorated among the place names on the map. What adventures, what historic achievements, and what painstaking labors have gone into their making! There is both learning and romance in maps for those who are able to read them.

7. Mathematical Scale Problems *

Scale is a basic element of all maps. It is essential to understand the scale of the map in order to be able to read and interpret it ef-

* Edward B. Espenshade, Jr., "Mathematical Scale Problems," *Journal of Geography,* Vol. 50, No. 3 (March, 1951), pp. 107–113. By permission of the *Journal of Geography,* official publication of The National Council of Geography Teachers.

The author (1910) is Professor of Geography at Northwestern University. A leading cartographer, he is editor of *Goode's World Atlas.*

fectively. Espenshade illustrates not only the difficulties involved in using or selecting a scale, but also points out the mathematical bases for solution of problems of map scale.

The earth is so large that the general layout and design of its surface features are beyond the range of man's vision. Only for a few features very close to him can he obtain an accurate impression of their size and other spatial relationships. He does not see even the somewhat more distant features, which are still within his limited range of vision, in absolute relationship, but in perspective, that is in respect to their relative distance and position. In other words, man's problem in visualizing and deciphering the earth's features is much like those confronting a fly who would alight on the headlines of a newspaper and would try to read them. Man's problem, however, is more difficult since he has an even smaller relationship to the earth than the fly to the newspaper.

The solution to this problem is to represent the earth's surface in a reduced form. Maps are an instrument thru which man obtains this reduction. They are graphic representations of the whole or part of the earth's surface. Of necessity they are many times smaller than the area they depict. The human mind accepts readily and accurately many reductions, without any hesitation. The child immediately recognizes the snapshot of his friend or the picture of a house or tree. These are objects within the compass of his vision. As a result he recognizes the degree of the reduction, altho probably not in mathematical terms. On the other hand, even relatively small parts of the earth's surface cannot be resolved by the eye. Their graphic representation on maps in a reduced form is an abstraction and therefore difficult for the individual to comprehend or to understand realistically.

The scale of a map is the means by which one expresses the degree of this reduction. The concept is a mathematical one. It is an expression of relations between quantities of two different magnitudes: ground distances and map distances. In the beginning the concept may be in relative terms only, such as "longer" or "shorter" and "larger" and "smaller." At advanced levels the concept should become more exact and precise.

Two Categories of Distance

The realization that scale involves two categories of distance is a fundamental and important point. For this reason the first step in understanding scale is the development of a knowledge of map and ground distances. Map distances which are given in small linear units, for the most part in inches in this country, present no particular problem. Ground distances, in contrast, present two problems. First, there is the great variety of them: among others, feet, yards, rods, blocks, miles, kilometers, latitude distance, and longitude distance, the last a variable. Second, except for a few smaller units, these ground units, individually or in the aggregate, are too large for the mind to comprehend directly. For example, a degree of latitude is an abstract ground distance value. Similarly a ground distance of 63,360 inches is without meaning until converted to its equivalent of one mile. Comprehension of ground distances becomes an indirect process related to field and travel experience and frequently requires a conversion from time factors. The graded training of the student should recognize the increasing difficulty of the map to ground distance concept. The simplest concept is that of map distances to the feet and yards of the classroom. More difficult are those of map distance to the blocks of the community. The more complex ideas are those of miles and of latitude and longitude distances associated with countries and continents.

Ways of Expressing Scale

The three ways in which the relation of map to ground distances can be expressed are well known. In order of difficulty they are the graphic scale, the statement of scale, and the representative fraction. The graphic scale is drawn for the student to see and facilitates visualization. It presents in its subdivisions actual units of map distance marked to represent any of a variety of ground distances. The use of the graphic scale for direct measurement is valuable in developing ideas of linear distances. The statement of scale, that is "inches-to-the-mile," appears to be a simple way, but actually presents difficulties in visualization and is a mixture of linear units. Further difficulty results from the practice of using either the map or the ground distances as unity. For example, "one-inch-to-four-miles," "one-mile-to-a-quarter-inch," and a "quarter-inch map" are all statements referring to the same scale. The representative fraction is the third way and the most advanced mathematically. It is a ratio of a single unit of map distance to the ground distance represented, measured in the same units. The difficulty of the concept, involving ratios and proportions, makes the use of the representative fraction questionable before the high school level. The great advantage of the representative fraction is its universality. It is equally applicable, as long as the same units are used in the numerator and denominator of the fraction, for all linear units whether they are inches, centimeters, verchocks, zolls, or cigarette lengths. If these proportions expressing map to ground distances were simple fractions such as one-half, one-fourth, or one-tenth, they would be expressions with real meaning to the student. Unfortunately they are small fractions which appear forbidding such as 1/10,000; 1/100,000; and 1/1,000,000 and, therefore, lack concreteness. Each of these methods, however, has certain advantages. They complement, rather than supplement, each other. Recognition of this is evidenced by the fact that the scale on many maps is expressed in two or three ways.

The Problems of Scale Conversion

With these fundamentals in mind, scales present two major types of problems. They are the conversion of scale from one system to another and the visualization of scale. Each of these, in turn, may be subdivided into problems of graded difficulty and presented at an appropriate time in the training of the student. The conversion of scales is largely a mathematical problem. It involves methods by which quantities sought are deducible from others which are known. The conversion of the graphic scale to a statement form or the reverse procedure is relatively simple. A statement may be read or estimated directly from the graphic scale in terms of convenient linear units. A statement of the scale can be plotted as a graphic scale.

The conversion of these forms of scale to a fractional scale, or the reverse, presents greater difficulty. In the first place, the numerator of the fraction must be unity. Second, the denominator must be expressed in the same linear units as the numerator. Thus the student must be able to convert readily units of one type of linear measurement into those of another, as for example expressing the length of one or more miles in inches, or the reverse. These are merely practical problems in multiplication and division. In addition he must be acquainted with the mechanics of handling fractions, and finally he must be able to express the values given as a simple equation and solve it. These procedures involve abilities which are taught in the various stages of the elementary and high school mathematics curriculum. The incorporation of scale conversion problems at the proper level within a partly correlated mathematics and geography curriculum can make both subjects more realistic. The knowledge and abilities involved can be utilized to obtain an understanding which is functional rather than purely mechanical.

The Problem of Visualizing Scales

The second major type of problem is the visualization of scale. Visualization of scale is the ability to observe ground distances in the landscape and mentally convert or visualize these same distances as map distances on a map of a given scale. It includes also the reverse process of observing map distances on a map of given scale and visualizing and recognizing these same distances in the landscape. In some cases the ability is largely one gained thru field experience and map study. In other cases the ability is obtained from a combination of training in the mathematics of scale and comparative map study.

Primitive peoples such as the Eskimos and Marshall Islanders had to develop this ability before they could make the maps which they utilize in their travels. I have seen an Indian guide in Canada, who had no formal knowledge of scale and who rarely used a map, mentally measure the ground distance to a number of pine-covered points on a lake and after a brief study of a map, point to his location on it. The student, similarly, can learn thru observation and the visualization of distances to make a map or plan of his classroom or immediate community. In the first stages the distances need not be in standard linear units nor expressed as a numerical ratio. The procedure should be as natural as that of drawing a picture of a tree or a house. The distances merely must be those familiar to him and within his range of vision. As his knowledge of linear measurement and methods of expressing scales increases, larger areas and numerical or precise ratios can be utilized. This process, then, is a direct one. Ground distances are observed, and then converted mentally into visualized and actual map distances, or vice versa. To become proficient in the process requires many hours of field experience in map reading. The ability is essential for anyone doing field mapping. It is essential also for anyone who must read a map accurately in the field. It may mean the difference between life and death for the soldier. The present military situation makes some graded training in this process an educational duty.

Visualization: Small Scale Maps

Visualization of scale on small scale maps such as one covering a state, continent or the world is a more difficult problem. Some of the linear ground units and most of the distances are beyond man's normal range of vision. Landscape or ground distances are not realities of observation. They are impressions derived by map comparisons or by conversion from travel time experience. Therefore, the process of visualization in these cases must be an indirect one.

Visualization of scale developed thru map comparisons raises the question, "comparison with what?" The comparison to be meaningful, must be made with some constant. A new frame of linear reference must be adopted to substitute for the realities of ground distances which the landscape provides as a constant. In the beginning, a twelve or sixteen inch globe can be used as a constant frame of reference. Others can be used, but the variety of scales used for reference should not be too great, or confusion will result.

There is another element which tends to add confusion to the visualization of small scale maps. It is the distortion and variation in scale which is inherent in any map projection. Without going into the details of the problem, two broad principles should be recognized. First, at the lower and intermediate elementary levels, the scale variation introduced by projections can be and should be disregarded. To do so at these levels requires, however, that the projections utilized be those whose scale distortion and variation from place to place is not excessive. The degree of inherent projection errors must be kept as near as possible within the ability of the untrained eye to measure and to the accuracy of scale comprehension expected at these levels. In the former case, the orthographic projection which is used in a number of elementary texts is an example of good practice. This projection presents on a flat surface the spherical surface of the globe with no more distortion than the eye obtains in looking directly at the globe. In the latter case a number of projections are suitable. The Mercator projection is an example of an unsatisfactory projection at this stage of training. It has not only an excessive degree of scale distortion in higher latitudes, but also a variable scale from one part to another. The second principle refers to the upper elementary and high school level. At these grades scale variation and distortion due to projections should be recognized as existing. The student need not know the exact degree of error involved. He needs to know, however, the relative amount of error which can be determined by a comparison with the basic facts of latitude and longitude distance values on a globe.

Exercises in Visualization of Scales

Two types of exercises should be practiced, using the few scale constants which are selected or available, in order to develop the ability to visualize scale on smaller scale maps. First the student should fix computed ground distances with map distances for well-known and significant features. These mental impressions should then be applied to map distances for other features, in other parts of the world. In other words the student should develop ideas of relative distances among a few given places, so that other and unknown distances will be meaningful and concrete to him. Second, the more advanced student should develop the habit of associating the ground area of a few states or countries with their map area. Thus, if he knows distances and areas for Illinois at a given scale, those of Korea on another map at the same scale will have greater meaning. These are the reasons why wall maps or textbook maps, particularly at the elementary level, should be on the same scale, if at all possible. Where this is not feasible, the relationship of scales among maps should be maintained as simple multiples such as two or four.

Once the student has developed certain linear and areal impressions for one or two constant scale references, that is, ideas of relative distances and areas, he is in a position to apply these impressions to the visualization of scale for other maps on different and variable scales. This process cannot be prosecuted, however, unless the student is increasing at the same time his knowledge and ability with respect to the other problems of scale mentioned. The mathematical skill involved in scale conversion is particularly important to facility in indirect visualization. The student must be able to compute readily how many times larger or smaller a given map scale is than his reference scale.

The visualization of scale thru conversion by travel time experience is not necessarily a separate process from the preceding one. It involves merely the development of additional mental impressions of ground distances related to map distances. As a result of travel experience, the time required to go between two points is converted to ground distance or vice versa, and in turn to map distance. On very small scale maps, air travel helps to develop this type of scale visualization. Travel by automobile does the same for road map scales. If the student knows it takes two hours of travel to cover a given map distance, his visualization of the ground distance between two other points with twice the map distance becomes more concrete.

Conclusion

In conclusion, visualization of scale should be recognized as more than a mechanical process. On the other hand, visualization of scale is impossible without the ability to think mathematically. The inherent problems of map scales are both geographical and mathematical. Understanding comes only from training in both fields, and only by correlation of this training in practical problems at each level of the student's education in the two fields.

8. The Uses of Aerial Photographs in Geographic Research *

One of the greatest boons of the "air age" for the geographer has been the development of aerial photographic techniques. Aerial photography has grown particularly in the United States where air views of nearly any area may be obtained easily and inexpensively. The aerial photograph is an invaluable aid for field research and map-making because of the detailed accurate information it contains.

Geographic Research and Its Problems

Modern research is the forerunner of all human progress, and today inquires into every phase of man's thoughts and endeavors. One of the very active segments investigates the intricately interwoven physical and cultural phenomena of the earth's surface. This investigation involves the distributional patterns and expressed character of the many physical landscape elements such as landforms, soils, water resources, climate and weather conditions, and natural vegetation, as well as the many superimposed "works of man" which take their form in crops and pasture lands, irrigation systems, transportation nets, urban developments, factories and mines—and, even man himself.

Much inventory and research work involved in the investigation of specific phases of these multiple elements of nature's complex landscape falls within the realm of Modern Geography, which may be thought of as a study of the structure and function of man's physical and cultural environment. The problems of Modern Geographic Research are tremendous, because the entire expanse of the earth's surface must be considered and studied. Of this whole vast areal complex not one small part or specimen feature can be brought into the geographic laboratory for consideration and evaluation, let alone several parts or several specimen features for comparative study. The geographer must carry out his inventorying and research strictly in the "field," *or,* through the employment of tools and techniques which permit him to reproduce a "miniature likeness" of the

* Clifford H. MacFadden, "The Uses of Aerial Photographs in Geographic Research," *Photogrammetric Engineering,* Sept. 1952, pp. 732–737. Published by permission Chairman, Publications Committee, American Society of Photogrammetry.

The author (1908), Associate Professor of Geography at the University of California, Los Angeles, is an advanced worker in the making and using of aerial photographs for geographical research. Co-author of *Introduction to Geography.*

geographic landscape phenomena which then can be utilized in the laboratory.

Nature of Today's Major Research Tools

The map has long been known and used as a method of reproducing landscape likenesses in the laboratory. Possibly its use dates back into early history, to the dawn of geographic thought in the minds of primitive men. The map has come to be a universal research and record tool, written in a universal sign and symbol language. The map has served the world of research essentially alone and unaided until very recent years, when the aerial photograph came into wide use as a second research and record tool of great utility and flexibility.

The aerial photograph is the first and only available device by which the geographer can capture a nearly complete and definitive full-detail miniature-likeness record of a given landscape complex, at any specified moment or series of times. As such, the aerial photograph is unique and becomes a priceless tool in the hands of the modern geographer. But it must be fully recognized that the photograph is no panacea, and does not spell doom for the maps now in use. Neither photograph nor map is fully complete within itself; they are definitely and conclusively supplementary to each other, and neither is in any way capable of supplanting the other. The geographer who does not today fully utilize their combined potentialities is sacrificing the cause of Modern Geography.

Uses for Aerial Photographs in Regional Geographic Research

It is universally recognized that in regional geographic research, aerial photography provides many vital links in the chain of inventory data and impression development, links which are important to the solution of geographic field problems.

Study-Region Selection

Probably one of the first and more elementary uses to which aerial photographs and mosaics are put in geographic research is that of suggesting field problems and in aiding in the selection of geographic regions for study. When the general study-region has been selected the aerial photographs further serve admirably in determining approximate regional extents, and in establishing the first basic regional concepts. Occasionally the study of an aerial mosaic strongly suggests important variances with established ideas already published in text and map form about a study-region, and thus commands a thorough investigation and restudy. Or, the study of a large-area set of mosaics may suggest the most logical localities within which to carry out a series of type studies to satisfy a regional geographic problem already conceived. Not only have untold numbers of geographic research hours been thus saved through the use of aerial photographs, thereby permitting more profitable expenditure by the geographer in other ways, but the net research results have undoubtedly been much superior.

Field Reconnaissance

The success of a geographic field reconnaissance may be largely measured by its completeness. Its completeness is most often determined by the investigator's pre-knowledge of the general conditions of the region involved and the peculiarities of its geographic problems. With the aid of aerial mosaics and stereo-pairs, a rather precise sketch map or series of maps can be constructed of a region, showing all the directly readable facts as well as many additional interpreted facts. Landform character, surface slope, drainage patterns, and vegetation cover, and the cultural imprints of man can frequently be recognized and partially understood from photographs, even before the first actual entry into the field. The physical accessibility and the best possible routes of entrance may be determined with considerable accuracy, and those portions of the region which give promise of furnishing the most needed and pertinent data can be selected with surprising correctness. Likewise, regional traverses may be plotted which can be later followed in the field, with practically no deviation whatsoever from plan. The geographer can "see," through the medium of the aerial photograph, the entire areal complex as nature has developed it. The field geographer usually in the past has utilized hill tops and other high vantage points for field observation; the geographer can now use the aerial photograph for the same purposes and with much superior results. The aerial photograph has become the geographer's "crystal ball," from which he may learn many things otherwise not possible even in the field. Thus, through the use of aerial photographs, the efficiency of the actual geographic field reconnaissance may be greatly enhanced, its completeness extended, and its cost in time, human effort, and valuable research monies enormously reduced.

In the field, the geographer finds the aerial mosaic or photograph of inestimable value. By carefully checking his field movements, the geographer may determine his exact position on the photograph at any moment, and thus read from the photograph the complete physical situation and character of the landscape on all sides—conditions which may be actually cut off from his direct on-the-spot view. The photograph allows him to "see" beyond the ridges or through a dense vegetation mantle, which his own vision can not possibly penetrate.

No other device can serve as efficiently and precisely as a base for field annotations as an aerial photograph. The physical and cultural features involved are already shown in their true form and in the exact areal location; this cannot always be said of a map. The explanatory notes need only refer to feature character—hill, stream, field, road, or house. These annotations can be inscribed in lines, symbols, or words, directly on the face of the photograph or preferably on an overlay of translucent frosted acetate.

Regional Appreciation

Regional understanding and appreciation can be acquired through the study of aerial mosaics and photographs to a degree far outreaching the possibilities through ground reconnaissance or map study alone. The only reconnaissance technique superior to aerial mosaics for gaining direct first-hand understanding of a region, is actual flying over the area in a slow low-flying airplane; this superior technique is further enhanced if the aerial mosaics are taken aloft for comparison study reference and for extensive annotations.

Regional geographic boundaries clarify themselves quite readily on aerial photographs; they may be actually seen and studied in true relationship and form, and not simply as abstract lines and symbols on sketches and maps. In similar fashion, regional "core areas" define themselves much more readily and accurately within the geographer's regional consciousness, if studied in true perspective from aerial photographs.

Patterns and Relationships

The broad regional patterns of landforms, drainage systems, or natural vegetation are frequently difficult to comprehend and to associate from field observations alone; and the patterns of the "works of man" are even more difficult to visualize and collate, because only relatively tiny pieces of the whole complex are "seen" at one time. But within the aerial photograph the landform likeness pattern, or any other specific landscape pattern, is displayed in total—spread out in a wealth of detail in panoramic perspective not obtainable through any other means or technique. Hills and valleys are displayed in true size, shape, character, and location, while the whole landform association is displayed in its true regional complex and its precisely correct space pattern.

In general, most pattern relationships are difficult to make on the ground, because on-the-ground observers become "lost" in the valleys or among the trees, and cannot properly and fully see their subject; the observer must rely almost exclusively on memory and on the art of image composition in the mind. Even the map cannot give the geographer the same completeness of pattern relationship that the aerial photograph is capable of because no single map, however large in scale and completeness, can carry *all* the detail of *all* the patterns in a region. At best there must be several maps in order to include all features, and comparisons must be made from one to another, a procedure definitely not ideal. Only through the medium of an aerial photograph, or through actual observation from an airplane above the region itself, can a full regional pattern-relationship complex be fully recognized, appreciated, and understood.

Uses for Aerial Photographs in General Geographic Research

The aerial photograph is a great boon to such research. This new versatile tool and technique makes possible for the first time a precise geographic study of "changes through time" of specifically selected phenomena of the geographic landscape, by means of a sequence of photographs taken at selected and controlled time intervals.

Landforms and Vegetation

Whether it be exceedingly torturous terrain, or in a broad flat plains area, the study of landforms is a relatively difficult task for the geographic field investigator. Even the very best maps fail to indicate the fine detail of surface configuration which falls within the tolerance of the contour interval; they do not show all the rock outcrops and the soil mantled areas, the faults and the scarps, the detail of broad rivers and the tiny rivulets, or even man's activities in the area and the scars he has inflicted on it. By on-the-ground field investigation alone, it is difficult, if not frequently impossible, to view as a "total area composite" either areas of great or small relief, where hills and ridges blot out the view, or where extreme flatness confines the horizontal view to short ground distances. But, through employment of aerial photographs, the geographer is able largely to overcome the difficulties associated with on-the-ground observation; the landform features are revealed in precise panoramic arrangement, without view limitations or space relationship confusions.

Vegetation-type patterns may be plotted very efficiently and correctly from aerial photographs, either directly on transparent acetate overlays or transfer-plotted onto prepared base maps. Zones of vegetation transition are readily observable in aerial photographs and the arbitrary boundary lines, so necessary in inventorying and mapping, can be adjusted with fine calculation by tree-crown counts and studying slight variations in tone and shadow. Aerial photographs are especially valuable to the geographer in areas of heavy vegetation, such as tropical forests and jungles.

Land Use and Classification

The geographer is frequently interested in the system of land utilization employed within a given area or political unit, or in the sequence of occupance through a period of time. In land utilization studies, the employment of aerial photography adds tremendously to the investigators efficiency, and probably even much to his research accuracy. Generally, a land use map can be made with great precision directly from an aerial mosaic, or such a map may be compiled from data gleaned from stereopairs or even from aerial obliques. Land areas may be measured with the planimeter, and precise data relative to acreages for each type of utilization can be very accurately determined. Also the aerial photograph bears witness to those areas of relatively good and poor crop production, even more effectively than an on-the-ground observer can ordinarily determine. The planning of agricultural policy, on both large-area scale and individual farm or field scale, can be most effective when based upon the study and evaluation of the geographic factors gleaned from aerial photographs—relief, slope, drainage, erosion, good or poor crop showings, and even evidences of mono- or multi-cropping.

In land classification, the geographer may consider a host of determining factors with relative ease from aerial photographs, to best establish a sound and utilitarian classification. Here the factors of relief, slope, drainage, vegetation cover, general soil types, house types, crop types, cultivation intensity, irrigation developments, and many others can all be studied in the complex form in which nature has developed and now exhibits them and not simply as piecemeal studies in unrelated fragment patterns.

Reclamation, Flood and Erosion Control

Thorough study of the geographical bases in land reclamation programs is essential the world over. Planning reclamation projects on any scale, and especially on a sub-continental or a national scale, requires a thorough knowledge of such fundamental geographic facts as the occurrence, distribution patterns, and areal associations of landform types, vegetation cover, soil types, climate and weather, developed agriculture and agricultural potential, as well as man himself. Most of these basic geographical facts can be partly obtained through the skillful use of aerial photographs. Research accuracy, speed, and economy are increased appreciably through their use, as compared with old on-the-ground survey and sketch methods.

Flood and erosion damage and control can be most effectively studied from aerial photographs. Floods appear and disappear so rapidly that it is only through the medium of the aerial photograph that they can be accurately recorded; mapping is too slow. Also, in erosion study and control, the aerial photograph makes possible inexpensive and absolutely authentic periodic records, which show accurately the stages and rate of erosion advancement or decline. Even large-scale maps, with very small contour intervals, could not as conclusively demonstrate to the geographer the actual stage conditions of erosion in the same complete and definitive way of which photographs are capable.

Settlement and Transport Patterns

Man's distribution and the settlement patterns he develops over the face of the earth are probably among the most basic and fundamental factors in Modern Geography, and at the same time probably among the most difficult to determine with any relative ease and precision. In sparsely populated areas the scattered nature of man's pinpoint dwellings make inventory and location difficult. But whether it be in tortuous mountain terrain where man's cabins and villages are nearly hidden from view among heavy vegetation, or in the broad expanses of the Great Plains where a few ranch-houses may be almost lost in tremendous flat distances, or in the towns and cities of the world, the study of man's location and geographical pattern, as well as the character of his settlements, can be greatly facilitated through the use of aerial photographs. Areas can be easily planimetered and man's dwellings accurately counted; per square-mile population-density results can be quite accurately computed.

The aerial photograph also serves the geographer excellently in the general understanding of regional transportation systems, especially their areal pattern forms and their relationships to the landform, drainage and settlement patterns of the landscape complex.

Some Limitations of Commercial Photography

It has been stated, "It is universally recognized that in regional geographic research aerial photography provides many vital links in the chain of inventory data and 'impressional development,' links which are important to the solution of geographic field problems." But, the geographer must recognize that unfortunately he is not generally in control of the tools for producing this extremely valuable aerial photography. Making these aerial photographs always has been and still is almost exclusively in the hands of commercial or governmental agencies; there is a very good reason, namely, the great cost of their production.

New Horizons in Aerial Photography for the Geographer

The geographer is now in a position whereby he can readily and cheaply provide himself with "personalized" aerial photographs, photographs of his own making which may well serve in most cases as completely workable substitutes, and in all cases as highly prized supplements to the already proven commercial aerial photographs.

In the light of the widespread and fundamental needs of the geographer for more and specialized aerial photographs, the author, during the last several years, has experimented with the combination light reconnaissance airplane and the ordinary and inexpensive 35 mm. camera in geographic field study and general areal inventory. Such general utilization of these two field tools is by no means new; it is only the specific form of utilization in geographic field investigations that is new. Nothing is needed to be developed, except a simple technique, or "know-how," of using these tools effectively.

The first experiments were largely in the nature of a hobby which had its beginning at World War II's end, but results were so promising that it was inevitable that these hobby tools would eventually be put to more serious uses. During the summer of 1947, a full-scale land use survey was made of the Santa Maria Valley in Southern Coastal California, using the 35 mm. camera from the light airplane at low altitudes. These two tools served as extremely versatile and dependable geographic field inventory aids.

Further experimentation continued within the Southern California region with increasingly satisfactory results. Numerous refinements in utilization were gradually developed, and color film soon replaced the customary black and white. In tropical Ceylon, during 1950–51, these same two field tools further demonstrated their great utility in geographic reconnaisance and inventory work, especially within those areas which were exceedingly difficult of access, due to heavy tropical vegetation and an almost complete lack of roads and trails.

With these two well-proven field tools,—the ordinary and inexpensive 35 mm. camera and the light airplane—the geographer may now make his own aerial photographs; he can make precisely the photographs he wants, when, how, and at extremely low cost in time, effort, and money. By this new procedure the geographer can greatly enhance his field source materials, and materially extend the horizons of his geographic field research.

One of the many major advantages this development offers to the geographer is that he may now avail himself always of up-to-the-minute aerial photographic materials—photographs which can be put to use in the laboratory the same day they are shot. Also, such photography has the great advantage of complete adaptability to the research needs at hand. The geographer-photographer has complete control over such elements as subject matter, composition, scale, detail, and the all important angle of view. High obliques, low obliques, and vertical photographs can all be obtained of the same landscape feature, from roof-top levels or mile-high heights, completely at the discretion of the geographer himself and, too, all in the short time space of an hour or so of flight.

But possibly the greatest advantage to the geographer lies in the fact that these personally made aerial photographs can be made in full natural color, as well as ordinary black and white. It must be remembered that up to the present no color aerial photographs have been available through normal commercial channels, and probably will not be for some time to come.

Conclusion

The methods of geographic research have been greatly advanced within recent years, by the adoption of aerial photography as an important geographic research tool. Now, with good photo likenesses of a region it is possible to simplify and to greatly improve on the old field-investigation methods. It is possible, with a minimum of ground inventory control work, to efficiently and accurately prepare regional reconnaissance and even final pattern distribution maps, in requisite detail for most regional geographic survey studies. It is possible now to dispense partly with the laborious and costly "ground-walk" over an area, in conducting a geographic field research investigation.

And with the tools now proven and available to make his own "personal" aerial photographs cheaply and quickly, the geographer should find still more profitable ways of utilizing the great versatility of aerial photographs in the geographic field research of the future.

CHAPTER TWO

Weather and Climate

WEATHER is probably the most consistent "front-page" news item in daily newspapers. This prominence indicates the significance of weather in the everyday life of people—even people who have no daily newspaper. Weather, simply expressed, is the condition of the atmosphere at any given time and place; without the atmosphere, no life as we know it could exist. Climate is the long-term average of weather—a generalization, therefore, of weather in an area.

Weather may have some influence on our behavior during short periods —from day to day or from hour to hour. It is climate, however, that often influences the larger patterns of all mankind on the surface of the earth. Where rainfall and moderate or warm temperatures prevail, there usually are concentrations of population. In areas of no rainfall, where extremes of temperature, either cold or hot, exist, man is found only in limited numbers and in limited areas.

Only recently has man been able to control the weather, and these efforts have been in very limited areas only. They point the way, however, toward a time when man may be able to do something more about the weather than merely talk about it.

9. *Storm* *

All of the elements of weather—temperature, precipitation, pressure, winds, and humidity—are found in the air masses that continually pass and meet over the earth. The resulting cyclonic storms are of particular consequence in the midlatitude land areas where tropical and polar air, dry and moist air masses, often meet in violent collision. Our weather in the United States is no exception, and this selection, taken from the novel *Storm,* show these various weather elements in the formation and movement of a storm. Here is the story of a storm: how it develops and forms, the resulting weather as it progresses over the sea and land, and the relatively puny, but nevertheless prodigious efforts of man to prepare for, to defend himself against, and to cope with the vast and almost omnipotent storm.

Enveloped in the gaseous film of the atmosphere, half-covered by a skim of water forming the oceans—the great sphere of the earth spun upon its axis and moved inflexibly in its course around the sun. Continuously, in the succession of day and night, season and season, year and year, the earth had received heat from the sun, and again lost into space that same amount of heat. But this balance of the entire sphere did not hold for its individual parts. The equatorial belt received yearly much more heat than it radiated off, and the polar regions lost much more heat than they received. Nevertheless the one was not growing hotter while the others sank toward absolute zero. Instead, at once tempering cosmic extremes and maintaining equilibrium with the sun, by a gigantic and complex circulation, the poles constantly cooled the tropics and the tropics reciprocally warmed the poles.

In this process, cold currents bore icebergs toward the equator, and warm currents moved poleward. But even these vast rivers of the oceans achieved only a small part of the necessary whole.

In the stupendous work of transport the paramount agent was the atmosphere, thin and insignificant though it was in comparison with the monstrous earth itself. Within the atmosphere the chief equalizers of heat were the great winds—the trades and anti-trades, the monsoons, the tropical hurricanes, the polar easterlies, and (most notable of all) the gigantic

* George R. Stewart, *Storm,* pp. 3–8, 30–32, 48–50, 76–79, 86–87, 89–94, 105–6, 139–47, 331–33, 349. Reprinted by permission of Random House, Inc. Copyright 1941 by George R. Stewart.

The author is a novelist and Professor of English at the University of California. His thorough and painstaking research has made his writing outstanding. His books *Fire* and *Highway 40* are also of interest geographically.

whirling storms of the temperate zones, which in the stateliest of earthly processions moved ever along their sinuous paths, across ocean and continent, from the setting toward the rising sun.

Early in November, had come "Election-Day rains." Chilling after the warmth of October, low-lying clouds blew in from the southwest, thick with moisture from the Pacific. The golden-brown hills of the Coast Ranges grew darker beneath the downpour. In the Great Valley summer-dry creeks again ran water. Upon the Sierra the snow fell steadily. The six-month dry season was over.

Between drenching showers the sun shone brightly, warming the earth. Thousands of hillsides were suddenly green with the sprouted grass. In the valleys, overnight, the square miles of summer fallow became fields of new wheat and barley. Stockmen talked jovially to one another—a good year! Farmers in irrigated districts thought comfortably of rising water-tables and filling reservoirs. In the towns the merchants gave larger orders to wholesale houses.

November ended with two weeks of good growing-weather. The grass and the grain sucked moisture from the soil, and spread lush blades in the sunshine.

December came in—days still warm and sunny, nights clear, with a touch of frost in the valleys and on the higher hills. Farmers began to look more often to the south—but there were no clouds. Stockmen no longer went about slapping one another on the back; instead, they went secretly and inquired the price of cotton-seed meal at the Fresno mills. As the weeks passed, storekeepers grew chary about granting credit.

By Christmas, the green of the pasture-lands and the wide grain fields showed a faint cast of yellow. In favored spots the grass was six inches tall; but the blades were curled a little, and at the edges were brownish red. Where cattle had grazed, the ragged ends still showed.

The city-folk went about congratulating themselves on the fine weather. The tourist trade was flourishing. On New Year's Day the sports experts broadcasting the football games talked almost as much about the fine weather as about the passes.

But just after the first of the year pessimistic crop-reports from California helped send the price of barley up a half cent on the Chicago exchange. That same day, six great trucks with trailers, heavy-laden with cotton-seed meal, plugged up the highway from Fresno; the richer stockmen had started to buy feed.

So, in the first weeks of the new year a winter drought lay tense upon the land.

From Siberia the wide torrent of air was sweeping southward—from death-cold Verkhoyansk, from the frigid basin of the Lena, from thick-frozen Lake Baikal. The great wind poured over the Desert of Gobi. Even the hardy nomads winced; the long-haired northern camels stirred uneasily; the rough-coated ponies shivered; all sound of running water was hushed. High in the air swirled the dust blown up from the desert. Over the mountain-jagged rim of the table-land the wind poured forth; through all the gaps and passes of the Khingan Mountains, down the gorge of the Hwang-ho. As in centuries past, it stormed across the Great Wall, asking no emperor's leave. Swifter than Tartar, more terrible than Mongol, more pitiless than Manchu, it swept down upon the plains of China.

Descending from the plateau and entering a warmer region, the air lost some of its arctic coldness; nonetheless, in the ancient northern capital the chill struck into men's blood. By day, a sun like tarnished brass shone without warmth through clouds of yellow dust. By night, the eyes saw nothing, but the dryness and smell of dust pinched the nostrils. The fur-coated foreigners (as was their birthright) blasphemed at the weather; the thin-clad, shivering coolies moved stoically about their business. Nightly in hovel and doorway, huddling in corners, some scores of the poor froze slowly to death.

Southward along the coast of China ran that river of air. Among the hills of Shantung it was still an iron-cold blast, but on the plain of the Yangtze its power was less. In Nanking and Shanghai the ice formed only in quieter, shallower pools.

The air at last swung away from the coast, and moved out over the sea; with every mile of passage across the water it grew more moist and temperate. Through a thinning yellow haze the sun pierced more warmly. Now the wind was no longer a gale, scarcely even a strong breeze. The polar fury was spent. But still, east by south, the river of air floated on across the China Sea toward the far reaches of the Pacific.

In mid-afternoon the front of the Siberian air-mass was pushing slowly across the island-studded ocean which lies east of China and south of Japan. Its cold heavy air clung close to the surface of the water. Advancing thus as a northeasterly breeze, it forced backward the warmer, lighter air ahead of it, and occasionally pushed beneath this air vigorously enough to cause a shower.

This opposing and retreating air had lain, some days previous, over the tropical ocean near the Philippine Islands. A storm had taken it northeast, shedding rain, clear to the Japanese coast; it had then moved slowly back before the pressure of the cold wave. By this northern foray it had lost its extreme humidity and warmth, and become temperate rather than tropical. Nevertheless it still remained warmer and more moist than the air which had swept down from Siberia.

The advance of the northern air and corresponding retreat of the southern were related, like all movements in the atmosphere, to conditions existing concurrently over the whole earth. The conditions of this particular day were such that the advance was losing its vigor and becoming slower.

An hour before sunset, one section of the front reached a small island—a mere mountain-peak above the ocean. A dead-tired man may stumble over a pebble and fall; but his weariness, rather than the pebble, is the cause. Similarly, a vigorously advancing front would simply have swept over and around the island, but now the obstruction caused an appreciable break, and a hesitant eddy, about a mile in diameter, began to form—weakened—took shape again. At one point the southern air no longer yielded passively to the northern, but actively flowed up its slope, as up a gradual hill. Rising, this air grew cooler, and from it a fine drizzle began to fall. This condensation of water in turn further warmed the air, and caused it to press up the slope more steadily with still further condensation. The process thus became self-perpetuating and self-strengthening.

The movement of this advancing warm air was now a little southwest breeze, where previously all the flow of air had been from the northeast. With this new breeze, air which was still warmer and more moist moved in from the south along the near-by section of the original front, renewing its vigor and causing a little shower. All these new and renewed activities —winds, drizzle, and shower—were now arranged in complex but orderly fashion around a single point.

As from the union of two opposite germ-cells begins a life, so from the contact of northern and southern air had sprung something which before had not been. As a new life, a focus of activity, begins to develop after its kind and grow by what it feeds on, so in the air that complex of forces began to develop and grow strong. A new storm had been born.

. . . . .

Around the curve of the earth, the day-old storm moved eastward, leaving Asia behind. Upon the opposite face of the sphere the sun now shone, but the storm swirled over darkened waters. Although among its kind it must be counted immature and small, nevertheless it had grown so rapidly that it already dominated an area which was a thousand miles across.

Around its center the winds blew in a great circuit—counterclockwise. In the whole half of the storm-area northward from the center there was little cloud or rain; dry, cold winds were blowing from the east and north. Most of the weather-activity lay to the south along the two fronts, the boundary lines between cooler and warmer air. Extending from the storm-center, like the two legs of a wide-spread compass—warm front and cold front—they moved rapidly eastward, and the storm-center moved with them. As a wave moves through the water without carrying the water along with it, so the storm-center and the two fronts moved through the air, yet themselves remained a single unit.

The southwest breeze which, thirty hours before, had first sprung up near that rocky island south of Japan, had now grown to a great river of air five miles deep, five hundred wide. From over the tropical ocean it poured forth its warm and moist air. Then, as it might have blown against a gentle-rising range of mountains, it met the slope of the retreating northern air, and spiraling upward, swerved in toward the center. Ascending, it cooled; its moisture first became cloud, and then quickly rain. Thus, like a great elongated comma—head at the center of the storm, tail reaching five hundred miles to the southeast—the continuous rain-belt of the warm front swept across the ocean-surface.

Not all of the southern air ascended that slope; some of it lagged behind and was overtaken by the advancing line of cooler northern air which formed the other compass-leg, the cold front. Here the northern air forcibly thrust itself beneath the southern air. And since the slope was much steeper, the warm air ascended with a rush, and the reaction was almost explosive. (Old navigators of sailing ships knew its like as the "line-squall"; most of all they feared its sudden treacherous wind-shift, which dismasted many a good vessel despite all seamanship.) Above a five-hundred-mile line of white-caps, the cold front swept forward. Dark thunder-clouds towered high above it. In contrast to the gentle rain-bringing warm front, its passage brought the terrors of the tempest—squalls, drumming rain-bursts, hail, thunder and lightning, the fearful wind-shift. The passage, however, was quick as it was violent. In a few minutes the front had rolled on eastward; behind it, here and there, heavy showers poured down, but before a cold steady wind from the north the clouds were breaking, and ever-widening patches of blue showed clear and clean.

. . . . .

In an age all too familiar with war the yearly cycle of the weather is well imagined in terms of combat. It is a war in which a stronghold or citadel sometimes beats off assault after assault. More often the battle-line shifts quickly back and forth across thousands of miles—a war of sudden raids and swift counterattacks, of stern pitched battles, of deep forays and confused struggles high in the air. In the Northern Hemisphere the opponents are the Arctic and the Tropics, North against South. Uncertain ally to the South—now bringing, now withdrawing aid—the sun shifts among the signs of the zodiac. And the chief battle-line is known as the Polar Front.

There is no discharge in that war, nor shall be until the earth grows cold. Yet every spring as the sun swings north through Taurus, it renews the forces of the South, and they sweep forward as if to final victory. Night vanishes from the Pole, and in unbroken day Keewatin and Siberia grow warm. The northern forces shrink back into their last stronghold over the ice-cap. The sun moves from Cancer to Leo. The Polar Front is no longer a well-marked battle-line; few and weak storms, mere guerrilla skirmishes, move along it close to the pole.

Then, as if thinking the victory won or as if wishing to preserve some balance of power, the sun withdraws into Virgo and Libra. Again night falls over the Arctic. The northern ranks re-form and advance. But the forces of the South still feel the sun at their backs and will not be routed. The line of the Polar Front becomes sharply marked—cold polar air to the north, warm tropical air to the south. And along the Front, like savage champions struggling in the death grapple, the storms move in unbroken succession.

In January the sun rides deep in Capricorn far from the northern Pole. Unbroken darkness lies over the Arctic, and from the ever-deepening chill of that night the cold air sweeps southward. Now it battles fiercely along the Polar Front, and now at some favorable point a lightning column breaks through and pierces clear to the Tropic. But still the forces of the South fight stiffly, and their ally never wholly deserts them. For even in mid-winter the broad equatorial belt lies hot in the sun, and high in the air through the great current of the anti-trades its reserves move northward toward the battle-line.

So in mid-winter the combat is fiercest, for then the forces of heat and of cold both are strong, and have drawn most closely together. At that time, as in many another war, the citadels of the combatants are quiet and peaceful. In the South the trade winds blow gently, week in, week out. Far to the North the stars shine in the calm polar night. Only in that No Man's Land which is the Temperate Zone the storms raid and harry.

Then the sun moves from Aries into Taurus, and the southern forces drive northward once again.

In meteorology the use of such a military term as "front" may be a chronological accident—that the theory was developed in the years following 1914, a time when such military expressions were on everyone's tongue. The theory has become much complicated, but men still talk of the Polar Front, and may even yet talk of it when the Western Front has happily become a dim memory.

Had the discovery been made in more peaceful years, men (who involuntarily try to humanize nature) would perhaps have derived a term from marriage rather than war. This comparison also is apt—love, as well as hate, arises between unlikes, and love like hate breeds violent encounters. Best of all would be to use words unrelated to human feelings. Those great storms know neither love nor hate.

. . . . .

Over all the top of the world rested unbroken darkness like a cap. Through that polar night the flow of heat off into outer space was like the steady drain of blood from an open wound. As the air thus grew colder and colder, it shrank toward the surface of the earth, and to fill its place more air flowed in at the upper levels. Upon every square mile of snow-covered land and frozen sea thus rested hourly a heavier weight of air.

Until two days previous this accumulation had been relieved by a great flow of cold air southward from Siberia into China. But since that time a series of storms had developed, and by their interlocked winds had blocked off this flow. All China now had mild temperature.

If the earth had not been revolving, if it had presented no contrast of sea and land, or even if there had been no mountains, the frigid air might merely have moved out in all directions from the pole, pushing beneath the warmer air in somewhat orderly fashion, as ink spilled upon a blotter seeps out to form an ever larger circle. But actually the cordon of storms surrounded the polar air, holding it back by the force of their winds as a line of police, now jostled back a little, now pushing forward, restrains an angry crowd. In Greenland, in Alaska, and in Scandinavia, high mountains also were barriers. But elsewhere, here and there, the line of the polar front bulged southward, as the crowd pushes forward against the police-line, not everywhere, but at spots where those who are boldest or angriest, most wronged or most desperate, whisper to one another and make ready for the sudden push.

Or, as a momentarily defeated army driven within a fortress daily restoring its morale and knowing itself too strong for the besiegers begins to renew the battle, so the polar air pushed out southward, now here, now there, feeling for weaknesses. Blocked in China, it thrust down the open ocean-corridor between Norway and Greenland; but a wide-spreading storm moving swiftly out from New England across the Gulf of St. Lawrence brought rain and snow to the mid-Atlantic and checked that sally. So the polar air pushed elsewhere, at every point where the mountain barrier was broken or the storms seemed weaker—into the broad arctic plain of Canada, at Bering Strait, under the lee of the Ural Mountains.

A fur-trader upon Victoria Island in the Arctic Archipelago, stepping from his cabin into the shadowless day-long twilight, felt a change of weather. He had long ago stopped bothering with the thermometer, but from experience he knew that the customary twenty or thirty below zero had yielded to something far colder. He spat experimentally, and the spittle crackled as it struck the ice-covered ground; that meant about fifty below. It was much too cold for snowflakes to form, but a few tiny spicules and ice-needles settled upon the fur of his sleeve, as the falling temperature squeezed from the already dry air some last vestiges of moisture. A steady breeze moved from the northeast. Along the lines of his cheek-bones above his thick beard, already he felt a numbness. The dog which had followed him from the cabin whimpered a little. "Softy!" said the trader; but he recognized the warning, and went back into the cabin. He brushed from his beard the frost which had formed from his breathing. Then he filled the tea-kettle, knowing that the dry air, when warmed inside the cabin, would suck the moisture from his throat and eye-balls. He decided to stay inside.

Undimmed by day the circling constellations glittered over polar ice and snow; the North Star stood at the zenith. Now and again, above the frozen ocean, the aurora flared bright. Hour by hour the heat radiated off. The temperature fell; the weight of air grew heavier; the pressure rose. And inevitably the hour of the break grew closer.

. . . . .

The storm centered now between the Hawaiian Islands and Alaska, somewhat nearer the latter. The dry east winds upon the northern fringes of its circuit swept Kodiak and Dutch Harbor, but the rest of its vast expanse lay over the ocean, and all its rain returned to mingle again with the salt water from which it had been drawn.

The storm had grown still in size, and might now be called mature. If it had centered at Chicago, ships a hundred miles at sea off Hatteras would have tossed before its south winds, and Denver would have been at its opposite edge. From Hudson Bay to the Gulf of Mexico it would have controlled the air, with its rain belt sweeping from Lake Superior to the Gulf. If it had centered over Paris, it would have extended from the Shetland Islands to Algiers. But as an elephant may be large but not among other elephants, so the storm was far from record-breaking among its kind.

Moreover, it was not likely to grow bigger. As most obvious symbol of its maturity, the cold front had overtaken the warm front along a line five hundred miles long, and was rapidly overtaking it along the remaining half. The elimination of the advancing front of warm air meant that no more moist tropical air could enter the storm system, and that, unless some new phase developed, the storm could only exhaust the energy which it already contained, and then die.

But to speak of a healthy man of twenty-five as dying, although in some ways justified, would be counted an over-statement. The man is no longer growing, and his physical condition probably shows a decline. Nevertheless, most of his life and his best years of power lie still ahead. So also the storm actually contained within itself an amount of energy which in human terms was the equivalent of many millions of kilowatt hours. To expend this energy, even if no trick of air movements served to augment it, might take a longer time than the storm had as yet been in existence.

In fact the activity of the storm was still rapidly increasing. Its recent maturity meant that it could no longer glide swiftly and easily as a wave; now, for every foot it advanced eastward, it bodily carried its air along. The pressure was falling at the center, the rainfall was heavier, the frontal winds had risen to the intensity of strong gales.

. . . . .

The J.M. [Junior Meteorologist] was working as chartman that morning. He lacked Whitey's machine-like speed and precision, but he did not let that worry him—just mechanical skill, he thought to himself. Ordinarily he would have looked at the twelve-hour map made up the preceding afternoon, but this morning he wanted to see the situation develop from the actual reports instead of getting a premonition from some other person's map. He was sure something was going to happen.

Recording station after station, he could sense the set-up. There was no need to wait for the Pacific chart, to find out about Maria.* She was close enough now to show, and she was a roarer! The *Byzantion* reported today, after skipping yesterday. A slack ship, if there ever was one! She was plowing head on into Maria, taking the wind right abeam. She reported a strong gale (nine-point intensity) from the south, overcast with rain, and pressure at the even thousand. She would be taking it even worse for the next few hours. Three hundred miles northeast, farther from the center, the liner *Eureka* had 1006, and a five-point southeasterly. Five hundred miles northwest the *Kanaga* reported 993; she was closest of all three to the center, but being to the north and far away from the fronts had only a seven-point gale, north-northeasterly.

After all, Maria was doing just about as expected. But there were some queer things beginning to show up elsewhere on the map—little matters

* Meteorologists commonly give names (or nicknames) to storms. Thus Stewart uses Maria for the principal storm of his book. Felicia and Cornelia, mentioned later, are other storms.—*Ed.*

which might not be important. Not even the best meteorologist could tell till he worked out his fronts and isobars. There were definite changes just the same, more than usual. Low pressure at Edmonton, rain, and rising temperature. Light drizzle at Galveston. Fog at Dallas, enough probably to button up the airport. And, wonder of wonders, clear sky on the Alaskan coast—at Sitka and Anchorage and Cordova where it had been raining for weeks—clear sky, and temperatures below freezing. It all pointed him on farther north, and he waited for the Arctic stations; they were late as usual. What about Coppermine? He remembered its 1023 of yesterday.

The Canadian Northwest must be on this page. There was nothing much else left. He let his eye run down the column, and found the Coppermine number. He almost started as he read the pressure—1032. She'd cut loose all right; there'd be plenty happening now.

He filled in the rest of the stations, not surprised now to find that Fort Norman was 1035. He sat back, and with some reluctant admiration watched as the Chief's pencil moved rapidly and deftly among the clutter of notations. Watching the map take shape, the J.M. felt his excitement grow. With every isobar the drama of the situation was clearer.

The Pacific High still stood firm, and also the eastern United States lay beneath another high-pressure area centering at Pittsburgh. But between the two the 1014 isobar showed a tongue of low pressure thrust up sharply from the tropics, covering Texas and reaching north through Oklahoma into Kansas. Following counterclockwise around the curve of the isobar, warm and moist breezes were blowing inland from the Gulf—thus the drizzle at Galveston and the fog at Dallas.

Farther north the drama was more obvious. Trapped and dying, Felicia lay over Hudson Bay and Ungava. She was not strong enough to break over the high mountains of Greenland; north and south, areas of high pressure blocked her off. But Cornelia had made the crossing of the Rockies, and now, rejuvenated on the Alberta plain, was ready to sweep south, moving again with the speed of a young storm. And beyond, dominating all the north, was the piled-up menace of the polar air. Behind Cornelia's cold front this mass could rush south across the plains, with no mountain range anywhere to check it. What sort of conflict might arise between Maria and the polar air?

He studied the map intently a moment, and decided what was likeliest. The great outflow from the north would deflect Maria from the usual course into the Gulf of Alaska; she would come on due east, smash the Pacific High, and let go her rain along the whole length of California.

"Golly, Chief," he burst out. "It's rain in forty-eight hours, plenty of it."

"Hn-n?" said the Chief, looking up.

The J.M. was embarrassed, interrupting with such childishness: "I'm sorry, Chief. I guess I'm excited."

"Well, why not? You haven't seen as many storms come across that map as I have." Then there was a miracle, for the Chief relaxed a moment from his work. "But don't go throwing out any forty-eight-hour guesses. Storms are hussies, in this part of the world anyway. I've known a lot of them—storms, I mean. You can't trust 'em twelve hours out of your sight." And he went on with his work.

The J.M., the Chief was thinking privately, was something of a whipper-snapper, but might have the makings of a good weather-man. Enthusiasm was proper in a youngster, and a forecaster needed imagination—not too much, but some. Rain in forty-eight hours would be his forecast too, if he had to make one that far ahead. Just the same, there were two possibilities which would prevent rain. The Alberta storm might not go south, but go east following that other storm which was hanging around over Hudson Bay; the polar air would follow, and the advancing Pacific storm move against the Alaskan coast as usual. Or the polar air, on the other hand, might sweep southward so violently that it joined with the Pacific High; then the advancing storm would be blocked a thousand miles to the west, and California would have only dry cold winds from the northeast.

In any case the next twenty-four hours offered no problem, and with confidence he began typing off a no-change forecast. Then Whitey shoved a telephone at him.

"You better take this, Chief—sounds bad!"

"Hn-n?" said the Chief, and then he heard someone plenty excited talking over the line.

"Weather Bureau, hello! Hello there! Weather Bureau, Weather—"

"Chief Forecaster speaking."

"Say, we got— This is the Brownington Steamship Company. We got a ship in trouble. She just let loose an SOS. The *Eureka* relayed it to us. She's making for her but she'll take six hours. What's the weather like out there?"

"Can you give me the position?"

"Not exactly—the *Eureka* didn't give it. But we'll get it."

"What ship is it?"

"*Byzantion.*"

"Don't bother then. We have her position when she reported two hours ago. She must have been all right then. Just a minute—"

But the man on the other end was almost wailing: "For God's sake, hurry. It's mostly a local crew; they got wives and families. The *Register* has an extra getting ready now."

Turning toward the map the Chief bumped into the J.M., dividers and slide-rule in hand.

"I'll have the gradient wind calculated in about—"

"Put that damn thing away!" snapped the Chief. "No, figure it. But get out of my road!"

The *Byzantion* was a slow ship, and once disabled would not move at all. He could figure her still being just about where she was before. But the storm had been tearing down toward her at a rate which would be around forty miles an hour. So the ship would be that much nearer the front. He looked at the close-spaced isobars. The ship's barometer, if anyone bothered to look, would be down around 997 by now; the wind might have risen a full point, maybe more.

"Hello—when she reported, the *Byzantion* had a nine-point wind—about, well, say fifty miles an hour. Now look here—don't tell all this to the reporters or to the families either. But you better know. It's going to get worse. In an hour it'll be blowing a whole gale, sixty miles an hour anyway. Then for another hour it'll be worst of all—gusts running over seventy. After that it'll fall off, but there'll be lots of wind for twelve hours, and a heavy sea after that. The storm out there is plenty big."

"Thank you—" the voice still had a wailing tone. "There isn't anything you can do about it?"

The Chief did not smile, for he recognized the appeal of despair.

"Not a thing. I'm sorry." And then Whitey was holding out another telephone to him. It was the *Register*.

For the next hour the Chief spent most of his time trying to tone down the language of editors. "No, it's not a typhoon. . . . No, it can't be called a hurricane." Since it could do no good, he dodged a public statement as to whether the storm was growing worse.

All the time, as the early sun flooded in at the east windows and the City basked in the calm of a cloudless morning, it was hard to realize that at a distance of a few inches on the map, even in reality only a small fraction of the earth's circumference, some of your fellow-townsmen were battling for their lives on a broken ship, and the front rushing down upon them.

. . . . .

From the Arctic islands and the ice-floes of Beaufort Sea, from the tundras and pine-barrens and frozen lakes, the polar air swept southward across the plains. Its overwhelming front rushed onward at fifty miles an hour.

This was the manner of its coming. Before it, there was clear sky, and the sun shining upon new-fallen snow, a soft breeze from the west, moist and not cold. Then to the north was a line of high-banked, slate-gray cloud, and the mutter of thunder. Next, suddenly, the clouds darkened sun and sky, the north wind struck frigidly, and the air was thick with furious snow.

All day Friday the line of that front had swept southward across Alberta and Saskatchewan. At noon it engulfed Edmonton; just before the winter sunset, Saskatoon and Calgary. In the open, life lost all semblance of pleasure or dignity or even of safety. From the Rockies to Lake Winnipeg animals and men alike sought shelter. The blizzard held sway.

About midnight the front approached the international boundary just north of Havre, Montana. No immigration officers demanded passports; no customs officials searched for contraband. Although the Weather Bureau had given warning, not even a hastily mobilized regiment of the National Guard held the border. At the very least, the Department of State might have sent a sharp note to Ottawa, warning that the Dominion Government would be held strictly accountable for damage done by the Canadian air.

Reasonable expectation could only be that a hundred or more citizens of the United States would lose their lives in the cold wave, and that wreckage of property would reach millions. Indirectly, through pneumonia and other means, the loss of life would run into many hundreds and the sum of such items as increased consumption of fuel, snow-removal, and delays in transportation would total an appalling figure. Yet the United States of America (often called by its citizens the greatest nation of the earth) merely cowered before the Canadian invasion.

The northern air crossed the border just after midnight on Saturday morning; by daybreak it had occupied much of Montana and North Dakota, and was advancing upon Minnesota, South Dakota and Wyoming.

. . . . .

While as yet he scarce walked upright steadily, man fashioned for himself many gods—of earth and of sea, of the nether world, but (most of all) gods of the sky. Of these, sometimes he imagined gods of the farther air, high and serene, celestial in the empyrean. Sometimes they were of the middle air, rulers of the four winds, of thunder and lightning, of rain. Still again, they were demons of the lower air, malignant, haunting headland and cliff and rim-rock, pouncing in squall or sand-storm. But most often, each god had many aspects, being now the far master of the sky, now the rain-bringer, and again the spiteful demon crushing the corn-field with hail.

Of all lands and peoples is the roll-call of the stormgods. Zeus the cloud-gatherer, lord of lightning. Adad-Ramman, the duplex, sender to the Babylonian plain alike of nourishing rain and devastating tempest. Jupiter of the rain; Thor, the thunderer; Indra, freer of the waters. Pulugu of the Bengal sea, before whose wrath the pigmy Andamanese cower low.

Kilima, Mahu, Dzakuta. Pase-Kamui of the Ainus; Asiak who rules the air above the far-off northern ice. Tlaloc of Mexico, thundering from his mountain-top.

Man walks the earth, but is of the air. Everywhere he pays homage, not to the air itself of which he is unconscious, but to the powers which move within the air. He bows his head before wind and rain.

And what of Jehovah? Jehovah who poured the Deluge forty days and forty nights, and then sent the rainbow, his sign and pledge! Jehovah who came as a thick cloud upon the mountain and spoke to his servant Moses through thunders and lightnings!

In that part of the western United States which the storm now dominated, a highly civilized race of men had hung so many wires upon so many poles that hardly a landscape was devoid of them. These wires served many purposes. The larger ones supported bridges, and served for trolleys and conveyors. A very great number carried electric current for power, light, telegraph, and telephone. Others served as guys, fences, aerials, and clothes-lines.

A common quality of almost all these wires was that they were erected in the open air, wholly exposed to the atmospheric forces. Yet such was the ingenuity of these men, and the tenacity of steel and copper that even a great Pacific storm could discommode only a few of the wires.

In the heaviest winds the wires swayed easily back and forth. Rain served only to increase their weight a little, and then dripped off harmlessly. Snow was scarcely more effective. In the higher mountains the snow clung to the wires, and frequently built up to a diameter of several inches. The wires sagged somewhat beneath this load, but sooner or later the very weight of the snow overcame its cohesive power. At that moment a small amount of snow dropped off; this sudden change caused the wire to vibrate sharply and to dislodge most of the remaining snow. Thus relieved, the wire swung back and forth for a few seconds, and then settled down to receive its next load.

In one zone, however, the attack of the storm upon the wires was more serious. Between the snow of the higher mountains and the rain of the foothills lay necessarily a region of transition in which the precipitation was neither rain nor snow but something about half way between and much more clinging and tenacious than either. This half-frozen rain and half-melted snow often built up a solid sheathing, not to be shaken off of its own weight, and steadily growing heavier as the storm lasted. A catastrophic snapping of wires was prevented only by the saving circumstance that the zone was seldom more than a few miles broad and frequently shifted location as colder or warmer air blew in from the Pacific. With each shift of position the wires of any particular region had a respite and might manage to relieve themselves of their loads.

So, although no storm passed without damage, the actual damage could usually be attributed to some pyramiding of accidents which managed to overcome the margin of safety which man's ingenuity had established.

During the early hours of Monday morning such a critical condition existed at a point where the transmission line from French Bar Power-House ran along the side of a foothill ridge at an elevation of about three thousand feet. The line was of a kind which may be seen almost anywhere in the United States. The sturdy spruce poles were sixty feet high; each bore two well braced cross-arms, and eight wires. The three topmost wires were the heaviest and served as the three-phase high-voltage transmission line. These wires were carried upon large insulators, one at the very top of the pole, and the others at the ends of the upper cross-arm. Upon one side of the lower cross-arm, smaller insulators supported the three service wires, operating at a lower voltage and supplying current to the near-by district; the other side of this cross-arm carried the two wires of the company's telephone.

The conditions of the storm were such that a strong south wind, funneling through a gap, was blowing up-hill and across the wires. Several miles farther south snow was falling from the clouds. As it fell, the snow half melted; then, as it was about to reach the ground, the strongly blowing wind swept it along and carried a large part of it actually up-hill. Since rising air grows cooler, the half-melted snow was quickly chilled below freezing, and in that condition was blown across the wires. Every particle which lodged upon them froze into solid ice at the moment of coming to rest. The lower wires were somewhat protected by the pine trees growing along the edge of the right-of-way, but the upper wires took the full attack of the storm.

Under these conditions the sheathing of ice built up rapidly. By the time it was a half foot in diameter each span of the three upper wires was supporting a ton of ice. The wires, however, were constructed about a steel core, and each was normally capable of supporting several times the weight which had as yet accumulated.

Some days previous, however, an owl had happened to alight on one of the cross-arms. The ensuing electrocution had caused a shower of electric sparks, and had burned and weakened one of the wires.

In the orange groves of Brownsville the norther lashed the branches, and the temperature at dawn was two degrees above freezing. Men made ready their fires for the bitter, still cold which follows the ceasing of the wind, and women prayed to God and to his Son. Across the Rio Grande in the orange groves of Montemorelos wind and temperature were the same; the brown-faced men shrugged their shoulders in resignation, and women prayed to the dark Virgin of Guadelupe.

Across the broad reach of the Gulf the storm drove on. It tossed the ships in its path—tankers of the oil ports, cotton- and banana- and coffee-boats. Over the warm waters the air grew less chill; and its lower levels, sucking up the spray from every white-cap, grew thick with moisture.

Beyond the Gulf, in the wind's path, lay the long crescent of the Mexican coast. *"El Norte!"* said the brown-faced people, and drew their serapes closer. In early morning the storm struck Vera Cruz; waves lashed the quays; spray wreathed the ancient castle of San Juan. Upon the mountain slopes by Jalapa the storm broke in torrents of rain; it tore the great leaves of the banana trees; it whipped the coffee-bushes and the gardenias. In their wattled tropical huts the people huddled shivering. Higher up, there was snow on the peaks—Orizaba, and Perote, and Malinche.

Through the passes—fiercer than Aztec or Spaniard—the storm poured down upon the Valley of Mexico. The wind stirred the lakes to foam; the cypresses of Chapultepec tossed wet branches; the flowers of Xochimilco were wet and sodden. Clouds covered Iztaccihuatl and Popocatepetl; snow was white upon Ajusco.

But farther away the storm could not go, for the great mountains blocked its passage. And by the swimming-pools of Cuernavaca the fair-skinned tourists lay in the hot sun, and wondered why that morning the little cloud-banners streamed off from the peaks to the north.

Blocking the norther's path, to the southwest lay the wall of the Mexican Cordillera; to the southeast, the highlands of Chiapas and Guatemala. But between were only the low hills of the Isthmus of Tehuantepec, and into that gap the wind poured as into a funnel. It spent the last of its rain upon the northern slope; dry and cool it started down toward the Pacific. Descending, it warmed; it ceased to be a chilling blast from the Arctic and became almost mild. But because of the funnel, the wind was stronger. On the Pacific it met the steamers from Panama, and buried them bows-under. "Tehuantepecker!" explained the stewards. "Have to expect them this time of year." The captains logged a ten-point gale.

Grown moist again from the tropical ocean, the wind skirted the coast of bananas and coffee. Striking the mountains the air exploded in thunderstorms. *"Chubasco!"* said the Salvadoreans. Like the men farther north, the soft Nicaraguans shivered in a cold wave, although the temperature did not fall below fifty-six. *"Papagayo!"* said the Costa Ricans.

At last, having penetrated to within ten degrees of the Equator, grown warm in the tropical sun, the far-sent invasion from the north felt the drag of that great current of air which belts the earth's central zone, and turning westward mingled with the steadily blowing trade wind.

Theoretically, the J.M. knew that such things could happen. At the Institute he had even heard a visiting specialist in dynamic meteorology read a paper on the synoptic preliminaries of a polar outbreak and demonstrate mathematically the sources of energy involved. Nevertheless, when he saw the map that morning, the J.M. almost gasped. To know that all this was in the actual process of happening was very different from thinking of it as equations—and at the same time to realize that as part of the Weather Bureau he carried his share of responsibility for charting it and forecasting its progress. He felt as if the government of the air had suddenly been overwhelmed by revolution.

In the orderly hemisphere of the text-books there was a high-pressure area over the Pole and another near the Tropic of Cancer in what were known as the "horse latitudes." Between the two, in the temperate zone, a succession of storms moved steadily from west to east. South of the sub-tropical high pressure was low pressure again, and the trade winds blowing from northeast to southwest.

But now, in two great tongues of cold air, the polar high pressure had broken clear through the chain of storms. It had joined with the high pressure of the horse latitudes, and even broken into the region of the trade winds.

He kept telling himself that such an outbreak was fully in accord with meteorological theory. The regular circulation of air was (like most things on the earth) imperfect; it resulted in too much air being carried northward, so that cataclysmic polar outbreaks such as this were necessary to restore the balance. But still, to be actually in its presence was fearful.

With pressure risen to 1050 the polar air mass centered over Fort Yukon. From it one tongue of cold air reached far south across the Pacific, and then in a long curve to the eastward joined the remnants of the old Pacific High off the Lower California coast. But the greater discharge of cold air poured southward across the plains of North America and even over the Gulf of Mexico. There also it had joined the remnants of the sub-tropical high, and that air (set in motion by the northern incursion) was now blowing a gale along the Pacific coast of Central America.

Surrounded almost entirely within the two arms of this polar outbreak, Maria was brought to a standstill off the coast. The J.M. looked at her with a fatherly feeling. First she had been an active little storm running her thousand miles a day, slipping through the air as a wave. She had matured, and with heightened winds had bodily carried the air along with her; she had broken a ship, and swept a man overboard. Then she had shrunk, and seemed to be declining. Now, caught between the two polar arms, she had become stationary, and again vast and vigorous, and in her nature more complicated than ever before.

In fact, she was so complicated that the J.M. had to admit he did not wholly understand her. She was no longer a baby; a baby ate and slept, and was a fairly simple affair. By now, Maria was more like a middle-aged person who has grown too individualized, not to say crotchety, to fit any rules. At first, she had been a storm right out of a text-book. She had had two fronts, and then only one front—just as you expected. But now, because of the complex mixing of her air and because of the mountains along the coast, she might have a dozen fronts and be developing new ones all the time. That would be the reason why the rain sometimes fell in torrents, and sometimes quit altogether for a half hour or so.

Yes, he had a fatherly feeling, but he was no longer in a position to say "Father knows best." The very fact that she had traveled across the Pacific and arrived off the coast in such vigorous state showed that she was not following the rules. Usually the storms which reached California were secondary developments from the storms which had formed off Asia.

Like a father whose child has suddenly become a powerful and famous person, the J.M. began to feel his affection mingled with awe. From Sitka to San Diego was now Maria's domain. She was a gigantic creature of the atmosphere, drawing moisture from the great Pacific and expending it as rain and snow upon a thousand miles of coast.

The Chief, that morning, moved about with a smile on his face. His forecast could have been no better if he had made the weather himself. And there was plenty of rain still to come.

. . . . .

The storm during its life had traveled a third of the way round the world; at its height, it had encompassed an area larger than the United States of America.

By mixing in gigantic proportions the northern and southern air the storm had helped adjust the inequalities of heat between equator and pole.

Next notable of its actions was the transfer of water from ocean to land. One inch of rain falling upon one square mile totals a weight of seventy thousand tons. Rain and snow from this single storm had fallen over a land area of more than two hundred thousand square miles, and the average precipitation of water was several inches.

Of all this water a little had already been reabsorbed into the dry air following after the last front. Another small amount had been impounded behind man-made dams. Somewhat more had passed through natural channels and returned to the ocean. Much remained as snow—attaining a depth of many feet—upon the higher mountains. Much was contained in the flooded streams, and was somewhat violently engaged in flowing toward tidewater. Another large part was held within the now saturated earth. Still another had gone into vegetation, for in many places the grass had grown an inch during the storm.

The third notable work of the storm was its lowering of the land-surface. Here by landslide, there by less spectacular erosion, the water had carried millions of cubic yards of earth a greater or less distance toward the ocean.

Beside these cosmic effects, the direct influence of the storm upon men seems small and secondary. *Good* and *bad* lose their meaning, and exist only according to point of view, within a limited range of vision.

"Sixteen dead by storm," declared the *Register*. This would doubtless be rated a bad effect, but perhaps the world was better off because of these deaths. And even the accuracy of the headline can be impugned. (Does the match or the powder cause the explosion?) The sixteen died not because of the storm but because of their own mortality. The storm was merely the occasion; after a few years they would in any case have died.

But if the editor was to hold the storm responsible for sixteen deaths, why not for hundreds? Many invalids died during the days of the storm, their deaths precipitated by chills and heart-depressions, attributable to the weather. Some healthy persons suffered wet feet which led to colds, pneumonia, and death within a few weeks. Other colds resulted in weakened resistance which opened the way to various fatal diseases.

"Million-dollar rain," was another headline in the *Register*. This, doubtless, would be rated a good effect. But the saving of a crop in California might quite possibly lead to bear raids in Chicago, foreclosures in Oklahoma, suicides in Florida, strikes in Massachusetts, and executions in Turkey.

As with the so-called bad, the so-called good was often far removed and difficult to appraise. Only a few entomologists realized that the rain, falling just when it did, destroyed billions of grasshopper eggs, and prevented a plague six months later.

Even aside from its cosmic effects the storm had thus vitally affected, in one way or another, the life of every human being in the region. It had accomplished all this without being itself catastrophic or even unusual.

• • • • •

Steadily the great sphere of the earth spun upon its axis, and moved in its unvarying course around the sun. From far-off Venus a watcher of the skies (if such we may imagine) viewed it as a more brilliant planet than any to be seen from the earth. It gave no sign that storms or men disturbed its tranquil round. Bright against the black of midnight, or yellow at the dawn, it hung in the sky—unflickering and serene.

10. Climate and Future Settlement *

Following the age of discovery were several centuries of great emigration, pioneering, and settlement in many areas of the world. This period of new settlement has virtually come to an end; yet there are still many parts of the earth where both climate and soil indicate that possibilities for population increases are good. Where are these regions? What are they like and why are they so thinly populated at present? What are the prospects for successful settlement in these regions in the future? This article answers these questions, and in doing so indicates a partial answer to one of the major problems of our time—overpopulation in many sections of the world.

Any attempt to prophesy is hazardous, and to evaluate climate as a factor in future settlement is particularly difficult. Not only is our knowledge of climate incomplete, but the function of climate varies with the cultural level of the occupying group. Man is not a passive creature who merely submits to the forces of his milieu. By setting his own standards, by rebelling against restrictions of the environment, he has gradually overcome obstacles and harnessed resources. There is no reason to believe that he has reached the end of his conquest.

This is not to say, however, that all climates are equally favorable. A study of the present distribution of population clearly reveals that certain zones offer stubborn resistance to dense settlement. In general, these regions belong to the following three climatic extremes: (1) Areas with low rainfall—the deserts; (2) areas with low temperatures—the polar regions; (3) areas with a combination of year-round high precipitation and high temperatures—the equatorial rain-forest regions. On the margins of these are the transition zones to the so-called temperate climates—respectively, the semiarid steppes, the subpolar forests, and the seasonally dry outer Tropics.

* Jan O. M. Broek, "Climate and Future Settlement," *Climate and Man, Yearbook of Agriculture* (1941), pp. 227–235.

The author (1904), Professor and Chairman of Geography at the University of Minnesota, has worked extensively in Southeast Asia and on population problems in both over- and underpopulated areas.

No doubt one could speculate in various ways on eventual changing relations between settlement and climate in the already well-populated regions; but this article will focus attention on regions with unsolved climatic problems in other parts of the world than the United States. The discussion will also be limited to the possibilities of settlement by peoples of European stock.

Settlement in Tropical Lands

Of the three climatic extremes, the equatorial lowlands with their excessive moisture and heat appear to be least repellent to human settlement. They may not have a high density of population, but neither do they show the empty spaces typical of the deserts and the polar lands. To high forms of cultural achievement, however, this environment seems unfavorable. There is no record of any advanced indigenous civilization in the Amazon and Congo Basins or in the equatorial parts of the Malay Archipelago.

Why this is so remains a matter of speculation. Perhaps the uniformity of climate is not conducive to foresighted action, as are climates with seasonal contrasts. More important, it may be that the overpowering vegetative growth and the leached soils offer tremendous resistance to human effort. Also the prevalence of diseases, which are carried from person to person by a multitude of insects, the monotonous and deficient diets, and perhaps the direct influence of the climate on human physiology should be considered. But one should take care to avoid purely environmental explanations. In many instances European exploitation, alcohol, disease, and the slave trade have caused the population to diminish and the native economic and social structure to deteriorate. Whatever the reasons, the fact remains that the equatorial lands are sparsely populated and are thus potential regions for immigration.

The majority of whites who at present live in the Tropics, either temporarily or permanently, belong to the social-economic upper strata, relying upon other races for physical labor. Immigration of whites in large numbers, however, implies the establishment of complete communities in which they would perform all functions. There are very few such colonies in the equatorial lowlands. The suitability of these territories for white settlement is still a hotly debated question.

There are two main aspects to the problem: (1) Can the whites maintain physical and mental health in the Tropics? and (2) can they be economically successful there? The answer to the first question was long held to be in the negative, as far as the tropical lowlands are concerned. But in recent decades there has been a definite swing to a more optimistic view, and for good reasons. Causes and cures have been found for such "tropical" diseases as malaria, dysentery, yellow fever, African sleeping sickness, hookworm, and others. Formerly physical labor in the Tropics was regarded as dangerous; modern evidence strongly indicates that it is instead an effective means of keeping fit, bodily as well as mentally. Moreover, air conditioning may in time become as significant in fighting heat as the traditional means of fighting cold are in temperate climates.

It cannot be denied, however, that the health problem requires constant vigilance, certain expenditures for sanitation, a balanced diet, and other precautionary measures. In other words, there must be a relatively high standard of living. This leads directly to the economic question. As a matter of fact, health and income are more closely intertwined in the Tropics than anywhere else. Although a discussion of economic problems is outside the scope of this article, a few points must be mentioned because of their fateful relation to the climatic struggle.

The leached soils of the tropical rain forest on the whole give low yields. This may be counterbalanced by obtaining two harvests a year, but that is not everywhere possible. Furthermore, there is reason to believe that cultivation requires more labor per acre of cropland than in the Temperate Zone, chiefly because of the need for frequent weeding. If these observations are correct, it means that the productivity of labor in the Tropics is low. This might be one explanation of why the white man usually has found small-scale farming unprofitable.

Even if this were not true, most tropical countries present problems associated with the presence of an indigenous population. Not only is the native because of his carelessness a constant source of infection, but, more important economically, he works for a far smaller reward than can the white man because he has much more restricted material and cultural wants. This competition naturally has a tendency to pull down the white farmer's income. Theoretically, this may be overcome in various ways—for instance, by producing high-value crops which the native does not raise or by using machinery for large-scale farming. But there is always the chance that the native will imitate him and plant the same crops; and as far as farming with machinery is concerned, there are various obstacles to success, especially the cultivation requirements of most tropical crops and, again, the presence of a cheap labor supply.

In view of these difficulties most experts agree that, although white settlement in equatorial lowlands is physically possible, the economic handicaps in comparison with those of other regions are such that at present intensive colonization seems inadvisable. Where colonies are contemplated, they should be preceded by experimental farms and established only under expert leadership.

Chances for settlement are considerably better in the cooler uplands of the Tropics. This is proved by a number of communities scattered through the Cordilleras of Central and South America as well as the African highlands. On the East African plateaus and the Rhodesian and Angolian uplands, at altitudes between 3,000 and 6,000 feet, white colonists raise cotton, coffee, sisal, maize, wheat, and livestock. Health conditions appear to be satisfactory. These colonies could be expanded if transportation were improved. It should be noted, though, that the Negro population, rapidly increasing in recent years, restricts the area available. Also, in most of these African settlements the white owner relies upon cheap native farm labor for much of the work; in other words, the farm economy resembles more the plantation or hacienda type than the small-scale family-farm community.

The highlands of Central Brazil may be climatically well suited to white occupation; moreover, the natives are comparatively few. But various institutional and social factors and lack of transportation facilities are formidable barriers to the development of this territory.

The lowlands of the outer Tropics have a comparatively cool season, which makes them better suited for the white man than are the equatorial lowlands. The climatic limitations lie in the distribution of the precipitation. Many parts of the outer Tropics have a protracted dry season and a highly variable rainfall. This is notably true of northeastern Brazil and northern Australia. In small areas irrigation may be possible. For the remainder, the great problem is to find commercial crops adapted to the short (and very warm) rainy season.

A good example of the effect of rainfall is the part of Australia located in the outer Tropics. Here the population is extremely sparse except on the east coast of Queensland, where there is sufficient rainfall for a variety of crops and sugarcane is the main commodity. The whites themselves do the heavy field work and seem none the worse for it. But two points should be noted: (1) Queensland is a white man's country since the colored labor formerly employed was forced to leave; (2) the Commonwealth subsidizes the cane growers by a high tariff on imported sugar. Even under these favorable conditions only the humid eastern part has been occupied. To the west and north lie almost empty semiarid wastes. The "white Australia" policy is understandable, but it places a heavy responsibility upon the leaders of the Commonwealth. There is an urgent need for effective occupation of North Australia by acclimatized whites.

Settlement in the Dry Lands

In comparison with the tropical regions, the desert offers no particular obstacles to acclimatization. As a matter of fact, the dry air and the absence of disease-carrying insects are, in most cases, favorable to health. Generally speaking, desert soils are rich in mineral nutrients; the fundamental condition needed for their development is the procurement of water. Modern techniques have greatly increased the means of conquering the desert, but they require a very large capital investment, profitable only if high-value crops are produced. The extensive irrigation works on the Indus, Nile, and Niger Rivers are well known. Obviously these areas are outlets for native rather than white farmers. Given favorable economic conditions, there is no doubt that the irrigated desert area could be enlarged. Outside the United States there are some possibilities in the west-coast deserts of South America and—probably of wider scope—in Mesopotamia, the lower Volga region, and Turkestan.

The rainfall in the semiarid fringes, although meager on the average, may in some years be considerable. These variations make the steppe a far more hazardous land with which to deal than is the desert. As far as climate is concerned, successful occupation depends upon how well the farming methods are adapted to these special conditions. It may be noted that substantially the same struggle characterizes settlement in the steppes of Argentina, South Africa, southern Australia, Manchuria, Mongolia, and southern Siberia. These semiarid regions, formerly the habitat of the roaming hunter or herdsman, have for the greater part been settled during the last century. This has been made possible through modern means of transportation and cultivation. In some of these areas the frontier is still moving forward, but in general it can be said that already the best steppe lands are occupied. The main task now is to consolidate the conquest in terms of a better adjustment to the peculiar environment. It is even quite likely that the forward surge into the dry realms has gone further than is wise under present conditions. Wherever further advance is possible it will require heavy capital investment. Clearly it is not production per acre that counts here, but production per man. Settlement, therefore, will always be sparse.

Settlement in the Polar Lands

The low-temperature climate appears to be the most formidable of the three extremes, if one may judge by the very scanty population. Even in the broad belt of the subpolar forest, or taiga, settlement has scarcely made a dent. Yet for the man from the middle latitudes acclimatization is fairly easy here; it seems that the contrast of light and dark seasons is harder to bear than is the intense cold of the long winters. The chief obstacle is the short season for growing crops. There are two other environmental factors, however, that restrict opportunities. One is the generally poor soils and the glacial morphology of the landscape; the other is the inaccessibility of most of this zone, since the continents of the Northern Hemisphere have their greatest width in these high latitudes and the Arctic Ocean has (or had until recently) no value as a communication route. But even in northern Scandinavia, adjacent to the open sea, the age-long struggle of European civilization against the subpolar forest has resulted in only a sparse population.

The areas of perpetual frost around the North and South Poles are obviously out of the question for permanent settlement, even though the establishment of meteorological stations, airplane bases, and mining camps may be expected as the ice caps gain in significance for the inhabited world. The tundra—the treeless, moss-covered polar steppe—has too short a summer to allow normal agriculture. The mean temperature of the warmest month is below 50° F., and only the top layer of the soil thaws during the warm season. For the settlement of people other than native nomads a new way of living must be found.

In this respect the recent policy of the Union of Soviet Socialist Republics is of great interest. The main goal is to create a safe navigation route through the arctic waters, practically a private corridor of some 6,000 miles, linking the western and eastern extremities of the country. In the last few years a score of ships have each season (July until October) made the through passage. The development of this route requires that various navigation facilities and ports of call be created along the arctic coast; this in turn will make possible the exploitation of the mineral resources as well as the export of timber from the southward forest zone. Because these extreme northern settlements are so remote, it is of crucial significance for the tenability of the whole position that the food problem be solved. The Central Administration of the Northern Sea Route, which has jurisdiction over the whole Russian Arctic (in Siberia as far south as the 62d parallel) is therefore charged with the development of its agriculture. The extreme north, as an official statement declares, must supply the industrial and trading population with vegetables and milk, organize forage bases for livestock, and establish hothouse production of antiscurvy greens.

Reindeer raising and hothouse culture are the only possibilities for the coastal fringe; it is claimed, however, that farther south, though still well north of the Arctic Circle, various berries and vegetables such as radishes, carrots, cabbages, and onions are grown successfully in the open. In view of the peculiar character of the Soviet regime and the baffling contradictions in the statistics, it is hard to say what the actual state of affairs is. Yet as an experiment in subduing the Arctic it deserves full attention.

Whatever the future possibilities of the tundra may be, it is unlikely that it will ever support a large number of people at a relatively high level of living. In this respect the taiga offers a somewhat better outlook. Climatic conditions there are not adverse to the production of well-selected crops. The limiting factors are principally the low temperature of air and soil in the spring and fall, but the shortness of the summer is partly counterbalanced by the great number of hours of daylight. Potatoes, flax, and various vegetables do well; even early-maturing grains and forage crops can be raised. The growing period of grains can be materially shortened by so-called vernalization, which consists in starting the germination process artifically, after which the plants are kept for a time in cold storage. If this procedure is economically feasible it will be an important means of pushing agriculture farther poleward.

The northward move of the farmer is determined not so much by the agricultural possibilities in themselves as by the demand for foodstuffs in areas of forest and mineral exploitation. Often he can supplement his income in winter by working in the mine, the forest, or the lumber mill. Agricultural expansion, therefore, depends upon the expansion of the latter industries and especially upon their degree of stability. When the policy is one of "cut out and get out," it leaves stranded farm communities in its wake and demoralizes the pioneer fringe. Only by carefully planning and coordinating the various activities can a thriving settlement be established.

In the Eurasian taiga the boundary of agriculture lies, on an average, farther north than in its American counterpart, owing to earlier settlement and greater population pressure. In the somewhat protected river valleys of central and eastern Siberia—as for instance in the Lena River Basin—farming is carried on as far as 65° N. In western Canada the 58th parallel is about the limit. The Northwest Territories of Canada beyond the 60th parallel comprise about 1,300,000 square miles but contain not more than 1,000 whites plus some 10,000 natives. Southern Alaska, while having no worse climate than Finland, has as yet only a very small farming population. Far-flung explorations, mostly by airplane, have been going on in the last decades, but no great undertaking like the opening of the Northeast Passage on the other side of the Arctic has as yet provided the inspirational stimulus for a determined assault on the Far North.

Conclusion

It is clear from the foregoing review that there are large areas still potentially available for human settlement. But it must be kept in mind that migration is essentially not a flow from densely populated areas to sparsely populated ones, but from areas of lesser to those of better opportunities. For some 400 years the European peoples have swarmed out into nearly empty lands, which were at the same time—broadly speaking—good lands. The situation is different now; land that has not yet been taken is mainly of a marginal nature, often because of its climate.

Controlling a new environment requires learning the laws of its behavior and devising ways to use them to the greatest advantage. No doubt science and technology will find further means of overcoming the present obstacles; even so, the borderlands with unfavorable climates can be won only with considerable effort and at high cost. This imposes a heavy burden on the modern pioneer, diminishing his chances of gaining a better living than he had in his home country.

This is not to say that the frontiers have become stagnant. At present there is an intensive search for lands suitable for European refugees. This need may well give new impetus to colonization of hitherto neglected territories. Nevertheless, it seems beyond doubt that the advance will take place more slowly than before. But just because expansion will be slower, it may be more substantial and may lead to a more secure grip on the climatic problem areas.

11. *Storms of the World* *

It seems almost impossible to believe, but the average number of thunderstorms per day throughout the world is 40,000. While thunderstorms may be mild as compared with hurricanes or tornados, they are often accompanied by violent winds and, not infrequently, by destructive hail. Thunderstorms, however, are only one type of storm. Others, such as the cyclonic type, although perhaps not so frequent, often are of much greater significance to man. Furthermore, storms as such are rarely discernible in climatic statistics and averages, yet, as Visher points out, they affect human activities to a much greater extent than any other weather phenomenon.

Storms have ever formed one of the most interesting features of man's environment. Throughout history they have disrupted his plans, from the time when he organized his hunts for the mammoth and the auroch

* Stephen S. Visher, "Storms of the World." Quoted, with omissions, from *Economic Geography,* Vol. 20, 1944, pp. 286–295.

The author (1887) is Professor of Geography at Indiana University. His field work and geographical interests have ranged far and wide, but he is best known for his research on human geography in the Middle West.

to the campaigns of the global war. They have destroyed his structures and hindered his progress, and wrought havoc among his crops and his cattle. They have changed the face of the landscape about him. They have complicated his problems, confused his courses, modified his adjustments to his environment. They have given him a vast share of the moisture he needs for life, much of the power he has used for travel and industry. Storms are interesting.

Of the many kinds of storms all are cyclonic in origin but one, and that exception is associated with cyclonic disturbance. All storms are related to local differences in atmospheric temperature and the rotation imparted to the air by the earth's rotation. They vary in size from the tiny whirlwinds only a few yards in spatial dimension that whirl dust and leaves and cornstalks across the midwestern prairie lands to the great massive geodepressions in atmospheric pressure hundreds, even thousands of miles across. Intermediate storms are waterspouts, tornadoes, and tropical cyclones. The features of such storms form the subject matter of this paper, without definite intent or purpose of explaining their cause or detailed character.

Thunderstorms

Most thunderstorms are minor, though important, features of the larger cyclonic disturbances—sort of local eddies. Although they are predominantly convectional rather than cyclonic, detailed studies have proved that convection sufficient or intense enough to cause thunderstorms almost never occurs except where the air is disturbed by at least a feeble cyclonic disturbance.

Thunderstorms are the most numerous type of storm with a world total of about 40,000 per average day, according to C. E. P. Brooks. They are most common in the rainy tropics, where each locality generally has one a day throughout most of the year and sometimes two or three. They are common in summer in the United States, where most localities have an average of one or two a week which pass at least within sight. In most subpolar regions, however, only a few occur, sometimes not a well developed one in a summer. Thunderstorms occur during every month of the year in tropical and subtropical regions, but are rare or absent during cold weather in regions with cold winters.

Most thunderstorms are only a few dozen miles across and as they commonly do not live to travel far, they affect only a relatively small area, often only a few hundred square miles. In the United States, however, they may travel a few hundred miles. Their average local duration is only an hour or two. Generally in the Westerly Wind Belt they travel in an easterly direction while in the Tradewind Belt, they commonly move westward. Their rate of average progress increases with the latitude; slow near the equator and usually 10–30 miles an hour in mid-latitudes.

Thunderstorms are significant in several respects. They form a major source of rainfall, cause a sharp drop in temperature, commonly have at least a little strong wind; their most distinctive feature is thunder, induced by lightning. Their cloud effects are noteworthy, some of the most imposingly beautiful seen anywhere. They often yield hail as well as rain. Altogether they are perhaps the most impressive atmospheric phenomenon commonly seen, highly useful in the aggregate, but locally often seriously harmful. The good they do, aside from the rain they bring to parched lands which often is highly welcome, includes the invigorating drop in temperature, the awe-inspiring display of cloud, lightning and wind, and the generally stimulating effect of the dramatic change of weather. The harm they do includes the squall wind, just before the rain falls. This gust often is violent enough to do considerable damage. The annual average property loss from "windstorms not tornadoes" in the United States is about $200,000,000. Much of this loss is due to thunderstorm squalls. Rain often falls torrentially, with the result that a large share of that which falls upon sloping ground runs away. Much of the soil erosion of our fields is due to thunderstorm rain. "Cloudbursts" not only cause erosion but they sometimes produce locally harmful floods. The lightning incidental to thunderstorms affords a spectacular display of usually harmless fireworks but also often does damage. Each average year more than five hundred people are killed by lightning in the United States. Many thousand livestock are also killed. Fires started by lightning annually destroy many million dollars worth of buildings and crops. Lightning starts many forest fires, some of which cause enormous losses. The lightning of thunderstorms does good as well as harm. Every flash combines some atmospheric nitrogen and oxygen to form ammonia, which when carried into the soil by rain adds fertility. Ammonia is an important source of increased fertility in the regions where thunderstorms are common. At the few stations where prolonged studies of this subject have been made, four to eight pounds per acre per year are added thus in England, six to eight in northeastern United States. Lightning flashes also create ozone, an unstable form of three oxygen atoms (O_3), instead of the stable two. Ozone has a pungent odor; some evidence indicates that it has a stimulating influence upon mental activity. Lightning is most dangerous at the beginning of the storm, just after the squall wind, when many lightning flashes travel downward. Later, lightning commonly is between parts of the storm or even upward from the ground.

Hail which falls in many thunderstorms is a convincing proof that the air is cold overhead even in hot weather. It also proves that the updrafts of air which make the imposing thunderhead are strong. Hail does much damage in various midlatitude regions and on tropical plateaus. In the United States the annual property loss reaches large figures. For example, detailed Federal estimates are that hail normally reduces the wheat harvest by some 15 million bushels, oats as much, and the corn harvest by some 24 million bushels. Considerable damage is also done to fruit, greenhouses, and poultry. Each year many people die in the United States as a consequence of hail bruises and annually some hundreds die thus in Europe, Asia, and on the plateaus of Africa.

Thunderstorms are most numerous in the doldrums or wet tropics. Many severe thunderstorms occur in Brazil, in the Congo basin of Africa, and in the East Indies. They are common throughout the rainy season in the parts of the tropics which have a wet season and a dry season, for example, the monsoon region of southeastern Asia and the Sudan of Africa. They are common during the summer months in the parts of the middle latitudes which have summer rainfall, for example in eastern United States, in Russia, and eastern Argentina. They occur occasionally in summer in subpolar regions and even in winter over the sea near Iceland. In the United States 60 to 80 thunderstorms occur in an average year in each locality in much of the Southeast, most in Florida, while 20 to 40 occur in most of the Northeast, and 20 to 50 in most of the West, except on the Pacific coast where there is little summer rainfall and hence few thunderstorms. Thunderstorms occur, however, in spring and autumn in the California type of climate; for example the vineyards of southern France suffer badly from hailstorms incidental to thunderstorms.

Tornadoes

Tornadoes, often called cyclones, are rare as compared with thunderstorms and are of minor importance, but in many cases they are so dramatically destructive that they attract undue attention. They are especially common and destructive in the United States; it is sometimes incorrectly stated that they are unique here. Typical tornadoes have repeatedly occurred in all the main parts of Europe, including England, in southern and eastern Asia, in Africa, and South America, while Australia according to the director of the Australian Weather Bureau has about as many per year (140) as the United States.

Tornadoes are violent tiny whirls started by opposing winds and associated with sharp vertical contrasts in temperature. They start in the clouds and extend to the ground only where the air near the surface is relatively warm, as compared with the higher air. Tornadoes rise above the surface again whenever the surface air is relatively cool. Hence, as to time of day, destructive tornadoes occur chiefly in the afternoon or early evening. The few destructive nocturnal tornadoes occurred on hot sultry nights. Weather Bureau experts can successfully predict the general occurrence of tornadoes, but not their exact location. As they affect such a tiny fraction of the large area in which they might occur on any particular day, the benefits derived from official forecasts are more than outweighed by the suspension of business, fear and even heart failure forecasts induce.

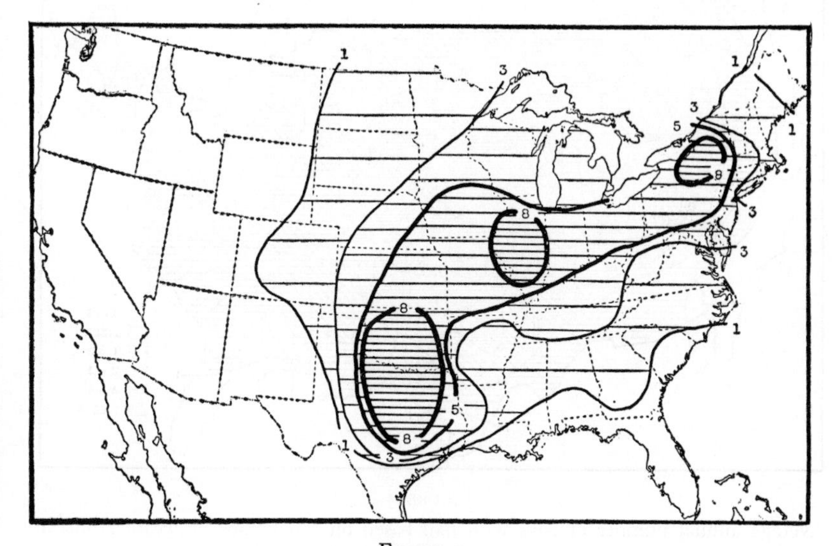

Figure 2

Lightning losses to farm buildings. Annual average, $100,000 (after Kincer).

Tornadoes are more than ten times as frequent near the center of the United States than in the Northeast or West. They are least common, however, in the most arid region, where violent almost tornado-like dust whirlwinds are frequent. In the approximately 2,800 tornadoes recorded by the Weather Bureau in the United States during the twenty years 1916–1935, 5,224 people were killed and property losses in excess of 230 millions of dollars were sustained. Losses in excess of $100,000 were caused by an average of about twenty tornadoes a year, losses in excess of $1,000,000 by about two. In that 20 year period, three caused losses of 24 to 43 millions of dollars each; one of these three and two others killed more than 100 people. The worst was that of May, 1925, chiefly in southern Illinois in which 689 lives were lost. The average American annual loss is 261 lives and about 12 million dollars worth of property.

Tornadoes have occurred in all of the States and Canadian provinces and in Alaska. They affect so small a strip (generally about a sixth of a mile wide by 10 to 30 miles long) that the chances that any spot will be hit are small. Even in the area where they are most common, the chances that a farm will be crossed in a century are less than one in a thousand. Many farms are crossed without damage to the buildings; many buildings are demolished without the loss of a human life.

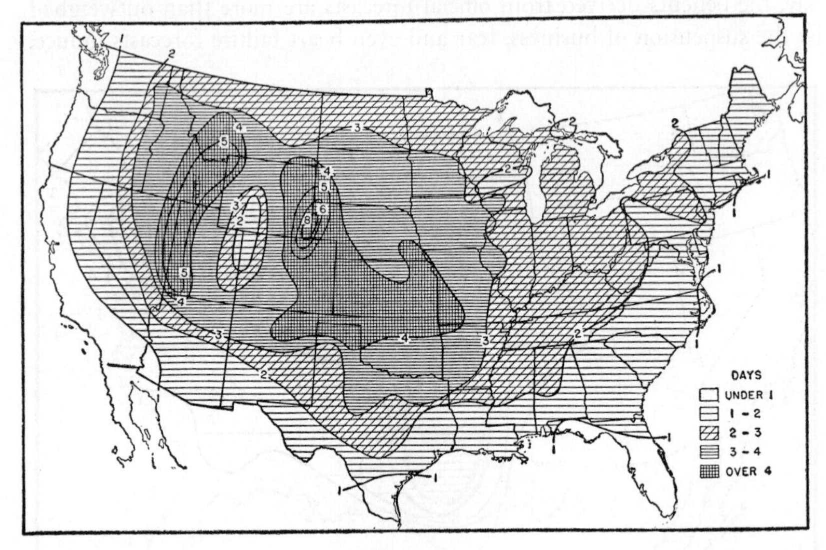

FIGURE 3

Average annual number of days with hail based on 200 first-order weather bureau stations, period 1899–1938 (*Yearbook of Agriculture 1941*).

Hurricanes, Typhoons, and Lesser Tropical Cyclones

More than 200 tropical cyclones, of which some 40 have hurricane winds, develop annually over the tropical and sub-tropical oceans. They affect significantly more than one-fifth of the globe and the world's population.

Although destruction they cause is often terrible, tropical cyclones benefit a much wider belt than they devastate. They do this chiefly by bringing rainfall to large parts of the tropics which otherwise would be too dry. Few tropical cyclones are destructive; the weaker ones usually do little harm and much good. The terribly destructive type rarely occurs, except in the Far East. Distant or incipient cyclones set up air movements which induce convectional over-turning, giving rise to thunder storms. Much if not most of the rainfall of these latitudes is induced by cyclonic disturbances, weak or distant. Tropical cyclones as a class certainly do more good than harm.

Tropical cyclones are whirling storms which vary in intensity from mild disturbances to violent hurricanes; they average about 300 miles across, develop chiefly in latitudes 10–20°, and travel generally roughly westward, pushed by the Trade Winds. They also move into progressively higher latitudes until they die away or leave the tropics. If they reach mid-latitudes, they slowly recurve and then are carried eastward by the prevailing Westerlies and become lows. Tropical cyclones usually travel rather slowly, generally only about ten miles an hour; the whirling winds about the center, however, have velocities ranging from about 20 miles an hour to more than 75. A few have wind velocities measured about 150 miles per hour, while the destruction which some have caused indicated even greater velocities. The wind's destructiveness is due partly to its sudden variations in velocity and direction.

Tropical cyclones are often destructive because of the strength of their winds, the torrential rainfall, and on bodies of water, the high and tumultuous waves. Typhoons, the name applied to strong tropical cyclones in the Far East, cause the death of an average of several thousand persons a year, few years pass without the death of more than a thousand, while occasionally huge numbers die. For example on August 3, 1922 more than 30,000 were reported killed near Swatow, China, while the next year the death of over 100,000 in and near Tokio, Japan is attributed to the typhoon which prevailed during the fires started by the earthquake of September 1. In India few years pass without numerous fatalities and occasionally the toll is huge; indeed there are competent estimates that more than 200,000 persons were drowned on October 3, 1876, and about 300,000 on October 7, 1737, in the delta of the Ganges-Brahmaputra River, near Calcutta. In the West Indies and neighboring regions, the toll is several hundred a year on the average, when account is taken of the heavy losses in exceptionally destructive storms. For example about 2,000 persons were killed in and near New Orleans in 1893, 3,300 in Porto Rico in 1899, 6,000 in and near Galveston in 1900, and 2,500 in Porto Rico and Florida in 1928. In Martinique and near-by islands as many as 20,000 were officially reported killed by a hurricane in 1781. Cuba has had hurricane fatalities of 1,000 or more during a number of years, and in 1791, 3,000 were reported killed there. The hurricane which demolished most of the houses of the capital of Santo Domingo, on the island of Haiti, on September 3, 1930, is reported to have killed about 4,000 people and done damage to property in excess of $40,000,000. Tropical cyclones that lack destructive winds often do serious damage by heavy rains, often more than 10 inches falling in a day and occasionally more than 30 inches in the two or three days as they pass. These deluges cause serious floods and severe soil erosion.

Tropical cyclones enter the United States chiefly from the West Indies and the Gulf of Mexico, but occasionally one progresses northward along the western coast of Mexico, affecting southern California or Arizona. Some storms which developed in the western Pacific (the Far East) as tropical cyclones (typhoons) also enter the United States from the northwest, as lows. Indeed a considerable share of our lows are of tropical origin. An average of about twenty cyclones a year enter the South or pass northward near the Atlantic coast. Of these, three on the average are hurricanes and two have gale winds (32–75 miles per hour).

Especially disastrous American hurricanes with the reported loss of life are as follows: 1881, August, coast of S. Carolina and Georgia, 500; 1893, August, coast of Carolina and Georgia, 1,000; 1893, October, New Orleans, etc., 2,000; 1900, September, Galveston, 6,000; 1915, August, Galveston, 280; 1915, September, New Orleans, 275; 1926, September, Florida-Mississippi, 399; 1928, September, Cuba, Florida, 3,000; 1935, September, Florida, 300; 1938, September, Long Island, New England, 682. American property loss was highest in the New England storm estimated at $400,000,000. The Galveston 1900 storm did an estimated damage of $30,000,000. The Florida hurricanes of 1926 and 1928 caused great tangible property loss, and in addition punctured the Florida boom, causing sharp decrease in real estate values.

Lows

The largest type of storm is the mid-latitude cyclone or low, of which somewhat more than a hundred occur each year in the United States and about as many in Europe, and produce an almost continuous change of weather. Other regions having many of these storms are the middle latitudes of Asia and the region around Antarctica, extending as far north as southern South America and southern Australia.

Lows have an average width of about 600 miles, ranging from about 200 miles to about 1,000 miles. They travel usually some 400–700 miles a day, two or three times as fast as an average tropical cyclone. Their normal wind velocity is about 10–20 miles per hour over the land, where ground velocities in excess of 30 miles an hour are rare. Over the North Atlantic and in the North Pacific, however, wind velocities of 40 miles an hour are common, and frequently cause seasickness to travellers.

Lows are important for five chief reasons: 1) they bring rainfall to large and important regions which otherwise would be dry, for example, most of interior United States; 2) they bring our changes of weather; 3) they afford the basis of our weather forecasts; 4) they cause considerable destruction of life and property, and much inconvenience, by the winds, rains, hot waves, and by the thunderstorms and tornadoes associated with some of them; 5) the changes of weather are stimulating to mankind both directly and indirectly. The importance of this influence is suggested by the fact that the more progressive, civilized peoples are in areas where numerous cyclonic storms cause frequent changes of the weather.

Lows of mid-latitudes are the great rain bringers of their region but many yield considerable rainfall only in the more humid sections of their paths. For example, in the United States, lows which cross from the Pacific to the Atlantic may yield no rainfall in the region between the Cascade-Sierre Nevada and the Rocky Mountains, and only a little over the Great Plains. But as they enter the humid eastern half of the country, they draw moisture from the Gulf of Mexico, and yield increasing amounts of rain as they pass eastward. Conversely, lows which pass from the Atlantic Ocean into Russia and Siberia yield less and less rainfall as they pass farther and farther from a sufficient source of moisture. In Central Asia they may cause only cloudiness, or perhaps yield a few drops of rain, as similar storms do in crossing our Great Basin. They bring rain by drawing moisture from the sea (as a result of the inblowing winds) and especially by inducing condensation and precipitation by the convectional disturbance which they set in motion.

Lows bring our change of weather by altering wind direction and velocity, by inducing cloudiness and producing rain. They change the winds because the fundamental part of a low is an area of below-average air pressure into which wind blows spirally. Thus on the western side there are northerly winds, which are usually relatively cold as compared with the southerly winds which are characteristic of the eastern side. Therefore a cyclone approaching from some westerly direction first causes the temperature to rise conspicuously, and then, as the center passes, to fall rather sharply. The warming as the low approaches is due not only to the warm southerly winds, but partly to the liberation of latent heat by the condensation of part of the moisture they carry. Clouds which are formed interfere with the escape of the heat, and help make the nights relatively warm. Cooler northerly winds which prevail shortly after the center of the low passes produce first a dash of rain or snow and then a clearing of the skies, with much cooler nights.

Lows afford much of our basis for weather forecasting since most scientific weather forecasting is based on a study of the approaching lows. The forecasters attempt to predict when they will arrive and whether or not they will have characteristics they had previously. Many lows are altered as they move eastward by the effect of other lows and highs. Their rate of advance eastward is not uniform and their courses are often changed. As a result, the forecasts are only approximately correct.

The general eastward movement of lows is due to the Westerlies, which prevail overhead most of the time in the United States, pushing the cyclonic masses east or east-northeast. That the highs move, in general, east-southeast instead of east-northeast, shows that the prevailing Westerlies are only one influence. The second influence is the result of the continual blowing of the Westerlies; air piles up in polar and subpolar latitudes. From time to time some of this air must return to lower latitudes or else finally much of the air would accumulate near the Poles. Our highs are masses of subpolar air which have broken away and are moving east-southeastward across the United States. A third, often highly significant influence which affects the courses followed by the lows is the air pressure conditions which prevail at the time in nearby areas.

Some Effects of Torrential Rains

Effects of heavy torrential rains resulting from severe thunderstorms are discussed in an article in the *Geographical Review*. Some extracts are relevant here. Buildings may be damaged by flooding of basements, weakening of foundations by runoff, and by water soaking. Buildings on lowlands may be partly submerged by the floodwaters of torrential rains. For example, the storm that brought 10 to 20 inches of rain in 24 hours to eight Weather Bureau stations in southeastern Alabama (March 14–15, 1929) flooded many towns. That rain caused an officially estimated damage of more than $3,750,000—not counting suspension of business.

City and town water supply, whether from shallow wells, reservoirs, or streams, and sewer disposal systems are seriously interfered with by torrential downpours. Heavy rainfalls injure roads, railroads, bridges, airports, and pipe lines by flooding, softening, and eroding. Although large-scale floods are caused by prolonged rains, the briefer storms often cause serious local floods. For example, on June 29–30, 1940, an estimated damage of $200,000 was done to roads, railroads and bridges in an area 50 miles by 100 miles in Texas, where from eight to 20 inches of rain fell in 24 hours and a number of people were drowned.

The damage to telephone, telegraph, and electric lines by torrential rains is partly due to the force of the water-laden winds that accompany most such downpours. But the damage is much increased by the softening of the ground caused by the large amount of water that runs down the poles. Electric light and power services may be disrupted by damage to the generating plant. If the plant is a hydro-electric one, the damage may be gradual, due to silting of the reservoir, or very rapid, due to breaking of the dam. Or the excessive rainfall may raise the water level enough to put the plant temporarily out of order. Fuel-powered plants, too, may suffer flood damage since their water requirements encourage location close to a stream.

Crops are damaged in several ways. Planting may be delayed; seeds and small plants may be washed out or buried beneath sediment; growth of weeds is facilitated, partly because cultivation is hindered. The value of unpicked cotton is greatly diminished when the open bolls are soiled with mud spattered by a hard rain.

The most serious long-term damage by torrential rains is that done by erosion and leaching. The South, where such rains are most frequent, is the large American region where soil erosion is most serious. Except for Florida and the low-lying land along the coast, fully four-fifths of the South has widespread "serious" or "harmful" erosion. By contrast, less than one-third of the North has either. It is obvious that the relatively extensive soil erosion in the South is due in part to the greater and more frequent hard rains.

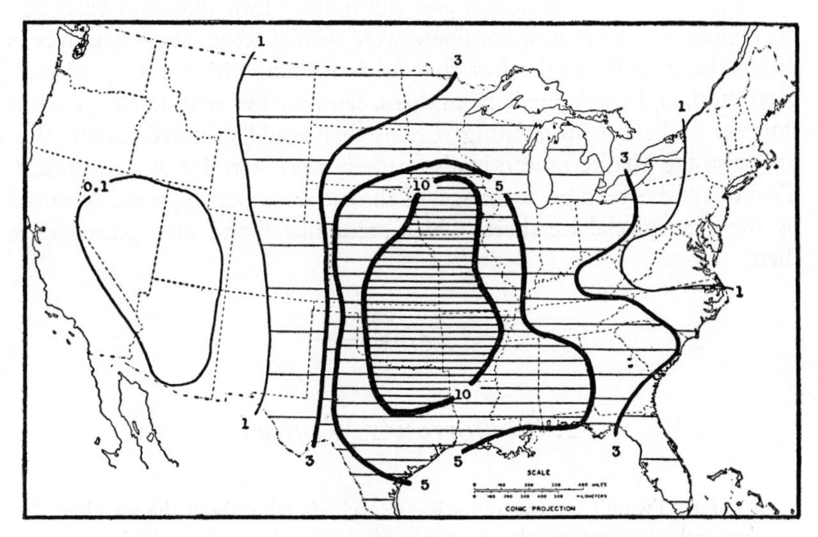

Figure 4

Average tornado frequency (number per year per state) in the United States (*Scientific Monthly*).

Cyclonic Storms and Civilization

The correspondence between the distribution of cyclonic storms and civilization has been discussed at length by Ellsworth Huntington in his *Civilization and Climate, Principles of Human Geography* and *Mainsprings of Civilization*. One-tenth or so of the land which has many lows is far ahead of the rest of the world in many respects. Analyses of production per worker, high achievements, and death rates have led Huntington to conclude that the main influence is the frequent change of weather. The many drops in temperature are stimulating, but also important are the many complications these storms impose. These call for continual adjustment. The many storms also insure a supply of moisture which is fairly dependable, as compared with that received in most of the world, despite the fact that the cyclonic regions have floods and drouths. People of Cyclonic Regions not only produce relatively large amounts of goods but lead in thriftiness, inventiveness, and in preparations for the future. The much disliked irregularity or uncertainty of the weather characteristic of cyclonic regions presumably has encouraged this forethought. In the parts of the world where weather changes are relatively few, people much more commonly "trust to luck."

Unquestionably the stormy regions now dominate most of the rest of the world politically, economically, and culturally. Two thousand years ago the regions which are now dominant were then of secondary importance is due perhaps partly to the fact that modern man, with the help of coal, glass, steel, and goods made from them, can now live with fair comfort in stormier and more stimulating regions than could primitive man. Possibly also the Mediterranean lands formerly were stormier than at present. That there have been great changes of climate since man appeared is proved by the great glacial ice sheets which accumulated and disappeared since then.

12. *Tomorrow's Weather* *

Mark Twain's famous remark, "Everybody talks about the weather, but nobody does anything about it," is fast becoming obsolete, at least insofar as doing something about it is concerned. Rainmaking has passed from the province of the medicine man into the laboratory of the physicist and the realm of the airman. Although these efforts are relatively small in scope and effect, they do indicate possibilities for controlling one of the greatest variables in man's environment—weather. Another major problem has been that of weather prediction. Improvements in instruments and communication, and, more important, the gathering of data by high-flying aircraft, particularly in polar regions, have made both short-range and long-range forecasting more precise and accurate. With these improved tools and techniques, weather prediction—of value to us all—may be expected to become more and more accurate. Current developments in research and practice are given in this selection.

"It may prove easier," remarked Irving Langmuir not long ago, "to make the weather than to predict it." However much this remark may irritate orthodox meteorologists, it illuminates the present state of meteorology and its baffling controversies. Ever since Vincent Schaefer made his first dry-ice run over a cloud in November, 1946, meteorology has been going through storms. As is normal in such periods, it is difficult to sort out biases and to separate fact from hypothesis. Since rain has high economic value, many farmers, ranchers, power companies, and others have decided to try the new rainmaking technology without waiting for meteorologists (and statisticians) to agree on its effectiveness. As one businessman explains, "Cloud seeding is so cheap that you can't afford not to try it." As a consequence, rainmaking has swiftly grown into a multimillion-dollar-a-year business that is spreading around the world.

As Dr. Langmuir's remark suggests, cloud seeding may be more than a local rainmaking stunt; conceivably it may trigger off large-scale atmospheric effects. At least this is his deduction from a remarkable twenty-month experiment which he asserts proved beyond doubt that periodic rainfall over half the U.S. was induced by silver iodide released periodically in New Mexico. The conclusion Langmuir draws is not that silver iodide is so powerful, but that the atmosphere is so unstable, so susceptible to faint proddings, that meteorologists can never hope to predict its behavior with certainty.

This most meteorologists are reluctant to concede. They are trying to improve forecasting techniques as if cloud seeding had never been discovered. While confident of doing better, they freely admit that present forecasts deteriorate rapidly beyond seventy-two hours, and that the Weather Bureau's experimental thirty-day extended forecasts, on balance, give results only somewhat better than climatic probability allows. On the other hand, the most successful industrial meteorologist in the country, Irving P. Krick, claims to have a sound method for predicting weather three and even six months in advance. . . .

Despite Krick, man's hope of predicting the behavior of the immense and restless atmosphere seems at least as chimerical as his attempt to define the limits of the universe. Yet the effort is going forward in many university and government laboratories, and, as in nuclear physics, the cost is being borne almost solely by the government. With plenty of money available, meteorologists are bringing some of the most advanced tools of modern technology to bear on their problems. They are probing the mechanism of storms with radar, plotting solar activity with coronagraphs, shooting instrument-carrying rockets (one or two a month) to the top of the atmosphere, and solving some of the most difficult equations known to mathematics with electronic computers. At the University of Chicago a young meteorologist has created a remarkable model of the atmosphere in a rotating dishpan. And at several cloud-breeding areas a private foundation, Munitalp (Platinum spelled backward), has installed movie cameras that, by time-lapse technique, make condensed records of cloud activity. Viewing these breath-taking, accelerated movies in color, one has the impression of seeing cloud behavior for the first time.

Yet the atmosphere cannot be examined in microcosm—despite the dishpan. Science must examine in detail and for long periods everything that may conceivably influence the weather, from variations in solar radiation to the temperature and circulation patterns of the oceans. "On some of our problems," says H. E. Landsberg, the Air Force's director of geophysics and weather research, "fifty years will not be too long to work."

Despite their complexity in detail, the basic motions of the atmosphere have a fairly simple origin. At the equator the earth's surface receives much more solar energy than it does at the poles. If there were no atmosphere, equator and poles would reach a temperature based solely on the rate at which they could radiate heat into space. The equator would be substantially hotter and the poles much colder than at present. The atmosphere, in obedience to the second law of thermodynamics, dutifully carries heat from hot regions to the colder. The currents generated by this process are deflected by the rotation of the earth, hence the prevailing winds at low altitudes and the so-called planetary waves at high altitudes. In its effort to reach dynamic equilibrium, the atmosphere is governed by self-regulating mechanisms, i.e., it has, in current jargon, various feed-back controls that provide a basic pattern of regularity, within which an infinite variety of small-scale adjustments may take place. These adjustments are the local weather.

Certainty vs. Uncertainty

There are two ways of looking at these grand atmospheric processes. The determinists hold that the atmosphere is a fluid that must conform to well-defined hydrodynamic equations of motion. This school owes much to the prodigious work of the Swedish-American meteorologist, Carl-Gustaf Rossby, director of the Stockholm meteorological institute, who established the meteorology departments at M.I.T. and the University of Chicago and taught in the U.S. from 1928 to 1946.

The other, and so far minority, school holds that the atmosphere is always on the verge of instability and that therefore weather is essentially probabilistic rather than deterministic. Irving Langmuir, the leader of this school, finds confirmation for his thesis in cloud seeding. In fact, he holds that cloud seeding is the most useful technique for removing the uncertainty from weather. Langmuir argues that precipitation is not an incidental but a fundamental part of the worldwide weather machine and that heat given off when water vapor condenses and freezes is great enough to influence significantly the motions of the atmosphere. Uncertainty enters, says Langmuir, primarily because water in clouds does not freeze spontaneously, as one might think, at 32° F., and in the temperate regions of the world precipitation seldom occurs until water inside a cloud does freeze.

The next question is, what induces water to freeze? It was while searching for the answer to this problem that Langmuir's General Electric associate, Vincent J. Schaefer, discovered that seeding a cloud with dry ice would turn the trick. Reason: it locally lowers cloud temperatures below —38° F., whereupon freezing appears to take place spontaneously. A little later another G.E. scientist, Bernard Vonnegut, discovered that particles of silver iodide would induce freezing, provided the temperature of the cloud was below 25° F. (General Electric holds the patents on both dry-ice and silver iodide seeding but has waived royalties.) It appears that natural nucleating agents, resembling silver iodide, customarily trigger the freezing that creates natural rain. These nuclei, however, seldom cause ice to form above 10° F. and often do not work until clouds reach —15° or below. Thus there is a critical temperature gap of at least fifteen degrees in which silver iodide will cause precipitation and natural nuclei won't. Moreover, most scientists now agree with Langmuir and Schaefer that the atmosphere is frequently deficient in freezing nuclei.

Langmuir thus concludes that natural rainfall is prone to uncertainty, and that there are in weather, as "in atomic physics, as well as human affairs . . . what we may call divergent phenomena where large important events grow from small beginnings . . ." Even Professor Rossby, the determinist, does not dismiss the Langmuir uncertainty thesis out of hand. "If Langmuir is right," says he, "we are wrong, and our attempts to forecast the weather will fail."

After more than six years of experimentation, meteorologists still cannot agree on cloud seeding's economic value. Moreover, the controversy has passed so completely into the stratosphere of higher statistics that it may be years before any agreement is possible. What makes the issue complex is this: if you seed a cloud and it rains, how can you be sure it wouldn't have rained anyway? Obviously there may never be proof enough to convince a complete skeptic. As one eminent statistician observes, "The more cautious we desire to be in asserting the effect of seeding, the less chance we shall have of detecting such effects if they actually exist."

There is no doubt that most of the first weather-modification experiments, including the early tests of Project Cirrus (a joint effort of General Electric, the Signal Corps, and the Office of Naval Research), were conducted without proper regard for the nasty questions that the statistician can pose. Any casual reader of the 1951 Project Cirrus report would conclude that cloud seeding clearly can produce gigantic effects. It mentions, for example, one seeding experiment in New Mexico that produced about 160 billion gallons of rain, and another that produced twice as much. (New York City's reservoirs hold about 250 billion gallons.) Dr. Langmuir calculated that there was only one chance in 100 million that these two rains were natural occurrences. Weather Bureau and university meteorologists found his statistics altogether unconvincing.

Rain at the Flip of a Coin

An independent series of cloud-seeding experiments conducted by the Weather Bureau and the Air Force during 1948 and 1949 gave astonishingly negative results. The results were so negative, indeed, that impartial scientists outside the controversy speculated that the Weather Bureau's experimenters might have succumbed, quite unconsciously, to bias. In any event, the results left statisticians almost as dissatisfied as did those obtained by Project Cirrus, so the Weather Bureau has now launched, in the state of Washington, a second series of experiments scrupulously designed in advance to meet all statistical objections. If all goes well, statistically significant results may materialize within the next two years. The basic principle being observed is randomization. When observers spot a likely-looking cloud, they will leave the decision to seed or not to seed to the flip of a coin, or to a list of random numbers. Rainfall under both seeded and unseeded clouds will then be compared. The tests are being conducted over two regions that historically receive almost exactly the same amount of rainfall. Any pronounced increase in rainfall over one region will have to be attributed to seeding.

Since the Weather Bureau plans initially to conduct cloud-seeding tests only from the air, professional cloud seeders have already protested that the experiments will not test prevailing commercial techniques. They argue that ground-based silver iodide generators must be operated throughout an entire storm and many hours per month to achieve ponderable increases in rainfall, and that brief seeding runs over a few clouds will prove virtually nothing. It would seem that the Weather Bureau might have speeded resolution of the controversy by copying commercial methods, which are based, after all, on substantial experience.

One other noteworthy series of cloud-seeding experiments was conducted in Australia by E. G. Bowen, a member of the Commonwealth Scientific and Industrial Research Organization. Both Langmuir and the Weather Bureau have derived comfort from Bowen's results. On the one hand, Bowen leaves no doubt that dry ice will produce "substantial amounts of precipitation which would not otherwise have fallen, provided conditions are right." * (No comparable statement can be found in the Weather Bureau's first series of reports.) On the other hand, Bowen seems to have had little success with a ground-based silver iodide generator. He concluded that in Australia, at least, airborne seeding showed more promise and that it might accomplish a 5 or 10 per cent increase in annual rainfall, "at the very outside." Since airborne seeding costs much more than ground-based seeding, Bowen doubts that rainmaking is of economic value except in marginal-rainfall areas where a little extra rain at the right time might greatly stimulate the growth of crops. He cites, for example, one Australian wheat area where every additional inch of rain in August and September would increase harvest value over $2 million.

Faced with the Langmuir–Weather Bureau split at home, many uncommitted meteorologists prefer to take their cue from Bowen. Thus, Henry Houghton, chairman of the American Meteorological Society's committee on weather modification, says that Bowen's 5 or 10 per cent figure represents his own estimate of the maximum value of seeding, though he says he has not seen even this figure confirmed by careful experiment. "If seeding produced more than that," says Houghton, "it shouldn't be so hard to find."

Is Optimism Unethical?

In the light of the foregoing, what is the businessman, farmer, or rancher to conclude about rainmaking? Is it, as Houghton suggests, almost wholly unproved and therefore a waste of money? The commercial cloud seeders feel that the furor over statistical validation has obscured the important fact that cloud seeding works. It works because the atmosphere is frequently deficient (the exact degree of frequency is arguable) in freezing nuclei; and, more to the point, natural nuclei are almost certainly less effective than silver iodide. The average businessman presented with comparable observations from his own laboratory would conclude that optimism was in order. For some curious reason most meteorologists have refused to be optimistic.

* In Bowen's report this statement also applied to the seeding of warm cumulus clouds with water drops, using a variation of a method first proposed by Irving Langmuir.

The commercial cloud seeders have been criticized by their academic friends for accepting money for applying an immature technology. The seeders retort that farmers and businessmen were anxious to try rainmaking and that if competent meteorologists did not accept the job, others less competent would. The seeders also point out that the technology could not be developed in the laboratory, that it had to be done out of doors, and that neither government nor university scientists seemed interested in doing the job. If one discounts some initial over-enthusiasm, it appears that the leading commercial rainmakers have been careful to acquaint clients with the uncertainties involved.

The seeders acknowledge that statistically significant results cannot be obtained in one or two seasons of operation over one target. Sometimes, as in the Cuban operation, the results seem tantamount to documentary evidence. In other cases the results are less striking. All the seeders agree, however, that results have been generally encouraging and that the sum of all their efforts is a strong plus. Their conclusion: *cloud seeding can usually increase precipitation 20 to 40 per cent.* They know as well as anyone that if this belief is not borne out during the next several years their business is washed up.

Pennies from Heaven

There are four large cloud-seeding organizations, all run by able meteorologists: Water Resources Development Corp. of Denver (Irving Krick); North American Weather Consultants, Pasadena; W. E. Howell Associates, Inc., Cambridge, Massachusetts; Weather Modification Co., Redlands, California.

Krick's organization, the first in the business (1950), is the biggest. Krick says that his rainmaking sales have topped $1 million in each of the past two years. (The usual cost to the client is 1 to 3 cents an acre.) Most of Krick's customers have been farmers and ranchers, but he has also worked for utilities, and last fall began seeding in Spain in a five-year effort to increase water supplies for hydropower. The Spanish contract is with Airfleets, Inc., one of Floyd Odlum's ventures, which will earn fees from several power companies if the project succeeds.

Last summer Krick had several hundred silver iodide generators spotted around the western half of the U.S. Usually they were turned on, at a phone call from headquarters, by a farmer or filling-station operator. Krick's procedure, followed in broad outline by others, is to watch the weather closely and, when he sees a storm brewing, to start seeding, using those generators located upwind from the target. "We work in step with nature," explains Krick, "and provide a catalyst to increase rainfall." As for the charge that he and others may be robbing Peter to pay Paul, Krick says nonsense. Nature, he maintains, has difficulty in precipitating even 1 per cent of the moisture available in the atmosphere during storms, hence there is plenty for everyone, even if silver iodide should double the rainfall in selected areas.

One of Krick's most impressive efforts: in the Rockies, where he has been seeding for three winters to increase the snow pack (to provide water for Denver), he reports that on target the three-year average snow pack is 175 to 288 per cent of the previous ten-year average.

Rain Every Tuesday

Since the professional rainmaker wants to produce local results for a specific client he has been anxious to disclaim responsibility for floods that may occur, coincidentally he hopes, hundreds of miles downwind from his generators. Thus even the rainmakers have not enthusiastically accepted evidence that over a twenty-month period Project Cirrus induced various periodicities in weather behavior over more than half the U.S. by releasing silver iodide at Socorro, New Mexico. It would be difficult to think of another experiment in modern science that seemed to prove so much, and yet was dismissed by the opposition as proving absolutely nothing.

Langmuir conceived his grand experiment, as part of Project Cirrus, after the Weather Bureau and other critics refused to credit seeding with the release of 480 billion gallons of rain on New Mexico in two days. Langmuir figured that if the weather were as capricious as his critics suggested, he would try to make it behave periodically by releasing, every week, about 1,000 grams of silver iodide. Initially Langmuir planned to run the Cirrus generator every Tuesday, Wednesday, and Thursday. The experiment had barely started in December, 1949, when heavy rains, concentrated chiefly on Mondays and Tuesdays, began drenching the Ohio Valley, causing near floods. Langmuir cut generator operation to Tuesday and Wednesday. Still the rains came. By April, 1950, the rainfall over the entire eastern half of the U.S. had assumed a striking weekly periodicity. Every Tuesday it rained from Alabama to Minnesota. One or two days later the storms had usually marched to New York and the New England coast. In subsequent months the periodicity became sporadic—upset, according to Langmuir, by commercial cloud seeders who had begun work in earnest. Nevertheless, an analysis by the Weather Bureau confirms that a strong tendency to periodic rainfall existed for the entire eleven months of weekly seedings.

In October, Langmuir began the second part of the experiment in which Project Cirrus tried to set up a weekly periodicity and then shift its phase.

The plan called for three generators to seed on Mondays for eight weeks, then shift to Fridays for eight weeks, then back to Mondays, and so on. This experiment lasted until mid-1951. If Langmuir could show that weather in the East followed the phase shifts of the generators, there would be virtually incontrovertible evidence of the power of silver iodide to modify weather.

Did Nature Obey Man?

Langmuir, who has still not published all his data, finds that the phase shift actually took place. Perhaps the only man who has tried to follow Langmuir's complex statistical analyses in detail is Glenn W. Brier, chief statistician of the Weather Bureau, for whom Langmuir has high regard.

On the crucial matter of rainfall behavior during the phase-shifting part of the experiment, Brier and Langmuir agree on observations, disagree on significance. They agree that some phase-shifting appeared to take place in the vicinity of Georgia, Alabama, Florida, and Tennessee, but not anywhere else. Brier maintains that the widespread absence of a phase shift makes its appearance in one region statistically insignificant. Langmuir says not so. He argues that many generators were operating north of his during the period, hence he could hardly influence the weather except in the Southeast.

Langmuir naturally feels that no one could hope to obtain more striking confirmation of a hypothesis than he obtained in his twenty-month experiment. Many meteorologists take the view that whatever happened, it was pure coincidence. Others, like Henry Houghton, frankly don't know what to think. "It's the most mysterious thing I have ever run up against," says Houghton. "How could one lonesome generator in New Mexico have the effect Langmuir says it had? If it wasn't chance, it was a totally new effect." Irving Krick's opinion is that the weekly seedings may have amplified and extended a natural tendency of U. S. weather to follow a five-to-seven-day cycle.

"The whole experiment was a great tragedy," observes one meteorologist. "If Langmuir actually influenced the weather, no one will believe him. If the periodicities were mere coincidence, nature played Langmuir a dirty trick."

Electronic Prediction

The real test of Langmuir's remark, that it may be easier to make the weather than to predict it, may come not from cloud seeding but from straightforward efforts to predict the weather. The most ambitious forecasting effort is being conducted with the aid of an electronic computer at the Institute for Advanced Study, under mathematician John von Neumann.

Prediction by computer is called numerical prediction and is strictly a determinist approach. It assumes that the atmosphere, as a fluid, is subject to dynamic laws that can be expressed in a solvable series of differential equations. The information fed into the institute computer consists of atmospheric pressure-level readings at 300-kilometer intervals on a grid covering most of the U.S. and part of Canada. (The readings actually represent various altitudes at which a given atmospheric pressure is observed. For example, the 700-millibar level usually lies between 9,500 and 10,500 feet.) Early computations took account of only one pressure level, represented by 361 readings. When the computer was fed 722 readings, representing two levels, the accuracy of prediction improved noticeably. The trick has been to develop a series of equations that will take observed readings and predict the readings that may be expected one hour hence, two hours hence, and so on. For the present, the goal is a good prediction twenty-four hours hence. (For one pressure level this takes the computer six minutes.) It should be stressed that the machine's product requires a good deal of interpretation before it resembles a conventional forecast of weather, but von Neumann sees no reason why, in time, the machine could not be made to give rainfall and temperature predictions in usable form.

The first man to examine the possibilities of numerical prediction was a British mathematician, Lewis F. Richardson, who worked out his equations while he was a stretcher-bearer in the first world war. Electronic computers had not been invented and Richardson estimated that it would take 64,000 people using ordinary desk calculators to keep pace with the weather around the globe. While Richardson had great vision, the equations he developed did not produce satisfactory forecasts.

When von Neumann, shortly after World War II, obtained government backing to build an electronic computer he decided that one of the problems he would like to tackle was numerical prediction. Jule Charney, a gifted young meteorologist-mathematician who had worked with Rossby, was brought in to take up where Richardson had left off. Collaborating closely with von Neumann, Charney has spent over five years refining mathematical models of the atmosphere. By July he expects to have tried out a five or six-level model, i.e., one that takes account of five or six pressure levels. "At that time," he says, "we will have exhausted our intellectual capital. If our predictions still leave much to be desired, we will have to think of something really new. Probably we shall have to worry much more about turbulence. We shall have to proceed inductively, using the computer as an experimental tool."

If Electrons Fail

Some meteorologists will not be surprised if numerical prediction "leaves much to be desired." In general they belong to what might be called the statistical school. This school holds that, turbulence aside, the Charney group "just doesn't have the stuff to crank into the machine." The alternative they suggest is to let statistics uncover pertinent relationships between successive weather developments. A leading advocate of statistical techniques is George P. Wadsworth, associate professor of mathematics at M.I.T. He writes: "According to a prevalent misconception, statistical methods mean the neglect of root causes and the substitution of shadow for substance . . . it cannot be too strongly emphasized that the use of statistical techniques for the solution of the behavior of the weather systems is equivalent to the setting up of equations of motion and obtaining the solution."

In general, Wadsworth's views support the beliefs of Irving Krick, who in addition to being the world's leading rainmaker, is perhaps the most audacious long-range forecaster. Krick thinks nothing of making a day-by-day weather forecast months in advance. Last winter he predicted this summer's weather (not in daily detail, of course) for Mitchell, one of the major air-conditioner manufacturers.

For about fifteen years, 1933–47, Krick was head of the department of meteorology at the California Institute of Technology. Toward the end of the Thirties he pioneered the field of industrial forecasting. During World War II he became one of the leading Army Air Forces forecasters and was on the team of six that made the fateful forecast for the Normandy invasion.

Krick bases his short and long-range forecasts on the analogue method—a method not featured in any U.S. curriculum since he left Caltech. The method rests on the assumption that weather patterns repeat and that a search through a classified file of past weather maps will uncover an "analogue" of current weather. Krick does not claim to have originated the method, only to have refined and improved upon it.

While the analogue method alone is adequate for six-to-nine-day forecasts, it has to be combined with something else to produce a long-range prediction. In Krick's method the something else is the upper atmosphere and the effect it has on a persistent high-pressure region in the Pacific, which serves as a convenient reference "cell." The high, in turn, depending on its position, exerts a strong influence on the path of storm tracks crossing North America. (For other parts of the world there are other reference cells.) Krick, moreover, finds that the high moves about the Pacific in a reasonably predictable manner, thereby providing a basis for long-range forecasts.

Under a Planetary Wave

Until Krick chooses to publish his methods in detail, meteorologists will have a hard time appraising the validity of his approach. Meanwhile the prevailing body of opinion favors the type of long-range forecasting practiced by Jerome Namias, head of the Weather Bureau's Extended Forecast Section. The section grew out of a government-sponsored effort conducted at M.I.T. during the Thirties by Professor Rossby. Namias, who worked under Rossby, transferred the project to the Weather Bureau in 1940. M.I.T. still continues to do background research.

The basic concept developed by Rossby and his group was that the upper atmosphere contains planetary waves—sinusoidal air currents that girdle the globe and provide the broad-scale setting for local weather. Rossby developed a theory making it possible to predict the general movement of the planetary waves, which, in turn, provided a rational basis for predicting the weather underneath. While the method cannot forecast the day-to-day weather, it permits one to find areas where temperature and rainfall may deviate from normal. Namias' section makes such predictions for five and thirty-day periods. (A year's subscription to the thirty-day forecast costs $4.80.)

During World War II Namias' five-day forecasts were compared with those made by Krick and by C. L. Mitchell, a top-notch Weather Bureau forecaster who had a system based largely on his long experience. (At that time only Krick had a thirty-day method.) The evaluation group concluded that there was, at that time, little to choose among the three methods.

Where the Jet Winds Blow

Until that remote day when thirty-day forecasts are made by electronic computer, improvements in present methods may come from several directions. One hope is that better knowledge of the jet stream will make it easier to predict planetary-wave behavior. The jet stream is a fast-moving (up to 300 mph) river of air that seems to define the core of planetary waves, 30,000 to 40,000 feet above the earth.

A recent observation made by Vincent Schaefer may simplify the task of keeping track of the jet stream's location. In studying the cloud movies made by Munitalp, of which he is scientific adviser, Schaefer concluded that about 80 per cent of the time the jet is accompanied by several telltale cloud types. The Air Force and commercial airlines hope they can use the jet stream to speed their aircraft, and Schaefer's clouds should help put them on its track.

Another extremely promising avenue of research, which could help both Namias and Charney, is the weather-in-a-dishpan experiments of Dave Fultz of the University of Chicago. His swirling liquids not only create patterns strikingly like planetary waves, they also generate thin swift currents that resemble the jet stream.

What's the Paper Say?

For the hard-pressed daily forecaster, trying to make his deadline, the feverish postwar research effort has not yet produced anything as helpful as the famous Norwegian polar-front theory, now some thirty years old. While the Weather Bureau's twenty-four-hour forecasts are approximately correct 85 per cent of the time, a substantial part of this score is built up during periods of easily predicted weather. When sudden weather shifts occur, the forecasters are frequently caught off base.

If Ben Franklin, who is credited with being the first to appreciate that weather moves across the map were forced to judge modern meteorology solely by the daily weather forecast, he might be dismayed at the lack of progress. If, however, Franklin could glimpse the rockets, the radar screens, the radiosonde balloons, Jule Charney's computer, and Dave Fultz's dishpan, his dismay might disappear. As a born experimenter he would surely recognize Langmuir and Schaefer as kindred spirits. And it would be difficult to conceive of his being pessimistic about the long-term prospects of weather modification.

13. *The Arctic in Fact and Fable* *

In a time when the two major world powers face each other over the North Pole, a knowledge of the Arctic—particularly of Arctic weather—is essential for security. Few areas of the world, however, are less well known than the Arctic, although defense requirements are increasing our knowledge of this region very rapidly.

* Vilhjalmur Stefansson "The Arctic in Fact and Fable." Headline Series, No. 51 (New York: Foreign Policy Association, March–April, 1945).

The author (1879–) has been a consultant on the Arctic for the United States Government and is now in the same capacity at Dartmouth College. He is one of the great Arctic explorers and is the author of many books on the Arctic.

Stefansson, who has spent many years in the Arctic, is more optimistic regarding the possibilities of settlement in the Arctic than are most other authorities. In this selection he debunks many popular misconceptions about Arctic life generally, and Arctic weather and climate specifically. Even so, his picture of the Arctic would hardly induce most of us to pack up and leave our more moderate climate.

There are two kinds of arctic problems, the imaginary and the real. Of the two, the imaginary are the more real; for man finds it easier to change the face of nature than to change his own mind.

Since they are the more difficult, we consider the imaginary problems first. Also, you cannot approach physical difficulties with the right mental attitude unless you first get past the mental hazards.

Our immediate purpose is to deal with "The Arctic" as that region surrounding the North Pole which is as yet little colonized. Generally speaking, this means a region that has been "discovered" within historic time and which still remains comparatively undeveloped, in the sense that there are few such institutions as cities, roads, schools. The population of European ancestry is small, and what there is of it is engaged mainly in frontier enterprises such as trading with natives, whaling, pioneer mining, law enforcement, missions. We cover the region usually called "Arctic and sub-Arctic."

In Canada something over 11,000,000 people dwell in the southern one-third of the country, a good deal fewer than 100,000 in the northern two thirds which, roughly, corresponds to the political subdivision Northwest Territories. This is our field in Canada—this and Yukon Territory. In North America we deal also with Labrador and Alaska.

Greenland is part of our sphere, but not Iceland, for conditions in Iceland are not such as we think of as Arctic, or even sub-Arctic; for instance, the average temperature of Reykjavik for the coldest month of the year is about like that of Philadelphia. For similar reasons, we do not deal with the western seacoast of Scandinavia, though we do include the northern interior, roughly Norwegian, Swedish and Finnish Lapland. Eastward from there in the Soviet Union we include a belt which is at first narrow but widens eastward to embrace large parts of the basins of the great north-flowing rivers, the Ob, Yenisei and Lena, streams comparable to the Mississippi, and the basins of the smaller streams which have a comparison range between the Hudson and the Missouri in the United States.

These are the mainlands with which we deal, and the islands to the north of them. On the north they are separated from each other by a mediterranean sea that is navigable around its edges during the summer months but otherwise covered by drift ice that prevents navigation by ordinary vessels. During winter the margins of the sea ice are landfast against various coasts. Apart from this, even in mid-winter, the floes are moving. There are no vast expanses of ice but millions and billions of cakes, ranging in area from the infinitesimal to several hundred square miles.

When floes break during summer they remain separate until autumn, dividing and redividing, becoming smaller and smaller. As winter approaches and frosts increase, the floes begin to be cemented together, and you have two processes going on side by side and compensating each other. Under stress of wind and current, perhaps through the impact of near-by floes, there are cracks forming, technically known as leads, in which open water appears where there had been ice. Thus the number of floes is increased, even during the coldest month of winter. But ice forms rapidly on the open water when temperatures are low, bridging the leads and cementing the floes, joining them up into new combinations and so decreasing the number of individual pieces.

The motion of sea ice is at all times sluggish. You can travel over it with comparative safety during winter, afoot or by sledge, for the floes are large, sometimes twenty or even thirty miles across. When you come to a break, you may be able to step across it; in any case, you can wait until the frost bridges over the lead, usually within two or three days.

In summer this kind of travel is difficult, for the floes are numerous and smaller, there is more open water, more motion, and, worst of all, there are ponds of water on top of the ice. These ponds are fresh water, incidentally, for sea ice, although bitterly salty when new, is gradually deprived of its salt content during the first year. Chunks from a floe which is nine months old can be broken off and melted into passable, slightly brackish drinking water. When the floe is more than a year old, you will have difficulty in noticing even a trace of salt, and when it is more than two years old you would need some delicate chemical test to determine that there is more salt than in rain water.

We shall talk, then, about the northern frontier lands of the New World and of the Old, with some reference to this mediterranean sea that divides them on the north, and to the rivers and lakes.

• • • • •

In its handicapping power second only to the belief that life is not possible in the remote North is the supplementary view that ordinary human beings would not like it. This general view comes under a number of specific headings, among them that it is too cold in winter, that it is not warm enough in summer, that the absence of sunlight in winter has a depressing effect on the human spirit, and that, in any case, activity in the North is possible in summer only, the winters being a time of confinement, a sort of hibernation.

As to the intensity of cold, it is fairly well agreed that if you were to spend a whole year at the very North Pole, latitude 90° North, or even a whole century, you would never observe a temperature colder than 55° below zero. Make it —60°, to be liberal; three states in the Union, according to *Climate and Man,* the 1941 Yearbook of the Department of Agriculture, have records that cold or colder. They are Wyoming, —66°; Montana, —63°; and North Dakota, —60°. There are people living at the special cold spots in these states some of whom will tell you that they like the climate.

We know that on the whole Arctic coast of the North American mainland there is no weather bureau record as cold as 55° below zero. There are five states of the Union which have records of —55° or colder. These are, in addition to the ones already named, Minnesota, —59°, and South Dakota, —58°.

As you go south from the north coast of the mainland, whether in the Old World or the New, the extreme minimum temperatures of winter get lower and lower until you have passed out of the Arctic into the north temperate zone. So far as we know at present, the coldest spot in North America is at or near Fort Good Hope, on the Mackenzie River, about 20 miles south of the Arctic Circle, with a minimum record of 79° below zero. In the Old World, the coldest spot is Oimekon, in Yakutia province, about 150 miles south of the Circle, with temperatures colder than 90° below zero, meaning something lower than 120 degrees below freezing.

Continuing farther south, whether in North America or Siberia, the lowest temperatures are progressively higher and higher; but as we have said, you have to go to and through the state of Wyoming in North America, and correspondingly far south in the Old World, to reach a point where it is less cold on the chilliest day of the year than the lowest theoretically possible record at the North Pole.

We are talking of low, level country in this entire discussion, for we are concerned with places where men live or can live, not with mountain tops. However mountain tops are not at all times colder than valleys. Mountain heights are relatively cool during summer and on comparatively warm days in winter; but on any day that is colder than 40° below zero in the valley you are sure to find it growing warmer gradually as you climb a near-by mountain slope.

Nor is it true, as formerly believed, that places which are very cold in winter are also very cold in summer. The cold pole of our earth, so far as we know, is at Oimekon; and this town is in a forested district, with some of the land in grain fields. Experimental stations of the Soviet Government may now be planting wheat; but according to our information, which is of some years back, the farmers around the cold pole were raising barley, oats, and rye.

When I first went north down the Mackenzie River, in 1906, I found at the cold pole of North America, Fort Good Hope, not merely a beautiful garden but the information that potatoes from it were shipped downstream for the trading posts of Red River and Mackenzie River and also upstream, southward. Today potatoes are grown both south and north of Good Hope and its preeminence as an exporting center of garden produce has disappeared; but the fact remains that, since the latter part of the nineteenth century, the cold pole of North America has been well known for its vegetable and flower gardens.

Great heat in the Arctic summer is found only on low, snow-free land; and, excepting Greenland, more than 90 per cent of all Arctic land is snow-free in August. Greenland is a mass of ice because it is a mass of mountains, but even in Greenland 15 per cent or more of the land is low enough to be ice-free. Peary Land, at the north tip of Greenland, is one of the largest ice-free parts of this island continent. Peary was there in summer and reported bumblebees and butterflies among the flowers just back of the most northerly coastline in the world.

It is never hot out on the polar sea, for the drifting ice and the cold water act as refrigerators; but it thaws even at the North Pole in midsummer and it rains instead of snowing. The Papanin expedition, in the immediate vicinity of the Pole, had their first rain of the season on June 28 and the last one on August 26.

We have disposed, then, of the first two points we just raised. The Arctic cannot be too cold for human habitation in winter, for if it were a number of our forty-eight states would be uninhabitable; it cannot be so very cold in summer or they would not be raising grain at Oimekon and potatoes at Good Hope.

But is the absence of the sun depressing to the human spirit and are conditions generally such that you would go into a gloomy sort of hibernation for the winter? We consider the last of these points first.

Up to and including the expedition of Sir Edward Parry, who wintered in uninhabited Melville Island during 1819–20, it was the general belief that polar exploration would necessarily consist of active summers and hibernating winters. We have already mentioned how the first Parry expedition confirmed this by going into a kind of winter house arrest. But his second expedition, a few years later, was in a country where there were Eskimos. Parry and his men soon found that the Eskimos liked to travel in winter and that white men could travel also. From this time on, the idea that winter is a good period for northern travel developed, though slowly. Twenty-five years later John Rae, of the Hudson's Bay Company, was apparently the first to believe, argue and show by his own example that winter is a good season for long journeys. He failed to make any substantial number of converts even among the explorers. It remained for Rear-Admiral Robert E. Peary to demonstrate to the satisfaction of his fellow explorers of the Arctic (though not to those of the Antarctic) that winter is the best traveling season of the year.

Peary laid it down as a principle that in the Far North summer is for preparation, and in that sense for idleness. The favorable time for long journeys, when the ice is strong enough to travel on, starts, according to Peary's view, in January, the second coldest of the months, or in February, which is the very coldest. Overland travel, or travel upon the frozen sea, would close in May or early June, when the snow begins to thaw in very high latitudes.

Those used to the Arctic climate have a general preference for mid-winter as against mid-summer. You will find that explorers whose expeditions were short, involving only one wintering, hardly ever affirm and sometimes strongly deny that winter is the pleasantest of the seasons. Explorers who have spent two or three winters begin to favor the cold season as pleasanter than the warm, this bias increasing with their length of service in the north.

The rule seems to be that you find in any part of the world a preference for the sort of climate to which the people there are most accustomed, this preference being the more clear-cut the more uniform the climate. Confining ourselves, then, to continental weather, which is more seasonal and less variable than that of northerly islands, we can lay it down as a safe bet that if in a given section the summer is longer than the winter, then the majority of the people living there are going to prefer the summer. But, if, as in Arctic Canada, Alaska or Siberia, the winter is notably longer than the summer, a majority will prefer the winter.

The proponents of summer will grow in number as you go south; those who prefer winter increase in percentage as you move north. The dividing line in North America is probably about the middle of Canada, somewhere near Great Slave Lake. In Alaska it is no doubt farther north, for Alaska is a peninsula and the ocean is permitted to give the southern part of the territory what is in effect an insular climate.

We come now to the last of our four points, the idea that the absence of the sun in winter has a depressing mental effect. We have, by implication, dealt with this common belief of Europeans; now we deal with it explicitly.

It is during the absence of the sun, as we have brought out, that overland and over-ice travel find their ideal conditions. Good travel conditions are particularly a requirement among hunting peoples, who must follow the game. This is easy in winter, when you can use dog sledges; it is difficult in summer, when the dogs carry packs and the people carry back loads, a cumbersome and laborious mode of travel.

The main transportation difference between the seasons is that you can walk on water only when it is frozen. In the summer boats can be used on large lakes or deep rivers and on the sea; being restricted to these channels is troublesome to the hunter, for the caribou do not obligingly travel along rivers, lake shores, or coasts, but tend to be on the open plains far from the large water courses.

In the whole North, and southward beyond the middle of Canada, the land on which grow the prairie grasses, as well as the trees of the forest, is permanently frozen when you get down a few inches or at most a few feet, and from there down in some cases to at least five hundred feet beneath the surface. Wherever the subsoil is frozen there cannot be any underground drainage. This means that on level or rolling land, anywhere except on mountain slopes, there is what may seem an incredible number of lakes; the surface of the country in vast areas is half water, in some large districts as much as 60 per cent water. The lakes, many of them shallow, are connected frequently by sluggish river channels.

Not only do you have to detour in summer when you come to a lake; you may detour in the wrong direction and find yourself an hour or two later at the tip of a peninsula. Moreover, even if the frost is only six or eight inches down, your feet keep slipping into mud-filled cracks between the hummocks of vegetation, and the clay is likely to stick to your feet, making them heavy and tiring you out.

Primitive Arctic man, therefore, does most of his traveling and a large part of his work in winter, except in a few special districts. European man soon adopts the same practice.

For instance, when the Canadian National Railways were building the road from The Pas to Churchill in the 1920's, they learned during the first year that much of their work was more easily done in winter than in summer. On the assumption that the railway construction would be a summer job, with idle winters, they had estimated that the cost per mile over the frozen muskeg would be three or four times as much as the average in southern Canada. But the engineers discovered during the first building season the advisability of reversing many procedures. For instance, instead of stripping off the topsoil with its vegetation, they learned to leave it where it was and to put additional soil on top of that—or, rather, things like peat and moss. By removing the topsoil the first year they had converted what appeared to be solid ground into seas of mud, when the sun got a chance to strike a black surface; it takes years at terrific cost of money and labor to fill in these mud sinks with gravel. But, through discouraging the thaw instead of encouraging it, they were able the second year to build large sections of the road upon frozen ground so that it remained frozen and therefore continued to be as solid year after year as if it were a bed of concrete.

In short, these railway builders, by discarding standard engineering procedures, built easily, cheaply, rapidly and solidly a railway that would have been one of the costliest in the world if constructed by regular southern methods. It turned out to be, mile for mile, one of the cheapest railroads ever built in Canada.

It is only during the present war that most Americans are getting a few ideas on how to behave in cold weather. The procedure and principles seem obvious when you once get hold of them, as, for instance, that crossing rivers when they are frozen is easier for an advancing army than when the rivers are unfrozen.

But go back to the newspaper files that deal with the first Soviet-Finnish war and you will see that only a few years ago we did not understand why the Red Army could advance the more easily the colder the weather. You will find our published comments on the first two months of that war filled with concepts that were in 1939 still almost exactly like those of our own Revolutionary War. Many things that look like advantages to us now, such as hard frost and the ice it produces, looked profoundly disadvantageous to us during the years that immediately preceded the Second World War.

It is in relatively southern countries like Italy, Greece, and Yugoslavia, even the Ukraine, where winters are only moderately cold, that summer campaigns are easier. As you go north, winter becomes more and more advantageous to those who know how to use it, particularly to an attacking force; when you are on the northern half of the Finnish-Soviet frontier, well north of Lake Ladoga, the winter becomes distinctly more favorable than summer, especially to heavily mechanized attacking forces.

14. *The Winter of 1948–49 in the Great Plains* *

Long-term averages of weather that make up what we call "climate" fail to give the details of day-to-day weather. The average January temperature at Lincoln, Nebraska, for example, is 24.6 degrees Fahren-

* Reprinted from Wesley Calef, "The Winter of 1948–49 in the Great Plains," *Annals of the Association of American Geographers,* Vol. 40, No. 4, Dec. 1950, pp. 267–292. By permission. The author (1914) is Assistant Professor of Geography at the University of Chicago.

heit, but this number indicates very little of the actual conditions in Lincoln as they occur from day to day, or in January of one year as compared with January of another year. Man experiences weather rather than climate, and when exceptional weather conditions prevail, they may affect climatic averages very little; however they are often catastrophic to the people living in the area. Extremes of weather are generally of greater significance to rural people than to urban people. This selection shows the effect of severe weather in a cattle-grazing region of the Middle West.

Highly unusual weather conditions prevailed throughout the entire western United States during the winter of 1948–49, but nowhere were conditions more extraordinary than in the Great Plains region. The fierce and protracted blizzards, the low temperatures, the long periods of high wind velocity and drifting snow, and the great sleet storms of the winter of 1948–49, by general agreement of old inhabitants, livestock men, meteorologists, and railroad, highway, and communications engineers, constituted the severest and hardest winter within their memory or on record. But, as one writer has shrewdly observed: "The winter's storms are spoken of collectively, which may be misleading. For not only were they different in calendar and geography, but they were different in kind and hence in effect." If climate is the sum of the weather of an area, the extraordinary conditions of the winter of 1948–49 must in the future constitute a major component in the climatology of the Great Plains region. This study deals with the distribution of the "kind" of storms and the "effect" of them in the Great Plains region during the winter of 1948–49, and is, therefore, a study in geographic climatology. It attempts to describe conditions during the storms, their duration, the pattern of their occurrence, the measures taken to cope with the storms' problems and effects, the effectiveness of these measures, their implications for the future; and, finally, both the short-range and long-range effects on the economy of the area.

The three major sources of information were local interviews, the files of the local and metropolitan papers, and several official or semi-official reports on some aspect of the storm. The area most intensively investigated includes roughly the states of Nebraska and Wyoming, and immediately adjacent parts of Colorado and South Dakota.

The Opening Storm of the Winter

On Wednesday, November 17, 1948 a small local snowstorm developed in central Wyoming. The center of the storm moved southeast at a speed

---

He has done considerable field work on land and water problems in the semiarid regions of the United States.

much lower than usual. As the low pressure area moved eastward it began to increase in intensity. A strongly developed "high" existed over Canada, and winds of gale strength began to sweep southward toward the center of the low pressure area. Kansas experienced the most severe November blizzard of record and it was among the worst in Nebraska.

A critical factor with regard to this storm, *as was true of most of the storms of the winter,* was the slow, leisurely manner in which the center of the cyclone moved to the east. On the morning of the 17th the center of the storm was in southeastern Wyoming, and 24 hours later it had moved in a southeasterly direction as far as southeastern Kansas. At this juncture, instead of moving eastward, the storm turned and moved very slowly almost straight north; on the morning of the 19th it was centered in southwestern Iowa. The result of this slow movement was to change what might have been an ordinary blizzard of the Great Plains into a fierce and protracted storm.

The storm varied in character and had differing effects in its various parts. A fall of snow of from 8 to 20 inches in northern and western Nebraska and northeastern Colorado, and 4 to 10 inches in Kansas accompanied by winds of from 40 to 70 miles an hour (with occasional recorded gusts up to 80 miles per hour) caused huge drifts of snow as much as 15 feet in depth to be formed at any point where an impediment to the wind caused the snow to collect.

The most serious effect of these conditions was on transportation. All highways in the area and all railroads with the exception of the Union Pacific were blocked for various lengths of time. One Santa Fe train was stalled for a half-day 12 miles west of Dodge City, Kansas. The Burlington main line was blocked from McCook to Hastings, Nebraska. Other Burlington lines and the Chicago and Northwestern lines were drifted in for various short lengths of time. The Union Pacific managed to keep its rails open though trains ran several hours late. During the night of the 18th the Greyhound Bus Lines took all their buses off the highways of western and central Nebraska. Numerous airline departures were cancelled out of Omaha.

At Wood River, Nebraska, between 200 and 300 cars were stalled because of the blocked highways. Numerous towns in Nebraska had all available lodging space filled by travelers and local people unable to return home because of the storm. . . . As previously noted all highways in western Kansas and western and northern Nebraska were closed for at least a short period.

The highway patrols of the states involved immediately began the task of clearing the highways, but, as would be expected, their equipment was inadequate to clear all roads immediately. However, the end of the storm period saw temperatures rise into the forties so that the work of clearing the highways was not hampered by low temperatures, high winds, or drifting. Steady progress was made. Within 24 hours after the end of the blizzard the main, transcontinental, east-west highway (U. S. Highway 30) was open all the way across the state of Nebraska to one-way traffic. Long stretches of other major traffic arteries had been opened, but none of the other highways was open across the storm area. Within three or four days most of the main highways had been opened; but it took an additional week to free the minor highways and the back roads of snow. Actually, from the beginning of this storm until the end of the winter there was never a time when there were not some local roads in need of plowing. These were local, minor occurrences typical of many winters in this Great Plains region.

As the storm moved into eastern Nebraska and Kansas the character of the precipitation changed from a dry snowfall to wet snow, sleet, and rain. Northeastern Nebraska experienced the heaviest snow in the entire area. Consequently, the effects of the storm were completely different in this area.

The principle damage in this section was to communications and power lines rather than to highways. The highways of the area were never closed by snow, though they were all described by the highway department as "hazardous" because of ice or a sleet cover on the surface.

The heavy accumulations of wet snow or sleet on telephone wires exposed to winds of high velocity resulted in tremendous damage to the lines. The number of breaks in telephone lines ran into the thousands. Numerous communities in Nebraska were cut off from 'phone service for varying lengths of time. The worst damage occurred in Butler, Seward, and Lancaster counties, Nebraska. In the general area of Iowa, Minnesota, and Nebraska the telephone company had over 700 linemen working as steadily as possible repairing the wire breaks.

Electric power lines also suffered severe damage, and a few of the smaller towns and many isolated residences experienced a complete power failure lasting from a few hours to three or four days.

Losses of livestock were almost negligible throughout the storm area.

The human death toll was set at seven. Two brothers died of freezing in their auto stalled on the highway. A farmer was found dead in the open country. One victim died of carbon-monoxide poisoning attempting to keep warm in his stalled auto. One person died of "exhaustion" and another of "heart attack" after shoveling snow. The last victim was burned in his farm home "unable to summon help on his severed telephone." The reader may decide whether the number of deaths attributable to the storm is four or seven.

Winter conditions were normal throughout the rest of November and

December. Temperatures ranged from average in the eastern Great Plains to a negative departure of four degrees in central Wyoming. No important snowfalls were recorded until the very end of the month of December.

The Second General Storm

The second storm of the winter occurred in almost the same areas as the first. The date was December 29th. As was true of the first storm, the character of the precipitation and the effects of the storm differed in different parts of the area. In western Nebraska, northeastern Colorado, and parts of western Kansas the snow was dry and accompanied by high winds. The strong winds caused drifting of the snow. Wind erosion of bare grain fields produced large dust storms. The amount of snow falling, however, was much less than in the earlier storm—from 2 to 4 inches. Consequently, except for some damage to grain fields, and a slight hampering of highway transportation (a few highways were blocked for a day or two), the effect of the storm in these areas was not noteworthy.

In a belt running entirely across the state of Nebraska from southwest to northeast and about 150 miles in width, precipitation was wet snow, sleet, or rain which turned to glaze upon striking cold surfaces. Highway travel though somewhat dangerous was not interrupted. Rail service was not affected.

As was true of the earlier storm the principal damage was to telephone and power lines; 124 Nebraska towns were cut off from telephone communication. The telephone company reported several thousand wire breaks. Power failures occurred in several small Nebraska towns. Though the effects of this storm were very similar to those of the November storm they were not nearly of the same magnitude. In fact, even in those sections of western Nebraska and northeastern Colorado where wind and snow made conditions most severe, the storm was essentially similar to dozens of blizzards which long-time residents had experienced, and would not be worthy of mention had it not been for the events that followed.

The Great Blizzard of January 2–5, 1949

The greatest blizzard of record in the Great Plains area began in western Nebraska and eastern Wyoming on the morning and afternoon of Sunday, January 2, 1949 and continued incessantly until the morning of January 5th. It arrived with very little warning. Following the blizzard of the end of December 1948 the weather had moderated greatly. On the day preceding the blizzard temperatures in western Nebraska and adjacent parts of Colorado and Wyoming were in the middle and high thirties, and the day was sunny and bright in many areas. Meteorologists were not anticipating any great change. Forecasts were for "light snow" and temperatures just below freezing. Nevertheless, when the storm struck it exceeded anything ever before recorded for the combination of snow, wind velocity, low temperatures, and duration. There have been cases of heavier snow falls, higher wind velocities, and much lower temperatures; but never a storm that remotely approached the severity of this storm in its combination of rigorous circumstances.

The Meteorological Conditions

The storm had its origin in an area of low pressure which covered the whole southern Rocky Mountain area on the day preceding the storm. Light snow was falling in the mountains. As the "low" moved slowly into eastern Colorado the pressure continued to drop. At the same time a mass of cold air with concomitant high pressures was moving slowly southward from southern Alberta and Saskatchewan. This caused a tremendous flow of air down the steep barometric gradient over the vast expanse of plains east of the Rocky Mountains. Simultaneously conditions in the upper atmosphere were almost precisely the opposite. Warm moist air was moving northward at elevations of 10,000 feet and over, and was forced over the much colder air at the surface. This was a matter of major importance, in that it was responsible for the constant fall of snow throughout the duration of the storm.

As with the big November storm, one of the major contributory causes of the storm's severity was the slowness with which it moved eastward. In fact, the movement of the center of this storm was extraordinarily peculiar. The storm was centered over the plains of eastern Colorado on the morning of January 2, 1949. Twenty-four hours later, the morning of January 3rd, the cyclone had moved only as far as western Oklahoma. But at this juncture the center of low presure suddenly turned and moved slowly east of north toward east-central Nebraska and then northwesterly to south-central South Dakota where it arrived on the morning of the 4th. It was not until 24 hours had elapsed that the storm reached central Minnesota bringing about an abatement of blizzard conditions over the Great Plains. Because of the intense development of the cyclone and anticyclone and their comparative proximity wind movement was of extraordinary velocity throughout the entire period.

The Blizzard and Its Effects

Though the storm started with moderate wind velocities and light snow, its intensity increased swiftly. Throughout eastern Wyoming, northeastern Colorado, and western Nebraska so intense was the storm that by noon on Sunday streets and highways were rapidly becoming impassable. By the end of the day all vehicular transportation was completely halted. Every highway and street in this area was drifted "tight shut." This does not mean merely that autos could not operate along the highways: taxis, buses, and private cars in the cities were absolutely unable to move. Travel on foot for even short distances was difficult for the hardy and strong and dangerous for anyone else. Railroads were drifted closed, airports were snowed in, and all intercity traffic was at a complete standstill.

Throughout the day winds averaged over 30 miles per hour with occasional gusts of over 60 miles per hour. The fiercely blowing snow constantly kept visibility below a quarter-mile and often dropped it to zero for short intervals. The temperature at the beginning of the storm was 22° F. and it fell steadily until the morning of the 3rd when it reached —7° at Cheyenne. Temperatures were similar but slightly higher elsewhere.

Paralysis of the region was almost complete by the end of the first day. Travelers only a few miles from home found it impossible to reach home. Passenger and freight trains were stranded in the open country. Military personnel from Ft. Warren at the outskirts of Cheyenne were excused from reporting on Monday morning. All state employees were excused from work. Schools were closed. Milk deliveries in the cities ceased. Garbage pickup was impossible. Over two-thirds of the stores in all the principal towns in the region did not open on Monday morning.

Little progress in combatting the storm's effects was possible on January 3rd or 4th. The blizzard was even worse on the 3rd than on the 2nd. For the two days January 3rd and 4th wind velocity averaged 41.8 miles per hour at Cheyenne. Temperatures were much lower on the 3rd than on the second. Temperatures never rose above zero on the 3rd at Cheyenne and were only a few degrees higher elsewhere. The only improvement in conditions on the 4th was a rise in temperature. One unusual aspect of the blizzard was the extreme dryness and fineness of the snow. In Colorado, for example, numerous cases were reported of damage to plaster, rugs, draperies, and other household furnishings by the extremely fine snow, which, driven by the gale-like winds, pushed through the cracks and crevices of closed doors and windows and then melted inside the homes. The same conditions made the operation of motors and machinery difficult.

The morning of the 5th saw conditions in the western part of the storm area moderate greatly. Though it was extremely difficult to make much progress in the rural areas, the cities were beginning to dig themselves out.

Every railroad in the main storm area had been completely snowed in. The Union Pacific alone had over 40 trains either definitely stalled and unable to move within the major storm area or being held at terminals on the border of the storm zone. Approximately 7,500 passengers were aboard these trains.

The emergency difficulties encountered with stalled trains on the Northwestern, Burlington, and Union Pacific were directly attributable to the unprecedented intensity and swift onset of the storm. In some of the railroad reports on the stalled trains it is emphasized and reiterated that when the train started on its run there was no reason even to suspect that it would not reach its destination. In one instance a lightly loaded, short train preceded by a wedge-type snow plow was unable to negotiate a run that only three hours earlier had been accomplished by a heavily loaded train without any assistance. The greatest difficulties occurred when passenger trains were stalled or halted at very small towns. The Union Pacific had five fast passenger trains halted at small towns along their main line in eastern Wyoming and western Nebraska. In some places local supplies of food and fuel were so limited and all forms of land transportation so completely stalled that it became necessary to fly food and supplies to the trains for a short period. The Burlington had to halt a passenger train at Seneca in central Nebraska, and it proved impossible to keep up steam in the locomotive. Some notion of the intensity of the blizzard can be gained by learning that not a single switch track could be cleared to enable another locomotive to be switched on. Snow drifted over the tracks faster than it could be shoveled off, and workers could endure exposure in the open for only a few minutes at a time. The passengers had to be transferred to the depot, a local cafe, and a small auditorium until the blizzard moderated.

Telephone and power lines were not disturbed. The fact that they remained intact greatly facilitated the work of relief and recovery from the blizzard's effects.

Two groups of people were, however, much more immediately and vitally affected than all others. To intercity travelers and to stockmen the blizzard brought pressing difficulties, problems, or hazards.

Intercity auto travelers who encountered difficulties fell into two groups —those that managed to reach shelter and those who did not. Many motorists traveling along the highway during the early part of the blizzard were making, as they realized, slightly hazardous efforts to reach either their destination or a large town with ample facilities for accommodating travelers. In numerous instances in this sparsely settled area their cars eventually stalled in the snow in open country with no shelter immediately available. Persons to whom this happened were faced with the alternative either of staying in their cars and awaiting rescue by road crews or others, or of attempting to reach shelter on foot. The greatest loss of life from the blizzard occurred among these stranded travelers. People froze to death in both circumstances. But from a consideration of all available data, keeping in mind the unusual severity and duration of the storm, it appears that it is safer (at least on any well-traveled road) to remain in the automobile than to leave it to seek shelter. South of Laramie, Wyoming, six people were rescued from cars in which they had been snowbound for 30 hours when temperatures were below zero. Seven people were rescued after they had been in their cars two and a half days near the Colorado-Wyoming border north of Fort Collins. Numerous other examples occurred throughout the Wyoming-Nebraska-Colorado area. However, several cases of frozen hands, feet, and ears were reported among travelers rescued from their cars after a prolonged wait.

One coincidence that increased the difficulties and discomforts of the blizzard was the time of its occurrence. It began on the first weekend following the Christmas and year-end holidays so that unusual numbers of travelers were on the trains and highways. In many sections of this region even hamlets are far apart with the consequence that, as the storm swiftly closed up the highways, dozens, scores, and even hundreds of motorists were forced to stop at tiny roadside settlements. Facilities and food supplies were totally inadequate to handle these sudden influxes. Though there were many rumors of suffering among the stranded travelers and of outrageous profiteering on the part of some of the establishment owners, discussions with people in the area, with travelers caught at small villages, and with truck and bus drivers make it seem certain that inconvenience, delay, and some slight discomforts were the extent of the "hardships."

The usual commercial establishments in even the largest cities were unable to accommodate all their involuntary visitors, but various civic organizations, the Red Cross, and impromptu local committees easily solved any problems with a minimum of difficulty for everyone.

The Process of Recovery

In view of the events that followed, one of the most favorable circumstances connected with the great blizzard was the rapid rise in temperature following the cessation of the storm. Temperatures had been either a few degrees above or below zero during the blizzard, but by the 5th the maximum temperatures had climbed very nearly to the melting point. On the 6th, 7th, and 8th the weather was surprisingly mild for this region. Daytime temperatures were in the 40's. With the simultaneous drop in wind velocities this gave excellent weather for clearing communication lines. The work proceeded rapidly, but so completely were communications blocked that most of the work in the first few days had to be confined to the main lines of the railroads and the major through-highways.

The Union Pacific opened a transcontinental line on January 6th. The blizzard had blocked the line from Laramie, Wyoming to central Nebraska. On January 6th the pass over the Laramie Mountains was opened, and the line north from Denver to Borie (a junction point on the main line seven miles west of Cheyenne) had been opened a little earlier. Consequently, it was possible to start moving trains east-west despite the long stretch of closed trackage in eastern Wyoming and western Nebraska. Trains were taken off the main line at Julesberg, Colorado, run on the Denver line to the junction with the Denver-Cheyenne line, and thence on to Borie where they could get back on the main line. As soon as this line was open a Red Cross train "rescued" approximately 600 stranded motorists in three little Colorado hamlets along U. S. Highway 85.

It was not until January 7th that the stalled passenger trains in western Nebraska and eastern Wyoming were released, taken back to Julesberg, and sent on west via the detour. Not until January 10 had all the passenger trains been moved toward their destination, thus permitting freights to move in numbers.

Pacific Fruit Express cars are a major component of west to east movement along this line; these cars, loaded with perishable goods, were a special problem. Union Pacific had to use three airplanes to haul charcoal from Laramie to Cheyenne to heat these cars until they could be moved east.

The Colorado and Southern Railroad was cleared without undue delay. But the Burlington lines and the Northwestern lines in northern and western Nebraska and eastern Wyoming were not yet opened on January 9th.

The Nebraska papers were still reporting the stretches of road that were open on January 8th; all the rest were still closed. In Wyoming road clearance proceeded somewhat more rapidly. By January 15th all main roads in Nebraska and Wyoming had been opened for traffic.

Throughout the period from January 5 to 15, there was no widespread blowing and drifting of snow, and no snowstorms of any appreciable dimensions. However, temperatures fell well below zero on January 9 and 10. There were numerous local instances where blowing and drifting occurred for a short time, and roads once cleared had to be plowed out again. But these were merely incidents in the general task of clearing the roads. Every main road in Wyoming, except mountain pass roads, was opened by January 10th. It was not until January 15th that the last main road in Nebraska was cleared. But as we shall see, the task had been too great for the length of time available to accomplish it. Tremendous drifts 10, 20, and 30 feet deep and from 50 to 3,000 or 4,000 feet long covered highways and rail lines throughout the storm area. Most small equipment was unable to cope with drifts of such dimensions. Moreover much of the equipment, being in a poor state of repair, had broken down one or more times and was out of service for various lengths of time. Private equipment that could be rented or contracted for was thrown into the job.

During this period local distress conditions developed at various spots. We have already noted the necessity of supplying the stranded Union Pacific passenger train by air even before the end of the blizzard. The Mountain States Telephone and Telegraph Company used a special vehicle, the "snow buggy," to bring hospital cases from isolated ranches and villages, and to deliver food and medicine in some unusual instances. By January 11th an airlift was being used to supply vitally needed commodities of various sorts to numerous towns and ranches in western Nebraska. Any distress conditions that arose were attributable to an inability to do without transportation, for whatever reason, for a period of 10 days or less.

Considering the size of the area, the number of distress cases was small. Almost all ranches had sufficient supplies of food, feed, and fuel to sustain themselves for a ten day period. Most villages and towns were able to supply themselves with everything that was needed from local stocks, and the majority of distress cases that developed resulted from shortages of one or two specialized items, generally of small bulk.

As road after road was opened, however, the number of these "emergency" situations decreased, and finally in Nebraska the period of emergency was declared to be over. This was a reasonable and logical assumption, because any ordinary course of weather events would have seen the entire transportation network completely cleared. But, while the main roads had been opened for travel in the major storm areas by the 12th or 15th of January, practically no progress had been made in clearing minor, back roads, access roads to ranches, and ranch roads themselves. Warnings were already beginning to be heard that isolated groups of livestock on farms away from ranch headquarters were beginning to approach the end of their feed supply and that farmers would need assistance in opening roads to these cattle in order to replenish the feed stocks. Other ranchers had not anticipated feeding their cattle for long periods and had not laid in large stocks of feed, and they noted that it would be necessary to open their roads to enable them to replenish their feed supplies from outside sources. Nevertheless, the situation was not deemed serious since, despite the fact that all these minor roads were still closed, it seemed a safe assumption that all the equipment for road clearing could now be turned to the job of clearing these back roads, access roads, and ranch roads.

The Later Winter Storms in the Central Great Plains: The Critical Period

The first general blow to this prospect occurred on January 17 when high winds caused extensive drifting in the Nebraska panhandle, northern Nebraska, and eastern Wyoming. The area of drifting enlarged the next day. All roads in eastern Wyoming and all roads in Nebraska west of McCook and Broken Bow and north of Neligh and Bloomfield were closed. The job of road clearing had to be started anew, and while the towns had all been opened to truck transportation during the intervening period many railroad branch lines had not been opened. By January 22 many long stretches on the main roads had been opened though there were still sections where drifts covered the highway. But on January 22 redrifting occurred over extensive areas within the central storm zone. On January 24 a new snowstorm occurred in northeastern Nebraska and effectively disposed of the possibility of transferring equipment to the affected areas further west. During this week temperatures dropped to lows for the winter. Thus far we have mentioned only those events that were fairly widespread. Throughout this entire period there were local snowstorms and "ground blizzards"* which would again block a few score or hundred miles of roads in some limited area, often times in areas where the main roads had been cleared previously.

The following is a report from the Norfolk area of north central Nebraska, where conditions were unusually severe.

Though there were no extensive and heavy snowstorms even very light snows had a profound effect, because every ditch, hollow, and cranny was already filled with snow. New snow would blow over the surface until it came to one of the cuts along the roads and railroads excavated from previous storms; it would fill these with fresh snow.

Storm on Jan. 9–10	Roads reopened Jan. 14
Redrifted " 15	" " " 17
" " 18	" " " 20
" " 21	" " " 26 (Except 150 miles)

New snow blocked all roads Jan. 28
500 miles reopened by " 29
912 " " " " 31 (488 miles still blocked)
All open by Feb. 9.
Redrifting Feb. 10.
Feb. 12—132 miles still closed.

* "Ground blizzard" is a local term designating a storm which whips loose surface snow into the air, but is not accompanied by a fall of new snow.

After drifting and redrifting had occurred several times, and after the snow had been pounded and packed by the wind the drifts became almost solid walls of ice, snow, and dirt. The early winds had removed all the snow from the upland surfaces; consequently, later drifts had a very considerable intermixture of dirt blown off these bare spots. Moreover, wedge-type plows, which simply pushed the snow off in piles at the side of the road, had been used extensively in clearing the roads after the first blizzards. After the cuts had redrifted and been plowed out once or twice there was no place beside the road to put any additional drifting snow thereafter. This combination made ordinary, light, snow-moving equipment practically useless. It was extremely hard on even the best and heaviest equipment. Blades on rotary plows would break against the ice formations. Transmission systems on bulldozers and plows would be torn out. The railroads reported several instances where livestock had sought shelter in a cut, died, frozen, and been buried by drifting snow. When rotary plow blades struck these carcasses it was like encountering a boulder, and another plow would be out of service for a time. Sometimes drifts would be so solid that even heavy bulldozers would scrape futilely across the surface. The railroads discovered that in many places flame throwers were the most feasible equipment for removing the walls of snow and ice, and several dozen of them were in use on the various rail lines. In other places it was necessary to use small charges of dynamite in order to loosen the solid ice masses.

The Nature of the Emergency

As we have noted in the previous sections, emergency situations which developed prior to the middle of January were isolated instances that resulted from an immediate need for transportation. But as the period of time without transportation lengthened the dimensions of the problem increased rapidly. As day after day and ultimately week after week passed with never more than partial clearing of the transportation lines more and more hamlets and, especially, isolated ranches began to feel the necessity of replenishing stocks of one item or another. This was the true nature of the emergency that arose.

The preponderance of the shortages were made up of three commodities —livestock feed, fuel, and food. Livestock feed was by far the most serious shortage.

The nature of the problem of livestock feed shortages was misunderstood at the time and the error has persisted. The crux of the error will be more apparent if it is understood that at no stage in the later storm period were there any serious local shortages of livestock feed anywhere. The problem was not one of importing livestock feed into a particular area, but of distributing it within that area. The difficulties arose from the closing of all local transportation lines and not from the closing of interregional highways. The difficulties arose in moving the hay from the haystack to cattle a mile or two away, or in transporting it from a town to a ranch a few miles out in the country. This point is stressed because many of the so-called relief measures taken showed a complete misunderstanding of the nature of the problem. Hay was flown into Wyoming by the Army Air Force from as far away as Kansas to help the unfortunate ranchers of Wyoming, who then had no way of moving the hay from the airport to their ranches a few miles away. Arrangements were made for long distance haulage of hay by rail into storm areas, and much of it was stacked near the sidings and remained there. Truckers and speculators bought hay in large quantities at high prices and trucked it into the "disaster" areas only to find in many cases that other truckers were buying local hay and hauling it back over the same route to alleviate supposed shortages in the first area. Many of the hardest hit counties exported almost as much hay as they imported during January and February. Much of the hay that was thus transported was never sold, or was sold at considerable loss to the seller. During the summer of 1949 huge piles of this baled hay offered clinching evidence of the fact that once local roads were open no market existed for imported hay.

The farm fuel shortages resulted from the recent widespread conversion of farm heating and cooking units to imported fuels. Local, indigenous fuels could no longer be utilized; hence the need for transport connections with the cities.

The Blizzard Relief Measures

As soon as redrifting had started in any area on an extensive scale it became apparent that unless weather conditions changed markedly for the better there was absolutely no hope for a general clearing of all the transportation routes in this region. And a change in the weather was not an eventuality that could be relied upon. It became necessary to establish some sort of area-wide coordinating body to allocate equipment to those areas where it was needed most urgently and to give financial assistance in sustaining those operations.

In Wyoming the magnitude of the storm of January 2–5 and the short period of good weather following the storm had, comparatively early, convinced people with long experience with the weather of this region that emergency situations were certainly going to arise. After a day or two of discussion with various citizens the Acting Governor of Wyoming, A. G. Crane, issued a proclamation on January 8 declaring that an emergency existed. A State Emergency Relief Board was appointed to deal with special problems as they arose. Radio broadcasts were initiated urging people faced with an emergency situation to telephone the Board office in Cheyenne.

At first the board was handling largely individual, special emergency cases, i.e., make arrangements to move isolated hospital cases to a hospital, assist a rancher to bring his cattle to a point where they could be fed or watered, procure and deliver emergency feed to a rancher, and similar circumstances all having the characteristic of being sudden emergencies which would not permit of any wait for the opening of regular transportation lines.

It was not until the snows and blows began about a week after the January 2–5 blizzard that the situation began to take on a more serious aspect, and the Board found the scale of its operations increasing greatly. As successive counties began to be seriously affected local county emergency boards were established consisting of a county commissioner, a resident employee of the Wyoming Highway Department, the County Agent, and a Red Cross representative. This board coordinated the work within the county and furnished liaison work with the State Board which directed the general, over-all work.

The Board was faced with the probability that there would not be a general freeing of the transportation network. But the need for transportation was not everywhere the same. Localized emergency conditions developed first in one area and then in another. A unique plan for dealing with these localized emergencies was worked out. This was the convoy system, and it proved to be singularly effective. Each convoy consisted of one or two big plows or bulldozers and a group of trucks. The greatest single item hauled was feed for the isolated livestock; but food or any other items that might be needed by the ranchers along the route was carried also.

Plows or bulldozers would go ahead clearing a path for the trucks to the ranches where the feed or supplies were dropped at some point where the rancher and his cattle could get to them. In the majority of instances it was necessary for the plows to reopen the road for the trucks on the way back.* Most of these trips were one-day or half-day runs, but occasionally one would take two or three days to complete.

Meanwhile it had become obvious that the light and meagre state and county highway equipment was totally inadequate to cope with the tre-

* Perhaps some notion of the severity of conditions during this period can be gained by noting that so rapid was redrifting in some instances, that convoys attempting to return to the base of operations found that drifting had been so extensive that the convoy itself was stalled and in turn had to be liberated by more powerful snow moving equipment sent out from the base of operations.

mendous drifts. What was needed was big equipment and more of it. On January 16th the Acting Governor of Wyoming wired the Wyoming senators in Washington "asking whether any heavy snow removal equipment was available for grant, rental, lease, or purchase." This incident is an excellent one to give a true perspective both on the views that were held with regard to the storms and the seriousness of the situation at the time. The U. S. Public Roads Administration succeeded in locating 60 pieces of Army equipment at Ogden, Utah, which could be released as soon as an emergency proclamation had been made by the governor. But since the weather moderated slightly at this time the governor waited until January 21 before issuing the proclamation.

On the same day Governor Val Peterson of Nebraska met with the state legislature to discuss action. On the 23rd of January he told the legislature that he was going to ask a special appropriation for acquiring road equipment, and two days thereafter on January 25 an appropriation of a half-million dollars was made. Wyoming had been a little earlier with similar appropriations. On January 18, the Wyoming legislature had appropriated $200,000 for emergency storm relief; that is, for renting and operating road clearing equipment and meeting the cost of the convoys. Of the total expenses incurred in fighting the storm conditions the state paid 60 per cent and the counties, 40 per cent.

It would not be worthwhile to review here all the governmental action (state and national) that was taken to assist with the relief work. Suffice it to say that a resolution was introduced into Congress on January 24 authorizing the Bureaus of Land Management and Reclamation to expend $500,000 for relief work, and this shortly made a large amount of heavy equipment available. The Forest Service loaned some of its heavy equipment. Congress appropriated a total of $41,300,000 for emergency relief work throughout the West.

The biggest single operation, however, was set in motion on January 29 when President Truman (after several days of temporizing measures by various branches of the federal establishment in Washington, which were the subject of considerable adverse comment in the Nebraska press) "ordered the Secretary of Defense to use whatever money and other resources were 'appropriate' for relief purposes."

The Army activities were in charge of Maj. General Lewis A. Pick of the Fifth Army; they were designated "Operation Snowbound." The Army operations were in part based on Army equipment, but mostly on the equipment of private contractors.

Every contractor in the Missouri Valley known to have equipment suitable for moving snow was asked to supply his equipment and personnel under contract to participate in the road clearing operation. By February

3, "673 bulldozers, 123 snow plows and patrols, and 116 Army weasels were either at work in the snowbound area or on their way." After only four days of operations (Feb. 4) according to Army figures over a half-million cattle had been given access to feed and slightly under 10,000 miles of road had been opened. By February 15 most roads throughout the entire storm area were open and by February 22 the operation was almost completed. The worst winter in the history of the central Great Plains was over.

15. Clouds *

Clouds are probably the most visible of all weather phenomena. In addition to their purely aesthetic attraction, they have other important functions. Clouds appear in a wide variety of shapes and sizes, each type having its own peculiar characteristics, and each a very reliable indicator of approaching weather. In this selection, Borland indicates the importance of each cloud type.

Clouds are among the earth's greatest travelers. Constantly in motion, continually being renewed, they are essentially the same wherever seen, yet never twice exactly the same. For they are creations of the earth's water vapors and of the winds; and of all changing things, winds are the most restless.

I look out of my study window and see cirrus clouds, mare's-tail streamers, riding the gales several miles or more high. Only six or eight hours ago, those clouds probably were over Chicago, nearly a thousand miles away. If conditions are favorable, I may look up tonight and see noctilucent clouds traveling in the stratosphere at the speed of an airplane, racing on the remote winds. Yet, because they are so far above the earth, they will seem to be standing still among the stars.

These are high-flying clouds, which zip along at spectacular speeds up where the eternal gales are blowing. But the everyday clouds that course the lower atmosphere are also travelers of consequence. Fog, which is merely a cloud in contact with the earth, seems to have little movement; yet it flows down the valleys and is wafted from one hilltop to the next.

* Hal Borland, "Clouds," *Holiday,* October 1949. Reprinted by permission of Willis Kingsley Wing. Copyright 1949 by Curtis Publishing Company.

The author is a writer of articles and stories. His articles cover a wide variety of subjects.

Scud, the ragged gray cloud which flies so low just before or just after a rainstorm, is whipped along by winds of 30, 40 and 50 miles an hour. The most spectacular of all, the big cotton-ball cumulus clouds, sometimes travel hundreds of miles, though at a stately pace of 15 or 20 and rarely more than 35 miles an hour.

Cloud names come from the Latin. *Cumulus* means a heap, and cumulus clouds are great, fluffy masses that look like gigantic heaps of meringue. *Nimbus* means rain, and nimbo-stratus clouds are those gray masses that close in on the earth, darken everything, and finally pour out a drenching storm. *Stratus* means a layer; and stratus clouds look like successive layers, or bands. *Cirrus,* meaning a curl or strand of hair, appropriately describes the high-flying cloud strands which sometimes resemble straight mare's-tails and often curl up at the ends in beautiful swirls. *Noctilucent* clouds are night-luminous, and *nacreous* clouds are mother-of-pearl. Both are visible only at night, occurring as they do at heights of 16 to 50 miles, where they catch and reflect the sun's glow long after sunset.

Everyday clouds are formed of water vapor. But it may be that the noctilucent clouds, which occur 35 to 50 miles above the earth, are composed of fine dust similar to that of comets and meteors. They are thought to move at 150 to 200 miles an hour, with occasional speeds much higher. Closer to earth are periodic clouds of smoke and volcanic dust, some of which travel long distances at notable speed. Smoke and dust clouds from a volcanic eruption may travel completely around the earth. The explosion of Krakatoa in the Dutch East Indies in 1883, most violent of modern times, threw up clouds which encircled the globe within a week. They remained suspended in the air, causing brilliant sunsets, almost all over the world, particularly in the southern hemisphere, for nearly a year.

Smoke clouds are common in the vicinity of industrial areas. Pittsburgh's notorious pall occasionally travels as far as Washington, D.C., the smoke from the New York City area often travels 30 miles, and that from Boston and eastern Massachusetts commonly drifts 50 miles. The real travelers, however, are smoke clouds from forest fires. One fire in Idaho sent up a cloud that turned midday into dusk in Minneapolis, and a northern Wisconsin fire sent its clouds to New England within twenty-four hours and to Texas within two days. Smoke from forest fires in Maine two years ago spread many miles at sea and over most of New England.

These smoke clouds, however, might be called unnatural formations, since they are caused by unusual circumstances. The clouds you can see from your window any day in the year, those we watched as youngsters while lying on our backs in a summer meadow, are as natural as rain and wind. Only a few of them are real storm clouds. Most of them are clouds of water vapor or ice crystals traveling from one place to another.

How far they travel depends on air temperature, humidity and the winds.

As a general rule , clouds ride higher in summer than in winter, higher over desert country than over well-watered regions, and higher near the equator than near the poles. On humid days the clouds ride lower; on warm, dry days they rise into the upper atmosphere and stay there.

The magnificent cumulus clouds characteristic of the West, and particularly of the high plains and the mesa country, usually ride with their bases from half a mile to a mile above the earth. From the base, they normally tower a mile or two to their billowy tops. But when they congregate and build up to thunderhead proportions their tops often soar to a height of four or five, occasionally seven miles. At that stage they appear dark and threatening, full of deep shadows, seething with an inner tempest of wind and rain. Their tops, up in the high winds, flatten off. Lightning begins to flash, and trouble brews.

Cumulus clouds, however, may sail across the sky all day—great puffs that keep to themselves—and bring only fair weather. Such clouds are the despair of those who live in arid lands, for they usually originate in the moist highlands and ride prevailing winds across the thirsting land to better-watered country, there to drop their rain. The hot, dry air of the arid plains keeps the cumulus clouds high and disdainful. The drought perpetuates itself, despite the parade of towering clouds, while the moisture of a wet valley calls down unneeded rain.

Cirrus clouds are less spectacular and ride much higher, sometimes as much as eight or ten miles up.

They are composed of ice particles or tiny snowflakes, and this accounts for their wispy shape and curled tips. The finely divided ice crystals are caught up and blown back over their noses by shifting air currents. At an altitude of ten miles the temperature may be —65°, and it is this biting cold which forms the ice particles.

Because the ice is heavier than the air, it tends to fall, thereby giving the cloud a ragged lower surface. Then, as the ice falls into a warmer layer of air, it melts, evaporates, rises again as water vapor, and once more is turned to ice. Thus the cirrus cloud is constantly renewed by the warm and cold layers of air.

Although cirrus clouds are usually seen by themselves, they are basically part of a storm area. That is why the weather axioms forecast stormy weather from these high-flying mare's-tails. A storm gathers, let us say, in the Midwest. It slowly moves east. As it proceeds, it sends out long streamers of cirrus clouds which, riding the winds of high altitudes, sweep over the horizon and warn of the storm's coming, sometimes two days in advance of the storm itself. The storm may rain, snow, or blow itself out and vanish after traveling only a hundred miles or so, in which case the outflung cirrus clouds are, in a sense, orphaned. But their warning is real enough. Storm conditions bred those cirrus streamers and sent them on their way.

There are any number of variations and combinations of basic cloud types and formations. Cirro-stratus clouds, for instance, are cirrus clouds that sweep across the sky in layers, like white-bread sandwiches with blue sky for filling. Cirro-cumulus clouds are puffs of cumuli flying in packs at great heights. Strato-cumulus clouds are woolly cumuli flattened at top and bottom by air currents, and traveling in clusters. The cumulo-nimbus is a thunderhead.

The tornado of the South and Midwest is essentially a dark-cloud mass with a twisting funnel reaching down to the ground, where the writhing tip does tremendous damage. Wind velocities in the vortex of a tornado's funnel are believed to reach 500 miles an hour. Occasionally a tornado vortex travels more than a hundred miles.

Clouds themselves carry relatively little rain. They are composed of water vapor, to be sure, but not all the rain they generate comes from the cloud itself. What happens is that a cloud, carrying more water vapor than the surrounding air, strikes conditions of temperature and atmospheric pressure which make that vapor begin to condense on the minute dust particles present in the air at all altitudes up to about 50,000 feet. These dust particles may be microscopic, but they serve as nuclei for tiny droplets of condensing moisture. The droplets, heavier than air, begin to flow earthward. If the air beneath the cloud is warm and unsaturated, these droplets may become vapor again and return to cloud formation. When that happens, no rain reaches the earth. But if the air is at or near the saturation point, the droplets falling from the cloud will accumulate more moisture from the air, increase in size, break up into small droplets again, and set off a kind of chain reaction. Each droplet becomes a point of condensation, and the moist air becomes filled with raindrops. The air's temperature falls. Cool air can hold less moisture than warm air. The cooling process "squeezes" still more moisture from the air. Rain falls, far more rain than was suspended in the original cloud.

The bulk of the rain, and its weight, is distributed through the air around and under the original rain cloud. Rain is heavier than is generally realized. One inch of rainfall, for example, deposits 113 tons of water on each acre of ground surface. An inch of rain on an average city block —approximately two acres—would weigh 452,000 pounds.

Clouds are the cause of colorful sunsets, even the soft pastel afterglow which seems cloudless. The water vapor, the smoke and dust of the atmosphere, and the minute ice crystals of cirrus clouds, all combine to split the long rays of sunlight into color, much as irregular prisms break light into its component parts. Low hanging clouds with a patch of clear sky beneath them make the most spectacular sunsets of all, with reflected light and color illuminating the whole cloud mass. Hurricane clouds result in breath-taking sunsets—particularly if the hurricane is not coming your way. And banks of cumulus clouds, accentuated by silver light around the edges, provide amazing color effects at sundown.

In the same way, clouds color our sunrises, though mostly with pastel tones, because the cool of night has partially cleared the air and the day's dust has settled. In winter sunrises, the presence of more snow particles in the clouds often causes the phenomena known as sun-dogs. These are vertical bars of rainbow colors, one at each side of the sun, and on bright mornings they can be dazzlingly beautiful.

Winter or summer, the clouds that trail about the earth, shading it, watering it and tempering its heat, are never absent from the sky. And they are always on the move, traveling, forever riding the restless winds that know no horizon.

16. How to Live Through a Hurricane *

The tropical hurricane, or typhoon, as it is called in the Far East, is one of the most violent and destructive forms of weather. Far greater in extent than the tornado, which originates over land, the hurricane develops great power over sea areas and may then move across land areas, causing widespread damage. Florida is well within the hurricane zone, but these storms have ravaged eastern coastal areas as far north as New England. So great is their violence that they must be experienced to be believed. Wylie, a well-known writer of short stories and critical essays resides in Miami, and, by virtue of having lived through a number of hurricanes, is well equipped to relate the measures necessary for self-preservation in a hurricane—certainly weather at its worst.

The sky was blue innocence, the air as washed and warm as on any tropic day, and the sun made the landscape glow. It was the morning after

* Philip Wylie, "How to Live Through a Hurricane," *Saturday Evening Post,* December 30, 1950. Copyright 1950 by the Curtis Publishing Company. Reprinted by permission of Harold Ober Associates.

The author is a short-story writer, novelist, and essayist. He is best known for *Generation of Vipers,* a collection of essays critical of many aspects of the American scene, and for his novels.

another hurricane. I came downstairs and began the usual inventory.

Our rooms would have been very dark—because of the cypress shutters over the windows and glass doors—but we had left one deeply recessed opening unbarred. Light came grayly from there; the outdoors, seen through it, was as brilliant as the color picture on the screen of a dim theater.

I flipped a switch. No light. I'd expected none. The telephone, lifted from its cradle, emitted no hum. It had gone out at eleven the evening before. In the kitchen I turned a tap unhopefully, but this time our city water flowed. I let the hot tap run, since the tanks would still be warm, filled a kettle and set it on the miniature stove beside the inert coils of the electric range. I struck a match, but its damp head smeared, so I snapped a cigarette lighter and set afire the can of solidified alcohol.

The louvers on the kitchen door opened with effort. The door itself resisted until I pushed hard enough to crack branches, of which there was a drifted heap in the carport where our two automobiles were jammed deliberately against each other and a concrete wall. The cars were polka-dotted with thousands of poinciana leaflets and stood hub-deep in debris. But no glass was broken and they seemed all right.

No morning paper on the steps. A glance down the curving driveway gave one possible explanation: it was blocked by limbs from our live-oak trees, limbs thigh-thick, heaped as high as the top of a big truck. The lawn lay invisible beneath vegetation, with pans, tins, pots, flower containers and other objects here and there—objects less careful neighbors or people somewhere had failed to take indoors. I walked toward the green barricade in the drive. Lo and behold, the newspaper lay there, after all! The boy had come as close to our house as he could and tossed it over the heap. Its headline read:

DAMAGE MAY REACH 30 MILLIONS

To the left was the poinsettia bed, a hundred feet long, hewn in hard rock by the gardener and myself, filled by wheelbarrow with special dirt and planted with choice cuttings which this year were expected to produce a wall of scarlet. Two great oak branches and a tree now lay upon the bed, poinsettias crushed beneath. The foot-thick trunk of the tree was splintered; it had been tossed by last night's wind from a nearby woods onto our floral border.

I walked around the high brick wall that masks the clothes-drying yard. A huge solanum vine, still in flower when the red-and-black hurricane-warning flags were hoisted, lay prostrate in the yard, and not a blossom left. Where the parasol-wide leaves of the taro had tented a corner of the house, was a green wreck. The pads of the tropical water lilies in the pool I'd spent months digging and cementing were turned up and tattered like flounces on the dress of a drowned girl. Rain that fell inches in minutes had brimmed the little pond; leaves, twigs and branches filled it.

The oak at its base was probably done for. Two branches of seven remained; the rest stood stiffly in the sunshine, like the shot-off fingers of a cupped hand. Beyond, in the acres of our land that are pine and palmetto, the blasted stumps of a few trees showed; but most still stood. And the house itself was unscathed.

I went back into the murky kitchen, slapping at mosquitoes, perspiring a little from the October sun and the dampness of the green-smelling morning. The kettle was hot now. I put a heaping spoonful of powdered coffee in a cup, added sugar and then cream from the still-cold but slowly defrosting refrigerator, poured the hot water, drank coffee and opened up the morning paper.

Mrs. Wylie came downstairs. Ricky, we call her. She looked at me for a moment and smiled. "How did we do?"

"Dandy," I said. "Just dandy!"

On the morning of the day before, a friend, knowing that we rarely listened to the radio, had phoned early. She had been a little bit jeering: "You should have stayed north longer! That hurricane fumbling around Jamaica is headed this way now! It's the ninth or tenth spotted this year, and I hope it misses, like the others!"

We were busy. We had other plans. But the same thing was true of all the half million people that morning in South Florida: the business went undone and the plans were canceled. Ricky, like tens of thousands of other housewives, has a routine for such occasions, and I, like as many husbands, have my set chores.

We tested our radio, but it didn't work. So that got priority on the list. We were warned at nine o'clock. By noon we'd had new batteries put in the radio, so it would work without its regular power supply.

Our gardener, luckily on hand, by noon had spread the solid board hurricane shutters on the lawn and commenced to carry them to the proper windows. Galvanized wing nuts and washers, brass screws and heavy bolts in glass jars marked "Hurricane" had been brought down from shelves. Both cars had been filled with gasoline, for there is no way to tell, when a hurricane is hours distant, how bad it will be, and therefore how many days may pass with the power off and gasoline pumps not functioning. The extension ladder was leaning against the house. The stepladders had been carried outdoors.

Ricky had shopped. The two-gallon kerosene can was full, for lamps. The can for "white" gasoline also was full, for the lantern. Extra batteries to fit sundry electric lamps and flashlights were on hand. She had stocked a fresh supply of candles, a dozen cans of solidified alcohol, powdered coffee, enough tinned staples to keep us fed without heat or ice for two weeks, if need be. People with freezer units can sometimes get dry ice to carry their produce over a period without electric power, but we have no unit. So she cooked the meat on hand. It would keep longer that way.

We have a spaniel named Popcorn; there was a three-weeks supply of canned food for him. Ricky had also bought a half-dozen bug bombs, against the good possibility that our screens might be damaged beyond easy and early repair, so that to sleep in any comfort we would have to seal up and spray a bedroom.

She'd set out raincoats and heavy boots and old towels in case of leaks just as I'd set out an ax in case of blockaded doors and fire extinguishers because of the lamps and the approaching wind.

Play by Play of Approaching Storm

Every two hours on the half hour, our radio stopped playing dance music or reporting world affairs or discussing the merits of advertised goods, and we—the half million of us—were transferred to the Weather Bureau. There, a calm but urgent voice made its reports, which are called advisories and were repeated at half-hour intervals by the regular announcers on all stations—stations which, in a few more hours, largely would fall silent as their tall steel towers crashed in a roaring night.

The storm, the voice would say, is at such-and-such latitude and longitude. Then it would translate: so many miles south and east of Miami and coming north and west at ten or eleven miles an hour. Or standing still for a while over some empty, tempestuous stretch of the sea. "Planes scouting the storm report wind velocities near the center at upward of a hundred miles an hour. This is a small but dangerous hurricane, and all safety measures and other preparations should be rushed!"

After the Weather Bureau, would come the voice of an announcer for the Red Cross. He would tell the listeners—sure of an excellent audience—what schools and other public buildings had been designated as shelters. Anybody who felt unsafe would be welcome—men, women and children, bearing their own food and water and flashlights, if they had them, but no pets. Pets were to be left behind with supplies of food and water. And expectant mothers were to be taken to Jackson Memorial Hospital; the storm might be so furious that the stork could get through, but not the doctor.

People in trailers, people in rickety houses, people living near the sea and frightened by the expectation of rising tides, packed up their families in family cars or took busses to the shelters—which were opened at two in the afternoon. Some other people, listening, but oversanguine, decided to ride it out where they were. Of those, some were subsequently regretful, and at least three lost their lives.

Toward one o'clock we decided to eat lunch downtown. The commercial buildings were already boarded up. But it seemed to us that Miami's pre-hurricane overture of hammers pounding wasn't loud enough in the residential sections. Perhaps the storms had called "wolf" and missed Miami too often that year. Or perhaps that word "small" sounded more cogent to many householders than the familiar word "dangerous." Most people with homes, at any rate, weren't doing much. But the boat owners were taking precautions. The city's many drawbridges went up and down as yachts, fishing cruisers, houseboats, sailboats and even outboards paraded up the rivers and canals to anchorages between high banks.

The restaurant was battened down, electric-lighted and full of people. Some seemed excited, but others looked tired and grim. Perhaps they'd been in hurricanes before and doubtless they'd boarded up for nothing several times that year. Near our table sat a group of badge-wearing delegates, members of one of the three conventions in town at the time.

A man among them proclaimed in a facetious shout, "If this hurricane misses, I'm going to ask the Chamber of Commerce for my money back! Always did want to see what happened in one!"

"If it hits," Ricky said to me quietly, "he may get his money's worth."

After all, we'd been through five.

Eating lunch in a restaurant saved our food supplies and saved energy and time. If the storm speeded up, time might become valuable. We drove home, part of the way in a hard shower that threw thunder across the green landscape and gave way to blue sky again in a few blocks. The storm, said the Weather Bureau, was stalling as of noon. Building up in force, they said.

Now the gardner and I began to fasten on the shutters. Each was lifted, fixed over threaded bolts in the window frame, pressed tight and secured by washers and wing nuts. One by one, upstairs and down, most of the windows of our house were thus darkened. Then the doors. Inside it became hot and gloomy. Outside the shower was repeated, the sky turned blue again and the wind picked up. The big garbage cans went into the shed where the shutters had been stored. The wheelbarrow and sawhorses were put in the concrete-block compost bin, on top of the heap, but below the walls. We brought in the gardenia and the potted plants. Porch furniture was stowed in bedrooms. With a garden hose I set a siphon going to lower our lily pond, knowing the rains might otherwise wash out its population of tropical fish.

Our grapefruit and papayas were too green to bother picking. We had no avocados. With a pole-handled tree trimmer, I cut off various fronds and branches which, in a tempest, might be expected to bat against eaves or the power lines leading to our house. I forgot to cut back the nine-foot tulip tree, and in the morning what was left was less than two feet high. And I thought of wrapping up the big, double yellow hibiscus at the corner of my workroom. But I didn't, and that was gone next day. I checked the hand pump on our well, and it was working; we'd have water—potable water—unless the concrete pump house blew away, and the pump with it.

Indoors, Ricky and our maid, Hester, had taken up rugs and hung away clothes, filled all the flint lighters, finished the cooking, locked or left open interior doors according to a plan, and set the hurricane gear at strategic points. Hester was dismissed early, and she joined the home-going throngs. School had been let out everywhere at noon and the yellow busses had already taken the children home. We were set now, and this was the time for the phone calls and the visits.

Other people, also finished with their precautions, came to see if they could help us. We got into a car and drove over to find out if our friends needed helpers. Some did.

Soon after our return, the contractor who had built our house the year before stopped by to see if we were snug, and decided my preparations needed reinforcements. He and I went back up on the ladders and the broad, flat roofs. Afterward he had a cup of coffee. More people phoned. We phoned to a few more, and the wind began to hiss in the treetops. It grew dark. Ricky cooked supper and we ate and then washed the dishes.

At eight-thirty the radio said South Florida was surely in for it. The Red Cross gave staccato lists of aid stations and shelters. People had been told everything they could be told. The wind downtown in Miami, in the next couple of hours, rose to hurricane force, which is seventy-five miles and above.

At five minutes of eleven our lights went out, after dying and coming on again a few times. We know the moment because the electric clocks stopped then, and the hands stayed there afterward. We had been phoning periodically to relay the advisories to a family whose radio had stopped working in the afternoon. The husband lay abed with a high fever, and one of the children, in trying to light a candle with a damp match, got a blazing coal in her eye. A doctor made it to their house through the rising tumult and found the child painfully, but not seriously injured. We phoned the ten-thirty bulletin to them, and none after that, as our line went dumb at about the same time our lights went out.

Outdoors it poured. As long as the power lasted, we kept our floodlights on, so we could watch the trees surge and glitter in the horizontal rain, catch sight of vague objects hurtling across the wet night and bounding anonymously on the lawn, and see our shrubs bend low, wave, twist and dig funnels in the earth at their bases. A steady wind steadily rose, giving the landscape just such an appearance and producing just such sound effects as the movies of hurricanes do. Over that wind, however, came the gusts, audible in the distance, screaming as they plowed troughs in the woods around us. The cinema is too feeble to reproduce such sounds as those. It was possible to go out on lee porches, but it was difficult to hear even shouts at any distance.

When our lights went, everybody's did near us; the comforting glow of other houses disappeared. It was replaced by flashes far and near—pink and blue and white lights—as transformers burned out and hot wires shorted on the ground or amidst the hurtling tree stems. Then utter darkness, filled with unspeakable din. The radio, now on batteries, stopped and we turned to another station. A tower had gone down, the new announcer said. His station had switched to a non-directional beam to cover for stations temporarily out of commission.

"Look at the barometer!" Ricky cried.

The eye could see it move. Down and down. Twenty-five hundredths in as many seconds. Our ears popped and hurt. Wind rushed from the house through the doors and windows we had left open for the purpose of keeping pressure equalized.

The radio talked fast now. Downtown in the main streets, it said, metal shutters were being ripped off many of the big stores. Their great plate-glass windows were bursting into the street as the outdoor pressure dropped. All firemen and police near a certain address were urged to hurry to it: a woman and two children were trapped there in an unroofed home. People were desperately ordered to stay off the streets. Casualties from the exploding windows were mounting where the foolhardy lingered in some supposedly protected spot to watch. More radio towers were falling. More roofs were lifting everywhere. Walls were collapsing. Huge electric signs were falling or dangling and grinding in the wind. The sea was up around thousands of houses. The sand it carried had made streets impassable where fallen trees had not already done so. *Cabañas* along the ocean front, torn up by the seas and the wind, were blowing around the beach.

Our house was now a dot in a pitch-dark world. The lamps guttered. A tongue of water slid under a door and spread out on the white terrazzo floor. Ricky threw some of the old towels over the little inundation and wrung them into a pan and left them at the wet crack. The noise was a tremendous roar overridden by the squealing gusts and punctuated by rare cracking sounds as trees broke. Most such noises, however, though loud in themselves, were lost in the general bellow.

Now the direction of the hurricane changed and our front porch became a protected place. We went out there. The screens still held, but we could see in the lightning and the beam of a big flashlight that our pines, slim and sixty or seventy feet tall, were bent low. The palms blew all one way, like the loose hair of a woman in a fast-driven roadster. The gusts had become appalling. Though the Weather Bureau had recorded nothing over a hundred and six miles an hour, I told Ricky I'd eat everything hurled into our yard if the gusts weren't hitting a hundred and a quarter by that time. They were . . . and in some places maybe a hundred and fifty, the bureau said later. We went back indoors, soon—a little afraid a branch or board might ride the pandemonium onto the porch.

The hurricane had reached its peak, but we had no way to tell. Our house, like all properly built houses in that area, was set on foundations of steel and of concrete poured in trenches in the underlying limestone. Ferroconcrete beams at the corners were tied by steel rods into similar heavy beams under the eaves; steel bands attached each separate member of the roof to the beams. Our rafters were double.

Ricky and I were far from terrified, but it would be untrue to say we were without apprehension. I've been worse scared by a California quake and in a burning building in Dakota, in a Canadian forest fire, in the 1913 Ohio flood and during a tornado in that same state. I've been more alarmed in a storm at sea. But hurricanes are tricky. Sometimes they contain tornadoes of their own which no construction can withstand. Occasionally a freak, twisting gust wreaks some particular havoc. And this was a strong storm. News of the falling steel towers—that had stood through other blows—and of the unroofing of many houses made that plain. As we felt the majestic mallet blows of the wind, we couldn't help glancing up where the rafters met the beams, to see if a crack showed there or if water was dribbling in.

Our exile, like that of all the rest in private homes, was absolute. For an hour, or possibly six or eight hours, we would be alone. The streets and roads were impassable. Communications were nil, except for radio and radio hams. A person might be able to flounder through the frantic night for aid; a person might fail in such an attempt. Any injury, acute sickness or disaster to our house would be our problem to deal with, probably without aid for hours. We sat on the divan and smoked limp cigarettes. Popcorn, our white cocker spaniel, stayed close in spite of the heat, shook, and eyed us with worry. We thought and spoke about the sleazy houses built for veterans in some of the outlying real-estate developments, and we spoke about the ramshackle sprawl of "colored town" where our Hester had lived until recently.

Morning was to see 20,000 houses, mostly the shabby or badly built ones, hit, unroofed or wrecked. Three dead and nearly a hundred hurt, and a miracle the total was so low. But that night the myriad disasters—bits and pieces of which the radio continued to report—were used by us and by hundreds of thousands like us as indices of personal hazard. Would we be next? And how long would we have to endure passively the effort of the elements to tear our house apart?

The October hurricane proved the old adage about the want of the nail for which the shoe was lost. The littlest violation of the building codes, the most minor skimping of material—nails too far apart or too small, mortar too poor or too sparingly used, a roofing felt lighter than the prescribed kind, flashing of too thin a gauge let in a finger of the tempest, and the hand and brawny arm thrust in behind. A tile rattled and flipped into the night; the tiles above it were plowed loose. Metal began to vibrate and then tore; the material beneath ballooned, ripped, raced into oblivion, and the roof after it, and then, sometimes, the walls buckled. In days to come, Miami would learn new lore concerning building against hurricanes and learn, shamefacedly, that among its capable builders there were a few cheats. Some people lost everything because a contractor had saved himself as little as ten dollars on a home.

"The barometer!" Ricky exclaimed again, after an hour or so. It was rising!

The terribleness of the gusts diminished; the general tumult lost energy. In another hour we had such a wind as might blow on any night of a gale, and soon only a stiff breeze. A neighbor—a man who said he liked to cook, but had no opportunity except before hurricanes—had brought us half of a cake. We ate most of that and drank a bottle of milk, which would sour if we did not use it. We were able to realize how tired we were. It was three A.M.

I let Popcorn out by a porch door and followed him a few feet through the rain. Not far. Overhead, branches still hung dangerously amongst the treetops; now and then we heard one let go and crash to earth. Somewhere nearby the wires were down, and of these some carried 13,000 volts; they might be alive still. There was another possible hazard in walking in the dark through fallen brush. It rains so hard in hurricanes that the effect is like that of a flash flood. When the adjacent lowlands are flooded, rattlesnakes sometimes scurry to such high ground as ours. The breed is *adamanteus,* the biggest of the diamondbacks, and we've found him on our lawn, bird hunting, even on pleasant days. I whistled Popcorn back presently, and let the damage census go till we'd had some sleep and until the light came.

The next morning, when we'd finished our coffee and made another tour of the premises, we toilsomely began the third part of every hurricane's routine.

While Ricky mopped up the mud tracks through the house, I chopped apart the limbs on the drive and manhandled them to one side. Then I tried starting both cars; neither was damped out. We drove over to see how the family with the sick father and the hurt child had fared. At the corner we saw the daughter of another neighbor playing in an uprooted and overturned mountain of trees which till then had stood for perhaps a century.

Our friends were safe and we went back, driving past houses with tile roofs like half-scaled fish, under leaning power poles, around roped-off areas where live wires lay, zigzagging through hastily cleared paths in the streets and noticing that not just the brittle trees, but even the mahoganies were riven. Heavy-husked coconuts lay everywhere like a giant's green marbles. Snapped palm and pine trunks stood conspicuously. Stone walls were notched where trees had fallen on them, and sidewalks were sundered where roots had lifted them. People in hundreds were outdoors, doing things or merely looking.

Already city trucks were collecting and carting off the mess. Portable cranes were straightening trees. On power poles among the snaggled spider webs of wire, umbrellas were lashed to shield from the hot autumn sun linemen who had begun to work as soon as the wind commenced to drop. Men were setting up concrete lampposts and moving up replacements for metal posts broken by the flung trees. A boy was staring morosely at the ruin of his convertible, and we saw a householder examining a car that had been rolled onto his crotons. Bulldozers shoved boughs and fronds about. Here a roof was gone, yonder a small building had become a pile of cement blocks, and in the distance the stump of a chimney showed.

Our shutters had to be set out to dry in such a way as not to warp. I began unbolting them. I next cleared the poinsettia bed, chopping up the large fallen tree to movable sizes. Since our house was dry inside, Ricky went to help people who had wet rugs, sodden draperies, soaked beds, bedraggled linen, drenched and often ruined clothes; people whose windows had broken because they hadn't bothered to put up shutters or whose windows and shutters had failed to keep out horizontal, pressurized streams of water that spurted even through keyholes and drowned whatever was in the rooms.

At lunchtime we knocked off and, since the restaurants were open, we met in one. From a human-relations standpoint, it is too bad hurricanes aren't universal and frequent. The restaurant was crowded, strangers doubled up at tables, everybody talked amiably to everybody else—talked a little excitedly and trustingly. Shared peril and subsequent release make all men brothers, briefly.

We worked all that day. Hester didn't show up and we worried about her. That night we bathed in the last of the warm water and read by kerosene lamps till we were sleepy.

In the morning Hester returned. Her house had suffered only a broken window, but her daughter and six grandchildren had escaped from theirs after the roof came off, but before the walls fell in. These seven, with all possessions lost, had moved in with Hester. "A bad storm," Hester said sorrowfully. "This one was just too bad."

By late afternoon of the second day, all the shutters were down again and the house was airy. The limbs and debris I'd piled up ran for fifty feet along the drive in a heap higher than my head, but you couldn't see the grass for the leaves, still, and there were acres I hadn't even investigated carefully. Our floors were spick-and-span, the lamps were full for another evening, spoiled food had been buried, because it breeds maggots swiftly in this climate, and I was raking oak leaves out of the lily pond—so their acidity wouldn't kill the fish—when Ricky came bursting from the house. "The light's on!" she shouted.

It seemed a great victory. We felt, for once, not the classic American impatience with utilities, but great pride in a company and in the men who could make swift sense out of the copper shambles the power lines had been. We wanted to thank somebody, but there wasn't a phone. Light also meant that our stove would work again and our bath water would heat, our fans would turn and we'd have ice and could store fresh food again. Two days! It might have been two weeks.

The following morning I trimmed back the beat-up shrubbery and straightened up those bushes, especially hibiscuses, which might reroot and live. I cut down the taro. Ricky put out food for her birds—cardinals and jays, quail and two kinds of doves, woodpeckers, towhees and flickers—which were extra hungry because their natural food had largely blown away. A plague of mosquitoes descended. But the big event that day was the ringing of our phone and the announcement by a technician that it would from then on be pretty constantly usable.

We—and 40,000-odd other people—went to the Orange Bowl that evening and watched the University of Miami defeat Boston University. During the first half, it is true, we were all a shade uneasy, owing to another phenomenon common in the hurricane latitudes: a new storm had been discovered in the gulf. It was headed toward us. Perhaps we'd have it all to do, go through and undo again. That had happened to Ricky and me twice before. But during the game the public-address system announced the blow was going to miss Miami—word that got quite a hand. Eventually that storm petered out, doing no damage.

A week after the hurricane, most of the streets were clear. Most of the tipped-over trees had been set upright and most of the ruined ones had been chopped up and carted off. Nearly everybody had lights and phones again. The open roofs were nearly all at least temporarily repaired enough to ward off the rains of the rainy season. The glass shortage was over and the stores were getting back their windows. Here and there, scraps of evidence remained: a boat aground, a plane demolished, a leaning tree, a cat's cradle of overhead wires, a missing cupola, a hotel with a wrecked sign. But our poinsettias were already coming up from the roots, the yellow hibiscus was growing anew, and the rapid vegetation of the tropics would soon obscure the wounds.

Long before the winter tourists arrived the landscape was normal—normal for a land where orchids bloom on trees. The tourists now look in vain for proof of what hit us in October. Only a few thousand people out of half a million remember the mid-October storm of 1950 as anything particular. The rest blur it with other, lesser or more violent recollections. But always, inland people and people who live up north, curious about our different way of life on the tropical big toe of Florida, will cap their inquiries with the question: "——and what about hurricanes?"

Well——

17. *Regions and Seasons of Mental Activity* *

Climatic determinism, the role of weather and climate in determining the activities of man on the earth's surface, has been one of the most maligned phases of geography. Although most geographers would not care to go quite so far as Huntington in defining the role of climate, his observations, data, and speculation are difficult to refute. In these selections taken from his provocative book, the

* Ellsworth Huntington, *Mainsprings of Civilization* (New York: John Wiley & Sons, Inc., 1945), pp. 343–367. Reprinted with permission of the publishers.

The author (1876–1947) is still one of the more controversial figures of American geography. Labeled a "climatic determinist," he has been the target of constant criticism, much of which is unwarranted and based on incomplete study of his work. He wrote several texts and other books in addition to *Mainsprings of Civilization*.

close relationship between certain behavior patterns and concurrent local weather conditions are well demonstrated. Any individual who is inclined to doubt the role of weather in these cases would do well to observe his own attitudes and behavior under varying weather conditions.

Geographic Variations in Mental Activity

"Thinking is as biological as digestion," says W. A. Price. Therefore, it is as readily influenced by climate, diet, and disease, as well as by education, mode of life, and other cultural conditions. This idea should be considered in connection with two important features in the history of civilization: first, the persistently increasing dominance of the north, and second, the variations from century to century in the general psychological status of individual countries and of the world as a whole. The first feature is obvious in the movement of the center of human progress from Babylonia and Egypt to western Europe. The second appears in the fact that sometimes confidence and assurance predominate widely among the nations, whereas at other times uncertainty and instability prevail.

These psychological reactions are generally supposed to arise from economic, religious, political, and other cultural conditions. This is true. Nevertheless, an hypothesis which inserts another factor may supply an additional element of truth. A peculiar psychological condition may arise because of (1) cycles of weather and hence of disease, diet, health, and temperament. This may lead to (2) economic, political, religious, and other changes. These latter produce (3) their own psychological effects, which in turn lead to further cultural changes. Thus for decades or centuries the weather may assist other conditions in giving a particular psychological aspect to certain periods of history. The Dark Ages and the Revival of Learning occurred at opposite phases of a long climatic cycle. Storminess apparently reached a low ebb in the Dark Ages but was abundant and violent in the fourteenth century. These two periods were likewise times of psychological contrast. The Dark Ages were characterized by widespread depression of mental activity, whereas the Revival of Learning ushered in a period of alertness and hope.

In order rightly to evaluate this hypothesis, and still more in order to appraise the validity of climatic efficiency, we must examine the distribution of mental activity geographically and also in relation to seasons and weather. The good sense and scientific temperament of northern peoples, such as Scandinavians and Finns are widely recognized. Some people call Denmark the most civilized of countries. Icelanders in the far north and Falkland Islanders in the far south are notable for their intellectual activity. In Alaska white Americans tend to become great readers. The Eskimos are reputed to have especially keen minds. Such facts suggest that mental activity is unusually great in high latitudes. On the other hand, the Arabs in their hot desert are often said to be mentally alert. Astronomy, geography, and our numerals bear witness to this. In China we have seen a reversal of the usual rule that the parts of a country in the higher latitudes make the most progress, provided they are not too cold for agriculture. In the high latitudes of South America, as far south as the Falkland Islands, the Alacaluf savages, with their bare bodies protected from furious winds only by fur capes, seem to be among the world's most backward and inert people.

Such contradictions indicate that mental alertness depends on a variety of factors. We have seen that selection through migration is one such factor. It apparently accounts, in part at least, for the alertness of Icelanders and South Chinese. Education is assuredly a powerful stimulant of mental activity. So are natural resources that can be used if people exert their wits. Climate and weather are simply other factors in this same series. They receive special treatment here because they are little understood as yet and because their cyclic variation seems to have influenced some of the greatest historical changes. The highest mental achievement is possible only when favorable conditions of many kinds exert a combined stimulus. Our task just now is to try to separate climatic effects from those of heredity, culture, and the non-climatic physical environment.

A good measure of intellectual activity on a large scale is the circulation of books by libraries, especially ordinary city libraries. People read serious books more frequently when their minds are active than when they are inert. Library statistics, most fortunately, are generally well kept. Librarians tend to be co-operative. Hence such statistics afford a vast reservoir of material for a study of intellectual activity. Data from thirty city libraries well distributed over continental United States, together with six in Canada, two in Australia, and one each in Hawaii, Cuba, Panama, New Zealand, and Argentina, provide a wide basis for study. Among those forty-three libraries, twenty-eight in the United States and Canada furnish data for the central library without the branches. . . . when these cities are divided according to latitude, there is a steady rise from 29 per cent of non-fiction in the most southern cities to 55 in the most northern. The circulation of magazines shows a similar distribution. For example, in proportion to population, northern states subscribe to the *Saturday Evening Post,* the *Ladies' Home Journal,* and *Country Gentleman* far more than southern states. The Dakotas surpass Texas and Oklahoma by 50 per cent or more, and Montana similarly surpasses Arizona.

An unusual but highly sensitive kind of evidence is found in the degree of accuracy with which people report their ages in the census. In 1910 or 1920 the total number of births was steadily increasing in practically all parts of the United States. Under such circumstances data obtained from mentally alert people give curves which slope regularly downward from earlier to later ages, like those for the native whites of native parentage in Minnesota in 1920. Even among such people there is some inaccuracy. Boys of nineteen or twenty, for example, sometimes report themselves as twenty-one, thus making a hump in the curve. Among mentally inactive people gross inaccuracies prevail. Even numbers are preferred to odd; twelve is an extreme favorite, as are multiples of ten among older people. Russian data suggest that such inaccuracy is due more to mental inertia than to lack of education. Although the settlers in Siberia are a vigorous and competent group selected by migration, their children are less literate than those of older regions such as the Ukraine. Nevertheless, these same children, when adults, state their ages more accurately than the Ukrainians.

In statistics of age it is easy to estimate the degree of inaccuracy by adding up the departures from a normal curve. A systematic increase in accuracy from south to north is outstanding. This breaks down in Florida because of the recent influx of people from farther north. It also breaks down in northern New England, partly perhaps because of the prolonged outward movement of the more alert types to cities and the West. Another noteworthy feature is that in all the more recently settled states from Texas and the Dakotas westward, except Nevada and Idaho, the errors in reporting ages are less than in states in similar latitudes farther east. The relatively small contrast between East and West may be due partly to an actual difference in innate capacity, but differences of this sort between the old white populations of the North and South can scarcely account for the large difference in accuracy. Both types of regional contrast may be due in part to education, but the educational differences in turn are dependent upon climate and migration, as well as upon other geographic conditions. Taken as a whole, the data as to ages suggest the same sort of association between mental alertness and low temperature which we have found in respect to German and Indian philosophy, the reading of serious books, and the circulation of magazines.

Seasonal Variations in Mental Activity

A connection between weather and mental activity appears also when one season is compared with another. A study of Danish school children long ago led Lehmann and Pedersen to the hypothesis that there is a mental optimum of temperature considerably lower than the physical optimum. Later studies seemed at first to confirm this, but library records suggest that temperature is by no means the only factor to be taken into account. For the present, however, let us merely look at seasonal variations, regardless of their cause. Townsend Lodge, for example, has found that intelligence tests of the same person vary according to the seasons. When four groups of children from superior social and economic backgrounds (171 children in all) were given four successive tests at six-month intervals, the average group ratings between November and April "were invariably higher than when the same children were tested between May and October." Students' marks at West Point and Annapolis, the percentage of persons passing civil service examinations, and the number of applications for amendments to patents received at Washington all have maxima in spring and fall, with minima in summer and winter. The spring maximum is systematically higher or more prolonged than the autumn maximum, whereas the summer minimum tends to be lower than that of winter.

Rossman has shown that patents afford an unusually good indication of seasonal variation in a high type of mental activity. During the year or more which generally elapses between the filing of an application and the granting of a patent an inventor often gets a new idea. Unless his original application is promptly amended, he must apply for a second patent to cover the new idea or leave the field to someone else. Naturally the inventor is eager to apply for an amendment as soon as necessary drawings and specifications can be prepared. Therefore Rossman's curve of average daily applications for amendments to patents gives an especially reliable picture of seasonal variations in mental activity. This applies primarily to the northeastern quarter of the United States where the great majority of American inventions originate.

The curve for patents shows several significant features. From a medium level in January it rises to a broad maximum including March, April, and, to a less degree, May. The date when drawings and specifications arrive at the Patent Office, however, is considerably later than the time when the new idea flashes into mind. Therefore, the maximum inventive activity presumably occurs as early as March or even February. In later months the inventive faculty apparently works at a progressively lower rate until midsummer. Inasmuch as August and September both stand low in the curve for patents, we infer that the inventive faculty is least vigorous in July and August. One might expect the opposite because vacations often provide opportunities for concentrated thought and the preparation of data. In October, applications for amendments to patents jump temporarily to a level higher than in April. Their prompt return to a low level in November and December indicates that the October peak is much less important than the one in the spring. Probably it represents ideas that have been simmering during the summer and are made use of under the stimulus of cool weather and the accompanying physical energy. The spring maximum, coming at the season of almost the poorest health, cannot be explained so easily and will be deferred until later.

One of the best tests of an hypothesis is its efficiency as a means of prediction and of inferring what must have happened in the past. Krynine, an engineer, has suggested that, if intellectual activity really varies throughout the year as indicated by students' marks, patents, and civil service examinations, the amount of discussion in scientific meetings ought to show a similar seasonal trend. This supposition has been tested by means of data for three large engineering societies (civil and chemical in New York and general in Chicago) which holds regular monthly or bi-monthly meetings from September to May or June. In each society the average number of persons who discuss papers presented at all the meetings for twenty years or more is counted as 100 per cent and the number for each month is expressed as a corresponding percentage. Of course, the number of persons who discuss a paper varies greatly according to the subject and the speaker. When many years and three different societies are considered, however, the chances of having a good speaker and an interesting subject are essentially the same in all months. This gives a good idea of the degree to which highly intellectual men feel inclined to comment on scientific papers. Its strong maximum in March and minor maximum in November agree almost perfectly with what would be expected on the basis of the hypothesis suggested. This agreement confirms the idea that mental activity of many kinds has a definite seasonal trend which is different from that of physical health.

. . . . .

Seasonal Riots in India

Returning once more to the seasonal relationships between mental conditions and the weather, let us examine religious riots in India. The files of *The New York Times* from 1919 to 1941 contain accounts of 148 major riots, excluding those connected with actual rebellions, or with political or social causes of a general nature, such as protests against taxes, unpopular arrests, enforcement of new laws, and popular movements, such as the agitation for Indian freedom. Most of the 148 riots were of a religious nature. They originated in clashes at times of festivals or in minor events such as the following culled from the *Times:* Moslems throw beef on the steps of a Hindu temple; others cut branches from a sacred

Hindu tree to make room for the banners of a procession; Hindus beat a Moslem vendor who drove away a sacred bull that feasted on his vegetables; a Hindu laundryman washes clothes in a pond attached to a Moslem mosque. Such riots usually involve Moslems and Hindus, but clashes between sects within each main religion or with other sects, such as the Sikhs, are also common. The greater number occur in the cities of the United Provinces and the Punjab, where Moslems and Hindus are intimately mixed, but they extend to Calcutta on the east and Bombay on the west. Minor riots by the hundred are a distinct and ominous feature of northern India.

SEASONAL DISTRIBUTION OF LOCAL INDIAN RIOTS

January	6	June	9	November	2
February	11	July	16	December	6
March	10	August	22		——
April	29	September	13	Total	148
May	19	October	5		

The nature of the conditions which immediately incite these riots has been often discussed but never settled. They obviously arise from tension between different faiths. They are a powerful factor in keeping religious antagonisms alive and tense. Hence a knowledge of their causes is highly important for the political and economic welfare of India. Religious festivals are often said to be the cause. The chief Moslem festivals occur at the New Year and the feast of Ramadan after the month of fasting when no food may be eaten between sunrise and sunset. The Moslem year, however, is so short that 33½ of them are equal to only 32½ true solar years. Hence during the period covered by our data these festivals occur almost equally at every season. This fact does not help much in accounting for 29 riots in April against 9 in June, or 22 in August against 2 in November. Hindu festivals, on the other hand, are so dated that they would lead us to expect few riots in midsummer and many in January, March, and October, but these three months with a total of 21 riots do not equal April or August alone (see Table).

Idleness and the congregating of villagers in the cities when there is little work in the fields are also said to set the date for riots. The course of events supports this idea at some seasons but opposes it at others. In northern India the agricultural year begins when the ground is softened by the first monsoon showers in June (May in Bengal). Thus the decline in riots from April to June accompanies an increase in agricultural work, and the rise in riots in August comes during a lull in farm work before the harvest. In August, however, the extreme muddiness of the roads, the heavy and almost daily showers, and the extremely damp, hot mugginess of the weather keep people at home, thus tending to reduce the likelihood of riots at the very time when they are most numerous. From September until November the harvesting of the summer crops and the planting of winter crops keep the peasants busy and coincide with a decline of riots to their lowest level. By the middle of December, however, the main work is at an end and the time is at hand when leisure, money, energy, and visits to the city, as well as the most important Hindu festivals, all combine to favor riots. Nevertheless, the riots remain at a low level from mid-December to mid-February. March and April, on the other hand, are again a busy season, for the winter crops must be harvested. Riots then rise to a maximum.

Another possibility is that scarcity of food, entailing high prices and hunger, leads to riots. The food supply is lowest in August and early September before the summer harvest begins. Riots then reach a maximum. Food is most abundant in the autumn when the main crop has been harvested. On this basis we should expect few riots, and that is what we find. On further investigation, however, we again find scanty food in February, before winter crops are harvested, and abundance in April after the harvest. At these times the number of riots is the opposite of what would be expected on the basis of food. Thus here, just as with idleness, close agreement at one season is neutralized by strong disagreement at another.

Weather as a promoter of riots has hitherto been neglected. Nevertheless, its effect seems to agree with the distribution of riots. The comfortable season in northern India begins in mid-October. By that time the average temperature for day and night from Lahore to Lucknow, where riots are especially common, has dropped to about 70°. The heavy summer rains are over and the mud is drying up, but the earth is still moist. Pleasant temperatures, about like New York in May, continue until February, but other things become less pleasant because drought parches the earth. After February the temperatures rise rapidly until monthly averages of 80° or even 90° are reached in April and 85° to 95° in May. The air is blistering hot, and the wind raises clouds of dust. The April maximum of riots occurs when extreme heat and drought are most widespread. We have seen that homicide in the United States and lack of sexual control in Italy also increase with hot weather.

May in Bengal and June farther up the Ganges see the "bursting" of the southwest monsoon and an extraordinary transformation. A comforting breeze blows quite steadily, clouds shield the sun, showers fall, the dust is laid, the temperature drops a few degrees, the death-rate lessens, and farm work begins. Naturally enough, all this is accompanied by a decided decline in riots.

Unfortunately these pleasant conditions soon disappear. During July the wind dies down, the air is saturated, and the monthly rainfall rises to 7 inches at Lahore, 13 at Calcutta, and 25 at Bombay. For week after week average temperatures of 80° to 90° make the weather as bad as the four or five most muggy days ever experienced in New York City. Tempers become short, and riots reach a second maximum in August. Then step by step with better weather serious riots decline from 22 in August to only 2 in November. Thus, though festivals, idleness, city crowds, and the food supply are doubtless important, the agreement between riots and the effect of the weather on personal comfort is so close that it appears to be the main cause of the seasonal fluctuations in riots. It should be noted, however, that in very hot cities—especially when rainfall is heavy—the number of riots declines at the most extreme high temperatures. As the weather gets hot, people apparently feel more and more uncomfortable and irritable, their power of self-control declines, and they riot under relatively small provocation, especially in dry weather. At still higher temperatures, however, the heat seems to sap people's energy so that greater irritation is needed to make them active. When the weather is rainy and humid, as well as hot, the tendency toward inertia is stronger than in dry weather, and the rain itself doubtless reduces riots by keeping people at home.

The conclusions derived from Indian riots are supported by the findings of Dexter years ago as to arrests for assault and battery. Basing his study on about 40,000 arrests during eight years in New York City, he finds that the seasonal curve of arrests

> is most beautifully regular, showing a gradual increase from January . . . to July . . . and a decrease for the remainder of the year. . . . One must conclude that temperature, more than any other condition, affects the emotional states which are conducive to fighting . . . except for the very highest temperatures, the number of assaults increases with heat. That is what Shakespeare had noticed, and the data corroborate in a striking manner the wonderful observational powers of the great master. . . . The general showing is one of marked deficiency for low temperatures with a gradual increase to . . . maximum excess in the 80°–85° group, at which point a sudden drop takes place. This final decrease . . . seems without doubt to be due to the devitalizing effect of the intense heat of 85° and above. . . . For fighting purposes one must have not only . . . inclination, but also . . . energy. . . . Heat of any considerable intensity seems productive of emotional states, furnishing the former (i.e. inclination), but at a certain point the latter is depleted by extra demands made upon it by the processes of life.

The important point is that people's temperament fluctuates in harmony with the weather. It is easy enough to accept this as an explanation of the seasonal cycle in religious antipathies and riots in India, but the general principle extends much farther. It applies to the actions of the Congress of the United States, for example, when tempers are frayed by hot weather, especially in the days before air conditioning was introduced. There is a widespread impression that hasty legislation and personal violence in the form of fist fights formerly rose to a maximum under such conditions. It is worth noting that in the United States Negro riots occur most often in unusually hot weather, as happened in 1943 during June in Detroit and early August in New York. Their primary cause was irritableness at a time when there was already tension between two groups, just as in India. The condition which brought them to a head was apparently the discomfort and lack of self-control associated with hot weather. In the world as a whole the tendency toward lack of self-control in politics, in sex relations, and in many other respects rises markedly in hot weather and in hot countries. This is not the only reason for the frequency of political revolutions in low latitudes, but it must play a part.

The Seasons, Insanity, and Crime

As final evidence of the influence of the seasons on mental reactions, let us examine the seasonal distribution of outbreaks of insanity and crime. Abundant evidence illustrates that (1) outbreaks of insanity in Italy, England, the United States, and Germany; (2) suicides in Italy, France, and England; and (3) sexual offenses in France and Germany are at or near maximum in June. All likewise show a minimum in winter. On an average the maximum in June is more than 80 per cent above the minimum in December. Homicides also are most numerous in June but remain abundant till autumn. Insanity, suicide, sexual crimes, and homicide all indicate mental weakness which causes people to do the wrong thing under conditions where stronger minds would behave differently. Curiously enough, these signs of weakness occur at just the time when other lines of evidence indicate physical wellbeing. June, as we have seen, is a time of good health and maximum conceptions, especially in western Europe. Children conceived then or a little earlier live longer and are more likely to be eminent than those conceived at any other time.

It is not difficult to understand why sexual crimes reach a maximum when the reproductive faculties are most active, but why do insanity and suicide also increase? The answer seems to be suggested in what has been said in regard to the excessive percentages of criminals, insane persons, and sufferers from tuberculosis conceived in June. At that time the physical stimulus which merely leads to health and increased powers of reproduction among normal people apparently overstimulates those who are poorly poised, weak of will, oversexed, or otherwise abnormal. Moreover, in the late spring many people who are physically below par and unable to produce children at other seasons appear to experience a reproductive stimulus which enables them to become parents. The results of the stimulus of the reproductive season upon both kinds of parents—the temperamentally weak and the physically weak—seem to appear not only in insanity, suicide, and crime among people of the parental generation, but in a crop of relatively handicapped children. These children suffer unduly from congenital defects. Like their parents, they are also the type which provides many individuals who experience nervous breakdowns leading to insanity or show the kind of lack of self-control which leads to crime. This, then, is what happens when people who are below par temperamentally or below the threshold of reproduction at most seasons are stimulated by the advent of the annual season of reproduction according to the animal cycle.

On the other hand, among temperamentally normal people who are also normal in being well above the reproductive threshold, the stimulation arising through the advent of the season of maximum reproductive capacity leads to the conception of children who are so vigorous that they raise the average span of life and provide much more than the normal proportion of leaders. Such relationships are significant as an indication that man's psychological as well as physical conditions are powerfully influenced by the changing weather of the seasons. If this statement is correct, it seems logical to suppose that a corresponding psychological effect is produced by different types of climate and by different phases of climatic cycles. Thus again we see that human history and the progress of civilization must be closely tied up with climate.

CHAPTER THREE

Landforms: Processes and Types

THE EARTH'S SURFACE is characterized by an infinite variety of shapes or forms. The arrangement of these landforms and their relationship to the underlying geologic structure is called *geomorphology* or *physiography* (the latter is the older term). Entailed in a study of landforms are their description, classification, and genesis. Such study is important to the areal differentiation of the world—the major objective of geography.

Current and past changes of the earth's surface demonstrate that its nature is dynamic. Internal processes such as frequent volcanic eruptions and earthquakes affect the surface of the earth; surface inequalities resulting from these internal processes are constantly being acted upon by the external gradational forces of weathering and erosion. The sum total of all these surface-shaping processes is not the same in any two regions of the earth—hence the tremendous variety of landforms. Attempts to describe this heterogeneity of landforms has resulted in their classification into such categories as plains, hills, plateaus, and mountains. Individual parts of these generalized types, such as valleys and peaks, can be further identified.

These varied landforms compose the background on which man must live. Some areas are favorable; others provide handicaps which man must overcome or avoid. Landforms play a part in the daily lives of all people —students, farmers, lawyers, and laborers. Type of climate, soil and soil erosion, water resources and drainage, isolation of areas, development of communications, location of settlements and agriculture: these are only a few of the items related to the nature, distribution, and genesis of landforms.

The readings in Chapter Three were selected for the purpose of giving the student specific examples of both internal and external surface-shaping processes. In addition, several background readings on the origin of present landscapes and examples of landform-type studies in central Africa and the Pyrenees Mountains are given.

---

18. The Face of the Land *

A quotation from the Greek philosopher Heraclitus: "There is nothing permanent in the world except change," closes this selection and emphasizes the theme presented. This portion of one of *Life's* "World We Live In" series explains, in popular style, how present landforms came into being through the opposing forces of internal uplift and surface degradation. Barnett emphasizes the constant change taking place in the earth's surface, and shows how rapid change as a result of earthquakes and volcanoes and slow change such as erosion are brought into balance. The reader might profitably consult the excellent photographs and diagrams in all of the "World We Live In" series.

In his own admiring eye man sees himself as the master of his environment and the author of all the changes he observes about him. The stony encrustations of his cities and towns overflow and atrophy the green countryside. His steel rails and concrete roads dissect the prairies and reshape mountain passes. His towering dams block entire river valleys and create huge new lakes.

As he makes minor alterations to suit his needs man seldom discerns that the natural world may be undergoing vaster changes through agencies beyond his control and at a rhythm too slow for him to perceive. He once thought that the features of the earth existed always—an illusion derived not only from the brevity of human memory, but from the brevity of human history. Although the great mountains and valleys, plains and plateaus of the earth are older far than history, they did not exist always, nor will they persist until the end of time. Every hill and highland, cliff, crag and rock is being eaten away by rain, frost, wind and ice; and in time the mightiest mountains will be leveled and washed away into the sea. The "everlasting hills" of the poet do not exist—there are no everlasting hills.

* Lincoln Barnett, "The Face of the Land," from *Life's* series on "The World We Live In," April 13, 1953.

The author (1909) has been a free-lance writer since 1946. He was a staff writer and associate editor of *Life,* 1937–46. He is the author of *The Universe and Dr. Einstein* and of *Life's* "The World We Live In" series.

Yet this does not mean that in the end the earth's surface will be reduced to a flat, featureless plain. For with every mountain that is obliterated from the earth, a new one comes into being. The face of the land is self-renewing and ever-changing, as mobile and inconstant in the long perspective of geologic time as its hovering cloud canopy appears in man's tiny temporal range. Even the earth's greatest relief features—the continental platforms and ocean basins—whose main outlines were molded in the planet's infancy do not preserve a wholly immutable relationship, but continually yield and recapture areas of their ever-shifting rival domains. And as the continental outlines recurrently change their pattern, now surrendering to the sea, now invading it, so the vertical profile of the land rises and falls in age-long cycles of upheaval and disintegration.

. . . . .

Knowing the processes by which mountains and valleys are constructed and destroyed, geologists find it possible to recapitulate the evolution of every land form on earth and guess its probable future. And so they speak of the earth's varied features in living terms as "young," "mature" or "old." In the long perspective of geologic history the eastern half of the U.S. is old and worn down; the West is a young, changing area.

In the East the destructive forces predominate over those of construction. The last major crustal upheavals which produced the Appalachians, the Adirondacks, and the Laurentian Mountains of Canada took place 200 to 250 million years ago. Today New England is a region of low promontories and rounded ridges, planed and scoured by millenniums of rain, ice and frost. The antique valleys of New England and the Middle Atlantic states, unlike the deep canyons and rugged V-shaped gorges of the West, are broad and gentle, possessed now not by swift, rushing streams but by slow, serpentine rivers. In many places its lowlands are carpeted with a thick cover of rich, arable soil which, geologically speaking, is a characteristic of old age. For it is only on the benign slopes of ancient landscapes, mellowed with age and protected by vegetation from the destructive pull of gravity, that soil can resist the forces of erosion and accumulate in a fertile mantle year after year, century after century.

In the West, where the forces of erosion work no less relentlessly, the earth's internal forces are far more active than in the East. Vast areas of the Western states are strewn with lava, cinders, ash and other debris of recent volcanic activity. The Columbia Plateau in the Northwest is one of the earth's greatest volcanic constructions, an immense lava field covering an area of more than 200,000 square miles and in places a mile thick, built by stupendous outpourings of molten lava. Lassen Peak, in California, is a dormant volcano that may erupt again at any time. Virtually all the mountains of the Far West are high and young, with barren rock and little soil cover; their pinnacles and spurs stand towering and jagged, not yet softened and rounded by the touch of wind and rain.

In particular, the West appears to be a region of great crustal uneasiness. Displacements recur frequently along great fault lines, producing earthquakes and upheaval of the surface rocks. Not long ago scientists of the U. S. Coast and Geodetic Survey discovered that linear strains have been building up along the huge San Andreas Fault ever since the San Francisco earthquake of 1906. Horizontal movements have been especially obvious; at the present time the earth mass along the west side of the fault is moving in a northwesterly direction at the rate of two inches a year. Hence they believe that the great rift will slip again some day, producing another earthquake perhaps as great as that of half a century ago. A new instrument designed to measure long-term strains in the earth's crust is now being tested by seismologists, who hope it may eventually make possible the prediction of future quakes. Elsewhere other slippages along other faults have produced great earthquakes in California at frequent intervals for many years past. One of the most recent was the Kern County earthquake of 1952, which was nearly as vehement as the historic San Francisco quake though less disastrous in its results.

And subtler crustal movements—broad regional uplifts, depressions and warpings—are imperceptibly altering the shape of the land. The Baldwin Hills area of the Los Angeles plain has been arched upward at the rate of three feet per century. The Buena Vista oil field in the San Joaquin Valley is rising at the rate of four feet per century. Trivial as these uplifts may seem, in a relatively brief interval of geologic time they could change the profile of California. If they continue for 25,000 years (discounting erosion), the Alamitos Plain will be a tableland 300 feet above the sea and the Buena Vista Hills will have grown 1,000 feet. If they continue for 200,000 years—only one fifth of the span of man's existence on earth—the Buena Vista Hills will be as high as the Cascades. If they continue for two million years—a not excessive interval, when one recalls that the uplifting of the Himalayas, the Alps and the Rockies require at least that much time—the California highlands will attain the height of Mt. Everest.

Thus everywhere on the planet there are signs that the earth's crust is not altogether stable. Surveys made by the U. S. Coast and Geodetic Survey over the last 20 years have shown that along the 1,000-mile stretch from Massachusetts to Florida the coast is being submerged at a rate of about .02 feet per year. There is reason to believe that this change in the relationship between land and sea is due not only to a rise in sea level but also to basic movements of the continental block. All around the world the uplift of mountains and plateaus is offset by the slow downward warping of shorelines and inland basins. The entire country of France, for example, appears to be tilting slowly northward, rising in the south, sinking along the Channel coast. If this movement continues, the waters of the Atlantic will ultimately inundate great areas of France from the Belgian border to Brest. Yet at the same time the Baltic coast of Sweden is rising at the rate of one-half centimeter per year. If this rate of uplift were maintained for 10,000 years it would tilt all the water out of the Baltic Sea and turn its shallow floor into dry land—as it used to be.

Although the active movements of the earth's crust are localized—upheavals occurring now in one place, now in another—the antipathetic processes of erosion are continuous and worldwide. Given time every land mass on the face of the earth would be destroyed and reduced to sea level by the chisels of rain and the wedges of frost, the abrasive breath of the wind and the massive tread of glaciers. If unopposed these forces would have swept all the land into the sea eons ago. But the restlessness and disquietude of the earth's crust proclaims that the internal forces responsible for the re-creation and rehabilitation of the land are as active today as ever they were in the geologic past. Present rates of crustal movement, if long continued, are sufficient to produce mountains as great as any that now stand on earth. So new uplands will arise, new plateaus will be warped toward the sky. And each uplift will create new rushing torrents to begin the work of obliterating the land.

It is only recently that scientists came to understand the antipathy of these natural forces of construction and destruction, and thus perceived that nothing on earth is eternal—no mountain or river, no continent or sea. Yet the flux of nature has been visible to some poets and philosophers of ages past. Two thousand five hundred years ago the Greek philosopher Heraclitus said, "There is nothing permanent in the world except change."

19. *Single Land Mass? U. S. Geologists Re-examine Continental Drift Theory* *

The amount of land and water on the earth's surface, the nature of the surface of continents and ocean basins, and the world position of the continents and the oceans are fundamental to an understanding of the world and the nature and distribution of its major

* "Single Land Mass? U. S. Geologists Re-examine Continental Drift Theory," *Christian Science Monitor*, December 3, 1953, p. 3. (Map by Russell H. Lenz)

landforms. Geologists generally agree that the continental surfaces are composed of lighter rock than the heavier oceanic basins. The loss of the moon from the Pacific Basin probably accounts for heavier materials being found there than in the other ocean basins. Geologists also usually accept the theory that the earth's interior is a molten, plastic, or viscous mass. The continental-drift theory has been proposed to explain the present position of land masses. This much-discussed theory postulates a world island that fractured into continental blocks; these blocks "drifted" on underlying plastic material to their present positions, owing, perhaps, to the force of earth rotation or to their attempts to achieve better balance on the earth's surface. This theory may explain the hemispheric land area differences, the present location of continents, and the shapes of continents and ocean basins. It has been largely discounted by United States geologists but recent evidence summarized in this article adds new support to the theory.

Startling changes are being considered in the outlook of American geology toward current theories explaining how continents got their form and structure.

Earth scientists are polishing up their best arguments on the hypothesis that existing continents were once a single land mass until unknown forces set them adrift some 180,000,000 years ago.

Several generations of school children now are familiar with the exercise of fitting continental cutouts together so the nose of South America nestles into the Gulf of Guinea; North America swings over to match up with Europe; and Australia, New Zealand, and Antarctica fit in at the south in the Indian Ocean.

Much Research Done

This was the supercontinent of Gondwana, or Gondwanaland, insofar as many overseas geomorphologists are concerned. But the geography seldom led much farther on this side of the Atlantic where geologists Schuchert, Bailey Willis, and J. W. Gregory gave the "continental drift" theory short shrift.

Lecturing before various groups of researchers of the American Association of Petroleum Geologists in 1951 and 1952, Dr. Lester C. King, University of Natal geologist from Durban, South Africa, noted "a new spirit of impartial inquiry and broad outlook" in his United States audiences. As a result, the AAPG, which now is finding room in its Journal for up-to-the-minute reports on South American geology, especially in Peru and Venezuela, is also running a series on "The Necessity for Continental Drift," by Dr. King.

Because a great deal of research has been done on this subject since World War II, and there is need for much more, Dr. King says he feels the time is peculiarly opportune for re-examining basic evidence.

While following the works of Taylor, Baker, Wegener, du Toit, Robert, Leonardos, Fermor and Windhausen in the main, Dr. King reassembles the continents a bit differently than his predecessors.

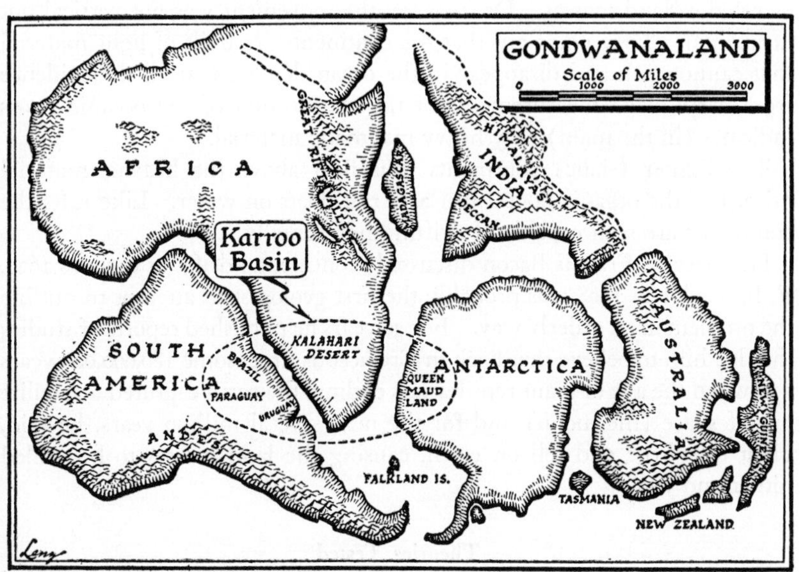

Russell H. Lenz, Chief Cartographer

Figure 5

Some natural scientists theorize that "existing continents were once a single land mass until unknown forces set them adrift some 180,000,000 years ago." This map, based on restoration by Lester C. King, South African geologist, shows how the coastlines might be fitted together to substantiate that view. This supercontinent was called Gondwana or Gondwanaland.

Based on the present distribution of late Paleozoic and Triassic land formations, including glacial deposits and coals, Dr. King swings Antarctica much farther north into the Indian Ocean than others have done, and visualizes Australia as having executed a counterclockwise turning movement of about 90 degrees while drifting eastward following continental dissolution.

He traces Africa's Great Karroo basin from a western beginning in Brazil, Paraguay, and Uruguay, across a sizable area of South Africa to Queen Maud Land in Antarctica.

Land Beyond Continents

Both driftists and nondriftists agree that at some time in the past there must have been land beyond the boundaries of the present continents. But it is in the manner of deriving these lands that the cleavage of opinion has come about. Some geologists backcast a time when deep ocean floors were elevated as land masses. Driftists say the movement was not vertical but horizontal. They point out that the continents are built of light material that cannot sink and disappear in the ocean depths; that all the evidence from earthquake measurements of the constitution of the oceanic floors indicates (in the main) only heavy magmatic material.

The lighter (sialic) continents thus float above the heavier material (sima) of the oceanic floors; just as a raft floats on water. Like rafts the continents are seen capable of drifting horizontally.

Historically, Francis Bacon discussed "continental drift" as early as 1620. F. B. Taylor in 1908 was probably the first geologist to attempt to outline the problem in an orderly way. For 30 years he published reports of studies that led him to believe that back in Cretaceous time, some 180,000,000 years ago when the age of giant reptiles was ending, the earth captured a satellite out of space (the moon) and for the next several million years, he said, giant tides rose and fell on earth, causing the land masses to be pulled hither and yon.

Theories Tested

In 1911 Howard Baker presented his "displacement globe" postulating a single supercontinent or pangaea which split from Alaska across the Arctic and down the full length of the Atlantic to the Antarctic, the unequal parts drifting off in opposite directions toward the Pacific region. Later, Alfred Wegener, German geophysicist, put prevailing theories to test and assembled the parts in the working hypothesis that bears his name. He quoted astronomical observations to support a claim that the continents still are drifting.

For a long time the drift theory languished in the United States. Then in 1948 at the University of Cincinnati, Dr. K. E. Caster reopened the question following four years of geological work in South America where he traveled thousands of miles gathering data under auspices of the United States Department and the Guggenheim Foundation.

"None of my findings in South America definitely proves or disproves the drift hypothesis," he says, "but they are significant enough to warrant additional field studies in South Africa, India, and Australia to make necessary comparisons."

Patterns Correlated

It was the late Alexander L. du Toit, another noted South African geologist, presenting a mass of detailed data published by the Carnegie Institution of Washington in 1927, who showed Africa to be "the key to the whole problem," the heart of ancient Gondwanaland.

Dr. du Toit stressed fossil relationships that indicated a widespread similarity of flora and fauna in the days before separation, increasing diversity since. Ten years later he presented a more finished work, "Our Wandering Continents."

He worked out beautiful correlations of fracture patterns as shown by the location and direction of sea deeps and rift valleys. He found fossil evidence and living species of plants and animals native to the Falkland Islands, South America, and South Africa, but known nowhere else in the world.

Following his own work in South America, Dr. Caster revised du Toit's work as it was published, translating this into Portuguese for the benefit of Brazilian geologists studying these problems.

In the current AAPG Bulletin, Dr. King calls attention to the manner in which the Great Karroo basin is cut off at both the east and west coasts of South Africa, asserting that this is evidence that widespread land areas formerly extended in those directions.

"Useful Hypothesis"

"The conditions of accumulation of the Karroo beds resembled those of the existing Kalahari basin," he says, "about which extend broad plains and uplands from which was supplied the detritus that accumulated in the basin.

"But the Karroo basin was on a vastly greater scale: the basin stretches beyond the borders of Africa to an unknown distance on both east and west; and the marginal lands beyond that, which supplied the sediment (maximum thickness of terrestrial sediments approaching 20,000 feet) must have been of continental dimensions."

Dr. King expresses amazement that "so useful an hypothesis should have been allowed to fall into neglect or provoke such violent opposition in other quarters." The arguments advanced by some opponents, he says, that similar fossil species and similar geologic sequences in sundered regions such as South America and South Africa are "merely fortuitous," amounts "to a negation of the scientific method. It denies the attempt to classify like data and to generalize from them. . . .

"The conception of drift harmonizes completely with what is known of the physical condition of the earth's crust: high-standing lighter continents, deeper, heavier oceanic sectors, isostacy (general equilbrium in the earth's crust) involving horizontal transfer of material at depth, the existence of at least one level of no strain."

Corroborative Evidence

The hypothesis of drift is not to be proved by idle armchair theorizing, but by hard work in the field, he concludes. Physicists and chemists insist that if an experiment is to be accepted it must be repeatable.

Therefore, "in the rocks that can be seen, sectioned, measured, hammered, and compared, individually and in sequence, structurally and in age, by anyone who cares, lies the geologist's repeatable experiment."

Also appearing in the same issue of the Bulletin is corroborative evidence offered by D. L. Niddrie of the University of Manchester, England, who recently visited the Falkland Islands and made comparisons between the rocks and fossils of South Africa, Uruguay, and the Islands.

He had been stationed previously as a Naval Meteorological Officer at Simonstown Naval Base (Cape Province), and later had access to geological museum collections in Montevideo. Gondwana and pre-Gondwana rocks and fossils were studied and many of the conclusions of Dr. du Toit were verified. For convenience he summarizes the rock types and sequences in tabular form.

20. *Parícutin* *

Recent dramatic evidence of the changing of the earth's surface through volcanic action has been provided by Parícutin, a new volcano in Mexico. It provides an excellent example of the crustal instability characteristic of the mountainous rim of the Pacific Basin. A cornfield, peaceful in 1943, now is occupied by a volcanic cone more than 1800 feet high. Lemert provides a graphic description of this area, the volcano, and the effects of the eruptions upon the area and its people. The account of an actual eruption is particularly revealing.

* Ben F. Lemert, "Parícutin," *Journal of Geography,* Vol. 47, October 1948, pp. 267–275. By permission of the *Journal of Geography,* official publication of The National Council of Geography Teachers.

The author (1892) is Associate Professor of Economic Geography, Duke University. He has done work in the southeastern United States and Mexico; his special interests include research in economic geography.

Parícutin volcano, approximately 212 miles by air and 350 miles by automobile in a west-southwest direction from Mexico City, is located in the state of Michoacán. The edge of the lava flow, near the buried town of San Juan de Parangaricutiro, is twelve miles from the Uruapan highway. The road which connects the highway with the edge of the lava flow is bad. Flimsy wooden bridges just wide enough for a car span some of the mountain streams, while others are crossed by means of two planks. Most of the streams are incised ten to twenty feet beneath the surface. Several miles of the road are thru areas covered deeply with fine ash, while other miles are over sharp rocks which are hard on tires and springs. The streets of one village are just wide enough for a car and the southern exit of that village is similar to a steep stairway. At Uruapan a Mexican taxicab driver will load any number of persons that can get into a new American car, and take them to the edge of the lava flow, waiting until they return from the lookout hill, for the sum of forty pesos. The driver expects a tip of five or ten pesos and he earns it.

Regional Characteristics

The state of Michoacán, in which Parícutin is located, is studded with dormant volcanoes. Tancítaro mountain, the dominating land mass, 13,000 feet above sea level, is surrounded by hundreds of cinder cones similar to Parícutin. From an airplane one can see many areas, covered with grass, grazed by cattle, areas, which by their contours, show they were once lava flows like those that spread over the valley in which San Juan de Parangaricutiro is located. The Uruapan highway that starts at Garapán, on the main road between Mexico City and Guadalajara, makes a ten-mile curve around the base of a beautiful cone, the diameter of which must be nearly two miles. The sides of the cones and the surrounding mountains are covered with pine and cedar forests, the intervening valleys carpeted with grass interspersed with fields of corn and sugar cane. This is one of the regions of Mexico that receives plenty of precipitation. Eastward in the vicinity of Mexico City, and westward around Guadalajara the landscape colors are gray, light green, and buff because of light rainfall, but the appearance of the region around Uruapan is dark green, the landscape color which is so familiar to people of northwestern Europe and the United States east of the Mississippi River.

The People

The Tarascan Indians who inhabit this region live on their corn, vegetables, and livestock. They make aguardiente, a colorless, fiery liquor from their sugar cane. They build their houses of pine lumber, and manufacture a wide variety of wooden objects ranging from furniture to chess sets. The Tarascans are short and stocky. Their black hair is straight, their eyes slant like those of a Mongolian, and their villages resemble those in wooded sections of Japan. Some of the Indians have skin that, where it is not exposed to the sun, is about as white as that of a northern European. These Indians pursue their horses about the high mountain pastures, sometimes running almost continuously for an hour at a time, yet they show very few signs of fatigue in spite of the elevation.

During the summer of 1947 the Tarascans welcomed visitors as a market for their wooden ware and guide services, but did not permit close inspection of their fields. Anyone leaving the highway was thought to be a government agent sent to examine their cattle and goats for signs of aftosa, the disease that livestock-producing countries strenuously try to eradicate. All over Mexico meat animals were destroyed by the thousands while the natives, unable to understand, stood by in helpless ignorance and were kept from violence by the presence of soldiers. The writer was forced to dismantle his camp, established in a mountain pasture twelve miles above Uruapan, in spite of rain and approaching darkness. Between two and three hundred Indians, clad in attractive red and black serapes, and armed with machetes and rifles, told him to come to their village where they could watch him, or remain where he was and be killed.

Prior to the appearance of the volcano, because of very poor means of communication of any kind, this section of Michoacán was subject to very little, if any, law enforcement. Today one Indian may kill another, the body of the dead man will lie where he fell until darkness, at which time members of his village will carry him away, and the perpetrator of the deed may continue his pursuits unmolested. It must not be concluded from this that the Tarascans in this region are vicious or hostile. They are really friendly and generous, but conduct their affairs in the manner that their primitive lives have proved best for survival.

The Volcano

Parícutin has built up a cone, the top of which is about 1800 feet higher than the floor of the valley in which it first appeared in February, 1943. The cone is not circular, but somewhat elliptical, with two sides higher and a sag in the middle. The crater has a central vent and two side vents, all of which sometimes erupt simultaneously. The surface of the cone is covered with volcanic sand, with here and there blocks of lava almost hidden in the loose material. The angle of slope is steep and the sand slides at the least disturbance. Ascent must be made by using both hands and feet, following a zigzag course. The only ways to descend are to double up and slide down on one's back, or wrap the arms around the head and roll. Both methods are uncomfortable and dangerous, especially if one strikes a sharp rock. The writer's companion rolled down that slope for at least 1,000 feet and survived, but such experiences rarely happen.

During violent eruptions the sides of the cone shake and heave and the sand slides. Prior to an eruption the surface trembles constantly and there is a sound similar to that given off by a boiler when the steam pressure is about to lift the safety valve.

Hardened lava almost surrounds the base of the cone, a groove-shaped depression between it and the sloping sand surface. This groove, about twenty feet wide and ten or fifteen feet deep, appears to have been formed by the immense amount of stones of all sizes from that of a pea to that of a piano, that hurtles down the volcano with terrific speed during heavy eruptions. Many of these stones are partially rounded, perhaps their shape being caused by the whirling motion while in a plastic condition in the air, and the pounding they get as they strike the side of the cone and bounce on their way to the bottom.

On the northeast and southwest sides of the cone lava is pushing out continuously and, beneath the broken crust that rides upon it, the molten rock looks like a mass of red-hot taffy. At one end of a graben where the plastic material was squeezing out it looked like a huge red ball or bubble, until the surface cooled and the hardened rock began to crack off. Usually such a situation produces a violent explosion, after which the viscous lava may move fifty or sixty feet a minute. After a few hours, or days, the speed slackens to thirty or forty feet an hour. Close to the cone the temperature of the molten rock is about 1900° Fahrenheit. At a distance of half a mile it usually registers about 1700°. However, new lava may burst up thru old flows at a distance of half a mile or more from the cone.

The former lookout hill that was used by tourists in 1946 has been completely surrounded by lava, preventing approach by the horses used for the ride from the edge of the lava flow at San Juan de Parangaricutiro. The present lookout hill is two or three miles from the base of the cone. Both hills are covered with a nine-foot layer of fine dust. At the base of the hills, on the side next to the volcano, the lava stands up like a wall, thirty or forty feet high. There are repeated explosions in this wall, each outburst announced by a blast of hot gas and dust, followed by rocks which crash to the bottom. All of the area between the lookout and the volcano is covered with merged tongues of moving lava, the surface of which is far from level. At frequent intervals there are deep grabens where the molten material has drained away, causing the solid mass to collapse. Descent into and the climb out of these depressions is very dangerous because many of the huge blocks of rock are delicately balanced and crash downwards at the touch of a hand or foot. All of the rocks are hot, those in some of the grabens too hot to touch with the hand. The rocks that make up the lava, for the most part, resemble coke material, hard, glassy, with a grayish, sponge-like appearance. Some of the material is solid, dense, porphyritic, and dark gray in color. There are also pieces of red material almost like burned clay, but full of gas holes.

At first glance when one is crossing the great heaps of debris, the rocks seem to be standing still. If he stops to rest, the rocks on which he stands, tilt; they sink a little, and move forward. Sometimes, when stepped upon the rocks sink several feet while others fall in to catch the legs unless the individual is quick enough to shove other rocks into crevices to hold the big ones back. During the afternoon, when thundershowers are prevalent, large columns of steam shoot skyward whenever a heavy fall of rain strikes the hotter portions of the lava beds. In addition to the heat remaining in the hardened portions, beneath much of the area is the still plastic rock which instantly turns the rainwater into vapor. For one who ventures across the lava field, in addition to the danger of being caught in the collapsing rocks, crushed by falling rocks as he climbs into and out of grabens, or scalded by live steam during a heavy shower, there is always the promise of a violent explosion from below.

An Eruption

Parícutin erupts frequently, but there is little regularity in the time between eruptions. A year ago last summer, it erupted violently all one night. The writer's camp on the side of a mountain twelve miles away was shaken repeatedly. The following day the only sign of activity was a cloud of smoke welling up from the crater. At that time two students climbed to the crater and took pictures, none of which were very clear because of the smoke. Last August the volcano remained quiet during the three or four hours necessary to cross the lava field. It was not until the author was about 500 feet from the top of the cone that another eruption occurred, an exceptionally heavy one, no doubt due to the hardening of the crust in the crater and the accumulation of immense pressure.

The eruption was announced by a deep rumble from beneath the quaking surface of the cone, the rumble closely followed by a booming explosion. The sound is not like that of a cannon, but prolonged as tho the discharge comes from great depths. An enormous mass of smoke, cinders, and rocks, punctured by great gashes of fire or bright, red-hot lava, rolled over the edge of the crater. Much rock material was blown high into the air, some of it exploding during the ascent. It takes some of those rocks eleven seconds to fall. For a few seconds after the eruption there was stillness. Then came an increasing volume of sound like a great wall of water rushing down a canyon. Twice during that short period the sides of the cone heaved and threw the writer far down the slope with each movement. Sand rolled over him and all around, and then came the rocks. Some of them were large and whirled and whistled as they flashed by. Others, small ones, were like a hail of whizzing bullets. To these sounds was added the heavy thump, thump, of rocks falling from high in the air. Some of those rocks disappeared in the sand. Others skipped as tho over the surface of water, and shot by with a shrill whine.

When all the rocks had finished their movement down to the groove at the base of the cone, the silence was oppressive. Clouds of smoke rolled slowly overhead. Everywhere was deep twilight. The volcano, extending up into that dim light was magnificent. The musical tinkle of the slowly moving lava in the background sounded like thousands of little glass bells.

Economic Effects

Parícutin has destroyed San Juan de Parangaricutiro and the village of Parícutin. It has covered up many fields that formerly provided means of subsistence for the people inhabiting the valley. The primary effect was disaster and despair. The result has proved to be somewhat of a blessing. Farther back from the volcano a large area that was covered with a few inches of fine ashes is now producing better crops than ever before. Much of the timber that appeared dead has put out leaves and is apparently as good as ever. The dead trees, closer to the volcano, still contain good wood. Many of the Tarascans are skilled in making lacquered wooden ware, wooden novelties and furniture. The crowds of tourists that come to see the volcano constitute a good market. At the point where the tourists have to use horses to get to the lookout, little shacks containing food and drink counters provide a good income for people who, a short time ago, saw their lands and homes disappear beneath masses of cinders and creeping rocks. The Indians who have horses rent them to the tourists and act as guides. If an Indian has only one horse he can make at least two round trips to the lookout, daily. The charge per trip is fifteen pesos. If he has several horses, his income is considerable. When the lava-covered land was an area of corn and sugar cane, his income, at the most, would have averaged about three pesos a day.

In Uruapan, which has long been a tourist town, noted for its lacquer ware, its aguardiente de caña, and its beautiful scenery, all business has increased, from hotels, taxicabs, and shops, to the individual workers.

Many people have more money than they ever had before, and they work less for it. If that twelve miles of road out to the edge of the lava flow did not remain in a dangerous condition, and the small turn-off sign on the main highway were not kept unreadable, the tourists could drive to the edge of the lava flow themselves, and spend their time in far more comfortable hotels in Morelia.

21. *The Long Beach Earthquake* *

The approximately 2700 shocks that take place daily on the earth's surface are another evidence of crustal instability. Of these, 300 to 400 are noticeable and many of them occur in the Pacific Rim. A number of fault planes are present in the California portion of this mountainous chain along which frequent earth movements take place. A few, such as the San Francisco earthquake of 1906, the Long Beach quake described here, and, more recently, the Bakersfield quake are very destructive of life and property. This reading discusses the impact of an earthquake on a community and the problem of "delayed response of human behavior to seismic environment."

The Long Beach, California, earthquake of March 10, 1933, will be less remembered by reason of its contributions to seismology—for as a crustal tremor there was nothing especially remarkable about it—than it will be for having broken down the "hush-hush" policy that has hitherto been followed by the commercial organizations of the cities of southern California. It has most fortunately compelled public avowal by the most important of those organizations that earthquakes are a recurrent risk in their magnificent region and that the risk must be met by safer construction of buildings. But the loss of 120 lives and property destruction estimated at more than $50,000,000 are a high price to pay for such wisdom.

The Long Beach earthquake may be described as a fairly strong local shock. The area seriously shaken extended southeastward from the south-

* William M. Davis, "The Long Beach Earthquake," from *Geographical Review*, Vol. 24, 1934, pp. 1–11; published by The American Geographical Society, New York.

The author (1850–1930) is often called the founder of modern American geography. Well known for his teaching and field work in the western United States, he developed the youth, maturity, and old-age cycle of stream erosion. He organized and was first president of the Association of American Geographers. Other writings by Davis include his *Elementary Meteorology, Physical Geography, Geographical Essays,* and numerous articles in professional periodicals.

ern border of Los Angeles, past Long Beach, for about 40 miles, with a breadth of 15 or 20 miles. The larger area of moderate damage included the business district and the southern part of the city of Los Angeles—the damage there approached $1,000,000—and most of the towns located on the coastal lowland in Los Angeles and Orange counties. The shock was felt over an area about equal to that shaken by the Santa Barbara earthquake of 1925 and was of about the same intensity as that shock; but its energy was vastly less than that of the San Francisco earthquake of 1906. It was not preceded by any so-recognized fore-shock, nor was it accompanied by any so-called "tidal wave," but it was followed by hundreds

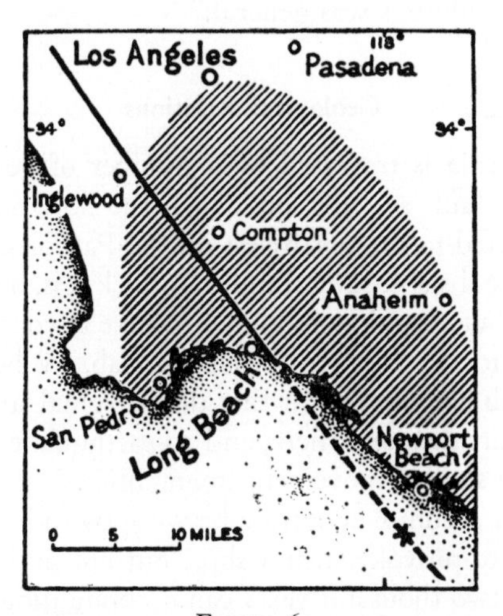

Figure 6

The area of principal damage (shaded) in the Long Beach earthquake. The epicenter is indicated (star) and the Inglewood fault (heavy line) and its probable extension (after a map by A. C. Chick).

of minor aftershocks. It is believed to have been caused by a small slip on the southeastward submarine extension of the Inglewood fault, which passes through a southwestern suburb of Los Angeles and on which a tremor was felt in 1920; but no displacement has as yet been discovered on the visible segment of that rift. The center of movement, as determined by automatic time records of the arrival of earth-crust waves at several stations maintained by the Pasadena Seismological Laboratory of the Carnegie Institution of Washington, lay beneath the sea at a depth of about six miles, under a point in latitude 33° 34.5′ N., longitude 117° 59′ W., or 3½ miles off from the shore resort of Newport Beach, which is 35 miles southeast of Los Angeles and 20 miles southeast of Long Beach. The shock is calculated to have begun there at 8 seconds after 5.54 p.m., Pacific standard time. It reached Long Beach a few seconds later. Movement there described as "hard shaking" lasted a number of seconds but less than half a minute.

In spite of exaggerated reports of its destruction, Long Beach was by no means reduced to ruins. On the other hand, many buildings suffered severely, as will be told below, and but for the fortunate chance that the shock occurred after the schools had been dismissed for the day the loss of life would have been terrible because of the disgraceful fact that "severe damage to school buildings was general."

Geological Relations

Southern California is traversed by a number of generally northwest-southeast-trending fault systems, on which the horizontal component of movement is directed to the northwest on the Pacific side. It is believed that the heavy crustal slabs, several miles in thickness, between these faults are in continuous but very slow motion. Where in contact they are under heavy strain due to the friction of slab on slab. When and where the movement of a slab has gone so far that the marginal strain overcomes the friction, a slip occurs then and there, and an earthquake is felt thereabouts, not because of any sudden movement in an entire slab, but because a local slip has relieved the accumulated strain between two adjacent slabs. It may require a century to provoke such a slip, "but not until man has lived in California one or two thousand years can accurate judgments be made of that matter."

The famous San Andreas rift, a 20-foot movement on which caused the San Francisco earthquake of 1906, is the farthest inland and by far the longest of the faults, passing from 30 to 50 miles from Los Angeles. The Inglewood fault is the southwesternmost and one of the shortest of the faults. The fissures of the fault systems are neither simple, rectilinear, nor parallel. The crustal slabs into which they divide the region have been tremendously tortured in the process of being dragged past one another and are subdivided by a complexity of minor faults. Slips may occur on any of the fractures. It is impossible to select any part of the populous southern California region, here considered, as exempt from earthquake hazard. It is otherwise with the area to the northeast, which, judging by its smoothly degraded surface forms, appears to have been undisturbed by faulting for a very long time. Unfortunately, however, this is the barren Mohave Desert, where settlements are few and far between.

The severity of earth tremors does not depend only on nearness to the fault slip that excites them; it depends also on the nature of the ground where the tremors come to the surface. Their oscillatory movement is less in firm rock than in alluvium; and if the alluvium is water-soaked, so much the worse, for its mobility is thereby increased. It was for this reason that both Long Beach and Compton, a smaller community midway between Long Beach and Los Angeles, suffered so severely last March, in spite of their considerable distance from the earthquake center. Both lie on an alluvial plain. Compton, which had a greater proportion of its buildings destroyed than any other town, is situated on a low part of the plain, some of which is swampy. On the other hand, the shore resorts of Corona del Mar and Laguna Beach, respectively east and southeast of the epicenter and less than half as far from it as Long Beach, suffered comparatively little damage, apparently because they are built on a rock platform of marine abrasion 50 or 100 feet above sea level and thinly covered with dry alluvium. In view of these facts, it seems that the fundamental cause of the heavy damage at Long Beach was unescapable; but the secondary cause of the damage, poor building construction, is escapable.

Report of the Committee on Earthquake Protection

Directly after the earthquake the importance of expert study of its effects was urged upon the California Institute of Technology, whereupon the Joint Technical Committee on Earthquake Protection was organized with members chosen from the most competent physicists, geologists, engineers, architects, fire underwriters, educators, and business men of the region. The chairmanship was accepted by Dr. R. A. Millikan, chairman of the executive council of the Institute, and the vice-chairmanship by Professor R. R. Martel, also of the Institute and a leading expert in the engineering problem of earthquake-resistant building construction. Thus a great advance was made, a step taken that for years past had been prophetically urged upon California municipalities by seismologists, notable among them Professor Bailey Willis of Stanford University.

The objective frankness of the committee's report will be shown below; but we must preface it with a quotation from an accompanying statement by the president of the Los Angeles Chamber of Commerce—a statement significant for its courageous recognition of earthquake risk in southern California as a matter of practical business as well as of scientific inquiry.

The entire intent of this report is to acquaint responsible public bodies generally with the fact that we have a natural condition to face, exactly in the same manner that we have heretofore faced and successfully met the need of a larger water supply . . . We believe that a comprehensive statement of the true facts, based upon scientific findings and building construction truths, is most timely and instructive and certainly should be considered carefully by all public bodies, institutions, and individuals, who are in any way responsible for the safety of lives and property in this area. . . .

Therefore, the Los Angeles Chamber of Commerce freely recognizes the truths as expressed in this report and commends the committee upon its findings and furthermore recommends to all governing authorities and responsible public groups that this report be seriously considered in the spirit in which it is presented.

And now for the report itself. It had for its declared object

To determine the effect of the earthquake, the reasons for the large loss of life and severe property damage, and the steps which should be taken to minimize the effects of future earthquakes. . . .

Earthquakes have occurred in California for a long period in the geologic past and it is extremely probable therefore that they will recur from time to time in the future. . . . Shocks of large magnitude were recorded in 1769, in 1812, and in 1857 . . . These earthquakes . . . were much greater in intensity . . . than the Long Beach earthquake, and it is not improbable that an even stronger earthquake may occur some time in the future.

Contrary to popular conception, the hazard of destruction by an earthquake is not limited to the area along a fault. Actually, the earthquake risk in southern California varies somewhat from place to place, but . . . in general it must be considered that the risk . . . does not differ greatly throughout this entire region . . .

There is reasonable probability, if not virtual certainty, that at some time in the future an earthquake of destructive intensity will cause great loss of life and damage to property, unless adequate protective measures are carried out. . . .

A summary states:

(a) Earthquakes of damaging or destructive intensity will continue to occur in California from time to time in the future.

(b) An earthquake is apt to occur in this region comparable in intensity and duration with the San Francisco earthquake of 1906.

(c) The risk of damage or destruction of buildings and other structures, and attendant loss of life, varies somewhat but not greatly throughout this region.

(d) The degree of risk is such that earthquake resistant construction is absolutely necessary in this region in order to avoid great loss of life and heavy damage to property.

And again:

An earthquake of the intensity and duration [about one minute] of that which occurred in San Francisco in 1906 may occur at any time at almost any place in this entire region. . . .

Had these emphatic statements appeared only in a scientific journal, they might pass unnoticed by the public; but they are actually published by an important commercial organization, with an approving note that begins by announcing that "the Los Angeles Chamber of Commerce not only has familiarized itself with the findings in this accompanying report . . . but has, through its own studies and investigations, arrived at the same general conclusions as are contained therein." Verily, the world does move!

Damage to Property

The statements concerning damage to property may be summarized as follows: Most of the modern office buildings in the zone of severe damage were of fireproof skeleton-frame construction; many of these buildings—although still standing, apparently unharmed—suffered considerable hidden structural injury. All too prevalent are "the stores and apartment houses which were built as cheaply as the inadequate building codes would permit by those who were interested only in speculative profits." In the zone of severe damage hundreds of unsound buildings were wrecked; as a class they account for a large part of the toll of property loss. While a great many of the residences in the affected area were likewise built to sell, they were almost always of wood-frame construction. A certain amount of diagonal bracing is customary in the erection of a wood-frame structure, and the weight of the building is small; consequently the inherent stability of the single-family residence is high. Injury to this type of structure was largely limited to cracked plaster, broken tile roofs, and fallen brick chimneys.

The most scandalous disclosure was that of the general weakness of the schoolhouses. On this point the report says:

> In every community where the earthquake was at all intense, severe damage to school buildings was general. Auditoriums collapsed, walls were thrown down, and the very exits to safety were piled high with debris which a few moments before had been heavy parts of towers and ornamental entrances. . . . Boards of Education were evidently most concerned with the size of the school buildings and their appearance. Actual or assumed financial limitations prevented the selection of the best type of construction, and legal requirements forced the letting of contracts to the lowest bidder who could secure bond. It is evident that this point of view is unsound and the economy false. . . . School buildings must be so re-designed and strengthened that a repetition of the recent disaster can not take place.

Earthquake-Resistant Construction

Inasmuch as the *Geographical Review* is devoted to a science in which the sociological factor is of large importance, we may appropriately dwell on this example of delayed response of human behavior to seismic environment. The delay is due in part to ignorance, for the population of southern California is derived largely from regions where the risk of earthquakes is small; but this ignorance is partly willful, for warnings of risk have been more scoffed at than listened to, and is largely actuated by selfishness and greedy snatching at immediate profit. Southern California has recklessly neglected to adopt standard designs of earthquake-resistant construction such as have already been adopted in Japan, Italy, and New Zealand. The main features of such designs are that all walls shall be capable of withstanding, at every level, a horizontal force equal to at least one-tenth of the superincumbent weight; that slender structures, such as towers, high chimneys, and elevated tanks, shall be able to resist at every point a horizontal force equal to one-third of the weight above; and that parapets, cornices, and other exterior ornamental structures shall withstand a horizontal force equal to their entire weight.

The extra cost of such safe construction is not forbidding if it is met during the growth of a community; but, when it has been so long neglected that a large amount of reconstruction is demanded after an alarming disaster, the total cost becomes burdensome. Thus Los Angeles now has had to meet as quickly as possible the expense of some $25,000,000 in re-strengthening its existing schools. The unequivocal conclusion of the Technical Committee's report on this matter is as follows: "Damage to schools, which children are required by law to attend, was widespread, and it was only by chance that thousands of children were not killed. . . . No one can question the imperative necessity of prompt and effective correction of the weakness prevalent in the school buildings." Because the reconstruction or reconditioning of schoolhouses could not be completed by the date when the schools opened in the autumn, the schooling of many children is now proceeding more or less irregularly.

Report of the National Board of Fire Underwriters

The conflagration that is liable to follow an earthquake adds an extra risk to insurance in earthquake regions. The insurance companies' committees on fire protection thus become interested in the planning of municipal waterworks and in the construction of quake-resistant buildings. It is for these practical reasons that their engineers have made critical studies of the effects of various earthquakes. Some additional details on the Long Beach earthquake may now be presented from an able report by the National Board of Fire Underwriters.

It is there stated that in the earthquake of March 10 "twenty thousand dwellings and two thousand apartment houses, stores, office buildings, factories, warehouses, theatres and churches were damaged in degrees varying from cracked plaster to complete destruction." In Compton the damage to business, industrial, and residential property amounted to 29 per cent of its total assessed value; in Long Beach to 9.4 per cent. The percentage for public and school buildings was considerably higher than these general averages. Complete collapse occurred chiefly in buildings in which the upper stories or roof trusses were supported on brick piers; partial demolition was greatest in front walls and parapets. The battering action of swaying roof trusses caused entire walls to be pushed out and thrown down.

The condemnation of schoolhouses is as severe as in the Technical Committee's report.

> Throughout the shaken area [they] suffered greater damage than any other class of buildings . . . Architectural effect seems to have predominated at the expense of strength and there was excessive use of ornamentation, towers, heavy copings on thin wall sections, and high parapets. A disturbing feature is that such unnecessary loadings of the structure were generally placed over doorways and passageways with the result that these exits were covered deep with debris. . . .
>
> Buildings in which the architectural effects were predominant, such as churches and public buildings, were damaged much more severely than the ordinary commercial structures of plainer design and more regular shape. Such structures generally involve tall unbraced walls supporting the concentrated loads of heavy roof trusses. . . .
>
> Poor workmanship contributed its share to the general destruction. The . . . mortar was frequently of a low grade and in some cases of wretched quality. . . .

Effects on the Tourist Industry

There are various southern California organizations that solicit the resort of tourists to their unquestionably attractive region. One is moved to inquire what effect on tourists the above-cited reports will have, in view of what is said in them as to the possibility of future earthquakes and the insufficiently quake-resistant construction of many California buildings. Geographers are familiar with the steep roofs of dwellings in regions where the snowfall is heavy and with the flat roofs of houses in warm and dry climates, that is with a relation of architecture to climate. Why should not a similarly appropriate relation of architecture to earthquakes be developed, that is a seismic architecture, where safety demands it? For instance, after reading the above warnings against the addition of parapets and cornices to roofs, it is somewhat disturbing to see, as one drives through the business sections of cities in the Los Angeles region, how very numerous such additions are. It would be a good thing if their removal were required as a measure of public safety. One of the cities in the region a few years ago displayed over its principal thoroughfare a sign reading, "Watch us grow." Might not that city now be persuaded first to remove its parapets and cornices and to strengthen its walls and then to display a sign reading, "Watch us grow safely"? But no, there is little probability of any such action or display. San Francisco is said to be relaxing already the building code it adopted in 1906.

It may be expected, however, that sooner or later the better hotels and apartment houses will be induced to have their construction inspected and certified by competent engineers, so that they may truthfully advertise such construction as quake-resistant. The inspecting engineers should not, for obvious reasons, be municipal appointees; they should be of the same independence and integrity as those employed, for example, by the Factory Mutual Fire Insurance Companies, which have been largely developed under the wise leadership of the late John R. Freeman, of Providence, than whom as authority on earthquake damage and insurance none stood higher.

These mutual insurance companies—or "Factory Mutuals" as they are known to the initiated—are carried on "without purpose of profit," solely for the protection of their members. They insure nothing but large manufacturing plants, of which they now cover upwards of 7500 in the United States and Canada, of a total value of more than ten billion dollars. The companies are wholly based on "fire prevention engineering." They employ more than 130 engineer-inspectors. By half a century of earnest and honest work they have reduced the fire loss in factories from an average of 33 cents per $100 a year, as it was from 1845 to 1875, to about 2½ cents between 1921 and 1931. Their service is of a special kind, applicable only to large concerns because of its high costs in inspection and engineering. It is referred to here in the hope that it may be possible to organize, in a correspondingly enlightened manner, a corps of inspectors under the direction of the various fire insurance companies that cover California hotels and apartment houses. How welcome would be an informing and thoroughly trustworthy report on California hotels similar to the one on Long Beach industrial structures recently made by A. C. Chick, who gained his engineering experiences by work under Freeman for the "Factory Mutuals." If visitors coming to California would make it a practice to inquire about quake-resistant construction before choosing their hotels, the preparation of such a report would be hastened; but not one in a hundred visitors will know that there is such a thing as quake-resistant construction.

The timorous talk in the East about the dangers from earthquakes in southern California has probably increased since the Long Beach shock; but, as far as actual danger to an individual is concerned, such talk is of the same order as that touching the danger from rattlesnakes when excursions in the deserts of the Southwest are mentioned. During the past eight years I have made such excursions without number and have seen but one rattler, which was promptly killed by other members of my party. During most of the same period I have resided in California and have felt only the earthquake of last March. Moreover, during that time I have seldom heard earthquakes and their risks mentioned as subjects of ordinary conversation. Earthquakes are, indeed, not talked about enough in California. They should be explicitly referred to whenever the building, buying, or renting of a house is under consideration, and certificates of quake-resistant construction should be secured from a competent and unbiased expert.

However, a visitor to Italy does not avoid Naples or Palermo because of their proximity to active volcanoes or because of their liability to disastrous earthquakes such as, for example, the violent shock that, in July, 1930, caused the death of about 1500 persons and the destruction of hundreds of buildings in a district some 50 miles east of Vesuvius. Many persons moved away from San Francisco shortly after the earthquake and conflagration of 1906, but in spite of their withdrawal the city is now larger than ever before. It is probably true that many persons left Long Beach last March. But in spite of that sort of exodus Long Beach is destined to grow as the seaside resort of a great city, just as San Francisco is destined to grow because of its unrivaled harbor. Life is full of hazards, and we must take our chances among them. The chances of an enjoyable life in southern California are, in spite of its occasional earthquakes, undeniably excellent.

22. *Erosive Forces in the Physiography of Western Arctic Canada* *

Jenness here analyzes the cumulative effect of all weathering and erosive forces in one area—the Western Arctic of Canada.† Even though mass wasting and fluvial erosion are the most significant forces, the work of other weathering and erosive agents is also considered. This reading discusses the relation of permafrost and mass wasting, the importance of water erosion (despite the small amount of Arctic precipitation), and debunks the idea that Arctic landforms are completely a result of continental glaciation.

In past years there has been a tendency to explain all landforms on the Arctic islands as resulting from extensive glaciation. It is true that in western Arctic Canada, in the southern half of the archipelago, there is abundant evidence of glaciation in the form of glacial grooves, striae, roches moutonnées, polished rock surfaces, and rock basin lakes, all of which seem to owe their origin to an ice sheet or sheets that moved into the Arctic islands during the Pleistocene. The northern half of the archipelago, however, probably lay beyond the limits of any continental ice sheet, and it seems possible to explain most of the major topographic forms both there and in the south without recourse to glacial erosion. At present the only island that contains a permanent capping of ice or snow is Meighen, and there the cap appears to be dormant or receding, so that it is the meltwaters emerging from it that are eroding the surface rather than the cap itself.

The question of the former extent of glaciation in the Arctic Archipelago and its influence on landforms will be discussed in another paper. Here we shall deal only with the processes of erosion that are active today, and their individual and collective role in bringing about the denudation of the Arctic landscape.

The principal erosive forces at work on the western Arctic islands are

* John L. Jenness, "Erosive Forces in the Physiography of Western Arctic Canada," from *Geographical Review,* Vol. 42, 1952, pp. 238–252; published by the American Geographical Society, New York.

The author is Associate Professor of Geography, University of Pittsburgh. He received his Master's degree from Cambridge and his Ph.D. from Clark University.

† The author has arbitrarily divided the Canadian Arctic Archipelago into western and eastern halves, along a boundary that coincides roughly with the meridian of 95° W. Meighen, Amund Ringnes, Cornwall, Cornwallis, and Somerset Islands are included in the western section; Boothia Peninsula, Devon Island, and other islands farther east in the eastern. This paper deals only with the western section as thus defined.

water, both fresh and salt, ice (except glacial ice, which is no longer active), and wind.

Erosion by Water

Water erodes when it falls as rain, flows in streams, or beats in waves along a coast. It also carries off the end products of weathering and mass wasting. In temperate latitudes precipitation causes a slow washing away of fine particles on the surface of the ground through the direct attack of raindrops. The process is usually referred to as "splash erosion" and is most serious where torrential rains fall on land that has little or no vegetation, such as newly plowed fields. In the western Arctic islands the pelting rains common in more southern latitudes are unknown; rain usually falls in the form of drizzle. Total precipitation is slight, averaging 10 inches or less yearly near the mainland and decreasing northward until on Ellef Ringnes Island, at the Isachsen meteorological station, the total for the year may be less than two inches. At the coastal stations near the mainland more than half the precipitation falls as snow; at higher latitudes and higher elevations nearly all of it is snow. Splash erosion is therefore not important, even though most of the land surface in the Arctic lacks plant cover.

Precipitation is by no means a negligible factor, however; for indirectly it causes more serious and widespread denudation than is generally realized. In all parts of the western Arctic snow falls in 11 months of the year, and in some places every month. Throughout much of this time there is no melting, so that the snow on the ground in early summer represents the accumulation of seven or eight months. Although the total precipitation of snow usually amounts to no more than two or three feet, much of it is blown against embankments or into depressions and stream channels, where it piles up to such thicknesses that even in August one may find lingering patches eight feet deep or more. The snow begins to thaw soon after the sun reappears above the horizon, and during the period of 24-hour sunlight, thawing may proceed continuously for days at a time. Runoff is then particularly violent. For example, at Resolute Bay, Cornwallis Island, 20 inches of snow that covered the ground at the beginning of June, 1948, had disappeared entirely by the end of the month. I myself have seen a surface of frost-shattered rock debris gullied by a stream to a depth of three feet in a single season. The journals of Arctic explorers, with their many references to swollen rivers and fords too deep to cross, offer additional evidence of fluvial activity during thaw.

By far the greatest amount of runoff is initiated within the stream channels, for it is there that most of the snow accumulates. Patches often persist long after surrounding slopes have become bare and may keep the streams running throughout the summer, even where they tap neither ponds nor lakes. In early summer, meltwater from adjacent slopes adds to their supply, and for an even longer time they are fed by water derived from the thawing of the ground above the permafrost table. Consequently, Arctic streams have a far greater capacity for erosion than is suggested by the size of their drainage basins, by the number of lakes at their heads, or by the amount of precipitation at any or all times of the year. Their erosive action is potentially greatest in early summer, but certain streams continue to scour their beds until they become frozen over again in the fall.*

Some streams have eroded their beds so effectively that they now flow through deep trenches cut in the underlying bedrock. Their ravines may be as much as 200 or 300 feet deep, even when they depend only on meltwater to maintain their flow; and their outlets are at grade, or almost at grade, with present base level, an indication that they are still adjusting their profiles to this level. Such streams are powerful eroding agents even though they operate mainly in a vertical plane. Most streams in the archipelago, however, are entrenched in bedrock to a depth of only 10 to 20 feet at most; many are not entrenched at all and have barely enough transporting power to remove the waste material supplied by adjacent slopes. Frequently these weak streams and the powerfully eroding ones lie within a few miles of one another; frequently, too, it is the weak streams rather than the powerful ones that tap many lakes for their water and have the longer courses and larger drainage basins. Why should there be so wide a difference in erosive power? Why should volume, gradient, and load be interrelated in such a manner that some streams become powerful while neighboring ones remain weak?

We may find a clue in a significant feature of the drainage, as revealed by the aerial photographs. Wherever in these photographs a deeply incised stream is traced to its source, this source will invariably be found to lie on an upland surface high above present sea level. All or most of the weak streams, on the other hand, seem to have their sources at lower levels, within a few hundred feet of the sea. This suggests that the former are second- or nth-cycle streams flowing off an old land surface which remained above the marine level and the latter are first-cycle streams originating on lands newly emerged from the sea. Three other phenomena support the hypothesis: (1) some of the deeply incised streams

* Large rivers that flow all winter, such as the Coppermine, must erode their beds in every month of the year. However, there seem to be no such rivers in the Arctic islands; even the long Thompson River on Banks Island is so shallow that it probably freezes to the bottom in midwinter.

(for example, on the west coast of Melville Island) empty into bays which seem to date from a period before the initiation of uplift; (2) in at least one area (the southern part of North Borden Island where it drains into Wilkins Strait) tortuously meandering streams flow at the bottom of deep trenches in the parent bedrock, a condition suggesting that they were once streams at grade on an old coastal plain which have been rejuvenated by uplift; and (3) the last few miles of many entrenched streams have a stumpy appearance as if only this part had so far succeeded in adjusting itself to a new base level.

Because the snowfall tends to accumulate in the valleys and ravines, the incised streams (that is, the second- or nth-cycle streams) have a pronounced maximum runoff in the early summer, coinciding with the critical melting period. These streams are capable of moving considerable bed load, and of acting as powerful agents of erosion within their own ravines. The first-cycle streams, on the other hand, are still initiating their valleys, which in most places are not yet deep enough to trap large quantities of snow. They are cutting their valleys slowly, if at all, because they have a relatively small flood peak in the critical melting period and their gradients are usually too gentle to permit rapid runoff during the season of flow. As a result, the first-cycle streams are not powerful eroding agents. They can move unconsolidated material seaward and ultimately deposit it at their outlets, but the process may be interrupted or greatly retarded by materials of mass wastage that slide into the channel from adjacent slopes.

Some of the most deeply incised streams have a total length of only five or six miles, though greater lengths are more common. The majority have no sources other than melting snow and thawing ground above permafrost. They may begin with just a little nick in the surface a thousand feet or so above present sea level, but by the time they reach their outlets they can produce ravines several hundred feet deep, cut entirely out of consolidated strata. McMillan mentions such ravines on Melville Island, inland from the south coast of Dundas Peninsula, that are 200 or 300 feet deep; and I have seen others, probably still deeper, on northeastern Banks Island: neither locality contains any lakes to feed the streams. Throughout the whole of the western Arctic the drainage from uplands a thousand feet or more in elevation produces ravines of these conspicuous depths. Many of the deepest and most spectacular possess the characteristic V-shaped profile of youthful streams. Many, too, show a box-canyon character, indicating rapid down-cutting with a minimum of sidewall weathering—features strongly suggestive of rapid uplift.

Water erodes also along lake shores and seacoasts. However, in the Arctic throughout the greater part of the year all bodies of water, both salt and fresh, are covered with solid ice. The largest lakes often remain bound well into August, and in unfavorable years many of them do not become entirely free at any time. Such prolonged ice cover is even more characteristic of the seas, straits, and channels. Consequently, wind, waves, and currents can act on shores and coasts for only three months, and usually for a much shorter period; in certain regions, indeed, their influence is negligible because there is so little open water at any season. Deltas at the mouths of streams on even the most current-swept and wind-swept coasts (for example, the west coast of Prince Patrick Island) prove that stream sediment is being deposited there faster than shore erosion can carry it away.

Erosion by Ice

Erosion also results today from the action of ice, both river ice and the ice along lake shores and marine coast lines. Ice that has frozen to a stream bed may carry off attached materials when it breaks up in the spring. Washburn counted 138 stones from one inch to a foot or more in diameter suspended in 30 square feet of river ice at Cambridge Bay, Victoria Island; and he concluded from the character of the ice and other evidence that the stones had been lifted from the bottom. Such underwater, or anchor, ice can produce erosion along a coast line also, especially when aided by the rise and fall of the tide. Rae saw stones in Repulse Bay weighing as much as one or two tons that had been torn up from the sea bottom; they had worked their way to the upper surface of the ice in a manner he explains as follows:

> At the commencement of winter the ice . . . had become frozen to the stones lying on the bottom, and raised them up when the tide came in. The stones would get gradually enclosed in the ice as it grew thicker . . . whilst by the process of evaporation, which goes on very rapidly in the spring, the upper surface was continually wasting away, so that in June and July there was little of the first formed ice remaining, and thus the stones which at first were on the under surface of the ice appeared on the top.

Anchor ice is probably less effective as an erosive agent than the ice jams that undercut banks in fresh-water streams and rivers and immense ice packs in motion along exposed seacoasts. Ice-pressure ridges are characteristic of many western Arctic shores and are common as well on nearly all lakes. At Point Barrow, Alaska, Stefansson noted that certain gravel ridges originally built up by ice pressure remained for several years, even though the summer season was long enough for waves to obliterate most or all traces of ice action. Floes laden with debris are not uncommon in Arctic seas; no doubt they usually indicate the erosion of the shore by sea ice, but sometimes the ice may be merely the transporting agent, laden with debris from rockfalls or with unconsolidated materials slumped in landslides.

On the whole, ice as an erosive agent seems to play a relatively small role. The destruction it causes is largely offset by the protection it gives the land during the long winter when rivers are frozen solid and ice protects seacoasts and lake shores from wave attack.

Wind Erosion

Winds blow fairly constantly in the Arctic and are the primary cause of the hard-packed snow of the coastal belt. We might imagine, therefore, that they would produce considerable erosion. However, the ground is frozen eight to ten months of the year, and at other times much of it is saturated with moisture. Winds can be effective only in the most exposed localities. Evaporation and runoff from melting snow and thawing ground make the upper slopes and hill crests dry out more rapidly than the low-lying ground; and broad expanses of level upland or lowland where the wind has a long fetch dry quickly, though the subsoil usually remains moist. Yet Washburn remarks that in snow-free land he noted wind action only in the form of deflation, and my own observations have revealed merely meager evidence of wind erosion.

Weathering and Mass Wasting

Erosion also results from weathering and mass wasting, which operate over the total land surface. In the western Arctic weathering and mass wasting have produced visible effects everywhere and in many respects appear to have a greater quantitative importance in the destruction of landforms than any of the erosion processes described above.

The term "weathering" refers to all processes working toward the decay of the rock materials on the earth's surface by either mechanical or chemical means. In high latitudes chemical weathering probably induces relatively small changes, even where the parent bedrock is limestone, the one sedimentary rock that decomposes readily by chemical change. This is because decomposition is held in abeyance just below the surface by the permanently frozen ground, which effectively hinders the circulation of ground water. Mechanical weathering, on the other hand, is evident nearly everywhere. I have noted in numerous places exfoliation of large erratic boulders and indications of considerable frost heave in the surface layers of sedimentary bedrock.

Alternate freezing and thawing take place almost daily from May to

October and make the disintegration of rock due to the freezing of absorbed water a potent and widespread force in landform destruction. The relative abundance of ground water above permafrost at this season is a significant contributory factor. Quantities of frost-shattered angular rock rubble commonly cover the surface. And it is not only at the surface that the materials become distributed and broken up, but also to some depth. Kindle even considered that "because of the depth of frost penetration, rock disintegration from this source is far more rapid in the Arctic than in temperate latitudes."

Under mass wasting one must include landslides, rockfalls, earth flows, slumps, solifluction, and soil creep, to which should be added mudflow and rillwork. All these processes are widespread in the western Arctic. For example, I noted landslides in the steep banks of unconsolidated material bordering Castel Bay, northern Banks Island, and rockfalls with resultant talus deposits at Minto Inlet, Victoria Island; rockfalls are particularly common where traprock is exposed at the surface. Also recognizable in many places are slumps, a form of landslide in unconsolidated material that leaves an amphitheater scar on the landscape. Solifluction movements that result in mudflow, rillwork, and the various forms of creep are seldom perceptible except through long observation, but their results are apparent in so many places that quantitatively they would seem to be the most powerful mass-wasting agent now operating in the western Arctic.

Mass wastage of the whole Arctic landscape continues uninterruptedly throughout the melting season. Even in winter it does not cease: landslides of frozen material are not uncommon on steep, unstable embankments. Mass wasting affects every part of the landscape where material can move downslope under the force of gravity. As Eakin points out, the ground generates its own movements; for the pressure exerted by the freezing of water in the soil heaves it upward and thrusts it out horizontally. Moreover, the conditions causing differential heave and thrust tend to accentuate themselves by their own activity, and centers of persistent heave not only are persistent but, within certain limits, become more and more pronounced.

As a result of mass wastage, the loose material on the surface of the ground moves steadily downslope. Movement varies in speed. Sometimes, as in the case of mudflows, the material moves so rapidly that the eye of the observer can follow it. At other times movement is slow, particularly where a slope flattens out. As the material descends from the hill slopes, streams may intervene and precipitate its advance, until it ends up in the most low-lying part of the region. By this means the lower slopes and valley bottoms are slowly becoming covered with unconsolidated materials derived from the upper slopes and hill crests. Where the hills are composed of bedrock, their crests are sometimes bared down to the parent material; more frequently they have been denuded to the level of the frost-shattered debris from the underlying bedrock. Again the steeper slopes tend to be less thickly covered with overburden than gentle slopes. If there is higher terrain near by to supply adequate water for the growing plants, uplands that are nearly horizontal may be covered with a relatively luxuriant carpet of vegetation, which slows up the downhill movement of loose material. Even then, however, to judge from the few instances I have seen, this movement does not cease altogether, for at each place vegetation overlapped the nearest downhill slope.

The cumulative effect of all these forms of mass wasting is so widespread that Washburn believes them to be "the most important leveling process operative, in this respect far outweighing fluvial action." His belief seems wholly justifiable; for the powerfully eroding streams that deeply incise their own valleys have little effect on the general denudation of the landscapes through which they pass.* They are making a significant contribution to the destruction of the land; but they are destroying it in an entirely different manner from mass wasting. Mass wasting tends to smooth off the slopes, giving the land a rounded and rolling appearance. The streams also carry off some material from the slopes, but because they are deeply entrenched, much of the material that falls into their channels is the coarse product of rockfalls, and so on, from the ravine sides. Hence instead of smoothing out the landscape, they accentuate the ruggedness by cutting it into blocks and ribbons as they lower their beds into the underlying materials.

Role of Permafrost

Finally, we must not overlook the role of permanently frozen ground. Permafrost, although not readily measurable, exerts an influence on Arctic landforms that is apparent to even the most casual traveler. Every-

* R. J. Lougee has pointed out (personal communication, April, 1951) that in the Arctic uplands of Alaska small streams may be repeatedly dammed by solifluction lobes into little pools, from which they break out again by flowing either around the edges of the lobes or over their tops. Such streams are plentiful in the Arctic Archipelago also, and are most evident in lands that have lately emerged from the sea. Either because they tap too small a source of water in the critical melting period, or because their gradients are too gentle—and often from both causes—these streams have accomplished relatively little downcutting. The ability of a stream to erode its bed at any given place must depend upon its ability to transport the material dumped into it. A high percentage of the material entering weak streams consists of such fine superficial overburden as is being removed from adjacent relatively gentle slopes by mass wastage. Thus these streams often lack the power to keep their channels clear; hence they erode their beds only slightly or not at all.

where the soggy surface it creates causes poor drainage, and this in turn contributes materially to the rapidity of denudation by mass wasting. What effects, if any, permafrost has on bedrock are not yet known.

In the Arctic Archipelago, just as farther south, the permafrost is separated from the ground surface by a shallow horizon, or "active layer," subject to annual freezing and thawing. The thickness of this active layer varies somewhat from place to place, for it depends in the main on two factors: temperature of the air near the ground, and the conductivity of the surface material. Thus it may be only a few inches in clay soils yet more than two feet in gravels. Permafrost may extend to ground level where a thick carpet of peat moss covers the surface, since peat is an exceptionally fine insulator; but it rarely or never does so where the ground is bare.

Several varieties of permafrost can be recognized if both soil type and percentage of water content are used as differentiating criteria. However, in Arctic erosion water content is a far more important factor than soil type, and it thus seems adequate for our purpose to distinguish only two major types of frozen ground: the relatively "dry" permafrost, low in water content, in which ice lenses normally will be almost invisible to the naked eye; and the "wet" permafrost, which contains an abundance of water and can usually be recognized by large lenses of clear ice. Thawing of wet permafrost produces mudflows much more readily than thawing of the relatively dry soil.

Permafrost provides an impervious base that prevents surface water from seeping into the ground to depths greater than a few inches or, at most, a few feet. At the same time it induces in the shallow active layer a much greater and more concentrated subsurface flow than would otherwise take place. Lakes and ponds are fed not only by streams but also by large quantities of water that move down the surrounding slopes through this shallow active layer.

Within the permafrost belt on the continental mainland, wherever the climate is temperate enough to permit a relatively luxuriant plant growth, some lakes are encroaching steadily on the land, and in others in the same region the hydrophytic plants that grow in great abundance around the shores are encroaching on the water.* On the islands north of the mainland expansion and shrinkage of lakes and ponds are harder to recognize. Probably the lakes there expand more slowly because precipitation decreases northward and drainage from the surrounding slopes is therefore less. But shrinkage too must be slower, because plant growth is far less abundant than on the more favored parts of the mainland. Low-lying ground is usually waterlogged and covered with more vegetation than the drier

* Some of the muskeg so characteristic of the Arctic and sub-Arctic owes its origin to this filling in of shallow lakes and ponds.

slopes; even so, the plant cover still seems insufficient to produce much infilling of the lake edges. In fact, I do not recall any lakes or ponds on the islands north of the mainland that had been completely filled in by vegetation.

In the parts of the Western Arctic, both mainland and island, that have been demonstrably glaciated, lakes and ponds occupy more of the land than remains unsubmerged. Here the water bodies seem to be expanding more than they are shrinking.* The low-lying ground is commonly filled with swamps, lakes, and ponds of various shapes and sizes that spill from one to another in complex and obscure drainage patterns. On the other hand, the islands north of Viscount Melville Sound, which I believe were never buried beneath a continental ice sheet, are almost completely devoid of lakes and ponds. In this part of the archipelago both surface and subsurface water apparently migrates downslope more or less unimpeded until it reaches the sea. The water may be checked temporarily at local base levels and cause localized puddling, soil saturation, and a somewhat richer plant growth, but it is not impeded sufficiently to permit the creation of real lakes. In this part of the archipelago, then, the impermeable substratum of permafrost has influenced the drainage much less markedly than it has on the islands south of Viscount Melville Sound and on the mainland.

In two ways, therefore, permafrost encourages mass wasting of the surface mantle: first, by concentrating underground drainage close to the surface; and, second, by creating a surface or slip plane on which the material above it can slide. Water moves through the active layer during the entire two or three months of the summer, and holes dug into this layer will encounter it everywhere except in the obviously best-drained places. In some places the water fills the holes almost as quickly as it can be shoveled out; in others it merely trickles in, becoming no more than two or three inches deep in a whole day. Yet everywhere it is moving, and slowly but surely the surface soil is moving downslope with it. Taber believes that freezing and thawing and excessive water are "the major factors causing mass movements of soil in cold climates"; and in the Arctic permafrost undoubtedly makes mass wastage far more severe than where there is no permafrost.

Permanently frozen ground sometimes becomes exposed to the air suddenly, as when a slide occurs in an unconsolidated embankment. Naturally, it immediately begins to thaw if the air temperature happens to be above freezing. Should the permafrost be of the "wet" variety, then, as the

* Some lakes have encroached on the forest margin, leaving many trees standing in the water. Others, beyond the limit of trees (for example, Tahoe Lake in the center of Victoria Island), are rimmed with a shallow submerged belt that suddenly drops off into deep water, which suggests recent expansion.

ice lenses melt, water oozes out of the embankment and trickles down its slope, carrying a certain amount of unconsolidated material along. The embankment begins to crumble away, exposing more of the frozen substratum, the thawing of which promotes a further release of water and more crumbling. The thawing and crumbling may continue all summer, until what at first was only a small earthfall becomes a huge scar on the landscape. Within the space of a single year this process can remove enormous quantities of materials, as I had occasion to note at De Salis Bay, Banks Island, in 1948 and 1949; for what in mid-July, 1948, had been only a small gully near the head of the bay had reached such prodigious size by the following year that I failed at first to recognize the place and identified it only after thoroughly checking my bearings with familiar landmarks that still persisted.

What, then, is the cumulative effect of all these forces which are striving toward the destruction of the landscape in the western Arctic?

In lower latitudes one is often impressed by the accelerated erosion of hill slopes provoked by their deforestation, but the devastation that is taking place on the treeless Arctic slopes has been going on far longer, and in a climate considerably harsher. If, geologically speaking, much of the Arctic has only recently emerged from the sea, nevertheless nearly all of it has lain exposed to the elements for many hundreds of years, and some of it for many thousands. Why, then, should we so often resort to Pleistocene glaciation to account for topographical features that seem much more readily explicable by the erosive processes we see at work in temperate latitudes?

In the western Arctic these processes do not operate equally. Most significant of them all are mass wasting and fluvial erosion.

Characteristic of the entire region are the rugged marginal parts of the high uplands that apparently stood above sea level at the time of maximum submergence; the deep canyons of streams originating on these uplands, canyons that may even extend across newly emerged land; and the only slightly eroded valleys of the streams that have their sources below the uplands. In many places the highest uplands are rocky and bare of vegetation because mass wasting and stream attack have carried off most of their overburden; and even where an overburden remains, plants seldom grow on it because of its extreme exposure to wind and its natural inability to retain ground moisture.* In contrast, in the lowlands it is frequently impossible to find bedrock exposed at the surface except in the channels of some major

* Yet another factor contributing toward sparse plant growth or the total absence of a vegetation covering must be the mobility of the soil itself. Highly mobile soil is an unfavorable substratum for vegetation on uplands and lowlands alike, wherever the ground is sloping.

streams or on very steep slopes that are too unstable to retain an overburden. On hill crests within the lowlands, as on the uplands, vegetation remains scanty; but in the lowest, most poorly drained places the ground is often carpeted with plants—the "Arctic prairies" described in the journals of so many explorers.

The western Arctic islands, accordingly, contain great contrasts, ranging from smoothly contoured surfaces to deeply dissected country. Although in general the distribution of upland and lowland reflects basic geological conditions, the topography of no one part seems explicable without reference to the effects of erosion by forces that are still active. These forces have subdued some of the boldness of the landscape, primarily through leveling by mass wastage; contrariwise, through fluvial action, cliff cutting, and other processes they have accentuated its relief and sharpness. I do not assert that they alone have produced the present-day landforms; for continental glaciation on the islands adjacent to the mainland and perhaps local glaciers elsewhere have certainly contributed their share. Nevertheless, so great have been the effects of these still active forces that we shall never properly understand the physiographic character of the region until we have allotted them their full weight.

23. *Swater* *

One of the less heralded, but nevertheless effective, means of water erosion is that caused by the splash of raindrops. The resulting fluid combination of soil and water aids in sheet erosion and accomplishes a great deal of work even in cultivated or barren soils of flat areas. Ellison has coined the term "swater" to describe the muddy liquid. The mechanics of soil erosion as a result of the splash process, and some of the resultant problems, are explained here. Particularly serious problems caused by "swater" are fertility losses from agricultural areas and pollution of streams.

Broad differences have been discovered in the behavior of rainwater after it falls on different fields. The rain that falls on fully vegetated lands

* W. D. Ellison, "Swater," *The Land,* Vol. 9, No. 3, Autumn, 1950, pp. 331–335. Published by Friends of the Land, Zanesville, Ohio.

The author (1898) has long been active in soil conservation and water-control work. He is at present a soil conservationist for the Department of the Navy, and has served as a special consultant for the President's Water Resources Policy Commission in Washington, D.C.

remains clear as it makes contact with the soil. But rain that falls on bare ground is splashed and churned into muddy mixtures as different from water as smog is different from fog.

They not only appear different, but they are different, and they present different types of problems. Fogs that fill the air over open lands, and the clear storm waters that reach the soil beneath full vegetal covers are products of nature. But the smogs that hang over many cities, and the muddy mixtures that are churned on bare soils are products of pollution.

I believe that it would help to clarify the problem before us if we selected a single word to designate the muddy mixtures that are churned on bare fields by splashing raindrops. I use the word swater. In searching for an appropriate term, I follow the pattern used in coining the word smog and combined letters from the words soil and water. Swater then, is a product of pollution which may be traced to the splash erosion process.

Differences in the behaviors of swater and water are indeed real. Consider, for example, the process of scour erosion which carves the gullies. We have heard much about the erosive power of water varying as the sixth power of the velocity. But, actually, the different characteristics of the swater will often cause this erosive factor to vary through much wider limits than do changes in velocities. Some mixtures of swater will be highly abrasive; so abrasive that it may carve channels in concrete. Or, I believe, this situation may even be reversed. If the swater contains only slick clay particles it may cause even less scouring than does clear water when acting alone.

The differences in swater that are stirred on the different soils also affect rates and amounts of water intake by a soil. The intake of each swater may be widely different from that of water. A general failure to recognize and account for these differences in past work has so limited some of our research findings that they are of little practical use. We have not only failed to obtain the infiltration that occurs with each different swater, but we have also failed to determine what kind of swater is produced on the different soils, with different crops, and for different types of storms. Differences in soils, crops and storms each have an important bearing on the properties of the swater that is produced.

The splash erosion process which breaks down crumbs of soil and stirs swater, will cause fertility elements to be released and churned into the muddy mixtures. When swater runs off it carries soil fertility from the lands. Even the creeping movements of swater as it leaves flat lands, at velocities so slow that they do not cause scour erosion, may float away the lighter fertility elements of a soil. The result is fertility erosion. This is an erosion process that cannot be eliminated by erosion control practices that merely slow down the runoff. The main thing, first of all, is to check the production of swater. This means checking the splash erosion process.

Plainly, the blasts of raindrops which produce the swater also break down clods and crumbs of soil and compact them, and this tends to close the pore openings. They beat the surface layer of soil into an impervious, structureless mass. After this happens the soil is devoid of clods and large crumbs; it has been puddled. It is no longer a soil, it is mud. In the past we have made little or no distinction between wet soils and muds. But the wet soils we find under full vegetal covers, and the muds we find on bare or partially exposed soils have widely different properties and they present widely different problems. It will be found that physical damages and fertility losses on a field will depend largely on the surface mud and the kinds of swater produced by the raindrop blasts.

The fine and light soil materials that are carried from the land by swater that flows very slowly, either from flat lands, from behind contour ridges, or through contour furrows and channels, are the very materials that pollute slow moving valley streams and fill large downstream storage basins. They are the materials that would stay in suspension for many minutes if placed in a pan of water or poured in a rain barrel. They are the kinds of materials that do not settle out of storm flow until it comes into the quiet of a large reservoir. The splash of the raindrops may release only very small amounts of this very fine and light material on each acre of exposed land. But when this release is summed up for large river basins, millions of acres, the total of these deposits may be tremendous.

Pollution of streams and lakes with swater runoff is injurious to many game fish. I was interested in a statement by Louis Bromfield a few years back, concerning the migration of game fish in Lake Erie, from near the mouth of a stream flowing out of very flat lands. He attributed this to filling in of the lake by erosional deposits. It would be interesting to know what part was played by pollution with fertility elements carried in swater runoff. Certainly most of the erosion on this flat land would be by the splash process.

We must recognize that much damage results from producing swater on the surface of the land. If there is runoff, fertility will be lost, and the materials carried away are the very ones that cement soil particles together to form the crumbs which are so important to a soil. To lose these materials may be compared with losing the cement out of a mixture of concrete. But, on the other hand, those that are carried far down into the soil may cause sealing of deep seepage ways through which underground water tables are replenished.

We are sorely in need of information on the properties and important field behaviors of swater that is produced by the splash erosion process. It is this swater that we must learn to control in order to have the raindrops absorbed where they fall.

I feel that progress in developing our soil and water conservation know-how has been slow. A friend once told me that such slowness in coming to grips with the basic and controlling factors of our problems often reminded him of a wrestler with a toe-hold on himself. Usually, he commented, it requires some help from outside the "ring" to bring these "bouts" to a close. He then went on to say that after looking into a number of studies that had reached a seeming impasse, he had found, in every case, the whole trouble could be traced to one or more faulty assumptions that were antecedent to the investigation. In other words, something the investigator "knew" and used as a basic fact, at the time he designed his study, was not so.

I feel that one of the principal faults in our present approach is our broad acceptance of field practices that were used as "palliatives" by the ancients. I feel we spend too much time and effort in trying to improve on these. This applies particularly to contouring and terracing practices which, although important, do not in themselves get at the beginning of the problem.

Soil and water wastes and most of the erosional damages to soils start with swater production. I believe our great need is for a more basic approach envolving an analysis of all fundamental details—minute though they may appear. Such an approach would reveal the true nature of all the destructive processes we must combat, and it would insure a far broader search for the essential curative practices. This more basic approach is needed to reveal the full importance and ramifications of the swater problem, and to guide us in the development of methods for effectively reducing the harmful effects of swater.

24. *Paradoxes of the Mississippi* *

What happens to the runoff from more than a million square miles of land in the Mississippi River drainage basin? How much silt, sand, and gravel is the Mississippi carrying in relation to other

* Gerard H. Matthes, "Paradoxes of the Mississippi." Reprinted with permission from *Scientific American*, Vol. 184, No. 4, April 1951, pp. 19–23.

The author (1874) is a retired consulting engineer. He has held positions as principal

rivers? Why is this great river not building its delta steadily out into the Gulf of Mexico? How many people are aware of the fact that clear blue water can be dipped out of the Mississippi? These and other questions are answered by Matthes in this reading. The intricacies of river erosion within the stream bed itself are effectively described here, as is the performance of the Mississippi during flood stage.

Ol' Man River, that thousand-mile stretch of the Lower Mississippi from Cairo, Ill., down to the Gulf of Mexico, is renowned in story, in song and in school books as our biggest and best-known river. Actually it has been our most misunderstood river. No stream in the U.S. has been the subject of so many persistent misconceptions. School books, college texts, technical writings and encyclopedias to this day contain a strange mixture of conflicting information concerning the Mississippi. It is given the reputation of being a very muddy river. The great load of sediments it carries is supposed to be building up the bed and banks of the river so that its flood stages will steadily continue to rise and require the raising of levees to ever greater heights. The river is asserted to flow down to the Gulf of Mexico on a broad ridge it has built up above the level of the surrounding country. There is a firmly rooted belief that the Mississippi's sediment discharge is steadily building its delta mouths farther and farther out into the Gulf of Mexico. Not one of these assertions and beliefs is correct.

The colossal proportions of the Mississippi—its 1,244,000-square-mile watershed, equal to 41 per cent of the whole U. S. area; its enormous floods, which discharge as much as two million cubic feet of water per second and make the river a mile wide and from 50 to 200 feet deep—have ever intrigued the imagination and furnished food for theorizing and controversy. The prime mystery has always been that the Mississippi, an alluvial (soil-washing) river, does not behave at all like other well-known alluvial streams, such as the Yellow River, the Po, the Nile, the Euphrates and the Tigris. The sediments carried by those rivers have built their beds and valley lands to ever higher elevations. Yet measurements covering more than half a century prove that no such build-up has occurred in the Mississippi. Why? In the past 14 years men have finally begun to collect the facts that make it possible to resolve the paradoxes of Ol' Man River.

In the winter of 1936–1937 a great flood began to gather on the headwaters of the Mississippi. Unusually heavy and protracted rains pointed to a record flood. It so happened that the stage was admirably set just

---

engineer in the office of the president, Mississippi River Commission (1932–45), and as director, United States Waterways Experiment Station (1942–45). His interests include: inland navigation, flood control, irrigation, and water power.

then for undertaking a highly detailed study of this flood from start to finish. A large number of engineers and surveyors were working on the shortening of the Mississippi by means of artificial cutoffs for the Mississippi River Commission. It was an organization trained in river work, fully equipped with instruments and boats. Ample funds were available. The result was that this flood, the greatest to flow all the way to the Gulf within its levees (without a single break) was given the most intensive study ever bestowed on a flood of its size. This investigation marked the commencement of an era of research on the Mississippi which continued for more than 10 years and to which many organizations and individuals contributed. Thousands of borings were made in all parts of the alluvial valley; the valley was thoroughly photographed from the air; elaborate hydraulic laboratory experiments were conducted on models of the river; river depths were traced by supersonic instruments; the early geological history of the valley was painstakingly investigated.

The geological work established that in its early history the Mississippi did build up its bed by alluvial deposits. During the waning of the last ice age some 30,000 years ago the ocean level was from 300 to 400 feet lower than at present. The beds of the Mississippi and the Ohio, then unconnected streams, sloped steeply down toward the sea, and the rivers therefore cut deeply into the rock bottom of the valley and were able to transport very coarse gravel. With the melting of the icecap and the rise of the sea level, the gradients of the rivers flattened. The coarse, heavy gravel then began to build up in the river beds and the sediment transported by the rivers became progressively finer. Eventually these alluvial deposits raised the river valleys an average of 150 feet.

Geologically the Mississippi still functions as an alluvial river. It continues to deposit sediment on its valley surface wherever it is not held in check by levees. But even before civilized man began to build levees to confine the river to its channel some 200 years ago, the rate of build-up of the valley had become insignificantly small. The evidence brought to light by geologists and engineers shows that during the past 1,500 to 2,000 years the river has not measurably built up its bed, its banks or its alluvial plain. Paradoxical as this may seem, the evidence is incontestable. It is confirmed by detailed investigations of the river's 1,500-year-old meandering courses, which have not been obliterated, of its channel and natural levees, of its sedimentary deposits and of its behavior during the last 70 years. Incidentally, these observations prove, contrary to what has generally been thought, that neither man's abuses of the land and water in the watershed nor the vagaries of droughts, floods and climatic fluctuations over the long course of time have left any measurable imprint on the behavior of the Mississippi River.

Now the Mississippi is known to carry a huge load of sediments. Each year it transports some 400 million tons of silt and gravel downstream, approximately 90 per cent of it in the form of fine particles suspended in the water and the rest heavier material that is dragged or rolled along the bottom. Yet despite that immense wash of soil the Mississippi has shown no appreciable build-up of its bed or valley lands for thousands of years. What is the explanation of this astonishing paradox?

Part of the answer is that the Mississippi's volume of water is so huge that its sediment load of 400 million tons is actually relatively light. Year by year its freight of suspended sediment averages 550 to 600 parts per million by weight in ratio to the weight of the water. This is about one tenth of the average annual concentration of suspended solids in other rivers such as the Missouri and the lower Colorado (before the building of the Hoover Dam). In flood the Mississippi's concentration of sediment steps up to 2,600 parts per million; in contrast, the concentration in the Missouri during flood may go as high as 20,000 parts per million, in the Colorado 40,000 parts per million and in the lower Rio Grande 40,000 parts per million. And the Yellow River in China carries a vastly heavier load: the weight of the solids suspended in it often exceeds the weight of the water itself.

Actually the Mississippi is a comparatively clear stream. During extremely low stages its concentration of sediment has been known to drop as low as 50 parts per million. In late September, 1936, during such a low stage, the Mississippi flowed water as blue as that of the Danube (which, incidentally, also is blue only during low-water periods). The normal turbidity of the Mississippi is due not to mud but to minute fragments of mineral matter, mostly sparkling silica grains, suspended in the water. A glass of water dipped up from the river clears itself quickly. The water is soft and pleasant to drink, despite the fact that it represents the runoff from more than a million square miles of soils and rocks. During dry periods, when much of the Mississippi's flow is derived from ground water (*i.e.,* from the valley soil and rocks), the hardness of its water increases noticeably.

Paradoxically the Mississippi's load, which according to theory should consist of nothing coarser than sand and silt, also contains gravel, some of it as large as potatoes two and a half inches in diameter. Most of this gravel is picked up by the river during floods, when it scours down 100 feet or more into the bottoms of bends and brings up coarse pebbles from the bottom layers of the deposit. Coarse gravel is contributed also by the Ohio River and by some of the small streams that descend from the eastern escarpment bordering the valley.

Another misconception about the Mississippi has been that most of the sediment load carried by the lower part of the river comes from the caving of its banks. Back in the 1890s measurements showed that the soil dropping into the river from its banks amounted to nearly a billion tons annually. Paradoxically, this was more than twice the annual load of suspended sediment. In recent years protection of the banks has reduced bank caving, yet the suspended load shows no evidence of a decrease. Hence bank caving obviously has little effect on the total amount of sediment that the Mississippi River pours into the Gulf of Mexico. Actually the bulk of the river's suspended material, some 280 million tons of it, comes from the Missouri River. The Ohio River, which flows on a rock and coarse gravel bed, brings in only 40 million tons of suspended matter; the Arkansas River about six million and other tributaries about four million. The bank cavings contribute only about 50 million of the 400 million tons of the river's suspended load. Most of the material from the cavings travels only a short distance along the bed and builds up the convex shore downstream. For this reason the river, despite its phenomenal caving, does not widen. As one bank caves, the bank opposite is built out by soil carried down from the caving next upstream on its side.

Perhaps the biggest paradox is the situation at the great river's mouth. It is popularly supposed that the mouths of the Mississippi are continuously building out into the Gulf of Mexico. Other great alluvial rivers certainly do so; the Euphrates and Tigris, for example, are advancing their joint delta into the Persian Gulf at the rate of about 160 feet a year. But the fact is that the Mississippi is not building out its delta at all; one obvious sign of this is that jetties constructed at its mouths as long ago as 1875 have not had to be extended. Furthermore, the Gulf of Mexico as a whole has not become more shallow. What, then, has become of the billions of tons of sand and silt dumped into the Gulf by the Mississippi River?

In 1939 the Louisiana State University geologists Richard J. Russell and Harold N. Fisk suggested the answer, and later studies confirmed them. The explanation, revealed by borings in the Gulf, is simply that the earth's crust there has sunk under the weight of the accumulated sediment load. The subsidence of the crust along the south shore of Louisiana began as early as 30,000 to 40,000 years ago, about the time when the icecap of the last glaciation started its final retreat. The rivers then flowing into the Gulf, probably larger than the Mississippi is today, unloaded enormous quantities of coarse gravel. Since the surface of the Gulf was more than 300 feet lower than at present, these rivers flowed on slopes steep enough to generate a tractive force capable of rolling gravel up to five inches in diameter. These ancient river courses, through shifting, brought into existence seven deltaic gravel deposits, strung out over a semicircular Gulf Coast front of some 150 miles. These deposits radiate, fan fashion, for 80 miles from a center near New Orleans. Each is bowl-shaped, with a maximum thickness at its deepest point of about 3,000 feet. Under the weight of this gravel the earth crust has been pressed down about the same distance. This large-scale subsidence of the crust in the Gulf has been accompanied by an uplifting of adjacent land areas, notably a marked rise of coastal lands in the state of Mississippi.

The modern Mississippi is in the act of superimposing on the early deposits in the Gulf a deltaic fan with a 17-mile radius, composed of fine silts, sands, logs and other remnants of vegetable origin. Its shape, in many respects similar to that of the earlier gravel deposits, has been likened to that of a ladle with a handle extending up the Mississippi River.

Anyone navigating the Mississippi soon after a flood has subsided cannot fail to notice the new layer of sand that the overflowing river has deposited on the tops of its banks. These deposits, varying in thickness from a few inches to as much as two feet, affords visual evidence that the Mississippi still is an alluvial river. What an observer cannot see from the river is that the deposit is heaviest on the rim of the bank and thins out rapidly on the landward side. The reason for this is that when the river overflows its banks, it drops the heaviest part of its load immediately, for the velocity of the water decreases suddenly after it charges over the bank. As the overflow advances slowly inland, willows and other vegetation conspire to rob the water of most of its sediment in a relatively short distance. The net effect of the deposits on the tops of the banks is to create a ridge 12 to 15 feet high along the river on each side. These structures, known as the river's natural levees, account for the fact that the Mississippi's valley lands have experienced no appreciable build-up through the long course of time.

Along the Mississippi it is an observed fact that the heaviest part of a sedimentary deposit on a high bank is the first to drop back into the river when the bank caves. In consequence, the natural levee does not continue to rise indefinitely but periodically caves and rebuilds anew.

The presence of the natural levees has misled many people into believing that the river flows on a ridge built up from its own deposits. This is not the case; actually the Mississippi is a very deep river. In many places its bottom is below sea level, even as far upstream as 470 miles, where the land is 100 feet above sea level. Throughout the entire 850 miles of the Mississippi between Cairo and Baton Rouge its mean low-water level is all of 30 feet below the adjacent land surface. Consequently the river must rise at least 30 feet before its water level equals the elevation of the land, not taking into account the additional height of the natural levee. The mean annual height of the river in flood ranges from 40 to 45 feet above the low-water mark in its upper section to 32 feet at Baton

Rouge. Most of the year the water level is not as high as the land. Below Baton Rouge the river assumes the form of a tidal estuary some 200 miles in length. Here the land surface on either side is low, in some places only a foot and a half above sea level. High artificial levees are necessary to keep the river confined during flood.

The fact that flood stages in the Mississippi have risen materially with time is due solely to the confinement of its flood waters between the high levees. In the course of a century the high-water mark mounted 6 feet at New Orleans, 13 feet at Baton Rouge, 8 feet at Natchez, 12 feet at Vicksburg, 15 feet at Arkansas City, 13 feet at Memphis and 8 to 9 feet at Columbus, Ky. Since 1932 the flood stages have been lowered by artificial cutoffs that have eliminated some of the worst bends and shortened the river about 170 miles. This operation has reduced flood stages 3 feet at Natchez, 10 feet at Vicksburg, 15 feet at Arkansas City, 5 feet at Memphis and 1.5 feet at Columbus.

It is common knowledge that the length of the Mississippi has not changed materially by natural means in the long course of years. Its length between Cairo and Baton Rouge was roughly 850 miles in 1765, 894 miles in 1825, 833 miles in 1882, 842 miles in 1910 and 846 miles in 1930. During this time the river made many changes in its meandering course, but evidently the wanderings that lengthened the river were offset by shortenings.

The general impression has been that the river shortens itself simply by cutting off some of its bends from time to time. Whenever a bend becomes too distended, flood waters erode a new channel across the narrow neck of the loop. Now there is no doubt that this process produces important shortenings of the river. Since 1765 a total of 19 natural cutoffs has occurred in the river stretch between Cairo and Baton Rouge. (Paradoxically, Yucatan Cutoff, the last natural one before the inauguration of artificial cutoffs in 1932, was not caused by a flood but unobtrusively made its debut during low water in the fall of 1929.) These cutoffs have effected individual shortenings ranging from 6 to 22 miles, and in aggregate the shortenings total 249 miles. But during the same period the lengthenings of the river have amounted to something approaching 500 miles, or nearly twice as much as the shortenings. Since the Cairo-to-Baton Rouge stretch of the river has not increased in total length, cutoffs cannot account for all the shortening that has taken place. Clearly other shortening processes must be at work.

Two such processes have been recognized by engineers. One has to do with the large sand bars that are commonly formed by cavings. These bars frequently build out a mile, sometimes as much as several miles, in the path of the stream, gradually forcing the river to detour by making a bend. Across such bars floods usually erode shallow swale-like depressions called "chutes." Because they are dry most of the time, the chutes are inconspicuous at first, but they slowly enlarge and deepen, and in the course of time they tend to become secondary river channels that act as short-cuts for the river. The time comes when a chute ceases to be a mere overflow route for flood waters and flows water the year round. It then robs the main channel of a part of its flow, thereby causing it to deteriorate by shoaling. Eventually the chute channel takes over and becomes the main channel. The entire process is so gradual, also so commonplace, as to lack the spectacular attributes of a cutoff across a narrow neck, hence it rarely finds mention in the press. At least one important chute, named Brandywine, is in process of development at the present time some 15 miles above Memphis. It will shorten the river about five miles.

The other generally unnoticed shortening process is a method by which the river gradually wears away and straightens out slight bends. This process is much less important than the other two, but it produces enough shortening to be recognized in the yearly revisions of river mileage on the Mississippi River Commission's navigation maps.

One of the most interesting paradoxes of the Mississippi relates to the advance of a major flood. The common conception pictures the crest of the flood as rushing with raging speed down the river. It is true that during a great flood the water on the top of the stream attains a velocity of 9 to 13 feet per second—from three to five times the speed of normal currents of the river at low water. But the crest of the flood as a whole actually moves down the river only half as fast as a small rise in water level during the low-water season.

The explanation of this paradox is as follows: During the rising stages of a major flood a large volume of water is continually being subtracted from the advancing flood-wave to fill that part of the channel ahead of it where the water surface still is low. In the case of the Mississippi the volume of water so required, technically known as "channel storage," is exceptionally large, owing to its channel width of 4,000 to 5,500 feet and its high banks rising 30 feet above low-water level. A great deal of water is also absorbed by sand bars and by the banks. Furthermore, when the flood wave overtops the banks an even heavier drain on it develops. In short, as the advancing flood-wave front moves downstream it is literally robbed of vast quantities of water, and this naturally slows its advance. Although the velocity of its top currents may be six to nine miles per hour, the flood itself moves at only about 1.5 miles per hour. If it does not overtop the river banks, the flood may speed up to three to four miles per hour. Before the river was artificially shortened by cutoffs of some of the bends, it commonly took a high flood crest about 25 days to travel from Cairo to Baton Rouge.

On the other hand, an entirely different situation controls the rate of transmission of a small rise in stage in the river at low water. The river then consists of a succession of deep pools, each several miles long, separated by shallow sand bars. A small rise in water travels from the upper to the lower end of such a pool with the speed of a wave, sometimes at the rate of 15 miles per hour. Because of this the "pop-rise," as it is called, moves downstream in about half the time taken by a flood crest; it makes the journey from Cairo to Baton Rouge in about 11 days.

The shortening of the river by artificial cutoffs has reduced the time of travel of flood crests noticeably, but just how great the effect will eventually be cannot yet be determined. The abandoned bends still take flood water, so retardation by channel storage continues undiminished. When the river has become stabilized, floods should pass down it in considerably less time than before man intervened.

25. *The Long Snowfall* *

An understanding of the slow accumulation of sediment on the bottoms of present seas throws light on the way in which sedimentary rock layers were formed. This "rock record" and the marine life fossilized in the sediments form the major "source book" for deciphering earth history. Carson likens this deposition to a snowfall that increases and decreases with climatic changes, changes in the rate of land erosion, and position in relation to land. Much recent work, aided by improved techniques, is enlarging our knowledge of the landform character of ocean bottoms and the rate of deposition thereon. Most sedimentary rock underlying present landforms was formed in the manner here described.

* Rachel Carson, "The Long Snowfall," *The Sea Around Us* (Oxford University Press, 1951), pp. 74–81. Copyright 1950, 1951 by Rachel L. Carson, reprinted by permission of Oxford University Press, Inc.

The author (1907) is Editor-in-Chief of the United States Fish and Wildlife Service. She has visited remote areas from the Rocky Mounains to the interior of the Everglades. Her work has also included considerable scientific observation of the sea and of sea life; she has taken part in several oceanographic expeditions. Her publications include numerous articles on natural history for periodicals and two books: *Under the Sea Wind* and *The Sea Around Us.*

Every part of earth or air or sea has an atmosphere peculiarly its own, a quality or characteristic that sets it apart from all others. When I think of the floor of the deep sea, the single, overwhelming fact that possesses my imagination is the accumulation of sediments. I see always the steady, unremitting, downward drift of materials from above, flake upon flake, layer upon layer—a drift that has continued for hundreds of millions of years, that will go on as long as there are seas and continents.

For the sediments are the materials of the most stupendous "snowfall" the earth has ever seen. It began when the first rains fell on the barren rocks and set in motion the forces of erosion. It was accelerated when living creatures developed in the surface waters and the discarded little shells of lime or silica that had encased them in life began to drift downward to the bottom. Silently, endlessly, with the deliberation of earth processes that can afford to be slow because they have so much time for completion, the accumulation of the sediments has proceeded. So little in a year, or in a human lifetime, but so enormous an amount in the life of earth and sea.

The rains, the eroding away of the earth, the rush of sediment-laden waters have continued, with varying pulse and tempo, throughout all of geologic time. In addition to the silt load of every river that finds its way to the sea, there are other materials that compose the sediments. Volcanic dust, blown perhaps half way around the earth in the upper atmosphere, comes eventually to rest on the ocean, drifts in the currents, becomes waterlogged, and sinks. Sands from coastal deserts are carried seaward on off-shore winds, fall to the sea, and sink. Gravel, pebbles, small boulders, and shells are carried by icebergs and drift ice, to be released to the water when the ice melts. Fragments of iron, nickel, and other meteoric debris that enter the earth's atmosphere over the sea—these, too, become flakes of the great snowfall. But most widely distributed of all are the billions upon billions of tiny shells and skeletons, the limy or silicious remains of all the minute creatures that once lived in the upper waters.

The sediments are a sort of epic poem of the earth. When we are wise enough, perhaps we can read in them all of past history. For all is written here. In the nature of the materials that compose them and in the arrangement of their successive layers the sediments reflect all that has happened in the waters above them and on the surrounding lands. The dramatic and the catastrophic in earth history have left their trace in the sediments—the outpourings of volcanoes, the advance and retreat of the ice, the searing aridity of desert lands, the sweeping destruction of floods.

The book of the sediments has been opened only within the lifetime of the present generation of scientists, with the most exciting progress in collecting and deciphering samples made since 1945. Early oceanographers could scrape up surface layers of sediment from the sea bottom with dredges. But what was needed was an instrument, operated on the principle of an apple corer, that could be driven vertically into the bottom to remove a long sample or "core" in which the order of the different layers was undisturbed. Such an instrument was invented by Dr. C. S. Piggot in 1935, and with the aid of this "gun" he obtained a series of cores across the deep Atlantic from Newfoundland to Ireland. These cores averaged about 10 feet long. A piston core sampler, developed by the Swedish oceanographer Kullenberg about 10 years later, now takes undisturbed cores 70 feet long. The rate of sedimentation in the different parts of the ocean is not definitely known, but it is very slow; certainly such a sample represents millions of years of geologic history.

Another ingenious method for studying the sediments has been used by Professor W. Maurice Ewing of Columbia University and the Woods Hole Oceanographic Institution. Professor Ewing found that he could measure the thickness of the carpeting layer of sediments that overlies the rock of the ocean floor by exploding depth charges and recording their echoes; one echo is received from the top of the sediment layer (the apparent bottom of the sea), another from the "bottom below the bottom" or the true rock floor. The carrying and use of explosives at sea is hazardous and cannot be attempted by all vessels, but this method was used by the Swedish *Albatross* as well as by the *Atlantis* in its exploration of the Atlantic Ridge. Ewing on the *Atlantis* also used a seismic refraction technique by which sound waves are made to travel horizontally through the rock layers of the ocean floor, providing information about the nature of the rock.

Before these techniques were developed, we could only guess at the thickness of the sediment blanket over the floor of the sea. We might have expected the amount to be vast, if we thought back through the ages of gentle, unending fall—one sand grain at a time, one fragile shell after another, here a shark's tooth, there a meteorite fragment—but the whole continuing persistently, relentlessly, endlessly. It is, of course, a process similar to that which has built up the layers of rock that help to make our mountains, for they, too, were once soft sediments under the shallow seas that have overflowed the continents from time to time. The sediments eventually became consolidated and cemented and, as the seas retreated again, gave the continents their thick, covering layers of sedimentary rocks —layers which we can see uplifted, tilted, compressed, and broken by the vast earth movements. And we know that in places the sedimentary rocks are many thousands of feet thick. Yet most people felt a shock of surprise and wonder when Hans Pettersson, leader of the Swedish Deep

Sea Expedition, announced that the *Albatross* measurements taken in the open Atlantic basin showed sediment layers as much as 12,000 feet thick.

If more than two miles of sediments have been deposited on the floor of the Atlantic, an interesting question arises: has the rocky floor sagged a corresponding distance under the terrific weight of the sediments? Geologists hold conflicting opinions. The recently discovered Pacific sea mounts may offer one piece of evidence that it has. If they are, as their discoverer called them, "drowned ancient islands," then they may have reached their present stand a mile or so below sea level through the sinking of the ocean floor. Hess believed the islands had been formed so long ago that coral animals had not yet evolved; otherwise the corals would presumably have settled on the flat, planed surfaces of the sea mounts and built them up as fast as their bases sank. In any event, it is hard to see how they could have been worn down so far below "wave base" unless the crust of the earth sagged under its load.

One thing seems probable—the sediments have been unevenly distributed both in place and time. In contrast to the 12,000-foot thickness found in parts of the Atlantic, the Swedish oceanographers never found sediments thicker than 1000 feet in the Pacific or in the Indian Ocean. Perhaps a deep layer of lava, from ancient submarine eruptions on a stupendous scale, underlies the upper layers of the sediments in these places and intercepts the sound waves.

Interesting variations in the thickness of the sediment layer on the Atlantic Ridge and the approaches to the Ridge from the American side were reported by Ewing. As the bottom contours became less even and began to slope up into the foothills of the Ridge, the sediments thickened, as though piling up into mammoth drifts 1000 to 2000 feet deep against the slopes of the hills. Farther up in the mountains of the Ridge, where there are many level terraces from a few to a score of miles wide, the sediments were even deeper, measuring up to 3000 feet. But along the backbone of the Ridge, on the steep slopes and peaks and pinnacles, the bare rock emerged, swept clean of sediments.

Reflecting on these differences in thickness and distribution, our minds return inevitably to the simile of the long snowfall. We may think of the abyssal snowstorm in terms of a bleak and blizzard-ridden arctic tundra. Long days of storm visit this place, when driving snow fills the air; then a lull comes in the blizzard, and the snowfall is light. In the snowfall of the sediments, also, there is an alternation of light and heavy falls. The heavy falls correspond to the periods of mountain building on the continents, when the lands are lifted high and the rain rushes down their slopes, carrying mud and rock fragments to the sea; the light falls mark the lulls between the mountain-building periods, when the continents are flat and erosion is slowed. And again, on our imaginary tundra, the winds blow the snow into deep drifts, filling in all the valleys between the ridges, piling the snow up and up until the contours of the land are obliterated, but scouring the ridges clear. In the drifting sediments on the floor of the ocean we see the work of the "winds," which may be the deep ocean currents, distributing the sediments according to laws of their own, not as yet grasped by human minds.

We have known the general pattern of the sediment carpet, however, for a good many years. Around the foundations of the continents, in the deep waters off the borders of the continental slopes, are the muds of terrestrial origin. There are muds of many colors—blue, green, red, black, and white—apparently varying with climatic changes as well as with the dominant soils and rocks of the lands of their origin. Farther at sea are the oozes of predominantly marine origin—the remains of the trillions of tiny sea creatures. Over great areas of the temperate oceans the sea floor is largely covered with the remains of unicellular creatures known as foraminifera, of which the most abundant genus is Globigerina. The shells of Globigerina may be recognized in very ancient sediments as well as in modern ones, but over the ages the species have varied. Knowing this, we can date approximately the deposits in which they occur. But always they have been simple animals, living in an intricately sculptured shell of carbonate of lime, the whole so small you would need a microscope to see its details. After the fashion of unicellular beings, the individual Globigerina normally did not die, but by the division of its substance became two. At each division, the old shell was abandoned, and two new ones were formed. In warm, lime-rich seas these tiny creatures have always multiplied prodigiously, and so, although each is so minute, their innumerable shells blanket millions of square miles of ocean bottom, and to a depth of thousands of feet.

In the great depths of the ocean, however, the immense pressures and the high carbon-dioxide content of deep water dissolve much of the lime long before it reaches the bottom and return it to the great chemical reservoir of the sea. Silica is more resistant to solution. It is one of the curious paradoxes of the ocean that the bulk of the organic remains that reach the great depths intact belong to unicellular creatures seemingly of the most delicate construction. The radiolarians remind us irresistibly of snow flakes, as infinitely varied in pattern, as lacy, and as intricately made. Yet because their shells are fashioned of silica instead of carbonate of lime, they can descend unchanged into the abyssal depths. So there are broad bands of radiolarian ooze in the deep tropical waters of the North Pacific, underlying the surface zones where the living radiolarians occur most numerously.

Two other kinds of organic sediments are named for the creatures whose remains compose them. Diatoms, the microscopic plant life of the sea, flourish most abundantly in cold waters. There is a broad belt of diatom ooze on the floor of the Antarctic Ocean, outside the zone of glacial debris dropped by the ice pack. There is another across the North Pacific, along the chain of great deeps that run from Alaska to Japan. Both are zones where nutrient-laden water wells up from the depths, sustaining a rich growth of plants. The diatoms, like the radiolaria, are encased in silicious coverings—small, boxlike cases of varied shape and meticulously etched design.

Then, in relatively shallow parts of the open Atlantic, there are patches of ooze composed of the remains of delicate swimming snails, called pteropods. These winged mollusks, possessing transparent shells of great beauty, are here and there incredibly abundant. Pteropod ooze is the characteristic bottom deposit in the vicinity of Bermuda, and a large patch occurs in the South Atlantic.

Mysterious and eerie are the immense areas, especially in the North Pacific, carpeted with a soft, red sediment in which there are no organic remains except sharks' teeth and the ear bones of whales. This red clay occurs at great depths. Perhaps all the materials of the other sediments are dissolved before they can reach this zone of immense pressures and glacial cold.

The reading of the story contained in the sediments has only begun. When more cores are collected and examined we shall certainly decipher many exciting chapters. Geologists have pointed out that a series of cores from the Mediterranean might settle several controversial problems concerning the history of the ocean and of the lands around the Mediterranean basin. For example, somewhere in the layers of sediment under this sea there must be evidence, in a sharply defined layer of sand, of the time when the deserts of the Sahara were formed and the hot, dry winds began to skim off the shifting surface layers and carry them seaward. Long cores recently obtained in the western Mediterranean off Algeria have given a record of volcanic activity extending back through thousands of years, and including great prehistoric eruptions of which we know nothing.

The Atlantic cores taken more than a decade ago by Piggot from the cable ship *Lord Kelvin* have been thoroughly studied by geologists. From their analysis it is possible to look back into the past 10,000 years or so and to sense the pulse of the earth's climatic rhythms; for the cores were composed of layers of cold-water globigerina faunas (and hence glacial stage sediments), alternating with globigerina ooze characteristic of warmer waters. From the clues furnished by these cores we can visualize interglacial stages when there were periods of mild climates, with warm water overlying the sea bottom and warmth-loving creatures living in the ocean. Between these periods the sea grew chill. Clouds gathered, the snows fell, and on the North American continent the great ice sheets grew and the ice mountains moved out to the coast. The glaciers reached the sea along a wide front; there they produced icebergs by the thousand. The slow-moving, majestic processions of the bergs passed out to sea, and because of the coldness of much of the earth they penetrated farther south than any but stray bergs do today. When finally they melted, they relinquished their loads of silt and sand and gravel and rock fragments that had become frozen into their under surfaces as they made their grinding way over the land. And so a layer of glacial sediment came to overlie the normal globigerina ooze, and the record of an Ice Age was inscribed.

Then the sea grew warmer again, the glaciers melted and retreated, and once more the warmer-water species of Globigerina lived in the sea—lived and died and drifted down to build another layer of globigerina ooze, this time over the clays and gravels from the glaciers. And the record of warmth and mildness was again written in the sediments. From the Piggot cores it has been possible to reconstruct four different periods of the advance of the ice, separated by periods of warm climate.

It is interesting to think that even now, in our own lifetime, the flakes of a new snow storm are falling, falling, one by one, out there on the ocean floor. The billions of Globigerina are drifting down, writing their unequivocal record that this, our present world, is on the whole a world of mild and temperate climate. Who will read their record, ten thousand years from now?

26. *Andorra: A Study in Mountain Geography* *

This selection by Peattie is a well-rounded geographic study of one of the major landform types—mountains. The complex physical character of mountain topography presents mankind with a great challenge in his attempt to utilize them; today most mountainous areas are sparsely populated except in the low latitudes. The tiny re-

* Roderick Peattie, "Andorra: A Study in Mountain Geography," from *Geographical Review*, Vol. 19, 1929, pp. 218–233; published by the American Geographical Society, New York.

The author (1891) is Professor of Geography, Ohio State University. Among his special interests are human, historical, and mountain geography; he is also interested in the area of Southern Africa. His books include *Mountain Geography* and *Geography in Human Destiny*.

public of Andorra, nestled in the Pyrenees between Spain and France, is an excellent example of the physical, cultural, and economic character found in this landform type.

The geographic factors back of the anomalous independence of Andorra, lying between two great countries, are Pyrenean rather than purely Andorran. The Pyrenees are not as sharp a divide between France and Spain as they are generally credited with being. At places along the summit of the range it is difficult to judge where the water divide may be. Nor is there a cultural divide, for the Catalans are found in almost equal strength on the two slopes of the eastern end, as are the Basques at the western. The summit of the eastern portion of the range is an uplifted and youthful plain. Here are vast pastures known by the Catalan as *plas*. With pastoral life as a prime element in the existences of both the Spanish and French mountaineers, these pastures are, in summer, the true focus of the local economies. The extent of pasture rights held by the people is as important a measure of the prosperity of the valley communes as is the amount of cultivated land. Indeed the communes frequently hold privileges upon the *pla* land in disregard of the national boundaries. The flocks and herds of the two people mix here. A bond, born of long contact with each other and a common set of economic problems, is established by people of two nations. Though more particularly so in the past, even today the Pyrenees are a zone of transition rather than a sharp boundary between governments and cultures.

So differentiated has this mountain zone been from the flanking plains that the separatist tendency, common to mountain peoples, is here well illustrated. As in Switzerland, there was in this range for three centuries a little-known federation. The mountaineers, regardless of national intentions of Spain or France, maintained a state possessing frontiers, public law, and a political consciousness. This federation was bound together largely by the *pla* terrain. Barèges, an elevated French village, had its communication with the outside world, French or Spanish, by the high-level route until the eighteenth century. It was a *pla* commune. Frequently communes on opposite versants had closer commercial and social relations with each other than with the plains to which they belong nationally if not linguistically. The treaties between such communes, known as *lies* and *passeries* (treaties of alliance and peace), were many, and they involved rights to pasture, water, wood, and commerce. Rights to resources and privileges to trade were exchanged without reference to the national governments and were clung to even when the nations to which the communes belonged were at war. Thus Barèges and Bielsa agreed in 1384 to continue friendly relations in case of war between Aragon and England. Ossau, Aspe, and Baretous were neutral during the Hundred Years' War. In the War of the Spanish Succession the transmontane commercial relations were maintained regardless of the wishes of kings. Indeed republican tendencies are common enough in these mountains. These were the natural results of agreements between communes. The government of Andorra itself is an example of the same historical movement. It is indeed merely a syndicate of villages, which for historical and geographic reasons has persisted into modern times.

Legend has it variously that Andorra owes its origin to the liberality of Charlemagne and to Louis I (*le Débonnaire*). The fact is that until the thirteenth century it was merely a mountain fief of a certain degree of independence under various seigniories and that at one time or another it owed allegiance to overlords on each side of the mountains. In feudal days rights frequently extended across the range. Thus the counts of Toulouse held Spanish Catalonia, and again the kings of Aragon held French Béarn and Foix. The quarrels between the Spanish bishops of Urgel and the French counts of Foix as to rights in Andorra led to the *Paréage* of 1278. *Paréage* is a feudal term implying equal rights of two lords to a seigniorage. That such a neutral situation should have lasted into the twentieth century may be explained in part by the definite geographic isolation of the little country.

Physical Circumstance

Andorra is officially known, in English, as the Valleys and Sovereignty of Andorra. Its 495 square kilometers (190 square miles) lie largely in one drainage basin, but its main stream, the Riu Valira, has two distinct branches and, in all, six open basins.* Hence the term "valleys." These basins are due to unequal resistance of the metamorphic rocks found in the southern part of the country. The northern portion, referred to previously as the *pla* country, represents the granitic core of the range. There is also much high-level land represented in the southern portion, different in character, however, for glaciation has been much more severe in the more easily eroded rocks. Cirques, compound cirques, glacial lakes, and hanging valleys are common. Both the northern and southern portions of the upland represent summer pastures, but the organization of the industry is different in the two cases. On the *plas* large droves of sheep and goats, largely transhumants from France and Spain, feed in the summer

* In order of increasing size the little countries of Europe are: Monaco, San Marino, Liechtenstein, Andorra. In number of inhabitants, they are in the reverse order, if the ranks of San Marino and Liechtenstein are interchanged. Andorra in 1920 had 4309 inhabitants, of which 224 were foreigners. Pyrenean communities have in general been losing population in the last ten years.

time. The increased precipitation due to the altitude, combined with the levelness and the impermeability of the granite rocks, provides excellent pasture for small stock. The highlands of the dissected southern portion consist of peaks and serrated ridges with steep cirque walls which separate cirque bottoms and high-level valleys. Here the steep slopes have only enough soil and ground water for the mountain pine. The pasture lands are excellent but small areas of valley-bottom soil, *comas*. There are, then, two topographic levels of life in the country—the pastoral and the agricultural. The difference in relief between these two levels is 1000 to 1500 meters. In distinction to mountain nomadism represented in many higher groups of mountains as the Alps, here only a few shepherds take part in the seasonal movement.

The valleys are distinctly glaciated. The forms of erosion are much more dramatic than in most parts of the Pyrenees, and the general aspect of the landscape is savage. The basin of Andorra la Vieja is a little Yosemite. Since glacial times there have been canyons cut, which are still so youthful as to offer serious barriers to communication between the basins. Thus the gorge of Sant Antoine between the basin of Andorra and La Massana has today but a mule path hewn from the rocks. The gorge from Andorra to Encamp has a road along its wall considerably above the stream, but from Encamp to Canillo the trail is forced up 320 meters over the shoulder of the mountain to pass the gorge of Meritxell. The climb is an arduous one for man or mule. The villagers of Mare de Deu and Prats along the route are a half-hour above their valley-bottom grasslands. These last-named villages are on terraces which are lateral moraines. Whereas the glacial terraces in places offer high-level agricultural land, elsewhere the morainic deposits are so rough and strewn with huge boulders as to be impossible for use except for pasturage between the rocks. The French call such an area a "chaos," and indeed they look as if they were portions of the earth unfinished on the day of creation. On the whole, glaciation has improved the Andorran valleys as a place of habitation. The greatest contribution made by the ice was the terminal moraine on which Santa Coloma stands. A lake of short duration existed in the valley upstream, upon whose lacustrine soils alluvial deposits from the side walls have since encroached.

Character of the Farming

In lieu of climatic statistics, which are totally lacking, the climate is best discussed in terms of natural vegetation and agriculture. The olive stops at the Spanish gate of Andorra. The chestnut and walnut are found only in the neighborhood of the lowest village, Sant Julia (950 meters). The live oak occupies sunny slopes in the basin of Andorra la Vieja. The climate, always rude, increases in severity very quickly with altitude. Many valleys are entirely subalpine and alpine in character. In less than three hours of thalweg road one may pass from harvest rye to green rye. On the plain of Andorra (1000 meters) grain is harvested from July first to the tenth. At Encamp (1300 meters) the harvest is nine days later. At Lo Serrat (1600 meters) harvest is not till the twentieth of August when some plowing of fields for the next season's crop has already begun. This rapidity of increasing rudeness of climate is shown by the table of duration of the dormant period of vegetation.

DURATION OF THE DORMANT PERIOD OF VEGETATION

			Dormant Period		
Vegetation	*Locality*	*Elevation (meters)*	Beginning	End	Duration (months)
Broadleaf evergreens	Plain of Andorra	1029	Dec. 15	Jan. 15	1
Deciduous	La Massana	1252	Dec. 1	Feb. 15	2½
	Encamp	1266	Dec. 11	Feb. 15	>2
	Ordino	1304	Dec. 15	Feb. 28	2½
Coniferous subalpine	Soldeu	1825	Oct. 15	Apr. 15	6
	Cortals d'Encamp	1860	Oct. 15	Apr. 15	6
	Lo Serrat	1600	Oct. 1	Apr. 30	7
	Bordes d'Inclès	1825	Oct. 1	Apr. 30	7
Alpine	Port de Soldeu	2407	Sept. 25	June 1	>8
	Portella Blanca	2515	Sept. 25	June 15	<9

The region is to be classed as of a mediterranean climate in distinction to the dry mediterranean climate to be found in Spain just outside the borders of the country. Farming is both of the irrigated and normal type. Hay, tobacco, and vegetables are grown by irrigation; the cereals are a dry-land crop. All land that is level or slopes that lie adjacent to and below canals on the valley walls are irrigated. These slopes are usually unterraced and devoted to grass. As in all regions where beasts are pastured in the high mountains in summer, the greatest part of the cropped land is devoted to hay production for feed for the animals during the winter stabling. Andorra has an excess of high pasture. Therefore economic pressure for hay land as against field crops is great. The more hay, the more beasts of Andorran ownership on the uplands. The number of cuttings of grass varies from one on the natural prairies at the edge of the *plas* to four on the irrigated fields. There is in Andorra, considering the Mediterranean type of climate, a remarkable flow in the streams. That the uplands have a significant duration of snow cover is an element in this condition, but the relative levelness of the uplands as well as the number of lakes plays a part. There is always an excess of water for the amount of land to which it can be easily conveyed.

The cereals are largely rye and barley. The people eat black bread. Where there are gentler breaks in the valley walls and farmable slopes extend up to the *pla* level, rye occupies the top fields. Elsewhere rye is grown on the shoulders of the canyon walls. These highest fields in Andorra lie at 1850 meters and are not infrequently an hour's tramp from the nearest house. The isolated position of the fields represents largely a search for sunlight. The deep gorges and their alluvial cones may have but a few hours of sun during the day: the high fields are out of the gorge on the sunny exposure of the valley.

The question of sunny slope and shady slope is of utmost importance in mountain climates, the more so because at high altitudes air temperatures in the shade are critically low. Each group of peoples has a set of names to correspond to the two slopes. The Catalan calls the sunny slope the *sola, solana,* or *solane* and the shady slope the *ubaga, obaga,* or *ubach.* Every inch of the *solana* is cultivated, but the *ubaga* almost literally belongs to anyone who wants it. In so far as production goes, the *ubaga* is almost negligible. And yet the *ubaga* is farmed, and the condition of slopes may be so favorable that it is farmed as high as the *solana:* indeed, frequently the greater the altitude on the *ubaga,* the greater the percentage of sunlight. But the crops on the shady side are commonly so slight or even precarious as to have relative unimportance. It may be stated as a principle of mountain geography that the shady slope can be farmed as extensively as the sunny but that the two vary greatly in economy. Also, the higher the altitude, the less the difference in the economy of the two slopes. However, I do not think that the climatic limit of agriculture of one sort or another has been reached by the Andorrans. Matters of accessibility, distance, difficulty of carrying manure to the fields and crops to the granges, and unwillingness to encroach upon pasture lands, as well as unfavorable soils on the *plas,* are factors which all obviously play a part. It would almost be easier to determine a lower climatic limit for grain in the gorges than an upper limit. In the valleys the sunlight duration is so short that the season necessary for maturing grain is lengthened. In places men may sow one grain crop in the autumn before in an adjacent field the grain of that year is harvested. The land must then either lie fallow a year or be put into field crops.

Tobacco is the most distinctive crop of Andorra. It had its start when smuggling was a recognized profession. Today smuggling is no longer what it was, partly because of the unfavorable exchange since the war. Andorra uses Spanish currency, and the peseta is much more nearly normal than the franc. But the amount of tobacco grown in Andorra is far in excess of national needs. I have no confidence that this tobacco pays duties when it is exported, and it would have been a breach of hospitality to have made inquiries. Climatically, the interesting thing regarding tobacco is that the highest cultivated fields in the basins of Andorra and the valley end of high Arinsal are devoted to it. The highest field in the basin

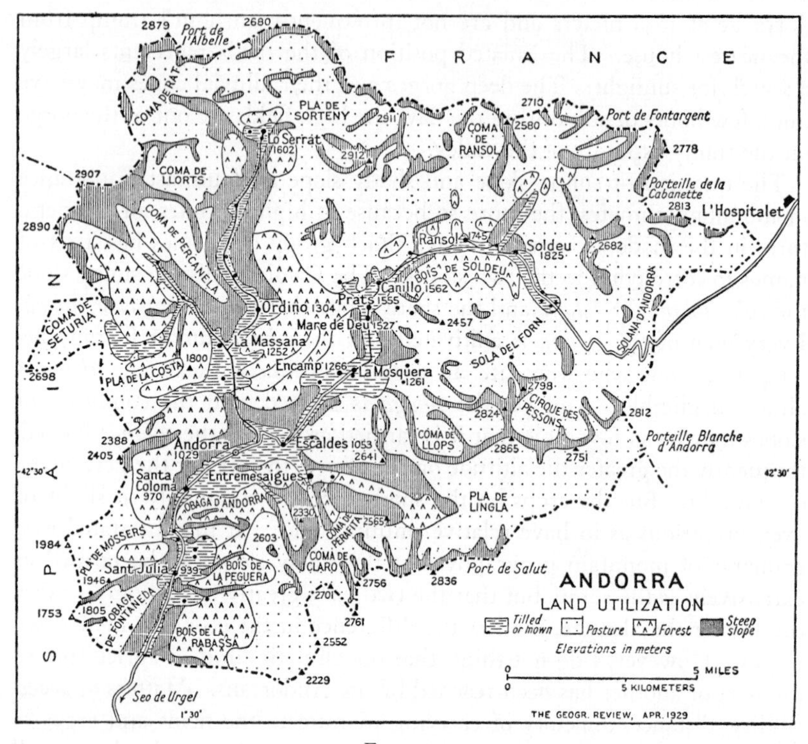

FIGURE 7

Land Utilization Map of Andorra. The area of continuous cultivated fields on the valley bottoms or alluvial slopes is shown, whether irrigated or farmed normally. Isolated fields upon the shoulders of the canyons are not included. Under forest are shown areas of accessible timber of commercial value, chiefly the mountain pine; but the stand varies greatly and generally the board-foot measure is not high.

Land of over 45° slope is distinguished: much of it has slight timber value; most is barren even of sheep forage; some of it has talus which menaces the tilled lands below. The upland pastures include the *plas,* grassy plateaus used largely for sheep, and the *comas,* green parks devoted to cattle and horses. Many of the high knobs of the north are covered with pasture of sorts to the summits; elsewhere it is topography rather than climate that limits the altitude of grass. Mixed forest and grassland has been mapped according to predominant use. The scale is approximately 1:290,000.

of Andorra (1500 meters) lies in the side valley of Entremesaigues. Sunlight duration is short (on September 15, with the tobacco still on the stalk, there was but eight hours of sunlight), the canyon is refrigerated by an icy stream, and it suffers in the evenings from cold mountain winds. Tobacco is everywhere given the best lands. These fields have the advantage of being close to summer pastures and so to manure.

Other agricultural products of Andorra are potatoes, garden vegetables, buckwheat, rye, and barley. A few vines exist near Sant Julia, the lowest community. Vine culture is restricted because with better transportation one is able to buy wines from the Lérida region of Spain, and the grapes are today used for raisins.

There are to the best of my knowledge no areal statistics on land utilization in Andorra. In lieu of exact data I offer the accompanying map. This is based largely upon personal observation, though certain facts for its construction were interpreted from the single existing contour map of the country.

Pastoral Activities

As with many mountain communities, the true basis of Andorran economy is pastoral. They have much more pasture land than they themselves can use. Hence great numbers of beasts, largely sheep, with a sprinkling of goats, come into the country annually from Spain and France. Spain alone will rent privileges for 30,000 head. The revenue from the rents amounts to many thousands of pesetas each year. The least desirable lands and the most remote are allotted to the foreign animals. They are in the country from June 24, the fête of St. Jean, to September 28, the fête of St. Michel. Other than that the shepherds keep their flocks to the proper pastures and that they be out of the country by a definite date there is but one requirement. It may be demanded that for three nights the beasts be quartered on the higher fields for the sake of the manure. It is a common custom in the Pyrenees to quarter animals on fields at night, the smaller groups being enclosed in a movable stockade. Thus the animals are forced to cover the field systematically with droppings.

The migration of beasts has brought about the Spanish fairs of Le Seu on November 6 and Organya from November 27 to December 4. The French transhumants descend earlier, and there is a fair at Aix-les-Thermes on September 13 and 14. The fairs within Andorra are yet earlier, and it is interesting to note that the farther downstream, the later the date of the fair. Thus we have the fair at Encamp on September 10, at Andorra la Vieja on September 27, and at Sant Julia on October 5 and 6. The fair in Andorra la Vieja is the most important, as this is the date of the descent of the Spanish beasts. The animals are largely sheep; about one in twenty of the Spanish animals in 1927 were goats. Mares and mules and even pigs are turned upon the *pla,* but rarely the cattle. They find better herbage on the *comas,* and they will feed on terrain too wet underfoot for the sheep.

This aspect of herding involves only a small number of men. The French sheep are guarded by Frenchmen. The Spaniards are inclined to bunch their herds and turn them over to Andorran shepherds. These men live aloft for three to four months in a crude stone shelter with a single blanket against the night. The herds are always under the sky. If at first too cold, the sheep are driven to lower altitudes for the night. A certain number of the beasts are locally owned. The communes of Encamp and Canillo have little farm land and much *pla* pasture and own most of the 16,000 or 17,000 sheep of Andorra. The local people keep their goats in the villages the year around, so as to profit from the milk. A small amount of sheep's and goats' cheese is made at a definite period in the summer, the cheese being divided between the shepherd and the owner.

The second phase of the transhumance is the migration of beasts of the Andorran villages to the better and usually less distant pastures. This involves mostly beef cattle, mares, and their mule offspring. Andorra is too isolated for dairying, and in any case the tradition of the Pyrenees favors beef cattle rather than milch cows. The raising of mules is one of the chief sources of local income. These animals usually descend earlier than the other animals from the *pla.* They come down in time to profit from the grass growth on the valley meadows after the last cutting of the hay and to fertilize the fields before the autumn plowing. The hay of the valleys is not even sufficient for the winter stabling of all the Andorran beasts. The Andorrans frequently buy rights to pasture sheep in winter on Spanish farms as far south as Lérida.

Industry and Communication

There is so little industry and such poor communication that not much may be said of either. An exception in the past was the contraband industry and today is the lumbering industry. Brutails, writing in 1904, said that the contraband industry was the chief source of revenue. Rios, writing in 1920, says it is negligible. Some of the well-to-do men of the country today are, however, the smugglers of a few years ago. The government took half-hearted steps from time to time to reduce smuggling, but one imagines that such legislation was merely a diplomatic gesture. It is more than likely that mules and tobacco are still smuggled through the lonely ports of the frontier.

That Andorra was heavily forested at one time seems beyond doubt. The name of the country is reputed to have come from a Moorish word, *Aldarra,* meaning "place thick with trees." There are iron ores of value in the country, and a very heavy drain was put upon the timber by the early Catalan forges, whose numerous ruins are still to be seen. Today fuel wood is an important item, but lumbering is carried on in every permanent community. The construction of a sawmill is an easy matter, for there are power streams everywhere; and large quantities of logs are shipped out of Andorra la Vieja by motor trucks into Spain. The communes have complete freedom to cut in their forests. There is, I should judge, a greater subtraction of trees than is supplied by the annual increase. If this is so it is especially unfortunate, for water resources constitute the outstanding asset of the country, and the stream flow may well be damaged by future excessive deforestation.

The manufacturing industry is very slight. Cigarettes and cigars are produced there by a tobacco factory as well as by cottage industry. Matches for local use are made. There is a factory at Escaldes for woolen blankets and scarfs, chiefly for Andorran use as wraps and capes. Escaldes has four inns, three of them of good size, which have flourished because of the curative properties of the local hot springs. The country has a modest summer tourist season, supported by Catalans from Barcelona. There are in all the villages primitive but decent inns; even in the remote villages hostelries flourished in the days when smugglers might be beleaguered en route to France.

The industrial future of Andorra lies in its iron ores, there being deposits in the region of Ransol, at Port Negre, the Coma of Claro, near the Pic de la Mariana, and in the valley of Ordino. I examined the first deposits. They were largely hematite with some brown limonite and carbonate ores. The deposit which outcrops prominently on the valley wall appeared to be important and could be obtained, at first at least, by quarrying. In the fall of 1927 a franchise for exploitation of iron ores was granted to a French syndicate. This involves the building of a road out of the Ordino Valley into France, perhaps by a pass 2546 meters above sea level. There was a time when it seemed as if a Spanish syndicate were to have the franchise; but at the last moment it was found that the Spaniards had inserted in the agreement a clause giving them the right to levy toll on all automobiles using the roads which they were to construct. The Andorrans were indignant: no one should ever levy tolls upon Andorra. The Spaniards were thrown out. The tradition of independence was maintained.

Andorra has two roads. One, a fine and much used highway built by Spain through the good offices of the Bishop of Urgel, runs from Seo d'Urgel past Sant Julia and Santa Colomba to Andorra la Vieja and has been recently continued to Escaldes and Encamp. Immediately upon proceeding beyond Encamp one is forced to climb a difficult mountain side through a chaos. It is little wonder that engineering difficulties here baffled further road construction. France has built a post road from L'Hospitalet (1436 meters) to Soldeu (1825 meters) over the Port d'Envalira at 2407 meters altitude. The postman does the route from Soldeu to Andorra daily on foot unless the weather is too inclement. The round trip takes about eight hours. From Andorra to Seo d'Urgel one travels by motor bus in an hour. Both France and Spain maintain telegraph systems in Andorra as well as postal systems. In the last year Andorra has instituted its own postal service. The country has had no money for public improvements, the taxes being merely a poll tax. No public official is paid a salary. No army or formal police force is maintained. The schools, Catalan and French, are supported by those who use them. The Spanish schools are supported by the Church. The ancient bridges, mule paths, the house of government —known as the Casa del Vall and perhaps as quaint a national monument as you will find—have had little care. The routes out of the country, other than those mentioned, are wild mountain trails developed by the smugglers and not overadvertised. The length of these routes to the outside world is eight to twelve hours, the true way of measuring mountain distances.

Quality of Life

The real Andorra is not easily discovered. Ordinarily a traveler sees only the permanent villages, which are not unlike other Catalan villages in France or Spain both in appearance and organization of life.

Villages such as Sant Julia, Andorra la Vieja, and Escaldes are in fine valleys, on a highway, and have a brisk trade. There one finds automobiles and farm machinery. There is plenty of food, and health and happiness abound. But life in Andorra can be very meager and primitive.

The most characteristic element in Andorran life lies in the high villages or in the little-visited hinterland, the *pla* country. The high villages, or *cortals,* are the equivalents of the *mayen* communities of the Swiss. They are situated on the lowest *alp,* or *mayen,* on a line between the highest fields and the lowest limits of high-level pastures. Thus the fields benefit from the manure deposits. There are in addition *bordes,* or isolated houses, frequently at higher elevations than the *cortals.* The *cortal* of Lo Serrat is at 1560 meters. The *bordes* of Encamp are at 2008 meters. The zone of precarious agriculture is between 1600 and 1850 meters. Above that are wild prairies, hence the *bordes.* The highest permanent habitations are at Soldeu at 1825 meters. In 1897 when there were 5210 persons in the country, there were 1042 houses.

There is a regular and characteristic sequence of seasonal migrations. When the cattle mount in the spring, the entire family may go to the temporary village to herd, mow, and plant. With the descent of the cattle in autumn, the temporary villages are again inhabited. Harvests are made, fields are manured, and plowing is done. Again in midwinter certain families may return to these villages with the cattle to profit from the hay stored there at a time when the hay in the lower granges is exhausted. Christmas is frequently celebrated in these high-level homes. The time which the family may spend in the temporary villages may be hardly less than that spent in the permanent villages. The differences between them lie in the size and number of the houses, the furnishings, and the unkempt nature of the higher houses. Essentially the upper villages are storage depots for hay and manure.

Changes, however, are coming fast. Roads now enter Andorra from two sides. Economic independence is giving way before a changing and improved economy and a growing import and export trade. This trade is more Spanish than French; indeed, because of the low-level route to Spain and the proximity of an active city there, Seo d'Urgel, Andorra has always been more Spanish in culture than French. There are two electric light plants in the country; it was something of shock to find the woman in the primitive *fonda* at Soldeu abandoning her hearth cookery for that of electricity. The national costumes are no longer seen. At the fêtes modern instruments have replaced the bagpipe and flute. The Charleston is danced on the streets. There was opened in 1928 a trans-Pyrenean railway which skirts the border of the little country. But there will always be individuality to Andorra. A mountain is always a mountain, a mountaineer always a mountaineer, and the country still holds its rustic mountain peace.

27. The Ahaggar: Heart of the Sahara *

Road and air routes are making the Sahara more accessible and better known than ever before; even a few tourists are being attracted into the desert. However many popular misconceptions concerning

* E. F. Gautier, "The Ahaggar: Heart of the Sahara," from *Geographical Review*, Vol. 16, 1926, pp. 378–394; published by the American Geographical Society, New York.

The author (1864), a Professor of Geography, University of Algiers, is an authority on the geology and geography of northern Africa and has written numerous articles on that continent.

deserts, such as that deserts are entirely flat, barren, sandy wastes, still exist. In this selection Gautier describes the largely mountainous portion of the central Sahara called the Ahaggar. His emphasis is on the physical character of the Ahaggar, but other aspects of the region are also covered—notably, the role of water erosion in carving the diverse landforms characteristic of this desert environment.

The name Ahaggar has dominated all exploration of the western Sahara during the latter half of the nineteenth century: it was the problem to be solved, the inaccessible core. Barth followed its eastern confines. Duveyrier gathered valuable data on the region though he did not penetrate it. Flatters with all the members of his expedition was massacred at Tin-Tarabin, where a memorial has now been raised by the French government. The Foureau-Lamy expedition crossed the Sahara but touched only the eastern margin of the Ahaggar. The name recalls a whole series of efforts, valiant indeed but futile or incomplete.

Solution of the problem remained for the twentieth century. Two successive reconnaissances by meharists from In-Salah finally dissipated the mystery. The first was under the leadership of Lieutenant Cottenest, the second under Lieutenant Guillo-Lohan. The first geographical account of exploration in the Ahaggar appeared in 1903 over the signature of the latter officer.

From this time the French meharists have policed the Ahaggar and the entire western Sahara of which the Ahaggar is the key. The credit for this work of pacification rather than conquest is due to General Laperrine, now dead and buried in the Ahaggar to which he had consecrated his life. The magnitude of his accomplishment has not received the recognition it merits.

Today the Ahaggar is one of the best known regions of the Sahara. The works on it have multiplied since 1903. We do not yet possess a topographic map on a large scale; but itineraries from the French posts have furnished traverses in all directions and are tied to a number of astronomically determined points. This is the basis of the General Staff's millionth map of the Sahara.

. . . . .

The People of the Ahaggar

The Ahaggar is inhabited by the people who have given it their name. The Arabs pronounce it Hoggar but, as there is no G in their alphabet, write it Hoouara, a name celebrated in medieval history in Tripolitania, Algeria, and Tunisia. The Ahaggar are the remnant of a well known Berber tribe, who from century to century ranged along the borders of the Mediterranean. Today they constitute a clan of the great Saharan tribe of Tuaregs. If not predominant in numbers they are at least the most famous, the fiercest, the most indomitable. They exercise direct control over three massifs, the Kudia, the Tefedest, and the Muidir in the heart of the desert. Of these the Kudia is most important because most populous. It is the only part of the Ahaggar where villages are to be found, if indeed the term village be not too ambitious. The villages are on the periphery of the Kudia at the debouchments of the great wadis. They consist of a collection of huts of hardened clay and are occupied by a limited number of slaves who water the miniature gardens from wells sunk in the wadi beds.

In the Tuareg tongue these villages are *arrem*. They are not true oases. For true oases one must look to the basins of the lower Sahara where converging slopes collect subsurface water. The Kudia on the contrary is a watershed. The best-known *arrem* is Tamanrasset, now on the way to becoming a little French center. Here are the tombs of Laperrine and Foucauld, and it has been proposed to build a hotel to accommodate future tourist traffic. Other *arrem* are Abalessa (site of the tomb of Tin Hinan), Silet, Ideles, Tin-Tarabin. These are their names, but they are of no importance, being insignificant enough in the general scheme of things. The Kudia cannot be an agricultural country. Thanks, however, to its altitude it arrests the passage of a greater number of storms than the surrounding wilderness. Kilian and Bourcart have observed on its summits, Tahat in particular, a persistent cloud cap from which an abundant moisture is deposited. It is sufficient, for instance, to saturate the paper of one's field notebook. Pasturage is found not only in all the valleys but even to the summits. The matter of temperature also is important. In winter precipitation on the highest elevations takes the form of snow which may last for the day. In summer the temperature of the Kudia is lower by twelve degrees or more than the neighboring regions of the Sahara. An important fact; for, after all, the Ahaggar are of the white race and live in the tropics.

Goats, sheep of a peculiar species, and asses browse on the herbage of the Kudia. Infrequently also zebus may be seen, brought from the Sudan; but it is the camel that is the important beast, the means of subsistence.

The pure-blooded Ahaggar does not engage in cultivation. Under no pretext will he handle an implement of toil. His hand, unaccustomed to manual labor, is small, quite out of proportion to his powerful frame and muscular body. The delicacy of his extremities is aristocratic. The hilt of the Ahaggar sword is too narrow for a European grasp. The Ahaggar is exclusively a gentleman of the sword. He has always lived on his courage. With the Kudia at the center of the Sahara as a retreat, mounted on his meharist camels trained admirably as their masters, the Ahaggar has been for centuries master of the transsaharan routes. According to his enemies he pillages the caravans; in his own view it is the levy of a legitimate toll. Certainly he gets his living from the transsaharan traffic.

This specialized life has developed a psychology, an ethos, which has forcibly struck all European observers from the time of Duveyrier to the most recent expeditions. It should be studied now before the old life changes and the Ahaggar become chauffeurs or garage mechanics or railway employees.

The Ahaggar have already been described many times; we shall here note only an aspect of the clan that is of particular geographical interest—what may be called its relict character. Certainly this is not a true description of the outward appearance of the individual, for he is a superb creature, tall, slender, muscular, keeping his force and agility to an advanced age. In a magnificent envelope a superb soul: of great energy, scornful of death, and yet possessing poise and moderation, courtesy and chivalry, one might say a sense of fair play. Nor is his mind to be underrated: refined by relentless strife against the exigencies of a hostile nature, it is a mind open, curious, eager to learn. The Ahaggar has the soul and body of a gentleman practicing for generations the hardest and most dangerous sport—a gentleman of the desert highway.

But when, instead of the individual, one considers the group the picture is less brilliant. Numerically the clan is insignificant in the extreme. The Ahaggar cannot assemble more than 400 warriors though all males between 15 and 60 to 70 years are under arms. Perhaps this fact increases the admiration roused by their former exploits, especially if one considers their armament—the buckler, broad-sword, and lance. They have always been poor, and they live too far from the sea to obtain more modern weapons. These 400 lances prevented the entry of Arabs and Europeans alike until 1903—an extraordinary exhibition of prowess. But so small a human group cannot offer indefinite resistance to the advance of modern civilization: they have a fine past but no future.

To what degree they are a people of the past certain details of equipment and customs bear striking witness. In the matter of writing, they alone amongst the Berber of North Africa have retained the use of Libyan characters which everywhere else disappeared not only before the Arabic but before the Roman alphabet. They use an iron ax, but the handle is attached in the same manner as the Neolithic stone axes. They make and wear polished stone bracelets. The most striking feature of their personal appearance is the veil covering half the figure, the *litham,* as the Arabs term it. Its purpose is to protect the mouth from harmful magic, for it is the gate of the breath, that is the soul. The family organization of the Ahaggar has a matriarchal basis: juridically speaking, the father is a nonentity; the nearest male relative is the maternal uncle. By a curious consequence the ultra archaic character of the Ahaggar family has a false air of modernity. The men are inferior creatures; the women have the monopoly of intellectuality; they are the literati, poets, musicians. The Ahaggar in good faith declare themselves Mohammedans. In reality their religion is an animism surviving from prehistory.

. . . . .

Physical Geography of the Ahaggar

Such are the people: let us now look at their country. A sketch of the physical characteristics of the Ahaggar is easily given, for its structure is very simple. It is a peneplain of old schists, gneisses, mica schists, and quartzites with intrusive granitic masses. The schists show evidence of intense folding, the folds extending approximately in a north-to-south direction, that of Tefedest on the map. Once there existed here an old mountain chain; but it long since disappeared, reduced by erosion to a peneplain. Suess proposed for it the name Saharides.

In the northern part, resting on the peneplain, are plateaus of red sandstone, very extensive and many hundred meters in thickness. There is the Muidir to the west, the Tassili to the east. Kilian has advanced a new and most interesting idea regarding these plateaus. In the uppermost layers Lower Devonian fossils were reported some time ago. In the middle clayey layers Kilian found Silurian fossils (Gothlandian). We draw the conclusion that the red sandstones are of Silurian age at least. Kilian believes that the basal layers are Cambrian; but this is purely hypothesis. His discovery has been fully confirmed by the Olufsen expedition. It is established beyond question and is a fact of importance.

The chain of the Saharides had already been reduced to a peneplain when the Silurian sandstones were deposited, since they rest horizontally on its surface. Hence the elevation of the chain dates from a very early geological period—Cambrian or Algonkian. There are other parts of the earth where ancient sediments—Silurian and Cambrian—are still found in horizontal layers, intact as they were deposited. To such massive and resistant areas the term of "shield" has been applied: as the Siberian shield, the Canadian shield. The Ahaggar is promoted to the rank of a planetary shield.

Yet rigidity does not signify absolute immobility. The Ahaggar peneplain, as we see it today, is no longer cut by a horizontal plane. Its surface as a whole is affected by an immense regular uplift in the form of an exceedingly flat dome. The slope outward from the center is so slight as to be imperceptible to the eye of the traveler. One can go from In-Salah, the last oasis of southern Algeria, which is in latitude almost 27° N. on the northern border of the shield, to the Ahaggar, the central dome of the shield, which is cut by the Tropic, without being aware that one is rising. In-Salah is 200 meters above sea level, and the pedestal of the Ahaggar is in the main above 2000 meters; but the difference, evenly distributed over a distance of 500 kilometers, gives only the insensible gradient of some 4 millimeters in a meter.

If this uplift, which presumably is the result of intense lateral pressure, has caused great ruptures in the shield in the form of extensive faults, they are yet to be discovered. Probably they do not exist. There are however numerous small ones, fissures by which volcanic eruptions have had play. Some volcanoes, the least numerous, are still recognizable by their form; but those which have been so worn down that their central chimney, at least on superficial examination, can no longer be found are represented by numerous lava flows too fresh to be considered old. They do not date back later than the Pliocene. This gives an approximate date for the uplifting of the peneplain: it is comparatively late in the scale of geological time.

To the north of the shield of the Ahaggar there runs a recent chain of Alpine age, the Atlas, whose overthrust folds attest the energy of the compression from the north. The volcanic eruptions and the uplifting of the peneplain are presumably connected with the uplift of the Atlas.

Volcanic eruptions took place in various parts of the peneplain, but they were far from being distributed evenly over its surface. They were most numerous in the most elevated part, precisely at the summit of the dome. Here is the thick lava cap that furnishes the chief relief and gives the Ahaggar its dominating position in the western Sahara. This lava cap, studied in particular by Bourcart, is composed of three successive flows piled one on top of another, at the base phonolites, above basalts, at the top trachytes. The whole series form a crust under which the old peneplain has completely disappeared. In diameter the cap attains a breadth of 70 kilometers: the thickness of the superposed flows is many hundreds of meters. The extreme summits attain heights of nearly 3000 meters in the peaks of Tahat and Ilaman. To this lava cap, so clearly individualized by its composition and altitude, the natives give a particular name; they call it the Kudia of Ahaggar. It is the Ahaggar par excellence, the geographical *raison d'être* of the country we call the Ahaggar.

Fluvial Erosion

The uplifting of the surface of the peneplain by modifying the slope gave new force to erosion and rejuvenated the land form. Although we have in the heart of the Sahara the finest example of a desert on our planet, the Ahaggar everywhere exhibits traces of fluvial erosion. It is the most distinctive feature of the physical geography of the country.

An examination of the map shows the Kudia of the Ahaggar as a watershed whence a great network of valleys diverges towards all parts of the horizon: towards the north the Igharghar, which ends in the depression of the great shotts near Biskra; towards the west the Tamanrasset with its affluent, the Tekwiat, which ends in the closed basin of the Juf, north of Timbuktu; towards the south the Tin Tarabin and the Irerrer, which after their junction with the Tafasasset join the lower Niger. Each of these great valleys has a close network of affluents. A first glance at the map suggests a normally well watered country. In reality these valleys so clearly delineated on the map do not carry rivers, large nor small; they do not even merit the term wadi, for they have not the tiniest trickle of running water. It is the skeleton of a dead river system; they are fossils.

Farther down in their lower courses in the zone of deposition the skeleton character is betrayed. The continuity of the network is broken; sections of the valleys have been effaced by the wind, invaded by sand; the work of dissolution has become apparent. But here in the heights and the borders of the Kudia one could be deceived from a study of the map alone, so admirably is the skeleton preserved.

It is an irrefutable testimony to a relatively rainy period which preceded the present period of extreme aridity. It is the Saharan equivalent of what we call the glacial period, what the French a half-century ago knew as the diluvial period, and the Germans still call the Pluvialzeit. As cicatrices left by the Pluvialzeit on the earth's surface the dead wadis of the Ahaggar are a good counterpart of the terraces of Lake Bonneville, the Quaternary ancestor of the Great Salt Lake, and they deserve to be as well known.

Morphological study of the dead valleys, as far as it is possible, leads to some interesting conclusions. The valleys indicate erosion arrested in the youthful stage. The simplicity of the pattern is significant. The valleys radiate regularly from the Kudia as center, each of them almost rectilinear; that is, in the terminology of the American physiographers, they are consequent or, as the French have sometimes termed it, primitive. It is true that at certain places subsequent trunk streams run contrary to the general slope and from an examination of the map one can discern captures. This is in particular the case in the great peripheral depression on the edge of the sandstone plateaus of Muidir and Tassili to the north. One suspects that the Wadi Amadror has been captured by the Igharghar. Above the point where the Amadror shows what appears to be an angle of capture its high valley is a long straight line in the exact prolongation of which the wall of the sandstone cuesta is deeply cut. Similarly it may be suspected that across the Muidir, pierced through and through by deep canyons, the Wadi Tarhemert-n-Akh, now a left-bank affluent of the Igharghar, was formerly the source of the Botha.

Much farther to the south at the very foot of the Kudia, upstream from In-Amejel, a group of little wadis, sources of the great Wadi Tekwiat, run in an east-west direction; they appear to have been captured by the Wadi Tekwiat to the detriment of the Igharghar. It is true that the erosion is not the sole cause; Bourcart thinks a lava flow has dammed the original valley.

These captures, which deserve further study, do not affect the impression of the youthfulness of the drainage as a whole; and this is accentuated if we take into consideration the profiles of the wadis. As the map shows at certain points, there is excessive enlargement of the stream bed, sometimes even bifurcation into great deltas (W. Tekwiat). Under another climate the enlargements would be lakes or marshes. In the Ahaggar these alluvial plains are sometimes encrusted with salt, Sebkha of Amadror for example, but most often they betray a dampness which supports pasture. Their importance the natives have recognized by naming them *maaders*. These valley steps are connected by narrow and deep canyons where the river, if it flowed, would form rapids. Such contrasts are characteristic of young valleys. The anthropologist by examining the dentition, sutures, etc. of a human skull can approximately determine the age of the owner at death. Examining in like fashion the skeleton of the dead rivers of the Ahaggar one reaches the conclusion that they died in adolescence, long before finishing their work of erosion.

These findings are in accord with those of geology. In northern Africa and the Sahara geologists have revealed a series of epochs in the past during which an arid climate prevailed. The relatively humid period which preceded the present appears to have been an incident in a long climatic past. And there remains the present climate of frightful aridity. Thus in the Ahaggar the desert physiognomy coexists with the forms of fluvial erosion. This gives the country its most picturesque, most photogenic aspects.

The Desert Landscape

One need not look in the Ahaggar for the sand dunes which imagination so freely associates with a desert country. The obstacle to their formation lies not in the climate but the altitude. The Ahaggar is the up-valley zone of the dead valleys. There is some sand with which the wind makes play but in insignificant amounts. The great mass of the dunes are found down valley, much lower, outside the Ahaggar in the zone of deposition where enormous quantities of alluvium furnish material for the building of dunes.

The Ahaggar is especially the desert of stones: of bare rocks or great plains of pebbles and gravel. It is said that the camels of the country, perfectly at home in traversing the rough rock edges, are less at ease in the low country on the yielding sand of the dunes. It is an extremely striking thing, this preponderance of bare stone swept and polished by the eternal wind and veneered by the desert patina in all shades of deep red, brown, or black. Desert erosion, furthermore, has sculptured the rock in fantastic forms.

It was long believed that the most elevated point of the Kudia was Mt. Ilaman, 2950 meters. Today it is certain that a neighboring peak Tahat is higher by some dozens of meters: it is estimated at 3000 meters. The error of earlier observers is readily explained by the arresting form of Ilaman, a slender rock pyramid, almost columnar. No one has made the ascent, and manifestly it could not be made without adequate equipment.

Another summit of the Ahaggar, said to be still more formidable, is Mt. Udan. It is somewhat less elevated but gains from its position as a solitary peak at the northern extremity of Tefedest, a region where the general base is appreciably lower. Its 2770 meters hang over the great Igharghar valley, here only 865 meters above sea level. This is the summit which has made most impression on the natives. They have named it Garet-el-Jenun, the needle of the Jinns. They consider it inaccessible to ordinary mortals, and legends of its fairy inhabitants and enchanted gardens have been collected by Kilian. These are the giant needles: there is an infinite number of medium-sized and small ones: the country fairly bristles with them. The abruptness of the slopes of which the needles are one expression has another in the innumerable canyons, one of the great beauties of the Ahaggar. The finest perhaps are in the highest part of Muidir, Ifetesen, where the sandstone plateau attains a height of 1000 meters. There are narrow canyons many thousand meters deep whose walls are vertical or in some instances indeed slightly overhung. This precipitousness of slopes is of course a classic product of the desert climate. The Alps also are strewn with innumerable needles, but these adorn the summits of a mountain chain enclosed by the glaciers that have sculptured them. There is nothing of this in the Ahaggar, no least trace of glaciation and no chain.

In the Kudia also a comprehensive glance easily discerns the level character of the lava flows dissected though they have been by the network of canyons and needles. Outside of Kudia plane surfaces largely predominate—here of the lava flows, there the uniform surface of the peneplain, and again of the gravel plains known to the natives as *reg*. From the level surface the needles rise with startling abruptness: they appear to be set on the plains, as Chudeau says, like bottles on a table.

This is the work of the climate in the modeling of the desert landscape. It is not as great as is generally supposed. All who have seen the western Sahara have been led to the conclusion that the potency of eolian action has been exaggerated. The desert climate, of which the wind is a fundamental agent, amplifies the contrasts of existing relief and thus produces results so striking as to be in the nature of caricatures; but it does not create. It is fluvial erosion that has originated the relief on the borders of the great sandstone plateaus as also the considerable mass of Tifedest, a region still little known, which Kilian and Bourcart tell us is a granitic massif. The granites and Silurian sandstones are in fact more resistant to erosion than most of the old schists, gneiss, and mica schists.

The Residual Fauna

The dead rivers have a souvenir not only in the relief they have sculptured: one must look back to the period in which they flowed to explain certain peculiarities in the fauna.

It is well known that two thousand years ago Carthage employed elephants in its wars against Rome. They were captured in the basin of the great shotts south of Biskra, today dotted with palm groves. The depression of the great shotts is the zone of deposition of the Igharghar. Evidently the elephant had passed from the tropical savanas of central Africa to the borders of the Mediterranean by following the then living rivers of the Ahaggar. This is historical testimony. A living witness may be seen in the towns of Tunisia, where snake charmers will make the cobra dance for the tourist. The famous Hindu serpent is a tropical beast; it is also found in Egypt, where the Nile explains its presence; in the depression of the great shotts it is today an absurdity, an anachronism.

In this depression tropical and Nilotic fishes unknown in Algeria and Europe—the chromis and the *Clarias lazera* (catfish)—have lately been found, a discovery that caused much surprise. They lie in the mud at the bottom of water holes and in the subterranean waters that feed the artesian wells.

At the other extremity of the Igharghar, at its head in the Kudia, Kilian reports on the other hand a Mediterranean fauna that has come from the north. These are the barbels and frogs in the water holes and the rare threads of running water.

But the most extraordinary case is that of the crocodile. A little colony has been discovered in the heart of the desert in the water holes of the sandstone plateaus. Paradoxical as is this fact, it is indubitable. A specimen has been brought to the laboratories. At latest reports, shameful to say, the French non-commissioned officers of the meharists were hunting the poor creature with the rifle.

This is what the zoölogist calls a relict fauna. These paradoxical beasts have all the characteristics, in particular degeneracy. The crocodiles do not exceed a meter in length, the catfish two centimeters. The cobra seems to have kept its proportions, but this reptile, so formidable in the Indies, is a languid and inoffensive creature in the Sahara.

The wadis have been dead since the end of the Quaternary, it would seem; but a certain number of the animals that peopled them still live, by a miracle, without doubt, and in diminishing number; but they live. The geologists date back the end of the Quaternary some thousands of years, an indefinite but lengthy period of time. Could the relict fauna of the rivers of the Ahaggar survive such a lapse of time? Has the Saharan crocodile lingered 10,000 or 20,000 years at the bottom of his little pool? It is evidently possible, such is the marvelous tenacity of life and its power of adaptation to new conditions.

This brings us back again to the question of more recent change. As we have seen in the earlier part of this paper, the human element seems to show characteristics analogous to the relict fauna. The tomb of Tin Hinan indicates wealth and resources far beyond the present-day population.

Must we then conclude that a thousand years ago the Ahaggar was more humid than today and supported a denser population? That hypothesis perhaps is not necessary. The Ahaggar, as we have said, bear the name of the famous Hoouara whose exploits were noised throughout Barbary in the Middle Ages. It founded in Morocco the great dynasty of the Almoravides which conquered Spain and shook all the western Mediterranean. This far-flung dominion, this active intervention in the affairs of Barbary necessarily had its repercussion in the fortunes of the central Sahara before the Arab invasions which drove the nomad Berbers to the Sahara.

It is true that such a historical explanation merely defers the difficulty. One may properly ask how it happens that the Veiled Ones, if they have always been as we see them today, could ever play so important a political rôle. This is for consideration elsewhere. However, one cannot help thinking of the Saharan crocodile.

The existence of the Sahara for many thousands of years is historically attested. In the Middle Ages it was almost as we now know it. But at "almost" we cannot lightly dismiss the question of change. In such a country the slightest trend towards deterioration may entail serious human consequences, a slow and progressive deterioration. Herein is the enigma.

CHAPTER FOUR

Natural Vegetation and Forestry

ORIGINAL VEGETATION COVER or lack of it plays an important part in the appearance and utilization of an area. Plant species differ with varying climate, soils, drainage, landform, elevation, and conditions of human use. A knowledge of plant distribution over the surface of the earth in its relation to the factors mentioned above is of vital concern in the establishment of the past and present geography of any region.

The populating of the world was both aided and inhibited by the nature of vegetation. In early history man occupied arid and semiarid grasslands, and avoided forests. In the early settlement of the United States, however, agriculture began in forested lands and grasslands were long retarded, owing to the inability of man to cope with the toughness of the sod. For example, the rough, infertile forested Shelbyville moraine of southern Indiana and Illinois was settled prior to the flat, fertile prairies just to the north.

There are two recognized approaches to the geographic study of plants. One is *plant ecology,* the study of the distribution of plant communities or associations and their relations to the physical and cultural environment. "Natural vegetation" is a term applied to the aggregate of plant communities of varying sizes and complexity. Plants reflect changing natural conditions of an area; thus vegetation realms of various scales have been identified. In most cases, however, man has disturbed the original vegetation.

The second approach is *floristic plant geography,* which concerns itself with the distribution of plant or taxonomic units, such as families and species. Here the interest is focused on the characteristics of individual plants or groups of plants that affect their distribution. Some families or species are found in extremely limited areas, whereas others are almost world wide and extend across major climatic and other natural boundaries.

The economic importance of the distribution of native and domesticated plants is considerable. Much of our food, clothing, and shelter depends on the availability of natural vegetation or on the ability of man to grow domestic plants. The selections that follow are indicative of the scope, distribution, economic importance, and problems of natural vegetation and forestry.

---

28. *The Role of Plants in Geography* *

The division between various bodies of knowledge is often fine or nonexistent, and there is often a great deal of overlapping. Geography is no exception. In this selection, Carter attempts to distinguish between the botanist and the plant geographer. He discusses, especially, the utility of the economic plant geographer who considers "economic plants of the earth in their regional setting." Many plants have wide climatic ranges but the boundaries of crop and plant regions do not necessarily coincide with climate or other physical barriers; historical and other man-made factors are often as important as environmental conditions in plant distribution.

Plant geography has been a neglected branch of our science. This is strange; for not only is it a fascinating study in itself, but both historically and philosophically it is a part of geography. Alexander von Humboldt, who with Ritter founded modern geography, is widely known as the father of plant geography; De Candolle, who did classic work in the nineteenth century on the origins of cultivated plants, was considered a plant geographer; and some of the recent great advances in our knowledge of the origin, distribution, adaptation, and use of plants have been accomplished by a group of Russian scientists who have worked under the appellation of "plant geographer."

There has been a tendency to label plant geographers "botanists." But

* George F. Carter, "The Role of Plants in Geography," from *Geographical Review,* Vol. 36, 1946, pp. 121–131; published by the American Geographical Society, New York.

The author (1912) is chairman, Isaiah Bowman School of Geography, The Johns Hopkins University. He is an authority on the geography of the southwestern United States, especially on Indian culture and agriculture. He is the author of *Plant Geography and Culture History in the American Southwest.*

this is no more reasonable than labeling geomorphologists "geologists." Just as in the geomorphologist we have a scientist with interests lying between the fields of geography and geology and acquainted with both, so in the botanist-geographer we have a similar combination. What is generally unrecognized by geographers is that the botanist's study of plant geography differs less in the material used than in the point of view. A botanist uses plant geography principally as a means of gaining understanding of the problems of plant diffusion, speciation, and speed, direction, and types of plant evolution and adaptation. In its specialized form this botanical plant geography is well represented by Stanley Cain's recent excellent book *Foundations of Plant Geography*. Less specialized in form, and hence more useful to geographers, is the recent translation of Wulff's great work *Historical Plant Geography*. These works are methodologically extremely interesting for the way in which distributional problems are handled. But for the botanical plant geographer the material with which he works is less interesting in itself than as a means of seeking out and exemplifying botanical laws. Conspicuously absent from the botanical plant geographer's work is consideration of the economic plants of the earth in their regional setting. Here is a proper and fruitful field for the geographer. It is this economic plant geography that I wish to discuss. For reasons both of space and of personal knowledge, I limit myself here to economic plants of America, drawing my illustrations from three groups of domestic plants: corn, beans, and squash, especially corn.

In dealing with such plants the methods are familiar and geographical. Plants, plant parts, or seeds are collected in the field. With the material it is desirable to have notes on season, planting and harvesting time and methods, location of fields, climatic data, and, whenever possible, data on the probable antiquity of the crop in the area, the native name for the crop, and so on. As an example of the usefulness of full data, consider the significance of the name given by the Hopi to one of their varieties of pumpkin—*Mormonvatna.* Translated this is "Mormon pumpkin." Tradition states that the Hopi received the pumpkin from the Mormons. This species of pumpkin is unknown archeologically in North America. But even though the archeological confirmation is lacking, the clues are present in name and tradition to indicate the late introduction of the plant. Similarly, the Hopi have particular names for other recently introduced plants that clearly indicate the time and agency of introduction.

It may be objected that to gather such intensive data is time-consuming in the extreme and that if one is to maintain balance in studying a region it is necessary to gather equally detailed data on soils, landforms, settlement, peoples, and so on and the time required for this would be prohibitive. But the worth of a regional study is proportionate to the degree of expertness acquired in knowledge of the interlocking details of the region. This is indeed where the geographer can make his unique contribution, and there is no short cut to such knowledge.

Corn Regions in the Americas

The question of what a "region" is and how one defines it has long vexed geographers. Ideally, regions would be defined in terms of a complex of traits. However, we have also defined regions on the basis of single factors, such as distribution of newspapers; in such cases we have been aware that we were measuring more than newspapers.

In defining a region we are most frequently concerned with the way of life of the people, and very often this means that we are concerned with agriculture. In America we are accustomed to recognizing agricultural regions, sometimes on a single-crop basis but oftener on a crop-complex basis. We have, however, virtually limited ourselves to the major, commercial crops, and we have shown amazingly little interest in the origins of these crops. I do not wish to belittle the commercial-crop approach, but I do wish to point out both the value of noting the minor, noncommercial crops and the utility of gaining perspective on regional problems through an understanding of the historical background.

Crops can be used to define regions either on the basis of single crops or by crop complexes. Corn (maize) furnishes an example of how a crop can be used to segregate regions. In the Americas the following broad regional corn divisions can be recognized:

There is a great Andean area characterized by flour corn, usually of giant grain size and with the kernels elongated and often pointed at the top and easily shelled off the cob. The plant is nonwoody, the roots are coarse and weak. The ears are relatively small-cobbed and irregularly rowed.

The Middle American lowland (northern Colombia into southern Mexico, and including Venezuela and the Caribbean) is characterized by flint corn of two subraces; one has large grains, the other small. In both races the rows are straight and closely spaced, the cobs are proportionately large, the tassel is large, the stem is large, the roots are fine and strong, and the plants, cobs, and stems are woody. The large-seed variety frequently has giant ears, often both of great length and of great diameter. In both varieties the seeds are uniform in shape and size.

The maize region of the Mexican plateau is characterized by plants of coarse, weak root system, great economy of water use, ears that are pyramidal in shape, often with irregular, wide-spaced rows, and kernels that are usually light-colored, relatively long, pointed at the top, and dented.

In northwestern Mexico and extending into the Gila-Colorado Valleys of the United States the principal maize is a small, nonsuckering plant, which produces small ears of light-colored flour corn, of moderately regular rowing, with tapering of the ear from the center toward both butt and tip, and with husk striation strongly present at the base of the ear. This corn is of extremely rapid growth and can withstand great heat.

On the Colorado plateau a mixture of varieties of corn is grown, primarily two races that have somewhat separate distributions. The first is a small-eared, straight-rowed, small, regular-seeded, freely suckering corn with an extreme adaptation for sprouting from great depth. This corn is commonest in the nonirrigated areas. The second is a many-rowed, enormous-cobbed, large-seeded corn, which is commonest in the irrigated parts of the Colorado plateau–Rio Grande area.

In the eastern United States there are in one sense several corn belts, roughly as follows: New England has large-seeded, few- and straight-rowed, small-cobbed, yellow flint corns. The Canadian-border area west of the Great Lakes has small-seeded, straight-rowed, small-cobbed, colored flint corns. In the South there is a wide spread of a great variety of dent corns, most of which are white or yellow. Our present Corn Belt yellow dents are clearly derived from these.

Obviously, even this sketchy division of the New World into corn regions has much meaning. Not only are corn regions set out, but it can be seen that these regions coincide with natural, cultural, and economic regions. And from the sketch of the plant types it should be plain that *what* plants are *where* is meaningful both historically and economically.

Relationships between Corn Areas

From the plant characteristics already given it should be clear that there are certain relationships between the corn of one area and that of another. How these relationships came about is an important anthropological, historical, and geographical problem.

Botanical, genetic, archeological, historical, and geographical evidence all points to the probability that corn was originally domesticated in South America, probably in the eastern Bolivian area. From there it spread northward, probably through the Andes, and across the uplands of Central America into Mexico, thence on into the United States, probably by two routes. Meanwhile in Central America this giant South American grass hybridized with *Tripsacum,* a near relative, and the result was teosinte. By repeated backcrossing, entirely new races of corn arose. These new races, possessed of new characters, began diffusions of their own.

The movements of maize seem to have been as follows: Andean maize, suited to growth at high altitudes, spread into the highlands of Central America and Mexico. Hybridization gave rise first to the small-grained tropical flints and later to the large-grained tropical flints. These were especially suited to tropical lowland conditons and spread widely through the lowlands of Central America, into at least northern South America, out into the Caribbean, and on up into the eastern United States. Another group of Andean corns, isolated on the Mexican plateau, received little *Tripsacum* mixture and became differentiated into the striking Mexican pyramidal dent corns. A separate race of small flour corn of little-known affinities spread up the west side of Mexico and eventually reached the Gila and Colorado river valleys.

Corn reached the eastern United States by some other route than the western Mexican one; for eastern United States corn, although racially varied, is not closely related to this western Mexican corn. Tropical flint corns are now the northernmost in the United States. This might be interpreted by application of the theory of age and area as evidence that they were the first to be introduced into the United States and reached their present position through long, slow adaptation.

But it might also be interpreted as evidence that special qualities permitted this corn to be grown on the northern fringe, and that these characters were not necessarily developed in this area. We have a partial check on this from the archeology of the Pueblo area. Here, the small-grained tropical flint corns stratigraphically precede most of the other corn types. It seems likely, therefore, that what we find today at the northern border of maize growing in the United States is the result of a very long period of selection and adaptation of a tropical corn variety until it has become fitted to an incredibly short season and poor growing conditions. In economic terms this means that this is probably the only corn in the world suited to such climates and, most significantly, that loss of such a corn would be irreplaceable.

It seems likely then that the more southern corn belts of the United States are occupied by later introductions. This is particularly true of the dent corn of the Southeast. This corn is clearly related to the pyramidal corn of the Valley of Mexico, and in turn to the Andean highland corn. It has both the faults and good qualities of Mexican pyramidal corn. Among its faults is a relatively coarse, weak root system, that makes the plant liable to topple over. (One suspects that the Indian practice of heaping dirt about the base of the plant may be related to this trait.) Among the good qualities is the characteristic of very deep grains, which give a large amount of kernel per cob.

The complexity in the Pueblo area is to be explained historically. Corn growing began in the Four Corners region about A.D. 200. The type was unusual, somewhat reminiscent of primitive Andean corn. About 700 corn related to the small-grained tropical flint corn appeared. About 900 dent corn almost identical with modern Corn Belt dents appeared. This race, however, apparently was little suited to the severe conditions of the Southwest and almost disappeared in the succeeding centuries. After 1400 big-grained, giant-cobbed corn was introduced into the Rio Grande Valley. All these corn varieties had to come from the eastern United States; for they are not found in the Gila-Colorado area or adjacent Mexico. We therefore gain an initial date of the beginning of the Christian Era or earlier for corn growing in the eastern United States.

How fast corn growing spread through the eastern United States must have depended on the plasticity of the corn varieties and on the cultural receptiveness of the native peoples. We can assume nothing on either count. Unexpected cultural lag is shown by such things as the fact that some of the Texas Indians and some of the Florida Indians never did take up agriculture. Botanically considered, corn arriving in the United States may or may not have carried a genetic factor for resisting the cold of high altitudes, and this factor if present may or may not have been useful in helping adapt corn to high latitudes, short season, and changing day length.

Surprisingly enough, we have a better knowledge of the probable spread of corn through the eastern part of the United States than one might suppose. Archeological-botanical-geographical research has shown that there was an independent agricultural beginning in the eastern United States. Here, before the agricultural contact with Mexico, the Indians had domesticated the *pepo* species of pumpkins and squash, the sunflower, and a variety of plants for seeds (*Chenopodium, Amaranthus, Iva,* etc.). With an agricultural life already established, it is probable that corn spread rapidly. Considering the near-tropical summer of this part of the United States, the grain should have spread until it was slowed by aridity to the west and short season and cold, damp springs to the north. If corn was introduced from Mexico into the eastern United States before the Christian Era, then we can probably think of much of the Mississippi and Ohio river valleys and Atlantic coastal plain as growing corn not long after the beginning of the Christian Era. Our historical perspective then, although dim, has considerable depth.

Application to Settlement Problems

It should be clear that all this is closely related to economic geography and that much of this type of knowledge is of considerable economic value. One of the fields of active geographical participation is settlement and resettlement. This involves regional planning. In regional planning one is often confronted with such agricultural problems as the finding of suitable feed and food crops. A knowledge of economic plant geography may make a choice possible; for example, we have just seen that there is a wide range of preadapted corn available for growth in almost any part of the world.

Some random notes on the possible extension of corn growing illustrate this point. Andean corn, for instance, might be successful in Tibet, Iran, and Afghanistan; Gila-Colorado corn, of exceedingly quick growth and great heat resistance, might prove useful in such areas as northern Australia, parts of India, Iraq, Egypt, and Africa; Dakota corn might be useful in northern Europe or in North China and Manchuria.

We cannot assume that because we know these crops exist and are so adapted they are actually in use elsewhere. Andean corn, Gila-Colorado corn, Mandan corn, and the others are probably unknown outside America. European corn is basically Caribbean corn, and this is of course a historical accident. European corn yields might well be greatly improved by careful geographical selection of American types best suited to European climates—the Russian plant geographers, for example, by surveying the entire world for useful plants have virtually revolutionized Russian agriculture.

Corn requires a relatively warm and long season, but in both the Dakotas and in New England adaptations are available that might permit corn growing far north of its present limits in Europe and Asia. Even Southeast Asia, a nearly ideal corn climate, seems to have an irrational, historically conditioned corn assemblage. Asiatic corn appears at least in part to be a relatively primitive type. There are almost surely available better corn types in yield, food and feed quality, and temperature and moisture adaptation. Particularly is this true in view of the limited variety of maize that was introduced into Asia, where it is now being grown under a great variety of conditions. Yet in America almost every Asiatic climatic condition can be duplicated and a corn type found that has been adapted to that condition for thousands of years.

One of the principal lessons, then, which the economic plant geographer has learned is that the world's agriculture is largely historical and nonrational. If this is true of the plants that went from America to the Old World, it must be true also of plants that came from the Old World to America. We should be extremely wary of assuming that agricultural plants are being grown in the climates best suited to them, or that the plants found in a region are the most suitable for that region.

Similarly we must be wary of assuming climatic barriers where crop frontiers exist. In the Southwest the crop division between the Gila-Colorado Valleys and the Colorado plateau is extremely sharp. This is also a major physiographic and climatic division. One might be tempted to assume that the crops are different primarily because of differences in climate. This, however, is only a half-truth. If the problem is approached historically, it is found that the agricultures differ because their sources differ: Gila-Colorado crops are west Mexican; Pueblo crops are from the eastern United States. Experiment shows that Gila-Colorado corn, beans, cotton, and squash can be readily and advantageously grown on the Colorado plateau. It is true that the plateau crops do not succeed in the lowland, but the complete separation of crop types cannot be said to be climatic when the lowland crops can be advantageously grown on the plateau.

Danger of Plant Standardization

There is another economic matter of which the historical plant geographer has become well aware. That is the present tendency to destroy useful plants. The trend is toward standardization of domestic plants. Wherever possible we in the United States tend to grow yellow dent corn. But there is inherent danger in "putting all our eggs in one basket."

Formerly, one family had an earlier bean, another a more drought-resistant corn, another a sweeter or fleshier pumpkin. Even though these differed but slightly in color or shape from the normal, they were cherished for their special qualities. We tend today to eliminate all variants. In our demand for a standardized product we are reversing the age-old tendency on which much of present agronomic success is built. It must not be forgotten that most frequently, when we seek new genetic material to meet an agricultural need, we turn to this broad genetic base of the primitive farmer. But we are discouraging the maintenance of these old crops. In the United States we have literally decimated the old Indian crops. Those who have worked with the Southwestern Indians and have listened to the old men telling how they used to have ten or twelve varieties of beans, now extinct because of the necessity of growing commercial, salable varieties, appreciate the magnitude of the loss.

When we have standardized the crops of Latin America, where shall we then turn for new, desperately needed corn, bean, and squash varieties? Consider the case of the lima-bean industry of California. This million-dollar industry had been virtually wiped out when a chance collection of Hopi lima beans reached the hands of an agronomist who discovered that this strain was resistant to the disease that was destroying the crop. By breeding, the resistance was transferred to the commercial strain. Had the Hopi lima already gone the way of the many other Southwestern beans, there would have been no way of saving this important crop. This is only one instance.

Bean root rot was similarly checked and when we needed an arid-land cotton, we got it from the primitive people of Mexico. But in the process of standardizing our agriculture we are destroying innumerable useful plants of great potential value. We are selling off the distributed securities we inherited from the past and concentrating all our wealth in one investment. This is economic, agronomic, and geographic folly.

The processes of standardization and extinction that are now in motion are probably going to continue. As our commercialized culture spreads, we shall have less and less material available for preservation. It seems imperative that we now undertake the task of collecting the useful plants of the world and studying them to determine their values. Even this will not suffice, however, for the scrawniest runt of a plant may possess the hidden virtue of resistance to a disease now of no consequence but potentially virulent enough to threaten the extinction of some useful plant. Such plagues are by no means uncommon; witness the great potato blight, or the phylloxera that struck the grape industry. We cannot foresee which of the plant diseases may become virulent, but we may be sure that some of them will. Moreover, the standardization of a few varieties of some useful plant, which then are grown in large continuous acreages, creates the perfect breeding ground for virulent outbreaks.

Now that we have shifted from subsistence to cash farming, we cannot expect the individual farmer to maintain strains without market value; yet we must for our own salvation see that innumerable strains are kept alive. The solution seems to lie in maintenance of "plant banks" or "libraries" where the plants or their seeds will be kept viable indefinitely. Our agricultural experiment stations are the most logical places.

If each experiment station were to keep going a number of strains of not immediately useful plants by planting the seed every few years to ensure a continued supply of viable seed, we should be taking an important step toward protecting our most valuable heritage from our agricultural ancestors. Eventually this should be a world-wide undertaking; for the good of the peoples of the whole world is at stake.

Regions and Complexes of Useful Plants

I have drawn most of my illustrations from maize and have attempted to show the use of plant geography in regional, historical, and economic geography. It should be noted, however, that similar single plant regions can be described for the other 50 to 75 American domesticated plants; that important plant geographical problems are not confined to domestic plants; and that outside America the same techniques can be applied to still other wide groups of plants.

Within the Americas I wish to point out another regional distribution. The cucurbits (the American squashes and pumpkins) were regionally distributed primarily as follows: *Cucurbita maxima* in South America; *C. moschata* in Middle America (Central America, southern Mexico, and northern South America); and *C. pepo* in North America. These distributions are related to many other phenomena. Thus the localization of *pepo* in North America, with its center of greatest variation in the United States, is related to its domestication here. Similarly, *moschata* seems to have been domesticated in Middle America and to be associated with the large group of Middle American plant domesticates. *Maxima* is apparently a South American domesticate and seems to be related to the domestication of corn, manioc, peanuts, and so on.

It is obvious, then, that there are complexes of domestic plants centering in various regions. There were in America several great centers of domestication, each with its complex of useful plants. To a little-recognized degree these complexes still survive and remain economically important. Thus in the United States we had, and in part still have, the following crop regions: The Northeast, with common beans (*Phaseolus vulgaris*), yellow field pumpkin and various summer squashes (*Cucurbita pepo*), sunflower (*Helianthus*), and specialized tropical flint corns. All but the corn are local domesticates with antiquity in the United States of more than five thousand years. To this assemblage there are added in the Southeast dent corn, the cushaw pumpkin (*Cucurbita moschata*), and the Sieva type of lima bean. In the Southwest the Pueblo area is now a hodgepodge of all types of beans and corn and squash. This reflects its rather wide range of edaphic conditions and the survival of the original complex of plants under the recent overlay of commercial varieties. The Gila-Colorado area, however, remains distinct in its possession of tepary beans (*Phaseolus acutifolius*) and its highly adapted corn. Until fifty years ago it was also characterized by a unique and valuable species of cotton and a unique pumpkin.

The Middle and South American agricultural regions are equally distinctive, much more complex, and much better preserved. The agricultural complex of highland Peru survives virtually intact. It is characterized by local races of corn, beans, and squash, which are agriculturally recent but chronologically ancient additions to the underlying and still important complex composed of potato (*Solanum* spp.), ullucu, nasturtium, lupine, quinoa, and others. In Mexico, in Colombia, in the Caribbean, and in Brazil there are similar important survivals of the pre-Columbian agriculture.

In summarizing all this the following facts emerge. Historically, plant distributional studies have long been associated with geography. Plant geography, and especially economic plant geography, is based on field study, with observations of soil, slope, climate, and culture supplying the necessary data for meaningful distributional studies. Few are as well prepared to make such studies as the geographer, especially the geographer who is thoroughly grounded in systematic geography. As a field, plant geography is as valid a study as any other systematic branch of geography. Plant geography in its broadest sense, not only in its domestic-plant aspects, is vital to a comprehensive regional approach and is especially important to regional planning. The historical approach to economic plant geography gives not only greater depth to our understanding of the problems involved but helps us judge the validity of apparent environmental limitations. Finally, from an over-all view of the past and present trends in economic plant geography it becomes clear that we are in danger of suffering a tragic loss through the continuing and accelerating destruction of useful plants.

29. *The Natural Vegetation of the Great Plains Regions* *

The natural vegetation of a given region depends on a number of physical factors, of which climate and soil are the most important. Tree growth is generally found in humid areas where subsurface moisture is constantly available. Natural grasslands dominate drier sections where a distinctly seasonal precipitation occurs or where only surface moisture is available during the growing season. The Great Plains area is one of the largest, most interesting, and most significant of the world's grasslands. Shantz describes this natural grassland and brings out the very close correlation between climate and soil differences and the resulting plant-community variations within that area. A study of vegetation, such as this, emphasizes the interrelation of aspects of the physical environment.

* Reprinted from H. L. Shantz, "The Natural Vegetation of the Great Plains Regions," *Annals of the Association of American Geographers,* Vol. 13, 1923, pp. 81–107. By permission.

The author (1876) is an Annuitant Collaborator, Department of Agriculture. Dr. Shantz has served as Head of the Botany Department, University of Illinois; President of University of Arizona; and Chief of Division of Wildlife Management, United States Forest Service. He has done a great deal of work on the plains of the United States and Canada, South America and Africa; his primary interest is plant geography and its relation to agriculture. He has contributed many articles, dealing chiefly with wildlife management, plant physiology, and natural vegetation, to journals and publications of the United States Government.

The Region Here Considered

The region considered in this paper (Fig. 8) lies between the Rocky Mountains on the west and the 97th degree of west longitude on the east. On the north it extends to the Canadian boundary and on the south to near the Mexican boundary. The line marking the eastern boundary of this region starts at the 98th degree of west longitude on the Canadian boundary and extends south along the western edge of the Red River valley. From a point west of Fargo, N. Dak. it leaves the Red River Valley and runs south and a little east until it reaches the 97th degree of west longitude in east central Nebraska. It then bends a little to the west and crosses the Oklahoma-Texas boundary at the 98th degree of west longitude. This line swings westward as far as the 99th degree of west longitude in Callahan and McCulloch counties, Texas, and then southeast, reaching the Gulf coast at about the 97th degree of west longitude. The western boundary follows the east side of the Rocky Mountains to the Montana-Wyoming boundary where it turns east to the eastern side of the Big Horn Mountains, extending south to the lower end of the Sangre de Cristo range where it turns west to the Manzano range, and east past the Sacramento, Guadalupe and Santiago mountains, thence east and later north to Fort Stockton, Texas. The western boundary line then runs north and west to the Texas-New Mexico line which it crosses about 50 miles west of the Pecos River. It then runs north to Roswell, New Mexico, where it swings across the Pecos, down the east side and crosses the New Mexico-Texas state boundary 50 miles east of the Pecos River. The boundary line runs parallel to the Pecos at a distance of about 50 miles east of the river except for a short distance where it touches the Pecos River in Ward and Crane counties in Texas. It then runs parallel to the Rio Grande River for a distance of 50 miles northeast. The boundary line strikes the Rio Grande 60 miles above its mouth.

Correlation of Vegetation with Climatic and Soil Conditions

Before discussing in detail the plant communities, it is necessary first to present a number of general considerations. The correlation between any single climatic or soil factor and the natural vegetation is often profoundly affected by change in the other factors. Similar distinct differences in the type of vegetation may be caused by any one of a number of factors. In correlating vegetation with conditions of soil or climate this consideration should be kept constantly in mind. When all other factors remain unchanged a close correlation can be made with the changes in any one factor of the environment. A change in either the rainfall, the soil texture, the soil depth, the available soil moisture, or the saturation deficit of the air, will be accompanied by a change in vegetation, if the other factors remain constant. If other factors vary, marked changes in one factor may produce no noticeable effect on the vegetation. The gradual decrease in the quantity of rainfall from east to west may be correlated with a gradual change in the natural vegetation. The greater quantity of rainfall in the south, as compared with the north, may produce no change in type of vegetation. This may be explained by the increase in evaporation and water requirement of the plants in the south as compared with those in the north. Differences in the depth of moist soil or in the available soil moisture may be closely correlated with changes in vegetation, provided the factors which control rate of loss of water do not vary in such a way as to equalize these conditions.

In dealing with plants we are equally concerned with the factors which determine the rate of loss of moisture from the plant and with the total available soil moisture supply. The quantity of rainfall is greater in the southern than in the northern portion of the Great Plains and a deeper layer of soil with moisture available for plant growth is produced. But this increase in moisture supply in the southern part is equalized by the higher water requirement. To produce a ton of dry matter, alfalfa required 518 tons of water at Williston, N. Dak., 630 tons at Newell, S. Dak., 853 tons at Akron, Colo., and 1005 tons at Dalhart, Tex. Field studies of the rate of use of water by a crop of spring wheat show the rate to be twice as great in the south as in the north.

A factor of importance for plant growth is the length of the drought period. This is normally long in the south and short in the north. The rapid-growing grasses utilize the short growing period in increasing the vegetative part of the plant and producing seed. These grasses are drought-enduring and thus pass through the long drought-rest period without injury. The habitat factors measured throughout the year do not properly express the condition under which the vegetation develops. Evaporation, for example, is greater during the periods of extreme drought, when the water loss from the plant cover is almost negligible, because there is no water present for it to use. When plants are well supplied with moisture and rapidly transpiring the evaporation is likely to be relatively low. The evaporation measurement expresses potential loss of water. In any given area on the High Plains the evaporation measurement for different periods of the frost-free season is probably more nearly inversely correlated than directly correlated with the actual water loss from the area.

If soils of similar texture are considered, the depth of the layer of periodically moistened soil is an indirect measure of the amount of available soil moisture. Throughout this region the subsoil is permanently dry to

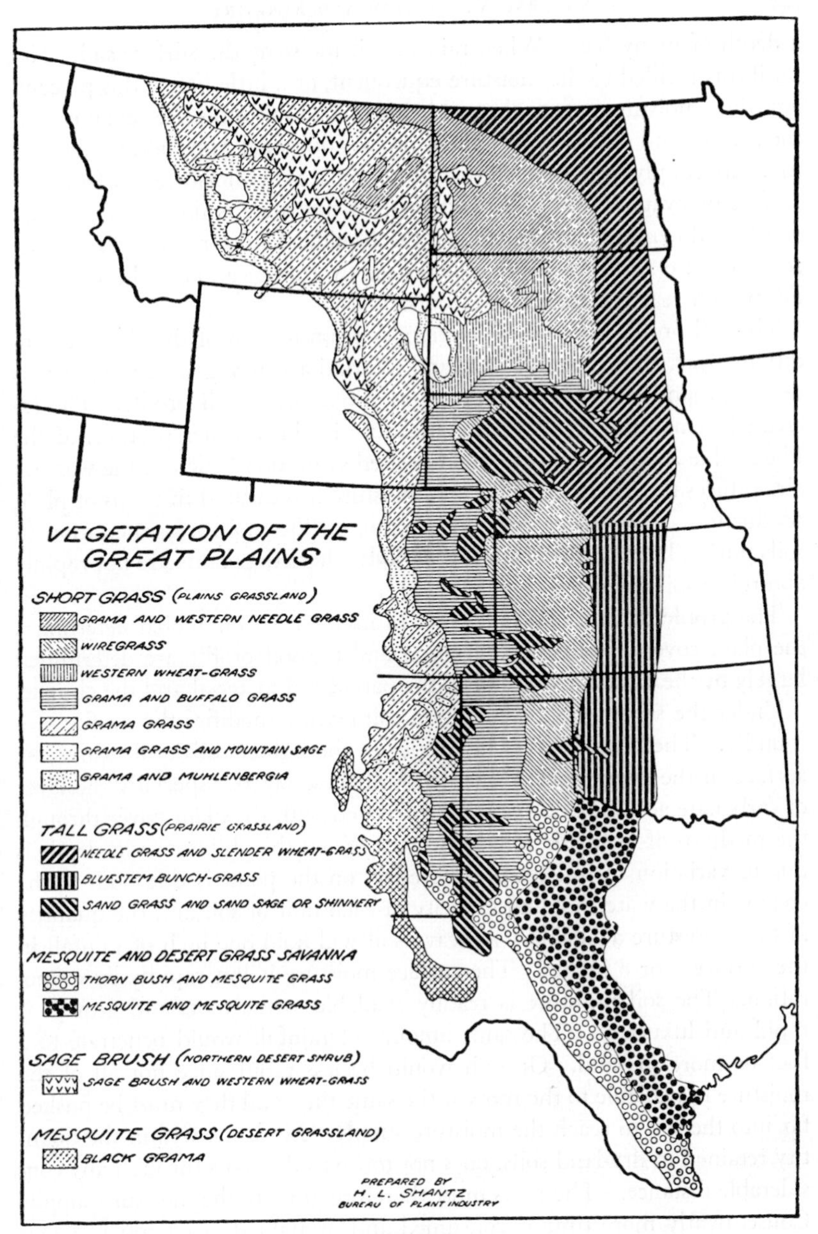

FIGURE 8

Sketch Map of the Great Plains Region Showing the Areas Occupied by the Principal Plant-Communities. In determining the boundary lines in the northwest the writer has been assisted by A. E. Aldous, U. S. Geological Survey, and in the location of the sandhill areas of the south, by C. F. Marbut, U. S. Soil Survey.

a depth of many feet. When rain falls it moistens the surface soil. Not until this is filled to the moisture equivalent, or a little below this percentage, does moisture pass to the soil below. The soil moisture remains near the surface and does not pass down unless additional rains add to the total moisture supply. It is not drawn up to replace the moisture lost from the surface by evaporation. The surface dries but there is no appreciable upward or downward movement of the liquid. Plants rapidly absorb the soil moisture and pass it off into the air by transpiration if the moisture lies within reach of their active roots.

The soil profile, like the vegetation, is a summation of the climatic conditions over a long period of years. Variations in vegetation are not as nearly proportional to total rainfall as variations in soil profile. The increased demand of the plant for moisture in the warmer portions of the Plains, due at least in part to the increased saturation deficit of the warmer air, reduces the efficiency of the soil moisture if measured in terms of plant production. This effect does not operate on the moisture penetration in soils during heavy rains or during periods where the plants are not rapidly absorbing soil moisture.

The profile or depth of soil is not in itself the factor which determines the plant cover. Both the vegetation and the soil profile are determined largely by the same factors, chiefly the parent soil material and the climate.

Under the same climatic condition soil texture modifies the profile profoundly. The profile layers lie deeper in the lighter soils and nearer the surface in the heavy soils. The depth of these layers, especially the layer of carbonate accumulation, can be correlated with the plant cover through the medium of available soil moisture. When this difference in depth is due to variation in soil texture the effect on the plant is due both to the change in the water-holding capacity of each unit of soil and the quantity of total moisture available. A heavy soil will hold one inch of rainfall in the surface 6 or 8 inches. The surface moisture is lost rapidly by evaporation. The soil moisture is readily available to the roots and growth is rapid and luxuriant. The same amount of rainfall would penetrate to a foot or more in sand. Growth would be less rapid since not all of the moisture is available to the roots at the same time and they must be pushed far into the soil to reach the moisture supply. Moisture, within the quantity retained in dry-land soils, does not move to the roots through any considerable distance. The roots must therefore grow to the moisture supply. Consequently more time is consumed and drought delayed much longer in sand than in heavy land. This is true of the cultivated as well as the native crops.

Vegetation has an important reaction on soil profile. In eastern Colorado the layer of carbonate accumulation develops at 14 to 18 inches under a short-grass vegetation. Had there been no vegetation to absorb the soil moisture the layer of carbonate accumulation would never have developed. When the vegetation is destroyed by cultivation the depth of moisture penetration is greatly increased, even if the land is continuously cropped. Alternate cropping greatly increases the penetration of soil moisture and crop plants normally grow in a soil which is moist below the layer of carbonate accumulation. Theoretically the layer of carbonate accumulation would be lowered under cultivation. The depth of soil to the layer of carbonate accumulation is a measure of the depth of moisture penetration under the natural vegetation during all but exceptional years. The soil profile affords, therefore, an indirect measure of the moisture condition during normal years. Unless other factors interfere vegetation and soil profiles can be closely correlated. This correlation is not perfect and the failure to correlate exactly affords an important means of interpreting the habitat.

In drawing general lines of plant distribution it is important that only mature soils of comparable texture be considered. Along the line between the tall grasses and the short grasses if the soil becomes light in texture, sand in other words, the eastern or tall-grass types will push west. A bluestem bunch-grass cover characteristic of a good loam soil in eastern Kansas will entirely disappear from the loam soils farther west and be confined entirely to the sands, on which it extends into the deserts of New Mexico. Where very heavy land occurs in central Kansas it is likely to be characterized by the short grasses, this vegetation type being carried eastward by a heavy soil. The vegetation types are, therefore, carried far out of their natural climatic range by a soil of either heavy or light texture. Bluestem bunch-grass which occupies the well-developed loams with a depth of about three feet will push west on crests where erosion is taking place and where moisture penetrates several feet into the soil. This penetration is due largely to the open spacing of the plants and the reduction in the rate of use of soil moisture. Bluestem bunch-grass is carried west beyond its range by flood water or by a sandy soil, since moisture penetration is relatively deep in both cases. This type occurs even in the blowouts of the heavy clay where clay granules blow about as sand. It is also characteristic of the pure gypsum sand dunes of New Mexico and occurs on eroded areas of caliche in the southern Great Plains. It is, therefore, not the depth of the layer free of carbonate accumulation which determines the growth of this species in central Kansas, but rather the depth of moist soil which is indicated in the well-developed soils by the depth to the layer of carbonate accumulation. On new or eroded soils carbonates may occur at the surface and the moisture condition still be favorable for the grass. Passing eastward from the high plains this type is soon shut out except on sand dunes or sandy land. Here it is evident that sand offers perfect drainage and consequently the best conditions for a relatively xerophytic grass. In the humid east the drainage is perfect in sand dunes, and bluestem bunch-grass succeeds well on sand in Illinois and Indiana, and on the Hempstead Plains of Long Island. Sand to some extent equalizes the habitat. In the arid country it furnishes the most favorable moisture condition, and in the more humid country the perfect drainage affords a favorable habitat for the xerophytic grasses. In short, the widest distribution from humid to dry habitat occurs on sand. Clay will often carry western types, especially short grasses, some distance east. The line of demarcation between the short-grass and the tall-grass vegetation must be swung east on heavy soils, and west on sands.

In making a generalized map of the plant associations it is necessary to recognize clearly the successional stages initiated by overgrazing or breaking. Before the vegetation can be successfully correlated with agricultural potentialities, successional and climax stages must be clearly recognized. Undeveloped sand dunes or areas of very young soils are characterized by a successional stage of vegetation. The sand hills on the Great Plains are constantly tending toward the normal short-grass type of the region. The soil profile enables one to discern clearly old and new soils. Climax types of vegetation occur only on older soils, those soils which have come into equilibrium with the climatic conditions. The soil profile affords a valuable means by which to determine whether the vegetation is a climax or merely a successional stage.

There are then two methods of evaluating the habitat, namely, by the proper interpretation of the vegetation and by the proper interpretation of the soil profile. The soil profile as an aid to the study of vegetation is now made available to the botanists in this country through the work of the Bureau of Soils and should greatly influence future study of vegetation.

From the considerations above it is clear that, in outlining on a generalized map, areas characterized by different types of vegetation, the occurrence of the type on mature soil, soil with a well-developed profile, should first be considered. These types of vegetation are climax types which have come into equilibrium with the soil and climatic conditions. Since a light soil or a heavy soil modifies the soil profile and the vegetation, it is well, if climatic climax vegetation areas are being outlined, to consider chiefly the vegetation which occurs on well-developed loam soils. Breaking destroys the vegetation and over-grazing often modifies it profoundly. It is therefore necessary to take these factors into consideration in deciding which type represents the original vegetation. These precautions are especially necessary in regions where most of the original vegetation has been destroyed. Failure to recognize the stages of succession would often lead to erroneous estimates of the importance of different communities.

The Plant Communities

The vegetation of the region here outlined is not uniform. Along the eastern edge in any portion north of the Canadian River the grasses are relatively tall and the area resembles a luxuriant meadow. Farther west the tall grasses disappear and the short grasses predominate. The short grasses resemble a well-grazed pasture. South of the Canadian River a scattered growth of trees over a relatively short-grass cover presents the appearance of an orchard of small fruit trees. In the southwest the grass cover may become sparse and the appearance is that of a desert grassland. In the northwest plants characteristic of the great desert push east on the poorer land and produce a vegetation consisting of scattered grasses and shrubs.

The region considered in this paper extends too far east and too far south to be regarded as a natural vegetational unit. It includes within its boundaries parts of the following plant formations and minor communities.

Short Grass (*Plains Grassland*).[a]—Grama grass (association), grama and buffalo grass (association), grama and western needle grass (association), wire-grass (association), western wheat-grass (association), grama grass and mountain sage (associes), grama and Muhlenbergia (associes).

Tall Grass (*Prairie Grassland*).[b]—Needle grass and slender wheat-grass (association), bluestem bunch-grass (association), sand grass and sand-sage (associes), shinnery (associes).

Mesquite and Desert-Grass Savanna (*Dessert Savanna*).[c]—Mesquite and mesquite grass (association), thorn bush and mesquite grass (associes).

Sagebrush (*Northern Desert Shrub*).[d]—Sagebrush and western wheat-grass (associes).

Mesquite Grass (*Desert Grassland*).[e]—Black grama (association).

Four criteria may be used in separating the formations, namely: physiognomy or general appearance, floristic composition, development of vegeta-

[a] A small portion of this grassland which pushes across the highlands of N. Mex., Ariz. and into Utah, is not included.

[b] Here are included only the two western associations and two developmental phases (associes) which push west on sandhills.

[c] The greater part of this community is included here, but it does not cover extensive areas in the United States.

[d] Only a few outstanding developmental areas of this type are included. These have pushed from the deserts into the Great Plains in Montana and Wyoming.

[e] Only part of one association located at the eastern edge of the formation is here included.

tion or succession within each area, and environmental conditions or the habitat.

. . . . .

Brief Generalization

In the area here considered the supply of rainfall is not sufficient to moisten the soil below the reach of the grass roots. No moisture is lost to the subsoil, and there is normally no storage of soil moisture from year to year. The subsoil is permanently dry. Over much of the area the soil is filled to its carrying capacity only to a depth of 1 to 4 feet below the surface. This soil moisture is absorbed and passed out into the air by transpiration before the first frosts in autumn. The growth period is therefore initiated by favorable temperature but terminated by drought.

The total quantity of water stored at the beginning of the season is equivalent to from 2 to 5 inches of rainfall. To this initial supply must be added the rainfall during the growing season. This may vary from 2 to 15 inches.

The moisture supply is greater in the south than in the north, but the water requirement of the plants is proportionately greater. For the growing plant the moisture conditions are therefore similar.

The needle-grass and slender-wheat-grass area is one of rich, deep, black soil moistened to a depth of 2 to 3½ feet at the beginning of the growth period. The water requirement of plants is lower than in any other area of the region considered. The area produces a good stand of relatively tall grasses valuable for forage and native hay. The land, under cultivation, has become the great spring-wheat area of the United States.

South of the needle-grass and slender-wheat-grass area the bluestem-bunch-grass association characterizes a soil moist from 2 to 4 feet. A good growth of tall grass is produced, valuable both for pasturage and native hay. This association characterizes the great winter-wheat area of the United States. This area is also productive of corn and alfalfa.

South of the bluestem-bunch-grass area, the mesquite and mesquite-grass area is one of alternating severe drought and good moisture supply. The area is not as favorable for plant growth as those just mentioned. Cotton is produced throughout the area and grain sorghums are grown chiefly in the north.

The groups of plant associations just considered represent land primarily valuable for crop production. Lying just west of this group of plant associations are the grama and western-needle-grass, the wiregrass, and the western-wheat-grass associations. Here crop failures are more likely to occur and agriculture rests both on crop production and grazing. Still farther west crops can only be produced during exceptionally good years, and the land is chiefly valuable for grazing.

On the basis of agricultural potentiality of the land the plant communities may be arranged as follows:

Land primarily valuable for crop production:

1. Needle grass and slender wheat-grass (spring wheat and other spring cereals)
2. Bluestem bunch-grass (winter wheat, corn, and alfalfa)
3. Mesquite and mesquite grass (cotton and grain sorghums)

Land valuable for crop production and grazing: (crop failures during years of less than normal rainfall):

4. Grama and western-needle-grass (spring wheat and other spring grains)
5. Wire-grass (winter wheat, corn, and grain sorghums in the south)
6. Wheat-grass (spring grains and corn)
7. Grama and mountain sage (spring grains)

Land valuable for grazing and crop production: (good crops only during years of more than normal rainfall):

8. Grama and buffalo-grass (grain sorghums, corn, and small grains)
9. Mesquite grass and thorn bush (cotton and grain sorghums during good years only)
10. Sand sage and sand grass (corn and sorghum except in the southwest)
11. Grama grass (spring grains during good years only)

Land valuable for grazing only:

12. Sagebrush and western wheat-grass
13. Black grama

Numbers 1, 2, 4 and 10 are best as hay land. As grazing land the numbers would run about as follows: 1, 2, 6, 4, 5, 10, 7, 8, 3, 11, 9, 13, 12.

---

30. *Forests and Human Progress* *

The 25 per cent of the earth that was originally covered by forest has played various significant roles in the history of man. "The primary stages of social development were reached in arid and tree-

* Raphael Zon, "Forests and Human Progress," from *Geographical Review*, Vol. 10, 1920, pp. 139–166; published by the American Geographical Society, New York.

The author (1874) was born in Simbirsk, Russia. He was educated in Russia, Brussels,

less climates" according to Zon who presents here an excellent discussion of the relation between forests and the progress of civilization. Only recently has man been able to conquer forests on a large scale—in some cases so completely that former forest areas are now the most densely populated portions of the world. The problem has developed, however, of maintaining forest resources adequate to fill man's many needs, and at the same time clearing sufficient land for crop cultivation to feed larger and larger numbers of people. Ruthless cutting has taken place in the areas where timber was the best "crop" for the poor soil or steep slope. Forest conservation was developed only after human domination of the forest became too complete.

Forests have had an important effect on the distribution of mankind over the earth's surface. They have deeply affected the spiritual and religious life of the tribes living within them or near by. They have been a source of raw material indispensable to the economic development of the human race. The relations between forests and man are manifold and varied throughout the course of human progress from the primitive stage to the present highly developed economic organization.

There may be recognized three stages in the relation of man to forests:

(1) Civilization dominated by forests.
(2) Civilization overcoming the forests.
(3) Civilization dominating forests.

Just as we had the stone age, the bronze age, and the iron age at the same time in different parts of the earth, so we have simultaneously the three stages of the relation of man to the forest. Thus in central Africa and South America man in his relation to the surrounding forest is in the first stage; in a considerable part of North America and in Asia he is in the second; and in Europe and in parts of the United States he is already in the third.

Civilization Dominated by Forests

If no attempt is made to go back into the mode of life of our simian ancestors, whose abode must have been the forest, and our survey is confined to the beginnings of civilization in Europe, Asia, and America, one fact stands out clearly; namely, that the forests in the early stages of human progress did not offer favorable conditions for the settlement of primitive

---

Belgium, and in the United States at Cornell University. He has served with the United States Forest Service, was director of the Lake States Forest Experiment Station, and has been a forestry professor at the Universities of Minnesota and Wisconsin. From 1905 to 1928 he was editor of the *Journal of Forestry*. His research interests include light in relation to forest trees, forest meteorology, forests and stream flow, and forest resources of the world.

man; on the contrary, they were always an element inimical to the spread of mankind over the earth.

The first and most striking evidence that this is so is the fact that only few traces of prehistoric man are found in densely forested regions. The chief memorials of Neolithic man in Britain, for instance, are found on the moorlands which in these ancient times appeared as islands of open habitable land above the vast stretches of swamp and forests. A study of the occurrence of human settlement from the earliest Stone Age tells the same story, namely, that the cradle of human civilization was not a primeval forest.

The first great nuclei of population, the seats of the earliest recorded civilizations both in the Old and in the New World, originated in arid regions, at best only scantily covered with forest. In the Old World the Egyptian, Babylonian, Assyrian, and Phoenician civilizations arose in hot and dry regions in climate not unlike southern Arizona and New Mexico. Within the "rainless belt" extending across North Africa, Arabia, Persia, and on through Tibet into Mongolia, or from the borders of it, have come all the conquering races of the Old World.

Similarly in the New World the nations which developed a high degree of civilization were those in the arid regions of Mexico and Peru—the Aztecs and the Incas.*

Primeval Forests an Obstacle to Human Migration and Colonization

Forests have acted as barriers to human colonization in all parts of the world. In the Alleghanies as well as in tropical West Africa the forest for many decades delayed the penetration of the white man into the interior of the continent. It took the American colonists about 200 years to reach the crest of the Appalachians. It prevented the spread of the Hamites from North Africa southward and stopped the movement into the Congo region of the cattle-keeping aristocracies such as the Bahima which had a social, political, and military organization superior to other tribes. In the heart of the Congo forest no traces of an ancient population have been found. All the evidence points to the comparatively recent penetration of man. The expansion of the Inca Empire from the high plateaus of Peru and Bolivia eastward was limited by the impenetrable forests of the headwaters of the Amazon River. Attempts to penetrate

* Remains of the Maya civilization are now found in the dense tropical forest. Huntington however suggests that this civilization arose and flourished during a time of drier climate. The succeeding moister period favored the growth of that type of heavy forest so inimical to human progress. Ellsworth Huntington: The Climatic Factor as Illustrated in Arid America, *Carnegie Instn. Publ. No. 192,* Washington, D.C., 1914.

down the eastern valleys brought feeble results. In contrast is the southward expansion of the Empire—to or beyond the river Maule—by roads where neither the frigid heights of the Cordillera nor the inhospitable desert proved so formidable as the barrier of the forest. The history of the Spanish conquest is similar: the forest continued to mark the boundary of effective control. Indeed much the same is true today.

The Ancient European Forests

The Romans, the greatest colonizers of olden times, were forced to stop in their expansion and Empire building at the boundaries of the dense, virgin German forests whose inhospitable and somber nature was pictured in dark colors by such ancient writers as Tacitus, Pomponius Mella, and Marcellinus, who spoke of the forests as of something horrid and inaccessible and unsuited for human habitation. The more recent European historians, such as Gradmann for instance, consider the boundary of the Roman Empire as coinciding with the western boundary of the coniferous forests of southern Germany. The strategic genius of the old Romans clearly perceived that it was not the German mountains themselves, which were only moderate in height, that formed the bulwark of the ancient Teutonic freedom but the vast primeval forests with which they were clothed. In their writings they referred to the *saltus* (break or forest) and not to the Montes Germaniæ.

Just as the Romans were compelled to stop in their colonizing activities at the boundary of the virgin forests of central Europe, so the successive later waves of the nomadic tribes which moved from the eastern prairies westward—Huns, Magyars, Avars, and the like—broke up when they reached the barrier of primeval forests. The routes of migration in western and central Europe were largely determined by the openings in the primeval forests.

The difficulty with which primeval forests could be penetrated made them always an obstacle to all great historic migrations of man. On the grasslands pack animals could be used, and here the wheeled cart originated. In the primeval forest where a path must be hacked out with the aid of ax and knife man must be his own burden bearer. Three or four miles a day is the average rate of travel in such forests. Not infrequently man depends here on the animal trails. Mammoth and rhinoceros in the ages past were the first trail builders in the forests of central Europe, just as the elephants are breaking trails now in the African and eastern Asiatic forests to be later followed by man. The bear trails served as roads for the Teutons in the primeval forests of Europe, just as they are now doing in the forests of Kamchatka and Siberia for the hunters of fur animals. In North America, as Humboldt remarks, the "bison pointed out to man the best roads through the Cumberland Mountains." In medieval Europe the wild cattle broke the first trails in the forest, just as in our own western forests the cattle trails were the first which many of us traveled.

Forests of the North

In the northern forests the main obstacles to the movement of man are vast swamps and muskegs. In winter the snow cover usually improves the facilities for movement. Light sleds, skis, and snowshoes are then the chief means of travel. In summer, however, this advantage of the northern forest over the tropical one is lost, and it is necessary to use the rivers for roads. Where these rivers are often interrupted by rapids or falls, light transportable canoes had to be used, as they are still being used by the North American Indians. Such means of transportation, although they are of great help, are not, of course, sufficient or adequate for easy communication. For this reason all world trade routes have always kept away from virgin forest regions. Not a single transcontinental railroad has yet been cut through the forest region of the Amazon or Congo, and such railroads as the Trans-Siberian and the Canadian Pacific skirt only the southern boundaries of the virgin boreal forests.

Middendorff in his travel through eastern Siberia was surprised at the scarcity of wild game, which became abundant only toward the steppes and in the vicinity of human habitation. In his travel through the forests he found an insurmountable obstacle in the vast swamps. In winter when they are frozen over it is possible for men to enter the forest and cut wood, but it is out of the question to establish a permanent dwelling on the unstable ground. The swamp forests, therefore, are not inhabited. Even where the soil is not swampy the foot sinks deep in decaying vegetation, while fallen, dead, or diseased trees lie athwart the dense upright trunks and thus impede movement. Darwin, in his ascent of Mt. Tarn in Tierra del Fuego, encountered difficulties of a similar character.

The records left by ancient writers regarding the primeval forests of central Europe agree with descriptions given by modern travelers of the forests of the north which still remain intact. Pliny presents a picture of the primeval forests of central Europe which is not unlike that given by Middendorff of the primeval forests of eastern and western Siberia. He speaks of gigantic trunks capable of holding up thirty men in the water, of oak roots lifted like arches or forming mounds of earth, and of great islands of wood floating on the rivers; just as the rivers of Siberia today are cumbered with trunks of trees uprooted and accumulated in huge natural rafts, so that to travel even by water is difficult.

Dense, extensive forests are perhaps the most formidable of natural barriers. Areas which otherwise would be easy of access, become unfriendly and inaccessible when covered with high and dense forest vegetation. Mountain slopes which if cleared would be accessible are inaccessible when covered with a dense forest. As Arrigo Lorenzi has pointed out, even the low and twisted forest vegetation characteristic of the dolomite region of the eastern Alps—and that of the San Bernardino Mountains of southern California might also be instanced—presents a serious obstacle to travel.

The Sparse Population of the Forest

Comparison of a map showing the density of population or settlement with one showing the distribution of the principal natural types of vegetation, such as desert, forest, grassland, shows at a glance that the most scattering population is found in the deserts and in the large stretches of primeval forest. This holds true of the northern forests of the temperate region and the tropical forests of the Amazon and of northern Australia, where the density of population is less than one per square mile, as well as of the Congo forest and the primeval forests of southeastern Asia, where the density of population is also very low. This belt of sparse population is clearly distinguished from adjoining prairie or otherwise treeless regions, where the density is considerably greater. Similar maps, only on a larger scale, for individual countries show that the timbered belt in the mountains has a thin population while the valleys below are densely populated. Even the alpine meadows above the timber line may have a denser though temporary population. In the timbered belt are found only a few huts of hunters and wood-choppers.

A primeval forest at the lower stages of human civilization is of little importance as a source of trade. The local demand for wood material is fully supplied from the fringes of the forest region. The export of large quantities of wood is out of the question because demand and means of transportation are lacking. There remains only hunting and grazing. It is true that throughout the Middle Ages hunting and pasturing of swine in the forest were not insignificant sources of revenue to many a king. This, however, was also possible only on the outskirts since the interior of the dense and dark primeval forests is unfavorable even for wild animals. Every one who has traveled through the virgin Douglas fir forest of Puget Sound has been impressed by the lack of animal and bird life. An occasional squirrel or chipmunk is about all that one is likely to see for days. The primeval forests of Asiatic Russia, the so-called Siberian *taiga,* and the tropical *selvas* of South America support very few wild animals. This is less true of temperate broad-leaved forests where abundant mast of beech and oak furnish food for animals and often for men. Such poverty and inaccessibility of the virgin tropical and northern coniferous forests make them almost entirely unsuited to human settlement. In the early colonial history of America the virgin forest was in true sense of the word "No Man's Land."

. . . . .

Civilization Overcoming the Forest

So much for the influence of the forest upon man. This influence was greatest when mankind was at comparatively low stages of civilization. At a certain stage there begins a reverse influence, namely, that of man upon forests.

Primitive man, possessing crude stone implements only, found but few parts of the earth's surface which were neither too barren nor too heavily forested to be suitable for his habitation. It is true that in recent times societies have to the greatest extent developed, both in size and complexity, in temperate forested regions. This, however, is not inconsistent with the fact that the first large human societies arose, and the primary stages of social development were reached, in arid and treeless climates. The earlier phases of progress had to be passed through where the resistances offered by natural conditions were least; only when the arts of life had been advanced did it become possible for societies to develop in regions where the resistance was greater; and it was only further development in the arts of life, with the further discipline in co-operation accompanying them, that enabled subsequent societies to take root and grow in regions where climatic and other conditions offered relatively great difficulties. At first man is the slave of his environment and only later becomes to a certain extent its master.

First Steps in Destruction of the Forest

The primitive nations could not change to any marked degree the forest cover of the earth. Their tools were too crude, and, moreover, their activity was rarely concentrated at the same place for any length of time because their mode of life was largely nomadic. The primitive agricultural system, kaingin making, of the Philippines could never have brought about the destruction of the forests, since the cultivators' efforts were never centered long enough at one place. For this reason the effective influence of man upon the forest in the early days was confined to localities where it existed under very adverse conditions of climate or soil, as for instance on sand dunes, on the edge of the prairie or desert, or at its upper or northern limit. The Batusi and other peoples have encroached on the northeastern edge of the great central African forest. Today Ruanda is practically deforested. The remnants of the ancient forests that remain on the hill tops are regarded as sacred by the natives. In Europe we find that man early succeeded in crowding out the forest in the Mediterranean region, where at best it had a hard struggle to maintain itself. This operation can be traced back even to classical antiquity.

The dense forests of central Europe did not give way before the efforts of the Romans or the ancient Teutons. Only in the Middle Ages, beginning with the era of Charlemagne, when there arose an imperative need for more room, did the Teutons succeed in clearing any large areas of the dense forests. This clearing was not the work of individuals but was the result of many concentrated and persistent efforts on the part of the religious and knightly orders.

Extent and Character of the Process of Clearing

Some idea of the extent and character of this process may be gleaned from a study of the geographic names of different settlements. There are in Germany alone not less than 6,905 names of places which indicate their origin in forest regions. An analysis of such names reveals also the part which different nationalities have taken in the colonization of forest regions and shows whether settlement took place on open land or on cleared forest land. In Bohemia, for instance, just as in the northern German lowlands, all areas poorly stocked with timber from time immemorial were occupied first by Slavonic nations, which had come to these lands long before the arrival there of the Teutons. The latter, therefore, were forced, as latecomers, to provide for themselves places of habitation amid the dense primeval forest by cutting it off, burning, and clearing the land for fields. In the same way the Romans in colonizing the Alps occupied the open places and left untouched the forested regions of southeastern Austria, which for a long time waited for colonists to come there from Franconia and Thuringia to turn them into fields and orchards. The same story has been repeated in the last century in southern Brazil. The creoles and negroes took possession largely of the prairie sections, leaving the forests to the nomadic South American Indians. The present settlement of the forest regions began only after the arrival there of European colonists who, not finding any more open land, began to clear the forest for settlement; and now some of the originally forested land is more densely populated than the open prairie.

Along the Atlantic shore of Central America the forests began to be cleared for human settlement only after the arrival there of negroes; and on the Island of Formosa clearing took place only through colonization by the Chinese, who, after having cleared the western part of the island, took possession of the entire island and crowded the original population to the eastern part of it.

The earliest settlements in the forest were comparatively small. In

Germany the extensive clearings are of a later date than the barbarian invasions, and only the areas which were by nature more or less clear of forest were inhabited in antiquity. Likewise in independent Gaul, especially north of the Loire, cleared and inhabited lands were like small islands encircled by vast forests. A striking example of the island-like character of clearings in the forest may be seen today to the south and southeast of Munich. Such small settlements, when made by a people of comparatively high civilization carrying on agriculture according to improved methods, may last a long time if the extent of the forest territory is very great in comparison with the population. Cultivation on a large scale involving the clearing and agricultural development of enormous areas of land was made possible only in modern times when man became armed with powerful machinery for removing trees and stumps.

The Forest as a Supplementary Source of Food

In the earlier settlements the surrounding forests served as a supplementary source of food for the primitive agriculturist. The cultivation of small parcels of cleared land was supplemented by grazing of stock in the oak or other adjoining forest. The forest also furnished acorns as food for animals and even men, while the wild animals provided meat and hides. During the period of such early agricultural settlements the forest was often protected from destruction because of its value as a hunting ground and as a source of food. There are many evidences of the economic importance of wild edible fruits in the forest in the early settlements of primitive man. In the prehistoric settlements the remains of beech mast have sometimes been found in heaps. Poets and writers of antiquity have preserved the record of the epoch in which the inhabitants of the country surrounding the Mediterranean were fed on acorns and other fruits of the forest. Aside from the Arcadians, called by other Greeks "the acorn eaters," and the statements of Pliny about bread made of acorns, there are many historic evidences of the importance of the acorn in the early economic life of Europe and at a later period. Even today the acorns of various species of oak are an article of food in all the Mediterranean countries. Cultivation of land within the forest, coupled with the gathering of wild fruits, is still going on in many parts of the world, as for instance among the peasants of Siberia and the Indians of North America.

As the gathering of wild plants is displaced gradually in the course of economic evolution by the regular production of cultivated crops, stock raising supersedes the hunting of game. As an intermediate stage from hunting to stock raising there is often domestication of animals, as for instance, the breeding of foxes, in a state of semi-domestication, in certain islands of the Bering Sea and in Newfoundland; or the raising of bees in the forest of the Ural Mountains, which is a step in advance of the gathering of wild honey as carried on, for example, by the Veddas but is not rational apiculture with food supplied by properly selected and cultivated crops. In the primitive horticulture of the primeval forest it is customary to cut down the trees in the portion of the forest destined for cultivation, then to burn all the wood or at least the branches and underbrush. The ashes serve as fertilizer; the ground is broken, and the seed, shoots, or tubers are planted. To remove the roots of the trees would be too difficult a task for primitive implements, hence the fields are very imperfect. The peasants of eastern Russia, as well as some agricultural colonists in South America, burn the forest and cultivate the ground for some years, merely to abandon it and repeat the same process every ten or fifteen years. Periodical change of the soil is necessitated by the lack of fertilizer and proper working. It corresponds to the rotation of crops in scientific farming. When one clearing is abandoned, another is opened, and, since the products cannot be abundant owing to inadequate preparation of the soil, the cleared areas are large compared to the small number of people to be supported by them. But such areas are in no sense comparable to those under intensive cultivation. They have the character of oases scattered through the unexplored forest and are exposed to its perils. Wild animals, for instance, may destroy in a few hours the fruits of prolonged toil. The size of the clearing may also depend on the need of the crops for light and space.

Exploitation of Forests the Chief Cause of Their Disappearance

Extensive as this form of agriculture may be, it in itself would not be sufficient to have reduced the forested area of the world to its present size. It is the increased need for the products of the forest itself, particularly its timber, that has made the heaviest inroads upon it. Next to food, wood has been one of the most important factors of civilization, particularly at the time when iron, brick, and other structural materials were either unknown or little used.

In the early stages of economic development, the forests furnished man with fuel for overcoming the rigors of winter cold. It furnished fuel also for metal working, and a number of secondary products such as charcoal, pitch, ashes, gallnuts, some of which were more widely used in the past than they are now. In places where intense cold causes a heavy growth of fur on the wild animals, man has made use of materials produced in the forest for tanning the hides, thus providing himself with clothing and with covering for his primitive tents. At a higher stage of civilization and with the development of means of communication and transportation the products of the forest are no longer merely the means with which to satisfy immediate needs; they become commodities of widespread use far beyond the forest boundary. Many industries which were dependent upon wood as fuel found their location in the forest. Thus the occurrence in the same areas of forests and mineral deposits gave rise to metallurgy and the art of glassmaking. In France about the fifteenth century, before the invention of high ovens, metallurgists and glassmakers took up their abode in the forest. In the Middle Ages an entire forest population employed exclusively in industries growing out of the use of wood lived in the forests of France. Kilns, charcoal furnaces, forges, glass furnaces, limekilns, and establishments where wood was worked up gave a peculiar aspect to the forests of that time.

Pallas describes the metallurgic industries connected with the forests of Russia in the Ural Mountains from which the necessary charcoal was obtained. In the forests of Russia also the coexistence of fur-bearing animals and plants producing tanning material has given rise to village industries, chiefly tanning. The forests of the eastern United States were once extensively used for charcoal making in connection with the iron industry.

Rivers as an Aid in Exploitation of the Forests

The penetration of the forests and the development of forest industries have been greatly favored by rivers. Watercourses penetrating forest regions are the natural means of access and with their banks constitute the first zone of attack on the phalanx of the forest. This was the case in Europe; the Rhine and its tributaries formed the principal routes by which extensive openings could be made in the German forests, and in the time of the Romans special corporations transported the felled trees on rafts. The same was true in Italy during the Roman epoch, when the Aniene, the Liri, and the Chiana served as means of transporting wood from the Apennines, and wood from the Alps reached Rome by way of rivers and the ocean.

The vast territory included between Hudson Bay and the Saskatchewan River was revealed to missionaries and fur dealers—*voyageurs, coureurs de bois*—by way of the St. Lawrence River. The development of our lumber industry in the early days would not have been so rapid had it not been for the proximity of the New England forests to the coast and the large number of navigable streams, such as the Penobscot, St. John, Androscoggin, St. Croix, and others. Wherever roads are lacking, wherever the rivers are not navigable, the forest cannot serve broad economic ends; in that case the primitive organization remains and the forest furnishes only a local means of livelihood, as is the case in the interior of continents or at high elevations.

In northern Russia forests are still intact because of lack of railways and roads; while the inland location and lack of communication with the coast, together with the long periods during which the rivers are frozen, present obstacles to the development of a wood-exporting industry. Much more favorable are the conditions in the adjoining Scandinavian peninsula, where from the time of the earliest commercial relations with neighboring countries forest products have played a very important part.

The modern development of railroad systems, however, is reducing transportation by water in many regions. Thus in the Vosges Mountains, as well as in our Lake states and Pacific Coast states, transportation by water is dying out altogether.

Psychological Influences

The psychological influence of the forest on primitive peoples has already been noted. At higher stages when man sets himself to overcome the forest he feels its influence none the less surely. Many of the specific pioneer traits of our own original settlers in this country may be traced to their battle against the forest on the slopes of the Alleghanies to provide a place for settlement. The hazardous work of hewing farms out of the virgin forest has bred a race of men of sturdy character and of enormous enterprise and self-reliance. It is true that life in the forest was not conducive to the cultivation of the graces of life characteristic of high culture. The virtues of the backwoodsman were those of a strong animal nature—courage, pertinacity, resourcefulness. In the delightful "Letters from an American Farmer," by J. Hector St. John de Crèvecoeur written in 1783, we find a realistic description of the influence of the forest environment upon the character of the so-called back settlers.

> It is with men as it is with the plants and animals that grow and live in the forests; they are entirely different from those that live in the plains. . . . By living in or near the woods their actions are regulated by the wildness of the neighborhood. The deer often came to eat their grain, the wolves to destroy their sheep, the bears to kill their hogs, the foxes to catch their poultry. This surrounding hostility immediately puts the gun into their hands; they watch these animals, they kill some . . . they soon become professed hunters. . . . The chase renders them ferocious, gloomy, and unsociable.

In spite, however, of coarseness and even brutality, these people were undeniably men. No weaklings were produced by the life of the forest. The boundless woods with the long stretches of swamp land, the rough trails, the isolated homesteads sometimes miles away from the nearest neighbor bred unwillingness to co-operate with others for common purposes or to submit to any kind of discipline.

During the slow process of hewing their farms out of the forest the settlers were compelled to rely for many necessities on their own skill with the ax. From the forest they obtained all the material for the construction of their cabins from the puncheon floor to the shingles of the roof and the moss that calked the crevices of the walls. All these, together with the rude furniture, they got from the trees on their homesteads. The forest also supplied them with meat to vary the monotony of salt pork, itself made from hogs that found every bit of nutriment in the spontaneous products of the forests.

The back settlers, however, in the course of time lost much of their coarseness and produced leaders such as Henry Clay, Jackson, Benton, Cass, and scores of others, who for over half a century helped to shape the destiny of their country. In Abraham Lincoln this type of leader, purged of all the repulsive characteristics of the early type, found its highest expression. The old characteristics of the back settlers disappeared in him and "nothing remained but the pure metal—strong, keen, tempered to perfection, and yet at other times as soft and pliable as gold without alloy."

The entire ancient history of Sweden may also be reduced to the same struggle with the primeval forest. It is the colonization of the forests of northern Russia that has developed in the Russian people the necessary qualities which enabled them to spread to Siberia and take possession of it. If of all the present nations, the Anglo-Saxons, the Teutons, and the Russians display the great colonizing capacity, may it not be attributed largely to their original impenetrable forests, in the struggle with which they have developed the persistence and unrelenting energy required for pioneer work?

Deforestation and the Progress of Civilization

With the growth of population and the spread of civilization the world's forested area has been progressively reduced. At present there is still under forest about five billion acres; if the brush land is included, considerably more, probably one-fourth of the entire land area. About another fourth of the land surface is covered with desert and tundra, which must be excluded from the possible area of human habitation. Therefore the land area available for human activities is none too large. If we compare the relative amount of the land under forest in the different regions of Europe which have comparable climatic and other conditions for timber growth, we find that England has only 4 per cent of its land in forest; France, 18 per cent; Belgium, 17 per cent; Germany, 26 per cent; Austria, 30 per cent; Russia, 32 per cent; Sweden, 40 per cent; and Finland, 60 per cent. These figures express also, although in inverse ratio, the relative density of population of these countries. In these figures, as in a mirror, is reflected the progressive movement of human civilization.

Other factors may undoubtedly act as a modifying influence. Legal protection of woodlands may have had some effect in preventing indiscriminate deforestation as agriculture, commerce, and industries have developed; but in a broad way the extent to which the forest is cleared is in direct relation to the density of population and therefore to the conditions of civilization.

While it would be misleading to lay down, as a general law, without any qualification, that the decrease in forested area and human progress always go hand in hand, it is nevertheless true that up to the present time the countries having the most highly developed economic organization have also a greater population and a proportionately reduced forest area. This was true in ancient times as it is true now. Thus, for instance, the deforestation of ancient Greece at its highest period of development had progressed much farther than that of the southern end of the Apennine peninsula—at that time in a lower stage of development. The Hellenes then looked upon Italy as a densely forested country. Thus Alcibiades, exiled from Athens, in the discourse delivered to the Lacedaemonians, urging them to aid Syracuse, which was menaced by the Athenians, advised: "build many triremes in addition to those we have, for Italy has wood in great abundance."

Reforestation Following Decline of Civilization

As the progress of ancient civilization, of which agriculture was an essential part, tended to the destruction of the primeval forests, so conversely, with the passing of this civilization, with the decadence of empire and the return to barbarism, the forests, aided by pestilence and devastating wars, gradually restored themselves. In a most striking description of the devastation of Italy Lucan states that brambles and trees spread over untilled ground at the time of the Antonines. After Venice was invaded by the Marcomanni and after the spread of pestilence accompanied by floods, earthquakes, and swarms of locusts, the population of Italy was greatly decreased, and the forests spread over the abandoned territory. In Roman Italy in the time of Augustus, according to the most probable estimates, the population numbered about 6,000,000, and the area of land under agriculture, which was a combination of field crops with pasture in oak forests, was comparatively large. As this area gradually decreased, the forests, no longer checked by the ax and the depredations of grazing animals, spread again over the natural domain which had been taken from them for agricultural purposes. In the great crisis of the third century desolating wars further aggravated the conditions. Lactantius, speaking of the exorbitant taxes levied by Diocletian, mentions that the colonists abandoned their fields and that the fields then became covered with forests. Incursions of the forest upon cultivated fields reached to the very walls of the cities and even to the centers of inhabited places.

In his history of the forests of France Maury mentions ruins dug up in the dense forests of the eastern region, and on the top of a ridge near Orleans was found in the midst of a forest a Roman *castrum* destroyed by the Vandals. In the Government of Smolensk in Russia fields and towns abandoned in 1812 as a result of the Napoleonic invasion, and later during the famine of 1840 to 1850, were very soon overgrown by forests. Similar cases are found throughout the United States from Virginia to Florida, where forests sprang up on fields abandoned after the Civil War. Even in New England with the migration of the population westward many abandoned fields have come back to forest and today are being cut over for the second and third times. If the climate is favorable and there is no interference from man a few decades are sufficient for fields to become changed into dense forests.

The Struggle Between Man and Forest

Cook in speaking of the effect of agriculture on natural vegetation in Central America says:

> Many localities which are now occupied by apparently virgin forests are shown by archeological remains to be regions of reforestation. Thus in the Senahu-Cahabón district of Alta Vera Paz relics of two or three very different types of primitive civilization indicate that as many ancient populations have occupied successively the same areas which are now being cleared anew by the coffee planters as though for the first time.
>
> It does not yet appear that any considerable region of forest has been explored in Central America without finding similar evidence that the present forests are not truly virgin growth.

And again, speaking of the evidence of antiquity as exemplified by the crumbling of large earthenware pots of an earlier civilization, he continues:

> We cannot know how long it has taken the pottery to crumble, but we can at least contrast the condition of these decayed pots with other pieces of pottery placed in caves of the same district in later prehistoric ages, which still appear fresh and new, as though recently burned. And yet the bones beside these apparently new pots have also crumbled nearly to dust, and there has been time for the surrounding country to be occupied with old forests of hardwood trees, like true virgin growth.

He also mentions terracing of the land as showing that agriculture was formerly extensively practiced and notes the presence of a type of terrace evidently designed "to hold drainage water and prevent erosion . . . . . [being] frequently met with in the heavily forested region in eastern Guatemala."

What is regarded by some geographers as evidence of a civilization that had arisen in the primeval forest is nothing but the remains of a civilization which succeeded in clearing the forest; with the decline of this civilization and favored by a warm and moist climate, the forest again took possession of the land.

In regions, however, where the climate is unfavorable or where there is even slight interference on the part of man the return of the forest is slow, the land is either merely run over with brambles and vines or becomes virtually a desert. Thus in the region of Friuli there are ruins of medieval castles destroyed during the last years of the Venetian Republic but not yet overrun by forest vegetation except ivy. Bishop Ennodio relates that the fields of Italy at the time of the wars between Theodoric and Odoacer were stripped of their indigenous covering and were overgrown with thorny plants. In many uncultivated areas which served as pasture during the last centuries of the empire the growth of forests was retarded, if not checked altogether, because pasturage on a large scale, as carried on in many parts of Italy, made it impossible for the forest to re-establish itself. The forests of beech and oak which probably covered the land about Rome in early historical times never returned.

The Original Composition of the Forest Changed by Man

There is another important influence which man has exerted upon the forest. The colonization of forest regions not only reduces the forest area but radically changes the entire structure and composition of the remaining forest. In analyzing the names of places, towns, and cities which are made up of words designating forest trees of one kind or another, one is at once impressed by the large number made up of the names of hardwood trees and the very small number designating pines, spruces, or even fir. Of the geographic names of central Europe which indicate the origin of the settlements in forested regions, nearly 90 per cent point to the existence of broad-leaved forests. One can find any number of names indicating an origin in a locality where linden was prevalent: Lindewiese, Lindenfels, Lindenau, Linden, Lindenhoff. With oak there is even a larger number of which it is enough to mention: Eichendorf, Eichorst, Eichrodt, Eichenfeld, Eichstat, Eichwald. Birch also takes a prominent part in giving names to many places; as, for instance, Birkenfeld, Birkenhain. Beech is also prominently represented, such names as Buchholz and Buchhorn being very numerous. Ash also contributed to the names of many towns; as, for instance, Eschenbach, Eschweiler. Even alder enters into the formation of geographic names, as, for instance, Erlau. One looks almost in vain, however, for towns or places whose names signify pine or spruce. Once in a while one finds such a name as Tannhausen.

From this it is natural to infer that in the past the conifers had not the same wide distribution that they now have. As far as Germany is concerned, the preponderance of coniferous over broad-leaved trees has undoubtedly been brought about artificially by planting pine and spruce as the most profitable species. It is also possible that the land first cleared was that occupied by broad-leaved forests because of the more fertile soil naturally found under such growth, while the poorer sandy soils occupied by the conifers remained uncleared and unsettled. In Michigan the repeated fires have undoubtedly helped the spread of jack pine and Norway pine at the expense of the hardwoods, just as in the South the scrub pine, loblolly pine, and the slash pine extended their range at the expense of other species also as a result of fires accompanying settlement. In the central Rockies fire has changed many a Douglas fir stand into a lodgepole pine forest. This change in the composition of the original forest is evidenced throughout the entire world. Thus in Sweden, pine successfully competes with fir only in the presence of frequent fires, since on burns it comes up and grows faster than fir. In Europe it is an interesting fact that the pine extends its range parallel with the advance of towns and villages.

Civilization Dominating Forests

Over a large part of the world the forest is now conquered. It is not only conquered, it is exterminated beyond any possible chance of natural recovery. It has now become important to civilization to preserve and restore the forest instead of struggling against it. Out of a land area of some 32½ billion acres there is little more than 5 billion acres remaining in forest—exclusive of brush land—or only one-sixth of the land area. The greatest change of course has taken place in Europe, where of a total land area of nearly 2½ billion acres there remain now barely 750 million acres in forest. Even of this, two-thirds are found in European Russia and Finland and about 250 million acres in the rest of Europe. In some countries—Great Britain, for instance—nearly 95 per cent of all the original forest is gone. In France, Spain, Belgium, Rumania, and Greece, from 80 to 90 per cent of the original forest has been destroyed; in Bulgaria, Serbia, and European Russia exclusive of Finland, from 60 to 70 per cent; and in North America the original forest has shrunk from some 822 million acres to 463 million acres in the course of three centuries.

The Increasing Need of Wood

The disappearance of the forest, however, has not done away with the use of wood by the present civilization; on the contrary it has only intensified it. Although steel, brick, and concrete are now more and more taking the place of wood for structural purposes, industries are arising every day which are dependent upon wood as raw material. As a striking illustration may be mentioned the pulpwood industry which within a few decades has assumed enormous proportions. In 1880 the consumption of pulpwood in our own country was barely 300,000 cords; twenty years later the consumption had grown to 2,000,000 cords; in ten years more this had more than doubled, and at present it has grown to around 6,000,000 cords. In Great Britain the total consumption of lumber during the period 1851–1911 increased fivefold, and the per capita consumption has also steadily increased, being in 1911 more than three times what it was 60 years before. In spite of the fact that production from German forests has doubled in volume within the past century, the imports from other countries have steadily increased in amount. While there are factors, such as the preservative treatment of wood and the substitution of other materials for construction purposes, which may tend to check the consumption of timber, it is a feature of modern commercial progress that, in spite of this, consumption per capita is steadily increasing.

Not only are the densely populated countries of Europe making heavy importations of lumber and other forest products. In our own country large sections like the Northeast and the Lake states, which not long ago had enormous forest areas and supplied the needs not only of the entire country but of other countries, are dependent upon wood from other regions, such as the Southeastern Pine Belt and the Pacific coast. This wood has to be brought from distances even greater than those over which some of the European countries are now importing. Backward countries in various parts of the world are now being called upon more and more to meet the growing deficit of wood in the world. Armed with powerful logging machinery and highly developed means of transportation the timber trader invades the remaining primeval forests and re-enacts there the same process which the European countries had gone through centuries ago—only at a more accelerated rate.

Social and Economic Evils of Forest Devastation

The clearing of the forest, aside from depriving the thickly settled and highly civilized countries of timber needed for their industries, has produced other bad economic and social effects. The stripping of the mountain forests resulted in the occurrence of torrents, in erosion, in floods, and in a general change in the régime of streams. The disappearance of the forest has also affected the climate and with the growth of industrialism has resulted in the physical deterioration of a large part of the population. Much of the forest land that has been cleared on mountain slopes, sandy plains, or rocky hills has proved unsuitable for agriculture and has failed to provide room for permanent settlement. Just as in the past the primeval forests proved a barrier to human settlement, today it is the vast stretches of cut-over and burned-over forest lands, unsuited to agriculture which are an economic barrier to permanent settlement in many parts of the United States, Canada, and other new countries. In the United States alone there are over 80,000,000 acres of such idle waste land. The soil too poor to maintain purely agricultural communities and the lumber industry gone with the disappearance of the forest and therefore no longer a source of livelihood to the local population—there is nothing left to keep the settler on the land. The dreary wastes, dismantled sawmills, deserted towns, so common throughout the Lake states, Pennsylvania, and other sections of the East, are depressing reminders of the day when these regions were the centers of lumber production for the entire country and sustained prosperous communities.

The products of the forest have now become altogether too valuable and no civilized nation can afford forest devastation on a large scale without regard to the future possibilities of the land. The demand for forest products is now so great that the cutting away of the forest, even on fairly good agricultural land, is far in advance of the possibility of actual land settlement. If the cutting is not followed by another forest growth or the land is not taken up by settlers for cultivation, the result is an economic waste and reduced production of the primary necessities of life.

Practically all of the civilized countries of the world have now come to realize that there is a point beyond which further clearing of the forest, no matter what the density of the population may be, proves detrimental to progress itself. Europe reached that point several centuries ago.

In central Europe the period of the greatest clearing of forest land for settlement was practically completed by the end of the thirteenth century, although considerable clearing has taken place since then in the more remote districts and particularly in the Alps. In the Canton of Zurich it is very definitely established that for the last 250 years the forest area has been reduced only 2.85 per cent. Better agricultural methods which made it possible to produce larger crops on smaller areas and the apparent evils resulting from the destruction of forests on mountain slopes led to adoption of legislative measures for the purpose of checking further clearing of forest on non-agricultural land.

The lesson of the older countries found a reaction also in countries still having abundant forests. In practically the entire civilized world a new economic force has now been born—a general appreciation of the value of forests and a movement toward the introduction of rational forest management. There is no doubt whatever that in civilized countries there is enough accessible actual and potential forest land not suitable for agriculture to produce under proper management timber enough to supply indefinitely the world's great demand.

The New Movement Toward Rational Management

Nearly every civilized country at the present time has adopted or is considering measures for the perpetuation of the existing forests, or even for extending their present area. Thus England which, because of her insular position and proximity to countries still possessing vast forest areas and because of her cheap water transportation, could best of all get along with a small forest area has now, as a result of bitter experience during the war, worked out a plan for planting some 1,700,000 acres and providing a forest area sufficient to sustain her domestic needs in case of emergency for three years. France, which for over a century has been carefully husbanding her forests, is further elaborating plans for their careful management and is enlarging her forest nurseries for extensive planting. Germany, Switzerland, Italy, Norway, Sweden, and New Zealand are also considering means of increasing forest products. Even in our own country the maintenance and protection of existing forests has become a pressing question of the day.

Nearly all of the forests now found in western Europe are man-made. With increase in population more intensive use of all resources became necessary, especially of those resources which through more intensive application of labor, knowledge, and skill could be made to produce more fully. Forests being a poor-land crop prove more profitable than agricultural crops on non-agricultural lands. The day of the forester—the timber farmer—has now arrived in practically all densely populated countries of the world, and his work is to secure forest crops by human skill just as food crops are now being secured. Nor is the less material rôle of the forest being overlooked. In order to offset deterioration in the physical and ethical well-being of the people crowded in industrial centers with poor housing facilities, state and municipal forests are being established as a source of healthy recreation for the densely populated countries of Europe.

The new forest may be different from the original forest which once occupied the ground. It certainly bears a more utilitarian aspect. The trees that are being grown are not always of the kind that nature would prefer to produce under given conditions of climate and soil, but are those which man needs most. Just as intensive farming has increased the production of the land, so the forester is now producing five to ten times as much useful material as nature unaided produced before. Although the man-made forest may not have the beauty and grandeur of the wild woods which were the result of the free play of natural forces, it has a new beauty

—the beauty of orderliness and usefulness. It is no less an important factor in civilization from the ethical and geographical point of view, because at present the economic principle is applied to it, as it is now being applied to the raising of agricultural crops.

31. *Natural Vegetation of the Guiana Highlands* *

These two passages from W. H. Hudson's book, *Green Mansions,* give vivid first-hand descriptions of the vegetation and rainfall of the borders of the rainy tropics. The locale is the western portion of the Guiana Highlands in northern South America. The gloomy, all-encompassing, and storied nature of tropical forests is well portrayed. The author catches the feeling of the transition zone between savanna grasslands and tropical rain forests.

When I reached the top and could see the country beyond, I was agreeably disappointed at the discovery that the sterile ground extended only about a mile and a quarter on the further side, and was succeeded by a forest—a very inviting patch of woodland covering five or six square miles, occupying a kind of oblong basin, extending from the foot of Ytaioa on the north to a low range of rocky hills on the south. From the wooded basin long narrow strips of forest ran out in various directions like the arms of an octopus, one pair embracing the slopes of Ytaioa, another much broader belt extending along a valley which cut through the ridge of hills on the south side at right angles, and was lost to sight beyond; far away in the west and south and north distant mountains appeared, not in regular ranges, but in groups or singly, or looking like blue banked-up clouds on the horizon.

Glad at having discovered the existence of this forest so near at home, and wondering why my Indian friends had never taken me to it, or ever went out on that side, I set forth with a light heart to explore it for myself, regretting only that I was without a proper weapon for procuring game. The walk from the ridge over the savannah was easy, as the barren, stony ground sloped downward the whole way. The outer part of

* Reprinted from *Green Mansions* by W. H. Hudson, by permission of Alfred A. Knopf, Inc. (Peter Pauper Press edition, pp. 29–32, 122–124.)

The author (1841–1922), an American by birth, was a nature writer who spent his early life until the age of thirty in Argentina. In 1870 he went to England and eventually became a naturalized English citizen. *Green Mansions* is his best work, but he has written numerous other books concerning nature, especially about birds.

the wood on my side was very open, composed in most part of dwarf trees that grow on stony soil, and scattered thorny bushes bearing a yellow pea-shaped blossom. Presently I came to thicker wood, where the trees were much taller and in greater variety; and after this came another sterile strip, like that on the edge of the wood, where stone cropped out from the ground and nothing grew except the yellow-flowered thorn bushes. Passing this sterile ribbon, which seemed to extend to a considerable distance north and south, and was fifty to a hundred yards wide, the forest again became dense and the trees large, with much undergrowth in places obstructing the view and making progress difficult.

I spent several hours in this wild paradise, which was so much more delightful than the extensive gloomier forests I had so often penetrated in Guayana: for here, if the trees did not attain to such majestic proportions, the variety of vegetable forms was even greater; as far as I went it was nowhere dark under the trees, and the number of lovely parasites everywhere illustrated the kindly influence of light and air. Even where the trees were largest the sunshine penetrated, subdued by the foliage to exquisite greenish-golden tints, filling the wide lower spaces with tender half-lights, and faint blue-and-gray shadows. Lying on my back and gazing up, I felt reluctant to rise and renew my ramble. For what a roof was that above my head! Roof I call it, just as the poets in their poverty sometimes describe the infinite ethereal sky by that word; but it was no more roof-like and hindering to the soaring spirit than the higher clouds that float in changing forms and tints, and like the foliage chasten the intolerable noonday beams. How far above me seemed that leafy cloudland into which I gazed! Nature, we know, first taught the architect to produce by long colonnades the illusion of distance; but the light-excluding roof prevents him from getting the same effect above. Here Nature is unapproachable with her green, airy canopy, a sun-impregnated cloud—cloud above cloud; and though the highest may be unreached by the eye, the beams yet filter through, illuming the wide spaces beneath—chamber succeeded by chamber, each with its own special lights and shadows. Far above me, but not nearly so far as it seemed, the tender gloom of one such chamber or space is traversed now by a golden shaft of light falling through some break in the upper foliage, giving a strange glory to everything it touches—projecting leaves, and beard-like tuft of moss, and snaky bush-rope. And in the most open part of that most open space, suspended on nothing to the eye, the shaft reveals a tangle of shining silver threads—the web of some large tree-spider. These seemingly distant, yet distinctly visible threads, serve to remind me that the human artist is only able to get his horizontal distance by a monotonous reduplication of pillar and arch, placed at regular intervals, and that the least departure from this order would destroy the effect. But Nature produces her effects at random, and seems only to increase the beautiful illusion by that infinite variety of decoration in which she revels, binding tree to tree in a tangle of anaconda-like lianas, and dwindling down from these huge cables to airy webs and hair-like fibres that vibrate to the wind of the passing insect's wing.

Thus in idleness, with such thoughts for company, I spent my time, glad that no human being, savage or civilised, was with me. It was better to be alone to listen to the monkeys that chattered without offending; to watch them occupied with the unserious business of their lives. With that luxuriant tropical nature, its green clouds and illusive aerial spaces, full of mystery, they harmonised well in language, appearance and motions;—mountebank angels, living their fantastic lives far above earth in a half-way heaven of their own.

I saw more monkeys on that morning than I usually saw in the course of a week's rambling. And other animals were seen; I particularly remember two accouries I startled, that after rushing away a few yards stopped and stood peering back at me as if not knowing whether to regard me as friend or enemy. Birds, too, were strangely abundant; and altogether this struck me as being the richest hunting-ground I had seen, and it astonished me to think that the Indians of the village did not appear to visit it.

. . . . .

By the time I reached the ridge I had discovered that she had prophesied truly, for now an ominous change had come over nature. A dull grey vapour had overspread the entire western half of the heavens; down, beyond the forest, the sky looked black as ink, and behind this blackness the sun had vanished. It was too late to go back now; I had been too long absent from Rima, and could only hope to reach Nuflo's lodge, wet or dry, before night closed round me in the forest.

For some moments I stood still on the ridge, struck by the somewhat weird aspect of the shadowed scene before me—the long strip of dull uniform green, with here and there a slender palm lifting its feathery crown above the other trees, standing motionless, in strange relief against the advancing blackness. Then I set out once more at a run, taking advantage of the downward slope to get well on my way before the tempest should burst. As I approached the wood there came a flash of lightning, pale, but covering the whole visible sky, followed after a long interval by a distant roll of thunder, which lasted several seconds, and ended with a succession of deep throbs. It was as if Nature herself, in supreme anguish and abandonment, had cast herself prone on the earth, and her great heart had throbbed audibly, shaking the world with its beats. No more thunder followed, but the rain was coming down heavily now in huge drops that fell straight through the gloomy, windless air. In half a minute I was drenched to the skin; but for a short time the rain seemed an advantage, as the brightness of the falling water lessened the gloom, turning the air from dark to lighter grey. This subdued rain-light did not last long: I had not been twenty minutes in the wood before a second and greater darkness fell on the earth, accompanied by an even more copious downpour of water. The sun had evidently gone down, and the whole sky was now covered with one thick cloud. Becoming more nervous as the gloom increased, I bent my steps more to the south, so as to keep near the border and more open part of the wood. Probably I had already grown confused before deviating and turned the wrong way, for instead of finding the forest easier, it grew closer and more difficult as I advanced. Before many minutes the darkness so increased that I could no longer distinguish objects more than five feet from my eyes. Groping blindly along, I became entangled in a dense undergrowth, and after struggling and stumbling along for some distance in vain endeavours to get through it, I came to a stand at last in sheer despair. All sense of direction was now lost: I was entombed in thick blackness—blackness of night and cloud and rain and of dripping foliage and network of branches bound with bush-ropes and creepers in a wild tangle. I had struggled into a hollow, or hole, as it were, in the midst of that mass of vegetation, where I could stand upright and turn round and round without touching anything; but when I put out my hands they came into contact with vines and bushes. To move from that spot seemed folly; yet how dreadful to remain there standing on the sodden earth, chilled with rain, in that awful blackness in which the only luminous thing one could look to see would be the eyes, shining with their own internal light, of some savage beast of prey.

32. *In the Piney Woods* *

The "cut-over" problem is widespread among the forested or previously forested districts of the United States. It was first thought that when the forest was removed successful farming would im-

* John F. Preston, "In the Piney Woods," *The Land,* Vol. 8, No. 3, Autumn, 1949, pp. 349–352. Published by Friends of the Land, Zanesville, Ohio.
The author is retired from active duty in the United States Forest Service.

mediately follow. Poor soil, steep slopes, or unfavorable growing conditions resulted in large-scale farm abandonment and tax delinquency. Some of these areas have since been turned into state or national forests. Others are being rehabilitated and a combination of forestry and farming is being effectively carried out. Preston describes such a program in the Piney Woods of northern Louisiana and southern Arkansas.

Ten years ago the piney woods looked much as it does today. There was the same mass effect of uncut forest interspersed by cut-over areas; some brushy and barren, some coming back with a new stand of thick-growing pines. There were big areas of company-owned lands. There were smaller spots of cultivated land with small patches of corn and cotton and larger patches of brushy pasture. Sharecroppers' cabins stood out in the clearings and there were occasional well-kept, attractive farm homes. Wandering cows and razor-back hogs moved about along the highways and in the clearings. There were broad river bottoms of hardwoods standing deep in water in the spring, dry in summer. Concrete highways led hither and yon, busy with fast-moving cars, trucks and trailers.

In perspective, this land was beautiful, mostly a flat country with pine trees as yet unspoiled by the inroads of civilization. If the traveler went fast enough along the roads, he would come away with an impression of what wonderful things Nature can do in a land blessed with plenty of water, and a climate and soil that permit her to dissipate in growing piney woods. If he stopped and looked closer at the rural scene, he would realize that here is being enacted the age-old struggle of Man against the wilderness.

Here, farmers were trying to convert forest lands into farms. Not all of it, because large holdings of timber land owned by individuals and corporations occupy much of the area. The open spots on farms seemed to be only a small percentage of the total, mere occasional breaks in the forest canopy. But actually, statistics for two representative counties show that cultivated and pasture land occupy 30 to 50 percent of the land area. A casual visitor would never guess it to be so much.

I visited this land some ten years ago. I saw then the general picture of beautiful pine woods, of luscious plant growth, of broad square miles of forest land. I saw some of the farms in detail. I saw successful efforts to carve farms out of the woods. But I also saw fields long abandoned and again grown up to dense stands of pine trees. I saw pastures inadequately covered with palatable grasses, gradually but surely being reclaimed by the wilderness. No wonder farmers apparently gave up the unequal struggle in the fight with Nature to make pastures, and turned the livestock out to wander at large where they picked a precarious livelihood along the highways and out in the "cut-overs."

I saw something else too. A surprisingly large part of the company lands were being selectively cut. A passerby often had to look twice to see that the timber was being cut at all. Forestry ten years ago was already established on many of the big holdings. Fire protection was rapidly gaining effectiveness. Company foresters were not only managing the company lands; they were trying to get farmers and small owners to manage their timber for continuous production. The companies not only wanted forest products to buy, but they wanted the communities to acquire appreciation of woods values. If they did, fires would stop and timber would grow and wood-using industries would be permanent. Timber production on farms is vital to industry because the farms include from one-third to one-half the timber-producing land of the region.

Company foresters were offering to selectively mark the timber offered for sale by small owners. They wanted them to start a program of continuous forest production. The wood-using industries needed pine logs and pine pulpwood every year. A "cut out and get out" policy would soon close the mills. That policy had already left many forest communities in other regions stranded. They did not want that to happen here where it seemed so easy to grow trees. Management for continuous production was their theme.

Some sawmill operators, too, were talking and practicing forestry. Extension foresters, federal and state foresters were doing what they could to encourage the growing of wood as a crop. This region seemed to be a sure bet if kept in growing trees; a doubtful bet if cleared and devoted to cultivated crops.

Nevertheless, the farms were here and more were being started. Man had to extract a living from the soil and this demanded that woods be converted to farms wherever there was a remote chance of success. And, of course, there were lots of good farms. The foresters saw the opportunity of combining forestry and agriculture. "Use the best land for the usual farm crops," they said, "but use the land best suited to timber growth for forestry. Grow wood as a farm crop. Make forestry an agricultural enterprise."

It was a good idea and it was sound farm economy. But it was very slow to take hold. Agricultural schools didn't have forestry in their teaching, agricultural workers (except foresters) didn't talk it, and farmers were not much interested. The old philosophy that a farm consisted of open fields, pastures, meadows, and orchards was still dominant. The woods must be cleared to make way for them. Once in a while a farmer accepted the new idea, tried it out, and found it good. It was a long ride, however, between farms where forestry was being practiced.

Today (the year, 1949), I was one of a dozen Soil Conservation Service foresters looking critically at the progress in farm conservation in the last ten years. We were particularly interested in the progress on farm woodlands for two reasons: First, we were partly responsible for the technical progress in this field through the farm conservation program of the soil conservation districts; and second, we knew that under conditions such as exist here, the farm conservation program could not succeed unless the timber lands in farms were included—unless the timber did its share in producing farm income. In this section we have perhaps the thriftiest, fastest growing pine trees in the whole United States. Its products—pulpwood, poles, piling and sawlogs—are readily salable. Good hardwoods are salable also as sawlogs and in some local markets, small inferior hardwoods are salable as pulpwood. Generally, the poor hardwoods are a drug on the market and a drag on the forestry enterprise.

A typical farmer in this region has more or less acreage of timber. Census statistics indicate that from one-third to nearly half of the average farm is in woods. Sometimes the farmer has already sold his timber stand. The purchaser has cut it all, big and little. The farmer then has no immediate prospect of any further income from his woods. If he can keep fire out and avoid severe grazing in his cut-over land, often he will have a new stand that he can manage. How long will he have to wait? Planted stands become marketable in ten to fifteen years. We saw ten year old plantations where better than ten cords have been cut per acre in order to give the best trees more room to grow, with an income better than $20.00 an acre. Some cut-over areas grow back to salable timber in an equal period, depending on protection against fire and overgrazing, and the number and the distribution of the seed trees which happen to be left. Unless these two factors are favorable, odds are against getting a good stand for a generation or more.

Ten years ago farmers were largely using the clear cut method of management. They were destroying the forest's growing stock of young trees along with the big ones. Often they destroyed any possiblity of further income except by incurring the further expense involved in complete clearing with fire, bulldozer, grub-hoe and plow. Such work would make the forest land suitable, if the soil were good enough, for cotton, corn or meadow. If the slope and the soil texture were good, such conversion might succeed, but the cost was very high and the results have often been disappointing. Proof of this is evident in the dense stands of pine grown to merchantable size on old abandoned fields.

On the other hand, a good stand of pine trees 6 to 16 inches in diameter can be managed to give farmers an annual income of $15.00 an acre where they sell stumpage, which is only collecting rent for the land. If the farmer sells on the same basis as he does other farm crops, he will cut his trees and sell products. In this case his gross income from his forest acre can easily be doubled. Management of farm woodland requires no fertilizer and no lime. No expenses are involved other than the taxes and interest common to all investments. Of course, labor and machinery are needed in harvesting the crops as they are in the case of all other farm crops. But their use is richly rewarded by the added income. Labor earnings for woods work in this section are several times greater than for cotton, the standard crop of the South.

The farmer who owns a 100-acre farm with 30 acres suitable for such crops as corn and cotton, 40 acres of pasture and 30 acres in a good stand of timber can double his gross annual income if he holds his timber growing stock and sells annually only the wood growth. He can do this if he markets his wood crop as he does his cotton. If he sells stumpage, he must be satisfied with only half as much income from his timber crop. This 100-acre farm happens to be the average size of farms in two representative counties as reported by the 1945 census. The 70 acres in pasture and cultivated crops also is representative of the average farm. Virtually every farm over 40 acres has some woods. The average is between 30 and 40 acres. Many farm woods comprise 100 acres or more. According to the 1945 census, the average gross income per farm is about $950. Thirty to forty acres of good pine woods can produce income equal to or exceeding this figure. The average farmer who hasn't over-cut his farm woods can soon get out of the sub-marginal level and into the class of profitable agriculture. Best of all, the farmer who includes management of his woodland as part of his farm business will have the money to inaugurate and maintain needed conservation measures on all of his land to insure the permanence of his own income, and he will have a successful farm to pass on to future generations. The forest must do its share to make farming a success.

So the foresters have a good story to tell. It was a good story ten years ago but only an occasional farmer listened and felt out forestry practices to find out for himself the result. A big change has taken place in ten years. Now, several hundred farmers have accepted the premise that their woods should help furnish their share of the annual farm income. Their woods are being cut on the basis of continued production. Under the general guidance of foresters, non-forestry trained agricultural workers are teaching the farmers how the woodland fits into farm economics. They are taking the next step by teaching them the necessary forestry techniques involved in managing the piney woods. Fortunately, these techniques have been simplified to the point where any farmer can successfully apply them and get satisfactory results. Appreciation of woods values in farm economy has taken hold. Private, federal and state foresters (the latter financed in part by Norris-Doxey federal funds) and extension foresters, all have had a hand in the changed farm philosophy.

Here in northern Louisiana and southern Arkansas is being set an objective pattern of agriculture that may well be the forerunner of similar ones in other regions. Here the pine trees are easily marketed and have a high value, but even here many worthless hardwoods must be girdled to get them out of the path of paying forestry. Few localities can show such tree growth or tree values, but the economic truth that agriculture cannot long prosper unless all parts of the farm contribute to income is universal in application. The larger the area of the farm in woods, the more urgent it is to make the woods pay whatever it is capable of contributing. There are surprisingly few places where farmers can afford to ignore the potential income from the woods.

These piney woods farmers are beginning to accept a new farm pattern. Come again ten years hence! The cut-overs will be healed with planted pine trees, the pastures will be made to grow good grasses, or if too tough, will be green with pine trees. Cultivated fields will still be in the picture and so will farm homes, more substantial and attractive because farmers have a more stable income. Conservation measures on cultivated land "to hold this soil" will be the accepted practice because agriculture will have a degree of permanence it lacked before. This is not speculative farming. Here is a solid foundation upon which to build an enduring agriculture; in fact, an enduring community economy.

33. *Southwestern Desert Vegetation: Its Adaptations and Utilization* *

About 19 per cent of the world's land surface is desert; it supports a mere 5 per cent of the population. Many desert areas are

* Jonas W. Hoover, "Southwestern Desert Vegetation, Its Adaptations and Utilization," *Journal of Geography,* Vol. 31, April 1935, pp. 148–156. By permission of the *Journal of Geography,* official publication of the National Council of Geography Teachers.

The author (1889) was chairman of Geography, State Teachers College, Tempe, Ariz. when this article was written. His special interests lie in the geography (especially anthropogeography) of the southwestern United States.

completely devoid of people, as the word "desert" implies. Actually, considerable variety exists in the climates, topography, and vegetation of the "too dry" areas of the earth. A knowledge of their character, as well as of their limitations and potentialities, would dispel many popular misconceptions. In this reading Hoover presents such information concerning desert vegetation.

A casual survey of the rainfall and vegetation maps of the world brings out the fact that about one-fourth of the land surface of the earth and nearly one-fourth of the area of continental United States is arid or semi-arid. Hence the significance of these lands should not be slighted. Altho sparsely populated there have risen from them dynamic cultural forces which have spread to the ends of the earth. Also they hold much significance for the future. We have been passing thru an era of cultural development and expansion based upon humid lands, but in looking for new worlds to conquer, the surge is against the barriers and restrictions imposed by aridity. As Isaiah Bowman puts it, "These are the regions where environment conspicuously affects the lives of men."

In the United States a line drawn across the southern end of Nevada and continuing southeastward along the borders of the northern and central highlands of Arizona, sets apart from other arid areas of the United States a province distinctive for its peculiar and picturesque vegetation. It is known to plant ecologists as the Sonoran Province and varies in altitude from sea level at the mouth of the Colorado River to about 4000 feet. The rainfall varies from less than 3 inches to about 15 inches. The vegetation increases in abundance eastward toward the highlands, due, not only to increased total rainfall, but to a larger summer percentage. At Barstow, California, in the Mojave desert only 5 per cent of the rain falls in the three warmest months, at Needles, 34 per cent; and at Tucson, 50 per cent.

To many the mention of a desert conjures up pictures of barren desolation in which the characteristic element is drifting sands, whereas bare areas, especially of drifting sands, are only occasional features. In a favorable season a desert may be lovely in its sweep of green and brilliant bloom, but it can be just as cruel with its burning summer heat with absence of water or shade.

Adaptation to aridity, as to other unfavorable life conditions compels low or slow metabolism, hence the desert plants are characteristically slow of growth and tenacious of sluggish life. Xerophytism expresses itself in highly specialized devices or modifications on the one hand for the securing of water, and on the other, for conserving it. In the case of the desert annuals, seed production is speeded up and the life cycle is shortened to bring it within the scope of the few weeks of moisture following rains.

The many varieties of cacti are especially interesting and unique among the plants of the Sonoran Desert, and illustrate several modes of xerophytic adaptation. The cacti, like camels among animals, are remarkable for their ability to absorb and store water. The bisnaga or barrel cactus, by way of illustration, will yield enough water to quench human thirst and to save life if its interior be pounded to a pulpy mass. Most of its roots are short, spongy, and shallow so as to absorb much water quickly during the heavy downpours which come at long intervals. It is therefore very easily uprooted, but will continue alive for months or years on its stored up water supply. Evaporation surface is reduced to a minimum thru a single cylindrical stem with leaves reduced to thorns. The surface is fluted, or ribbed, enabling it to expand or shrink according to moisture content. The disposition of leaves necessitates the relegation of their functions to the stem surfaces, which are therefore green.

The leaves of the desert plants, if at all present, are small and are either cast off in the dry periods, or their edges are turned to the sun. Leaves of shrubs are further protected from evaporation by waxy, scaly or hairy surfaces.

The root system of the creosote bush is typical of the desert shrubs. Even when it would seem that not a particle of moisture could be left in the soil, the plant is able to find enough moisture to keep going the spark of life. The roots ramify widely near the surface and penetrate deeply, but the plants must be widely spaced to share the limited moisture. The ability of the roots of the creosote bush to gather moisture where there is a minimum of it, and to penetrate the *caliche* or hard limey precipitate general beneath the surface of arid soils, enables it to thrive on the long sweeping areas of gentle slope of the arid basins, often to the exclusion of any other perennials. So, altho one of the most useless of plants, its presence relieves, what otherwise would be complete desolation of extensive areas. At no great distance from the observer the bare spaces between the plants seem to disappear, and unless the season is unusually dry, the receding plain appears as a vast expanse of green.

On the lower flat bottoms of the basins, more moisture accumulates, but escapes almost or entirely by evaporation. Hence the soil becomes charged with salt and alkali. Here the salt bushes have undisputed domain, except perhaps for a scattering of greasewood. Most common of the salt bushes are Suoeda and several varieties of Atriplex, which superficially resemble sage brush. If a permanent or temporary stream has entrenched a flat below the general level of the plain, this will be covered with the thorny mesquite, trees or bushes. The presence of mesquite is an indication of ground water. The plant requires plenty of moisture but is able to send its roots 30 to 40 feet to secure it. Along the channels of the main streams such as the Colorado, Gila, and Salt Rivers grow occasional groves of cottonwoods; and where soil or sand is subject to shifting, the long reed like arrow-weed or the recently introduced tamarisk takes hold.

Most varied and most luxuriant is the vegetation of the long rocky and gravelly slopes of the Arizona desert mountains or highland residuals. Here there is more moisture and less alkalinity, because there is more rainfall over the highlands, and the drainage follows the sub-areal rock extending from the mountains. Here the cacti grow in greatest abundance. Lines of the thorny palo verde, and ironwood, mark the courses of the washes and between them the gray Franseria, also suggestive of the sages, is the characteristic shrub. In the higher elevations of the mountain margins, the yuccas and agaves become conspicuous.

Utilization of Desert Plants

American settlement in the Southwest is very recent and is exotic to the desert. Beyond some grazing of indigenous forage plants, and cutting of the stunted trees for fuel, little use has been made of the desert plants. The many Indian cultures, prehistoric and recent, however, developed in the desert, entirely dependent upon their desert environment.

The present day Indian tribes of the desert, including Papagos, Pimas, Maricopas, Yumas, and Mojaves, number about 13,000. Formerly they sustained themselves entirely from the desert, and largely by the use of wild plants. But today, the Indian tho still using a variety of foods made from desert plants is becoming, like the white man, dependent upon the can opener.

The uses of desert plants may be classed as food for man and for domestic animals; materials for fibers, shelter, fuel, medicine, soap, and other manufactured products; and protection from erosion. Frank Russell in his ethnological report on the Pimas, lists among the native plants used by them for food, 22 of which the stems, leaves or flowers were eaten, 4 which furnished roots or bulbs, 24 seeds or nuts, and 15 which supplied fruits or berries. He also lists 18 plants used for medicine, tho it is not certain that all these remedies were effective.

Outstanding among the desert plants for their importance in the economy of the native peoples, have been the mesquite, the shuaro or giant cactus, along with other varieties of cacti, and the yuccas and agaves.

Food Plants

The beans of the mesquite were a very important item in the diet of all the southern Indian tribes, including the Apaches. The Pimas, Mojaves and Yumas who lived on, or adjacent to the river flats, where the mesquite beans grew so abundantly, were especially dependent upon them. They are fattening and hence these river Indians have always shown a marked tendency to obesity and indolence. Especially the Mojaves depended upon these beans to such an extent that they developed only a trifling part of their productive agricultural resources. Olive Oatman, who was captive among them for several years in the early 1850's, stated that they produced insufficient wheat to maintain one-fifth of their population. The mesquite beans were gathered for miles around and were thoroly dried to be used when their vegetables and grain were exhausted. They failed to provide for lean years, and when occasionally the mesquite crop failed there was distress and even famine. The screw bean is another variety of mesquite whose spiral pods were gathered and prepared in a variety of ways. Mesquite beans are still much consumed by all the southern tribes, and even the Apaches made regular trips into the southern mountain valleys to gather them. The supply is now much curtailed by the livestock which feed avidly upon them.

The palo verdes or Parksonias also produce beans which may be eaten as gathered, or after being pounded in a mortar. The ironwood makes similar contributions.

Next in importance among the desert plant foods comes the fruit of the sahuaro and other cacti. The sahuaro fruit may be eaten raw, dried, cooked into preserves or jam, or the juice may be made into a drink. The seeds are used to make seed cakes, or are ground into meal. The Papagos to whom the fruit of the sahuaro is especially important, have made the time of its harvest the occasion for feasting. The blooming of the sahuaro marks the beginning of the Pima New Year. Each June finds many Papago and Pima families going out to gather the fruit, perhaps working a half day and obtaining about 50 pounds of the huge berries from which the wine ("tis-win"), is made for the fiesta or other future occasions.

The fruit of the prickly pears was eaten in moderation and prepared for future use also. The famous Burbank spineless cactus is a cultivated variety of the prickly pear. Prickly pears are also cultivated by the Mexicans, and is then called by them, "Napal." With plenty of moisture, the joints or segmented stems grow much larger, have fewer thorns, and assume a bluish green color. The fruit also grows much larger, has a better flavor and remains a pale yellowish green.

Even certain species of the Cylindropuntias, as Opuntia arborescens, a long stemmed thorny branching cactus, were collected in large quantities. The usual method of preparing the fruit for future use was to dig a pit and heat stones in it. After the fire died down the stones were removed and a layer of the Suoeda salt bush was placed over the coals. Above this was placed a layer of the cactus fruit, then the hot stones and so on alternately to the top. After a night, the fruit was taken out, dried, and stirred to remove the thorns, and stored away. The smaller cacti of the genus Cereus also bear edible fruit, but are less abundant. One large plant of the hedge hog or strawberry variety will yield about one to two quarts of fruit which the Papagos eat raw or cook into jam or conserves. The bisnaga or barrel cactus also yields an edible fruit, but the plant is becoming increasingly scarce due to its slow growth and its popularity for use in the commercial cactus candy. The Indians ate it after cutting it into strips and boiling it all day. Sometimes it was boiled with mesquite beans, a layer of each, in the cooking olla.

The favorite vegetable of the Apaches and a delicacy with all the desert tribes was "mescal," obtained from the agaves, commonly known as century plants. The entire plants were cut when signs of the flowering stalk appeared. These were trimmed down and prepared in large pits somewhat after the fashion of the Opuntia-arborescens described above. After cooking for several days with a fire on top, the mescal became a sweet pasty mass which was dried in the sun. The fruit of the Spanish bayonet was dried, ground on the metate, or boiled with flour by the Pimas, and cooked in ashes and dried for future use by the Apaches.

A number of small plants were cooked as greens. Salt bushes were often boiled with other foods to give them a salty flavor. The stems were also boiled with wheat and used as stuffing for roast rabbit. The heads were pounded and screened to separate the seeds, which were washed, dried, parched in an olla, then ground on a metate and eaten as "pinole."

If we include the higher and rainier mountain slopes of the highlands marginal to the desert, then to the list of important food plants may be added pinon nuts gathered by the Apache Indians for the American market, and acorns which are stewed by them, parched and ground into meal.

Forage Plants

The wide spacing of the desert perennials, their thorns, or their leathery, scaly or hairy surfaces, together with their paucity of leaves or bad taste, as in the case of the creosote bush, render them generally unsuitable for browse or pasture. But since the annuals of the desert are so ephemeral, it is upon the perennials the grazing must depend most of the time. Yet this is the only important use to which the white man has put the desert vegetation. The nutritious gramma grass, abundant in the northern highlands, formerly grew with some luxuriance in the higher moister parts of the desert province. It is still found growing in the protection of thorny bushes and would if given opportunity come again to its own. After rains, the floor of the desert becomes carpeted with alfilaria, a low tiny geranium, which is fattening to cattle. In long periods of drought the food on the desert becomes so scarce that most of the cattle must be removed or large numbers perish. Some of the desert shrubs including the salt bushes are fairly good natural forage. If better feed is scarce, the cattle will eat the prickly pear or munch the spiny jointed chollas, the most vicous of opuntias. The chollas supply water as well as nutriment. Stockmen sometimes chop up the stems of the yucca and feed them to the cattle.

Yucca Fiber and Soap

The yuccas and agaves have played the most varied rôle in the economic progress of the native southwestern cultures. Especially important were the long strong leaf fibers which were woven into textiles since prehistoric times. Thus they were used for textiles, skirts, head bands, martial cloaks, laces, belts, sandals, and leggings. For many centuries the fibers of the long wiry leaves of the yucca have been used by the Indians in the making of heavy cords, ropes for ladders, burden carriers, saddle bags, and lariats. The leaves themselves were used in making sleeping mats and crude saddle blankets. The spines terminating the leaves were used as needles. The fibers were also used as bead strings, or were made into crude brushes. The Apaches still tie the poles of their "wick-i-ups" with yucca fibers or narrow strips of their leaves.

The roots of the yuccas have marked saponaceous qualities and are used by Mexicans and Indians alike for washing the delicate fabrics or woolens. It is also favored for shampooing, leaving the hair soft, fluffy and glossy. The Navajoes are said to wash their hair with this soap before participating in sacred ceremonials. It has also been used to some extent by white people and the demand for the roots has depleted large areas of the yucca plants, especially in the vicinity of Mexican or Indian settlements.

Uses of Desert Vegetation in Construction

The desert shrubs and trees have had a significant rôle in providing shelter, not only to the native Indians, but to the Mexicans and American settlers, especially before importation of materials became easy. All the trees, but particularly mesquite and cottonwood, were used for supporting uprights, roof beams and poles. Sahuaro ribs, or the stems of the ocatilla, have been most commonly used as the framework for the walls of the wattle houses of the southern Indians. The ocatilla is an odd plant which grows in bunches of straight stems covered with blunt thorns to a height of 8 to 10 feet. When there is a fair amount of moisture the stems are covered with tiny rich green leaves, and in the spring each shaft is crowned with a raceme of torch red blossoms. These are suggestive, as the stems contain a resin which burns with a bright flame, and the Indians sometimes light the ends of the dead stems using them as candles or torches. The stems are sometimes set close together in the ground and bound for fences. The stems take root and when in leaf and bloom, these flowering fences are novel and attractive. Along the rivers where ocatilla stems and sahuaro ribs may be distant, arrow-weed stems may be substituted in wall construction. At any rate they afford the best of roofing material, laid across heavier poles to support the cover of weeds and adobe.

In making the solid earthen floors of the Indian and Mexican huts, the stems of prickly pears are sometimes beaten into the adobe. The water in the stems has a peculiar cementing property when mixed with a proportional amount of loam and it imparts greater durability to the floor.

Except for barbed wire used by the United States Indian Service, the Indians have depended entirely upon poles from the aforementioned trees, or ocatilla, to build their fences and corrals. On the isolated cattle ranches of the white man, they are used in the same way. Ironwood, as suggested by its name, is exceedingly hard and too heavy to float in water. It is very hard to cut, but posts made of it more than 50 years ago are still sound. It is fine grained and susceptible of high polish, but unfortunately it is not abundant enough and grows too slowly to become of commercial importance. It is used somewhat in the manufacturing of novelties.

Many other plants have entered into the construction and decoration of the various household articles and artifacts of the native peoples of the Southwest, but as these plants are generally unfamiliar except to the denizen of the desert they need not be listed here. Many of these articles and uses have become obsolete with dependence upon the trading post, altho some are used in the rather incidental manufacturing of commercial souvenirs and novelties.

Medicinal Uses of Desert Plants

The Indian medicine man did have some knowledge of healing herbs and did not always rely entirely upon magic. Investigations by competent medicinal botanists in the Arizona deserts might greatly enrich medical science.

Even the creosote bush, here came in for some use. Poultices were made by boiling the leaves. The boiled down liquid was taken internally for a cathartic. It is also said to be a good tonic for the scalp, but its odor debars its use. The mesquite, during the summer months, exudes a liquid which has the properties of gum arabic. The gum was boiled by the Indians, diluted and used as a wash for sore eyes and open wounds. The bark of the arrow weed was used in a similar manner. Yucca also has some medicinal value, as it contains gum, grape sugar and saponin. The wood of the stems makes excellent splints because of its lightness and flexibility. The value of a number of other plants, known to have been used by the Indians, is open to question.

Scientific Investigations

Several institutions have been set up in the Southwest aiming to investigate the economic possibilities, of not only native desert plants with possible modifications, but also of plants which may be introduced. The latest step is the establishment of a division of the Bureau of Plant Industry at Tucson, Arizona, with branch stations at Safford, Arizona, and Gallup, New Mexico, for the investigation of plants which may aid in the utilization of these arid and semi-arid areas. The immediate problems are to find plants which will thrive and at the same time afford good forage or will check erosion. This work is to be under the able direction of F. J. Crider who has been conducting similar investigations at the Boyce Thompson Desert Arboretum near Superior, Arizona, and from which unfortunately financial support for scientific investigation has been largely withdrawn. For a number of years the Desert Laboratory of the Carnegie Institution, located at Tucson, Arizona, has been unfolding much of what has been learned about the life of the Desert, but more from the viewpoint of pure science.

The Desert Beautiful

Aside from the conception of utility of the desert which is concerned only with the physical welfare of man, there are other values, esthetic and intellectual. The vegetation of the Sonoran Province is so unique and so varied that it has definite scenic values. To the practical man of affairs an appeal may therefore be made for the preservation of these unusual, and in some cases rare plants, in support of a thriving and increasing tourist industry. Fortunately the cacti and some other desert plants adequately protect their gorgeous blossoms from ruthless pickers. But the fad for potted small cacti thruout the country has played havoc with a number of the rarer varieties which propagate with difficulty. Legislation without adequate policing, has not solved the problem.

When the desert is at its best, carpeted with alfilaria and wild flowers, with the gorgeous golden bloom of the palo verde, the brilliant flowers of the cacti and the ocatilla, the rich green expanse of the creosote bush, all stretching to mountain ranges rising clean cut and angular, perhaps a hundred miles away, with the bright light of the day fading to a horizon of opalescence, for the ones who love it, it is hard to withhold a little wish that the quest for utility may perhaps not be too altogether successful.

34. *Biggest Christmas Tree Grower* *

The problem of utilizing cut-over or worthless land faces many sections of the United States. Such factors as erosion, strip-coal mining, soil depletion, and others, cause many areas to become unproductive. This reading, taken from *Fortune,* indicates how poor land in a coal-mining district of Pennsylvania was successfully planted to Christmas trees. This venture gives promise that reforestation may prove economically feasible on a much larger scale than is now in operation. Many private and government-sponsored conservation programs are desirable and necessary to save our vital timber resource.

Fred Musser always wanted to be worth a million dollars. He wanted to make the million in Indiana, Pennsylvania, a town of 11,700 about fifty miles east of Pittsburgh, and he says now that he wasn't particular about the kind of business so long as it didn't take too much of his time. Indiana is in a hilly, hard part of the Alleghenies and the surrounding lands are moderately rich in coal. By the time Musser started out, most of the farming that could be done in the area had been done, and the farmers had become miners. There was no other industry. It would be hard to find a part of Pennsylvania that offered less to an ambitious young man without a coal mine.

In 1928, at the age of twenty-four, Musser decided that if he planted evergreens on the cheap, almost abandoned farms nearby, he could sell them

* Reprinted from the December 1952 issue of *Fortune* by Special Permission of the Editors;

in five or six years as Christmas trees. He figured that 1,000 acres worth $10 per acre could be planted to two million Christmas trees, and it took the simplest of figuring to turn that into the kind of money Fred Musser wanted to make. The idea appealed to him also because all of the hard work would be done in two months of spring (for planting) and in two months of winter (for harvesting).

At the beginning Musser planted only 405 acres with about 600,000 trees, just to see if the thing was nearly so good as it appeared on paper. Today he has 8,500 acres planted, and by adding 400 to 500 acres of land annually he will be able to continue each year to cut 200,000 Christmas trees worth at wholesale $200,000 more or less. He also has three tree nurseries from which he sells some 25 million baby Christmas trees a year to thousands of people who are either reforestation enthusiasts or who are simply trying to copy Musser by making money out of land good for little else. This year these nurseries produced $600,000 worth of business and earned 20 per cent net after taxes. Musser has the million dollars plus leisure.

. . . . .

Musser didn't go into the growing of trees completely blind. His father, since Fred was twelve, had been active in reforesting his coal company's lands with quick-growing pines and Fred knew what it took to plant and grow a tree. It was Musser's contention that even though pines had never been sold generally for use as Christmas trees, they could be sold. He knew, of course, that pines would be more difficult for housewives to decorate than the traditional balsam firs or spruces, with their short needles. On the other hand, he pointed out, whereas balsams and spruces start dropping their needles practically the minute they are cut, pines off their stumps will keep their needles almost all winter. Housewives, Musser argued, would like that enough to offset the difficulty of decorating. And dealers would like it; they could buy early, sell early, and take no loss from spoilage. The thing to do was create the demand, and the product would take care of selling itself. "You can sell anything," Musser kept repeating to his skeptical partners.

There was another idea in the back of Musser's head but it didn't impress his partners. Selling Christmas trees is a $55-million industry, and except for Musser it is mostly disorganized. It is a highly irregular industry, fly-by-night operators think nothing of loading bundles of trees with worthless branches, and Christmas-tree buyers, out to make a killing in six weeks, try every known trick to keep from paying for what they buy. Musser's idea was that a regular supplier of a standard product would provide a degree of stabilization unknown in the industry, and business would automatically come to him from the most reliable people in it. In practice, however, this theory proved to be merely something pleasant to contemplate; the market was and is still governed solely by supply and demand. Musser's position as a reliable supplier permits him to sell cash-in-hand; only old customers with a record for payment are shipped sight draft.

The economics of the Christmas tree is short and simple. Most of the 28 million trees cut annually for Christmas must be harvested and sold within eight weeks. Their value is equal to minus zero on Christmas morning because it costs money to cart them off. Since the time factor throws such a high degree of speculation into the business, markups are high and normal gross profits all along the line are based simply on multiplying cost by five. For example, it costs Musser about 6 cents to raise a tree five to seven years old, and about 15 cents to cut, bale, and haul it. He sells this 21-cent tree for $1 up, and when the market drops under this he stops selling. A dealer gets about $1 a foot for these $1 trees, which range in height from five to seven feet. The dealer's problem, like Musser's, is to be in and out of business as quickly as possible.

In 1930 Musser made his first big market test. He cut trees from various plantations, including his father's coal-company lands, and shipped eleven carloads to one dealer in Buffalo on consignment. They were worth at wholesale $1,000 per car. Musser got only $198 for all eleven cars. Tests in other cities were not quite so disastrous, but the season's sales added up to just $1,920. Fred Musser alone remained undismayed. "We've got a lot more missionary work to do with this new product," he told his partners. The missionary work consisted of continuing to ship pines on consignment, and under this prodding markets gradually opened up in Chicago, St. Louis, and Cleveland. But not in New York or New England, which to this day remain committed to conventional balsams and spruces. (Last year, however, Musser managed to make a dent in Philadelphia.)

. . . . .

He learned about all there was to know about cropping trees for Christmas. He found out that no two pieces of land grow trees the same way and that all trees, even of the same variety, grow at different rates. Some reach five-foot height in five years, others of the same variety can take twelve years to become salable. (Acres planted by Musser as early as 1940 are still producing.) He stopped buying land not readily accessible in winter, or land too steep to plant and cut easily. He cut planting losses by training planting teams, and worked out methods of getting more trees into the ground per man-day. By shearing trees that grew too rapidly he made them bushier and more salable. After he became dissatisfied with his suppliers of seedlings and decided to grow from his own seeds, he hit the jackpot.

Musser started his first seedlings in 1938, and in 1940 came up with a fine crop of young trees for transplanting. It can be called luck that practically all the seeds grew, and that the sixty 4-by-100 feet raised beds of seedlings held a crop of about 3,600,000 perky young trees—some three million more than he could possibly use to plant the 400 acres of land he had bought that year. Musser didn't view all those seedlings as luck; they merely appeared to him to be something that had to be sold—which he proceeded to do, handsomely.

By this time Musser had developed a reputation as the country's outstanding Christmas-tree grower. Forest conservationists from many states (even nations) had journeyed to Indiana (Pennsylvania) to see how to get a cash crop out of spent land. Even more important to the conservationists was the fact that from 500 to 1,000 trees per acre were always unsalable as Christmas trees and the best of them would develop into timber. Musser learned from the foresters that several varieties of evergreens should be planted in a block, particularly the high-value, slow-growing spruces, which would do their duty as a cash crop of Christmas trees but would be even more valuable in a half century as timber. Stories were printed in all kinds of publications about the Musser system of growing wood for cash, and inquiries poured in. When Musser found that the nursery crop of seedlings far exceeded his requirements, it seemed logical to let the envious public know that it could buy seedlings right from headquarters. He wrote his first catalogue, a two-page folder, in 1940. Although most of his $126,000 gross that year came from his expanding sales of trees for Christmas, the demand for seedlings was so brisk that he decided to expand the nursery and add more varieties of evergreens.

Mail Order Pays Off

In preparing his 1945 catalogue, Musser hit upon the low-pressure formula that tells all about raising Christmas trees from Musser seedlings. The catalogue as a piece of printing is strictly utilitarian. Like most mail-order nurserymen, Musser doesn't bother about changing the pictures from year to year, although he does shuffle them around, adds one or two new ones to each edition. Some of the pictures date from almost the first edition, particularly one of the three Musser children, all practically adult now, posing self-consciously beside a Musser HEMLOCK hedge. The catalogue is full of similar capitalized words—YEWS, JUNIPERS, PINES, and SPRUCE. It is full of directions and hints, all calculated to prove that a Musser tree is the easiest thing in the world to grow ("no cultivation required"; "the poorer the land the better the Christmas tree") and that Musser trees can only expand miraculously into cash. The section headed "Musser's Christmas Tree Growers' Guide," a masterpiece of simple exposition, contains everything Fred Musser has learned about growing Christmas trees, including a cold-turkey talk on the problems of marketing them. Only one point is missing. Musser grows his Christmas trees on land on top of natural gas that provides royalties of from 50 cents to $1 per acre per year to pay the taxes.

. . . . .

The volume of all Musser's growing operations has shown tremendous increases since 1942, and if next year's gain is even close to this year's, he will be a member of that small and elite group of nurserymen, most of whose businesses have been in the making for fifty years or more, who gross more than a $1 million annually. He has discovered that slower-growing ornamental evergreens like Japanese yews and some of the hollies are even more profitable than forest stock, and it won't be long before his new $200,000 nursery will contain acres of them. They and some of the flowering shrubs appear to be so profitable that Musser has decided to learn how to pronounce their botanical names. He has hired a Dutch propagator and a professor of horticulture to work at Musser Forests with the idea that something unusual—and possibly salable—might come out of having a scientist and a practical horticulturist working together.

It appears that his children are already well provided for and his grandchildren will have no worries about inflation. To them will fall the timber left from Christmas-tree plantings on thousands of acres of land planted by Fred with Musser seedlings. Just the 8,500 acres planted now will be worth about $5 million on the stumps in fifty years, which is that added value from planting Christmas trees for a cash crop, just as it says in the Musser Forests catalogue.

CHAPTER FIVE

Soils and Agriculture

BECAUSE MAN MUST EAT to survive, and because nearly all of man's food is either directly or indirectly a product of the soil, agriculture is one of the most important activities on the earth. As the world patterns of landforms and natural vegetation are diverse, so also is the pattern of soils. The correlation between similar regions of climate, vegetation, and soils is, however, one of the most significant facts of geography.

Man has established diverse patterns throughout the areas of the world where agriculture is possible. These different patterns are not merely the result of climate and soil variations, but, more significantly, the result of many other factors—history, tradition, population density, and technology, to mention only a few.

Shortage of productive land is one of the major problems facing the world, and the development of world agriculture is that of too little land for the rapidly increasing population. Although this problem hardly exists in the United States today, it is nevertheless a situation we cannot ignore, for it is, no doubt, approaching even this country.

Associated with agriculture is animal husbandry, the growing of animals for their products. Grazing is often found in areas where the climate and soils are too poor to support agriculture; feeding and fattening of animals for meat production are often found in connection with agriculture, primarily in areas containing an urban population with a sufficiently high standard of living to afford the relative luxury of eating meat.

35. *Soil and Democracy* *

The ratio of land to people is basic to agricultural productivity and consumption rates. As the maximum productivity per unit of land is achieved, the amount of food available per person must decrease as the population continues to increase. The total food production in the United States, for example, has not increased since 1944. The disparity between the two curves—the rising population curve and the flattening food production curve—points up a growing problem. This problem, as Fink shows by examples from the past, has serious political implications for the continuation of the democratic way of life.

Land and people are the two foundations of a bridge that determines the economy of a nation and the limits of its cultural development. The traffic across this bridge is an interchange in goods and skills. It conveys the fertility of the land to meet human needs and wants, and it likewise conveys technical skills and discoveries that are achieved by the whole population to increase basic productivity and raise the standards of living.

A farmer in a jungle, working by hand and alone, can clear and crop only about two acres a year. He works alone not only in the physical sense, but without the partnership of machine makers, research technicians, bankers and business enterprisers in making the job of farming easier and more productive. The improvements in tools and methods that originate *off the farm* and flow back to the farm in an advanced interdependent society provide vivid illustration of the productive possibilities when bridge-traffic between the two great foundations of progress, land and people, becomes a complex, modern interchange of goods and skills.

Here with us, a Corn Belt farmer can operate 300 to 400 acres. A wheat farmer can cultivate 1,000 acres. Here, the capacity to produce is in proportion to our command of new knowledge, power and machines. Here, research and technology have substituted wheels and levers, electronic devices and other gadgets for the mind and muscle of human drudgery. As human drudgery is reduced and research is applied to man's use of resources, the traffic across our bridge changes from a narrow single lane to the ever broadening super-highway span with its many lanes of traffic.

* Ollie E. Fink, "Soil and Democracy," *The Land,* Vol. 11, No. 1, Spring, 1952, pp. 34–39. Published by Friends of the Land, Zanesville, Ohio.

The author is Executive Secretary and Program Director of the Friends of the Land, an organization dedicated to the wise and constructive use of land, and to the conservation of natural resources.

The jungle farmer represents a single lane traffic. The wheat farmer represents the superhighway. And if the lanes were marked, they might well be designated—Research—Industrial Research, Medical Research, Agricultural Research, and Governmental including Military Research.

But technical progress can never exempt a land or a people from obedience to fundamental laws. "Earth and the life on it," Paul B. Sears has pointed out, "were well set in their way before we came. We did not make and we cannot change the laws under which we work, but at least we can understand them."

"There is no wealth but life," wrote Ruskin at the beginning of his essay, Unto The Last. When we think of the deserted mining camps or the wastelands of the desert we may feel as he did; yet to apply this maxim unreservedly is to initiate national suicide. Whether we like it or not, we are bound to consider what happens when there is *too much life*. A realistic consideration of the man-made ratio is as essential under advanced conditions of civilization as it is under primitive conditions; and adjustment to an effective ratio has become a major purpose of conservation.

Consider China: "To die without offspring," Confucius said, "is one of the gravest unfilial acts." Yet China, with a stabilized population of around 60 million before 1600 A.D. did not have the problems of population pressure that were encountered when the population there rose to 450 million, or a man-land ratio of one-half acre per person. Human life has almost no value on land so heavily laden. In the light of history and of present experience, it takes the product of from two to two and one-half acres to keep one person in good health for one year.

Two acres of arable land per capita gives a working formula that we can apply. If the man-land ratio is less than that, the consequences may well be such as led a sympathetic observer of the plight of India to report, in grim earnest, after successive years of drought and famine in 1943 and 1944: "The famine was a failure because it did not kill enough people." And in 1948 there were reliable news reports of wealthy families in India paying from $400 to $1,000 to have their babies smuggled into South Africa and other less crowded parts of the world.

Such humanitarian standards as well-fed lands can afford to express through benefactions of the Red Cross and the like can have little place in economies where overpopulation imposes hunger and malnutrition on the majority of the population from birth to death. Our military forces now are killing more great numbers of the Chinese in Korea, and the more of them we kill the more successful that war must be accounted from our point of view. It is a grim thought, but probably just as true, that the starving and malnourished Chinese living apart from the army, fatalistically accept or even welcome the massacre of so many of their own countrymen because it will mean more food per person. The psychology of any people is quickly reduced by hunger to an animal level.

The present population of the world is about 2¼ billion; the total cultivated acres are 2½ billion. This ratio of less than an acre per person leaves approximately three out of every four people in the world hungry. "The history of man is the story of a hungry animal in search of food." Hendrick W. Van Loon wrote that in his Story of Mankind, a quarter-century ago; and since he wrote it the number of hungry animals has increased daily.

When Germany moved into Poland on September 1, 1939, acres divided by people in Germany gave only nine-tenths of an acre per person. Mussolini moved into Abyssinia when acres in Italy divided by people gave three-fourths of an acre per person; and on Pearl Harbor Day, December 7, 1941, Japan had only one-fourth of an acre per person of arable land.

We in the United States are still on the favorable side of the land-man ratio. The most recent population figure is 151 million people and we have 345 million acres under cultivation. That gives us at present about 2½ acres per person. But in order that an Atlas does not confuse us, we must remember that arable land means good crop or pasture land. Really productive lands must have favorable temperatures, sufficient rainfall, but not too much; good topography, not too steep; and a fertile soil. A realistic listing of our really agricultural lands, omitting the deserts and swamps and mountainous areas, coupled with the fact of a mounting population load, and a diminishing store of basic fertility, warns of a day not too far in the future when overpopulation may be an enemy within our own gates.

The United Nations reports an increase of nearly 60,000 people per day the world over. This would create an immediate need for over 100 thousand acres of productive land per day if the newborn were to be well-fed and nourished. Meantime, the most crowded parts of the world become even more overcrowded and more oppressed by hunger. Asia, with one-tenth of the Earth's surface, now has one-half of all the people. The population of Japan is today increasing 1½ million per year, with the United States spending $1½ million per day to help support what must in the end prove to be an unbearable burden. And in Puerto Rico, on our own doorstep, a half-century of American aid reinforces the grim conviction that a humanitarian saving of lives through medical advances and hospitals and sanitary improvements only makes the overall tragedy worse by increasing the total of hungry mouths.

Now to examine the other end of our bridge—the resources: Americans are accustomed to think in terms of mass production with great supplies of raw materials being fabricated and turned into useful products for ourselves and the rest of the world. These natural resources and their development and fabrication forms the basis for the economic structure and our machine civilization. We have the greatest physical production plant in the world. We have more newspapers, churches, colleges, hospitals, more modern homes, more paved streets and highways, more running water, more retail stores and a wider distribution of consumer goods than any other people in history. We possess four times as much gold as all other nations combined, and about the same ratio of automobiles. We have approximately three-fourths of the trucks and more than two-thirds of the telephones. We produce more than half of the world's production of many materials such as petroleum, cotton, wheat, corn and a third of the steel, pig iron and coal.

We have more than one-third of the world's wealth and approximately half of the world's productive income. Those in higher income levels spend a smaller share of the total income for basic necessities such as food, and a large share for clothing, travel, recreation and education. The high national income determines the character and size of the market and its changing demand upon resources.

We have used our metals as mechanical slaves. A Pharaoh, Khufu, used seven million forced laborers for thirty years to build the pyramid of Cheops. This is about equal to 66 billion horsepower hours. It is estimated that in 1944 we had the tremendous total of 310 billion horsepower hours per person. This means that an average American had the services of about 4.7 times more energy in one year than all the work that went into the building of one pyramid. A small electric motor for a few pennies can do more work than the strongest laborer. What a contrast—with 33 million slaves working for each of us each year—and all the toil, poverty and despair on the other side of the world?

When Columbus arrived it is estimated that there was less than 20 million dollars in gold and silver in Europe—less than $2 per person. But when gold from the Americas started streaming into Europe, the 200 million gold of 1492 rose eight times by 1600; 20 times by 1700; 37 times by 1800 and over 100 times by 1950. Writing recently in Harper's Magazine, Walter P. Webb points out that since 1493 not less than $85 of every $100 of precious metals produced in the world would have been supplied by the frontier countries, and not more than $15 from Europe and Asia. This change of ratio between money and material things provides a key to the thesis of Webb's article, entitled, "Ended: 400 Year Boom." The amount of goods flowing into Europe was like a horn of plenty emptying its wealth from the frontier of our nation and from the Great Frontier, including practically all the world except Asia and Europe.

These waves of wealth included products from the land and precious metals from lands where there was an excess of land in ratio to population —where, in other words, there were great fertile areas of fertile acres and only a few people. The taking of this wealth brought people in migrating waves to each of the countries. The wages of labor were high because there was the wealth from the land for those who would work for it. Labor scarcity was the key—scarcity in the man-land ratio.

A committee of the Pennsylvania Legislature stated in 1752 that immigrating workers soon set up for themselves, which keeps up the price of labor, and makes it more difficult for the old settler to procure working hands. This committee concluded: "For as long as land can be easily procured for settlements between the Atlantic and Pacific Oceans, so long will Labor be dear in America." Adam Smith stated that the circumstances which in our colonial period made for high wages and all around good prosperity was "plenty of good land."

The favorable man-land ratio of the American past accounts, then, in great part for a change from a subsistence level of living to the living conditions of the modern Western world with its concern for money and commodities. The end result is a great advance in human betterment. The four-century boom which Webb analyzes continued as long as there was practically free land. But now that the free land is occupied—what next?

Two men working a ten acre grain field can produce more than one man can produce but he cannot produce as many bushels per man. If the number of farmers in Ohio were doubled the total production would not be doubled. One man with modern tools on 100 acres can produce a comparable amount to eighteen workers; *but the modern tools have not increased the total food supply.*

Higher production per man with fewer farmers will not, then, in itself avert a shift downward in living standards. The population curve goes up daily, arable acres are being farmed down to marginal or useless acres, and the general fertility of our land is on the decline. In spite of all the emphasis that has been placed on outbursts of food production, all the ballyhoo, all the USDA surplus payment, *the total food production of the United States has not increased since 1944.*

Biological laws are at work here—the area of leaf surface which can have its life-giving place in the sun, the water and soil moisture limits, the limited soil nutrients—all these are factors which determine limits of production regardless of the number of men. Again, when we speak, for instance, of price control efforts to roll back meat prices, we would do well to first examine the meat situation in terms of the roll-back which our given store of soil fertility has already brought to pass.

With the protein requirements of an individual 70 grams daily, it takes about 1½ acres to provide in 320 pounds of meat (750 pounds gross weight) the protein (and fat) that an individual requires in a year. This clearly explains why the world cannot be on a beefsteak diet and why meat prices must be high, relatively, under competitive land-use pressures of supply and demand. Consider this: In 1900 there were about 2,114 head of livestock for each 1,000 persons in this nation. Today this figure has been reduced to 1,174—little more than fifty percent of the amount available to our parents. Wages and salaries have increased and made more buyers; the demand increases; increased demand in the face of an ever decreasing supply per capita lifts prices; and governmental efforts to roll back prices cannot counteract the fact that basic fertility and the total demand upon it regulate prices in a permanent manner.

Food is the basic resource. So it is that man or groups of men who in any particular period of the history of a nation control the supply and are in possession of the basic foods are supreme in power. A government is stable and supreme only if it has control or can take over the rationing of food. In frontier countries where there is adequate food in the hands of those who produce it, plenty of good land, then the government cannot effectively control the food supply. Our "Land of the Free" tradition stems directly from plenty of good land.

As acres become too few and people too many, the government steps in and regulates the distribution of food. Egyptian history back to 2830 B.C. *records governmental agents as overseers of the grains.* The story of Joseph in the Bible shows how *government can reduce a people to slavery by control of the food.* In China, the two sets of interest—the consumers and the producers—were recognized and controls designed to regulate the supply and demand by price fixing. About 1122 B.C. it was recognized that if the price of grain were too high it would hurt the consumer and if too low it would hurt the producer. High prices cause emigration and low prices for the farmers made the nation poor. Either extreme, with prices high or low, produced final bad results.

In Athens the history records that Xenophon in 404 B.C. counted it an important quality of a statesman to have knowledge of the grain business. A century later, 303 B.C., Rome was experiencing the problems of man-land ratio, and *price controls* were listed for more than eight-hundred articles of commerce. England tried in 1199 to control both retail and wholesale prices and again in 1815, but these as well as all other arbitrary measures failed. Belgium failed in 1584 and 1585 to regulate prices by government at Antwerp. India following rice failures in 1770, in which one-third of the population died, passed laws designed to prohibit speculation in food.

On December 20, 1777, Sir Henry Clinton in charge of the collection of taxes for the British at New York, proclaimed the legal rate for the sale of wheat, corn and other foods. The proclamation specified that the farmer's supply would be confiscated if he refused to sell at the specified prices as set by the government agent. But because there was plenty of good land the controls proved fruitless and were discontinued after six months. In France at this same time price-fixing became a major factor in the Reign of Terror.

The lesson of history here is that first population increases overtake the productive ability of the declining fertility of the soils and that governmental efforts to limit the price artificially are doomed to failure.

After the government takes over the controls of the food supply—when acres divided by people is less than two acres per person—we recognize a trend in type of government to be socialistic, fascist or communistic. Democracy as we know it was created by and grew out of the independent food supply of farmers. We still live under the benefits of personal and political freedom fruiting from plenty of good land, land of the free. But our days as a democracy as we know it will reach the critical day when we shall no longer have the two acres per person.

Rationing foretells the end of a free republic. Four hundred years of boom at an end, the free-land frontier gone—this sounds most discouraging. What can be done? A great deal. A new frontier lies at our feet in the acres we now have. Science has now revealed that from most soils in this nation we can not only make two blades of grass grow where one grew before—but better.

An old Italian fable comes to mind: An old man left instructions: "I bequeath to my sons my olive orchards and equal shares in the treasure that lies buried therein." The three lazy sons after hearing the report of the buried treasure exclaimed, "We must dig until we find it." They divided the orchard into three parts and began to dig carefully around each tree and in the rows between. They upturned the soil of the entire orchard, but found no treasure.

That year a strange thing happened, the crop was the largest they had ever seen, and the income seemed like a fortune. One of the sons remarked, "Our digging has brought us a treasure." And so they in the fable continued to dig year after year and the soil yielded its treasure.

To protect our treasure of independence and freedom, to enrich the source of all our strength and prosperity, we must restore and rebuild God's greatest gift, the soil. Conservation is the new frontier.

36. *Grass and the Soil* *

Soil is the basic ingredient of both agriculture and grazing; the latter is dependent on the natural or cultivated vegetation of an area. Interrelationship between soils and plants is of great significance to man and his understanding of the nature of soils, their physical characteristics and productive capabilities is essential. Maintenance of the soil, vital to continued productivity, is a problem of increasing importance as soils are becoming more and more exhausted through constant cropping or grazing. Kellogg indicates the important facts concerning soils, as well as the significance of the relationships between different soil types and vegetation.

The great variety and complexity of the country scene appeals to most people whether they are professional naturalists or not. Each rural landscape has its own set of characteristics. Any one may be just a little different from the thousands of others, or very unlike any of them. Through science modern man tries to understand these landscapes—to unravel their many interlocking relationships—in order to discover principles that can be used to guide the great producing powers of nature to his own ends.

But the job is so big that scientists have had to divide it among them. Thus botanists, geologists, foresters, climatologists, horticulturists, agronomists, soil scientists, farmers, and others are each concerned with some part of the whole. Yet at some stages in scientific work the facts and principles discovered in these specific lines of inquiry must be brought together if principles of prediction value in the real world are to be developed. That is, plants growing in even the simplest farm, or garden, or forest are subject to all the influences of the environment acting together and they contribute to this environment as well.

Nothing illustrates this complexity better than grass. In some landscapes tall, luxuriant grasses grow naturally and help make black soils that are naturally productive for cultivated plants. The invasion of such landscapes by forest degrades these soils—they lose part of their great producing potential for crops. And this may happen quickly—not in terms of a man's lifetime perhaps, but in 200 years or so.

Yet in other places more productive soils are found under forest than

* Charles E. Kellogg, "Grass and the Soil," *Grass, Yearbook of Agriculture*, 1948, pp. 49–55. The author (1902   ) is Chief of the Division of Soil Survey of the United States Department of Agriculture. He has written extensively on soils and soil science in the United States, chiefly for government publications.

under grass. Here invasion of the soil by grasses degrades it rapidly, within the period of one man's life or much less.

These are two extremes. But often it is by looking at the extremes that we discover principles of great importance to the soils between them, where differences are not so easily seen.

The Soil

Suppose we look at the soil itself. What is it? First of all, it is the natural medium in which plants grow. It is a mixture of mineral matter and organic matter, some of which is living. Things are being added to it and taken away from it. The soil on the very surface is not like that just beneath it; in fact, the soils in most places consist of a series of unlike layers, one over the other, each from a few inches to several feet in depth.

Then, too, the surface is gradually changing. Some soils are slowly being eroded, bit by bit, so that all the layers move down. To each layer a bit of the one beneath is being changed and added to its lower side as it loses its upper part by erosion or to another layer above it. Finally, new fresh minerals from the rock beneath are incorporated into the lower part of the lowest layer of the soil.

Other soils, of course, receive additions to the top instead of the bottom. Along great rivers silty alluvium settles out of the water over the soil. Dust settles from the air—perhaps just a little; often a great deal. Volcanoes add ash or cinders to soils, sometimes lowering their productivity for crop plants but more often increasing it.

When water enters the soil, air is forced out of the pore spaces. Then as the soil dries, air returns. In this process grasses like carbon dioxide escape and others like ammonia enter the soil to be absorbed.

The entering water, either as rain or irrigation water, brings soluble materials with it too—usually just a little, but sometimes a great deal. The excess water beyond what the soil can hold seeps out into deep drainage and carries soluble materials away.

Then, of course, plants are growing on the soil, extracting nutrients, and producing organic matter from these soil nutrients and those from the air and water. Depending on the kind of vegetation, the total organic matter may be a ton or so per acre up to several hundred tons. Thus, in the living organic matter the soil has a great storehouse of nutrients. When the plants and animals die, the remains serve as food for microorganisms. As it decomposes, the nutrients in it are made available to new plants.

Thus a soil changes between day and night, from season to season, and over long periods of geological time.

Yet soils are not quite so difficult to understand as this recital might suggest because many of the processes go together. Ignoring for the moment man's interference, a soil—an individual set of soil characteristics that we call a soil type—results from a particular combination of five genetic factors—climate, vegetation, parent rock, relief, and time. Thus soils are not distributed promiscuously over the earth, but in an orderly discoverable geographic pattern. A given set of the five genetic factors everywhere produces the same set of soil characteristics—the same soil type.

But to these natural types of soil must be added the changes caused by use—often drastic changes for better or for worse, in terms of crop production. That is, many soils developed originally under forest in the humid temperate regions have been made ever so much more productive by careful husbandry, including the growing of grasses, the use of lime and manures, and improved drainage for hundreds of years. Other soils have been deprived of their essential cover of grass or trees and exposed directly to the sun, wind, and water, with serious degradation by erosion, blowing, burning of organic matter, and loss of structure.

Soil scientists have been and are now attempting to discover precisely what types of soil exist in the world, where they are, and how they respond to that whole group of practices we call "husbandry."

One cannot understand a soil by looking simply at one or two of its characteristics. Slope, depth, texture, color, structure, chemical composition, and many more must be seen in combination. Not only that, a soil must be seen in relation to those around it. A soil is three-dimensional. It occupies discreet areas of the earth. Around each area are boundary lines that separate it from the other soil types with different sets of soil characteristics. These boundary lines come in places where there is a change in one or more of the five genetic factors.

So a soil is a solid, the upper surface of which is the surface of the land. The lower surface is defined by the lower limits of biological forces, and the sides are the boundaries with other soil types. One cannot take a soil into the laboratory any more than he can a mountain or a river; but one may take samples of rock, water, or soil into the laboratory for important investigations to determine some of the characteristics of mountains, rivers, or soils.

Even further, a soil is a landscape with a characteristic climate and vegetation. Thus plants and soils are essential parts of one whole, each influencing the other and both reacting to the climate.

Soil Productivity

A central problem of inquiry in soil science is soil productivity for various crops, grasses, and trees and how to increase it or maintain it efficiently. The two principal aspects of soil productivity are its structure, or tilth, and its fertility, or content and balance of available plant nutrients.

Let us consider the fertility. Commonly, soil scientists attempt to express the amounts of nutrients available to plants in terms of "pounds per acre" of available phosphorus, potassium, calcium, and so on. These figures permit the comparison of soils only in the narrow sense, not as landscapes.

Suppose, for example, that we compare the black grassland soils (Chernozem) of eastern North Dakota with the light-colored forested soils of northern Michigan (Podzol). We shall see at once that the content of available plant nutrients is considerably higher in the Chernozem than in the Podzol. But to compare the total plant nutrients in, and available to, the biological cycles of the natural untouched landscapes, we shall need to add to the amount in the acre of soil that in the living matter—in the trunks, branches, and leaves of the trees, in the animals, and in the other plants and micro-organisms. This additional amount will be large for the forest and relatively low for the grasses. Of course, the nutrients tied up in living matter are not subject to much leaching—not until the material dies and begins to decompose. It is mainly the material in the soil that is subject to leaching. Thus, of this total, more will be subject to leaching under grass than under forest.

Generally, the percentage of mineral plant nutrients in the organic remains from grass is higher than in those from forest. Thus more organic acids result from the decomposition of forest litter, even though the total of minerals supplied is somewhat greater. Per ton of dry matter produced, grasses return to the soil more bases, like calcium, potassium, and so on, than trees, other conditions being comparable; and, with nearly equivalent synthesis of organic matter, grasses produce more humus—black, stable organic matter—because of their chemical nature and their dense, fibrous root systems.

Then because of the relatively drier climate, the Chernozem soil is much less subject to leaching than the Podzol. Grass, side by side with forest in the moist Podzol region, holds less against leaching than the forest; grass side by side with forest at the boundary between the Chernozem and Podzol zones gives a darker soil, higher in organic matter and plant nutrients, than forest. The dark, fertile, granular surface soil is deeper under the grass and more suitable for crop plants than that under forest from the same rock material.

Thus, the figures selected for a comparison of an acre of Chernozem with an acre of Podzol vary greatly, depending upon whether we think only of the soil in a narrow sense or of the total landscape, including soils and plants together. In both scientific and practical work, both sets of comparisons are needed.

If the light-colored Podzols are fertilized, it is possible to have soil fertile for grass, despite the leaching. If this grass cover is maintained, the cultivated soil itself then takes on some of the physical and biological characteristics of the Chernozem of the black grasslands. But if we do not make up for the greater leaching in the Podzol landscape by the proper use of lime and fertilizers, the pastures and meadows are likely to be poor—indeed, not only poor, but the soil may actually become less fertile under the grass than under the forest. (Young alluvial soils or others too young to have received normal leaching are exceptions.)

In practice a farmer on the Podzol soils, let us say in New England, will produce pasture more efficiently by using lime and fertilizer on a small area to develop a soil approaching the less-leached Chernozem in fertility than to use a far larger area for untreated pasture. That is, a hundred acres of untreated pasture will, ordinarily, give less return in the Podzol landscape than the same area with 20 acres of well-treated pasture and 80 acres of forest, to say nothing of the fact that the long-time productivity of the soil will be better.

In this comparison both landscapes have a cold season when the ground is frozen. Let us look at the contrasting relationships between grass (savanna) and soil, and forest and soil in the humid Tropics with only a short dry season. In these comparisons it must be clear that reference to "grass" or "forest" includes all the plants, animals, and micro-organisms associated with them, not simply the trees and grasses themselves.

First of all, leaching under the heavy rainfall in equatorial regions is very severe. At high temperatures all chemical reactions are accelerated. (Generally the speed of chemical reactions doubles with each rise of 18° F.) Thus at any moment the (unfertilized) soil is low in all available plant nutrients (again except for very young soils like those on fresh alluvium or volcanic ejecta). The deep-rooted trees of the tropical rain forest draw nutrients from a great volume of soil. A large amount of these nutrients is collected and stored in the great tree trunks, in the branches and leaves of trees and other plants, and in micro-organisms and animals. At equilibrium, a small amount continually returns to the soil surface as the plants drop their leaves, and some is returned on or near the surface as the other living matter dies. And the amount lost by leaching balances the gains from new minerals and from the atmosphere. But the total amount of nutrients collected in the savanna is relatively small.

Thus, if we compare equal areas of the two landscapes under the same climate, one with a cover of tropical rain forest and the other with a cover of savanna, we shall find an enormous amount of material held by the living plants and not subject to leaching under the forest, and only a small amount held by the plants in the savanna with the rest subject to leaching. And, of course, that which is subject to leaching is leached out of the soil. Matters are made worse by fire. Whereas the tropical forest does not burn unless it is cut and made to burn, the savanna burns like gasoline-soaked rags when dry and so usually burns in the dry season. Moreover, tropical soils are relatively low in their capacity to absorb plant nutrients. Thus, a large part of the ash from burning the savanna is lost with the first heavy rains.

In such landscapes, then, we find the most productive soils, other things being equal, under the forest—the reverse of our comparison at the boundary between Chernozem and Podzol. In the Chernozem region where leaching is low and temperatures are relatively low, grass acts as a great soil builder and conserver of plant nutrients. In the hot humid Tropics, grass has the reverse effect and becomes a degrader of soil.

After cutting the luxuriant forest, crops may be grown in rotations and mixtures for periods of 2 to 7 years—sometimes even longer—depending upon local soil conditions. But it is necessary for forest to return to this soil again before the nutrient supply built up under the forest has been seriously depleted. Otherwise, the savanna will come into the cleared land and injure the soil for both trees and crops. After 10 to 15 years of forest growth, the land may again be devoted to a rotation of crops.

Soil Structure

Soils productive for crops are permeable to roots, water, and air. The productive soil has the individual grains grouped into aggregates so there are pore spaces for passage. Generally speaking, tillage by itself tends to destroy structure, tends to break up the soil crumbs and granules, and causes the clay particles to "run together" into masses. This effect of tillage varies enormously with different soil types and within one soil type, according to moisture conditions at the time of tillage and other cultural practices. In fact, a few soils become too granular with tillage so that contacts between roots and soil particles are too few for the proper transfer of water and the nutrients.

Even though tillage has the effect of injuring soil structure—scarcely at all with some soil types and a great deal with others—it often cannot be eliminated. Soil structure must be good in the lower layers as well as in the upper ones. Since an active population of micro-organisms is essential for good structure in most soils, organic materials and fertilizers must be added to many soils to make them productive for crops and grasses, and added not only to the surface, but also to the sub-soils. This may require deep plowing or chiseling to get the materials into the lower layers so that roots may go deeply.

The exposure of many soils to the hot sun injures structure by decreasing the micro-population, hastening the decomposition of organic matter, and causing a hard crust at the surface. Excess erosion, beyond that normal for the soil, may remove surface layers with good crumb structure and expose lower layers with poor structure. In fact, this type of injury by erosion is, generally, far more important than the nutrient losses from erosion.

Vigorous, close-growing, deep-rooted vegetation is the best builder of soil structure. Generally, the deep-rooted legumes and grasses are best for cultivated soil, provided, and only provided, that proper varieties are grown with adequate fertilization or manuring as needed on the individual soil type. But a well-growing forest produces better soil structure than poorly growing grasses. The best structure of all is produced under tall grasses in subhumid regions, as in Chernozem. Where leaching is low, organic matter and nutrients are conserved, and a deep fibrous root system develops. In areas of high leaching, like the humid Tropics, where the forest grows much better than grasses and conserves the nutrients, forest is superior to grass in developing and maintaining good soil structure.

In temperate regions, like most of the United States and Europe, the growing of vigorous stands of the deep-rooted grasses and legumes is generally the most effective way to develop soil structure, provided the soil is properly fertilized, as needed, in depth as well as in the surface. Of course, in the humid parts of the country soil structure can be maintained under a stand of forest also. But it is usually more efficient in the United States to work out a cropping system that does not require the periodic use of forest for the regeneration of soils for cropping.

The Place of Grass

Grass is the natural cover of many soil types throughout the world. It is the natural cover of the Chernozem—the famous black soils of subhumid temperate regions. But we must not conclude that grass is everywhere a conserving cover or that it always improves the soil. In moist regions where there is a great deal of leaching, the forest is generally a more conserving natural cover because it gathers a large body of plant nutrients, holds them in living forms, and gradually returns them to the soil.

In hot humid regions it is especially difficult to have good grass and productive soil together—one must make up through practice the great ability of the forest to shade the soil and keep it cool, to maintain structure, and to conserve plant nutrients against the strong forces of leaching. Unless management practices can offset these changes in environment, grasses will not grow well and the soils will deteriorate.

The same principle holds in all humid regions, like the eastern part of the United States, where the natural cover is forest, except for young soils that have not been leached importantly, even though the contrast may not appear to be so great as in the Tropics. Grass can often be established and maintained in naturally forested regions simply by seeding and by fire, mowing, or cutting to keep out the young shrubs and trees. But under such conditions, without fertilizers or manures, most pastures and meadows will be poor and the soils will deteriorate, perhaps rapidly, perhaps slowly.

Farmers really should make a clear decision between grass or forest. Although wild grass is a good soil-building cover in semiarid and subhumid regions if protected against overgrazing, it usually is not in humid regions except for relatively unleached soils. Wild, uncared for, frequently burned grassland in humid regions produces little. The soil is made more productive and yields more if forested.

Thus grass cannot be classified definitely as "soil-conserving" or "soil-depleting"; it may be one or the other on the same farm, on the same soil type, depending on cultural practices.

Except for young alluvial soils, most soils in the United States must be periodically devoted to the grasses and grasslike plants to remain productive for crop plants. Thus proper liming and fertilization for deep-rooted legumes, alone or in mixtures with grass, are the first steps for either production or soil conservation on millions of American farms. The amount of lime and the kinds of fertilizers vary from soil to soil but emphasis needs to be given phosphates, potash, and boron, roughly in that order, although each field has its individual needs for these and other nutrients according to the soil type and previous management.

For the efficient production of grasses—efficient in terms of equality, yield, and good effects on the long-time productivity of the soil—practices must be used to maintain within the soil conditions similar to those in the natural Chernozem. This means abundant plant nutrients and good structure for considerable depth. Such a deep layer of fertile soil with good structure often needs to be made by the farmer from the natural soil. An individual set of practices to this end will be required in each individual landscape.

With the proper practices, grasses can be grown efficiently in most parts of the world, but not everywhere. One of the great problems of agricultural science is to learn how to make these practices more efficient and especially how to adapt them more precisely to the individual soil types. Then too, we need to discover practices for growing good grass efficiently on those soils for which we have as yet no satisfactory methods.

37. *Fertilization: Route to a New Continent* *

Soils that have a rich natural vegetation may or may not have a high yield when planted to a particular crop. It is now recognized that certain crops require specific soil minerals for high productivity; with the use of fertilizers, crop yields have been increased greatly in many areas. This reading presents a somewhat optimistic view of the possibilities of higher yields through the selective use of fertilizers. Despite its somewhat glorified estimate, wise use of fertilizer can undoubtedly increase yields as well as farm income. Availability and accessibility of mineral fertilizers is another aspect of the problem, since some agricultural areas of the world are poorly endowed.

A few centuries ago Christopher Columbus made a long voyage looking for a new route to the riches of the East Indies. Instead he discovered a continent, a land which has added enormously to the world's food supply. Recently, what amounts to the discovery of a new continent may result from widespread use of modern crop fertilization formulae. In short with proper application of nitrogen, phosphorus and potash, crop production can be doubled and the continent of Columbus can become equivalent to two as a producer of food.

One of the most arable sections of North America is the Mid-West Corn Belt which waited until the middle of the last century before starting its great contribution towards American food supply. Commercial farming developed slowly but by the decade of the 1890's, the grain producing qualities of this great farming region became known thruout the world.

In the early 1900's, Professor Cyril G. Hopkins of the University of Illinois, believing that limits of crop production were still far above the yields at that time, discovered that Corn Belt soils lack sufficient phosphorus

* Earl B. Shaw, "Fertilization: Route to a New Continent," *Journal of Geography*, Vol. 47, No. 7, Oct. 1948, pp. 284–290. By permission of the *Journal of Geography*, official publication of the National Council of Geography Teachers.

The author (1889) is Professor of Geography, State Teachers College, Worcester, Massachusetts. He has published articles on a variety of subjects in geographical journals.

for a maximum clover harvest. As a result, he developed a plan to increase crop yields and to maintain soil fertility—a plan which included (1) the application of phosphorus to aid clover growth and (2) the growth of clover every fourth year in a crop rotation cycle.

Hopkins was one of the first to advocate the well known four year rotation of corn, corn, oats and clover. The cycle worked well, especially when a heavy phosphate application was made at the time oats were seeded as a nurse crop for clover. If land became acid, lime was added to correct soil acidity and to permit phosphate and clover to react most efficiently. The lime-phosphate-clover program and the four year and similar rotation cycles high-lighted Corn Belt crop production for many years. Hopkins became famous; students from his classes carried his theories to other Corn Belt universities; farm papers and extension bulletins encouraged the Hopkins Plan. It was regarded as the answer to practically all major crop production problems of the Mid-West.

Modern Fertilization Programs

A few years ago, certain agronomists, who believed the Hopkins Plan good, but not the final answer to increased crop yields, discovered that larger production will result if nitrogen is added to the original Hopkins Plan. Increases from a phosphorus-nitrogen fertilization are almost unbelievable. The use of this combination with oats may be cited as an illustration.

Corn, the principal grain crop of the Mid-West, is usually planted for two or three years on the same field. Then the land may be seeded to oats or other small grain, and almost always clover is planted with it at the same time. Oats shades the clover from the hot sun until the legume gets well rooted and able to make its way alone at the time oats are cut.

Clovers have the ability to take nitrogen from the air and fix that soil builder in the soil, but the task is not started until oats are harvested. Consequently oats, which in recent years has averaged only about thirty bushel an acre in Iowa, gets no help from the crop whose early growth it protects. The old recommendation of applying phosphorus to the oats at seeding time, to help the clover, never did help the nurse crop appreciably because the major deficiency affecting oats was nitrogen. Now when phosphorus and nitrogen are both applied, the oats yield may be more than doubled. One authority sums it up this way.

> To help the yield of oats, simply add as many pounds of nitrogen as you want to increase the yield of grain in bushels per acre. One pound of nitrogen adds one extra bushel of oats if that nitrogen is applied in combination with phosphorus, but only if it is applied in combination with phosphorus.

Basically the same fertilizing program will hold true with wheat or barley that holds true for oats. The only difference is that because wheat is twice as heavy as oats, it takes approximately two pounds of nitrogen to increase the yield of wheat one bushel, and approximately a pound and a half for an increase of each bushel of barley.

In general, the increases available thru using nitrogen with phosphorus when seeding oats, wheat and barley are also available if such fertilizers are applied to the land at the time of corn seeding. Of course corn yields received a big boost within the last decade in response to the development and widespread use of hybrid seed corn. Largely as a result of this progressive step, corn averages have jumped several bushels an acre within the last few years. But farmers are not satisfied with this progress. Dr. W. L. Burlison, head of agronomy at the University of Illinois, states "The average corn yield here in the heart of the Corn Belt is about fifty bushels an acre. Why is it not more than fifty? The first factor is nitrogen. Put in the nitrogen and you get seventy-five. Add phosphorus and you get ninety. Put in potash also and you get one hundred. When we add nitrogen, phosphorus and potassium for thickly planted high-yielding hybrid corn to normally 90 bushel corn land, the sky is the limit. Under favorable weather conditions yields have already jumped to 150 and more bushels. Our better farmers here in the Corn Belt do not talk any more about seventy-bushel corn. They are shooting at a hundred and fifty bushels and more."

The revolution in crop production brought about by increased use of chemical fertilizers is not confined to the Corn Belt. J. Sidney Cates, writing in the June, 1947, *Country Gentleman,* "War Lessons With Fertilizers" and in a personal letter to the author says that

Corn yields in Southern United States rise to Corn Belt heights when thick-planted hybrid corn is grown in fields treated with nitrogen. In one North Carolina experiment, ten dollars worth of nitrogen pushed up corn yield from 19 bushels an acre without fertilization to 107 bushels with it. Nitrogen not only feeds the crop, but also insures against or cuts down drought damage. Without heavy nitrogen application, a severe drought, coming just as the corn is in silk, has a devastating effect. But put out as much as sixty pounds of nitrogen to the acre, and when a drought does come the corn leaves do not fire. They may curl and look pretty sick, but they stay dark green and alive; and it's in a drought year that the biggest difference shows between no nitrogen and heavy nitrogen.

Mr. Cates also says that

An increase in nitrogen and potash on tobacco and cotton soils with a relative lessening of phosphorus provides increased harvests in the South; and

North Carolina soy bean growers have discovered that doubling or trebling potash applications will encourage a big boost in yields.

It should also be added that many people have thought only of the poor lands of the United States when considering fertilization potential. The nation's farmers are now beginning to realize that it may be even more profitable to use fertilizer on the rich lands than on the poorly cropped, eroded and so-called worn out lands of the country.

Much is yet to be learned, however, concerning the best methods of applying nitrogen and other commercial fertilizing materials, and as to what are optimum amounts to be used for highest yields. For example in 1946 at the University of Illinois, corn production tests were made using nitrogen in amounts of 20-40-60-80 pounds of elemental nitrogen per acre and of application by broadcast before plowing, at planting time, at second cultivation, at third cultivation; side dressing at planting time, at second cultivation, and at third cultivation. The fields with the 40 pounds elemental nitrogen applied as a side dressing at the second and third cultivation produced at the rate of 104 bushels of corn per acre, while the field with an application of 80 pounds broadcast at second cultivation and the field with a similar application at planting time only yielded 89 bushels of corn per acre.

Again, old tried and proven practices such as the establishment and maintenance of good drainage; the judicious utilization and careful conservation of legumes, crop residues and animal manures; contour farming; terracing; grass waterways; correction of soil acidity by use of limestone; cropping systems with proper balance between intertilled, small grain and grass-legume sod crops—none of these should be abandoned because of exciting results obtained by the addition of commercial nitrogen, phosphorus and potash. Commercial fertilizers such as these should supplement the time-tested crop practices rather than replace them.

Fertilizer Resources of the United States

One of the main problems facing the farmers of the nation is to obtain, cheaply, enough commercial fertilizer to raise food production to the status of a new continental discovery. The United States supply of phosphorus is large, and prior to the war this country produced more phosphoric acid and phosphate rock than any other country in the world. In four western states, Idaho, Montana, Utah and Wyoming, billions of tons of phosphate rock are available and five states of the Southeast, Florida, Tennessee, Arkansas, South Carolina and Kentucky possess phosphate resources probably less than ten per cent of those in the West. Because the deposits of the Southeast lie closer to the nation's greatest farming country they account for well over three-fourths of our annual production. Of nearly five million tons of phosphate rock mined in 1941, only about 300,000 tons were produced from the far greater resources of the four western states.

Large supplies of potash are available in the United States, but the greatest deposits also lie far from the market. Two major areas supplied the bulk of the 1941 production. These are the Permian Basin of the Carlsbad section of New Mexico and the brines of Searles Lake, California. Sub-surface brines of the Salduro Marsh near Wendover, Utah contribute slightly to United States production. In 1942 the total national production approximated 617,000 tons of K_2O in the form of refined salts, a great increase over the 1930's 61,000 tons when most of our potash came from Stassfurt, Germany and Alsace, France.

Cheaply available natural occurring nitrate reserves are limited in the United States, but nitrogen fixation plants offer adequate substitute where low cost power is available. However, plants with cheap power are not in abundance at the present time and here is one of the greatest drawbacks to the utilization of the "newly discovered continent."

The present nitrogen fixation capacity of the United States is only about 700,000 tons, and of this amount, something like 70,000 tons are being exported under the rehabilitation program. To show how inadequate the supply of ammonium nitrate is, consider the following excerpt from a letter written by Garst and Thomas Hybrid Corn Company, Coon Rapids, Iowa.

> There are about 200,000 farmers in Iowa. Each could profitably use the nitrogen equivalent of five tons of ammonium nitrate on his farm annually. This means that Iowa farmers could profit by using the nitrogen equivalent of something like a million tons of ammonium nitrate. They would, of course, have to use far more phosphorus and potash than they are now using to balance it—but they could use something like that much nitrogen.
>
> As against a potential demand for a million tons. Iowa was able to procure only about 7,000 tons last year (1946) and will only be able to acquire about 12,000 tons next year (1948). In other words only one farmer in every twenty, or thereabouts, could have one ton if it were equitably distributed, and it is not.
>
> The Iowa situation is only representative of the national picture. Nebraska farmers know even more about the use of ammonium nitrate than those in Iowa. Kansas and Missouri will know as much about it soon. In all four states the demand will exceed the supply for some time. In the whole nation this will probably be true.

Europe is also badly in need of nitrogen. In speaking of Europe's need, the Krug report states: "Altho European production of nitrogen is almost back to pre-war levels, total production abroad is still below capacity, owing chiefly to an insufficiency of coal and electric power." The report suggests "giving high priority to coal and industrial equipment shipments for increased nitrogen fertilizer production in Europe." Another item of the report is also of interest to American farmers seeking increased nitrogen supplies. "Considering transportation and cost, it appears desirable to export nitrogen for increased food production abroad rather than to continue to ship the much greater tonnage of equivalent food from the United States."

Some say that nitrogen fertilizers are as easily available as the air we breathe, the water we drink, and the gas our coal fields can produce, but it must be stressed that nitrogen fixation plants are very expensive. An economical sized operating unit may cost twenty or thirty million dollars and many such units are needed for United States production.

The new continent has been discovered but its blessings wait upon supplies of chemical fertilizer for its own use and that of other continents. Yield estimates made cooperatively by the United States Department of Agriculture and the Land Grant Colleges show that with proper land use practices food production can be increased by 1950 as follows: corn 31 per cent; hay 28 per cent; wheat 18 per cent; rice 13 per cent; peanuts 20 per cent; sugar beets 17 per cent; potatoes 22 per cent and sweet potatoes 31 per cent. And these probably are not ceiling figures for the future. Many believe that fully fertilized, the agricultural production can easily be doubled. The sooner we get to building the nitrogen plants either by private industry or government enterprise the sooner the new continental discovery will really come into its own.

38. Major Agricultural Regions of the World *

Despite the great diversity of climates, landforms, and human activities over the surface of the earth, the fundamental agricultural pattern developed by mankind shows a distinct area specialization. Furthermore, this agricultural pattern is one of the most stable and fixed patterns that man has established. Although this outstanding analysis of agricultural regions was published in 1936, it is only slightly

* Reprinted from Derwent W. Whittlesey, "Major Agricultural Regions of the World," *Annals of the Association of American Geographers,* Vol. 26, 1936, p. 199. By permission.

The author is Professor Emeritus of Geography, Harvard University. His geographical interests and writings cover a wide range of subjects. His book *The Earth and the State* is a standard work on political geography.

outdated. The highly diverse regions here described were selected either because they occupy areas significant in supporting large groups of the world's population or because they extensively utilize relatively large uninhabited areas of the world.

Of all the modes of using land, raising crops and livestock covers the most space and is the most easily observed in the field. It therefore lends itself better than the others to geographic classification—that is to say areal analysis and synthesis.

Tillage of the soil and pasturage of animals are postulated on indefinite anticipated continuance of collaboration between man and the ground, a relation embodied in the term husbandry. In this respect these occupations differ from the extractive industries, which take from the earth nature's bounty with no provision for replenishment, and also from manufacturing, trade, and the professions, which use the earth chiefly or solely as a localized site for their operations. Oddly, the English language has no term to cover both plant and animal husbandry. For lack of a more fitting word, "agriculture" is used in these pages.

. . . . .

Livestock Ranching

Livestock ranching everywhere has been instituted by sedentary folk of European antecedents who have settled in dry country. They have taken with them habits, attitudes, and beliefs of humid regions, and with few and temporary exceptions, they have kept in contact with the outside world. Many of their inherited ways of life have become modified in the harsh and unsympathetic environment of their adopted lands. In extreme cases, as the Boers of South Africa, the pioneers had to turn nomadic, but succeeding generations are generally able to live a life more nearly in accord with their humid-country traditions. This is largely owing to the improved transportation of the past 150 years, which has brought the livestock ranching regions progressively closer to the outside world—their market and their supply store.

Ranching postdates the discoveries of the New World by Europeans, because until cattle, sheep, goats, and horses were introduced to America and Australia-New Zealand, the basic elements of the business were lacking in the new continents. In the Americas some imported animals, turned loose, became progenitors of a half-wild race. The Indians promptly caught them and spontaneously became nomadic herders as an advance over their traditional practice of collecting what they could from the natural environment. This system was extirpated, along with the plains Indians, when a world market for wool, hides, and meat developed. This market is the creature of the Industrial Revolution and the consequent rise of cities full of people who raise no animal products for themselves. The regions of the new continents akin in natural environment to the nomadic herding regions of the Old World, are remote. They have been grappled to these growing city populations by instruments of the Industrial Revolution itself—the steamship and the railroad, the telegraph, and the refrigerator.

The livestock ranch is semi-sedentary. The ranch house forms a permanent center, where a good deal of capital is fixed in the shape of dipping vats, shearing sheds, and paddocks—facilities calculated to maintain the high quality of the products and to expedite their shipment. Usually the ranch is fenced, a refinement over the pioneer days of the open range. Some land may be tilled to raise forage for winter feeding in cool regions, or against the day of drouth. Wells or ponds distributed over the ranch supply the herds with water, which usually outlasts the forage. Ordinary movements of the herds are confined to the ranch, although in mountainous regions transhumance follows the seasons to remote pastures—often rented. During years of extreme drouth enforced nomadism drives stock from ruined grazing lands to less afflicted pastures. In all these movements "cowboys" attached to the ranch move with the herds, but at roundup and occasionally at other times they live briefly at the ranch house.

Great care is taken to improve the breed, and the rancher is a business operator on a large scale. Each region tends to specialize on the animal and the product for which it is best fitted. This is in line with the technical proficiency of the business.

Although all the leading ranching regions are in the new continents, inroads are being made on nomadic herding regions wherever railroads have tapped them. Stimulated by outside markets, European methods or settlers are intruding themselves, notably in Russian Turkestan, in the Atlas, and in the East and South African highlands.

Statistics are available for the chief livestock ranching regions. In the stock and crop association the ratio of browsing animals—cattle, sheep, goats—to total area is very low, and the ratio of cropland—mostly hay—to the total area is even lower. The percentage of draft animal units in the total animal population is likewise very low. Careful methods result in a high return per animal. The land is used extensively, since it requires several acres to feed an animal. This means huge holdings and a small and scattered farm population. Isolation urges absentee ownership; some holdings are organized as stock companies.

Livestock ranching is likely to be the mode of occupying an expanding frontier. Near the margin of settlement the number of both people and animals may be negligible. This is notably the case in the southern part of the Amazon Basin, and scarcely less so in interior Australia.

. . . . .

In summary comparison of the two types of agricultural occupance based on livestock and occupying the drylands of the earth, contrasts appear. One is a subsistence business, the other commercial. This results in a different cultural landscape and a widely divergent return for effort. It is a neat example of the utilization of essentially the same natural landscape in contrasting ways, the distinction being based on different stages of technology.

Shifting Cultivation

Within the humid low latitudes another pair of agricultural types may be recognized. Their character and regional distribution are less clean-cut, because the climate and interrelated vegetation and soils range from rain forest on laterite to park-savanna on friable soil, and from oceanic deltas to mountain basins at 14,000 feet elevation. Besides, there are large areas in almost identical natural environments which do not practice either of these agricultural systems. Some historical relation between them can, however, be traced.

Shifting cultivation, the archetype, is widespread in the rain forest and on its borders. There lateritic soil, infertile at best, leeches and erodes rapidly when removal of the natural vegetation exposes it to sun and rain. This has led all primitive peoples inhabiting such lands to move their farmed plots every few years (usually from one to three, depending on local conditions), and to seek new land in the adjacent forest. After some years (five to a dozen), the plots being tilled are inconveniently remote from the village, and the tribe removes to a site in the deep forest, a new center from which another block of land is gradually cleared. The absence of domestic animals in aboriginal America restricted the farm products to crops, except for llama hair, as did the presence of the tsetse fly in Africa, save for poultry, pigs, and goats. In the true rain forest the large domestic animals languish, but in somewhat drier regions hardy strains survive, outside tsetse infected regions. Crops were few and monotonous until outsiders, especially Europeans, began moving from continent to continent, carrying seeds and slips, as well as livestock.

The forest dwellers live in small tribes, segregated from their neighbors by abandoned and jungly clearings or by virgin forest. They build huts of thatch, sometimes thatch over mud, and have no more paraphernalia than they can move when the old home has to be abandoned. They are likely to be animists, and no major religion has ever affected most of them.

Tillage is crude, fire being used to clear the ground, with some assistance from hand tools. Many tribes make sticks serve as plows and root up the plants by way of harvesting them. The return is inevitably very low, and food shortage is common toward the end of the growing period, after the old crop is consumed, and before the new one is ready for gathering. Little clothing is needed, and materials for housing are to be found everywhere.

Shifting cultivation extends beyond the rain forest, into several of the combinations of small trees and coarse grasses commonly called "bush." In this environment it lacks some characteristic features, and has to compete with nomadic herding or livestock ranching. Only in Africa, where the tsetse is the enemy of animal husbandry, does shifting cultivation spread far beyond the margins of the rain forest.

As in the case of Nomadic Herding, no statistics are available on the migrant tillers of the soil. Descriptions of their life and landscape are few, most of them being incidental notes tucked away in anthropological discussions, and incomplete from the geographic viewpoint.

. . . . .

Intensive Subsistence Tillage with Rice Dominant

In the humid regions of South and East Asia and adjacent islands, another pair of agricultural types is found, very different from all the rest, but distinguished from each other chiefly by the presence or absence of rice in the crop association.

Where the season is long enough for paddy rice to mature, the highly intensive agricultural system supports the densest rural population found over large areas anywhere on earth. Although three sorts of crops are associated with three types of farmland, the key to this mode of land occupance is the paddy—irrigable deltas, floodplains, coastal plains, and terraces planted to rice. Two crops a year are garnered where the climate is hot, one where water fails or a cool season intervenes. Rice yields more grain per acre than any other crop. Land out of reach of irrigation, but not too rough, is devoted to varied crops, chiefly grains, oil-seeds, and cotton. Hillslopes too steep to till are planted to trees—mulberry, tea, pepper, and others.

Waters as well as all types of lands are compelled to furnish a share of the food supply. Fish is taken from the rivers and backwaters, and cultivated in artificial ponds. Aquatic plants yield a living to numerous ducks, or are pulled to spread on the fields as green fertilizer.

All the work is performed by hand, except plowing the paddies. Plows are pulled by carabaos, animals which are at home in watery mud. Hand tools are moderately effective, being made of iron or steel, but plows and irrigation pumps are primitive. Some of the tasks are incredibly arduous. Grain must be hung up to dry after being cut, tea and mulberry leaves must be carefully gathered, and the rice plants must be transferred one by one from seed plots to fields. Besides the routine jobs water must be pumped on to the paddies, and irrigation works must be kept in repair.

Natural flooding, annually or occasionally, helps maintain fertility in the paddy silts. On unirrigable lands two or more crops may be planted in the same field to minimize drain on the soil. The seeds may be mixed or planted in alternate rows. Rotation is likewise a well understood principle. In these regions of few animals the land is fed by every available sort of fertilizer, including nightsoil.

Because of the careful methods in vogue and the excellent tilth maintained by hand weeding, it is doubtful if the introduction of farm machinery would increase production. More likely the yield would be less. Certainly the rice paddies would produce less per acre if transplanting should be abandoned.

In spite of indefatigable labor, per capita production is not high and the people are abjectly poor. They live in close-set and close-packed villages crowded upon the smallest possible acreage, to preserve the precious land for tillage, or standing, sometimes inconveniently remote from the fields, on sand spits, tongues of unirrigable land, or other inferior soils. In delta districts whole populations may dwell on houseboats. The furnishings of homes are meager.

Few statistics are published for China, but Japan and especially India are covered by numerous reports. Where an all-year growing season permits, two crops a year are grown on the same land. This results in more than 100% of the total cropped area being in crops in the course of the year. Rice occupies the ground during the favored season, when nearly the total tilled area may be under this one crop. Studies of particular regions are more detailed, if not more numerous, than for the agricultural types previously discussed.

. . . . .

Specialized Horticulture

Production of fruits and vegetables in kitchen gardens and home orchards is the rule in most agriculture of humid regions. Among the occidental systems of middle latitudes horticulture as an important phase of the business occurs only in Mediterranean agriculture. Elsewhere fruit and vegetable growing, if on a large scale, is specialized on exceptionally favored spots. . . . Each district concentrates on one or a very few crops, which it sells to a market as particularized as the producing area itself.

Perhaps the most ancient districts of specialized horticulture are the vineyards of Europe outside the Mediterranean climate. Some of them were instituted in Roman times, although they were put on a cash basis in the modern sense only two or three centuries ago. The most famous are the *côtes* of the Eastern Paris Basin, where southeast slopes and limestone soils offset the cool, dark climate and produce the prized light wines known under generic place names, such as Burgundy, Champagne, and Moselle. Similarly situated, and only a little less famous, are wines from slopes overlooking the Rhine, the Loire, the Swiss lakes, and the plain of northern Hungary. Near Bordeaux special soils and a quasi-Mediterranean climate produce wines ranking with Burgundies. In a very different climate and under irrigation, Argentina supplies itself with wine from the specialized oases, Mendoza and San Juan.

Other aspects of intensive fruit and vegetable growing had to await the market created by city populations which live by manufacturing, mining, and trading. Producing little or no food themselves, they purchase large quantities of horticultural crops.

This demand is satisfied in part by market gardens within a few hours trucking of populous cities. There, on the types of land which favor early harvest, intensive labor and consummate skill are devoted to raising the maximum of crops on the minimum of acres. Warm soils bring into bearing successive crops, each a bit earlier than in ordinary nearby gardens. Lavish application of purchased fertilizers enrich the light soil and produce high yields and quality. The value of market garden land averages higher per acre than that devoted to any other sort of farming. The crops are vegetables and bush fruits.

No outlay for housing is required, apart from a residence, unless the business has progressed to the stage of growing crops in winter or starting seeds under glass. In such cases greenhouses are built over the gardens, to utilize the same prized soil. During peak periods the farmer and his family must work almost incessantly. Therefore they usually live on the place in a small house, well-kept like the garden itself. This gives the market garden district the aspect of a scattered residential village.

Farther from the city market, in belts progressing into warmer climates, extend districts of truck farming. Lacking the market garden's advantage of nearness to market, truck farms make up for it by exceptionally favorable soil and by the climate, which matures the desired crops earlier than in their competitors' suburban gardens. Only in Europe and North America does the urban population induce truck farming. Districts in Europe lie in three regions. (1) Along the Channel coast of Brittany and the Netherlands, to supply the markets of Britain, Germany, and North France. In the Low Countries the business is conducted under glass as well as outdoors, and is favored less by climate than by soil, and by cheap labor with a long-standing tradition of meticulous tillage. (2) The narrow Rhône Valley, the bit of Mediterranean climate nearest to Northwest Europe, is a continuous ribbon of truck farm. The superposition of truck farming on the original Mediterranean agriculture entails merely a different group of crops and not a marked change in the character of agricultural land occupance. At the head of the Rhône Delta this belt changes direction and runs along the Riviera into Italy. (3) Similar districts, which market their vegetables and fruits still earlier in the season, are the Algerian and Tunisian coast of North Africa, the plains of Morocco, and the nearer oases in the Sahara.

In North America two zones extend southward from the major urban region. The larger follows the sandy soils of the Atlantic coastal plain. In Florida it merges into low latitude climate. The smaller follows the Mississippi Valley and the Gulf Coast, but only intermittently. In the Rio Grande Valley it occupies irrigated land which has some of the qualities of a low latitude desert oasis. A quite distinct area in which truck farming occurs is the dry country west of the 100th meridian. Scattered through it from southern Canada to northern Mexico are irrigated patches producing a wide climatic range of fruits and a number of vegetables. The climax of this region is the low latitude desert of the Lower Colorado Basin and the Mediterranean Climate of California. These areas are functional counterparts of the truck farms in the Sahara and on the shores of the Mediterranean Sea.

Commercial fruit orchards are found in many of the truck farming regions. All but hardy fruits, such as apples, cherries, and pears, are confined to climates milder than the urban regions of either Europe or North America can boast. Irrigation has evolved the large and handsome fruits common in the United States. In humid regions there are orchard districts in favored belts and spots. . . . Islands of more favorable climate are created in the sea of continental conditions by water bodies, which retard blossoms in spring and frosts in autumn, and by hills which set up air drainage. Examples are the apple district of southwestern Germany, and the fruit zones of Nova Scotia, the Lower Great Lakes, the Middle Appalachians, and the Ozarks. The wine districts of North Europe also belong in this category.

The landscape of the truck farm district or fruit belt looks much like a market garden area. Small houses, each on its own land, crops very carefully tended, and no livestock, except perhaps a horse or mule for plowing and hauling.

Besides fruits and vegetables a number of other crops are produced as specialties, at least in some districts. Many a crop of this sort is only one item in several produced by every farmer of the neighborhood. Always it is sold for cash, and it may provide the principal income of the farm, even though the acreage occupied by it is but a small fraction of the tilled land. Sugar beets in humid regions, tobacco in the middle latitudes, flax and hemp for fiber, and many less widely distributed crops belong to this group. In the classification of major agricultural regions, these crops may properly be thought of as variants of the cash crops more usually characteristic of the association in which they are found.

Much the same sort of crop is cotton in humid climates. It is being grown increasingly as a specialty crop in regions which otherwise bear many of the earmarks of commercial livestock and crop farming.

In dry regions where irrigation must be practiced, cotton may dominate the business of small districts. Oases within Russian Turkestan, spots in the Levant, a district in the Argentine Chaco, coastal oases of Peru, and places in the Lower Colorado Basin are examples. Sugar beets in the Platte and Salt Lake oases of western United States, and sugar cane in irrigated districts of coastal Peru and northern Argentina are in similar case. These irrigated spots are designated as specialized horticulture, because the agricultural system is much the same as in vegetable and fruit growing of nearby oases.

Specialized poultry production is a minor business, carried on chiefly in the United States, which resembles market gardening wherever it is found near large cities, and truck farming in the two large producing districts of California.

The small districts devoted to commercial horticulture and the other crop specialties rarely coincide with administrative divisions for which statistics are collected. In the field they are easily observed, because the break between horticulture and surrounding, extensive land utilization is sharp, adhering strictly to frost lines and changes in soil or slope. Some truck farms of the Atlantic and Gulf coastal plains, carved out of deep forest, are as strikingly set off as are irrigated oases in deserts. Perhaps because they are clean-cut, many garden and orchard regions have been carefully studied. From these studies a composite picture of this manifold agricultural system can be seen.

39. *Agricultural and Forestry Potential of the Tropics* *

With the major exception of tropical southeast Asia, which is densely populated, most tropical areas of the world remain relatively uninhabited and little used. Although these regions are characterized by little climatic diversity, the vast variety of trees and other plants found in the tropics gives some indication of their possibilities and potentialities. The major problems are those of exploitation, and here political and social considerations seem to have inhibited, to some extent, the rapid development of the tropics.

In this discussion we shall consider the humid equatorial lowlands, especially the vast Amazon and Congo River basins. Since Hevea rubber, vegetable oils, and cordage and textile fibers are important plant products of these regions, we will include them along with food crops; also since much of the land in these regions is still under tropical high rain forests, we shall briefly consider some of the points relating to forestry and the utilization of tropical woods. We must not overlook tree crops because they are especially appropriate for many equatorial soils.

Erroneous Popular Opinions

In higher latitudes, and particularly in the United States, a widespread opinion prevails that such humid tropical regions as the enormous Amazon basin, now occupied by luxuriant and apparently limitless tropical high forests, must certainly have rich soils, and hence, great potentialities for the production of food, fiber, and other agricultural crops. These opinions continue to be expressed not only in the Sunday supplements but in other periodicals; this wishful thinking also has a large place in at least one recent book. It is also perfectly natural for foresters, especially, to feel that the great quantities of hardwood timber should not be destroyed in clearing, but sawed into lumber and marketed into those portions of the world where there is such need for wood.

It is true that certain regions such as those with recently active volcanoes, and those recent alluvial soils in humid equatorial lowlands which are not deeply flooded, do have great crop growing potentialities; they are

* Robert L. Pendleton, "Agricultural and Forestry Potentialities of the Tropics," *Agronomy Journal,* Vol. 42, No. 3, March, 1950, pp. 115–123.

The author is a specialist in tropical soils and land use (particularly of southeast Asia) at the Isaiah Bowman School of Geography, The Johns Hopkins University.

producing and can continue to produce much from the soil. Nevertheless, on the whole, the soils of humid equatorial regions have distressingly limited possibilities for plant production. In addition, the economic problems of utilizing and marketing the enormous number of different kinds of tropical lumber are very different and more difficult than the problems of utilizing the well known temperate zone woods.

This pessimistic attitude is no longer the result of mere opinion, for in a number of widely scattered regions in the humid low latitudes agricultural scientists have been and still are seriously at work. Their findings are, as a whole, not at all encouraging for the possibilities of intensive production of annual grain and fodder crops and the maintenance of pastures of the types we are used to, for example, in the corn or wheat belts of the United States.

Kaingining of Equatorial Forests

A stranger flying hour after hour over the vast, magnificent, and beautiful equatorial forests, seeing scarcely a sign of any human activity, much less of any serious agricultural cultivation as we know it, but rather only small, often isolated clearings here and there—holes of an acre or so cut in the forest, when he sees the towering trees being cut and burned to make a clearing where will be produced a few sacks of food—a little upland rice, maize, or mandioca (casava, *Manihot utilssima*)—he cannot help but think: What a shocking destruction of beautiful and valuable timber! Why not have sawmills to work up the timber so that it can be marketed, and then cultivate the soil assiduously year after year rather than destroy more forest for new clearings each year? Even after extensive travel and study in Brazil, Lynn Smith erred seriously in criticizing "fire agriculture," as he called it, and believed that it could be replaced by more intensive types of land use. In the Philippines, where this method of crop production is known as *kaingining*,* with the best and most highly trained Ameri-

* A *kaingin* is the clearing made by *kaingining:* this involves felling the forest, burning the slash, and then dibbling the seeds or cuttings of food or fiber crops into the unstirred soil. The *kainginero* is the one who produces crops in this way. (*Kaingin,* to *kaingin,* and *kainginero* are Philippine vernacular words, used in technical agricultural and forestry publications in English since about 1910.) This method of crop production is used even where the soils are not so infertile, and is generally employed by peasants in most humid equatorial lowlands and up to midaltitudes. Draft animals are not used, nor would plowing be possible, for the soil is full of stumps and roots. But plowing is quite unnecessary. Many vernacular names have been applied to this practice: *canuco* or *roça* around the Caribbean, and in Brazil; *taungya* in Burma; *cheena* in Ceylon; *rai* in Siam; *ladang* in the N.E.I., etc. In 1919 the Mexican word *milpa* was proposed by O. F. Cook, but this is an inappropriate term, for in Mexico *milpa* means a permanently cultivated corn field. There is no connotation whatsoever of the use of forest as a cover crop to kill the weeds and improve the soil structure, thus restoring soil fertility. The term "shifting cultivation" is also inappropriate, for it implies a nomadic or semi-nomadic

can tropical foresters, the official policy was to combat kaingining; kaingineros were often punished by jail sentences. On the other hand, as in Burma and India, under certain circumstances foresters gave permission to kaingin certain forest lands, where they were desirous of planting out special forest crop trees. In the Philippines, with its often much better than average tropical soils, and better than average stands of rain forest and marketing conditions for tropical timber, there was some justification for the official attitude against kaingining.*

Failure of Permanent Cropping with Annuals

An observant traveller is not long in the Amazon valley before learning why some of these seemingly very irrational ways of growing crops and destroying timber are used. In Pará State the once heavily forested Bragança region, east of Belem and of the mouth of the Amazon River and almost under the equator, illustrates well the great difficulties in attempting to convert one of these forest regions into an intensively cultivated agricultural one. Many years ago a railroad and roads were built eastward from Belem through this Bragança region and people were encouraged to come in and settle. It was expected that this district would soon be settled and prosperous through agricultural production, for less than a thousand miles to the southeast are the sertões, the arid region of shallow soils, from which there is a continual migration of laborers seeking work, while coastwise shipping provides an easy method of transport. The sertões are the semiarid portions of northeastern Brazil from which people have to migrate more or less continuously in order to find work. Moreover, about once a decade in that region there has been a disastrous famine with many deaths by starvation. This is the source of much of the labor which has developed central and southern Brazil, and also for rubber collecting in the Amazon Valley. Thus, it was reasoned, why not develop sound agricultural colonies in the immense rainy forests just to the east of Belem, with some of this population needing farms in less

---

type of population, when actually the kaingineros often live most of the year in permanent villages of substantial dwellings.

* It is evident that professional foresters, mostly, it is true, with temperate zone experience continue to be opposed to kaingining. For example, in The Report of the Panel on Forestry and Forest Products, to Commission II of the Fifth Session of the Conference of the Food and Agriculture Organization, Document C49/II/F Panel 15, presented December 1, 1949, we find on p. 4: "The Conference stresses again the urgency of dealing with the problem of shifting cultivation and other forms of destructive land use so widespread in tropical and subtropical countries." Upon presentation agricultural members of Commission II called attention to the fact that while such methods of "shifting cultivation" may be destructive of forests they are *not* destructive of soil; that on the contrary kaingining protects the soil from erosion, and that kaingining is often the only way by which peasants can produce any food from poor soils.

droughty regions as has so often been the case elsewhere? The peasants who pioneered here soon found that while they could get a good crop of food the first year after cutting and burning the primeval forest and could get a following crop or two of mandioca (cassava), no further cropping was worthwhile for them, even though very little labor was needed to cut down and clear the second growth (capoeiras) that came in after they abandoned their 2 or 3 years' cultivation of crops in the new clearing.

The reason for the rapid decline in productivity is that practically all of the plant nutrients within reach of the roots of the forest trees have been taken up and are in the growing trees. Almost all the plant offal (dead leaves, twigs, fruit, fallen trees, etc.) which falls to the ground is quickly attacked by termites and decay organisms; as a consequence it rapidly disappears. Organic matter can not persist long on the soil; leaf mold as it is known in the north temperate U.S. does not develop. However, the heartwood logs of certain very durable sorts of trees will last a couple of years or more. The nutrients thus released and washed into the soil by the frequent drenching rains are quickly taken up by the tree roots lying in wait just under the soil surface. All the nutrients within reach of the tree roots are in the vegetation, and are being cycled. When the forest is cut and burned the cycle is broken, the plant nutrients being released in soluble form in the ash. The soil itself is extremely acid, often being around pH4. The burning slightly reduces the acidity and supplies available nutrients for the crop plants which may be planted in the clearing. But before the annual or biennial crop plants can develop extensive root systems sufficient to absorb any considerable proportion of these liberated nutrients, most of the soluble materials will have been washed down deep into the subsoil by the almost daily rains—thus quite out of reach of the roots.

Now after 60 years Felisberto C. de Camargo, director of the Northern Agricultural Research Institute at Belem, has courageously admitted and set out the reasons for the failure of this agricultural development on upland soils of the Amazon valley.

In describing the "development" of virgin tropical forest lands which he saw in Trinidad and in British Guiana in 1938, Milne emphasizes the fact that the tropical forest fertility lasts "only so long as the reaction of forest upon soil properties was maintained without interruption." He continues, "an estimate of fertility had been based on the stature and luxuriance of the virgin forest, and though the estimate was valid enough for that particular forest crop on its own unaltered soil, it proved to be at fault for crops of cultivation."

Jurion and Henry have succinctly summarized the failure of the Belgian efforts in the humid equatorial portions of central Africa Congo to replace the forest fallow of the native ("Bantu") methods by the use "of so-called improvements crops, such as leguminous plants, and by the use of farming operations such as plowing. . . ." They found that the results were the reverse of what had been hoped for and that these modifications of methods introduced from Europe which had been expected to be improvements, all led, sooner or later, to serious impoverishment of the soil. Attempts were even made experimentally to remedy this state of things by the use of mineral fertilizers but the results were disappointing and often negative. In the end, the Belgian agricultural scientists were forced to admit that the native forest fallow cropping system, in spite of its extravagant use of land and labor, especially in felling the forest cover crop, does give soil protection against the destructive effects of sun and rain, keeps the exploitation of the soil within reasonable bounds, and allows a sufficient fallow period to restore the fertility. Jurion and Henry describe how they have been able to rationalize the "Bantu" methods through the development of their corridor system and by so doing to stabilize the population, encourage the return of the forest fallow (forest cover crop), reduce the labor needed especially for clearing, and at the same time obtain desired additional crops for export and for diversifying the local diet.

Soil Degradation in Clearings

As has been mentioned, most of the nutrients in the forest cover are liberated in a few hours by the burning of the slash. In the central Amazon, observant farmers know that the loss of organic matter and nutrients is less if the burn is "quick"—*i.e.,* when the slash and felled trees are burned early in the season. If the brush and down trees are allowed to remain through the dry season too long after cutting, they become very dry. If then burned, much more of the wood and the little organic matter on the soil are destroyed by the hotter fire.

It should be noted that upon clearing the forest the soil is relatively loose, so there is no need of plowing or otherwise stirring it. Nor are there any weeds to turn under. In kaingining there is no need to stir the soil except to peck or to dibble the seeds into the surface soil. This is fortunate, for plowing or otherwise stirring the soil intensifies oxidation and other chemical changes, and the loss of the organic matter hastens the loss of exchangeable bases, hence a decline in the productive potentialities. Also, soil erosion is not accelerated.

Deterioration of Coffee Soils

The world is dependent upon tropical and subtropical regions not only for natural rubber, industrial vegetable oils, sugar, cordage, and sacking fibers, but also for many of its other needs, coffee, tea, and pepper and other spices. Brazil has long been and still is the world's greatest producer of coffee, but the methods of growing coffee in Brazil are more than usually exploitive of the soils, especially by contrast with practices in some other coffee producing countries where at least some of the forest trees are left, other shade trees are planted, and the coffee bushes are planted on the contour. In Brazil the forest is entirely cut and burned and the stumps grubbed out, so that the coffee bushes can be planted very neatly on the square, even on steep slopes. Most serious of all, the soil is exposed to sun and rain, for shade is not used for coffee in most of Brazil; after the first year's mulching neither fertilizers nor organic matter are added to the soils of the coffee gardens. Even the best coffee soils in that country can not produce coffee indefinitely, although the life of gardens with good care on the best soils may be as long as 50 to 100 years. On the poorer soils coffee bushes will produce hardly more than five or eight annual crops before the soils deteriorate so seriously that further production is hardly worth-while. There is an actual physical and chemical deterioration of the friable red clay soils on which the best coffee is grown in Brazil. This physical and chemical deterioration is greatly accelerated by the clean culture practices which expose to sun and rain the soils of the coffee plantations. These soils, developed from the weathering of basic igneous rocks, are in Brazil relatively very limited in area.

Careful estimates indicate that Brazil has lost 1 billion coffee bushes in the last 20 years, in spite of planting 600 million bushes, and that they will lose another billion bushes in the next twenty. More serious soil deterioration and losses of coffee bushes occurred during the great depression of the 1930's when the owners could not afford to maintain their coffee gardens. The dismissed laborers left to go west to pioneer regions where they could get work or better to obtain land of their own. Cattle were pastured in the neglected coffee gardens; their tramping of the soil hastened its further deterioration, while the coffee bushes were soon ruined by browsing. This soil deterioration is believed to be an irreversible process, hence such treatment seriously jeopardizes the future coffee producing capacity of Brazil. Where there is still some forest soil left which can be cleared, new coffee plantations are being made higher and higher on the mountains; other plantings of coffee are being made farther and farther into the forests of the west and northwest, where spots of suitable soil can still be found. Reports indicate that there are but few remaining bodies of forest on soils suitable for coffee. This situation, combined with the lack of rain at the beginning of the current rainy season in Brazil, is undoubtedly a factor in the recent price increases of coffee.

Poor Pastures and Backward Cattle

Soils considered not good enough for coffee growing in the coffee regions of Brazil have been kaingined. The first crop is usually upland rice or maize, often followed by mandioca. After 2 or 3 years cropping the land is usually used only for pasture, with wild and at times some planted grasses. However, at best the soils are not high in plant nutrients, so that the pasture grasses are relatively poor in mineral nutrients. From time to time the pastures may be plowed and planted to annual cotton.

Frequently 25 acres of pasture are needed to support one head of cattle, and even at this rate the growth of the cattle is undoubtedly very slow. Furthermore, prior to Pearl Harbor transport from the interior was so inadequate that the producer seldom got more than about $5.00 per head (U. S. currency), and he sold only one out of 10 animals. This return was so low that the cattle raiser felt he could not afford even to salt his cattle, much less supply them the additional minerals and micronutrients that would certainly have assured better health and earlier maturity for market. If the Brazilian cattle rancher had been willing and able to supply his cattle with adequate mineral supplements, he would likely have been able to get them ready for market in one-third to one-half the time it customarily requires in subtropical and tropical Brazil. The considerably higher prices now being obtained by cattle raisers should make it possible for them to break the vicious circle by supplying their stock with salt and minerals, thus hastening growth. In such regions, where herbaceous leguminous fodder crops do not seem to thrive, the possibilities for leguminous browse shrubs should be great.

The development of cattle is certainly further retarded by cattle diseases which are particularly serious in humid tropical regions. Not only are great areas in Central Africa infested by many kinds of tsetse flies, which transmit sleeping sickness; but warble flies and ticks are generally very serious. The latter, however, respond readily to certain simple and inexpensive treatments such as sprays or dips which in Brazil have been proved of distinct merit for dairy farmers. These difficulties with cattle are added reasons for kaingining.

Belterra Hevea Rubber Plantation

The development of Belterra, the second Ford rubber plantation of selected clones of *Hevea brasiliensis* on the Tapajoz River, has shown some interesting differences between the potential of the virgin as contrasted with the second growth forest soils. The soils of Belterra, unusually uniform over considerable distances, are on an almost flat mesa about 500 feet above the river. The slope of the top of this mesa is so very slight that there is no surface erosion; moreover, man has not abused the soil in the usual sense. This plantation was established and developed under the supervision of competent and experienced Americans and Brazilians. It should be kept in mind that rubber is a native in this region and does not require, in fact it seems to object to, a soil high in nutrients. This is clearly shown by the less satisfactory growth of these rubber trees planted on the little spots of better, darker soils here and there near the escarpment of this mesa, the sites of prehistoric Indian villages, where wastes and the nutrients they contained had accumulated. In the course of the development of the Belterra rubber plantation, which now occupies an area of about 7,000 hectares (17,300 acres), a block of virgin forest was cleared, burned, and at once planted to budded rubber trees in 1942, that is, 7 years ago. At the same time an adjoining block of regrowth brush and young trees, originally cleared 2 years earlier, *i.e.,* in 1940, after again clearing, was also planted to Hevea. Now, 7 years later the trees planted on the land freshly cleared from virgin forest are roughly twice as large as those planted on the recleared land. It is evident that the freshly cleared land had more nutrients available for the roots of the rubber trees than that land which had been cleared 2 years previously and leached by the heavy rains for 2 years and which during this period had produced only a poor regrowth brush. It should be added that the method of clearing used on the Ford plantations was not the most advanced: their practice has been to burn at least most of the logs and to remove the stumps; this more rapidly dissipates the little fertility left by the forest: The cleared land under the rubber trees is kept covered by *Pueraria javanica.*

Rubber Forestry

A better method for the establishment and maintenance of Hevea plantations is rubber forestry. In this method the slash from clearing the virgin forest is not burned; instead the logs are moved into lines or windrows across the slope, while the tree stumps are left. As often as necessary, sprouts and young brush of other than the Hevea trees are slashed to keep the planting fairly open, while only the paths from tree to tree and a meter circle about each tree are kept clear. A leguminous vine, such as *Pueraria javanica,* is planted and encouraged to clamber over the brush, stumps, and logs. These logs and stumps rot within a few years, liberating the nutrients contained in them; at least more of these can be used by the young Hevea trees than if all were liberated at once by burning. Haines graphically describes the striking and serious physical changes in the soil of rubber plantations; these changes are a part of the serious and rapid deterioration suffered by all tropical forest soils when they are cleared and utilized by man.

Certain crops which thrive in humid tropical regions either require or can tolerate a considerable amount of shade. Cacao trees, for example, need a certain amount of shade. In the Gold Coast, where great quantities of cacao are grown, the forest undergrowth is cleared, but only part of the tall trees are felled. Bananas may be planted at the same time as the cacao. If the latter thrives, the bananas are cut out. Or other crops may be raised the first year after clearing. In any case there is at least a partial conservation of the forest conditions.

In the Bicol region, S.E. Luzon Philippines, much of the older abacá (*Musa textilis*) plantings were in only partially cleared tropical high forest. So few of the tall trees were cut that from a mile or so distant I could not distinguish an abacá "plantation" from untouched high forest. The production of fiber was not high, it is true, but continued for perhaps hundreds of years. In Davao, by contrast, the Japanese abacá plantations were set out on clear-felled slopes and carefully tended horticulturally. There were thousands of acres uninterrupted except by roads. This was indeed intensive exploitation of the soil and naturally gave higher yields than abacá under forest conditions. But already in 1939, after at most a few decades, we noted that considerable areas of abacá in Davao had died. Was this because of a lack of forest conditions?

It is also interesting to note that subsequent reports from the Davao region indicate that where tractors and other agricultural machinery had been used in the development of abacá plantations, the soil structure was very unfavorably altered.

Chemical Fertilizers on Tropical Crops

The reported responses to the application of commercial fertilizers applied to humid tropical lowland soils have varied widely. This is to be expected when there is such a wide range of crops, soils, and kinds and combinations of fertilizers. In Malaya, only low rates of application were reported to be effective on *padi;* when more was applied, little or no additional grain was obtained because of some unexplained "block" which soon appeared. On the other hand, before Pearl Harbor the Dunlop rubber plantations in Malaya were importing "shiploads of rock phosphate and ammonium sulphate" for application to their rubber plantations. These fertilizers were believed to give returns which amply justified the expense. In Belterra, in the central Amazon, commercial fertilizers were effective in pulling rubber trees through a difficult period. In this case, however, we have no information as to whether or not it was financially justified. Preliminary trials in Thailand indicate big increases in *padi* from the use of bone meal. In central Thailand before the war native truck gardeners used annually several thousand tons of ammonium sulfate on sugar cane and vegetables.

Fertilizers can at times be used very effectively and with profit where capital is invested in facilities for the transport and processing of tropical crops such as sugar cane, or for the transport and cold storage of bananas. Under such circumstances not only can fertilizers be obtained and transported to the fields at reasonable cost, but also credit arrangements can be made which are not too heavy a burden upon the agriculturists. However, in most cases in the tropics it has thus far been impracticable and uneconomical to use commercial fertilizers for the production of peasant subsistence crops. Not only is transport expensive and the cost of the fertilizer in many tropical countries extremely high, but there is the more difficult problem of financing the purchase of fertilizers by subsistence farmers. Most tropical products are sold by the peasants at what the world market will pay rather than at what it costs to produce the crop. Moreover, the peasant thinks in terms of his own subsistence; enough to feed him and his family for the year, enough for seed for the coming year, and something to give to the merchant against his usually never-fully-paid-up-debt. It seems all too likely that if the peasant purchases fertilizers from his merchant, too often he will merely be under greater economic bondage to him. And though he may get a considerably bigger yield in the end, he is not likely to be any better off.

Fire—Climax Savannas

The striking fertility and continuous crop producing capacity of the former grasslands in the middle United States give Americans a false notion of the character of the grasslands bordering and invading the equatorial rain forest zones of the Amazon and Congo basins. In Central Africa, in southeastern Asia, and in the Indo-Malaysian region, cogon, or lalang (*Imperata cylindrica*), quickly invades the kaingins after the crop has been harvested. This pest, very much worse than our Johnson grass, burns rapidly even when relatively green, and in burning destroys seedlings and suckers of forest trees endeavoring to reestablish themselves in the clearings. As Lebrun says, when young this grass supplies some little poor pasture. In South America the indigenous *Imperata brasiliensis* is not so serious a pest as *I. cylindrica*. Nevertheless this weed is serious and agriculturists who have to fight it refer to it in very unflattering terms. These and other species of *Imperata* and related grasses are important in humid tropical savannas. As Kellogg has pointed out, soils under these fire-climax savannas are even poorer and have a lower agricultural potential than neighboring soils that continue undisturbed under tropical forests. While the vast llanos of the northern part of the Amazon basin and of other extensive tropical regions have not yet been studied pedologically, they are almost certainly fire-climax savannas. If so, their soils are quite useless for other cultivated crops than lowland rice.

Lowland Rice, a Unique Crop

Lowland rice is a unique food plant, for if the soil on which it is planted can be kept free of weeds, and flooded a few inches deep during the growth of the rice, this crop will produce something to eat year after year, and even twice a year, on all but the very poorest of soils. Experience in China is even more encouraging. Buck states that with sufficient water, the Chinese find that rice provides greater food production per unit of land than any other crop. For as yet unexplained reasons the roots of lowland rice are able to obtain sufficient nutrients from extremely poor soils to produce at least some food. As Gourou says, rice growing on all possible lowlands is one of the reasons that southeastern Asia has such a large population. It seems certain that as the population of the world increases a continually greater proportion of the population will come to live mainly upon rice produced on the soils of the humid tropical lowlands.

In most parts of humid tropical Asia and of the Indo-Malayan region where suitable land is the limiting factor but labor is relatively abundant, most sorts of *padi* are transplanted. (So-called "floating rice," which is raised in naturally flooded areas where the water may be 10 feet or more deep before maturity of the crop, is broadcast early in the rainy season.) Floating rice is limited, however, to certain river delta regions. In desert coastal Peru, where water is the limiting factor, *padi* is transplanted to conserve water and get the crop started sooner. Except where East Indians are cultivating lowland rice in Africa and British Guiana, transplanting of the 3 weeks' old seedling *padi* is as yet hardly known nor can the labor yet be afforded for this outside of Asia.

Possibilities of Recent Alluvia

Jurion and Henry call attention to the possibilities of the low-lying alluvial lands along the Congo River and remark that the reason why the natives have neglected to cultivate this land is unknown. Jurion and Henry recently obtained yields which show the high productivity which can be obtained by cultivating these lands, and they propose to utilize them. A fact they emphasize is that such relatively recent alluvial soils contain much more plant nutrients in available form than the uplands which have long been leached by the heavy rainfall. Camargo also contrasts the hopelessly poor forest soils on the old Quaternary uplands in the Belem region of Brazil mentioned above, which have failed to support permanent agriculture, with the recent alluvium in the adjacent fresh water swamps along some of the smaller tributaries of the lower Amazon. He believes this alluvium has sufficient potential fertility to permit permanent cropping and to support nutritious pastures. Already Camargo is having considerable areas of swamp soils along the Rio Guamá cleared and diked. Drainage canals and automatic tide gates will make possible removal of excess rain water as well as seepage water from the extensive uplands behind the swamps. When needed for irrigation, silty Amazon river water which will thus supply some plant nutrients can be applied to the rice fields. Since permanent settlement, with even a low degree of density, has failed in the uplands, Camargo proposes that these fresh water lowland swamp areas be made the permanent cultivation areas for the colonists now in the Bragança uplands. Their new farmsteads and roads would be on the lower edge of the uplands, just back of the swamps, where there is good drainage and plenty of iron concretionary material for road surfacing and use about the buildings.

Unfortunately the level of the Amazon River varies widely during the year; thus it is quite different from the Congo River. For example, at Santarem 350 miles up the Amazon from the ocean, the differences in levels between the flood and low water are more than 20 feet. Marbut and Manifold's map of the alluvium along the Amazon shows it to be astonishingly narrow. Furthermore, this alluvial plain is seriously and frequently interrupted by old channels, oxbow loops, and other irregular bodies of water. No extensive plains of fertile recent alluvial soil, free from serious flood hazard, are known in the Amazon valley. It would of course be possible to dike some of the alluvium and so control the water level and produce lowland rice. Dikes high enough to keep out 20-foot floods are enormously expensive, and might have to be nearly double that height, for the constriction of any considerable portion of the narrow Amazon lowlands would raise the flood level on the undiked portion to a much greater height than at present, when there are no dikes to confine the flood waters. In short, the reclamation and cultivation of any considerable part of the alluvial plain of the Amazon itself seems extremely unlikely. On the other hand, there is some production of melons and other short-season crops on exposed sand banks, islands, and shores during low water periods.

Estimating Tropical Soil Potentialities

In the past false standards for estimating the potentialities of tropical soils as a whole have been used. Salter, for example, used the Philippines as a yard stick to estimate the productive capacity of such soils as those supposed to be in the Amazon and Congo Basins. Unfortunately this "yard stick" is hardly appropriate, for the Philippines have as a whole much better soils than those in most tropical regions for two reasons: (1) the Philippines are young topographically, hence, at most but few of the soils are "suffering from too little erosion," while in the Amazon and Congo Basins almost all are senile—they have been exposed so very long to weathering and leaching at continuously high temperatures; (2) many of the soils of the Philippines have been developed from relatively young volcanic ash (rock powder); consequently these soils often have considerable quantities of plant nutrients, very much greater quantities than in the vast expanses of senile soils in practically all of the humid tropical lowlands.

The importance of volcanic soils in plant production and human population is well shown by contrasting the population densities of Java and Borneo. Before Pearl Harbor these two islands were for the most part subjected to similar political and economic conditions. Moreover, although Java does have a much wider range of rainfall than has been recorded for Borneo, the climates of Borneo and Java are similar as a whole. Java has roughly 50 volcanoes over 2,000 meters high. Since many of them have been active in modern times, their ash has often rejuvenated the soils. The population of Java averages about 825 persons per square mile, with more than double this number in the most fertile volcanic regions. Borneo, by contrast, is without active volcanoes. It is for the most part made up of humid tropical lowlands and intermediate elevations. By and large, the soil, rainfall, and drainage conditions are probably quite similar to those prevailing in the Congo and Amazon River valleys and the types of vegetation also similar. As a consequence, the population of volcanoless Borneo is only about eight persons per square mile, or less than one-one hundredth of that of Java! The difference is undoubtedly mostly due to the difference in soils—volcanic soils on Java; senile infertile soils on Borneo.

Chemical and Physical Characteristics of Tropical Soils

In general mature or senile upland humid tropical soils have practically no silt, for the silt has long since broken down to clay. Hence, in the tropics the prevailing soil textures are sand and clay. In reaction humid tropical soils have low to very low pH values. In other words, they are very acid to extremely acid. The iron for the most part occurs as secondary discrete concretions or as more or less massive laterite. This secondary precipitation of iron is of particular significance in that it involves the co-precipitation of phosphorus, *i.e.,* the resulting concretions are stable under these weathering conditions, thus effectively locking the phosphorus up with the iron so that the plants cannot obtain it. This is why phosphorus is the most generally deficient of the "major" elements in mature humid tropical soils.

In the Philippines and in Java the presence of iron concretions ("pea-iron ore" or "limonite") was used as a rough and ready index of the need of sugar cane soils for phosphorus fertilization. In recent alluvial low-lands where no iron concretions were to be seen, the effective element for sugar cane was nitrogen, most cheaply applied as ammonium sulfate. On the other hand, on the older uplands where small spherical iron concretions, "pea iron," indicated that there had been time and suitable conditions for formation, in addition to nitrogen, phosphorus fertilizers almost invariably gave economic and significant returns.

Reserves of Phosphatic Materials

Bear has just stated that the supplies of phosphorus in the United States are sufficient for a very long time. But let us consider the situation, not in terms of our lifetime, but in terms of the future of our country, and of the world: The consumption of phosphorus fertilizers in the United States in 1938 was about 3,800,000 tons, while in 1948 it was 10,500,000 tons. In addition, perhaps 10 million tons of rock phosphate were used. The total U. S. reserves of phosphate rock are estimated at 14 billion tons, more than all the rest of the world, and almost double those of the next largest, Russia. At the present rate of consumption of U. S. reserves in this country, they should last over 700 years. However, with the relatively rapid depletion of available phosphorus from any of our agricultural soils, increased through the growing of hybrid corn and other high nutrient demanding crops, and with an increasing realization of the advantages to be gained through the application of phosphatic fertilizers to agricultural soils in the humid low latitudes, the rates of consumption of the reserves of phosphorus are certain to increase greatly. Moreover, there are increasing uses of phosphorus in the detergent and other industries.

Taking the long view: in the centuries ahead, where can be obtained the phosphorus to fertilize the ever increasing quantities of food and other crops which will be needed? Nitrogen can be obtained from the air, and magnesium from the sea, but from where can the phosphorus be obtained?

Tree Crops Ideal for Humid Tropics

For most humid tropical regions, tree crops maintained under forest conditions appear to be the most practicable, permanent, and useful way to utilize those soils. Unfortunately there are not many tree crops in which we are interested and which it pays to grow—rubber, Brazil nuts, coconut and African oil palms, chicle, gums, resins, and some others. However, to bear well, coconut palms especially require a relatively fertile soil. In the Orient there is a saying that the coconut palm does not do well beyond the sound of the sea or of the human voice. As Mohr says, within the sound of the sea, salt spray is blown inland and supplies elements essential to the growth of coconut palms. If planted on poor soils farther inland the palms may grow moderately well but will not produce many nuts unless growing near a house or barn where animal and other wastes accumulate and can supply the necessary nutrients. The most productive coconut growing regions are on the volcanic soils of the Philippines and Indonesia.

It is desirable and often imperative to avoid the exposure of tropical soils to sun and rain; as far as possible the transition should be from the wild forest to the desired forest or other crop without the exposure of the bare soil at all. For example, it is the practice in certain banana producing regions of Central America to clear out the underbrush, plant out the young bananas, then fell the larger trees. A moderate amount of brush cutting will permit the bananas to come up through the brush, and by the time the fruit is ready to be gathered, most of the trees and brush will have disappeared through decay and the action of termites. Thus there need be no burning of the brush or slash.

Similarly, in very wet regions, where burning of the slash is difficult or impossible, maize is planted before felling, and comes up through the brush. On the slopes of Irazú volcano, in Costa Rica, kikuyu grass pastures have been established in a very similar manner: The underbrush of the forest is cut, after which the grass is planted. Then the trees are felled and in the course of a couple of years are consumed by termites and decay. By this time grass has dominated the vegetation, with the exception of the stumps and logs of a few very durable trees.

In describing conditions in Trinidad, Milne emphasizes strongly the importance of preserving the continuity of forest conditions. In discussing two examples he points out that

both these soils had, in fact, a fertility quite sufficient to maintain natural mixed forest, or to grow satisfactory forests of commercial timbers, but they had this fertility *only so long as the reactions of forest upon soil properties were maintained without interruption.* It was not expressible through field crops, because the clear felling, burning and tillage necessary in preparation for such crops had as it were dismembered the soil as a working system, and the 'scrap' that was left did not provide the makings of an agricultural soil. Not even a good forest soil could be rebuilt from it; there had been loss of essential parts and the mechanisms of a year or two before could not be restored to working order.

Summary and Conclusions

Only the very small areas (much less than 5%) of soils developed from certain volcanic products, being better drained and supplied with plant nutrients, measure up to the popular conceptions as to the potential fertility of the soils of the humid low latitudes. Consequently, generally held notions as to the unlimited fertility of soils of the tropics are quite wrong.

Seldom can intensive agronomic and horticultural practices of Europe and the United States be used successfully on tropical soils.

Where it is impossible to avoid exposing the soil to sun and rain, for the production of upland grains and fiber crops, a forest fallow of from 8 to 15 years is often effective in restoring soil productivity. Kaingining (shifting cultivation) is often the only way natives can produce food and fibers.

Cogon grass and fire often prevent regeneration of the forest fallow. The Belgian Congo leads in rationalization of forest fallow methods.

In humid equatorial forested regions tree crops are preferable, avoiding the clear felling and the destruction of the forest conditions during the transition, for once destroyed, forest conditions can seldom be restored.

Partial thinning and under-story clearing of the native forest may preserve forest soil conditions and at the same time permit long time production of such forest crops as cacao, abacá, and coffee.

Where coffee is grown without shade, serious chemical and physical deterioration of the soil results.

Phosphorus, often deficient in humid tropical soils, is one of the limiting factors for both plant and animal growth. Pasture grasses on these poor soils are poor in nutrients. Production of livestock and dairy products is difficult: growth is apt to be both slow and unhealthy.

Rapid increases in use of phosphorus as a fertilizer, exhausting the reserves, may be the factor limiting healthy population increase in the world.

Where the soil can be kept at least slightly submerged under water during the growing season, and puddled to control weeds, a crop of *padi* (lowland rice) can be grown annually or oftener, even on soils very low in plant nutrients. In the long run, rice will feed increasing proportions of the world's population.

40. *Evolution of the Banana Industry of Costa Rica* *

Single-crop plantations financed by foreign capital for an outside market has been characteristic of much of the development of tropical agriculture. Investment has been high, but so, too, have been the returns. Often, depletion of soils, plant diseases, and other difficulties have resulted in a shift of production centers. Transportation to a remote market and the maintenance of a quality product have also been problems. The banana industry has had a development pattern typical for many tropical crops, and this detailed study of the industry in Costa Rica is representative of many other products of tropical agriculture.

As is so often the case with a new industry, the commercial banana industry in Costa Rica began as a side line of another activity. It was developed to supply a freight income for the railroad being built by Minor C. Keith from Puerto Limón across the low, swampy, hot, rainy, heavily forested, insect infested and disease ridden lowland, up the deep rugged Reventazón Valley, over the continental divide at 5137 feet, and down across the Meseta Central to San José.

. . . . .

As construction of the railway proceeded, Keith planted bananas in the Zent and Matina Valley areas tributary to the line. . . . When the plantings began to bear, the first shipments from Limón were made to New Orleans in 1878. . . . In March 1899 the United Fruit Company was formed through the consolidation of the Boston Fruit Company, obtaining fruit from the West Indies, and the companies headed by Minor C. Keith, which

* Clarence F. Jones and Paul C. Morrison, "Evolution of the Banana Industry of Costa Rica." Quoted with omissions from *Economic Geography,* Vol. 28, 1952, pp. 1–19.

Clarence F. Jones, Professor of Geography at Northwestern University, is widely known for his work on Latin America. *Economic Geography* and *South America* are two of his important books.

Paul C. Morrison, Professor of Geography at Michigan State College, has done extensive field work in Middle America. He has also served as consultant to the Inter-American Institute of Agricultural Sciences at Turrialba, Costa Rica.

secured their bananas from Central America and Santa Marta, Colombia.

In 1883 exports from Costa Rica, all through Limón, totalled 110,000 bunches, valued at $47,000. With large new plantings coming into bearing, the exports from Limón reached 1,035,000 bunches in 1890, valued at $410,000. The experimental work of the first 20 years set the stage for the tremendous growth of commercial banana production not only in Costa Rica, but also in other areas of Caribbean America, and paved the way for the great consumption in the United States, Canada, and United Kingdom. . . .

Rapid Growth of the Industry in the Caribbean Lowlands of Costa Rica

Exports from Limón rose from 1,035,000 bunches in 1890 to 3,420,000 stems in 1900 and to 10,166,550 bunches in 1907. Up to this time only the area tributary to Limón contributed bananas for export (Fig. 9). However, about 1906 the United Fruit Company, having brought the plantation area in Bocas del Toro, Panama, into production as far west as the national boundary, crossed the Río Sixaola and began developmental work

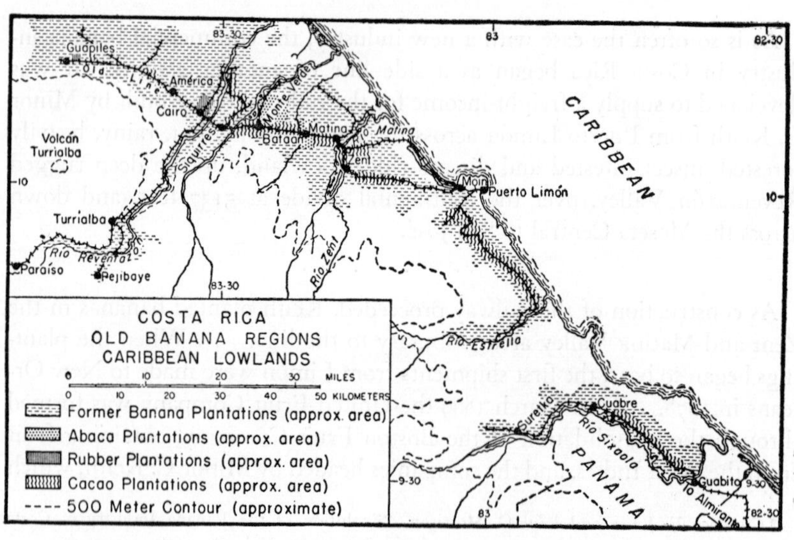

FIGURE 9

Old Banana Regions of Caribbean Lowlands of Costa Rica. Although the United Fruit Company has withdrawn from all fruit activities in the Caribbean Lowlands, it still operates 23,500 acres of cacao and 10,063 acres of abacá here. Also, on or near the old banana plantations are about 2,500 acres in rubber, 20,000 additional acres in cacao, about 5,000 acres in individual banana plantings, and thousands of acres in corn, beans, rice, cassava, other food crops, and pasture.

in that district of Costa Rica (Fig. 10). The bananas from this area moved by rail across the Costa Rican-Panamanian boundary and were exported via Almirante, Panama. In 1912 the Sixaola district exported 1,020,000 bunches. The all-time peak in the exports from Costa Rica was reached in 1913, totalling 11,170,800 bunches, of which the area tributary to Limón supplied 9,319,100 and the Sixaola district 1,851,700 stems.

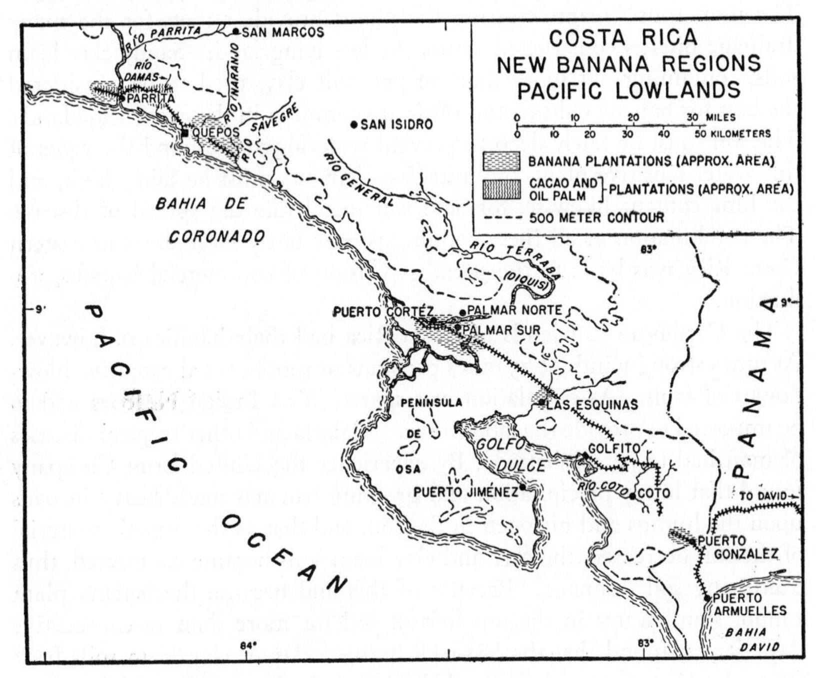

FIGURE 10

Banana Districts on the Pacific Lowlands of Costa Rica.

During this period of great expansion the Caribbean Lowlands of Costa Rica were considered by the Fruit Company and by independent growers as just about ideal for large-scale commercial plantation banana culture. The coastal, alluvial, and gently sloping piedmont plains of these areas were near the seaports, so that bananas could be moved by cart or mule from company plantations and independent farms to railways and thence to the ship-side within 24 hours or so. Rapid movement of cut bananas from field to steamship hold is desirable in order to prevent ripening from setting in.

The physical conditions of these areas in many respects are favorable to banana production. In one year the plant grows to full size—about 25 feet high and 14 inches in diameter at the base—and bears a bunch of fruit which, when mature, weighs from 50 to 80 pounds. For such a rapid growth the plant needs heat, moisture, adequate drainage, and fairly fertile soil. The annual precipitation at Limón is 121 inches. In districts nearer the foothills of the mountains the precipitation is greater. No month receives less than five inches; six months get more than ten inches each. At Limón the mean monthly temperatures range between 77°F. and 81°F. The numerous streams crossing the plains provide outlets for the many drainage ditches constructed across the low-lying land. Sandy clay loam soils, containing not more than 40 per cent clay, used to be considered the best for banana culture and these are common in the eastern lowlands. The soil must be fairly deep to prevent waterlogging around the roots of this water-sensitive plant, the nutritive elements must be fairly high, and the lime content likewise, for acid soils accelerate the spread of disease. The combination of all these conditions over fairly large areas in eastern Costa Rica was basic to the great expansion of commercial banana production.

The Caribbean Lowlands of Costa Rica had their handicaps, however. At times strong winds of 25 miles per hour or more caused extensive blowdowns of fruit. As population was sparse, West Indian Negroes had to be imported to provide the labor force. Malaria and other tropical diseases of man had to be combatted. By experience the United Fruit Company found that heavy precipitation and growing bananas made heavy inroads upon the humus and nitrogen in the soil, and that as the organic material of the soil decreased, the clay and clay loam soils became compacted, thus decreasing soil drainage. Because of this and because the banana plant cannot stand water in the top foot of soil for more than 12 consecutive days, it was found that the less-well drained clay or clay loam soils back from the rivers were short-lived, lasting only from five to eight years, whereas sandy soils on the natural levees were the best and longest-lived. Furthermore, the Panama disease (*Fusarium cubense*) or wilt disease appeared in the older plantings, causing their abandonment. Typical infestations of the Panama disease were observed as early as 1890 and the disease had obtained alarming proportions in Panama and Costa Rica by 1904.

Decline of the Banana Industry of the Caribbean Lowlands of Costa Rica

Following 1913, the peak year of banana shipments from Costa Rica, the exports from the Caribbean Lowlands declined irregularly to a low of only 1,411,000 bunches in 1941. This was true despite the fact that the exports from the Sixaola district increased from 1,851,700 stems in 1913 to 3,312,450 bunches in 1919. The decline has been attributed to several things. Among these are soil exhaustion and increasing distances of rail haul to the ports. However, two banana diseases, Panama disease and Sigatoka, have been advanced as the chief causes for the decline.

In the early years some planted areas lasted for only five to eight years, whereas other plantings lasted for as long as 25 years. Thus, in its operations in the Caribbean Lowlands the United Fruit Company was early forced to adopt a policy of regular abandonment of old fields and planting of new ones. This policy was possible only because of the large area of suitable virgin land available under contract agreement to the company. In general, individual private growers could not adopt this policy because most holdings were too small to permit it.

While soil exhaustion might in time have contributed to a decline of the banana industry in this region, evidence points to the fact that this was not a major factor in the decline which occurred. "Actually, unlike many crops, bananas are not exhaustive of the general fertility of the soil, their demand being largely for nitrogen." While it is true that, as banana plantations were developed farther and farther from the ports, the bananas had to be hauled by rail longer distances, this also was a minor factor in the decline. The longest rail haul for bananas to Limón was less than 75 miles. In Guatemala millions of bunches each year are shipped by rail from the Pacific Lowlands to Puerto Barrios on the Caribbean Sea, a distance of more than 350 miles.

There seems to be no question but that the Panama disease was the major cause for plantation abandonment and the decline of banana growing in the Caribbean Lowlands of Costa Rica. It is reported that by 1910 at least 15,000 acres of banana land had been abandoned in Panama, that many thousands more in that country were seriously affected by the Panama disease, and that the damage in Costa Rica was even greater.

Panama disease attacks the plant through the root system, causing the leaves to wilt and the plant to rot off at the ground. An infected plant does not produce a bunch of bananas. Infected soils cannot be used for growing bananas again for years. Despite intensive research and the expenditure of much money, no cheap and effective method of controlling the spread of this disease has been discovered. . . .

The peak year of banana production in the area tributary to Limón was 1907. . . . By 1926 the United Fruit Company had abandoned 29,500 acres of banana land in eastern Costa Rica. From 1929 to 1934 the United Fruit Company was planting in the Limón hinterland new land that went out of production in two or three years as a result of Panama disease. Production consequently declined to 2,611,800 stems in 1935. About this time the United Fruit Company decided that it was fighting a losing battle with this disease. Because of the great cost of developing plantations which were short-lived, the company could no longer maintain profitable production of bananas by the plantation method in this area. In 1935 and 1936 the company started a program of encouraging independent growers to plant bananas for sale, of contracting to purchase these bananas at about 50 cents per stem, and of leasing the growers company land. Many such plantings were put in to provide temporary shade on cacao farms, belonging chiefly to the company. The increased exports of 1937 and 1938 resulted primarily from these efforts.

In 1938 Sigatoka (*Cercospora musae*), a leaf spot disease, first appeared in the lowlands of eastern Costa Rica. This disease attacks the leaves and prevents the plant from producing large bunches of high quality bananas. Soon after Sigatoka appeared experiments were made to control it by airplane dusting of the plantation with a mixture of copper sulphate and lime. The dust did not adhere readily to the glossy top side of the young leaves, or was soon washed off by heavy rains, and the system otherwise proved impracticable. The disease is now controlled in other banana areas by spraying plants with Bordeaux mixture.

When the effects of this new disease became important in 1939 and 1940, causing the quality of the bananas to decline, it became less and less profitable for the United Fruit Company to purchase fruit in the Limón area for export. Although the United Fruit Company had abandoned plantation production of fruit in eastern Costa Rica before Sigatoka appeared, this disease hastened the withdrawal of the company from all fruit activities in the area. Exports from the Sixaola district, owing largely to the ravages of the Panama disease, had practically ceased by 1938. So far as the purchase and export of bananas is concerned, the United Fruit Company pulled out entirely from the Caribbean Lowlands of Costa Rica in 1942. The last ship in 1942 was sunk at the Limón dock by a torpedo from a German submarine, and no ships called in 1943.

The United Fruit Company has had no part in the renewal of shipments from Limón since 1943. The exports from Limón in 1948 were 1,130,670 stems. Independent buyers are operating in the area, paying fairly high prices. This results in many small plantings by Negro and white farmers. These consist chiefly of scattered groups of plants, varying from as low as 25 to 50 plants to as much as four acres. No large plantings are present. The plantings are usually mixed with cacao, cassava, or other crops. Panama disease kills out the plantings in two or three years. Sigatoka, although it may not seriously affect the plant the first two years, does reduce the quality of the fruit. No spraying to control Sigatoka is done. It would be impracticable to spray such scattered banana plants, especially in an area where it rains nearly 200 days in the year and where there is no distinct dry season. As a consequence, most of the fruit stems produced weigh only 25 to 30 pounds, which is much below the standards maintained by the United Fruit Company. . . . If buyers continue to pay 45 cents or more per stem, shipments will continue and there will be a constant shift in land used for production.

. . . . .

Shift of the Banana Industry to the Pacific Lowlands of Costa Rica

For many years bananas have been produced in the Pacific Lowlands of Costa Rica. The first shipments from a Pacific Coast port were in 1927. For several years independent operators purchased bananas, grown in the coastal valleys, and moved them in launches and small boats north to Puntarenas for shipment to foreign markets. In 1935 the United Fruit Company began buying bananas from independent producers and transporting them by tug and barge to Puntarenas for export. The 57,000 to 235,000 stems exported through Puntarenas annually between 1928 and 1939 thus came by coastwise pickup chiefly from the Río Parrita and Río Naranjo areas. . . .

By 1938 the United Fruit Company had decided to shift its banana operations from the Caribbean Lowlands to the Pacific Lowlands and signed a contract with the Costa Rican Government for this purpose. Development work began at once. The new dock at Quepos was opened late in 1939, causing shipments from Puntarenas to cease. . . . In the Pacific Lowlands the company organized two banana divisions, the Quepos and the Golfito divisions.

The Quepos Division

As noted above, banana culture by independent growers had been developed in the Río Parrita and Río Naranjo valleys in what is now the Quepos division before the United Fruit Company became active in that area. In the Parrita area the company purchased some 1500 independently established acres and contracted to spray and purchase the fruit from another 600 acres. It also continued to purchase fruit from 2000 acres of independently established plantations in production in the Naranjo Valley until late in 1946, but these acres, abandoned because of Panama disease, are now in a cattle farm. The Quepos division consists of four districts: the Naranjo; the Savegre; the Savegre East in the coastal valleys to the south of the Naranjo; and the Damas to the north.

In 1941, owing to the rapid plantings by the United Fruit Company in the preceding two years, the Quepos division produced and exported 3,296,000 bunches of bananas. The shipments dropped off rapidly during the war years because of the lack of ships and abandonment due to Panama disease. Until 1946 shipping was scarce. In 1948 exports totalled 2,128,100 bunches.

Banana production and exportation from the Quepos division will probably reach a peak in 1951 and then they will rapidly decline and eventually disappear. Large acreages were planted in 1948. The year 1949 was the last year of large plantings. Most of the land in this division is short-lived, commonly yielding for only about five years before it has to be abandoned.

• • • • •

It is the present policy of the United Fruit Company not to plant any soil with a life expectancy of less than five years. As pointed out above, the best soils will produce for as long as 25 years. In the Quepos division land suitable for banana culture has been largely developed. Land contiguous to the plantations either has a life expectancy of less than five years, is too hilly for use, or lies along the coast in a narrow one-mile wide strip which is national land that by law cannot be sold or leased except for the construction of a port.

As land in the Quepos division is abandoned for banana growing, the United Fruit Company follows a policy of planting other things, such as cacao, African oil palm, pasture, and small areas of mahogany and teak. At the end of 1948 the company had in the division 2500 acres in cacao, mostly consisting of high-yielding, disease-resistant strains. The annual precipitation of 100 inches or more, the long rainy season from April to November, and the subsequent dry season all should favor the growth, ripening, harvesting, and preparation of high quality cacao beans. In this area there are also approximately 8000 acres in African oil palms, some of which began to bear in 1949. The soils and the rainfall regime in this area are apparently well-suited to the growth of this palm. Judged from experimental plantings over several years, no serious disease or insect pest problems are anticipated. The Damas district, referred to above, is now all in oil palm and cacao. Tentative plans of the United Fruit Company call for eventually planting in the Quepos division some 16,000 acres of cacao and 10,000 acres of oil palm as banana fields are abandoned. Of course, very low prices or the lack of markets for these products could alter these plans materially.

The United Fruit Company is now consciously following the policy of putting something productive on banana lands as they are abandoned, so as to prevent or lessen distress such as has occurred in the past in some areas of abandonment. The company considers this "good business." It is certainly enlightened policy insofar as utilization of resources and the expanding of economy in tropical areas are concerned. . . .

The Golfito Division

Before the United Fruit Company began development work in late 1938, much of the area of the present Golfito division was either uninhabited or very sparsely settled tropical rain forest. However, there was a small production of bananas at Palmar on the Webb farm before the company came. Also, there were a few people along the Térraba River, as at Puerto Cortéz, and several small settlements along the coast.

In a decade the United Fruit Company brought the activities of the division up to high level. It built 246 kilometers of railway lines; constructed modern banana shipping facilities at Golfito, with equipment for loading 4000 bunches of bananas an hour; built a town of some 7000 people, with a modern hospital, stores, construction shops, communication, recreation, and other modern facilities; developed near Golfito a dairy farm with 50 head of cows and a modern pasteurizer; and brought into production thousands of acres of bananas. The main line railway from Palmar and the port at Golfito were completed in 1941, the port being finished before the railway. It also brought into the area, in addition to company officials, some 15,000 white and mestizo persons as workers from Guanacaste and other west coast localities. In addition to workers living on the plantations or in Golfito, the company has encouraged settlers to establish themselves along the main line railroad between banana districts. These people provide the extra labor needed at the wharf during banana loading operations, the extra workers required in development and new construction, and at times labor for other rush activities. Between periods of work of this character these settlers grow on small plots much of their own food and also food for the population of Golfito.

. . . . .

Each of the districts in the Golfito division is divided into a number of farms, the number varying from five to nine; seven is the ideal and the most usual number. The typical farm, rectangular in shape, consists of 800 acres of bananas, with about 20 acres devoted to campsite and buildings, and may have as many as 150 acres in pasture land. Each 800-acre farm requires the labor of 150 workers employed the year round. Included are about 81 workers who weed, prune, and harvest the bananas, 40 spray men, 8 fruit washers, 8 stevedores, 5 irrigation men (during the season of irrigation), 3 foremen, 2 timekeepers, 1 overseer, 1 stockman, and 1 sanitation man. Once a plantation is established, 54 per cent of the labor on a farm is engaged full-time in weeding, pruning, and harvesting. Weeds and other undergrowth are chopped out every two months; alternating with cleaning, pruning is done every two months; each farm is gone over twice weekly to harvest the fruit. A farm is called a "tractor farm" or a "mule farm," depending on the method of bringing the bananas from the fields to rail sidings. Diesel tractors pull trailers for hauling bananas. Each small mule, two mules to one driver, packs out two bunches at a time. Oxen are not used. However, each farm may have some cows, and generally has several riding mules and horses.

Some of the operations of developing banana lands and the production of bananas in the Golfito division are not unlike those on the former plantations in the Caribbean Lowlands. On the other hand, some operations, owing to the necessity of irrigation and of spraying for control of Sigatoka, differ greatly.

In the Golfito division the low-lying lands have to be cleared of the forest, drainage ditches constructed, transportation facilities provided, and the bananas planted as these things were done in the former plantations of the Caribbean Lowlands. Master drainage canals are spaced at about 500 yard intervals and secondary drainage ways about every 75 meters. Most of the drainage canals are laid out on a contour drainage system, but in some new farms on flat land a grid system with straight-line drainage ways is used. A straight-line grid system facilitates spraying and harvesting operations. As pointed out above, adequate drainage of land for growing bananas is necessary because the plant cannot stand water in the top foot of soil for more than twelve consecutive days.

Owing to three or more months of light rainfall in the Pacific Lowland banana districts, irrigation is necessary during the dry season in contrast to the former plantations in the Caribbean Lowlands. Drainage canals and irrigation intake canals are separate. Water flows into the intake canals from rivers or estuaries. It is pumped from the intake canals through a system of pipes decreasing from fourteen to four inches in diameter. The irrigation system runs 24 hours a day in season and requires five men to irrigate each 1000 acres. The standard pump handles 5000 gallons of water a minute and works ten towers at a time. Each tower, or riser, puts out 500 gallons of water a minute and irrigates three and one-third acres. The towers are laid out in systems and are spaced on a hexagonal pattern. Each system consists of 36 risers. There are ten systems on each pump. At any given time only one riser in each system is supplied water from the pump, or ten risers at once. If each of the 36 risers in a system is worked four hours, it takes six days to irrigate the land covered by the risers. This pipe system is so constructed that a water pressure of ninety pounds is maintained at the base of each riser. The nozzle on each riser slowly revolves, taking about 30 minutes to make a complete turn. Water is thrown out from the riser nozzle with a 205-foot radius of spray. A minimum of one and one-half inches of water is applied to the area covered in four to five hours time. Each banana field is supplied with this amount of water once a week during the irrigation season. Irrigation on any particular piece of ground is synchronized with spraying, cutting, and weeding, and with irrigation on surrounding areas, so that one activity does not interfere with another.

It has been said that growing bananas with irrigation on the Pacific Lowlands offers many advantages over production with natural precipitation on the Caribbean Lowlands: water can be applied in the correct amounts as the plants need it, weed control is easier and soil leaching is less, laborers can work more consistently, and building roads and railroads is easier on lands with low rainfall. It is true that during the dry season of three or four months field work is not interrupted and that construction can proceed more easily. On the other hand, the annual precipitation at stations in the Golfito division is about as heavy as it is in the Caribbean Lowlands of Costa Rica, and at least six inches of water per month are sprayed on the fields during the dry season. The water sprayed on the fields is apparently equivalent to that much precipitation in causing weeds to grow and in leaching the soil. According to soil scientists, the abandonment of soils due to Panama disease seems to be more closely related to drainage conditions and acidity than to leaching alone or to the presence or absence of a dry season. In addition, the provision of irrigation facilities is expensive, and five men on each farm are needed to run the irrigation equipment. Furthermore, although until now blowdowns have not been great, the chief danger from wind is in May and June at the beginning of the rainy season.

Up to the end of 1948 Panama disease had appeared in only a few areas in the Golfito division, and these were not seriously infected. In both the Quepos and Golfito divisions, however, the banana fields must be sprayed every two or three weeks to control Sigatoka. High-pressure pumps force spray from central mixing houses through two-inch main pipes, one and one-quarter inch laterals, and three-quarter inch sublaterals. Laterals laid out on a straight grid system are 500 meters apart. Sublaterals are spaced 60 meters apart with angle valves every 30 meters to which can be hooked a 140 foot hose handled by two men. The spray mixture used consists of a 5/5/50 ratio, or five pounds of copper sulphate and five pounds of lime to 50 gallons of water. In 1948, about 1250 men worked continuously on Sigatoka control in the Golfito division, one man for every 5110 bunches produced. The company uses each year in this area as much as a million pounds of copper sulphate and a million pounds of lime.

Controlling Sigatoka is expensive, but without it good banana land would not for long produce large bunches of high-quality fruit. The total cost of pipes, pumps, and other spraying equipment is said to be about as much per acre as the initial expense of preparing and planting an acre to bananas. In addition, 30 per cent of the laborers on each farm are engaged full time in spraying the fields and in washing the fruit. Before the bananas are loaded in cars at rail sidings, the bunches are dipped into a tank containing a dilute solution of sodium acid sulphate to remove the Bordeaux mixture and then dipped into a tank of water to remove the sodium sulphate.

For decades the popular impression has been that bananas serve only to skim the fertility of the soil and that then the areas won by costly development revert to jungle. There has been and there still is ample evidence for this impression through the abandonment of banana plantings after a cycle of production of from five to 25 years. However, will the Golfito division prove to be the exception for which fruit men have been looking for more than half a century? Bananas are not exhaustive of the general fertility of the soil; their demands are largely for nitrogen. In this area the United Fruit Company regularly applies nitrogen fertilizer, the amount used varying with the character of the soil and the age of the planting. As yet there has been no abandonment due to Panama disease, but few farms have been in bananas for more than ten years. The soils in the Golfito division are classed by United Fruit Company men as long-lived. The long productivity of these soils may be due to several conditions: better drainage facilities provided by taking advantage of years of experience, fairly high pH, calcium-magnesium ratio, application of nitrogen fertilizer, and the influence of the dry season on the spread of Panama disease. While these soils may have some characteristic inimical to the spread of the Panama disease, the likelihood is that the longer life is due in part at least to more modern methods of soil management.

The above discussion demonstrates that the achievements of the United Fruit Company in the Quepos and Golfito divisions in only a decade, which included the greatest of World Wars, have been remarkable. Banana exports from the Pacific Lowlands of Costa Rica in 1948 totalled more than 8,500,000 bunches. It seems certain that within a few years the annual shipments from the Quepos and Golfito divisions together will surpass the record combined exports from the Limón and Sixaola regions in 1911 of 11,170,810 bunches. The exports from the Golfito division probably will not reach a peak for another ten to fifteen years. In the vicinity of Palmar some four to five thousand acres more can be planted. But the only land between the Palmar area and Golfito that at present seems suitable for bananas lies in the Esquinas district, and most of the suitable land in this area has been planted. However, in the Coto region southeast of Golfito and farther south toward the Panamanian boundary a large area is suitable for banana growing. Certain developments such as installations of roads, drainage ditches, communication facilities, etc., have already occurred in this land. The presence of this potential banana land influenced the establishment of port facilities at Golfito. . . .

Conclusion and Outlook

The shift of United Fruit Company activities in production, purchase, and exportation of bananas from the Caribbean Lowlands to the Pacific Lowlands of Costa Rica has been complete. The main cause of this shift must be attributed to the increasing rapidity with which the Panama disease spread to new plantings in the Caribbean Lowlands. In 1935 the company abandoned plantation production of bananas in that area. Apparently, Sigatoka had no part in causing the company to cease plantings, for it did not appear in the eastern lowlands of Costa Rica until 1938. However, Sigatoka, owing to its lowering the size of bunches and the quality of the fruit grown by individual planters and sold to the company under contract, caused the company to cease purchase and export of bananas from this area in 1942. That soil exhaustion, that is the loss of the humus and nitrogen in the soil growing bananas, in itself was a major cause for the shift is questionable. . . . Although some soils are more resistant to Panama disease than others, no soil entirely immune to Panama disease has been discovered in either the Caribbean or Pacific Lowlands. An earlier contention that the spread of Panama disease in an area with a dry season could be retarded greatly has not been demonstrated by experience in the Quepos division, where in a little over a decade about 12,000 acres of both company and individual holdings have been abandoned because of Panama disease. The Quepos division will probably be largely out of production in another 15 years. . . . Unless an effective method of controlling the spread of Panama disease is discovered the banana lands in the Golfito division will in time also go out of production. Commercial banana production at present must still be considered a relatively impermanent system of agriculture.

41. *Land Occupance in the Southeast* *

The southeastern part of the United States has had great changes in its land-use pattern. In the past, the single crop system prevailed throughout the area, with resulting economic dislocation as well as rapid soil depletion. The changes that have taken place and are continuing, are indicative of the nature of diversification as well as the advantages of a varied agricultural economy. As in any area where great land-use changes take place, new regional emphases will develop. This article is particularly valuable for its treatment of the emerging southern agricultural regional specializations.

For more than 150 years leading Southern agriculturists and enlightened landowners have crusaded for freedom from one-crop bondage. Early agricultural societies propagated a doctrine of diversification not too different from that of today's farm-management experts. In the ante bellum Southeast † agitation for diversification did not progress much beyond comments in newspapers, journals, and private letters, except for occasional agricultural-society debates. The great agricultural benefits resulting from the Morrill Land-Grant Act of 1862, which established state agricultural colleges and their attendant services, were slow to appear on the Southeastern scene. "One-cropism's" hold on Southeastern farms, strengthened by the economic misery of post-Civil War reconstruction, restricted the influence of agricultural research on land occupance in most of the region. Although other factors were contributory, many scholars believe the dominant factor in the one-crop fixation was the grinding poverty caused by loss of most capital goods, except land, during the Civil War. The results of agricultural research and education therefore have been partly vitiated, until recently, by absence of liquid capital with which to apply them.

In the past 25 years the South has experienced a rapidity and variety in land-occupance changes never before witnessed in its rich history. Diversi-

* Merle J. Prunty, Jr., "Land Occupance in the Southeast," from *Geographical Review,* Vol. 42, 1952, pp. 439–461; published by the American Geographical Society, New York.

The author (1917) is Professor of Geography and Geology at the University of Georgia. He has done extensive field work in the southeastern United States.

† This discussion is confined to the traditional South, comprising Virginia, North and South Carolina, Kentucky, Tennessee, Georgia, Alabama, Mississippi, Texas, Oklahoma, Louisiana, and Arkansas, and nonpeninsular Florida. The terms "South" and "Southeast" are used interchangeably to refer to these states, which constitute the southeastern quadrant of the country. Principal emphasis is on the middle and lower South.

fication benefits are already apparent in higher income levels, greater purchasing power, and greater productivity from basic resources; but no one is certain today what the geography of the new South will be. Change, undoubtedly. A new regionality? Probably. Several or many new Southeastern regions in what was once the Cotton Belt? Quite likely. One point is certain: the land-occupance upheavals of recent years have destroyed the validity of the easy epithets and alliterative titles so long applied to the South.

In a discussion of limited length it is impossible to treat fully all phases of Southeastern land occupance. An effort is made here to describe and analyze salient features of rural occupance, the landmarks of the South today: forests; cropping systems related to changes in cotton production; cash specialty crops; and livestock and recent increases in hay-pastureland use. Urban and manufactural land occupance is omitted except for occasional direct relationships. Certain future developments in land occupance can be discerned—albeit "through a glass, darkly."

The Forests

The greatest single common denominator to landscapes of the South is its forests. If geographical classification by a single criterion is necessary, the South is more nearly a forest region than anything else. Exclusive of western Texas and Oklahoma, more than 55 per cent of the area is in forest—slightly more than 30 per cent of the national total. About 40 per cent of the nation's commercial forest is in the South, and half of its privately owned commercial forest. Public ownership of forests is less significant than elsewhere: roughly 86 per cent are privately owned, and about 40 per cent are on farms. There are some 1,650,000 small-forest landowners, whose holdings average 75 forested acres. Pulp-and-paper companies own vast tracts of forest land, especially in the Coastal Plain east of the Mississippi. At present the South supplies almost half of the national annual timber growth; and about 55 per cent of the annual growth of saw timber—on only 21 per cent of the national saw-timber stand. In 1944 the Forest Service estimated that Southern forests were producing roughly 42 per cent of the nation's lumber and timber, 53 per cent of its fuel wood, 44 per cent of its pulp, and virtually all of its naval stores. The Service estimated that total drain on the region's forests exceeded growth by at least 2 per cent and pointed to thin, inadequate stands on hundreds of thousands of acres as uneconomic production units.

In recent years restocking and replanting have proceeded rapidly. Inadequate stands are being upgraded. Production goals in 1949 for state-owned tree nurseries were set at 98.5 million seedlings total (almost entirely pine seedlings), and the Forest Service indicated that this output—about double that of the preceding year—would not remotely satisfy demand. In Georgia alone 45 million seedlings were planted in 1950, and even these were not enough. Most planting is now done with mechanized planters; as these machines have become more numerous, seedling demand has increased greatly. There is little doubt that forest growth could be doubled if restocking and management of stands proceeded in accord with approved forestry practices. A vast acreage in bush and brush could be put to productive use simply by adequate planting. Rising demand for seedlings indicates that forest restocking in most of the South is increasing, but this does not necessarily mean increased forest acreage.

The greatest change in Southern forest utilization in recent years is reflected in construction of new pulp-and-paper mills. By 1951 there were at least 670 paper and paperboard plants in the South, including a mammoth new newsprint plant at Childersburg, Ala. In 1950 these plants produced a gross volume worth more than two billion dollars; within the last five months of 1951 construction of half a dozen large new plants was announced. It is the writer's opinion, based on plant increments since 1944, that the South now produces at least 55 per cent of the national pulp-paper output (by volume), instead of the 44 per cent reported by the Forest Service in 1944.

Percentage of area in forest in certain parts of the South is so great that, by almost any reasonable measure, they must be considered forest regions. One region occupies most of the Appalachian Highland from northern Georgia through South and North Carolina and eastern Tennessee to northwestern Virginia (Fig. 11). Another extends from southeastern South Carolina through most of southeastern and south-central Georgia and encompasses Florida north of the peninsula. This very large region, site of the naval-stores industry, contains county after county with more than 90 per cent of area in forest. Southwestern Alabama and southern Mississippi constitute a third region. Another extends from central Louisiana into eastern Texas (this region includes nearly half of Louisiana!). Southern Arkansas is another, as are the Ouachita and Boston Mountains in Oklahoma and Arkansas. Throughout these regions, roughly 80 per cent of total area is in forest. Smaller areal proportions characterize the Cumberland Plateau forest of Alabama, Tennessee, and Kentucky.

There is extensive demand in the lower South for moderate to large tracts of land suitable for forests. This demand comes primarily from paper mills who wish to ensure their sources of supply; some mills are purchasing land as much as 150 miles from the mill site. Private individuals with capital to invest make up another purchasing group. This group is interested because (1) the return from reasonably managed pine forest averages at least 10 per cent on capital invested, (2) the income received may be treated as a long-term capital gain in income-tax returns, and (3) land in the South today is underpriced in comparison both with national average land prices and with its inherent production capacity. Even low-grade forest land constitutes an excellent inflationary hedge.

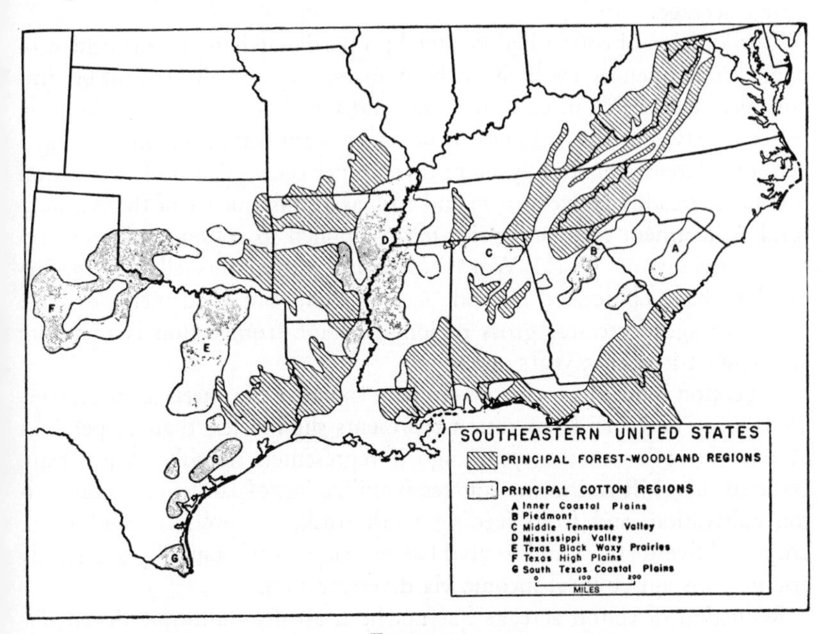

FIGURE 11

Forest-Woodland and Cotton Regions, 1950. Regions shown as forest and woodland average 75 per cent or more of total area in forest. Cotton regions average about 9 per cent of total area in cotton acreage harvested. Compiled from Census of Agriculture, 1950; Bureau of Agricultural Economics, "Major Land Uses in the United States, 1950"; and forest service publications. Boundaries are approximate.

On the other hand, small farmers now tend to replace low-grade forest with more intensive forms of land use, especially improved pastures. Since the bulk of the region's forests are in small landholdings, the writer's opinion is that the small farmer's shift to pasturage will at least counterbalance acreage accessions in large landholdings. A slight decrease in forest acreage, especially about the periphery of the forest regions, is anticipated.

Changes in Cotton Production

Perhaps the most far-reaching change in Southeastern land use has been the decrease in acreage planted to cotton. Between 1924 and 1944 cotton acreages decreased about 48 per cent in 11 Southern cotton-producing states. Since 1945 gross acreage in cotton has increased only slightly, except in 1948–1949, when it was well above the 1940–1950 norms. Virtually every important producing area in the old traditional cotton South except the West Texas High Plains has undergone large reductions in cotton acreage.

If production of cotton had declined proportionately to acreage, the economic consequences could have been disastrous and diversification impossible. But yields in eastern Texas and Oklahoma increased about 25 per cent between 1925–1929 and 1946, and eastern cotton regions averaged per acre increases of slightly more than 50 per cent. Prices of raw cotton rose fairly steadily between 1929 and 1946 as a consequence of the Agricultural Adjustment Acts and price parity applied to cotton, and more recently because of World War II demand. In a nutshell, acreage reductions have obliterated the old "Cotton Belt," but yield increases have offset acreage decreases; gross regional income from cotton is therefore about what it was 25 years ago.

But cotton is no longer the pre-eminent source of Southern farm income. Today's gross return from cotton represents slightly less than 25 per cent of total farm income; 25 years ago it represented roughly 50 per cent. Basic to this shift in income sources is utilization of land freed from cotton cultivation, and from feeding work stock, for production of other crops and livestock. Land so used has contributed substantially to a steady rise in gross agricultural income via diversification.

Reduction of cotton acreage has not been areally uniform. Seven distinct cotton regions now produce almost two-thirds of the crop within counties that together contain a little less than 10 per cent of the total land area in 11 Southern cotton-producing states (Fig. 11). The seven regions appear destined to remain "cotton regions" for many years because of inherent cultural, economic, and physical advantages.

Land occupance within the seven cotton regions differs from that of the traditional cotton-farming areas of 1900–1930. Average farm and field size is greater than in the South as a whole. All seven regions are susceptible of complete mechanization, though in the Georgia-Carolina Piedmont mechanization is beset with difficulties. The regions are characterized by soils of relatively high fertility, a high soil imbibitional rate resulting from a large proportion of soil clay fractions, and low angles of slope in comparison with the rest of the South. These conditions combine to favor large-scale cotton production.

In each cotton region the percentages of area and available cropland devoted to cotton do not approach 50, and commonly some other form of land use occupies greater acreage. One-cropism is gone: a three-way pattern is emerging.

In the West Texas High Plains the three-way association consists of grain sorghums, cotton, and hay forage for beef cattle; grain sorghums occupy a larger acreage than cotton, and beef cattle are more numerous today than 30 years ago when most of the area was in large ranches. The cotton-cattle combination characterizes each of the other regions, but with a different "partner." In the Mississippi alluvial valley it is soybeans, except in east-central Arkansas, where it is rice. In northern Alabama it is soybeans or corn; the Piedmont area has become a significant producer of small winter grains. Peanuts and corn complete the relationship in the inner Coastal Plain of Georgia and South Carolina but are displaced by tobacco in North Carolina. The Black Waxy Prairies of Texas are becoming more important as peanut and legume seed producers, but the predominant associated field crop is still corn.

Occupance types are emerging that concentrate on one high-unit-value commodity plus those activities which fit into both conservational rotation systems and maximum use of specialized machinery necessary for production of the dominant crop. Beef cattle fit these requirements well. Specialization for optimum productivity from both land and equipment is proceeding rapidly. Instead of "general" or "diversified" farming on the *individual* farm, what is emerging throughout the South—including the cotton regions—is *diversification within each region or area* through specialization of its individual farm components.

Mechanization of Southern farm power deserves special mention. The cotton regions have been leaders in the swing to tractors. There are about four times as many tractors in Mississippi today as there were 10 years ago, in Texas twice as many. Increase since 1940 has been threefold in Arkansas, tenfold in Georgia. Millions of acres formerly devoted to feeding work stock now support livestock grazing, or expanded cash specialty crops, or forage. The South still lags behind the rest of the country in ratio of tractors to cultivated acreage, and further mechanization can be anticipated. The writer estimates that in 1950 at least 3,500,000 acres in Mississippi, Alabama, and Georgia alone still were devoted to feeding work stock. If freed for use as pasturage, this acreage could support 1,000,000 beef cows plus calves. In other words, potentialities inherent in mechanization are far from realization.

Complete mechanization of cotton production is now possible. Almost half the cotton acreage of the West Texas High Plains is harvested by 3500 mechanical stripper-harvesters produced by two implement manufacturers. Three other large implement companies manufacture picker-harvesters for use in humid areas. Picker-harvesters are economical if operated close to capacity—about 200 acres annually—but are inefficient on less than 100 acres; consequently they are best suited to large farms with large fields. Pre-emergence herbicides, applied by tractor-drawn machines during planting, have been developed recently; other new herbicides, also machine-applied, can control weeds and grass in young cotton. Availability of the new herbicides means that laborious hand hoeing, weeding, and chopping can be supplanted by machine work. The "field hand" of old now rides a tractor, and "one mule and forty acres" cotton farming is a dodo. Not merely in the cotton regions but throughout the South average farm size is increasing, in large part, apparently, as a result of expanding production units to utilize machinery efficiently.

A great deal has been written about displacement of Southern rural-farm population by mechanization. One of the most cautious estimates calculates a total displacement of more than 2,000,000 people between 1945 and 1965 and a nonfarm employment potential for the same period in the South alone to exceed 2,300,000. Manufactural absorption potential is based on the 1946 ratio of farm to manufacturing employment in the region and is held constant throughout the 1945–1965 period, a condition that cannot apply because of rapid increments to the manufacturing plant of the South during the past seven years. These calculations also make no allowance for the widespread increase in intensiveness of farming.

Instead of tractors pushing workers off the farms, landowners more often than not have been forced to mechanize because of labor shortages. Those who cried "Calamity!" 15 years ago, when tractors appeared in numbers in the South, missed a basic point: industrialization and urbanization have been proceeding regionally at rates greater than those for the country. Farm workers have migrated voluntarily to cities and factories in response to relatively high wages.

Consumption of fertilizer is great—for which some have criticized the South. Applications of lime are up 840 per cent (1944), and fertilizer consumption 33 per cent (1944), over 1929 figures for Southern farms; characteristically, the region pays slightly more than half the nation's fertilizer bill. In many respects the South leads the country in adapting fertilizers to intensive farming practices. Fertilizer consumption undoubtedly will increase, as it will throughout the country, in response to the necessity for higher per acre yields to feed and clothe a growing population. Ten years from now today's fertilizer consumption in the South may look small.

Rotation systems capitalizing on legumes are utilized throughout the South to an extent not even remotely anticipated 20 years ago. Research to produce still better cotton varieties continues on experiment stations and commercial seed farms throughout the region. Mechanization, fertilizer, and farm-specialization trends cited above point toward more intensive cultivation. Consequently, the gradual rise in per acre cotton yields should continue for some time. It would seem that the competitive position of the South's cotton farmers is much better than heretofore and that national cotton demand can be satisfied from the present acreage in the seven regions, or even from a slightly smaller acreage.

Cash Specialty Crops

Corn

Corn is generally considered about equal to cotton as a soil depleting crop. Total corn acreage has decreased from a peak of 32.5 million in 1938 to some 24 million—nearly 25 per cent. Decrease has been greatest in Texas and Oklahoma, somewhat less in the Mississippi Valley States and Alabama, and least in the Atlantic Seaboard States. Corn is grown throughout the South, though in the western sectors it has been largely replaced by grain sorghums. The upper South still produces greater per acre and total yields than the Gulf Coastal States: Virginia averaged corn yields of 46 bushels an acre in 1948–1950; Georgia, despite an increase of nearly 50 per cent in recent years, awaits a consistent trend average exceeding 20 bushels. Yield increases in the upper South may be explained partly by more rapid dissemination of adapted hybrid varieties and by greater utilization of improved corns in legume and small-grain rotations. Good hybrids adapted to Coastal Plain conditions, especially to late summer droughts, have yet to appear. Grain sorghums may prove to be a more satisfactory source of feed grains than corn on the Gulf and Atlantic Coastal Plain; research on the sorghums in these areas to date is meager and inconclusive.

Most corn now produced in the South is grown for sale. "Hogging off" of corn is expanding, and about 60 per cent of the feed consumed by poultry is produced within the region. However, the South is still a grain and feed importer. Corn and small grains move regularly down the Mississippi-Tennessee waterway to such points as Florence and Decatur, Ala.; Florence is becoming a major feed milling and distributing center for the lower South.

With local markets aplenty, research under way, and yields climbing rapidly, a region-wide increase in corn productivity should continue, probably from slightly less acreage in the future.

Tobacco

For many years well-defined tobacco regions have existed in seven Southern states. The Atlantic seaboard regions of southern Georgia and north-central Florida, North and South Carolina, and the south-central Virginia Coastal Plain are flue-cure producers and cornerstone areas in cigarette-tobacco production. About 60 per cent of all United States tobacco is flue-cured from these areas. Southern Maryland produces a fire-cured tobacco of somewhat less desirable grade. Central and western Kentucky and north-central Tennessee concentrate on burley, and a smaller burley area flourishes in eastern Tennessee and extreme southwestern Virginia. In value, tobacco is the second most important agricultural crop in the South.

No other type of land use in the South is as distinctly regionalized as tobacco cultivation, and as unlikely to change in distribution. No other crop has been subjected to as many regulatory procedures and aided as greatly by preferential price treatments under the parity arrangements of the Agricultural Adjustment Acts. These preferential arrangements have been exhaustively studied and are too complex for repetition here. Their cumulative effect has been to push tobacco prices to much higher proportionate levels than those for other commodities, even in years when parity levels for most other agricultural goods were reduced.

A strict AAA-enforced acreage-control program has fixed distribution of tobacco production—seemingly permanently—in those areas and on those farms which have a history as tobacco producers under acreage regulations; acreage allotment remains the same year after year. If a newcomer wishes to enter tobacco production, he must petition his county Production and Marketing Committee for an acreage allotment, which is obtained only at the expense of established growers. For this reason virtually all new applications are denied. The only device open to the newcomer is to purchase a farm that traditionally has grown the crop under allotment, but he finds that the allotment each farm carries has value far beyond the customary value of the land.

Geographically, tobacco has had little effect recently on Southeastern land use. That tobacco, which geographers have always considered noteworthy for its wide range of adaptability to various soils and climates, should be so restricted in distribution is, to say the least, anomalous. The crop probably serves as the best agricultural example of a new brand of determinism—political determinism.

Peanuts

Peanuts now occupy third place among Southern cash crops. "In the last 35 years commercial production of this crop has increased sixfold; acreage 'hogged-off' has gone up about four times [to one million acres]. Peanut hay now runs nearly 15 million tons a year." Between 1929 and 1948 acreage planted to peanuts more than doubled (4,146,000 acres, 1948), average harvested for nuts increased 162 per cent (3,311,000 acres, 1948), per acre yields remained constant at about 706 pounds, and prices increased from an average of 3.7 cents a pound to 10.5 cents. The 1948 production of 1,169,235 tons was nearly three times as great as the 1929 production, and the United States has changed from a net importer to an exporter of some magnitude: since 1944 exports have increased sharply.

The first upsurge in peanut production outside the traditional Virginia-Carolina area occurred in response to World War I demand for vegetable oils; large plantings were made on the Texas Black Waxy Prairies, in the Red River Valley, and on the Georgia–Alabama–Florida–South Carolina Coastal Plain. World War II demand for oil accelerated a 1930–1940 trend toward peanut displacement of cotton in southwestern Georgia, southeastern Alabama, and northern Florida, which together now produce more than half the nation's peanuts (Fig. 12). The peanut has also made substantial inroads at the expense of cotton in the Georgia-Carolina inner Coastal Plain and in the eastern Alabama Black Belt. On part of the 1925–1929 cotton acreage of the northern Black Waxy Prairies peanuts have replaced cotton, and the middle Red River Valley still continues as a secondary peanut region. During World War II peanut production increased about 2.5 times in central Texas and southern Oklahoma, but only about 15 per cent in the old Virginia–North Carolina Coastal Plain region.

The recently emerged peanut regions will probably continue in about their present areal pattern. The peanut is subject to price and acreage controls of the Agricultural Adjustment Acts; its price under parity is relatively more favorable than 20 years ago. The Bureau of Agricultural Economics believes that consumer incomes will exercise a major influence on the market for peanuts, and since the national income outlook is promising, demand for peanuts should be steady. Even with fluctuations, the outlook is anything but dark under the AAA price-parity program.

Another promising factor is research under way for new products from peanut hulls, nuts, and oil. Vines are frequently recovered after harvesting and fed to livestock to supplement other feeds. Peanut oil and food processing plants are being built near principal production regions;

Moultrie, Ga., has become an outstanding center. The peanut has succumbed to mechanization, and mechanical harvesters are increasing rapidly in all the peanut regions.

Soybeans

The soybean, introduced into the United States via the South Atlantic Coastal Plain, was insignificant as a source of cash income in the South until about 15 years ago. During the 1930's the Soil Conservation Service, county agents, and others promoted its cultivation throughout the South as a forage, hay, green manure, and supplemental nitrogen crop. Expansion in acreage was greatest in the alluvial upper Mississippi Valley, where the crop was used largely for forage, but soybeans also gained a firm toe hold in the northeastern North Carolina Coastal Plain.

In 1943 the Secretary of Agriculture established a parity price for soybeans. Parity increased the average oilbean price about 50 per cent at a time when Mississippi Valley farmers—traditionally cotton producers—were unable to expand cotton acreages significantly because of labor shortages but could greatly expand machine-cultivated and -harvested crops. During the 1930's per acre oilbean yields in this region had been low, because of poorly adapted varieties, but immediately before World War II locally adapted varieties were disseminated in the valley, which virtually tripled per acre yields; certain of them that mature in 100–110 days offer many double-cropping possibilities. Oilbean production in the Mississippi Valley rose steadily from 1943 until the end of the decade: by 1944 it had increased to more than 900 per cent above the 1939 output; in 1947 it reached more than 12,000,000 bushels, and the total has since increased.

Soybeans threaten the areal supremacy of cotton and corn in the upper half of the alluvial valley today. In several parts of eastern Arkansas and southeastern Missouri cotton and corn acreages have been exceeded by acreages planted to harvested beans. Oilbeans are receiving increasing attention in the "Delta" of Mississippi, Arkansas, and other parts of the lower valley; research for adapted varieties by experiment stations is particularly significant.

A cotton-soybean dualism has developed in the Mississippi Valley that is not duplicated elsewhere. Since rise of the soybean is attributable to price supports, the extent to which this regional dualism will expand, or continue, depends on federal actions. For the time being the pattern will continue; for the future the competitive position of the soybean appears strong.

There is little doubt that soybeans will expand farther, especially southward, and that soybean displacement of cotton will become greater. Landowners now recognize the strongest competitive facet of the soybean throughout this region: although net return *per acre* is less than from cotton at prevailing prices, the net return *per dollar* invested in capital and labor is greater.

In the other large soybean district—northeastern North Carolina—production increase paralleled that of the Mississippi Valley, but on a smaller scale and at a less rapid rate. Since World War II this region has been producing about 3,000,000 bushels of oilbeans annually. Both production and areal extent appear stable.

During 1950–1951 soybean plantings increased substantially in the middle Tennessee River Valley of northern Alabama, the Georgia-Carolina Piedmont, the northern Texas Black Waxy Prairies, and the lower Arkansas River Valley. Whether or not these increases portend new trends in dissemination of soybean culture is not yet clear; however, the multifunctional nature of the bean ensures more widespread cultivation in the future.

Market Vegetables and Small Fruits

For the South as a whole, total cash income from truck crops has risen more than 150 per cent since 1924. A trend toward greater production of market vegetables appears under way in several small areas, including south-central Louisiana; northwestern Tennessee, especially Gibson County; southwestern Mississippi; south-central Georgia; the central Coastal Plain in South Carolina; extreme northeastern Tennessee–southwestern Virginia; and northwestern Arkansas. (Fig. 12).

Large tomato crops are produced in the lower Rio Grande Valley by irrigation, in northeastern Texas, and in northwestern Arkansas. Watermelons are grown intensively in many small isolated areas from eastern Texas to Delaware, with greatest production in south-central and southwestern Georgia. So also with a few other truck crops; but true commercialized trucking is carried on only in the areas mentioned above.

Four forces have combined to create the specialized truck areas: railroad agents interested in expanding freight volume; agricultural extension work, especially in improvement of plant varieties; gradual influx of frozen foods and canning industries; and small farms, with rather large labor forces in the truck areas.

The outlook for truck crops is steady expansion of existing areas and creation of new ones. Geographers have recognized for many years the inherent soil and climatic advantages of most of the Gulf South for truck crops; reliable markets have been needed for expansion. These markets are now at hand through the mediums of canning and freezing plants, expanding regional and national consumer demand, and organized transportation facilities for marketing outside the South.

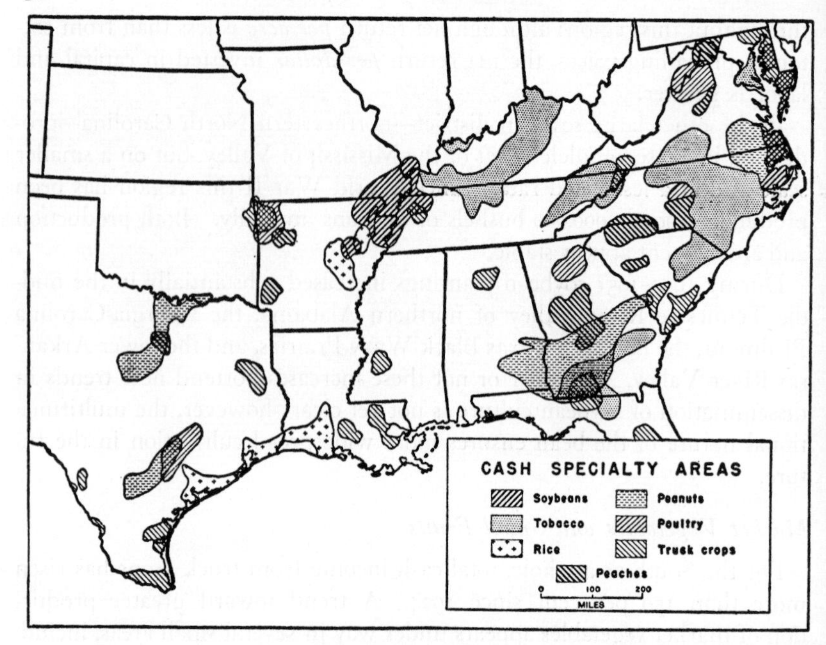

FIGURE 12

Principal Cash Specialty Areas Other Than Cotton, 1950. Compiled from Census of Agriculture, 1950, and publications of the Bureau of Agricultural Economics and the Office of Foreign Agricultural Relations. Areas delimited are principal production regions for the commodities mapped. No uniform statistical component was applied to boundaries shown; regions are the writer's interpretation of cash specialty areas.

The Livestock Industries

Grazing and livestock industries represent the greatest changes in the South's land occupance in recent years and promise most for the future. The more significant changes have to do with poultry, dairying, and beef cattle.

Poultry

Since 1924, for the South as a whole, income has increased more than 160 per cent from the sale of eggs, and about 270 per cent from the sale of other poultry products. Poultry, especially chickens, are raised on most farms in the South in conjunction with other forms of land use, and primarily for the farm table, but four regions are noteworthy for commercial poultry production: northwestern Virginia, the upper Chattahoochee Valley in Georgia (centered on Gainesville), northwestern Arkansas, and the Guadalupe–San Marcos Valley region of Texas. No other form of land use receives more than minor attention on farms that specialize in poultry. Poultry farms, like tobacco farms, are highly specialized and utilize a small acreage intensively.

The amazing growth of the broiler industry in the Chattahoochee Valley indicates the high degree of specialization that Southern poultry producers are achieving. In 1935, after an inauspicious beginning during the depression, this region produced a modest total of some 500,000 broilers. By 1950 production had increased to more than 62 million birds (Georgia Crop Reporting Service estimates), and gross sales value to about 50 million dollars. Between 1948 and 1951 gross dollar volume increased more than 120 per cent, and the Crop Reporting Service asserts that the Gainesville area now leads the country in broiler output. Accompanying the growth of the broiler industry have been other new activities—feed and grain stores; hatcheries; dressing, freezing, and processing plants; and the like. Grain is shipped from the Midwest into Gainesville continuously and accounts for half, roughly, of the area's feed consumption. The extensive demand for feed grains is reflected in increased small-grains acreage in neighboring parts of the Piedmont, and recently in the organization of a company to construct and operate grain elevators in a near-by county. From cotton gin to grain elevator on the same landscape in 15 years is indeed a change.

A typical broiler farm in the Chattahoochee Valley consists of 50 acres or less, a third or more of which is woodland. Owner-operated, these farms in the past were devoted principally to cotton-corn and subsistence production. Today the universal item is the broiler shed, a long, low, one-story structure with few or no windows, artificially lighted inside, heated by either oil or electric brooders, and sheltering 15,000 chicks or more at a time. Since the chick never sets foot outdoors, the weather is significant only as it affects heating costs. Chicks are fed to market size in two months or less, and marketing proceeds the year round. The poultry farmer keeps a close check on daily market quotations.

In a real sense the Chattahoochee poultry industry has been an agricultural-factory operation. Until recently, all that the region supplied in the production of broilers was a series of hillside sites and labor for assemblage of raw materials; chicks, grains, protein supplements, commercial grits, and antibiotics came from outside. Today hatcheries are expanding in the region, and feed-grain production is increasing in adjoining areas. Now even grit is produced locally, just south to famous Stone Mountain (east of Atlanta). Expansion of local raw-materials production to supply the broiler industry would appear to signify approaching maturity for the Chattahoochee poultry region.

Dairy Expansion

Despite winter grazing potentialities throughout the South not remotely approximated in any major dairy region, there is a current unbalance between fluid-milk production and growing urban populations. Total Southern urban population has increased 35 per cent in the past decade alone; individual income—hence per capita milk consumption—has expanded roughly fourfold since 1924. Both production and value of dairy products also increased substantially between 1924 and 1948—in value, milk products have increased about 225 per cent. But the industry is still far from satisfying regional demand, and the South seems destined to continue as a dairy importer for some time. Present dairying is almost entirely urban-oriented; dairy farms are found interspersed among other farms in crude "rings" of uneven width around the principal urban centers. There is no true dairy area in the South today in the sense that the Housatonic Valley or West Chester, Pa., are dairy centers; the closest approaches are middle Tennessee, the upper Holston Valley, and northeastern Mississippi.

The hill lands and rolling plains of eastern Tennessee, the upper Piedmont, northern Alabama, and adjacent areas provide superior opportunities for dairying; for example, year-round grazing on improved pastures of high potential productivity, relatively low essential dairy housing and equipment costs, expanding urban centers near by, and adequate local transportation. All these areas are characterized by many small farms, mostly owner-operated and in need of relatively intensive land use. Continuing soil-conservation problems on the rolling to hilly terrain point the necessity for a grass-forage economy, and the relatively high but stable farm income that dairying provides is also needed here. Dairying is due for long-range expansion in the South. Conditions within a radius of 150 miles of Chattanooga seem especially favorable, and rapid expansion is already discernible.

Beef-Cattle Grazing

The swing to beef cattle and attendant improved pastures and hay crops is so pronounced, widespread, and rapid that it constitutes the most important new trend in Southern land use.

Many factors operating together have contributed to the growth of the Southern beef-cattle industry. From 1924 to 1944 livestock grazing expanded partly in response to decreases in cotton acreage. The boll-weevil invasion of the 1920's forced a reduction of cotton acreage; the economic depression of the early thirties brought such low cotton prices that production was scarcely justifiable; in 1933 the first cotton-acreage limitation program further intensified emphasis on feed and forage production. Soil Conservation Service incentive payments encouraged farmers to adopt approved land uses such as legume and seed production, permanent pastures, and hay-forage rotation. During World War II high beef prices and labor shortages accelerated the trend. Mechanization also contributed substantially by freeing acreage previously devoted to support of work stock; that process continues. During the 1930–1944 period many new feed and forage crops and grasses were introduced and developed. Forceful farmer-education programs promoted by agricultural extension workers have paid dividends recently through rapid adoption of new forage varieties.

Since World War II additional influences have become apparent, especially market demand and market orientation factors. Rapid increments in per capita incomes in the South (about a 400 per cent increase in the last 20 years), plus urbanization, have expanded Southern markets for beef products more rapidly than for the nation as a whole. Despite an increase in its beef output, the South still imports about half its meat supply. The High Plains ranch regions, traditional sources of calves fattened and marketed in the Midwest, are now shipping regularly to the West Coast to meet the demand for beef created by large population growth in California during the past decade. Eastern markets, also more densely populated than a decade ago, must look elsewhere for more beef. Pennsylvania, Maryland, and Ohio cattle buyers are already purchasing feeder stock in the Georgia-Carolina area for fattening close to Eastern markets, though on a small scale.

It is becoming clear that the South can probably produce most grades of beef at lower unit cost than other large livestock areas. Climatic advantages minimize barn, shelter, machinery, and other equipment costs, and year-round grazing on green forage greatly reduces the need for stored winter feed. Under proper management and with relatively small investment, low-grade or even abandoned land can be converted into a high-protein grass-legume pasture that will support a cow plus calf on three acres or less; highly improved permanent pastures are carrying cow-calf on 1½ acres.

Exclusive of Virginia and Kentucky, beef cattle ("cattle other than dairy" in census reports) increased in the South from about 11,000,000 head in 1925 to about 15,200,000 head in 1947 and yielded 390 per cent more cash return in that year than in 1925. Pasturage in the Mississippi Valley and states to the east increased about 42 per cent, to a total of some 41 million acres.

These figures do not begin to tell the story: the most rapid and significant grazing changes have occurred since 1947–1948. For 1949 and 1950, the 10 top states in the country in percentage gains in cattle population were all in the South, with Alabama, Georgia, and North Carolina leading. The Bureau of Agricultural Economics reports a 1949–1950 cattle increase of 23 per cent in Alabama, 21 per cent in Georgia, and 20 per cent in North Carolina. Increments for 1950–1952 apparently are equally great.

The South is stocking its pastures by importing commercial beef breeding stock—especially heifers, registered beef bulls for crossbreeding on native cattle, and whole registered cattle herds. Crossbreeding with Brahman cattle proceeds rapidly. Heifer calves are being retained to augment herds. In a few years, perhaps as few as five, stocking will diminish, and a flood of steers and calves will roll from the South.

There is, as yet, no clear-cut regionality; in some ways the whole South has gone into the cattle business. It appears to be most pronounced in the following areas: (1) lower Coastal Plain of southeastern Alabama, southern Georgia, northern and northwestern Florida, and southeastern South Carolina; (2) the Alabama-Mississippi Black Belt; (3) the inner Coastal Plain in North Carolina; (4) the northern Black Waxy Prairies; and (5) the alluvial Mississippi Valley from approximately Baton Rouge, La., northward. The first area seems to be rapidly expanding northward and eastward. Well-established cattle grazing has been characteristic of the Louisville-Nashville Basins and the upper Holston, Roanoke, and Shenandoah Valleys for some time.

Beef-cattle production currently consists almost entirely of grass-hay fattened calves and feeder cattle; many are marketed at maturity as grass-fattened. When stocking has ended, more emphasis will be placed on grain feeding for finishing and fattening cattle on locally produced grains. Land can be used to provide winter pasture for four months, then yield a grass or legume seed crop, grow grain sorghums or soybeans during summer, and return to pasture during fall. Or winter grains can be grown in conjunction with a winter legume, pastured for most of the winter, cut for grain in early summer, and followed by a summer annual legume for summer forage or hay. There are many possible combinations. Grain sorghums appear to hold especial promise for the Coastal Plain from Texas eastward because they mature more rapidly than corn, can be used in a winter-forage rotation, can be machine-harvested, and probably will prove to be greater per acre producers in the lower South than corn. The significant point seems to be that many conservational rotation schemes are possible for most of the South that will enable substantial increase of grain output without competing with existing forms of land use and without reducing livestock grazing potentials. To date cattle grazing does not remotely approach potential capacity; expansion is ahead.

Forecast: The Trends

Within contemporary Southern land occupance lie clues to the future. Trend analysis and prediction always involve dangers in an area undergoing profound changes, and geographical tools for prediction are somewhat inadequate. Not without trepidation, the writer ventures to forecast a few land-use trends in the South for the decade 1950–1960.

It has been assumed that agricultural parity prices under AAA, relatively high commodity prices, and gradually expanding consumer markets will continue without significant alterations; these factors underlie most of the changes in the South during recent years.

Cotton yields will increase, and acreage will decrease slightly. By 1960 the seven cotton regions will exhibit accessory, diversified forms of land occupance more clearly. The inner Coastal Plain and Piedmont cotton regions will experience major developments in beef-cattle grazing.

Cattle grazing will expand for some time, achieving a high degree of intensification. Concentrations will become pronounced on the lower Gulf–South Atlantic Coastal Plain, on the northern Black Waxy Prairies, and in the lower Mississippi Valley. Conservational land-use practices will increase areally, in large part to accommodate more grazing. Acreage in highly developed pastures will exceed that of any other form of land use except forest.

Small grains will expand in response to livestock increments. The expansion probably will be greatest east of the Mississippi and will involve double cropping. Corn productivity will increase, but acreage will remain as at present or decrease slightly. Expansion in grain sorghums is overdue now, especially east of the Texas prairies.

Dairying will expand in all areas adjacent to major cities, and a true dairy region is in sight in the uplands within a 150-mile radius of Chattanooga.

Oilbean crops, both peanuts and soybeans, will increase still more: they are sensitive to national vegetable-oil demand, are leguminous and hence desirable for rotations, and fit livestock production-management needs. Except for distinct regional patterns already created, tobacco culture will contribute little to the "new look" of the South. Success in small, highly specialized poultry and vegetable areas will cause other small areas to emulate them; expanding national markets provide a major incentive. Supplemental irrigation will increase substantially, not only in truck specialty areas but also in response to expansion in intensive production of forage crops for dairy and beef cattle.

A slight decrease in gross forest acreage can be anticipated, coupled with increased output of all forest products; better forest management, fostered especially by commercial concerns, will more than offset any slight acreage decrease. Industries utilizing wood cellulose will increase in number and in output; the South will continue to produce about half of the nation's timber regrowth.

Late in the decade grazing and forestry will become more competitive in an areal sense; that is, because of greater gross and annual returns, grazing will begin to replace lower-grade forests. This trend will probably be noticeable first on cutover land in southern Alabama, Mississippi, and Arkansas.

More mechanization, larger farms with larger fields, and a smaller total farm labor force are on the way. Migration from farms to cities and factories will continue. Both regional and individual farm incomes will go on rising.

The South has already diversified; it is now engaged in intensifying. The process is rapid and visible, with readily measurable benefits. The geographical consequences are somewhat bewildering. Gone is the old regionality; in its stead are new regions, not yet fully emerged, and not identifiable by single criteria. New geographical procedures and new criteria will have to be applied for adequate assessment in the future.

The Southern color scheme from now on is shades of green the year round: green forests, green fields—and greenbacks!

42. *Herdsmen and Husbandmen* *

The domestication and use of animals and animal products has been a mark of the progress of mankind. As time has passed, a cleavage between the Herdsman and the Husbandman, between the transient, or nomad, and the sedentary farmer has slowly developed. The historical growth of various uses of animals in different areas of the world underlies many of the differences in land utilization and culture patterns in similar climatic regions.

* From Carl O. Sauer, *Agricultural Origins and Dispersals,* published by the American Geographical Society.

The author (1889) is Professor of Geography, University of California, Berkeley. His has been a strong voice in establishing the fields of human and historical geography, and anthropogeography, in the United States.

Herd Animals Belong with Seed Agriculture

The household animals I have associated with vegetative planting in origin; the herd animals belong with seed farming. The only exception is the reindeer, living in margins of the Arctic beyond the lands possible to cultivation. The notion that nomads domesticated herd animals stems from the age-old fancy that hunters became pastoralists and finally farmers, that hunters were the animal domesticators and that collectors learned how to grow plants. I know no evidence for such views, nor for the assumption underlying both, that growing scarcity of food gave the impetus to domestication. The dependence of the nomadic pastoralist on agricultural communities is well known and general, and his way of life is derived from the sedentary farmer.

• • • •

The hearth of domestication of herd animals lies in Southwest Asia. To the myth of the wolf that became a dog by joining the campfire of hunters and the one that hungry collectors began to sow and thus originated the noble grains, we may add the fancy that enclosure of game animals by hunters was the means by which our herd animals came to be.

The bones of cattle, sheep, and goats are found with early village sites of seed farmers, dated as about seven thousand years old, and ranging from the base of the Cilician Mountains to the basin of Persepolis in south-central Persia. Tell Hassuna in upper Mesopotamia and Tepe Sialk in central Persia, are among the oldest known. These records of the life and arts of ancient seed farmers and stock raisers exhibit conditions far removed from the beginnings of domestication, perhaps more different from their beginnings than they are from modern village life in the same parts. No more than for the crops has the archeologist discovered the beginnings of animal domestications, nor the order in which they appeared. For such reconstruction we must turn to the distribution of the wild forms, to bits of genetic evidence, all too few as yet about the descent of the domestic forms, and to folkways and folklore in different societies.

To confine bands of adult wild and lusty animals until they became domestic herd animals was not within the power of any early folk. The building of enclosures which could not be leaped or breached was hardly possible, nor was taming by starving into acceptance of food and obedience to man. Taming of the wild again may be thought of as beginning by infant capture, nursing by a foster mother, and raising the young in close association with man. I should start the procedure therefore in much the same manner as among the tropical planters, by fully sedentary folk, in this case seed farmers, who had no want of food and were not interested in the captured young as future roasts, but for entertainment or ceremonial. Pigs as well as dogs were already widely distributed, I have inferred as acquired from the planting cultures of the East. The pig, it should be remembered, was generally raised all across Southwest Asia and farther west until it became despised in the rise of newer religions. If any domestic mammals were already present, lactation of captured infant stock was simplified. A plausible reconstruction is thus: man returning from the hills with a kid or lamb, woman rearing it, and children growing up with the young animal and leading it out to browse. In such a gentle captivity, breeding might occur and thus domestication begin. In any case, hungry and errant hunters were not the ones who thought of domestication or could practice it.

Milking Common to Herd Animals

All the domestic herd animals are milked or have been thus used in the past. Milking may, therefore, have been both part of the process and purpose of their domestication. The wild forms of such animals are not more desirable sources of milk, either as to quality or amount, than a lot of other herbivores, accessible to man but never domesticated. Early in Hahn's study of economic geography he found that milking had a continuous distribution which could not be explained by climate, pasture, or anything else in the environment. Beyond this milking line there were people who had an aversion to milk and its products. In other words, here Hahn inferred a non-environmental culture trait that originated in one center and spread thence until stopped by other cultures that would have nothing to do with it. The original center, he judged correctly, lay in Southwest Asia. It was unknown in America, nor did the natives of the New World care for the strange practice when it was brought by the Europeans.

In the Old World, milking is not practiced in two agricultural areas, the Far East and the Pacific islands in Asia and the tropical forests of Africa. Some of the animals milked elsewhere are kept in numbers and of old both in the Orient and inner Africa. The explanation that the Chinese do not use milk because they got cattle and goats before milking was invented is an assumption unsupported by any evidence. I think it more likely that the Orientals and central Africans accepted some domesticated herd animals, but did not take on the habit of milking because it was strange to their ways and they did not like it. We know that the Orient remained in communication with Southwest Asia and that there was continuing transfer of ideas that were congenial. The cultures that rejected milking were the two ancient planting cultures, and the basis of rejection is probably only antipathy.

That milking began for economic ends is, I think, also unlikely. At the beginning of domestication, the animals secreted milk enough only for their young, or very little more. That small children might on occasion share milk of goat or ewe with the animal young is hardly a sufficient basis for starting a milking economy.

. . . . .

Domestication as to Kind

The kinds of animals that were domesticated are curious and meaningful. There was high diversity of game animals in the Levant and its borderlands: antelopes and gazelles in the plains; wild cattle, bison, and buffalo in forest, brush, and grassland; deer of various kinds and habits; goats and sheep in rocky and mountainous lands; camels in deserts; horses and asses in continuous distribution from the Cape of Good Hope north to the Siberian taiga. Of this multitude only a very few were domesticated, though the ancient sculptures and paintings abound in hunting scenes of diverse sorts and also tell of the keeping of numerous kinds tamed.

The selection was not based on propinquity to man, nor on sharing his habitat. It was not based on declining abundance, for most of the domestication took place near the margins of the natural range occupied by the species. It was not based on docility: antelopes, gazelles, and deer, easily tamed and much kept for diversion, provided no domesticate except the reindeer. This animal of the cold north seems to be a belated substitute added when pastoralism spread into the margins of the Arctic. Rather, one might say that animals were chosen for domestication that were not easy to take, which were not common, and which were difficult to make gentle—the wild mountain goats and sheep that avoid the vicinity of man, the formidable wild cattle and buffalo. Hunting the urus (*Bos primigenius*) was a sport of major hazard and elaborate organization to the time of their extinction in the seventeenth century of our era. Yet this is the ancestor of our domestic cattle. The feared wild cattle of India, the garur, are no more dangerous than was the urus. The Old World bison, a very near relative of our American bison, never had such a reputation for ferocity. It occupied a very great range that extended well into the lands of ancient civilization. It was desirable for meat, hide and wool, but no domestication was undertaken; the failure to do so was not due to its nature, habitat, or economic suitability.

The eleven domesticates are: the common cattle, zebu, water buffalo, yak, goat, sheep, reindeer, dromedary, Bactrian camel, horse, and ass, all now or once milch animals. Except the reindeer, all are first known from ancient seed-agricultural centers and their wild ranges are in or marginal to such areas. The coincidence of the west Asiatic centers of seed domestication and of herd animals is such that they appear as complementary features of one cultural complex.

Goats and Sheep

The goat may possibly begin the series of herd domestications. It has been distributed all the way across Eurasia and to the south end of Africa, penetrating both the non-milking cultures of the Far East and of tropical Africa quite generally. Among African forest folk it is often the most important domestic animal, especially a dwarf race which has been thought to be akin to the turbary Neolithic goat of Swiss lake dwellers. There are very many domestic races in the Old World and they have not been well studied. It is probable that the blood of several wild species has been introduced into the domestic forms, but the main descent is traced from the southwest Asiatic bezoar goat (*Capra aegagrus*), a mountain animal ranging west of the Indus to the Caucasus. Adametz thought the earliest pictorial representations in the Near East to be a domestic version of the screw horned *C. falconeri,* native to the western Himalayas, Afghanistan, and east Bukhara, and known to be fully fertile in crosses with the house goat. First choice as to place of origin therefore goes to the cis-Indus country (area B of the seed hearths). The wild forms live in the mountains well above, but at no great distance from the ancient agricultural valleys.

Culturally there are a number of suggestions of high antiquity. The goat is both herd and household animal and is found among people who have none of the other herd animals, but who keep pigs and fowls. It is sacrificed, but usually as second choice to sheep. Goat gods, such as Pan, and the ritual scapegoat, may be traits of degradation such as elder gods and elder rites have often suffered.

Sheep were domesticated in the same general area as the goat, the chief parent being considered *Ovis vignei*. Adametz ties an early domestic form with horizontal spiral horns to a variety of *O. vignei* living from the Salt Range of the Punjab to Baluchistan, emphasizing "the outstanding role which these parts of Asia played, in part as centers of origin, in part as staging areas of domestic animals and peoples in the early history of mankind, moving from East to West." Independently, therefore, the seed plants of Area B and sheep and goats have been assigned to the same area as to domestic hearths, from which they passed into the Near East and beyond. Fat tails and woolly fleeces were later developments of domestication. In Ethiopia parallel selection formed races of goats and sheep so much alike as to confuse travellers and lead to stories of crosses between the two.

. . . . .

Cattle

The original ceremonial domestication of cattle was proposed by Hahn to much academic headshaking. In brief, they were, in his view, the originally sacred animals in the moon cult, their horns symbolizing the crescent moon. Milking and castration were fertility rituals. Sacred oxen first drew the ceremonial cart and pulled the plow, a phallic symbol for the insemination of the receptive earth. Cattle, cart, plow, broadcasting, and drilling all began as ceremonies of a rising fertility cult of the Near East in which the officiants were males, and henceforth the care of the cattle, the hand at the plow, the sower, was male. The husbandman thereafter takes over the agricultural operations, the women retire to the house and to garden work. Paternal societies are formed, with priests and kings, politics and states, aristocracies and subjects. The male hierarchies prevailed where cattle, plowed fields, and wagons became dominant institutions. The thesis was repugnant to materialistic rationalism. It also offended because it placed sex at the center of esoteric religious matters. It remains a great contribution, still acceptable in large part.

. . . . .

The Camels

Camels were on the verge of extinction when they became domesticated. No wild dromedaries have ever been known, and prevailing zoologic opinion considers the living "wild" two-humped camels of Chinese Turkestan as feral. The dromedary is linked with Semitic peoples and an Arabian domestication is commonly assumed. There are a few early Egyptian representations, none, it is said, being known after the First Dynasty until the time of the Ptolemies. This early Egyptian knowledge suggests a center in western Arabia, where quite early agricultural settlements may be inferred, though such have not been proven. The spread of the dromedary was late and then rather rapid when states and trade required a transport animal for desert crossings. For the Bactrian camel, domestication is inferred because crosses with the dromedary are sterile. no other locality is indicated than the one that gives the name. A separate

Such hybrids were fairly common in Asia Minor in classical times, where it is thought also that the breeding of mules originated. Neither dromedary nor Bactrian need be assigned to nomad origin. Bactria is a farming land more ancient than the probable time of camel domestication. So too, it is surmised, is Yemen, and probably Hejaz; there are botanical indications that point that way.

The Horse

. . . Historically the horse is associated mainly with the Indo-European migrations, martial bands that poured across Anatolia into the Fertile Crescent, through Media into India, and out of the Russian plains into the Mediterranean peninsulas and western Europe. With the horse came the war chariot and the cavalryman, new forms of war and conquest, military aristocracy. To Indo-Europeans it was the animal of prestige, the sacred animal above all others, the high sacrifice, the flesh of solemn festivals. To the nomads of interior Asia it became the provider of fermented milk, kumiss. To our ancestors it was a source of meat, though much less so than were beeves. Christianity stamped out the eating of horseflesh among our people since it was a main link to pagan ways.

. . . .

Separation of Herdsmen from Husbandmen

The separation of herdsman from husbandman came about insensibly and imperfectly. "Abel was a keeper of sheep, but Cain was a tiller of the ground," and both were of one family. Beyond the tilled lands of the villagers lay the open range where herds grazed or browsed in hills and mountains and on plains too dry to farm. In the off season, the fallow fields provided additional grazing. Feed from browse was important, probably more so than grass. As the numbers of people and stock increased, herdsmen and herd moved farther and farther away from the villages and became more permanently detached from the settled lands. This about describes the roots of pastoral nomadism. As with village Arab and Bedouin, sedentary folk and mobile tent dwellers are mostly one people. In Inner Asia, earlier hunting peoples took on herd animals from other kinds of folk to the south, but still there is some dependence of herdsman on farmer for grain. The original and absolute pastoralists can scarcely be said to exist or ever to have existed; they derive from a farming culture in which livestock was an original element.

Hamitic and Indo-European migrations were largely driven by a strong bent toward herding. The former, stemming out of a common background with the Semites, moved across north and east Africa, bearers of a cattle culture in which the beasts were—and are—prized far beyond their economic utility. Hamitic cattle lords spread over the native hoe-tilling peoples in a sort of symbiosis in which the privileged group were masters of the cattle, the peasant mass grew the field crops. The Aryan invasion of India had similar aristocratic quality. In Europe successive Indo-European waves overran and mingled with the older sedentary cultivators. The latter are still partially recognizable in "Mediterranean" racial stocks in the south and west and Alpines in the central mountains and hill lands. Some of the Indo-European bands came by way of Asia Minor, others by way of the Russian plains, all with their herds of cattle and horses.

North European Husbandry

Our forebears, drifting west and north, got into lands of shorter and cooler summers and of mixed forests or woodlands. The farther they went the more did climate restrict their habits. By the time they settled on the Baltic and North Sea lowlands, they were stockmen, not cultivators. Studies of pollen that drifted into bogs have enabled a pretty accurate reconstruction of vegetation. The earliest clearing of land was not for sown fields but for pastures and meadows; the newly-immigrated plants were only pasture weeds. Somewhat later, the first grains appear, wheat and barley; still later, rye and oats. The pollen record is checked by seed impressions in potsherds of known age.

Rye and, in part, oats are wild grasses at home in western Asia, mingling in fields with wheat and barley but only as weeds. Primitive methods of harvest and winnowing did not separate weed seed from grain and so the ryes and oats marched along with the wheat and barley in their westward travels. Meanwhile, a partial domestication had taken place quite by chance, for the strains of rye and oats that remained intermingled with the cultivated grains were those that had become non-shattering, matured at the same time as the cultivated plants, had similar grain and stalk sizes, and hence became part of the harvested crop. As the growing of cereals spread into lands of colder and wetter summers and acid soils, barley and in particular wheat did less and less well, the volunteer rye and oats relatively better and in the end these became the cultivated crops and the north Atlantic lands came to depend on them for human cereal.

Thus arose a distinctive farming system north of the Alps and west of the Russian steppes. This was a balanced, mixed farming, primarily an animal husbandry. Milk products were most important and, with dairying, the calf crop increased the meat supply. Clearing of new ground was primarily to gain more pasture and meadow. The limiting factor always was the amount of feed that could be grown for the animals, the grazing available during open weather, the hay that could be stored against winter. The economy produced the barn for hay and the stable for stock. Field crops took second place to hay crop. Rye had increased importance because, being fall sown, it provided some winter pasture. Fertility was maintained because the stable manure was returned to the fields. Long continued pasturing and mowing selected an association of forage plants that prospered under the bite of cattle and cut of scythe in a closed ecologic cycle, as Gradmann liked to point out. Man took from the ground no more than he returned; he did not lose topsoil by overcultivation nor was it lost to winter rains. Production was not at a high level, nor was the life of the husbandman easy, but man lived durably on the land and could expect his descendants to do so.

Such were the systems of culture across northwestern Europe for two to three thousand years, systems not seriously modified until the eighteenth century. Then, with the introduction of the potato, the development of stock beets and field turnips, and the cultivation of clovers, the new agricultural revolution arose and, in part, prepared the way for the industrial revolution.

• • • • •

We are at the end of this summary review of what man has done with the plants and animals at his disposal. His mastery over the organic world began with his employment of and experiments with fire. Sedentary fishing peoples perhaps commenced the cultivation of plants and became the first domesticators of plants and animals. The earliest plant selection was by vegetative reproduction and the early domestic animals were part of the household. Later came plant selection by seed reproduction and the keeping of flocks by seed farmers. I have thought to link these inventions in series, possibly beginning from a common center, and to follow their dispersals and divergences. If this be exaggeration of the processes of diffusion of learning, the proposed thesis may be taken as an invitation to study the various lines of evidence as to the growth of the agricultural arts.

Our civilization still rests, and will continue to rest, on the discoveries made by peoples for the most part unknown to history. Historic man has added no plant or animal of major importance to the domesticated forms on which he depends. He has learned lately to explain a good part of the mechanisms of selection, but the arts thereof are immemorial and represent an achievement that merits our respect and attention. We remain a part of the organic world, and as we intervene more and more decisively to change the balance and nature of life, we have also more need to know, by restrospective study, the responsibilities and hazards of our present and our prospects as lords of creation.

CHAPTER SIX

World Water Resources

APPROXIMATELY 71 per cent of the total earth's surface—81 per cent of the Southern Hemisphere and 61 per cent of the Northern Hemisphere—is water. These figures seem to indicate a superabundance of water for man's use; the larger part, however, is the salt water of the oceans, the direct use of which by man is limited. Ocean water provides an efficient, inexpensive, international water highway that connects the world land masses; in addition, it supplies an abundance of raw materials and food, for example, salt, magnesium, seaweed, sponges, whales, and fish. Perhaps the greatest value of these salt-water bodies, however, is as source regions for the fresh water of land areas. Evaporated water vapor from the oceans is brought inland by winds and the hydrologic cycle of precipitation, runoff, evaporation, and replenishing of surface and ground water is set up.

Unfortunately, the distribution over the continents of usable fresh water is extremely uneven, owing to differences in climate and to surface and subsurface storage conditions. Vast areas of the earth remain unsettled, or practically so, as a result of the lack of an available water supply. Egypt's survival as a nation and the present disproportionate distribution of its people result almost entirely from the water supplied by the Nile River. The economy of other areas is endangered by man's use of surface or ground water much more rapidly than it can be renewed by nature. Water is a renewable resource normally taken for granted and its critical significance is realized only when it is not available.

Knowledge of the regional distribution of water on the earth and of the problems involved in man's use of water in various regions provides an important link in the understanding of our environment. These aspects of the world's water resources are covered in the readings of this chapter. In addition, the challenge of Antarctic whaling and the effect of a changing climate on the occurrence and numbers of fish also are presented.

---

43. *Our Nation's Water Wealth* *

Considerable publicity has been given recently to water shortages and water pollution in various parts of the United States. The future of large industrial communities as well as of many agricultural and residential areas depends as much on water as on any other one resource. Carhart in this selection emphasizes the importance of water, by giving figures of water consumption for selected industries and crops. He stresses some of the problems that result, despite the apparent abundance of surface and ground water, and speculates on the effect of drier climates and increased use of sea water. He perhaps overemphasizes the seriousness of water problems in the attempt to get his points across.

On three things on which all earth life depends: the particle of soil, the green cell in plants and the raindrop. They are inseparable. They underwrite the entire complex of life.

The raindrop falls, it enters the soil, it puts nutrients in solution, and the plant draws these into the leaves. There in the green cell, under activating sunlight, the chlorophyll performs the alchemy that is the first link in every chain of life and living.

From that point, life and living we enjoy is carried on a flow of water. Wherever you may look at the complex we call our civilization, you find this carrying flow of water supplying necessities, facilities and luxuries.

Seventy percent or more of your physical being is water. You need a minimum of six to eight pints per day under normal activity to replace body losses. That's the first demand.

But in these United States, to supply you average necessities, comforts and luxuries, requires about 13,000 gallons of water consumed or in service every twenty-four hours.

You shave and shower, flush a toilet and drive your auto to business.

* Arthur H. Carhart, "Our Nation's Water Wealth," *The Land,* Vol. 10, No. 4, Winter, 1951–52, pp. 441–445. Published by Friends of the Land, Zanesville, Ohio.

The author (1892) is an author, conservationist, and landscape architect. He has written numerous articles and twelve books, of which the most recent are *Water—or Your Life* and *Son of the Forest.* He is now editor of *Conservation Please.*

The steel in an auto required from 65,000 to 80,000 gallons of water per ton produced. Every gallon of gasoline burned in your car involved the use of seven to ten gallons of water in its production.

If you ride an electrically-driven transit system, the steam plant producing the energy uses 600 to 1000 tons of cooling water per ton of coal burned or water in a hydro plant turns the turbines.

You read the morning paper and throw it away. It takes 70,000 gallons of water to produce one ton of newsprint pulp by the sulphate process. To produce one ton of magnesium from sea water requires 300,000 gallons of water. 200,000 gallons to produce a ton of viscose rayon, 380,000 gallons for a ton of butadine, and a distiller requires 600,000 gallons of water in fermenting 1000 bushels of industrial grain.

Those suggest demands of existing industries. Mention of one new process will illustrate what can lie ahead in the way of mounting demands.

The hydronization of coal to produce petroleum products is on the threshold of commercial operations. Colorado alone, has enough known coal to supply the nation at current consumptive rates for four hundred years. The potentials in this new field are tremendous.

A plant with a 10,000 barrel capacity per day requires 5½ to 6½ million gallons of water per day. That water would be eighty percent consumed. In addition to plant needs, there would be those of the surrounding community.

The needs of industry for water are not the greatest. Growing crops are the super-extravagant drains on our gross supply of water.

Crop water requirements vary with what is being grown, soil type, and climate. Experiments at Akron, Colorado, on the western great plains, showed that 334 tons of water were involved in growing one ton of dry matter in a crop of barley. That wasn't the grain alone; it was dry matter of root, stem, leaves and seed. Beans required 738 tons of water to a ton of dry matter produced, clover 797 tons of water, oats 599, peas 788, potatoes 636 and wheat 544.

No data at hand shows how much additional water is required in producing each pound of beef, pork, or mutton, but a dairy cow consumes about 500 pounds of water as she furnishes 100 pounds of milk.

Timber production involves water. Mixed evergreen stands in eastern forests require a precipitation of 30 to 40 inches; in west coast forests, Douglas fir needs 60 inches of precipitation, 40 for ponderosa pine.

These demands will not lessen. With mounting drains on our water wealth, it is business sense to see what we have in our account against which these drafts will be drawn.

Water is not inexhaustible. Here in Detroit, it seems like crying "wolf" to refer to grievous water shortages plaguing many other communities.

This area, with the Great Lakes embracing it, is endowed with bountiful wealth in water, of useable quality. There is a temptation to think of water here as being without limit—and the expansion it may service in all fields as also practically unlimited.

But Milwaukee learned that squirting municipal sewage into Lake Michigan deteriorated the quality of water, while not affecting mere volume. The city was compelled to take drastic steps to recapture quality. Their treatment and disposal facilities, making use of wastes as well as protecting the integrity of their water supply, is a trail-blazing accomplishment that no municipality can disregard.

The loss of useability in water is sharply indicated by the case of distillery and synthetic rubber plants near Louisville during World War II. The whole flow of the Ohio river was at their doors. But that stream carried wastes from the communities up valley. These industries required clean water and preferably of low temperature.

As in so many other places, where we have destroyed use-value of our streams, the Louisville industries turned to nature-filtered, nature-cooled ground water to meet their needs. Wells were sunk. In 1944 from 20 to 30 million gallons of water per day were being pumped from those wells. The ground water dropped to within a few feet of casing bottoms. Lack of useable water threatened full production.

Mechanical means for stretching water were installed. It was cooled and re-used. Water also was pumped back into the ground to recharge that supply. The cost of doing this ran to about 5 million dollars.

Then the U. S. Geological Survey was called in, and found that by going up-river a little distance, laying collection lines in water-rich gravel beds, wells could be pumped and pumped without much danger of depletion—and at a cost of about one-tenth the money already spent on the cooling and recharging schemes.

There have been other warnings that water is not inexhaustible all across the nation. Air conditioning on Long Island during the 1930's pulled ground water down to where sea water was beginning to invade the land mass. Now water is filtered after use and pumped back to recharge ground supplies. Inevitably this will gradually stop the pores of the earth around the recharge wells.

Los Angeles has over-pumped the basin southwest of the city at twice the rate of natural recharge. Salt water has crept two miles into the shore area at Redondo Beach.

Texas City drew on its ground water supply until the mass of water removed was so great the earth sunk as much as one and a half feet. The water level in one 1000 feet well dropped to 102 feet below sealevel; a well 610 feet deep, dropped to 165 feet below the adjacent gulf. The Pan

American Carbide and Carbon company reached out to obtain 275,000,000 gallons of water a day from the Brazos river. The Celenese company secured water from the Nueces river.

New York City's water shortage was highly publicized. The irony of that was, the Hudson river, with an average volume of water sufficient to supply the city nine times over, flows past Manhattan. It couldn't be used; it is a great sewer for upcountry communities.

For this and other reasons, we are confronted all over the country, and perhaps in your own community, with paradoxal water shortages. Given fabulous quantities of water, we still lack enough.

The sun is the power plant that energizes the gigantic machinery which delivers water to our land masses. Although it is 93 million miles distant, the sun constantly pours heat equivalent to a quatrillion horsepower on the earth's surface and vaporizes moisture. About 6¼ feet per year is vaporized from the Atlantic Ocean between 8 and 30 degrees north latitude; about 4 feet from the Pacific in a similar belt.

This vapor is picked up by great air currents sweeping inland, clouds are formed, and when the moisture-carrying winds bring these cloud masses in to meet masses of cold air from polar regions, the clouds are chilled and drop their water loads.

There, at the point of impact, the arrival of rain on earth, is the initial point of water management.

We too generally think of water as it is present at some particular spot; in lake, reservoir, river or ground storage. Actually, from the moment a raindrop hits the earth it and all its kind struggle to rejoin the ocean. Whatever use we may make of water must be made while it is in transit. As a corollary, the longer we may delay water in its return to the ocean, the more uses it may serve. And unless we do delay raindrops and put them to service, they combine, gather destructive force, erode the land, mount into floods, and not only do damage but are lost to beneficial service.

If the sky water delivered within the boundaries of the nation were spread evenly, it would amount to about thirty inches of precipitation annually in all regions. That is the equivalent of *15 million-billion* gallons.

Three fourths of this water never returns to the oceans through river channels. The combined flow of rivers emptying into the oceans from the United States is equivalent only to 8.6 inches of precipitation. The 21.4 inches of precipitation that does not flow back to the oceans through rivers is mostly accounted for by the transpiration of plants and direct evaporation from land and water surfaces. That still leaves a quantity of water for other purposes, since the normal flow of all U. S. rivers at their mouths approximates 15 million gallons per second.

Precipitation is superabundant in some areas, sparse in others. At Grays

Harbor in Western Washington, the skies deliver ten feet of water per year—120 inches. At Boston the average is about forty inches. Between the east coast and the Sierra Nevada mountains, there is a progressive decline in the average annual precipitation. West of a line that runs roughly north and south through Kearney, Nebraska, the evapo-transpiration drains equal the precipitation. Only in the western mountain areas, generally above the 7500 foot elevation, where cloud masses are trapped and chilled, is there snow and rain that supplies any volume runoff.

This is but a glimpse of our status in regard to surface water resources. The second division of our audit is water stored in the ground. There has been an almost explosive turning to water in the ground as a source of supply. Often ground water is the only remaining source that we have not damaged beyond usefulness.

Drawn from thirty to sixty feet below the surface, ground water generally is only 2 to 3 degrees above the average of the year-around temperature. It is cool; and that is a quality necessary in many uses. It is nature-filtered, generally bacteria free and clean.

Here we find encouragement. Geologists have estimated ground water reserves total several times all water above ground including the Great Lakes. If the Great Lakes were spread evenly over the states, that water alone would cover the land about ten feet deep.

We do not know in any exact terms just what we may have in the water bank that is underground. Only about 5 percent of our ground water supply has been surveyed. But one thing is certain: Unless we look ahead, secure the data necessary, and show some reasonable intelligence in management of the community wealth in ground water, we may be headed toward misuse, dissipation and destruction of this part of our water bank as we have our surface water. It is shocking to look at the measly funds Congress has pinched out to the Ground Water Division of the U. S. Geological Survey, for example—only $180,000 last year. Compare this with a third of a billion handed to the Bureau of Reclamation and over a half billion to the Army Engineers for flood control and navigation.

Neither this nor any fifty foot shelf of books and reports now available can give a full appraisal of water wealth in this country. All that can be done is to indicate supply and demand. In 1950, Albert Nelson Sayer of the Hydrological Division of the U. S. Geological Survey said: "As a matter of cold fact, we do not know what our water resource potential is nor do we know accurately what our present use of water is." This being true, we had better get busy, fast, and find out, for we are heading into water trouble.

Other questions arise—bewildering, perhaps frightening, but demanding exploration. First is the question whether or not we are moving toward increasingly drouthy days. Nobody can prophesy the future of our climate but there are some trends that should be noted.

Humans are creatures of the Ice Age. Prior to 500,000 B.C., for some millions of years, the earth climate was milder and drier than now, with no ice caps at the poles. Then the earth entered what is termed a "revolutionary" period, with more volcanic action and strangely, the Age of Ice.

At some remote time, now reckoned by some authorities as long ago as 100,000 years, the man creature appeared on the scene. Every day of human existence has been in an environment which is keyed to this Age of Ice.

Why fuss at all about something that involves half a million years; we'll never live to see anything different?

That's probably a logical query. But we should realize the significance of our living in the Ice Age.

It is the masses of cold air that pour out from the refrigerated north that trigger the clouds to drop snow and rain. It is even the differences of temperature in the atmosphere at the equator and the poles that set the moisture carrying air streams into action. The mechanism of rain delivery to land masses is tied in closely with the fact that there is cold and ice at the poles, warm and hot climate around the earth's girdle.

If then, there is even a slight rise in the over-all temperature of the earth it affects the long-range operation of the delivery of the raw product that is water. The smallest sort of increase in temperature can do a disproportionate amount of mischief to the machinery of wind, atmospheric moisture and water delivery to land surfaces.

Authorities differ as to whether or not we are heading toward drouth. Some capable men declare we are. Charles G. Abbot, former secretary of the Smithsonian Institution predicts a big drouth for the Great Lakes area, serious decline of water levels, in 1975, with fluctuating progression toward that condition. Directly contradicting this, the 1941 Year Book of the Department of Agriculture declares there is no proof one way or another of any real climatic cycle or swing. But still others point out that some degree of milder climate increases the loss of water through evapo-transpiration, and while there continues to be the same average precipitation across the country, there is lessening of water flow in streams —and that is a matter of record. For fifty or more years there has been a progressive, demonstrable decline of runoff in most principal rivers of the nation.

The only thought that should seriously be raised in connection with this indicated trend away from Ice Age conditions toward the so-called "normal" climate is this: If we are intelligent, we will consider more drouthy days as a possibility, and since such a change would decrease the amount of water that we might receive on the land masses, we are fools if we do not fortify against such a possible future by developing the most efficient water management policy and plan human intelligence can devise.

Again, we should take a questioning peek at what may lie in tapping the oceans for useable water. There are today giant stills which will deliver 1,350,000 gallons of fresh water from 1,500,000 gallons of sea water. It costs from 20 to 30 cents per 1000 gallons of fresh water to do this, but it is being done. The potential of putting nuclear energy to work as a source of power in this process may make the oceans a final place to which we may turn to get needed useable water. Or the terrific energy of the sun may eventually be harnessed to power this distillation process.

All such conjectures have a certain tinge of the Buck Rogers world. But it was only a decade or so past that the rockets and jet-propelled airships of the slightly comic strips were the stuff of pseudo-science writers and illustrators. They are facts today. Or—think of television—fantastic a quarter of a century ago and in your living room now. That is my reason for digressing on these three detours from the main subject.

44. *Water Problems in the United States* *

A basic study of the nature, uses, and problems of the water resources of the United States is given in this reading by Meigs. It is a sound and somewhat more cautious appraisal than Carhart's and emphasizes the distribution of water consumption as well as the occurrence of available surface and ground water. This regional evaluation is fundamental to an understanding of the water problems of this country, and, as the author indicates, too little has been done in this field. Students, regional planners, and others can benefit from this approach.

Water, as an element of the natural landscape and as a powerful factor in the development of social geographical patterns, is a theme worthy

* Peveril Meigs, "Water Problems in the United States," from *Geographical Review*, Vol. 42, 1952, pp. 346–366; published by the American Geographical Society, New York.

The author (1903) is a climatologist with the Research and Development Division, Office of the Quartermaster General, Washington, D.C. He was a geographer with the Office of Strategic Services during World War II, and was later editor-in-chief, Joint Intelligence, Study Publishing Board. His research and writing deal with climatology, water resources, and geography of the United States.

of comprehensive, systematic treatment by geographers. Until recently, however, it has been neglected by them; too often "drainage features," "water supply," or "hydrology" has been tacked onto regional description rather as an afterthought without integration or interpretation.

The great droughts and dust storms of the early thirties, and, perhaps even more important, the coincidental economic depression with its pressure for more jobs, gave enormous impetus to the study of, and action on, water problems. Subsequent publicity on the water problems of, for example, the Missouri Basin, Kansas City, Los Angeles, New York, the Rio Grande, and the St. Lawrence Waterway has kept America water-conscious. Books and articles on the subject, both popular and scientific, have appeared in great numbers, written mainly by engineers, meteorologists, soil technologists, and, especially, conservationists. Happily, geographers have shared this growing awareness of water problems.

Though some of the recent writing leaves one with a feeling of impending disaster, through desertification, flood destruction, or soil loss, a dispassionate appraisal indicates that the basic situation is hopeful. In total water resources we are well off. Precipitation over the continental United States averages about 30 inches a year, or nearly five billion acre-feet of water; annual consumption for irrigation and domestic, municipal, and industrial uses is less than one inch (about 160 million acre-feet). Even with an evapo-transpiration of 21½ inches, about 1⅓ billion acre-feet remains for runoff and use, leaving a comfortable surplus about eight times as large as the amount of water consumed. Furthermore, precipitation presumably will continue to provide us with fresh supplies year after year; opportunities for intelligent use of water are perpetual, though bungling or unavoidable delays may postpone the rewards.

Obviously, the difficulty is one of distribution and development, and undeniable critical water problems do exist in nearly all parts of the country. Failure to solve them promptly and effectively may result in damage to nonrenewable resources and deprive the nation of current income.

The Need for Water: Consumptive Use

Estimates of total amounts of water used in the United States for different purposes are little more than intelligent guesses based on incomplete data. There can be no question that drinking is the essential use, but even with an assumed per capita intake of one gallon a day, drinking water constitutes only a minute fraction of total water consumed. In the United States the consumptive use (withdrawal of water from ground or surface sources and the return of at least part of it directly to the atmosphere through evaporation, transpiration, or perspiration) has been estimated as follows, in millions of gallons a day: rural (not irrigation), 3600; municipal, 14,000; industrial (private), 77,000; irrigation, 79,000.

The rural figure is based on a use of 10 gallons a day per capita for homes without running water, 80 gallons per capita for homes with running water, and graduated amounts for livestock. Municipal consumption includes city use, domestic use, and some business and industrial use, at an average of 145 gallons a day per capita. The United States is no exception to the truism that per capita use of water increases as the economic structure becomes more complex and the standard of living rises. Along with the higher standard of living there appears to be also a certain wastefulness. Whatever the reason, per capita use of water before World War II in New York, Philadelphia, Baltimore, Chicago, and Detroit amounted to 155 gallons a day, as compared with 39 gallons a day for London, Paris, Vienna, Edinburgh, and Berlin.

Irrigated lands and industrial establishments are by far the largest consumers of water. The two are about equal in total amount of water used, but are strikingly different in regional distribution (Fig. 13). The development of irrigation expresses one of the basic regional contrasts of American hydrology: the aridity of the West and the abundant precipitation of the East. From pre-Columbian Indian days to the present, large areas of the West have depended on irrigation. Under white occupation irrigated

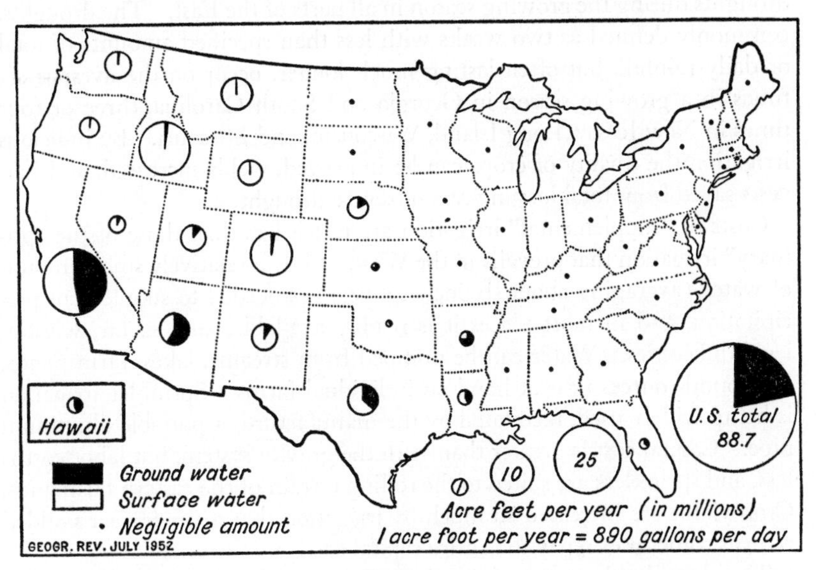

Figure 13

Water used for irrigation, 1950. Adapted from Figure 5 in *U. S. Geol. Survey Circular 115*, 1951.

lands have steadily increased to more than 26 million acres today for the states west of the Mississippi. California is now the largest irrigator, with 6,618,595 acres of irrigated land in 1949; Texas is second, with 3,148,115, a 210 per cent increase since 1939; Colorado, Idaho, Montana, Wyoming, Utah, and Oregon follow, with between one and three million acres each. The total amount of water for irrigation delivered to farms in the United States in 1950 was about 89 million acre-feet, an average of more than three feet per acre.

A significant recent trend has been the increase in irrigation in the eastern United States. Incomplete returns from the 1950 census show large percentage increases in land under irrigation throughout the East. In the five years 1944 to 1949 the amount of such land doubled or more than doubled in New Jersey, Virginia, Arkansas, Florida, and many other states; the increase was ninefold in North Carolina, sixteenfold in Connecticut. In most of the Eastern states the total of irrigated lands is still small (8088 acres in Connecticut, for example), but it has reached 362,909 acres in Florida and 418,644 in Arkansas. Although the potential value of irrigation in the East has long been recognized, in the last decade the idea has begun to "catch on" extensively, as the result of effective experimentation and increased publicity by state, federal, and private agricultural agencies.

The basic natural justification for the current trend is the occurrence of droughts during the growing season in all parts of the East. The droughts, commonly defined as two weeks with less than specified amounts of total or daily rainfall, but often lasting much longer, occur on the average six times in a growing season in Georgia and South Carolina, three or four times in New Jersey, Long Island, Wisconsin, and Missouri. By judicious irrigation the quality of crops can be improved, yields increased, and harvests saved from total loss in years of severe drought.

Costs of "supplemental" irrigation are much less than those of the "primary" irrigation that prevails in the West. Only a relatively small amount of water (averaging about six inches a year) is needed to supplement precipitation, and in most places it is readily available, and, so far, without legal difficulties. Water can be pumped from streams, lakes, farm ponds, or ground sources near at hand on individual farms. Sprinkler irrigation is being widely used, facilitated by the manufacture of portable aluminum pipe. Capital cost is greater than with the gravity system, but labor cost is less, and sprinklers are suited to the rolling terrain of the eastern farmlands. Crop yields are increased so much by irrigation that a single year's added returns sometimes repay the entire capital cost.

The slow development of supplemental irrigation is partly attributable to the difficulties of the terrain before the advent of modern sprinkler systems, and partly to the fact that the rainfall could be counted on to produce satisfactory crops in most years.

Industrial demands for water are obviously greatest in the manufacturing area of the northeast (Fig. 14). Here the abundant precipitation provides easily obtainable supplies, and industries are commonly able to meet their needs locally and individually without calling on the government for aid.

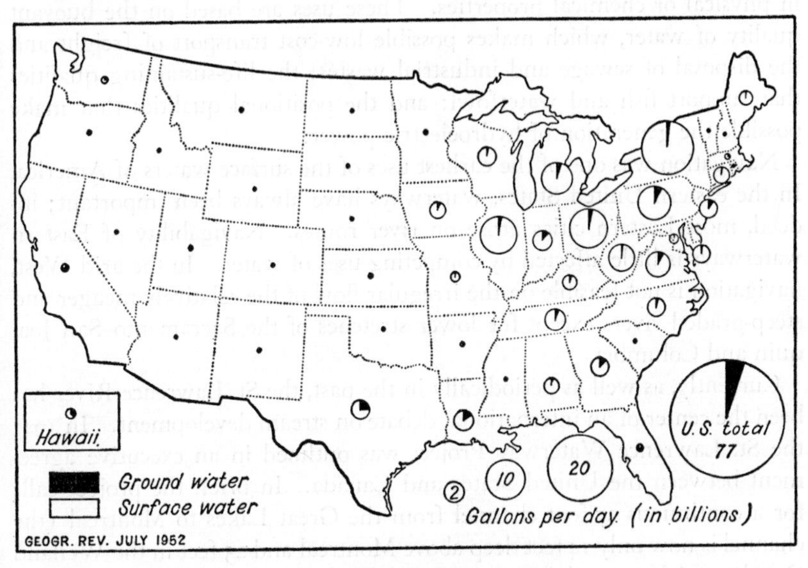

FIGURE 14

Water used for industrial supply from private sources, 1950. Adapted from Figure 4 in *U. S. Geol. Survey Circular 115*, 1951.

Altogether industry uses between 20 and 25 billion gallons of water a day, and many industrial processes consume enormous amounts. It has been estimated that the manufacture of one net ton of rolled steel requires 110,000 gallons; a ton of rayon yarn, 250,000 to 403,974 gallons; and a barrel of aviation gasoline, 1050 gallons. If gasoline is manufactured synthetically, more than 15,000 gallons a barrel is needed. Some of the processes, such as cooling or washing, return the water to the ground or to surface water bodies with little evaporative loss or pollution, though the discharge stream may become seriously overheated. The generation of steam power totally consumes water, and many chemical processes destroy its value for other uses and cause serious stream pollution.

Per capita water consumption for all uses in the United States totals about 1100 gallons a day, more than half of which is returned to ground or surface supplies and can be re-used. In addition, cultivated crops consume an unmeasured amount of water through evapo-transpiration.

Nonconsumptive Uses

In its nonconsumptive uses water ordinarily does not undergo changes in physical or chemical properties. These uses are based on the buoyant quality of water, which makes possible low-cost transport of freight and the disposal of sewage and industrial wastes; the life-sustaining qualities that support fish and waterfowl; and the positional qualities that make possible the generation of hydroelectric power.

Navigation was one of the earliest uses of the surface waters of America. In the eastern United States, waterways have always been important; indeed, most Eastern cities arose on river routes. Navigability of Eastern waterways is little affected by competing uses of water. In the arid West, navigation is not feasible on the irregular flow of the relatively meager and steep-graded rivers except for lower stretches of the Sacramento–San Joaquin and Columbia.

Currently, as well as periodically in the past, the St. Lawrence River has been the center of an international debate on stream development. In 1941 the St. Lawrence Waterway Project was outlined in an executive agreement between the United States and Canada. In brief, the project calls for a continuous 27-foot channel from the Great Lakes to Montreal (the channel is now only 14 feet deep above Montreal and 25 feet in the Welland Canal), and for one of the largest power plants in North America at a dam in the international rapids section below the Thousand Islands to utilize the river flow stabilized by the vast natural reservoirs of the Great Lakes. The Canadian Parliament has approved the project enthusiastically, but the United States Congress has not, for reasons reflecting the regional divergences of interest that arise in connection with all proposals for large-scale governmental projects for water development. Many business groups of the Hudson-Mohawk route, from Buffalo to New York City, think that a St. Lawrence seaway would become a bypass for much of their present commerce; Atlantic and Gulf coastal ports from Maine to Texas fear the loss of as much as 25 per cent of their traffic. The production of large amounts of electric power at low rates might affect the mining and hauling of coal; on this issue the National Coal Association, the United Mine Workers, the Pennsylvania Railroad, railroad brotherhoods, the Boston and New Orleans Chambers of Commerce, and the New York longshoremen's unions are among those united in opposition.

Supporters of the project include the western lake terminals, such as Chicago, Milwaukee, and Duluth, hopeful of becoming seaports for ocean-going vessels. The prospect of reduced electric rates, among other factors, appeals to the New York State Power Authority, the National Grange, Farm Bureau, and Farmers' Union, and the electric cooperatives. The major steel corporations support the seaway, influenced by the potent consideration that large shipments of iron ore might move up the St. Lawrence toward Great Lakes steel plants from the reserves now being opened up in Labrador and Quebec. With an eye to the national interest, in war and in peace, all departments of the federal Executive Branch favor the project, which Major General Lewis Pick of the Army Engineers has called "sound in engineering, economically justified, vital to the national strength and security."

Recreational use of water, including boating, swimming, fishing, and waterfowl hunting on streams and lakes, is not impaired by navigational use. Indeed, lakes formed by the construction of dams to aid navigation, control floods, or generate power can at the same time provide recreational opportunities. Properly managed for water-level maintenance, shore-line development, and protection from pollution, such water bodies can add incalculably to the joy of living. Commercial fishing, important on some rivers, particularly in the Pacific Northwest salmon area, may be greatly affected by developments for other water uses. High dams, especially, present problems that require considerable ingenuity and expense to solve.

City sewage and industrial wastes can be removed most cheaply by pouring them into the nearest river. When towns and industries were small and few, natural oxidation and dilution disposed of the wastes with reasonable adequacy. With the growth of population and, particularly, the rapid installation of city sewer systems after 1890, pollution increased, and likewise the need for consumptive water supplies and for attractive recreational areas. These considerations, together with the danger from water-borne epidemics, have led to increasing control to minimize stream pollution, culminating in the passage of the Water Pollution Control Act of 1948, which provides for coordinated action by federal, state, and local agencies under leadership of the Public Health Service. Unfortunately, lack of regulatory powers and shortage of staff leave many areas of severe pollution in all parts of the country. Even in the nation's capital, the pollution of the Potomac is notorious; it has been estimated that between $300,000 and $400,000 could be saved annually by reasonable abatement practices.

Hydroelectric Power and Multiple Use

Hydroelectric power, the last of the nonconsumptive uses of water, has become economically one of the most important. More than six times as much water is used for power production as for all consumptive uses.

The inclusion of hydroelectric power in a water development program often makes the difference between a self-liquidating and a tax-supported project. During the depression of the thirties scores of irrigation districts depending for revenue solely on sales of water to farmers were forced to default on their obligations; the farms could not produce enough income to pay all water production costs. Sales of electricity, however, can cover part of the cost of development and thus permit irrigation water to be sold at reasonable rates. Aside from its role in cost apportionment, the growth of diversified industries in the Tennessee River Basin and, more recently, the development of large aluminum industries in the Columbia Basin show how availability of low-priced power stimulates the development of private industries in areas where other fuels are lacking or uneconomical.

In order to get maximum advantage from low-cost hydroelectric-power production, steam plants must be integrated into the transmission network, to maintain power output when water may be insufficient for maximum hydroelectric generation. In 1950 about one-quarter of the installed electric-power capacity of the country was hydroelectric. The installed hydroelectric capacity of 16.5 million kilowatts represents not quite one-sixth of the estimated total potential hydroelectric power. Currently authorized construction would increase installations to 35.5 million kilowatts but still would leave nearly 70 million kilowatts of undeveloped power. The North Pacific drainage basin has by far the greatest power potentialities among the major basins, with 37 per cent of the entire potential hydroelectric resources of the United States.

In early water development, and to some extent still, water resources have been used to satisfy immediate single needs. As experience has accumulated and economic pressure on resources increased, the tendency has been more and more to plan a given water-development project so as to take best advantage of several of the various possibilities. Some of the interrelations among different uses of the same water supply have already been suggested. In the operation of a large modern reservoir, for example, decisions must be made as to how much water shall be released for power generation, irrigation, or navigation, how much stored for emergencies, how much space reserved for silt accumulation and for storage of surplus floodwaters. Where there is a series of interconnected reservoirs or other works, decisions are still more difficult, but greater control of the supply is possible. Most of the elements of our present water-supply systems were not designed with regard to over-all maximum benefit; comprehensive projects now must fit the existing structures into the master plan in the best manner possible. In most instances, however, the existing structures can be considered assets in the broader scheme.

Since initiation of the Tennessee Valley Authority in 1933, much thought has been given to coordinated development of entire river basins, and discussion of water problems has acquired a broader view. Lessons of coordination among federal, state, and local governments and private industries have been learned from the TVA example. Even earlier, in 1922, a memorable compact was signed by the seven states of the Colorado River Basin for the division of the river water, and the United States later reached agreement with Mexico on international water problems of the Colorado and the Rio Grande. Whether organized on the basis of a government corporation, like TVA, or by looser arrangements, coordination throughout a basin is inescapable.

The Supply of Water: Precipitation

Water is used by man chiefly at four stages in its movement through the hydrologic cycle: as precipitation, soil water, surface water, and ground water. Small amounts of sea water are also used. Precipitation is, of course, the basic supply, and any large change, cyclic or irregular, in the normal amount of precipitation in a region may upset the economy.

Whenever a serious shortage of water occurs, as in the Great Plains in the thirties, New York City in the fall of 1949, or the Southwest from 1942 to 1952, an uneasy feeling arises that perhaps the climate is becoming drier. Existing records, however, give no indication that the country is experiencing a long-time trend toward greater aridity. Annual precipitation data for three sample sites representing three different climates illustrate the cyclic character of precipitation. In the curve for Pierre, S. Dak., representative of the Great Plains, the drought of the mid-thirties stands out as the most intense on record, though not as prolonged as the drought of 1885–1895. Computed trend lines indicate a widespread decrease in precipitation in the Great Plains since 1875, and mixed trends in the eastern and western parts of the Missouri Basin. The direction of the trend depends partly on the date of beginning and ending of the period of record. A majority of the stations whose records begin in the dry nineties show an upward trend to the present, in spite of the effect of the drought of the thirties in depressing the recent end of trend lines. Since 1934 the short-term trend has been sharply upward.

Neither of the Missouri Basin droughts extended to the east or west coast. New York's dry periods centered about 1850 and 1914. The year of the last memorable shortage, 1949, was about eight inches below normal, following a year 11½ inches above normal. In San Diego the three principal droughts of the past hundred years centered about 1860, 1898, and 1947.

The recent dry period in San Diego is part of a widespread drought in the Southwest from the Pacific coast to Texas, a drought that has been exceeded in intensity but once in the past hundred years. This drought began in 1942 in Arizona, 1943 in New Mexico and western Texas, and 1945 in Southern California; 1941 was the last unusually wet year for the area. By the fall of 1951 conditions were critical at many points. Reservoirs were nearly empty, and feverish drilling of new wells accelerated the already rapid drop in ground-water levels. Nevertheless, ground water was still providing an invaluable reserve, but a reserve that was being "mined" far above the rate of recharge. Although irrigators below Elephant Butte Reservoir on the Rio Grande were being allowed only 1.75 acre-feet of water for irrigation instead of their usual 3.1 acre-feet, the supply in the reservoir had been reduced to 17,600 acre-feet, the lowest since its construction in 1915. Grazing lands were even more severely affected than irrigated lands, and a catastrophic decrease in livestock occurred in the Indian lands. Many farmers had been desperately turning to cloud seeding for the past two years, though other farmers were attributing the intensity of the drought to the same operation.

On the Pacific coast the Santa Barbara–Ventura area was experiencing the severest drought in its history. At Ventura, with river-fed reservoirs almost empty and water no longer running from many faucets, only an energetic city well-drilling campaign averted disaster in 1948. In Santa Barbara, whose reservoir was half filled with silt and almost empty of water, the voters in 1949 decided to approve construction by the Bureau of Reclamation of the Cachuma Dam on the Santa Ynez River. San Diego, its local supplies wholly inadequate for war-expanded industries, joined the Metropolitan Water District of Southern California to obtain help, and in 1947 water from the Colorado River poured into San Diego's San Vicente Reservoir from the new pipeline.

The winter of 1951–1952 has broken the drought, at least temporarily, on the Pacific coast. Rainfall in November, 1951, was above normal, and for December–February was 50 per cent above normal, with the usual accompaniments of floods and landslides. However, in much of southern Arizona, New Mexico, and Texas the drought continued through the winter, with only 25 to 50 per cent of the season's normal in large areas. The rains of March, 1952, were normal or above in most of the area. Winter snowfall in the southern Rockies was unusually heavy, and the spring melt should begin to replenish reservoirs and ground-water supplies, though several seasons' surplus would be necessary to counterbalance the existing overdraft.

Availability of water depends on evapotranspiration as well as on precipitation. The widespread slight upward trend in temperature must to some extent reduce the effectiveness of precipitation. Runoff trends in the

Missouri River Basin show a distinct decline, which appears to be at least partly related to the temperature rise.

In arid areas, and in times of drought in humid areas, attempts have been made to increase precipitation by various devices. Some 60 years ago the federal government supported a project to test the theory of explosions as the cause of rainfall, and in the first quarter of the present century one of the most famous of a large class of "pluviculturists," Hatfield the Rain-maker, amassed a fortune in California by chemical rain making. During the past few years rain making has been revived on an unprecedented scale, sparked by a government-financed "Project Cirrus" from 1947 to 1950, using dry ice and silver iodide for cloud seeding. The results are the subject of violent controversy, which has been aired and documented exhaustively and inconclusively in the course of Senate hearings on bills for research and for control of experimentation.

Scientific experiments, similar to those of August Veraart in the Netherlands in 1930, were conducted by dropping dry ice in clouds. Local portions of thin clouds were dissipated, and slight precipitation resulted. The official statement on the subject by the council of the American Meteorological Society in May, 1951, pointed out that there is "no present scientific basis for the belief that we now possess the ability to modify or control the weather and climate of a major portion of the country." The council advocated additional well-designed experimentation. Experimentation continues, but for the most part not well controlled, in the form of burning silver iodide in ground generators. A rancher, with a generator and two dollars' worth of silver iodide and fuel, can produce enough nuclei to seed about 30,000 cubic miles of air in an hour. In addition to individual activities, about half of the West is under contract to rain makers, at charges of about one to ten cents an acre. Controlled tests now under way should shed light on this heated controversy. In the meantime, most scientists not involved are maintaining a wait-and-see attitude.

Surface Water

The maintenance of as large and steady a flow of streams of water carrying as little silt as possible is certainly a major objective of land and water use. More than 80 per cent of our water consumption is supplied by surface water sources, chiefly rivers and lakes. Hydroelectric power is based on running water, and inland navigation uses both rivers and lakes. Reservoirs are artificial lakes, under somewhat more control than natural lakes but having a similar function of stabilizing stream flow by holding back surplus water for release during periods of deficiency. The loss of farmland inundated by a reservoir, often a tragedy to those affected, must be weighed against the total benefits resulting from the project.

Water runoff may often be the most valuable economic contribution of a watershed, particularly where the land is rough. For example, the annual economic return from the 135 million acres of national forests of the western United States has been valued as follows: grazing (grazing-fee receipts, 1947), $3 million; timber (stumpage sales, 1947), $18 million; recreation (at private commercial rates), $20 million; water (147.5 million acre-feet, at $1.75), $258 million. Such figures leave little doubt as to the desirable direction of primary emphasis in management of the forests, particularly since sound lumbering, recreational, and grazing practices are compatible with the best use of water supplies.

The restraint of unwanted water may be equally valuable. It has been estimated by the Corps of Engineers that flood damage on the major streams alone averages about $465 million annually in the United States. If to this is added damage on tributary streams and loss of soil through floods, the total losses must amount to more than a billion dollars annually. Flood damage tends to mount as cities grow. The Kansas City flood of July, 1951, was the most devastating in the history of the country, with damage estimated at one billion dollars and an equal loss due to interruption of business. Because of effective forecasts, only 17 people were drowned, as compared with 350 in the smaller flood of 1903. The floods resulted from four days of heavy rainfall, centered in the basin of the Kansas River, following an unusually wet spring and the wettest June ever recorded. The ground was so wet that on July 12 runoff approached 100 per cent of rainfall.

Definite measures can be taken to increase the use of runoff water. Water can be held back by protective vegetation and small dams in headwater areas, and by large dams farther downstream. Capacity of reservoirs can be increased by reducing the intake of silt through watershed management, or by diverting tributary streams that are most heavily silt-laden. Dredging is uneconomical: prevention is the only practicable plan. Siltation, particularly serious in the West, where bare ground between native plants is the rule, is reducing the capacity of our reservoirs at the rate of 350,000 acre-feet a year. Sedimentation is a normal physiographic process, but the rate is now about two to four times the natural amount. Ordinarily space is reserved for silt when the capacity of a reservoir is planned. In the Missouri Basin, for example, allowance is made for sedimentation for about 50 to 100 years—time enough to amortize the investment. The problem remains of what to do with the irreplaceable reservoir site when the reservoir has become silted up.

For a given area, water can sometimes be diverted from another basin.

Southern California has already tapped supplies from the Sierra Nevada and Rocky Mountains, and some consideration has been given to the abundant supplies of the Columbia Basin in case of additional need.

Still another possible source is the ocean. Sea water is already used to some extent for certain industrial processes, such as cooling. Fresh water can be obtained from sea water by several methods, but so far even the cheapest, involving vapor-compression distillation, has been much more expensive than natural sources—about $1.25 per 1000 gallons of distilled water, including cost of amortizing the plant.

A final source of increased surface-water supplies is re-use. Irrigation water, sewage effluent, and industrial water can be used for other purposes, and such uses can be considerably increased above present levels.

Ground Water

Only about one-sixth as much water (25 billion gallons a day) is drawn from ground water as from streams and lakes. Although the use of ground water has increased three or fourfold during the past 20 years, there is plenty of room for further increase in the United States as a whole; for the total amount of water stored in the ground is estimated to be the equivalent of 30 years or more of precipitation. Data on amounts and movements of ground water are far from adequate; there has been no systematic program of measurement and gauging such as has long been in operation for the precipitation and runoff phases of the hydrologic cycle. The difficulty of appraising ground-water conditions has resulted in widespread misinformation on the subject. Intensive measurements have been made in connection with local development of water supplies, and the principles of ground-water occurrence are reasonably well known. The recent work by Thomas is a major contribution to our regional knowledge of ground-water resources.

Ground water has several advantages over surface water. A huge supply is held in natural storage, with natural conduits leading to the place of use. Although there is a slow downslope movement of the water, fluctuation is much less violent than that of surface supplies, so that a reserve is provided which can be counted on at all seasons (unless overdrawn by excessive use). Loss by evapotranspiration, if it occurs at all, is usually much smaller than from surface water. Pollution is less likely to be a serious problem, and cost of purification is therefore less. Finally, ground water can be tapped quickly and cheaply by an individual, without community campaigns, interstate agreements, or water-rights litigation. Consequently, much of the recent feverish activity to gain additional water supplies to meet the drought in the Southwest has been in the form of well drilling.

California uses nearly half of all ground water pumped for irrigation in the western United States, chiefly in the San Joaquin Valley (Fig. 13). Texas is second, and Arizona a distant third. In the drought areas of these three states the drilling of new wells and the deepening of old ones have helped stave off disaster for irrigated crops, but ground-water levels have dropped seriously, so that current rate of use can be maintained only if natural recharge is resumed over a period of years. There is a growing tendency in some of the Western states to recognize ground water as public property, and a body of laws to ensure long-range equity in its use is gradually developing comparable with the long-recognized laws covering surface water.

Ground water can be conserved in several ways. In parts of the West the number of wells in a given basin is being restricted, so as not to overdraw the available resources. "Spreading works" designed to distribute surface runoff or stream flood surplus in recharge areas are being used to replenish ground water in many drainage basins of the West; and in a very few areas—for example, in Brooklyn—water after use for cooling or air conditioning is added to wells to maintain ground-water levels and prevent incursion of salt water from the sea.

Large savings of ground water are possible through the destruction of phreatophytes—plants whose roots penetrate to the moist capillary fringe overlying ground water. In the arid West such plants cover an estimated 15 million acres and may waste as much as 20 to 25 million acre-feet annually. In Nevada alone, perhaps 25 per cent of the waste could be prevented—about 400,000 acre-feet, or enough to irrigate 133,000 acres of alfalfa. A recent study has found that in the Gila River Valley in one year phreatophytes consumed ground water at a rate ranging from about a foot for miscellaneous brush to 7.2 feet for salt cedars. The salt cedar (tamarisk), introduced more than a hundred years ago from the Old World, has spread rapidly and established itself in dense thickets on bottomlands in the southwestern United States. At the delta heads of reservoirs, such as Elephant Butte Reservoir on the Rio Grande, it has become a jungle, and not only consumes large quantities of water but clogs the inlet to the reservoir. Control of the plant, by mechanical or more effective chemical means such as use of 2,4-D, is a serious need. Native cottonwoods consume nearly as much water as salt cedar but are less aggressive in their spread.

Even in the humid East phreatophytes consume large quantities of ground water. Periodical cutting of vegetation on one watershed in the Coweeta Experimental Forest of North Carolina resulted in a total increase of about 65 per cent in yield of water to streams, and a doubling of yield in the hottest summer months. Evaporation of rainfall intercepted by foliage is a source of water loss, as much as six inches a year in some places. Lumbering can greatly reduce such loss, but any cutting program must balance the benefits from increasing water yield against the need for preserving slope soils. Riparian growth, as distinguished from slope growth, can usually be spared safely.

Some Regional Comparisons

The differences in problems between the dry West and the humid East, already touched on, can be illustrated by specific municipal and regional examples.

The water-supply systems of the largest urban centers of the East and West provide a striking contrast. New York City, with its nearly eight million people, satisfies most of its water needs from the relatively small Catskill and Croton watersheds, with total reservoir storage capacity of about 870,000 acre-feet (284 billion gallons). Cities of the Metropolitan Water District of Southern California, with a total population of 3,593,000, draw their water all the way from the Sierra Nevada and Rocky Mountain watersheds, by way of the Owens River Aqueduct of Los Angeles and the 242-mile Colorado River Aqueduct. Lake Mead on the Colorado has a storage capacity of more than 31 million acre-feet, most of which is not intended for municipal use; the capacity of Lake Havasu, from which the Colorado Aqueduct leads, is 717,000 acre-feet. In 1950–1951, only 165,472 acre-feet of Colorado River water was used by the District's 18 constituents (35 cities). Nearly half of the consumption was taken by San Diego, which obtained 82 per cent of its water from this source. Los Angeles obtained only 1.4 per cent of its water from the Colorado; the remainder came from local supplies and the Owens River Aqueduct.

The New York "drought" of 1949, with its serious temporary reduction in the city's water supplies, simply accentuated the long-time trend of increasing demands for water. The Croton watershed, east of the Hudson, reached its present capacity in 1890; the Catskills were first tapped in 1915 and reached present capacity in 1927; the Delaware River watershed has begun to be used, through the new Delaware Aqueduct, and by 1956 the three major dams are due for completion, nearly doubling the present water supply of New York. The need for the Delaware system has long been recognized. As early as 1927 a plan had been presented to develop the Delaware system, scheduled for completion in 20 years. But for delays caused by legal opposition of New Jersey, difficulty of financing during the depression, and a shutdown of construction during World War II, development would have been adequate to prevent the water shortage of 1949. Pending completion of the Delaware system, in 1950 a battery of huge pumps was installed 60 miles above New York to add 100 million gallons a day of Hudson River water to the aqueduct system for emergency use. The East has plenty of water close at hand, awaiting only the application of engineering to make it available.

Water resources of the East have been less well developed than those of the West, partly because of a lack of pressing need for additional water or power supplies, partly from opposition by the established population and vested interests that would be affected by large-scale development. The successful opposition to the creation of a series of lakes along the Potomac River for recreation and power generation is a case in point. The destructive flash floods in the Potomac are almost uncontrolled; only 5840 kilowatts is developed of a potential 777,340; pollution from 50 municipal plants that pour untreated sewage into the river system adds to the cost of water and injures downstream fisheries; recreational facilities are underdeveloped for the hundreds of thousands of government workers in Washington; and watershed deterioration is proceeding rapidly in an area that originally had a magnificent forest cover.

The Tennessee Valley, the only large river basin in the East that has been extensively developed on a comprehensive plan, has been a model for basin development throughout the world. Even here, however, there is a great need for extensive watershed improvement. At least a million acres is virtual wasteland in the form of eroded and abandoned farms, heavily cut or burned land, and land almost bare of vegetation.

. . . The [Missouri River] basin forms a link between East and West, with precipitation ranging from more than 40 inches annually in Missouri to less than 15 inches in most of Montana and Wyoming except the mountains, and less than 10 inches in the Big Horn Basin. In most of the area yearly potential evapotranspiration exceeds precipitation, though the cool Western mountains have a surplus of water that maintains river volume across the arid plains. Annual runoff, reflecting a balance between precipitation and actual evapotranspiration, is less than an inch over more than half of the basin. In very dry years the strong winds that sweep across the arid plains lift the powdery soil into the air in terrific dust storms.

The water interest of the downstream population differs from that of the headwaters population. Navigation, which requires a dependable body of water, is feasible on the large, gently flowing lower Missouri River. Upstream, rivers are looked upon first as a source of hydroelectric power in the steep mountains, and second as a source of irrigation water for the dry but fertile alluvial fans and valley floors. The irrigation and navigation needs are opposed, but in the need for flood protection the region is united.

Solution of the problems has been approached piecemeal, with the Bureau of Reclamation and private firms largely attending to the upstream power and irrigation development, and the Corps of Engineers handling the problems of navigation and flood control downstream. Since 1944, when an agreement was reached on a coordinated plan of construction (the Pick-Sloan Plan), development has proceeded more systematically, though the ultimate form of control is still a subject of controversy; a unified government authority, similar to the TVA, has many advocates.

The main construction features of Missouri Basin development (Fig. 15)

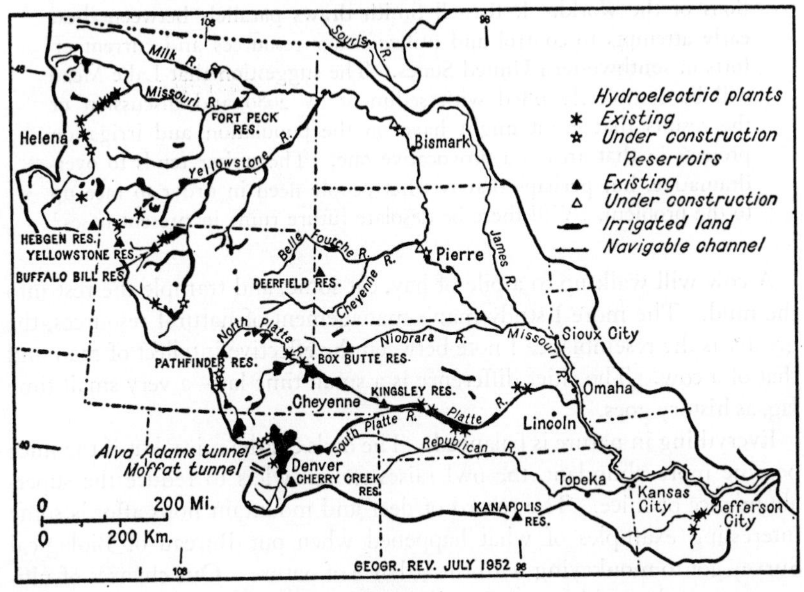

FIGURE 15

Hydroelectric power development in the Missouri Basin. Adapted from Figure 8 in "Report of the President's . . . Commission," Vol. 2.

are the dams and power plants in and near the mountains; two tunnels to bring additional water into the basin from the Colorado River watershed; a nine-foot channel, flanked by massive levees, from the mouth of the Missouri River to Sioux City; and a series of three long reservoirs (now under construction) on the "main stem" of the river, for flood control, power generation, and recreation. Numerous smaller dams are planned, to bring the Missouri system under wider control. Finally, the Department of Agriculture is furthering a far-reaching plan for protection of the soil by correct management of cropland, pasture, forest, and runoff.

45. *Regional Suicide* *

Mismanagement of water is not a fault peculiar to present-day man. Evidence to the contrary is abundant for many of the ancient civilizations of the world. J. Russell Smith draws parallels between these early attempts to control and utilize water resources and current efforts in southwestern United States. The suggestion that Lake Mead will be completely filled with sediment by 2080 and discussion of the results that event might have on the population and irrigation projects in that area is a provocative one. The writer tends to overdramatize, but perhaps that is what people need in order to face up to the problem. Will there be desolate future ruins in present oases?

A cow will walk up to a pile of hay, eat some, and trample the rest into the mud. The more I study man's management of natural resources, the greater is the resemblance I note between the effective intellect of man and that of a cow. The chief difference is a small time lag—a very small time lag, as history goes.

Everything in nature is balanced. The owls eat the mice, but if the mice become more abundant, the owl raises more owlets to reduce the superabundance of mice. The record of deer and mountain lions affords some interesting examples of what happened when our Bureau of Biological Survey got to monkeying with the balance of nature. Our chances of ultimate survival would be much enhanced if we realized that every change we make in nature's balance creates a problem that must be met—or else.

When it comes to water, we seem to think it is like air, to be breathed and used, and taken for granted. But water is no exception to the laws of nature. Water, too, exists in a series of balances. In all climates except that of the ice cap, nature works out a balance between water, plants and soil. For ages primitive man, like the other animals, lived without any serious disturbance of that balance. When man began to grow crops, he began to destroy other plants to make place for crops. That broke the balance of nature, but it was in a small and harmless way. The Indian with his planting stick and digging stone hoe could not clean a patch large enough to let a gully get started. When plowing began and fields re-

* J. Russell Smith, "Regional Suicide," *The Land*, Vol. 8, No. 3, Autumn, 1949, pp. 314–318. Published by Friends of the Land, Zanesville, Ohio.

The author (1874) is Emeritus Professor of Economic Geography, Columbia University. He is a well-known author of geography books, including *Industrial and Commercial Geography, North America,* and *Tree Crops, a Permanent Agriculture.* Dr. Smith's interests lie primarily in the geography of North America, and in conservation and economic geography.

mained as fields the trouble began. A field could wash away. I am glad that agriculture did not get started 100,000 years ago. We probably wouldn't be here today if it had; there probably wouldn't have been any *here* to be *at*.

Perhaps Japan and parts of China have given us the best examples in the recognition of water as a friend to man's survival or a deadly enemy, according to how rain is used and controlled. Japan's total crop acreage is about 15 million, and yet, with the assistance of much fish, these islanders are supporting about five persons to the cultivated acre, with very little pasture land to furnish meat.

In China, the lowlands, fertilized with human excrements and by the mud of flood waters, have produced good crops for thousands of years and are in high productivity today. The Chinese hill countries present great contrast between productivity and ruin. In the more humid south, in the latitude of our Gulf Coast, Florida and Cuba, millions of acres of hillsides are terraced and kept. But in north China, the land of little rain, near the Great Wall, I saw this situation: The rainfall here was so light that only the valleys were cultivated. The steep hills had been overpastured. Gullies thirty feet deep had developed. The outwash covered the valleys with coarse sand and pebbles and stones as big as your fist. Ruined hill—ruined valley! Here stood the wall of a town, but there was no house within the wall. When the valley was ruined the town was ruined, and perforce, people moved away.

In Syria, east of the Jordan River and the Lebanon mountains, a section called the Haan shows ruins of stone houses and villages now standing deserted on bare rock—bedrock. This was once good farmland, with a California climate and in the second century A.D. this section of Asia was about as populous as the farm areas of Illinois. You can still read the inscriptions on the walls of the libraries and other public buildings in the dead towns of what was then a prosperous Roman province.

Mesopotamia, the Valley of the Tigris and Euphrates, is the land of the Sumarians, the Assyrians and Babylonians. It is an archeologists' paradise as they go out into the desert to dig into the unpeopled ruins of Babylon, Ur and other cities. The railroad from Bazra, the port of this valley to Bagdad, the present capital, runs much of the way through desert. At one place the train stopped. I got off and walked beside the track—desert—flat desert—nothing in sight but the railroad and a string of camels winding their way along the horizon. The flat bare desert beside the railway was almost paved with pieces of broken pottery—glazed and colored like kitchenware. Perhaps it had been there for 3,000 years, perhaps 4,000. This flat piece of desert was once the site of a village, perhaps for centuries the site of a village in the ancient days of irrigation.

Babylon, once the capital of the world, is just a large mound and over it I saw a shepherd leading a flock of sheep, nibbling a blade of grass here and there. The shepherd with the flock of sheep is the final scavenger to pick the bones of dead civilizations. Let us hope that we may be smart enough to escape him. If so, we must change some of our ways.

The greatest ruins of Mesopotamia are not the ruins of Babylon or of any other city. They are piles of earth. In the distance you often see across the level plain something that looks like a railroad bank. When you reach it you find that there are two running side by side. You are beholding the ruins of an irrigation system, which once made this desert plain the home of millions, the seat of empire. Muddy water filled the ditches with silt and man shoveled it up in baskets and carried it out and piled it beside the canal. They carried it out and piled it, generation after generation until they built these two railroad banks—one on each side of the canal. Finally the mud got ahead of man—man went. The desert returned. After exposure to the patter of rain drops for centuries these twin railroad embankments are often from fifteen to twenty feet high.

Every schoolboy knows of the annual Nile flood and its automatic fertilization and the long continued productivity of the Nile Valley. The people of Egypt have had great cause for thankfulness because of the kind favors that geology has bestowed upon them. The head waters of the Nile coming down from the mountains of Ethiopia load themselves with mud as is the habit of such streams in flood, but the upper Nile flows through wide areas in which great blocks of the earth's crust have sunk, making depressions like the one of which the Dead Sea occupies the bottom. This area is storing the mud, the heavy silt loosened by the Nile floods, so that the water that finally reaches Egypt carries only very fine sediments and has built up the valley at the rate of about an inch a century, and fertilized as it built. For some six thousand years man has utilized this flood and its resulting thin layer of slime—this marvelous gift of nature. As the flood waters receded, the man of the Nile has walked through the shallow waters and sowed grain broadcast. The seeds settled in the mud, planted themselves, sprouted, and there was enough moisture and enough fertility to bring the grains through to a ripened crop—automatic fertilization—no plowing—a crop every year—manna couldn't touch that!

But in recent years Egypt has entered into a new era. This one crop system did not produce enough for the population that is now increasing rapidly under the influence of our new knowledge of preventable diseases, sanitation and public health, accompanied by uncontrolled birth rate. To meet this new emergency the Egyptians are cutting out the flood system, have built a huge reservoir at Assuan and are using the water to irrigate two crops a year. A new problem enters, soil exhaustion; and the Egyptians are beginning to buy fertilizer almost as recklessly as the cotton growers of our South. Thus Egypt has lost its automatic source of wealth, and its economic independence. That country has given hostage to fortune by this new dependence upon foreign supplies and therefore upon foreign markets to get the wherewithal to meet its food needs. Incidentally, also, they are getting the irrigation problems of salt and alkali which did not exist with the ancient flood system. By that automatic and benign donation of Providence, the ground dried deeply in the dry season, it cracked open, the salt settled on the insides of the cracks and sometimes on the surface, but the oncoming flood dissolved it and carried it on down to the sea. Now the Egyptians have begun to find they must fight the alkali problem as we do in our own West, where it is said we destroy almost as much land by alkali as we add by reclamation.

From ancient experiences in water mismanagement and the consequences we come thus to consider like examples of regional suicide in our own land and time. Here is a great valley watered by the inflow from distant mountains—the Valley of the Colorado River, of Arizona-California, in which we are showing the Asiatics some new fangled ways of handling such a stream. Never has a river been treated with such complex, complicated, and far flung devices, and it is quite likely that never before did man make for himself a more complete and finally destructive trap. When we started in to irrigate the Imperial Valley we soon discovered that the 2 or 3 per cent of silt which the river carries filled up the ditches as it did in Mesopotamia, but we seem to have solved that by preparing extensive desilting works beside the river, so that perhaps we may keep the advantage of irrigation without fighting too much silt. We may keep silt out of the irrigation canal, but the river still carries silt.

The real menace of the Colorado River system to southern California lies in the filling of Lake Mead, the reservoir back of the Hoover (Boulder) Dam. This astounding engineering structure can now hold the water of the year one until it is wanted in year three. It can let out as wanted for irrigation, city use and power, the power that is used to lift some of this water over a mountain in southern California where it is used for municipal, industrial and irrigation needs in the Los Angeles Basin. This is so satisfactory that a hundred mile extension was recently made to carry Colorado water on down to San Diego. Splendid! But what will it be in a short time hence in 2080?—when mud has filled the Boulder Dam, and southern California has filled itself to the limit of people, dependent upon the water that was stored in Boulder Dam before it filled with mud.

One would think that the people of southern California would be going and taking heroic steps to guarantee their future by the control of erosion and siltation of the Colorado Drainage Basin, if it could be controlled.

But instead, they seem to be using its waters and letting the dam fill up as cheerfully and with as little concern as the grasshopper has for next year—less indeed, because the grasshopper lays eggs which will hatch next year, when grass comes again.

One of the most appalling examples of the American, or should I say, the general human inability to read history and profit by it, is afforded by the Rio Grande Valley in New Mexico and West Texas, with West Texas playing the part of chief victim. A large section of the upper Rio Grande Valley drains into the magnificent Elephant Butte reservoir which was built some years ago. After having done this, we permit overpasturing to break nature's balance, of water-plant-soil. Nibbling beasts destroy the grass in wide almost level upland valleys. After the sod is broken, gullies start and become little canyons and the fertile soil of the upland valley becomes millions of tons of silt that go on down to choke the Rio Grande River.

As a result this river at Albuquerque has so filled its channel with sand, men have built dykes to keep the river from flowing over the valley. That was done years ago. It is still filling up its dyked channel with sand until now the stream bed is higher than the adjacent city. Yet more, the valley which once was good irrigated land can no longer drain into the river. Therefore it becomes waterlogged and farms are being destroyed by alkali, but the river is unable to carry its complete load on down to fill the Elephant Butte reservoir.

I think this is one of the most perfect examples of regional suicide to be found anywhere in the world. First we ruin an upland pasture. Second this ruin causes wash to fill a channel of a river so that men must build artificial banks, dykes. Third, the filling of the channel raises the water table in the valley and irrigated land in the valley is ruined. Fourth we build a great dam and turn a part of the valley into a reservoir to hold water to irrigate hundreds of thousands of acres farther down, but this needless silting is needlessly filling this beautiful reservoir. Fifth, the filling of this reservoir will stop most of the irrigation in fertile valley lands below and must inevitably turn many towns into batroosts, the inevitable future of an irrigated settlement when the water is gone.

And yet the Yankee boasts about how smart he is. Is it any wonder that he has become an object of international contempt?

46. *Food Shortages and the Sea* *

Several articles in this chapter as well as in other parts of the book emphasize conservation and the need for enlightened practices if sufficient food and other resources are to be available for future generations. This possibility of food scarcity undoubtedly is one of the most serious problems facing the world today; one solution that has been proposed is an increase in the harvest from the sea. Merriman analyzes the effect of new techniques, inventions, and gear on the amount of fish landed, but states that the expansion of "fish farming" is a far more important factor. He concludes that "if we should double the world's landings of fisheries' products in the present decade . . . the ocean would still contribute less than three percent to the supply of protein required for the world in 1960."

Since World War II our attention has been drawn in forcible manner to the problems created by a rapidly increasing population in a world of food shortages and diminishing natural resources. Such books as Osborn's *Our Plundered Planet* and Vogt's *Road to Survival* paint dramatic and frightening pictures. The press follows with alarmist statements about future depletion or speaks with undue optimism about anything that offers the slightest hope of alleviating critical conditions. Here the oceans come in for a large share of attention, especially with reference to supplying the ever-increasing need for protein. This is wholly natural; the oceans cover nearly three-quarters of the earth's surface, and recent technological advances have led to a number of eminently newsworthy "miracles" of modern fishing, such as electronic aids, "atomic" trawls, electrophysiological fishing, the deep scattering layer, and detection of fishes by the noise they make.

More fundamental than new techniques in fishing, however, is the problem of what food is to be taken from the sea—or, to put it another way, at what point can man most advantageously break into the sea's cycle of life?

This cycle can be said to begin with the vast assemblage of minute floating plants (phytoplankton) and animals (zooplankton) which populate the upper levels of the sea. The microscopic phytoplankton comprising

* Daniel Merriman, "Food Shortages and the Sea," *Yale Review,* Vol. 39, No. 3, Spring, 1950. From the *Yale Review,* copyright, Yale University Press.

The author (1908) is Director, Bingham Oceanographic Laboratory, Yale University. He received his Ph.D. in Zoology and worked with the United States Bureau of Fisheries and the American Wildlife Institute before going to Yale. His special interests are ichthyology, fisheries' biology, and oceanography, on which he has written numerous articles.

more than 99 percent of all marine plants, creates organic matter from inorganic materials in the presence of sunlight, by the process known as photosynthesis. No animals have this capacity; they must feed either on plants or on other animals that have first fed on plants.

It has often been suggested that the sea's cycle of life might be interrupted right here; and if a way could be found for harvesting phytoplankton and zooplankton for human consumption it might be comparable with the best agricultural practices. But without human interference, these minute forms of life are eaten in fantastic quantities by other ocean dwellers. The zooplankton, for the most part, live by eating the phytoplankton. They may then sink to the bottom, where they provide food for shrimps, crabs, worms, mollusks, and smaller invertebrate animals (which in turn may be eaten by large invertebrates or by bottom-living fishes like flounder and cod), or they may stay in the surface layers—only to be eaten by such fishes as herring, menhaden, sardines, or mackerel, or, paradoxically enough, by the largest of all marine animals, the whalebone or baleen whales. The phytoplankton and zooplankton, the bottom invertebrates, the fishes, the whales—all eventually meet their fate. If they escape predation, they die a natural death and release their inorganic matter for use once again in the continuous cycle of life in the ocean.

Or these plankton, these bottom invertebrates (shrimps, oysters, clams), these fishes (herring or flounder), these whales, may be removed from the sea by man for his use.

The question, then, is this: at what stage in the cycle is it best to take "the harvest of the sea"? G. A. Riley, writing in the October 1949 *Scientific American,* directed attention to this problem in exemplary fashion:

> . . . the fishes and other large animals in the sea represent the end product of a long and complicated food chain. Through a series of predations, the tiny bits of plant life are transformed into successively bigger bundles of living material. But all along the way from plants to fishes there is a continual loss of organic matter. During its growth to adulthood an animal eats many times its own weight in food. Most of the organic material it consumes is broken down to supply energy for its activity and life processes in general. It follows that the total plant matter in the sea outweighs the animals that feed upon it, and the herbivores in turn outweigh the carnivores. Fish production is believed to be of the order of only one-tenth of 1 percent of plant production.

To put it another way, we can say that the average annual phytoplankton crop in well-known fishing areas is roughly 500 to 1,000 times as great as the commercial catch of fishes; in short, if an acre of sea bottom yields 50 pounds of fish a year, the phytoplankton production in the overlying waters in that period might be 25–50,000 pounds. At a given time the phytoplankton crop might be only about four times the weight of the fishes, but the microscopic plants grow and multiply so fast that the production in the course of a year is hundreds of times as much as the fish production. And if the annual phytoplankton crop is of this order of magnitude, the zooplankton crop—the next step in the chain—is perhaps 100 times the poundage of the commercial fish catch in the course of a year. Clearly then, by harvesting the fishes, which are at the end of the chain, we are working at the most inefficient level.

Unfortunately, however, nothing can be done about it. There have been devices for the collection of plankton on a limited scale through the utilization of tidal energy, and by special processing this nutritious material might be made quite acceptable as human food. But the harvesting of a plankton crop would require the continuous filtering of stupendous quantities of water and would demand such an enormous output of energy that any large-scale process of this sort is completely impractical—at least until atomic energy is turned to constructive rather than destructive ends, and even then the problems would be complex. Such harvesting still belongs in the realm of fantasy; to collect the plankton in water of average depth overlying only an acre of fishing bottom would require the filtration of perhaps 50 million gallons of water through the finest sort of bolting cloth many times over in the course of a year. As Riley puts it, "By and large we must leave the plankton to the fishes."

But though we must leave the plankton, are the fishes necessarily the consumers to whom we must leave it? Are there perhaps, other organisms that might be harvested at a more efficient level in the food chain? Oysters, clams, mussels, and other molluscan species feed directly on microscopic plankton; hence there is less loss of organic material than in the end product of a food chain which has involved a number of steps. On this account production is relatively efficient. But as a rule such animals are extremely slow-growing, and since they live in the shallow part of the ocean and are sedentary, they are readily accessible to man; therefore natural populations are likely to be fished out.

For example, Connecticut oyster grounds showed a decline as early as the eighteenth century, and by 1830 the supply had decreased to such an extent that oysters from Chesapeake Bay were imported in large quantities. In the second half of the nineteenth century the highly specialized business of oyster culture developed in Long Island Sound. Then the Chesapeake oyster began to show signs of serious depletion, and by 1900 importation from the South had ceased. As Gordon Sweet points out in the *Geographical Review* (October 1941), oysters were now removed from the low-priced staple food class and the price rose to such an extent that they became a luxury.

Present-day oyster farming in Long Island Sound is a difficult and skilled type of agriculture. Land under water is leased by an act of the Connecticut legislature. The beds must be protected from starfish, which open and feed on oysters by means still not fully understood, and from small snails which riddle the shells with holes, and the oysters must be transplanted to different areas for optimal growth at different stages of their life history. After preparing clean beds of shells on which the baby free-swimming oyster larvae settle and become "spat" during the summer, the oyster farmer transplants his growing crop at least three times in the next 4 years. Sometime between the fifth and ninth year of life the oyster is ready for human consumption and the edible product is dredged once again and prepared for shipment. Small wonder, under conditions of such a highly developed system of cultivation, that the oyster is a luxury item. Among recent developments in this industry are dredges based on a vacuum-cleaner principle, which can suck up as much as 3,000 bushels in a morning; this mechanism has enormously speeded the transplantation of oysters to different grounds, and obviously it provides for far more efficient control of destructive pests. It is probable that there are still some molluscan sources which are untapped, and there is little doubt that the cultivation of oysters, clams, and other bivalves can be developed on a wider scale. But it is totally unrealistic to look to these sources for any substantial alleviation of world-wide food shortages; the best that might be expected would be limited developments in certain areas which might serve directly or indirectly to relieve critical conditions in minimal fashion.

So we are left with the fact that the great bulk of our harvest of the sea must come from the animals at the end of the food chain—the fishes, which represent the most inefficient level of harvesting. That is to say, they are "inefficient" in terms of total organic production, although admittedly "efficient" in terms of man's ability to catch fish as compared with his ability to catch plankton.

What, then, can man do to increase the landings of fisheries on a world-wide scale? Are these resources inexhaustible? For example, is the stock of herringlike fishes, which constitutes a major item in the world's fish production, being depleted to the danger point by the ever more intensive and efficient efforts of man? The world's annual landings at present amount to perhaps 20 million tons. Can we double those landings in a decade by exploiting the present stocks much more fully? Can we also find new and untapped resources so that the world's production might be increased many times over—say, ten-, fifty- or a hundred-fold? How much will the expanding science of oceanography and the rapid strides in technology help us to increase the production of our fisheries?

These questions are difficult to answer with any degree of accuracy.

Sober thought and judgment are needed lest the misconception that the ocean offers a panacea for food problems become widespread.

Reference has been made earlier to the miraculous aids to modern fishing, some of which can be called electronic. About 20 years ago the conventional sounding lead and line gave way to the fathometer, a machine that measured the time required for sound waves sent out from the ship to reach bottom and return an echo to the ship. Given the speed of sound in water, it was possible to construct the instrument so that the depth of water was recorded on a dial, and measurements could be made continuously under full steam. In the early days of fathometers on trawlers on the Banks, we would simply turn a switch and a light would flash at short intervals opposite the appropriate depth on a dial reading from zero to a hundred fathoms. With such a mechanism the skipper could drag his net in a gully or depression where he had reason to think there were heavy concentrations of fishes.

The fathometer underwent rapid improvement, and the utilization of supersonic frequencies made it a precision instrument so delicate that it could detect much more than absolute depth. Double "echoes" began to show up on occasion, one clearly from the bottom and the other from intervening layers at mid-depth or less. It became clear that the second reflection, or false bottom, could only arise from concentrations of fishes or other organisms. In the herring fishery of the Pacific coast, schools of varying size occur at mid-depths.

In the old days the fisherman had to depend on a combination of intuition, knowledge, and experience. When a herring seiner arrived in an area where there might be fish, it was common practice to let down a great length of piano wire with a weight attached; a skilled man could tell whether the concentration was light, medium, or heavy by the frequency of pings as the schooling fish hit the wire, and on his say-so was based the decision to set or not to set the net. Nowadays the echo-sounder performs the same function; it, too, can judge the size and concentration of the school by the intensity and depth of the recorded echo. Amazing hauls are made on occasion, as this story from *The Pacific Fisherman* for January 1950 shows:

Something close to an all-time record for a single set of herring off the British Columbia coast was achieved by Nelson Bros. Fisheries' Seiner *Western Ranger,* Nov. 2, with a haul of 1,180 tons of fish. . . . [This] was made possible through the practical application of electronics to fishing. The great school of herring was detected by Capt. Hans Stoilen on his vessel's echo-sounder in weather so foggy that no sign of fish could be seen. Acting on information provided by his sounder, he set his net blind and made this enormous catch. . . . *Western Girl,* the flagship of the Nelson Bros. fleet, was close by. . . . The two boats were in constant radio telephone communication with each other while the operation was being completed.

But the echo-sounder alone has not served to bring about a vast increase in the catch of Pacific herring. To be sure, it has replaced a more time-consuming method, it has made fishing more mechanical, and at times it has made possible the detection of herring that might otherwise have escaped the fishermen. But it has not, singlehanded, brought about an increase in the catch of the order of magnitude that here concerns us. The fisherman's accumulated knowledge, his gambling instinct, and other personal factors will not quickly be subordinated to mechanical aids of this sort.

Another discovery resulting from the perfection of echo-sounding devices is the "deep scattering layer," a new term in oceanography. During and following the war, fathograms in deep water in both the open Pacific and Atlantic have shown the presence of layers, of dubious constitution, that scattered the outgoing signal to varying degrees so that a false bottom appeared at levels down to several hundred fathoms. The nature of this scattering layer has been the subject of inquiry and controversy ever since it was first detected. (See the discussion by R. S. Dietz in the *Journal of Marine Research,* November 1948.) At first it was believed that some physical discontinuity in the water, such as a temperature change, might produce the effect, but the intensity of the scattered sound was often so great as to rule out a temperature change or other physical boundary.

. . . . .

During the war the underwater noises made by marine animals became a matter of great importance to those operating listening devices for the detection of surface vessels, submarines, or other enemy activity. The instruments were developed to a high degree of perfection, but animal noises interfered with accurate interpretation to such an extent that investigations were carried on in the British Isles, America, and also Japan to identify particular sounds with the species that made them. A considerable body of literature on the subject is now available; indeed, certain investigators, instead of sending out the customary scientific reprints, produced actual recordings of their findings; only the other day there came to my desk a record (78 revolutions per minute) of the underwater calls of *Delphinapterus leucas,* the white porpoise—a form of crepitation unrivaled in the annals of phonography.

The underwater soundmakers are of many kinds, such as shrimps, all sorts of fishes, whales, and porpoises. The character of the sound is highly variable, and a recent United States Navy publication on sonic fishes of the Pacific lists the types as follows: Breathing, click, croak, crunch, drum-tap, growl, grunt-groan, hum, rasp-grate-spit, squeak, toot-whistle, and whine-pipe. This same publication states that "subsurface listeners described unidentifiable contacts running the gamut of sound from mild beeping, clicking, creaking, harsh croaking, crackling, whistling, grunting, hammering, moaning and mewing, to the staccato tapping as of a stick rapidly and steadily drawn along a picket fence, of coal rolling down a metal chute, the dragging of heavy chains, fat frying in a pan, simulated propeller noises and the pings of echo ranging." It has been suggested that the identification and association of particular sounds with definite species might be of practical significance to the industry in detecting schools or concentrations of commercial fishes. There appears to be little justification for this optimistic view; it is not likely that the sounds made by fishes will be used by commercial fishermen to any greater advantage in the future than in the past. There is, however, some possibility that certain shrimps, which make a characteristic crackling noise, may be of utility in the commercial sponge industry. These shrimps live in the pores and channels of important sponges, sometimes in great abundance, and there is reason to believe that the shrimp crackle might be a useful tool in establishing the whereabouts and extent of sponge colonies.

New methods of catching fishes, new gear, always excite the imagination and catch the public fancy. Since the war two inventions have attracted particular attention. One, a new Danish floating trawl, has been dubbed the "atomic trawl" because of the reports of its effectiveness. Trawl nets are normally dragged along the sea floor to catch bottom-dwelling species; the problem is to catch those forms that exist in large numbers near the bottom but above the vertical limit of the relatively flat cone-shaped net. The Danes are said to have developed a method of making a trawl work some distance above the bottom and to have made enormous catches thereby. Two boats work some 300 feet apart and the gear is manipulated by a system of floats and balances and by slackening and tightening the towing ropes and wires. Published descriptions are complex and not encouraging to those who might like to experiment. It is probable that the gear is effective in limited areas and under special conditions; the Danes have always excelled in net construction and gear handling. But the "atomic trawl" will not revolutionize the industry, nor will it be a gear which will bring about a great increase in the world's catch of fish.

The other invention, developed in Germany by Dr. Konrad Kreutzer since the war, has been given the spectacular name "electrophysiological fishing." Previous experiments had shown that fishes are responsive to the polarity of electric fields, and when two electrodes are placed in the water, with a varying positive voltage on one, the fishes are forced in that direction. Kreutzer has carried on experiments in Lake Constance and, on a small scale, in salt water; he reports great success and hopes to obtain a patent on the electrode arrangement and on the pulse shape and rate, the pulse form being critical to the success of the whole endeavor. Last summer (1949) he was seeking funds to equip an experimental boat in order to attempt to apply his method to the trawling industry. The anode would be incorporated in the net and the cathode kept near the boat. He has not published quantitative results of his experiments to date and is not willing to reveal all details until he has obtained patents.

However, his accounts are highly enthusiastic and an American Consulate report from Bremerhaven states, "Kreutzer's invention, if successful, will revolutionize commercial fishing." The principle would be applicable not only to the trawl fishery, but to other types of gear, and the inventor believes it would be especially adaptable to the capture of large forms such as sharks, tuna, and whales. Kreutzer himself grants that practical experimentation with electric fishing at sea will unquestionably pose many technical difficulties. For example, the fishes will react differently according to their size, and the problem of varying the voltage effectively may prove an obstacle, although Kreutzer discusses this feature only in terms of the conservation of small fishes which are detroyed in normal trawling operations. Also, in his account, the gear, as applied to a special trawl, sounds unwieldy and highly impractical for operation at sea. More fishing gear has been designed on land and failed in practice than any skipper cares to think about. Electrophysiological fishing remains to be demonstrated as a means of increasing the commercial catch, and it must still be regarded with more than a little skepticism.

In short, it is not probable that inventions, new techniques, or modifications of existing gear will immediately bring about such a huge increase in the world's annual landings of fishes as to make notable contribution to the need for protein. The increase in human population appears to be outstripping the ability of science to produce by new inventions the requisite food—at least food from the sea.

The expansion of present fisheries and the development of new ones hold more promise in this regard. For example, the Japanese tuna fisheries in the prewar period were of vast extent; in all probability their precise magnitude will never be known. At present the United States Fish and Wildlife Service has embarked on an extensive study of the biology of the Pacific tunas and a survey of the potentialities of this resource. The area involved is so huge and the problems so complex that results are bound to be slow. However, it is certain that expansion of our tuna fisheries, not alone in the Pacific but elsewhere, will follow in time. Here again the degree of optimism in terms of increasing the world's supply of protein should be restrained. Tuna is costly to produce, and therefore it is not the sort of food that can play a large role in raising the standard of human diet in, let us say, southeast Asia. Other fisheries—notably those devoted to the herring and cod families, will unquestionably expand and develop in new areas.

The biological productivity of the ocean is incredibly high in certain localities, such as the west coasts of Africa and South America; the pattern of current in both places causes upwelling from the bottom resulting in a rich supply of fertilizing nutrients for use by the phytoplankton. Thus the quantities of fish off Peru, where the Humboldt Current exerts its influence, are phenomenal; the cormorants on the three small Chincha Islands (once famous for their guano deposits) have been estimated to consume each year a weight of anchovylike fish equivalent to one-quarter of the entire United States catch of all species. These areas are notably underexploited by man; surely our fisheries will in time exploit them to a much greater degree. How can it be otherwise with Diesel and gasoline engines replacing steam and sail, with a vastly increased cruising radius, radiotelephone communication, quick-freezing, radar, and other technological advances? But the extent of exploitation will depend on economic, marketing, and other factors, and it is not likely that these expansions will raise the world's fisheries' production by two or three times within the next decade.

Curiously enough, the development of an ancient practice, fish farming, holds greatest promise for supplying protein in areas where it is most needed and where nutrition is notably below minimal standards. This sort of fish culture, involving the construction of special ponds (either fresh-water or salt) in which all the operations of animal husbandry are practiced, has existed for centuries in China and India, as Hickling relates in *Nature,* for May 15, 1948. The ponds are shallow, roughly 3 to 5 feet in depth, and range in size from less than an acre to 15 acres or more. Frequently they are used for agricultural as well as fish crops—rice, water chestnut, watercress, and arrowhead for human consumption; water lilies and water hyacinth for pig food. These plant and animal crops may alternate—paddy from February to June and fish from July to January—or they may be simultaneous. The ponds are often operated concurrently with vegetable gardens and the raising of pigs and ducks; they are fertilized both naturally and by the application of farmyard manure and compost, resulting in rich growths of plankton and hence tremendous production at the lower levels of the food chain. As Hickling points out, these fish ponds fit in well with a system of peasant small-holding. In some localities the production of fish runs as high as 4,000 pounds per acre annually; contrast that figure with the animal production of 50 pounds per acre from the sea bottom referred to earlier.

The significance of fish farming is by no means as widely understood as it should be. Although the farming of milkfish, carp, mullet, gourami, tilapia, and other species calls for special knowledge, sometimes involving immensely skillful techniques, there is no reason why it should not be practiced more widely and introduced into other areas where it could be developed on a high scale. Production is cheap and yields are high; many areas where human nutrition levels are low are suitable for fish farming (protein shortage is the bane of many tropical populations), and with modern means of transportation the introduction of foreign species is now possible as never before.

Fish farming can be expected to boost the world's production of fish in considerable amounts and to relieve dietary deficiencies in critical areas to no small degree. Expansion of this time-honored practice may yield more than all the atomic nets, electric fishing, electronic aids, and other technological advances put together. This is not to imply that fertilization of large tracts of the ocean by human agencies holds any promise. During the war experiments in Scottish lochs produced greatly increased growth rates in flatfish. Widespread and unfortunate publicity resulted in the popular misconception that important sea-fishing areas could be similarly treated with comparable results. This is not so; the magnitude of such an undertaking renders it utterly implausible.

Another source of encouragement is to be found in the much fuller utilization of marine products in the last two decades. In some fisheries close to half the fishes caught, many of them killed in the process, were discarded as inedible or nonmarketable during World War II. But we are making rapid advances in this field. New species, heretofore unknown to the housewife, are attractively packaged. Others, until recently unsought, are taken for the vitamin A in their livers. Still others, not readily marketed, are turned to fish meal for domestic animals. Thus there has developed in the past year a "trash" fishery of no small proportions on the North Atlantic coast; nonmarketable species, previously discarded as useless, have been landed in quantity for the purpose. That is why the Bingham Oceanographic Laboratory has paid particular attention to such species as the small skate in southern New England waters. Not marketable directly for human consumption because of its small size and sharp spines (although its larger counterparts are widely eaten, particularly in Europe), the small skate is now being caught in great numbers for use in the fish-meal industry. We need to know how the supply will stand up under intensive fishing, and how its large-scale removal will affect marketable fishes which compete for the same food in the same area. There is reason to believe that catching such skates will benefit other bottom species, such as flounder, which eat the same small animals.

At least 60 per cent of the fisheries' products throughout the world are inedible, nonabsorbable, or otherwise unfit for human consumption, but we are learning how to utilize what heretofore has been almost pure waste. These scrap products are useful. Herring scales have recently been worth more to the commercial fisherman than the herring itself—for use in certain "gun-metal" and other paints so common on automobiles. Other byproducts in filleting are used for fish meal or for oil. Some whole fishes are ground up for cat and dog food. No longer do we discard with abandon, and the far more efficient utilization of these resources augurs well for the future.

In the final analysis, however, we must maintain the most cautious optimism about the resources of the sea as a means of alleviating world food shortages. Particular areas and populations can increase their fish production and relieve local protein deficiencies. Our total landings can and will go far above the present catch by using new gear and by exploiting oceanic resources to the full, and we shall learn how to make the most complete use of what we take. But it is unrealistic to think that the ocean is likely to supply a large proportion of the food required for the world. Let me put it bluntly. Using figures from the United Nations Scientific Conference on the Conservation and Utilization of Resources this past summer (1949), and taking into account the present rate of increase of the human population, if we should double the world's landings of fisheries' products in the present decade—almost beyond the realm of possibility—the ocean would still contribute less than 3 percent to the supply of protein required for the world in 1960.

47. *Whaling and Its Antarctic Problems Today* *

The whaling industry is colorful, but nevertheless very destructive to the ocean's resources. At one time whales were hunted primarily for their oil, which was the principal source of artificial light in many parts of the world. After the discovery of petroleum whaling declined, but by that time the whale in the North Atlantic had become

* Harry R. Lillie, "Whaling and Its Antarctic Problems Today." Reprinted from *Canadian Geographical Journal*, Vol. 38, No. 3, March 1949, pp. 104–113.

The author comes from Dundee, Scotland. For some years before taking up surgery he was a civil engineer. In 1946–47 he was in the Antarctic as surgeon to one of the Scottish whaling fleets. Since that time he has been traveling, lecturing, writing, and carrying on research in Canada, the United States, and Newfoundland.

almost extinct. In the twentieth century other uses were found for whale oil and other parts of the animals, and the hunt was on anew; this time the hunters turned to the Antarctic as the major source. In Norway, England, and Japan whale meat is not an uncommon item on the menu. Methods of whaling have today become so efficient that international control and co-operation are necessary if this resource is to be saved. Harry Lillie, a surgeon on a Scottish whaling expedition, provides in this reading considerable information concerning the nature and problems of Antarctic whaling.

Over a thousand years ago man started the active pursuit of the cetaceans, both baleen and toothed whales, following his discovery that specimens stranded on the sea beaches could provide him with food and fuel. An era of relentless hunting coincided with the industrial age, when by the middle of the nineteenth century, whale oil was mainly used as a lubricant, illuminant, and in the tanning and textile industries. The fame of Dundee in Scotland, as a whaling port, was a direct result of the use of the oil for batching in the jute industry. Only in certain isolated areas of the northern hemisphere was the meat used as food by the human inhabitants.

A depression in the industry followed in the second half of the nineteenth century, when whale oil as a crude lubricant was largely replaced by mineral oils, and gas came in for lighting; but in the early part of the present century, physics and chemistry developed the conversion of whale oil into edible fat such as margarine This, soap (with glycerine as a by-product) and high grade lubricants, are some of the many products from the oil today.

In the early days, iron harpoons thrown by hand were used from row boats, based on land at first, and later working from sailing "Mother" ships, alongside which the whales were stripped of blubber, and the rest of the carcass discarded. Right whales and sperms were then the animals hunted, species which floated when dead. Catching the blue, fin and sei whales which are chased today was not then practicable as they swam too fast and sank when dead, so that no rowing boat could hold them. Those big blue whales today may be over ninety feet long and weigh well over a hundred tons; equal to a troupe of twenty elephants.

At the middle of the last century, America was the leading nation in whaling, with over seven hundred vessels engaged mainly on sperm hunting; but her interest was gradually lost to the counter attraction of the development of the western prairies coinciding with depletion of the whales. Then came the day in the latter half of the century, when the Norwegian Svend Foyn put his developed harpoon gear into action, mounted on steam chasing vessels; and this, firing an explosive harpoon, finally displaced the old hand weapon, and made the catching of all species of the larger whales easy.

Uncontrolled commercial exploitation by several countries followed, and by the beginning of the present century, the stock of whales in the northern hemisphere had been almost destroyed. A Norwegian company started whaling from a base at Durban, in South Africa, in 1908, and in the next three years a number of companies operated from shore stations on the African coast. But the main attention turned to the still virgin waters of the Antarctic, when the Norwegian Captain C. A. Larsen aroused the interest of the Argentine. The Campañia Argentina de Pesca, founded in 1903, and at present operating from Grytviken, in the Island of South Georgia in the Falkland Islands Dependencies, was the first to develop the industry to any extent in the Antarctic, followed by Norway and Britain from shore stations in both South Georgia and the South Shetlands. Soon after, floating factories made their appearance, a development of the old days of the sailing "Mother" ships. The animals were caught by the same steam catchers, but instead of being towed long distances to shore stations, were treated on board these parent ships, completely self contained units, now steam propelled and able to move to wherever whales were plentiful. This modern version of pelagic whaling soon became a new menace to the stock of baleen whales in what was previously their one remaining sanctuary on the globe.

By 1930 there were forty-three of these factories, mainly operating in the Ross Sea area. In September, 1931, not a day too soon, the League of Nations drafted the International Convention for the Regulation of Whaling, concerned with the conservation of baleen whales from indiscriminate slaughter. It became international law in 1935, and, condensed in a few words, it prohibited the taking of any right whale, blue whale under sixty feet in length, fin whale under fifty feet, or any female accompanied by a calf. As a true conservation measure it was a failure. There was no limitation of total catch, and the allowable lengths of whales captured was far too small. In spite of the Discovery Committee's findings in 1929, that the blue whale becomes sexually mature at over seventy feet, whales only sixty feet long could be destroyed, which was long before they had a chance to reproduce themselves even once.

Now, after two world wars, with a tremendous increase in the human population of the world, food production has dropped to a very low level. Whale oil, which before World War II was valued at $60 per ton, has now reached over $400 per ton, and whale meat, from having been wasted for the extraction of a trivial three per cent of oil, has become the most valued product at $800 per ton for human consumption as meat. In

Britain today it is the same price as the best Canadian beef. Only by the local inhabitants of certain areas of Norway, the Faroes, Greenland, and Japan had its real value been appreciated in the past.

Since the onset of pelagic whaling, Holland, Germany, and Japan have come into the industry in the Antarctic, followed by Russia on a small scale, while South Africa, with interests previously centred in Durban, has also come south. New Zealand and Australia are taking an increasing interest. In the 1946–47 season, fifteen factory ships operated in the Antarctic, three large vessels from the United Kingdom, seven smaller Norwegian craft, one Dutch, one South African, two Japanese, and one Russian ship. Germany has not yet resumed activities. Four of these factories were over 30,000 tons displacement. The number of whales killed was nearly thirty thousand, and nothing in statistics of length of animals caught would indicate that there had been any recovery of the stock during the non-whaling war years; a more serious warning is to be taken from the fact that it would appear that the percentage of females pregnant has dropped considerably. Two more new Norwegian factories brought those operating in the 1947–48 season to seventeen, when over 31,000 whales were killed, and the number of blue whale units taken was over 17,500, considerably in excess of the internationally allowed quota. Everything points to the onset of a repetition of the unfortunate history of the industry in the northern hemisphere. A present internationally agreed quota of 16,000 blue whale units * as the maximum allowable total Antarctic catch appears now to be far too high for an animal which produces only one calf every two to three years. Not all countries engaged in whaling co-operated by observing the International Convention. The Japanese have never done so until recently, and indiscriminate slaughter on their part has had a still more unfortunate effect in their sector of the Antarctic.

There have been various amendments to the 1935 agreement, and the last whaling conference at Washington in 1946 established an improved International Whaling Convention, which was proclaimed on February 5th, 1948, following its acceptance by Australia, Canada, Denmark, France, Great Britain, Iceland, New Zealand, Norway, South Africa, Soviet Russia, and the United States. Japan, under the administration of the United States, has now to abide by the convention laws.

The main features in it are that the permissible Antarctic catch of baleen whales is still 16,000 blue whale units, but this will be under constant review. The minimum lengths of whales which can be taken are increased—blue whales to be not less than seventy feet, fin whales not less than fifty-five feet, and other species in proportion; except in cases where whales are taken by land stations for the consumption of meat by local in-

* A blue whale unit is equivalent to two fin whales, or six sei whales.

habitants, when permissible lengths are slightly less. The taking of any female accompanied by a calf is of course prohibited. The taking of grey whales or right whales is not allowed anywhere, except when the meat and products are used by local aborigines. The South Pacific from approximately Cape Horn to the Ross Sea south of 40° south latitude, is a sanctuary for baleen whales at all times, and no humpback whale can be taken anywhere south of 40° south latitude.

All factory ships have to report details of their catch weekly by radio to the Whaling Regulation authorities in Norway who decide the date on which whaling shall cease, should it appear that the quota allowed would be reached before the provisionally agreed date for ceasing operations.

This quota of 16,000 B.W.U. for the 1947–48 season was approached ahead of time, so all countries were notified that the Antarctic season would end at midnight on 31st March, a week before the provisional date. This was due mainly to the two extra Norwegian factory ships at work. The Russian expedition was the only one which did not report its catch on time as required. Including those attached to shore stations, one hundred and eighty-four catching vessels were active, while twelve ships of various sizes transported meat and whale oil to Europe and Japan.

Since the last war, radar, azdic, and even aircraft have been added to the whalers' equipment, in addition to still faster catching vessels capable of over fifteen knots. But the sad fact remains that with all these inventions and improvements, the actual killing today with the explosive harpoon is more cruel and economically unsound than was the original method at the dawn of the industry. More cruel than it would be to a human, for in a whale, wound shock gives no relief; and economically bad, for the explosive harpoon is the most wasteful weapon possible. The harpoon head explosion in the majority of cases bursts the intestines and spreads putrefactive organisms throughout the circulation. Early putrefaction of the entire carcass sets in, with rapid loss of oil yield, and the production of a meat marketed for human consumption which has so far been anything but popular. Only in the comparatively few cases when the whale is speedily killed by a harpoon striking a vital spot away from the intestines altogether can a satisfactory meat be produced. Fresh whale meat consumed on the whaling grounds can hardly be distinguished from prime freshly killed beef in either appearance or flavour, but the complaints so often heard in Britain that the meat is oily to taste or smells fishy, means only one thing—putrefaction has already set in. Only by giving up this primitive explosive harpoon can whale meat ever come into its own as a reliable and valuable food for humans. Meanwhile hundreds of millions of dollars' worth of it is being wasted annually, enough to feed Europe for over three months on present rations.

A whale swimming is a wonderful sight, the poetry of majestic motion, and to see one of these beautiful creatures pouring blood and gasping along on the surface towing a four-hundred-ton catching vessel on the end of a heavy harpoon rope is pitiful. Anything up to an hour is the usual time taken for them to die, but time and again it takes two or three hours and three, four and more harpoons to tear and blast the life out of one of them. One extreme case witnessed by the author was five hours and nine harpoons to kill a female blue whale in advanced pregnancy. These mother whales fight desperately for their lives and those of their babies. Occasionally a whale will be killed in less than five minutes and even instantly by a lucky shot, but gunners able to do that more than very occasionally are few indeed. If we imagine a horse having two or three explosive spears driven into its stomach, then made to drag a heavy truck through the streets of one of our cities or on the prairie, while it poured blood until it finally collapsed an hour or more later, then we would have a slight idea of what a whale goes through. Why in the last fifty years of whaling nothing has ever been done to overcome this unfortunate state of things is difficult to understand. One Norwegian explained to me that some gunners do not want any improvements that might throw them out of employment or require fewer catching vessels. But the Norwegians with whom the writer sailed on the catching craft on the whaling grounds invariably agreed that reform was needed, and more than once commented that if whales could scream, nobody could stand it and the industry in its present form would come to a speedy end. But these creatures have no vocal cords.

There has been a definite passive resistance on the part of some gunners and others in the industry where the trial of new methods is concerned, and this has held up field research to some considerable extent in the past. But there are now indications of an awakening among whaling countries generally to the realization that the present obsolete methods must be superseded by a clean, humane, economical way of killing.

Some years ago the Norwegians went into the question of electrocution, and investigations into other methods were started in the Antarctic in the 1946–47 season. Research has gone on steadily since then, with the cooperation of United Whalers Ltd. of London, and the Universities Federation for Animal Welfare, also with its headquarters in London. Drug manufacturers, gas specialists, manufacturing chemists, cable and electrical firms, and others have been most helpful, and given liberally of their time and advice.

Four possibilities have been explored.

1. The use of a drug such as curare or hydrogen cyanide.
2. A gas such as carbon dioxide or nitrous oxide.

3. Alteration in the type of explosive in the harpoon head.
4. Electrocution.

The use of curare or hydrogen cyanide was primarily to cause paralysis of the whale, and prevent diving, enabling the catching vessel to close in and kill by a harpoon or lance into a vital spot at close range. The aim was to fire the drug in a two-foot dart from a shoulder gun of the anti-tank type the moment the first harpoon, which would be non-explosive, was seen to strike; the poison being in a capsule which could burst in the muscle after penetration. Curare would have been suitable, but had to be ruled out as supplies are not available in sufficient quantity. Hydrogen cyanide has been considered too dangerous in view of the possibility of pockets of the drug being left unabsorbed in muscle and later consumed by humans.

In using a compressed gas, such as carbon dioxide, or nitrous oxide, it would be fired into the whale in a container, with the object of possibly forming a gas embolism or giving the animal sufficient excess buoyancy to prevent diving. Such buoyancy would require about 150 cubic feet of expanded gas, requiring a compression container too large for fitting to an ordinary harpoon. But carbon dioxide may act both in the formation of an embolism, and as a narcotic. An experiment carried out on one ship in the 1946–47 season with compressed carbon dioxide in the harpoon head was promising. An advantage of the use of carbon dioxide is the increased acidity of the meat which results, with consequent improved keeping qualities. Comparatively slow release of the gas is essential to avoid rupture of the intestines. But this method is likely to be very inefficient if the harpoon does not strike somewhere in the forepart of the body.

The present explosive harpoon carries a bursting grenade head charge of one pound of gunpowder, and the idea of replacing this with a reduced charge of high explosive was considered, but abandoned in view of the danger of handling misfires embedded in the whales. Also, of course, high explosive would in no way lessen the damage to the intestines, which is the cause of the failure of the present harpoon.

Electrocution is almost certainly the solution of the problem. It has already proved a workable proposition, using current of approximately 200 volts, 30 amperes, generated on the catching vessel, and passed into the whale through a flexible copper cable leading along the harpoon forgoer rope to the harpoon itself. Two hundred whales are reported to have been killed by the Norwegians in a similar way in 1934, and half a dozen catchers fitted with electrical gear the following year; but the whole thing appears to have been shelved soon after. About the same time a British company tried it and gave it up after a rather half-hearted experiment, in which careless handling apparently led to a gunner receiving a minor shock and a whale being inefficiently electrocuted. It appears now, however, that only a little more adjustment in the detailed design is needed to make the equipment already evolved thoroughly reliable.

By the co-operation in Britain of the firms of United Whalers, and the General Electric Company of London, with the Universities Federation for Animal Welfare, a British harpoon vessel has now been fitted out with electrical equipment for the Antarctic season 1948–49. New Zealand and Australia are co-operating in use of the new gear, and the results, it is hoped, will speedily revolutionize harpooning. Nylon whale ropes and lighter harpoons are coming in with the electricity, and the new methods will shorten considerably the length of time the expeditions have to remain in Antarctic waters. The season is now one of three months active whale catching, and with an inevitable reduction in the quota of whales allowed to be killed, this period may well be down to two months within the next two to three years.

One of the British whaling companies during the past year has tried to reduce the waste from decomposition of the meat, by using converted naval corvettes as butcher ships. Their function was to take over the whales from the catching vessels, eviscerate them and let the cold sea water into the intestinal cavity, and then speed up the time of towing back to the factory ship. This is necessarily only a temporary expedient until the explosive harpoon is abolished, as the real damage is done to the meat while the creatures are in their long struggles before death.

Reform is needed throughout the industry. Seven days a week of catching is too much, and attention should be given to the whaling stations, some of which are extremely squalid; the stations should be orderly and clean (as some are) and the waters around kept free from that scourge of animals and birds—the fuel oil which traps them.

To the Scottish whaling fleets the Island of South Georgia is the first outpost of the frozen south. Over one hundred miles long by fifteen miles wide, it lies out in the Atlantic, twelve hundred miles east of Cape Horn. There most of the catching fleets remain at the land based stations through the long dark winter, to refit and prepare for November the first month of the Antarctic summer, when the big factory ships will call on their way from Britain to the whaling grounds many hundreds of miles still farther south on the edge of the pack ice.

To those whose lives are not entirely devoted to worship of the god of whale oil, South Georgia also means elephant and leopard seals, penguins, and a fascinating, ever changing pattern of other bird life. This island must have more glaciers packed into its tortuous coast line than almost any other spot on earth, and in winter is just a glorified iceberg. But for an all too brief summer, the snow clears from some of the lower slopes of the mountains, and amid the areas of grey green tussac grass the elephant seals, penguins and other creatures have their short breeding season before returning to the ocean for another year. Happy, trusting, lovable people all.

Enough has been said of the horrors of the whale catching in its present antiquated form, but even as seen from amid the blood soaked welter of a factory ship's deck, the Antarctic is a place of real beauty. As the big bergs go drifting by in the summer twilight, fantastic shapes with weird emerald lighting, and caves of gradually deepening translucent sapphire, you have serious doubts as to whether you are in the same world as the so-called civilization experienced a short time previously; and you wonder if perhaps you are really in the company of Alice and the White Rabbit, and the penguin sitting on a whale moored alongside is just the Dodo after all.

48. Climate and Our Fish Supply *

Considerable information has been gathered recently about the trend in the world's climate toward increased warmth, as evidenced by the receding glaciers in Alaska, Norway, and elsewhere. The physical and economic implications of this trend are tremendous. The water level of the ocean may gradually be raised to inundate many coastal cities and lowlands. The oceans are now 0.4 of an inch higher than they were in 1900. Higher temperatures will affect the lengths of Arctic growing seasons and the type of vegetation found in that region. Today Iceland's farmers are growing barley in soil that prior to 1900 was completely frozen; Eskimos are catching and eating cod—a type of fish they had never seen before approximately 1920. Water temperatures in the more northern and southern latitudes are also being altered. Lee describes these modifications and their effect on fish habitats in the North Atlantic and the North Sea. Because this is one of the world's leading commercial fishing areas, any changes there have great significance for the nations frequenting those waters.

During recent decades there has been a world-wide change in climate. Its effects have been most marked in the arctic and sub-arctic regions. There air temperatures, especially winter ones, have risen by as much as

* Arthur Lee, "Climate and Our Fish Supply," *The Listener,* Vol. LI, No. 1314, May 6, 1954, pp. 779–781.
The author is on the staff of the Fisheries Laboratory, Lowestoft, England.

seven degrees centigrade. On land this amelioration has brought about the shrinkage of glaciers: at sea it has led to a big reduction in the amount of pack ice. For instance, in the Russian sector of the Arctic, the area of sea covered by drift ice has decreased considerably: by nearly 400,000 square miles between 1924 and 1944. As a result navigation has become easier, and ships can now sail along the northern shores of Russia from the Atlantic to the Pacific: that is, through the North-East Passage where the sixteenth-century explorers Willoughby and Barents died.

The rise in air temperature has also changed the distribution of land plants and animals: the bird life of northern Europe and America, for example. Southerly species of birds have immigrated into Iceland, Greenland, and Scandinavia, and have bred there. The growth of trees and crops has improved at the same time. In many northern countries trees have spread rapidly above the former timber lines. Farmers have been able to increase the cultivation of crops such as oats, because the growing season is now longer. They can also keep animals farther north than before, so that in West Germany sheepfarming is now an important part of the economy. While these spectacular events have been taking place on land, similar changes of great economic importance have been occurring in the sea. Changes in the distribution of fish have allowed some fisheries to expand. But they have also brought about the decline of others. Northern fishes, such as cod, haddock, herring, and halibut, have extended their distribution northwards, and some have increased in numbers. By contrast, arctic and sub-arctic fishes, like the capelin and Greenland shark, do not come as far south as they used to.

The present-day British distant-water trawl fishery depends on the increased cod stock found in northern waters. It extends over an area that stretches from Greenland, Labrador, and Newfoundland, in the west, to Spitsbergen, Novaya Zemlya, and Norway, in the east. It yields nearly 400,000 tons of fish each year: two-thirds of the total catch of trawled fish landed in England and Wales. On being landed this fish is worth more than £18,000,000.

The West Greenland fishery can be used to illustrate the rapid expansion that has taken place. We know that the cod was abundant off the west coast of Greenland during two periods in the nineteenth century: about 1820 and just before 1850. After that the fish became practically nonexistent. American schooners visited the Davis Strait regularly to fish for halibut, but they took few cod. Danish and Faroese vessels also explored the area and caught very little. But in 1917 the cod reappeared in numbers on the banks and in the fjords along the southwest Greenland coast. Then, during the nineteen-twenties, they started to extend up the David Strait; so that now the area of heaviest coastal fishing is 300 miles farther north than it was in 1917. The total catch has increased enormously. In 1917 the Greenlanders caught only 250 tons: now they catch 15,000 tons every year. British and other European vessels regularly fish the area, and their catch has also risen: to 400 times what it used to be. The other Arctic cod fisheries have grown in a similar way. Trials were carried out before the first world war on the Bear Island Bank, halfway between Spitsbergen and Norway. Nothing was caught then; good catches were taken for the first time in 1925. British trawlers soon developed a regular fishery there throughout the year. They landed 15,000 tons in 1929 and 135,000 in 1938. Since the war, catches have not remained at this high level, but they have been between 50,000 and 100,000 tons a year.

These increases in the total amount of fish caught in Arctic waters are not in themselves proof of an increased density of stock. The number of vessels fishing has greatly increased and methods of capture have improved. But it is possible to calculate the catch of cod per unit effort for British vessels fishing at Iceland and in the Barents Sea. In 1906 a trawler fishing at Iceland caught only a ton of cod for each day it was away for its home port: but in 1937 it caught two tons, and in the last few years it has caught nearly three. The figures for the Barents Sea are even more impressive: the catch there has increased fourfold and it is now about seventeen tons a day. These increases are so great that we cannot account for them solely by increased efficiency in fishing.

Changes have also been taking place in the Baltic and the approaches to it. In this area such changes have often occurred in the past, some of historic importance. The Hansards from Lübeck used to catch Baltic herring for salting and so obtained much of their wealth. But in the early part of the fifteenth century the fish suddenly disappeared. As a result the North Sea herring fishery became more important. This was to the advantage of the Dutch and to the detriment of the Hanseatic League. Today the Baltic is being invaded, not evacuated, by fish; but this time the important fish are the cod and sprat, not the herring. At the northern end of the Baltic they have entered the Gulf of Bothnia for the first time, and have increased in numbers in the central and southern parts of the sea. So much so, that now the Baltic cod fishery amounts to 40,000 tons a year, whereas in 1935 it was only 10,000 tons. As a result it has become the second biggest cod fishery in Europe and is only surpassed by the Norwegian fishery at Lofoten.

Herring in the Western English Channel

In contrast to these examples of expanding fisheries, we might look at the herring fishery in the western part of the English Channel. Each winter over eighty Lowestoft drifters used to visit Plymouth to fish herring. They often caught as much as 4,000 tons. But after 1936 the average weight of fish caught per vessel rapidly declined; so that the drifters stopped going to the western Channel and the Plymouth herring fishing has become practically non-existent. It is perhaps significant that in the early part of the nineteen-thirties the composition of the catch changed. Before that only a third of the fish were over six years old: but then these older fish became more important, so that by 1937 they made up four-fifths of the catch. Surveys made in the western Channel show that after 1931 there was a marked decrease in the abundance of herring larvae. This meant that recruitment to the stock of herring was reduced. So it looks as if the herring catches were maintained at a good level for a few years by drawing on stocks of older fish. Once these were used up catches rapidly declined.

What causes these changes in fish stocks? Are they due to a rise in sea temperature, for example? Water tends to be conservative. It heats slowly and cools slowly, and we would expect any rise to be small. In fact, the ocean has been called the global thermostat. If we analyse the available temperature records, we do find that the surface layers of the sea in the North Atlantic region have been getting slightly warmer. The warming dates from 1915, but it is small, half to three-quarters of a degree centigrade at the most in areas like the Davis Strait and the Norwegian Sea. It is more difficult to show that there has also been an increase in the deeper layers. There, observations are much fewer and they have not been collected systematically at fixed stations at definite times for long periods. But we do have some evidence that the water in the Arctic Ocean is getting warmer.

The Gulf Stream system carries Atlantic water northwards and eventually it reaches the North Polar Basin: not at the surface, but as a relatively warm layer sandwiched between two very cold layers. Between 1893 and 1896 Nansen drifted across the basin in the *Fram* and found that the warm layer had a temperature of 1.2 degrees centigrade. It lay beneath a very cold layer 800 feet thick. A series of Russian expeditions also explored the basin between 1927 and 1935. They found that the warm layer was over a degree warmer, and that the thickness of the overlying cold layer had become less by about 600 feet. Recently we have been able to narrow down the date at which this rise in temperature took place. This has been done by studying all the observations ever made off north-western Spitsbergen, where the warm water enters the Arctic Ocean. The main increase in temperature seems to have taken place between 1912 and 1922. Observations made by our research vessel *Ernest Holt* in 1951 show that the temperature reached in the nineteen-thirties has been kept up.

The decrease in the amount of sea ice in the Arctic has obviously allowed fishing vessels to visit more and more distant banks. But how has the rise in sea temperature brought about the great increase in the cod stocks that live on those banks? It may have caused an increase in the number of fry produced. We know that low temperatures can have a lethal effect on fish larvae. This can either be direct or by making the time necessary for development too long. But the higher sea temperatures are unlikely to have brought about increased production at the centres of old spawning grounds. Their most vital effect has been to bring the northern margins of those grounds into production.

Have the higher temperatures opened up new feeding grounds and new nursery grounds for the cod? We now know that the answer to this is no. Cod can feed well in cold water; and, what is more, the younger fish are always found in colder water than the older ones. Even so, more and more nursery and feeding grounds have been brought into use. To explain this we have come to the conclusion that the strengths of the ocean currents in the arctic and sub-arctic seas is an important factor. Spawning always takes place down-current from the feeding and nursery grounds. The cod that grow up on the Bear Island and Spitsbergen Banks feed in the cold water that covers most of these banks; they are spawned in the first few months of the year on the north coast of Norway; and they eventually spawn there themselves. From Norway the fry are carried to the banks by the West Spitsbergen Current. When the current is strong we would expect the fry to be carried to more northerly nursery grounds than when the current is weak. In this way the vast marginal nursery areas become populated. We would also expect the fry to be transported more rapidly, so that early in life they would reach a large area with ample food. On the other hand, when the current is weak we would expect the fry to remain close to the spawning grounds. They would then be in a small area of dispersion that quickly becomes over-populated, and a high mortality will result.

To test this idea we had to find out if the strength of the current varies at the vital time when the fry are being transported. Work by the *Ernest Holt* over the past five years shows that it does. When it is strong the current transports twelve times more water northwards than when it is weak. And we have found that it is strongest when southerly winds are blowing over it.

Meteorologists have shown that the rise of air temperature in the Arctic is owing to an intensification of the atmospheric circulation. As part of this there has been an increased transport of air northwards over the Norwegian Sea; this means that the West Spitsbergen Current was strong during the recent mild decades. So the increased atmospheric circulation is primarily responsible for the more extensive distribution of the cod fry in northern waters. More than that, it is the cause of the increased fish stocks in the Baltic. There has been an increase in the south-east wind over the entrances to this sea. At the surface this has increased the outflow of low-salinity water, but it has also brought about an increase in the compensating inflow along the bottom. The inflow brings in high-salinity water from the North Sea, resulting in an increase in salinity throughout the whole of the Baltic. As the salinity has risen the cod stocks have grown and spread northwards.

Let us look at the decline of the herring fishery in the western Channel. This has been investigated by the Plymouth laboratory. It appears that the decrease in the herring stocks is connected with a decrease in the fertility of the water that took place after 1930. Each winter the amount of phosphate present dropped to a third below normal. The subsequent production of phytoplankton in spring is known to depend upon the winter stock of nutrients. Also herring are plankton feeders. So there is a clear association between the decline of the fishery and the decline of fertility.

"Upwelling in the Nineteen-twenties"

But why did the fertility decrease? The present suggestion is that during the early nineteen-twenties Channel waters were enriched by a process known as upwelling. This took place off the mouth of the Channel during spells of easterly winds. The surface water was blown offshore and deep water was brought up to replace it: a process which has been aptly described as deep ploughing of the ocean, because it brings up a store of nutrients from the depths. There is no corresponding enrichment today, because the level of the rich, deep water is now much lower. It has become inaccessible even to deep ploughing.

We must study the origin of this water to find the reason for this. It is formed in winter off southern Greenland and Iceland and in the Norwegian Sea. There, surface water with a high salinity is cooled so much that it becomes the heaviest water in the North Atlantic. It sinks and fills the bottom of the basin. The amount produced will obviously depend upon the severity of the winter. The winters of the first twenty years of this century were very cold, and it is thought that so much deep water was produced then that it reached to a level 1,300 feet higher than now. As the reduced severity of our present winters is related to the increased atmospheric circulation, this once again becomes the primary cause of the change in fish stocks.

It is not possible at present to forecast whether the warming of the Arctic will continue or whether there will be a recession. Recession is the more likely at the moment. In the last few years the amount of warm water transported into the West Greenland area has decreased to a third of what it was in the nineteen-thirties. Also sea temperatures are falling here. Elsewhere the rise is slowing down. If the position were restored to that of earlier decades, the herring and the drifters might return to the western Channel. But our Arctic fleets would have to look elsewhere, and the peoples of West Greenland and northern Norway would have to readjust their economies. In the meantime we must push ahead as quickly as possible with research designed to discover the laws that govern the behaviour of the cod. If these could be found for all stages of the fish's existence, it might be possible to know how to proceed should a recession of climate occur.

CHAPTER SEVEN

Mineral Production

IT HAS been said that the quantity of mineral products consumed during the twentieth century, including all the more important minerals and metals that provide the sinews of modern industry, far exceeds that for the whole preceding period of man's existence on earth. The present importance of minerals varies with the stages of industrial development of a nation or region. Other factors, such as accessibility and world market conditions, enter into the importance of any particular mineral deposit. The three key minerals of modern society are coal, iron, and petroleum. These minerals, of low value per unit weight, are used in huge quantities and usually cannot stand the cost of transportation as well as minerals less utilized and of higher value per unit weight. Large industrial areas are generally concentrated near deposits of one or more of the above key minerals, or they have easy access (by efficient transportation) to abundant supplies of the minerals.

The world pattern of mineral production is extremely irregular and unpredictable. The existence of exploitable minerals is very closely related to the rock or geological structures of the earth; many minerals such as iron are extremely abundant in the earth's crust, but generally in such small amounts as not to be considered commercial deposits or "ore." Concentration by nature or man must take place for the deposit to become profitable.

Some minerals, such as copper, may be concentrated by the heat and pressure associated with changes in the earth's crust through diastrophism and vulcanism. Others, like gold, are accumulated in stream beds (as in California) by the action of weathering and erosion. Thus most metallic minerals are found in mountainous regions, old eroded mountain cores, or other disturbed areas. A close correlation exists between the distribution of mountainous and other deformed crustal areas and the occurrence of metallic minerals.

Coal and petroleum, on the other hand, are found in sedimentary basins or large geosynclines. Petroleum may often be found on the flanks of mountains where the proper trap structures to concentrate the mineral exist. Coal, too, is often found on the edges of highlands or old crystalline rock areas.

The uneven distribution of minerals is a geographic fact of great economic and political importance. No nation possesses all the minerals necessary to supply the needs of its industry. The number, abundance, and quality of minerals and the need for them varies from nation to nation. Often the "haves" must trade with the "have nots," illustrating the interdependence of nations.

Many problems occur in the mining, distribution, and utilization of the world's mineral resources. Some mining areas are abandoned as a result of the discovery of a substitute for the mineral—for example, synthetic nitrates are now replacing natural nitrates. Other areas boom because of the sudden rise in importance of a mineral—uranium, for example. Inaccessibility, depletion, and economic difficulties may render a mineral resource worthless. The following series of readings illustrate some of these problems as well as treating the importance of selected minerals, the significance of new sources of iron ore, and the effect of mineral exploitation on an area such as South Africa.

---

49. *Geographical Factors in the Utilization of Mineral Deposits* *

Minerals are often exploited in many remote corners of the earth under exceedingly adverse geographical conditions; nitrates in the driest desert in existence (northern Chile), and gold in barren, cold northern Siberia are only two examples. "If a mineral deposit is indicated to be valuable, adverse geographical factors are a hindrance,

* Alan M. Bateman, "Geographic Factors in the Utilization of Mineral Deposits," *Proceedings of the United Nations Scientific Conference on the Conservation and Utilization of Resources,* United Nations, Department of Economic Affairs, New York, 1951, pp. 13–16.

The author (1899   ) is Silliman Professor of Economic Geology, Yale University. Dr. Bateman is an outstanding authority on the formation and economic occurrence of minerals. He is the author of a textbook, *Economic Mineral Deposits,* and of 70 papers to scientific geological journals. At present he is editor of *Economic Geology.*

rather than a preventative, to utilization" according to Bateman, one of the leading economic geologists of the United States. Although man has the ingenuity and ability to overcome many of the handicaps of nature, various environmental factors play an important part in the successful exploitation of the world's mineral resources. Some of these factors are discussed in this reading.

This subject may perhaps best be approached by a brief glance at the mineral background. If we study the development of the industrial nations we will note that their rise coincided with their utilization of mineral resources, notably that of coal and iron. Coal supplied the energy that made the wheels go around and the wheels were made of steel. We have come to realize that the energy of fuels and the solidity of metals spelled industrial growth and those countries abundantly endowed with both attained predominance over their competitors and became the great manufacturing and trading nations. It is no accident that great industrial cities sprang up in central England, in the Ruhr, in France, and around the Great Lakes regions of the United States; for there coal and iron met and the products of the junction spread to the far corners of the world. Those nations lacking these substances became agricultural or handicraft nations and mineral resources came to be regarded as one of the chief goals of economic sufficiency.

The world realization that industrial development of modern life depended upon a liberal endowment of mineral resources, or access to them, created such an insatiable appetite, for minerals that within the period embracing the two world wars we have dug and consumed more minerals than in all previous history. This has made deep inroads into unreplaceable mineral resources. They do not grow again like a crop of corn. Former adequate supplies now look meagre, and sources of large supplies are becoming fewer and fewer. The more manufacturing proceeds, the greater the inroads upon the very basis of manufacturing, and the greater the depletion in mineral resources. It is fitting therefore that conservation and wise utilization of mineral resources should command the attention of this congress. It is further fitting that attention should be directed to all factors that bear upon the development of new resources to replace those that are undergoing such rapid depletion, and this includes geographical factors.

Background

Geographical factors in the development of the Western Hemisphere offer a clue to the part that such factors may play in the development and utilization of other mineral resources in the future.

The lure of a gold strike in California one hundred years ago initiated a gold rush that spread rapidly over California. Crude mining was initiated, followed almost immediately by farming to supply the miners with food, and small hand-craft industries to supply them with tools and equipment. Then, further farming and industries arose to supply those who were supplying the miners. A little known, sparsely settled region, was rapidly transformed by the initiation of development of mineral resources into a productive, flourishing, and wealthy state.

The gold rush of California in 1849 spread to the search for gold and silver in the unsettled states of Nevada, Arizona, New Mexico, Utah, and the Rocky Mountain states of Colorado, Montana, Idaho. Wild regions, roamed by bands of Indians and herds of buffalo became dotted by scattered mining centres. Local resources were tapped to supply these centres, transportation was initiated, supplies began to flow, and communities independent of mining came into being and existed for their own account and for export. The discovery of bulky non-ferrous metals created more lasting communities and demands for heavy transportation facilities. Likewise the gold rush to the forbidding Yukon and Alaska in 1898 midst hardship and tragedy was the forerunner of geographic changes that led to the development of this harsh country.

Today, in the unsettled wilderness of northeastern Quebec and Labrador, two new large mineral deposits, one of iron ore and the other of titanium ore, are undergoing development and exploitation. Geographic factors had to be carefully studied before decision was reached to go ahead with expenditures that would amount to scores of millions of dollars. The geographic factors chiefly involved are present lack of land transportation; availability of water transport at the rail terminal for ocean-going vessels, whereby transportation costs could be cut; bulk of product versus cost of transportation and market price of product; questions of freezing of ore in railroad cars, and consequent unloading difficulties, during the long sub-arctic winters; problems of mine operation during the many low-temperature and high-snowfall months; problems of protecting water supplies during the winter months; availability of timber for mining operations; availability of fuel or water power in sub-arctic lands for mining and domestic purposes; effect of a bleak, lonely country, and harsh climate on retention of labour. These, and many other geographical factors, had to be carefully studied and balanced against cost of mining, processing, transportation and the value of the product at the place of delivery. In these two cases the effect of geographical factors is largely that of determining feasibility, and of costs. If the deposits had been located in New Jersey, for instance, practically all of the geographical factors mentioned above would not need to be considered and one could consider at once that, provided the quality of the ores was satisfactory, economic exploitation could be assured.

Similarly, geographic factors, although of different character, will have to be considered in the contemplated development of iron ore deposits in Venezuela, low-grade chrome deposits in Turkey, iron-ore deposits in Brazil, zinc deposits in Bolivia, manganese deposits in the hinterland of Brazil, and in many other cases.

The Geographical Factors

Geographical factors may determine whether a mineral deposit can be utilized, or whether it is economic to attempt to utilize it. In general, if a mineral deposit is indicated to be valuable, adverse geographical factors are a hindrance, rather than a preventative, to utilization. Mostly, they can be overcome provided scientific and engineering skills, ingenuity, and venture capital, are available. Geographical obstacles become then chiefly a matter of cost and economics. The intrepid British, American, Canadian, Australian, French, Dutch, and Belgian mineral pioneers, with their knowledge and skills have not hesitated to initiate mining developments in far off remote parts of the United States, Canada, Alaska, Mexico, South America, Australia, Africa, Russia, and other parts of Asia. They are the ones who have developed most of the world's mineral resources.

The various geographic factors that bear on the utilization of mineral deposits may now each be considered separately, with some examples of deposits in which such factors have had to, or will have to, be taken into consideration. Although each factor is dealt with separately, it should be realized that in actuality several geographic factors may enter into the problem of development and utilization of a single deposit.

Location

The geographic situation of a mineral deposit is perhaps the most important single item that determines whether it may be utilized. Location immediately raises a number of questions as to utilization that must be resolved before consideration of development can proceed. As an extreme case, the location of a non-ferrous mineral deposit on Northwest Greenland would entrain many geographical problems that would be absent with a similar type of deposit located alongside the Canadian Pacific railroad or on the banks of the River Plate. Location may involve not only transportation but elevation, climatic and health conditions, labour supply, availability of water, timber and fuels, accessibility to market and other conditions. Most obstacles of location, however, can be overcome provided the increased cost of doing so is not prohibitive, or provided the material is desired regardless of cost.

Transportation

Transportation ranks first among geographical factors in the utilization of mineral resources. For the most part recent discoveries of minerals take place in sparsely settled regions where transportation is absent. Two questions immediately arise, namely the feasibility of establishing transportation, and the transportation cost of shipping the product to market. These in turn depend upon the character of the mineral product to be utilized and whether water, rail, truck or air transportation is utilized.

Low-value, bulk mineral products such as coal, iron ore, or phosphate rock must move in large volume at low transportation cost to compete in world markets and require therefore, water or rail transport. If such means of transport are not available it requires that the mineral deposits contain tonnages large enough to repay the capital expenditures of transportation installation. If the rail or water transport cannot be installed because of the physical geography, or because the tonnage would not justify the expenditure, the deposits are then uneconomic under present conditions. If the tonnage of the deposit does not justify the capital expenditures for transportation construction, other geographical factors may weigh in favour of construction, namely, the development of the products of forest or agriculture that may spread the cost of transport, and lower it on the mineral products. Or, transport construction may be politically advisable for the development of a frontier region.

In the case of ores amenable to beneficiation, concentration processes may be installed at the place of extraction and the volume of the shipping product may thereby be so greatly reduced that the cost of transportation becomes a minor part of the cost of the product. For example, a copper ore containing 2 per cent metal, may be concentrated so that the copper minerals in twenty tons of ore are reduced to one ton of concentrates, thereby reducing the cost of transportation to approximately one-twentieth of the cost on the original ore. If the concentrates can be smelted at the point of extraction, the volume is further reduced, with additional saving in transportation costs. Although rail or water transport is most desirable for the shipment of such non-ferrous metals, movement by trucks may be feasible if the terrain and accessibility to market permits.

High-value, low-volume, products such as gold and silver may not even require the building of railroads or roads, but may be serviced by air. The output of a successful gold mine may be packed in hand bags. Successful gold mines at Bululo, New Guinea, in British Guiana, in the Andes, and in Northern Canada, are serviced entirely by airplanes.

Topography

Topography generally determines the means of transportation to be used and the effect of cost of transportation on the utilization of mineral deposits. Flattish topography such as that of the African plateaus favours construction at low-cost of railroads or highways and this feature alone may determine the utilization of a given mineral deposit. Rugged mountainous areas may defy the building of railroads or highways but oftentimes the inaccessible parts may be spanned by aerial tramways, or tunnels may be bored beneath them. Few valuable deposits, however, have been left undeveloped in rugged mountainous regions because of inability to bring them within reach of some kind of transportation.

Water Supply

The availability of fresh water supply may be a determining geographical factor in the utilization of mineral resources. This problem is, of course, particularly acute in arid or desert regions, and may be the largest single cost in development, or even render a deposit uneconomic. Most mining operations are accompanied by ore beneficiation which requires huge quantities of water and in Chile and Australia water supplies have to be brought distances of scores of miles and involving large capital expenditures. In one large Chilean mine the quantity of water available determines the capacity of operations. Water scarcity is not restricted solely to arid regions; it is a problem of many flattish regions and of regions of perennial frost. Water purification commonly has to be resorted to in many areas, particularly in tropical ones.

Power Sources

Sources of available power supply rank next to transportation and water supply in the geographical factors affecting utilization of mineral resources. Much power is required for mineral extraction and its generation usually constitutes one of the chief items of capital outlay and cost. Most new mineral developments of the future will come from frontier regions where existing power supply is lacking. Consequently, power must be developed and one must look to the availability of water power, coal, oil, gas, wood, subterranean heat or atomic power.

Water power is the most preferred energy since it saves transportation and storage of fuels but unfortunately it is not often available. Because of its high installation cost, the ore reserves of the deposit must be sufficiently large to repay over their life the capital cost involved. Lacking water power, other energy sources, presumably fuels, must be utilized and the choice is determined by the geographic location of the deposit and of the fuel. The preferred fuel, of course, is natural gas or petroleum if available. In the case of deposits of small to medium size one must resort to the less expensive power installations, using fuels, and the proximity of the fuel may be the determining economic factor. Even a diesel plant using fuel oil might not be economic under adverse transportation. In many places for small deposits where transport cost prohibits the use of imported fuels, local wood has been used, as in parts of Africa, Northern Canada, Alaska, and South America.

In most cases, large deposits that indicate a satisfactory margin of profit, will justify the building of transportation to them and this solves the problems of power supply.

Climate

The factor of climate is seldom a deterrent to the development of mineral resources. Man has an amazing ability to adapt himself and his operations to climatic conditions, however severe. Hence, an unfavourable climate imposes only additional costs of operation made necessary to provide physical comfort or satisfactory operating conditions. A sub-arctic climate requires for many months additional heating for plants and houses, at a cost; it requires special means of handling and transporting ores to prevent freezing, or methods of defrosting; it involves problems of winter water supply and of snow disposal; it involves high expense to keep lines of communication open; it may even restrict operations to a short summer season as in the placer-mining operations in Alaska. Water transportation may also be restricted to summer months, necessitating much winter storage capacity for the mineral products. All of these features add to the cost of operations, and in the case of "near-marginal" properties may even render them uneconomic.

At the other extreme, a humid tropical climate, likewise adds to the cost of operations although to a lesser amount. This comes about by lower labor and managerial efficiency in a debilitating climate and the necessity for long vacations. Also, air conditioning may be necessary, as in the oil regions of Saudi Arabia. The problems of health and sanitation in tropical climates also generally add to the cost of operations.

Timber

The availability of timber is another geographical factor pertinent to the development of minerals. Mines are great consumers of timber and lumber, both for surface and underground operations, and a large mine needs its own forest. If local timber is not available or suitable, it must be brought in and that demands a means of transportation.

Labour Supply

In the development of minerals indigenous labour is desired but the geography may decree that none is available and an added cost to the minerals is imposed in recruiting, transporting, housing, and returning labour. For the New Caledonia nickel operations labour had to be imported from far off Java; Northern Canada and Alaska labour has to be brought in; this is true also of the hinterland regions of South America; and for most African operations labour has to be recruited elsewhere.

Food Supplies

If local food supplies can be raised in the region surrounding mineral deposits it adds to health, comfort, lower living cost, and lower operating cost. The lack of nearby fertile areas has been no great handicap in the utilization of mineral deposits in such unfertile regions as Saudi Arabia, Alaska, Northern Canada and parts of South America.

Health and Sanitation

The geographical location of mineral deposits often necessitates elaborate precautions for health and sanitation—problems particularly pertinent to unsettled tropical and subtropical regions where fevers, plague, dysentery, or other diseases are apt to be present. Such problems are generally absent in cold northern and high mountain climates. Thus, in the development of the Northern Rhodesia copper belt an intense and successful health and sanitation programme was initiated to inhibit malaria, typhoid, dysentery and other diseases. Similar steps were taken in Katanga, Belgian Congo, Tanganyika gold districts, Bulolo, New Guinea, Persian Gulf, Venezuela, and Colombia oil fields, Netherland Indies and Malayan tin fields, Gold Coast manganese fields, and in many other localities. Such precautions are essential for the safety and maintenance of labour, and have to be considered as an integral cost of mining operations.

Juxtaposition of Resources

The most ideal conditions for the utilization of mineral resources are the juxtaposition of several favourable geographic factors. Indeed, for some mineral industries, such as a steel project, it is almost essential for economic operation that supplies of iron ore, coal, and limestone flux, be closely grouped. That has been a fundamental factor in the development of such great steel centres as Pennsylvania, Great Lakes region, Birmingham, Alabama, and the Ruhr. The lack of such grouping near the large iron ore deposits of Itabira, Brazil, Orinoco region of Venezuela, Chile, or even Kiruna, Sweden, is a deterrent to large steel industries in those localities. The iron ore, perforce, must move to coal and limestone. Similarly, a precious and base-metal smelting industry, must have available to it ores that can serve as collectors for precious metals, ores to supply the proper proportions of bases and silica, and necessary fluxes.

Markets for By-Products

Oftentimes the economic possibilities of a mineral deposit may depend upon the utilization of by-products which can find a market near by. This in turn may depend upon the physical, geographic and industrial development, and the density of population. To illustrate, the forthcoming exploitation of the large titanium deposit in northern Quebec, referred to earlier, will be economically feasible only because by-product iron can be marketed in the industrialized St. Lawrence waterway. The sale of by-product pyrite for sulphur burning for paper pulp industry has made marginal copper deposits profitable. Similarly other by-products whose utilization nearby has helped make marginal deposits economic are: fluorspar for steel making or chemicals; manganese carbonate for manganese ore; magnetic iron from titanium ore; barite for industrial use and oil drilling; feldspar for ceramics; quartz for silica glass and abrasives; crushed rocks for highways, building construction and concrete aggregates; and minerals for abrasives, lithium, strontium and other compounds.

Some Recent Mineral Developments

Some new large mineral developments going on today, where geographical factors have had to be carefully weighed and overcome, illustrate the relationship between geography and utilization.

In addition to the huge iron-ore and titanium properties undergoing development in sub-arctic Quebec, a sub-arctic gold district at Great Slave Lake, Northwest Canada, is being developed where the heavy transportation is by water for only a few months, and the airplane is necessary. In the unsettled tropical hinterlands of Venezula, near the Orinoco River, large iron ore deposits are undergoing development for ocean transport delivery to northeastern Atlantic ports. There, geographical factors revolve around transportation and the problems of developing a low-cost product in a low-lying tropical region. Similarly, large manganese deposits are being investigated in the sparsely-settled, tropical regions of Brazil where transportation is crude or lacking. New large sulphide copper ore installations are taking place in Chile, Northern Rhodesia, and Katanga. Large-scale new gold developments are being pushed under the favourable geographical conditions of the Orange Free State in South

Africa, and lead-zinc-copper developments in the remote regions of South West Africa.

These are but a few of the many new mineral deposits undergoing exploration or development in remote lands where geographical factors are ever to the fore.

Again, some of the noteworthy developments completed in the last decade or so have demonstrated the successful overcoming of severe geographical factors in utilizing mineral resources. A few examples will serve as illustrations.

In the rigorous sub-arctic of Canada the uranium-silver deposits of Great Bear Lake were brought into production where transportation over a distance of 500 miles from railhead was by inland waterways open only from June to September. In Finland, the development of nickel deposits at Petsamo, on the Arctic Ocean, was under way when World War II broke out. In Africa, the great Northern Rhodesian Copper Belt was opened up in forested wilderness, infested with fever and roamed by lions, and numerous other mineral deposits of lesser importance have been brought into production throughout other parts of geographically difficult Africa. Latin America has witnessed the recent development of the $33,000,000 Nicaro Nickel project in northeastern Cuba, the large copper deposit of Yauricocha in the high Andes of Peru, the development of oil in Eastern Bolivia and southern Chile; and the further development of the Itabira iron deposit in Brazil.

Each of the above examples of recent successful utilization of mineral resources has demonstrated the necessity of the co-operation and interweaving of technical skills. The mining geologist has been called upon to appraise the size, value, and potentialities of the deposit and whether the tonnage involved and its value merits further consideration. He had also been called upon to guide the exploration to obtain data to furnish answers to the above questions. The mining engineer has been called upon to appraise the mining possibilities, to determine the location of mine openings, to choose the mining and beneficiation methods and to determine the means and cost of transportation and power development. The metallurgical engineer is called upon to determine the character and design of beneficiation, refining and smelting plants. The mining or civil engineer may be called upon to design and construct, aerial or gravity tramways, haulage ways, highways or railways adapted to the topography and climate of the region. The engineer's skills are also utilized to design and construct housing, public utilities and health and recreational facilities adapted to the peculiarities of the people, or the topography, and the climate. All of these are interwoven with financing.

Thus, the utilization of mineral resources necessitates the co-operative effort of the skills of geologists and of engineers to investigate and attempt to overcome the many and varied geographical factors in order to strive to make the property an economic success. But skills alone will not avail unless the costs of production and transportation can be made less than the selling price of the product.

50. *Outlook for Steel* *

Despite the abundance of iron as an element, high-grade iron ores are rapidly being depleted in some parts of the world. The possible exhaustion of high-quality ores in the iron-rich Lake Superior district, long our major source, is a new problem to the United States' "iron and steel" economy. The average metallic content of ores mined in the Lake Superior district decreased from 51.7 to 50.4 per cent in the years 1944–49. Either beneficiation (the refinement of low-quality ores) or supplementation of the supply by new foreign sources, or both, have been suggested. Kimble summarizes in this selection the pre- and postwar world iron ore production and suggests possible future trends.

This is still the age of steel—the atomic bomb notwithstanding. The United States citizen uses more steel than any other commodity except water—some 1,200 pounds of it per year, and he is using more all the time. Without steel our American economy would collapse overnight. The airplane, automobile, and ammunition industries would close their doors; international, even local, trade would be at a standstill; most of us would be without light, heat, and power, and all of us would go hungry.

Fortunately, there is little danger that any of these things will happen, since the world supply of iron ore, the main ingredient of steel, is going to last a very long time. This is not to say that every country has enough of the right kinds of iron ore, or that there is enough to provide every Hottentot with a refrigerator and every teen-ager with a jukebox. On the contrary, the terrestrial distribution of economic deposits of iron ore is un-

* George H. T. Kimble, "Outlook for Steel," *Focus,* Vol. 1, No.7, April 15, 1951, pp. 1–4. Reprinted from *Focus,* American Geographical Society.

The author (1908   ) was, until recently, director of the American Geographical Society, New York. He is now director of the African Survey of the Twentieth Century Fund. He was formerly chairman of the geography department, McGill University. Books published by Kimble include *The Weather, Geography of the Middle Ages,* and *The World's Open Spaces.*

even, and the present demand for war matériel is such that even the most favored nations will have to restrain their enthusiasm for chromium-plated fixtures and canned goods.

Precisely how uneven this distribution is, nobody knows, since there are still large blanks on our geological map of the world, but we can get an inkling from the fact that, up to World War II, 75 per cent of the world's iron ore was being produced by five countries, namely the United States, France, Sweden, Great Britain, and the U.S.S.R.

For many years now the United States has been the "Number One" producer of iron ore. The Mesabi range of Minnesota and neighboring ranges in northern Michigan have alone consistently produced between one-fifth and one-fourth of the entire world output, amounting in boom years to the fantastic figure of 85 million tons. Reasons for the preeminence of this field come quickly to mind: no other place in the world has so large a deposit of such high-grade hematite ore capable of being worked open-pit fashion and located so conveniently to water transportation. The Birmingham (Alabama) ore field is, by comparison, small, and it must be mined by underground methods. However, it enjoys at least two sizeable advantages over the Lake Superior ore region: good coking coal and limestone for fluxing are both available close at hand. Its annual output of ore is steady at about 8 million tons.

Next, on the prewar list, came France. The limonite (oölitic) ores of Lorraine and nearby Luxemburg are among the most extensive in Europe, perhaps in the whole world. They are easily worked, by open pit, and because of their high lime content are self-fluxing. On the debit side, however, they have a rather low iron content—about 25 per cent, as against 50 to 60 per cent for United States hematite—and a high phosphoric content, a condition that effectively retarded their exploitation until the open-hearth and Bessemer smelting processes were perfected in the late nineteenth century. At the same time, the proximity, in the Saar and Ruhr Valleys, of coking coal has proved to be a tremendous asset. In 1938 more than 25 per cent of the world's ore output came from this region, though because of its low grade the yield of metal was considerably less than that from the comparable Mesabi production.

Sweden, third on the prewar list, has a number of iron fields, but only one of the first magnitude, the Kiruna-Gällivare. The ore here is a very high-grade hematite (about 65 per cent iron content), and ample for all the country's foreseeable needs. In addition to the climatic obstacles to its exploitation (the mines are north of the Arctic Circle), this Swedish ore labors under the disability of being remote from supplies of coking coal. It is largely for these reasons that most of the ore is exported, and that the country does not rank among the world's great steel producers.

The British ores, located for the most part in the Cleveland Hills–Northamptonshire Uplands region, compare in kind and quality with those of Lorraine and likewise gain by being situated near satisfactory coking coals. However, they have long been inadequate for British needs, and the growing deficiency is made good by imports from Sweden, Newfoundland, Spain, Sierra Leone, and North Africa.

Principal Steel Producers, 1948
(In thousand long tons)

	Steel Ingots and Castings	*Iron Ore*	*Coal*
United States	79,143	102,200	583,547 (d)
U.S.S.R. (a)	16,400	31,000	200,600 (e)
Great Britain	14,877	13,089	197,646 (d)
France	7,121	22,664	43,127 (d)
Germany (b)	6,677	7,161	163,251 (f)
Belgium	3,855	95	26,258 (e)
Canada	2,858	2,677 (c)	15,054 (g)
Luxemburg	2,414	3,345	—
Italy	2,092	558	957 (d)
Poland (a)	1,800	600	69,152 (h)
Japan	1,687	549	33,192 (h)
Australia	1,380	2,042	14,544 (h)
India	1,257	2,284	30,124 (e)
Sweden	1,237	13,077	368 (e)

(a) Estimates; (b) American, British, French zones, including Saar; (c) including Newfoundland; (d) anthracite and bituminous; (e) unspecified; (f) bituminous and brown; (g) bituminous and sub-bituminous; (h) bituminous.

The fifth of the great prewar ore-producing countries was the U.S.S.R.* In 1940 two-thirds of the 28 million tons of ore produced in the Soviet Union came from the Krivoi Rog mines, in the elbow of the lower Dnieper. The ores here are of excellent grade, with an iron content approaching 70 per cent, which makes them just about the richest in the world. Most of the remainder of Russia's ore output came at that time from the flanks of the southern Urals, notably from the Magnitogorsk region.

While all these fields are still disgorging their substance as riotously as ever, at least one is beginning to show signs of exhaustion. The Mesabi ore is no longer what it was, and at the present rate of consumption the bottom of the barrel, so far as the better grades are concerned, will be reached by 1970. American metallurgists have not been slow to grasp the meaning of this situation: to survive, new sources of supply must be found. Fortunately such supplies exist in many parts of the earth.

* In 1948 Soviet production was estimated to be the second largest in the world.

Across the Canadian border there are at least three promising deposits, two of them right on the Mesabi doorstep. The open-pit Steep Rock mines, some 140 miles west of Port Arthur, and the Helen mine near Michipicoten (near the northeast extremity of Lake Superior) are producing between them about 3 million tons a year and could easily produce 10 times as much, according to the most recent reports coming from the Dominion. (Cyrus Eaton, chairman of the Steep Rock Board, recently said that the reserves in that area alone exceed a billion tons, or more than "those of any other range, old or new, on the continent.") Of scarcely less promise is the northern Quebec-Labrador field. Here in the sub-Arctic bush some 750 miles northeast of Quebec City are two major deposits. One of them, at Burnt Creek, is known to have 400 million tons of high-grade (65 per cent) hematite; the other (still unnamed, since it was only discovered in the past season) may prove to be even larger. By 1954, when the railroad now being built in from the north shore of the St. Lawrence will be finished, 10 million tons of ore a year will start moving down to the Great Lakes and East Coast smelters.

WORLD PRODUCTION (1948) OF LEADING FERROALLOYS
(As percentage of total)

	Chief Producing Countries			
	(1)	(2)	(3)	(4)
Chromium	U.S.S.R. 21% [a]	U. of So. Africa 19%	Turkey 14%	Philippine Rep. 12%
Cobalt	Belgian Congo 70%	Canada 11%	No. Rhodesia 6%	Fr. Morocco 4%
Manganese	U.S.S.R. 46% [a]	Gold Coast 16%	India 8%	U. of So. Africa 7%
Molybdenum	U.S. 89%	Chile 4%	Canada ½%	Norway ½%
Nickel	Canada 80%	U.S.S.R. 16% [a]	N. Caledonia 3%	U.S. ½%
Titanium [b]	U.S. 44%	India 37%	Norway 10%	Australia 3%
Tungsten	China 38%	U.S. 11%	Portugal 9%	Bolivia 8%
Vanadium [b]	U.S. 56%	Peru 25%	S.W. Africa 16%	No. Rhodesia 3%

[a] Estimate
[b] 1947

South of the Rio Grande the search for new ore deposits has been even more rewarding. Latin America, earlier thought to be a "deficit" region for iron ore (the Chilean deposits have been the only ones to figure in world commerce until now), may soon prove to be one of the richest. The Cerro Bolívar ore deposit in southern Venezuela, discovered in 1947, is already being asserted by the United States Steel Corporation to be the largest in the world. Whether this is so remains to be seen, but there can be no denying that Cerro Bolívar, rising some 2,000 feet from the surrounding savanna lowlands, is literally an iron mountain. The first boatload of ore from this field recently reached the United States; the shipment is expected to exceed 15 million tons a year by 1960.

The Bethlehem Steel Corporation is developing another major deposit at El Pao, also in Venezuela. In March (1951) 22,000 tons of high grade hematite were shipped out to Maryland, inaugurating a service designed to bring 3 million tons of ore annually to the United States.

Over in eastern Brazil near the headwaters of the Rio Doce is a second field, likewise of generous dimensions and impressive quality. Some of the ore is already being processed locally (at Volta Redonda), using coal from Santa Catarina, 600 miles south of Rio de Janeiro; some is being shipped down to the coast port of Vitória; and more will be exported as land transportation and terminal facilities improve.

Across the South Atlantic in tropical Africa, the latest estimates of iron ore potential are equaled only by the optimism they have inspired. From all accounts, there is enough high-grade ore in Northern Rhodesia (near Lusaka), Southern Rhodesia (near Que Que), Liberia (in the Bomi Hills), and Kenya (in the Elgon-Tororo district) to take care of the needs of the entire continent for generations to come; only Latin America would seem to have a higher per capita reserve. Near three of the ore fields coking coal is available, and in one, the Southern Rhodesian, chrome, limestone, asbestos, mica, and copper—all basic ingredients of a modern metallurgical economy—are also found. Small wonder, therefore, that the British are already talking of the area as "one of the future arsenals of democracy!"

The continent with the greatest reserves is undoubtedly Asia. Even if we exclude the U.S.S.R., these reserves are roughly twice those of North America and more than 50 times those of Australia and New Zealand. The largest are located in (1) India, in the Mayurbhanj fields, a hundred miles or so west of Calcutta (the estimated metallic content of these deposits is now set at 10,000 million tons), (2) China, mainly in the provinces of Hopeh, Hupeh, and Anwhei, and southern Manchuria (the corresponding figure here is only 1200 million tons), and (3) Indonesia (720 million tons).

Estimates of the Soviet Union's iron reserves vary according to the source; some would seem to be propaganda rather than the result of prospecting. One writer, for example, states that they "exceed all other countries" and asserts that the ferruginous quartzite of the Kursk region alone contains between 80,000 million and 100,000 million tons of metal and could "supply the world for hundreds of years at the present rate of consumption." On the other hand, the recently published United Nations report on the subject puts Russia's entire reserves at considerably less than those of Cuba! Be this as it may, three things seem fairly certain: first, the reserves are more than adequate for Russia's needs; second, the present

Soviet output of steel is only about one-fourth or one-third as large as America's, which would mean that it is still smaller than the American output 40 years ago; and, third, the center of gravity of the Soviet steel industry is bit by bit shifting eastward. In the past few years steel mills have come into production in the Georgian Republic near the Dashkesan hematite deposits, in the southern Urals near Orsk, where there is a rich field covering some 600 square miles, and in the Khazakh Republic near Karaganda, where good coking coal and iron ore are found in close proximity. Nevertheless, there is little or no ground for believing that Asiatic Russia will oust the Ukraine from its steel-making supremacy.

But the high-quality steel demanded by modern industry needs more than iron ore, coke, and limestone for its fabrication. It also needs such ferroalloys as manganese, vanadium, nickel, molybdenum, cobalt, chromium, tungsten, and titanium. Without these, the production of high-speed tools, engine parts, guns, and other articles subjected to intense heat would be impossible—and, for that matter, automobiles, which as long ago as 1935 commonly contained no fewer than 80 different alloy steels. So important are these ores nowadays that access to them has become as necessary to an industrial nation as the ownership of iron ore itself, yet the quantities used in a given metallurgical operation are so small that their importance is frequently overlooked by the layman. For example, only some 14 pounds of manganese are required to produce a ton of manganese steel.

Like iron ore, ferroalloys are widely distributed throughout the world, and the major workings in each case have so far been limited to two or three countries. This is well brought out in the accompanying table.

The steel outlook, then, as far as the North American continent is concerned, is anything but dismal. Quite possibly, as time goes by, some of the older manufacturing centers will find themselves increasingly hard pressed in the battle for survival; in fact, there are already signs of a locational trend away from the Pittsburgh-Chicago-Buffalo "triangle" to the eastern seaboard. Even more likely, the present decade will see new plants springing up in parts of the world (such as Latin America, tropical Africa, and Indonesia) that this country formerly supplied, and it is certain that the steel output in the Soviet sphere will rise as more and more mills come into operation. At the same time, there is very little to indicate that the metallurgical dominance of America is going to be challenged within the next generation. On the contrary: in viewing the supplies of high-grade ore, coking coal, and ferroalloys available to this country, and those of its friends on both sides of the Atlantic, it may fairly be asserted that the steel-making potential of the United States is unmatched by that of any other nation, or association of nations. This may be cold comfort to an American public called upon to accept a diluted austerity, but it must be even colder comfort to any aspiring aggressor!

51. *The Labrador Frontier* *

A somewhat more detailed analysis of one of the new iron-ore areas mentioned in the previous reading, the Labrador-Quebec field, is treated in this reading. The nature of this wild, unsettled, and previously little-known region and the problems involved in its development and the exploitation of its varied resources are summarized here. With the passage by the United States Congress (in 1954) of the St. Lawrence Seaway Bill, this new source of iron ore will be of great value to the future of iron and steel industries of the Great Lakes and Ohio Valley-Pittsburgh districts.

The peninsula of Labrador-Ungava, in area equal to Western Europe, is a little-known land, a land whose forbidding exterior has repelled both settlers and explorers. "J'estime mieulx que aultrement," wrote Cartier, "que c'est la terre que Dieu donna à Cayn." Today, four centuries later, official Quebec dissents so strongly from Cartier's obloquy that she refuses on her official maps to admit the claim of Newfoundland to a share in the peninsula.

The dispute between Canada and Newfoundland over the Labrador "frontier" is of long standing. The boundary at present acknowledged by the Dominion follows the award of the Judicial Committee of the Privy Council on March 1, 1927. It is a physiographic absurdity, wandering in an unpredictable manner across a heavily glaciated, lake-strewn terrain. In many places its position is only vaguely known.

The award gave the Atlantic drainage slope to Newfoundland, now a Canadian province. The Hamilton and Naskaupi Rivers belong to this drainage, so that Newfoundland's share includes a part of the central plateau. Quebec province has in recent years objected vigorously to the

* F. Kenneth Hare, "The Labrador Frontier," from *Geographical Review,* Vol. 42, 1952, pp. 405–424; published by the American Geographical Society, New York.

The author (1919) is Professor and Chairman, Department of Geography, McGill University. He received part of his education in England, but his Ph.D. degree was conferred by the University of Montreal in 1950. His interests lie in Europe, Canada, and the polar regions. He has done considerable research and has written several articles on the geography of eastern Canada.

award and has inscribed her official maps with the political squib that heads this article. For Labrador has now at last become a frontier in a new and dramatic sense. The curtain of ignorance is being drawn aside, with the aid of the aircraft. As the potential wealth of the interior has been realized, the full implications of the 1927 award have dawned on the two provinces concerned. The iron-ore field, for example, has been found to lie squarely on the boundary, which even bisects some of the ore bodies!

Structural Details

There is still much to be learned about the Labrador-Ungava peninsula: five years of intensive exploration have barely begun the process. The peninsula is, in fact, the least-known third of the Canadian Shield and is usually dismissed by geographers in the impatient way they have with Pre-Cambrian rocks. Actually its surface is considerably differentiated both by structure and by recent physiographic history. Some of this differentiation is geographically significant.

Vast areas are underlain by granites and granite gneisses and form a monotonous plateau verging on peneplane relief. A complete absence of pattern characterizes most of this landscape, though in some areas major joint systems have been etched out by water and glacial scour and give a geometrical appearance to the map; one such area lies in the center of the peninsula among the headstreams of the Kaniapiskau River. This featureless plateau on Archean (older Pre-Cambrian) gneiss is the ordinary Labrador landscape. Occasional low, rocky hills rise some hundreds of feet above the surface, and every hollow is filled with a lake or a patch of muskeg. Most of the low ground is plastered with glacial till, in places drumlinized. Eskers, sand plains, and, in certain areas, marine and lacustrine clays complete the superficial overburden, which has been estimated to obscure no less than 90 per cent of Quebec's bedrock.

In places, however, the ancient plateau has been markedly uplifted. The steep cliffs of the Northern Ungava Plateau (Fig. 16) and the famous Torngat Uplift have been given abundant attention in the literature. The Mealy Mountains, with summits probably reaching 4000 feet, have received less notice; the Otish Mountains, south of Nichicun Lake, are not even shown on the average map, though they are almost as high. Much more significant for our present purpose is the continuous mountain wall that confronts the Gulf of St. Lawrence between the Manicouagan and Little Mecatina Rivers. For want of a better name, the writer calls this wall the *Laurentide Scarp*. It is simply the uplifted rim of the interior plateau. In places it exceeds 3000 feet, especially north of Seven Islands and Mingan, but it has never been surveyed; in general, it lies 40–100 miles inland and is irregular in cross profile. The rivers from the interior flow placidly across the plateau to the north at 1500–2000 feet but plunge abruptly into gorges as they cut through the rim; not one of them is navigable. They are believed to be antecedent streams, having succeeded in maintaining their courses across the scarp as it was uplifted in Pliocene time. The importance of the scarp is the obstacle it offers to communications and the very heavy winter snowfall it attracts.

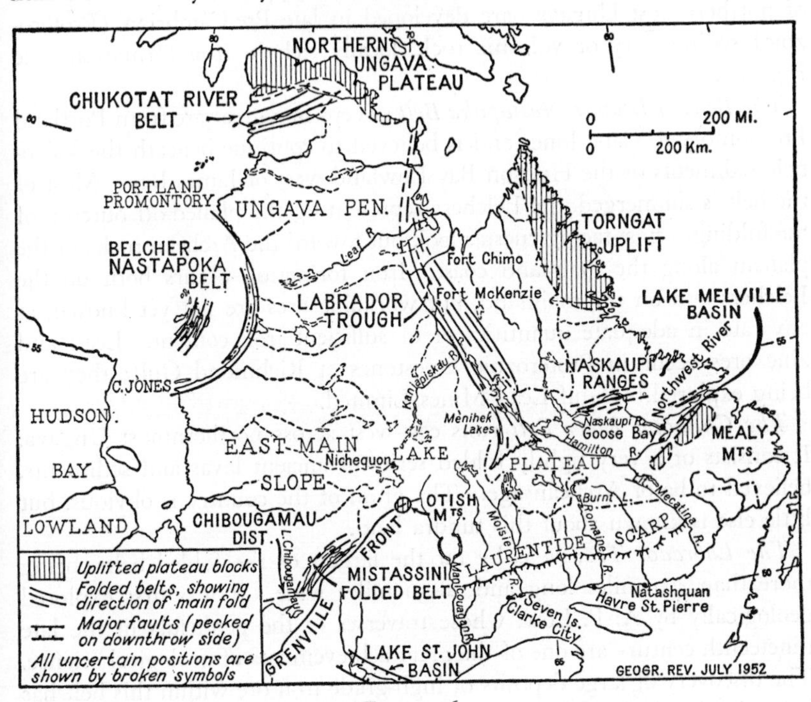

FIGURE 16

Some physical details of the peninsula. Note (1) the folded belts, especially the Labrador Trough, and (2) the Grenville Front, which separates the Grenville and Temiskamian provinces. The Laurentide Scarp is shown only by symbol, since its exact position is not known.

Before we leave the Archean areas, we must note one vital distinction. Canadian geologists recognize two principal provinces within the peninsula, the Temiskamian province, containing the ore fields of Abitibi and northern Ontario, and the Grenville province, in the southeast. The boundary between them is a major structural divide, the Grenville Front (Fig. 16), whose course is known only up to the Otish range. The Grenville rocks contain a curious suite of types quite dissimilar to those of the Temiskamian province, including crystalline limestones and extensive masses of anorthosite. The Grenville province is less extensively mineralized than the rest of the shield but has certain resources (notably titanium) that are uncommon elsewhere.

Perhaps the most significant of the new facts relating to the structure has been the recognition of the vital economic importance of the great folded belts long known to be present in the Pre-Cambrian rocks of the peninsula. All but one of these Appalachian-type structural belts—that of northernmost Ungava—are developed in late Pre-Cambrian (Proterozoic) sedimentary or volcanic rock, locally rich in iron formation (see Fig. 16).

The Belcher Islands–Nastapoka Belt sweeps in a great arc from Portland Promontory to Cape Jones and is believed to continue beneath the Paleozoic sediments of the Hudson Bay Lowland west of James Bay. Most of the belt is submerged, the Belchers representing the planed-off outcrop of the folding. East-facing cuestas look out toward the Archean rocks of the plateau along the mainland coast. Iron formation occurs both on the Belchers and on the mainland, but workable ores are not yet known, at any rate in adequate quantities or of sufficient iron content. Lead and zinc ores occur in Proterozoic limestones at Richmond Gulf; they are being explored by Gulf Lead Mines Limited.

The Chukotat River Belt runs east-west across northernmost Ungava. It consists of a very tightly folded series of ancient lavas and sediments, believed to be of Archean age. The grain of the country is obvious, but little else is known about this tundra land.

The Labrador Trough is by far the largest of the folded belts, being more than 400 miles long and 20–50 miles wide. It was first explored geologically by A. P. Low, whose traverses of the peninsula in the late nineteenth century are one of the great achievements of geological science. The discovery of large deposits of high-grade iron ore within this belt has led to its thorough exploration. This and the exploitation of the ores are discussed later.

A small belt known as the *Naskaupi Ranges* lies across the upper Naskaupi River. The grain is east-west, and the structures are believed to be younger than those of the Labrador Trough. Frobisher Mines Limited have an exploration license covering part of this belt.

The Mistassini Belt lies in the southwestern part of the peninsula. It consists of a series of gently folded Proterozoic sediments just west of the Grenville Front. Ridges on resistant beds form the islands in Lake Mistassini, whose shore line makes the structural grain apparent even on atlas maps. The rocks are not known to be extensively mineralized.

The only remaining structural feature requiring attention is the Lake Melville Basin, about whose origin there is much controversy. The steep southern wall, leading to the lofty summits of the Mealy Mountains, suggests that at least in part this great inland waterway occupies a graben, though the corresponding feature on the northern flank is not known. Lake Melville affords a sheltered, tidal waterway deep into the interior, accessible to ocean shipping as far as Goose Bay airport, 130 miles inland.

The Labrador Trough

The term by which the chief folded belt has come to be known is confusing, for the belt consists of an alternation of parallel ridges and valleys, closely akin to the Pennsylvania Appalachians. There is no suggestion of "trough"-like relief; the word is purely structural in application, being used in effect as a synonym for "geosyncline."

The folds are developed in a thick series of Proterozoic sediments and volcanics accumulated in a late Pre-Cambrian trough that was later compressed from the northeast. The sediments were corrugated and in places overthrust by the compressive forces and are today disposed in tight folds running approximately north-northwest–south-southeast. Throughout the trough the sediments are rich in iron formation. The stream banks are often stained brown by rust from these highly ferruginous beds, which can be clearly identified from low-flying aircraft.

Most of the trough lies within the zone of permafrost; that is, the regolith and upper parts of the bedrock are frozen throughout the summer. Nevertheless, fair stands of lichen woodland with black spruce and larch occur on much of the lower ground. North of latitude 57° permafrost seems widespread, but to the south it is patchy. There are probably patches of it in the Knob Lake area, but it has in no way interfered with the operations of the Iron Ore Company of Canada.

Geological prospecting of the trough has been in progress for 15 years. The observations of Low did not stimulate interest, since few were willing to face the grim physical toil and risks entailed in penetration to the interior. With the coming of the aircraft, and especially the bush pilot, the search was cautiously begun. In 1929, J. E. Gill and W. F. James discovered the large iron-ore bodies at Ruth Lake (Fig. 17); to them must go the credit for providing the earliest evidence that workable ores exist in the trough.

In 1936 a Canadian mining group commissioned J. A. Retty, a Quebec geologist, to survey a 20,000-square mile concession in the great bend of the Hamilton. Retty discovered iron ore on the property in the following year, and in 1938 he proved its existence beyond the watershed in Quebec. A concession was obtained on this Quebec area, and the pattern of the present Iron Ore Company of Canada's territory was more or less established. Though the control of the companies concerned has changed, Retty has continued to be the pioneer and dominating spirit in the exploration. Until 1945, however, the search for iron ore remained subsidiary to that for gold and base metals; interest was in the type of development that has taken place in Abitibi and northern Ontario. During the decade before World War II there was little demand for iron ore: the steel industry was depressed, and older sources of supply seemed adequate for many years to come.

The change came immediately after World War II. Retty's exploration has been supplemented since that time by intensive and detailed study of the concessions held, and more than 400,000,000 tons of high-grade iron ore is now known to be available in readily accessible form. The discoveries have coincided with a continued demand for ore by the American steel industry. Fears have been expressed that the high-grade Superior ores are approaching exhaustion; both Bethlehem Steel and United States Steel have sought overseas ore fields and are developing their east-coast quays and plants. The possibilities of the Labrador field have at last been realized, and a tremendous upsurge in interest in the exploration for ore has begun. The entire southern trough has been assigned since 1945 (Fig. 17).

The Hollinger Concessions

The large areas explored by Retty under license from the Quebec and Newfoundland governments came under the control, in 1942, of Hollinger Consolidated Gold Mines, a Canadian group, with the Hanna Corporation of Cleveland, Ohio, as minority partner. Hollinger has taken the foremost role in the development ever since; Retty is consulting geologist in the company. In 1949, after the exploration had reached fruition, the group was reorganized, and several large steel companies joined it. The Iron Ore Company of Canada was chartered in Delaware in November, 1949; the subscribing companies included the Armco, Republic, National, and Wheeling Steel Corporations, the Youngstown Sheet and Tube Company, and the Hanna Coal and Ore Corporation. With them were associated the Hollinger interests controlling the Labrador and Quebec concessions. Hollinger-Hanna Limited was incorporated in Canada a short time later to implement the program. The magnitude of American interests will be noted; and it will further strike the economic geographer that their producing units are in the interior, in the Lake Erie–Ohio Valley regions. The other large American companies are not in the group, though Bethlehem Steel has contracted to purchase part of the production.

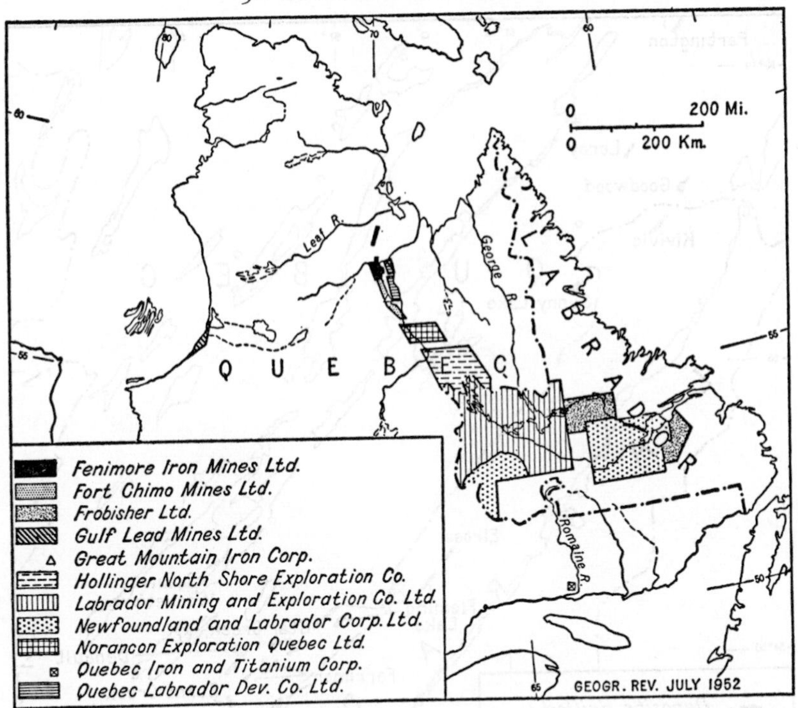

FIGURE 17

Areas Licensed for Exploration to Mining Companies, 1951. The Hollinger North Shore Exploration Co. and the Labrador Mining and Exploration Co. are the two halves of the Hollinger concessions, in Quebec and Newfoundland, respectively. Data supplied by Quebec Department of Mines and Newfoundland Department of Natural Resources.

Figure 18 shows the productive area. The ore bodies are strung out along the geological strike in a narrow belt more than 90 miles long; the largest cluster lies across the Quebec-Labrador boundary, which actually bisects three of the ore bodies. The map shows the height of land along which the boundary is supposed to lie. More than two-thirds of the ore lies in Quebec, but it will all be exported across Newfoundland-Labrador before regaining Quebec territory. The ore assays in natural state at about 55 per cent metallic iron. Roughly 55 per cent of the ore is nonphosphoric (that is, within the Bessemer range of less than 0.045 per cent phosphorus content), and 12 per cent is manganiferous. At the estimated annual production rate of 10,000,000 tons, more than 40 years' supply is already proved, and most of the drift-covered terrain remains unexplored.

Retty has outlined the remarkable work of the airlift that has flown all

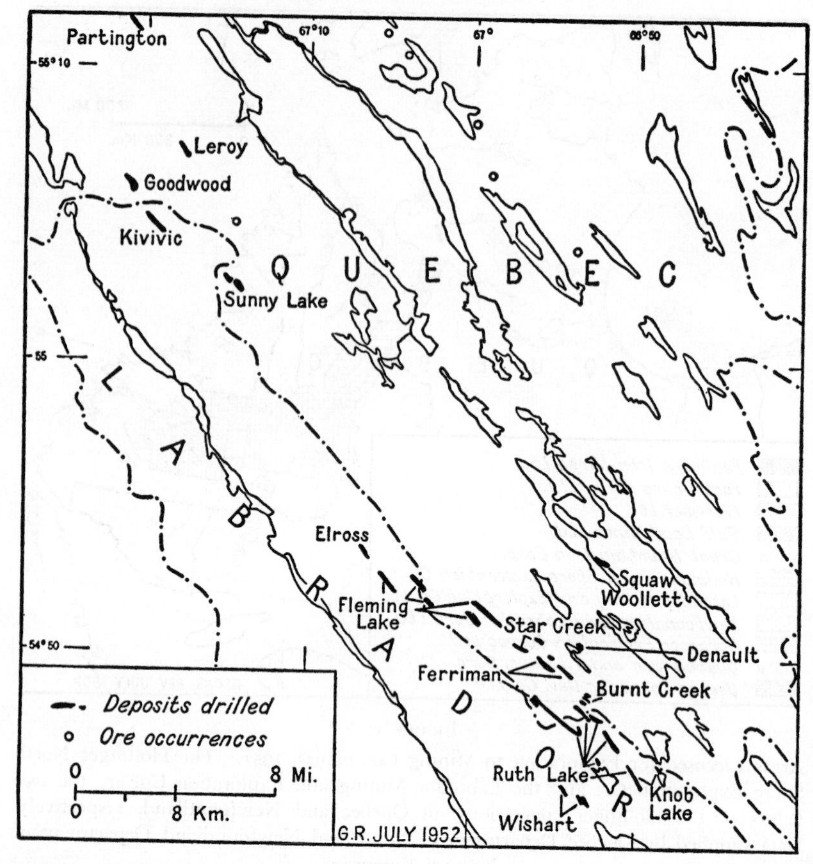

FIGURE 18

Detailed map of the central part of the Iron Ore Company of Canada's ore field. Because of the structural control of drainage, the grain of the country is clear. Note that the interprovincial boundary bisects some of the ore bodies. Data supplied by Iron Ore Company of Canada.

men and supplies to the area. In his most recent review he describes the establishment of the new townsite at Burnt Creek, where the senior personnel and their families now live. The railway to the coast, to be called the Quebec North Shore and Labrador Railway, is already under construction, as is the new harbor at Seven Islands; it is expected that the initial exports will move south along the new railway in 1954.

It is a curious coincidence that these Labrador ores should resemble so closely those of Minnesota and northern Sweden (Kiruna and Gällivare districts) in local environment. All three lie within Pre-Cambrian shields and in regions of cold winters.

There is no doubt that the Labrador area has the severest climate. The intense cold of winter is accentuated by the high winds that drive blowing snow across the treeless interfluves. The summer is similar to that of Lapland, but wetter and more changeable. Black flies and mosquitoes are a plague that will require stringent control: as Retty says, after many summers in the area, "undoubtedly this region is the source of supply for the entire universe." However, because of the southerly latitude, there is a considerable period of daylight even in midwinter, and the settlers in the new town will not face the darkness of the Swedish districts. Life will be hard, but stimulating. Mining and living conditions may be comparable with those of the Swedish areas, but one can hardly agree with the promoters of the project that they compare favorably with those of the Mesabi range.

	Jan. Temp. (°F.)	*July Temp. (°F.)*	*Thaw Season (Days)*	*Mean Ann. Snowfall (Inches)*	*Daylight, Dec. 21 (hr. & min.)*
Knob Lake District	−10	57	155–160	100–125	7 08
Mesabi Range	+5	65 to 68	215–220	45–50	8 25
Northern Sweden	+10	54 to 58	155–170	45–50	nil

Snow is likely to be a major problem. All the mining is to be opencast, and deep gashes in the terrain will quickly be formed. Any small hollow on the Labrador plateau fills to the brim with drifting snow, and there is little doubt that enormous quantities will accumulate annually in all the workings. The fresh snowfall of more than 100 inches a year is much greater than that of either of the two comparable areas. Present plans call for a five- to six-month mining season, which will necessitate vigorous snow removal as soon as the thaw begins in May. The new railway has to thread its way through the deep gorges of the Moisie, Nipissis, and Wacouno Rivers, in many places following grades blasted out of sheer rock walls. These gorges penetrate the Laurentide Scarp at its highest point, and very heavy snowfalls are to be expected on the valley sides. At least 200 inches must fall over wide areas, and 185 inches on the coast itself. Plainly, protection of the roadbed during the off season (ore will be shipped to the coast only during the mining period) will call for considerable care.

Diesel power will be employed on the railway. In spite of the incredible richness of the peninsula in hydroelectric potential, the company seems to have little use for hydroelectricity. Within its Newfoundland-Labrador concession lies Grand Falls on the Hamilton, a drop of more than 300 feet, with an estimated potential of 1,250,000 horsepower; and all the streams of the southern part of the peninsula offer abundant reserves of power. So far, however, the company proposes to develop only about 20,000 horsepower. One site is on the Menihek Lakes of the upper Hamilton, where 10,000 horsepower is to be generated—the first development on one of the world's greatest undeveloped rivers. A further 10,000 horsepower is to be generated on the Ste. Marguerite River to supply the installations at Seven Islands.

The Hollinger enterprise is thus well launched, and by its success it has stimulated intense interest and exploration in various other parts of the Labrador Trough.

Other Developments in the Labrador Trough

Several other groups have obtained exploration licenses in the Labrador Trough from the Quebec government. Figure 17 shows the concessions in 1951; they cover most of the folded belt south of the Leaf River. All these companies have reported promising showings of iron formation, but so far no claims have been made of ore bodies on the scale of those of the Hollinger company; it seems likely, however, that considerable discoveries will be made in these concessions in the near future. In some areas permafrost has added to the problems of exploration.

The charter of the Quebec North Shore and Labrador Railway includes provision for an extension to Fort Chimo, the proposed course to run through most of the remaining areas of the trough. Furthermore, although its promoters are wholly concerned with the Hollinger concessions, the new railway has common-carrier obligations; in other words, it will be in effect a public railway. However, it is doubtful whether the cost of rail haul to the Gulf of St. Lawrence could be borne by companies operating in the northern parts of the trough.

The proposals of Fenimore Iron Mines Limited are of the greatest interest. This group, with headquarters in Toronto, has been actively exploring the northernmost parts of the known iron-ore areas of the trough (Fig. 17). The chairman of the board is H. A. Brassert, well known as an iron and steel engineer in Pittsburgh, and the president was formerly an executive of the United States Steel Corporation. Once again the paramount interest of the American steel industry is obvious. In 1951 the company discovered 18 high-grade ore showings, some of them as far north as the Leaf River, and many of them manganiferous. Drilling began in October, 1951, in three of the most promising showings to determine the volume of ore.

The Fenimore group proposes to develop Fort Chimo as a deep-sea port, and to export the ore via Hudson Strait to Atlantic coast ports of the United States; for the northernmost ore bodies they are investigating the possibility of using near-by Leaf Lake as a harbor. Trucks would haul the ore to tide-water, though engineers employed by the group are exploring the possible improvement of the Koksoak River. The Fenimore interests assert that a five- to six-month navigation season can be maintained. At present Hudson Strait is officially open for navigation only in August, September, and early October, though Canadian government vessels regularly navigate the strait earlier and later. With modern navigational aids the official season could be greatly lengthened, but whether to the extent claimed by the company the writer does not care to guess.

These northernmost concessions are in areas whose climate is a little more rigorous than that of the Hollinger area. July temperatures are 3° to 5° F. lower, and the season of persistent thaw is shorter by a week or two. On the other hand, the winter is little, if at all, colder, and the annual snowfall is much lighter.

The Titanium Strike

The iron-ore discoveries in the interior have stolen some of the lime-light from another enterprise in the peninsula that deserves attention. In many places the anorthosite of the Grenville province is associated with small masses of ilmenite (an oxide of iron and titanium containing 30–40 per cent by mass of titanium oxide). In 1941, J. A. Retty reported that such masses occurred near Lake Allard, on the Laurentide Scarp about 25 miles inland from Havre St. Pierre, wholly within Quebec territory. Extensive exploration of these showings since 1946 has proved the existence of more than 125,000,000 tons of high-grade ilmenite. These bid fair to make Canada the leading producer of titanium oxide, of value chiefly as a paint pigment, and of metallic titanium, whose manifold uses are now beginning to be realized.

Development has been undertaken by the Quebec Iron and Titanium Corporation, a Canadian subsidiary of two United States base-metal corporations, Kennecott Copper and the New Jersey Zinc Company. A 28-mile railway, diesel-operated, connects the crushing plant near the deposits with the new harbor facilities at Havre St. Pierre. The crushed ore is shipped by boat to Sorel, at the Richelieu–St. Lawrence confluence, where it is refined with the aid of power supplied by the Shawinigan Water and Power Company. The products are pig iron and titanium slag, which contains about 70 per cent titanium oxide. It is hoped that production will reach about 175,000 tons of pig iron and 250,000 tons of slag a year, which is comparable with the normal annual output of oxide in the United States. In 1951, the first full year of production, close to 372,000 tons of ilmenite was extracted.

Ilmenite occurrences have been reported from other parts of the peninsula, chiefly in the south. Promising showings are being investigated near the Mealy Mountains anorthosite mass.

The Chibougamau District

The extreme southwestern districts of the peninsula are also being developed. The highly mineralized Temiskamian province has for a long time been the mainstay of Ontario and Quebec production of gold, silver, and base metals. All the established areas, however, are along or south of the National Transcontinental Railway (Canadian National Railways) from the St. Maurice Valley westward; the extension of the structural province northeastward into Labrador-Ungava has remained unproductive.

The area immediately northwest of the Grenville Front around Lake Chibougamau (Fig. 16) has for almost half a century been known to possess numerous small showings of gold, copper, iron, lead, and zinc ores, with small amounts of asbestos and silver. The area is rugged and thickly forested; it lies on the height of land between James Bay and Lake St. John drainage, and its drainage is therefore erratic; there are no large streams to afford ready access by canoe. In the 1930's, however, considerable prospecting took place, much of it air-borne, and interest in the district increased steadily.

In 1949 the Quebec Department of Mines built a road from St. Félicien, in the Lake St. John Basin, to the new Chibougamau townsite, more or less following the line of an old winter road. The ease of access stimulated fresh interest in the area. There are now eight properties in the mineralized belt, and the townsite bustles with activity. Potential ore valued at about $70 million has been proved. In late 1951 three of the companies were engaged in operations designed to bring their properties into production. It seems almost certain that the Chibougamau district will become a considerable producer of copper, and secondarily of gold, within the next few years.

Forest Resources

Although mineral wealth has been the prime reason for the new developments in Labrador-Ungava, most of the earlier interest in the interior was focused on the forest resources, which were rumored to be vast. The forests along the southern margin from Clarke City on the east to the Clay Belt on the west have been exploited for many years. This area, within the main Boreal forest zone, has long been known for its rich reserves of spruce, both white and black. The forests offer close stands of spruce and less desirable pulpwood species of size ideal for the industry; furthermore, abundant power is located precisely where it is needed.

It seems unlikely that the area of vigorous pulpwood cutting can be extended much beyond this southern belt. Along the North Shore east of Clarke City the face of the Laurentide Scarp and the narrow gorges cut by the major streams support good stands of black spruce and balsam fir; but the zone is narrow. It has suffered badly from fire in recent years, and extensive areas are economically useless. The coastal-plain lowlands are largely covered with bog and spruce muskeg. East of Natashquan the cooler summers do not permit dense forest growth.

The interior plateaus are unattractive to the pulpwood cutters. The "forest" here is primarily of the woodland structure; black or white spruce stand isolated in an ocean of reindeer lichen. The areal density of trees is low, and they often adopt a habit unsuitable for the pulping process. There are probably patches of exploitable forest within the woodland zone, but they would hardly be likely to sustain industries on the scale of those of Lake St. John, at any rate until more accessible supplies were exhausted. Natural regeneration is very slow, and fire has destroyed large areas during the past half century.

Special interest attaches to the remarkable "soft spot" in the Lake Melville Basin. The writer has already called attention to the considerable stands of close forest in the basin, which has a thermal climate like that of Clarke City. These forests exist primarily on the slopes and terraces of the Naskaupi, Hamilton, and Kenamu Rivers. In view of the superabundance of power available on these undeveloped rivers, and of the access to the sea offered by Lake Melville, it is natural that people should turn their minds to the establishment of a pulpwood industry in the basin. The present Newfoundland government has been loud in its praises of the district and has undertaken to establish a local industry, employing in part Newfoundland labor.

The writer is less sanguine than he was about the Lake Melville country. Some of the estimates of the potential annual cut seem excessive. Detailed mapping (unpublished) of the Kenamu Valley by I. A. McKay, as well as of the southern terraces flanking Lake Melville itself, has demonstrated that large areas of muskeg occupy terrain confidently designated by promoters as "forest." Many of the sand plains are covered with lichen woodland rather than forest. There is no doubt that there are extensive areas of good forest capable of cutting on a large scale, but the relief restricts these to a small part of the total.

. . . . .

Labrador and the St. Lawrence Seaway

In the future development of the peninsula much may depend on the St. Lawrence navigation. It has been pointed out that the iron ore to be extracted from the Labrador Trough is intended primarily for steel companies whose present plants are in the Lake Erie or Ohio Valley producing centers. It is therefore vital that deep-water navigation be made available between the Gulf of St. Lawrence and Lake Erie.

The new port of Seven Islands is 952 miles from Cleveland, Ohio, by the St. Lawrence route. It is 1366 miles from Philadelphia and 1550 miles from Baltimore, which in turn are 300–500 miles from the producing centers of the interior. To reach these, the ore will therefore have a rail haul as long as that from the ore bodies to Seven Islands. (Ed. note: Railway completed and first shipments made in July, 1954.)

The existing St. Lawrence canals are quite incapable of providing adequate service. The maximum draft of 14 feet is too shallow for the large ore carriers that will have to be used. The present lock capacity is inadequate for the 10,000,000 to 20,000,000 tons of ore that will ultimately move along the route. There is no doubt that the development of the peninsula as a source for bulky ores would be materially aided by the proposed seaway. Moreover, it is the policy of the Hollinger interests that some part of the production should be diverted to permit an expansion of the steel capacity of the Dominion itself. It has recently been announced that the existing facilities at Hamilton, Ont., are to be enlarged with this in mind. Here again the seaway, when built, will be an enormous stimulus.

52. *Britain's Coal Crisis* *

No other major nation has an economy based so completely on a single mineral as has Britain; that mineral is, of course, coal. The

* L. Dudley Stamp, "Britain's Coal Crisis: Geographical Background," from *Geographical Review*, Vol. 38, 1948, pp. 179–193; published by the American Geographical Society, New York.

The author (1898) is one of England's leading geographers. At present he is Professor and Chairman of Geography, University of London, London School of Economics. He has traveled and conducted research in widely diverse areas of the world. He is perhaps best known for his work in land utilization and mapping in the British Isles. Among his numerous books may be mentioned *Asia, a Regional and Economic Geography, The British Isles; a Geographic and Economic Survey, The Face of Britain, The Land of Britain, its Use and Misuse, Our Undeveloped World,* and *Africa.*

decline of coal production and export in Britain has been a severe blow to the economic life of that country. A prominent British geographer, L. Dudley Stamp, presents in this reading an excellent analysis of all aspects of the postwar situation. The relation of coal quality and mining problems to geological structures and erosion in Britain is well brought out. The successful exploitation of coal depends not only on the possession of a coal resource but also on other physical and economic factors, as conditions in Britain well illustrate.

It is a commonplace to say that Britain's industrial development has been based on coal. The statement not only is true of the past but remains true at the present day. Britain's immediate recovery, indeed her whole prosperity, depends essentially on her ability to obtain the coal that still exists in quantity in her coal fields. The difficulties in which the coal industry finds itself after World War II are widely misunderstood, and the mistaken belief has gained unfortunate currency that the chief difficulty is the exhaustion of the reserves—which is, happily, far from the truth.

Coal has been worked in Britain since very early times. The discovery of coal cinders in the ruins of Roman towns makes it probable that the Romans used coal during their occupation of the country. The "Anglo-Saxon Chronicle" records its use in monasteries in the ninth century. By the thirteenth or fourteenth century there was a well-established trade in sea-borne coal from Newcastle and Tyneside to London. The early workings were naturally along outcrops, but coal at or near the surface is apt to be badly weathered and unobtainable in lumps suitable for transport and burning, so that commonly a seam was followed from a scarp-face outcrop into the hill by means of adit or drift. Such outcrop workings were abandoned when water caused difficulties or the roof collapsed, and their place was taken by shallow mines, from which the coal was removed by haulage up a shaft. As a rule, no records were kept either of outcrop workings or of the early mines, with the result that many seams near the surface are honeycombed with irregular excavations. Much coal remains, but any attempt at more systematic exploitation by modern methods is likely to reveal old flooded workings, and the amount of coal still available is unknown.

With the coming of the Industrial Revolution the coal fields became the focus of a new urban development. In earlier times a close correlation existed between population density and land fertility: the counties most productive agriculturally supported the most people. The basic rural settlement pattern of scattered farms, hamlets, villages, market towns, and county towns remained, and to a considerable extent still remains, but the new urban pattern of colliery villages, factory towns, and great centralized ports became superimposed upon it. According to official figures

Britain has become so urbanized that 80 per cent of the population are classed as "urban." This means people living in the properly constituted cities, towns, and "urban districts" and excludes people living in towns —often of several thousand inhabitants—in "rural districts." Actually, nearer 90 per cent of the British people live in towns. In the late eighteenth century and the whole of the nineteenth this increasing urbanization was concentrated on, or was associated with, the coal fields. The only major exception was London itself; on the other hand, only one or two of the minor coal fields failed to exhibit the fundamental change to an industrial region.

In general terms the story of development is the same for all the British coal fields, though they may be in different stages at the present time. There was first the spasmodic local working in open pits or shallow mines; then came shaft mines and colliery villages and towns and the growth of factory industry, with all the attendant network of services and communications—the improvement of roads or construction of tramways, later the extensive building of canals, rendered obsolete by the advent of railroads. The industrial regions took on the higher degree of specialization characteristic of Britain—Lancashire with cottons, the Leeds-Bradford area of Yorkshire with woolens, the Sheffield area with iron, steel, and cutlery, the Black Country with iron smelting, and so on.

But coal winning is a robber industry, and in due course the available coal becomes worked out. In Britain this has happened, in part at least, in the old Black Country of southern Staffordshire and neighboring parts of Warwickshire. In most of the fields, however, only the more accessible seams in the shallow parts have been exhausted; workings have become concentrated in the deeper parts, often in the "concealed" fields, where large units and large-scale organization are both essential. The Report of the Royal Commission on the Coal Industry (1925) demonstrated most realistically that in every British coal field there were large, modern, well-equipped collieries producing coal at competitive prices and small, old, uneconomic collieries whose costs of production were much higher. Out of 114 undertakings that in 1926 were operating at a loss of 3 shillings a ton or more, no fewer than 110 had a yearly output of less than 400,000 tons.

Nationalization and the Manpower Problem

At first thought the obvious course would seem to be to shut down all the old, uneconomic collieries and concentrate on the large, modern ones. But this would involve destroying the *raison d'être* of the well-established towns in all the older coal-field areas. The government consequently instructed colliery owners to carry out voluntarily a grouping of collieries so that the large, modern units could each carry a share of the old small units. Where this "rationalization" was not done voluntarily, it was done compulsorily. It may be asserted that this was a prelude to the several steps to nationalization that followed. The coal resources of the country were made the property of the state by the Coal Act 1938 (effective from 1942), but it was left to the Labour government, elected in the summer of 1945, to nationalize the industry itself. The Coal Industry Nationalisation Bill was introduced on December 19, 1945, passed through all stages in both houses, and received the Royal Assent on July 12, 1946. It established a National Coal Board charged with the task of reorganizing and re-equipping the industry. The Board is required to pay its way on the average of good and bad years but has a government advance of as much as £150 million spread over five years for capital expenditure in the sinking of new pits and installation of modern machinery.

The real crisis faced by the National Coal Board was primarily one of manpower. Before World War I more than a million men were employed in the industry. In 1927 the figure was still 1,024,000, but after that there was a steady drop, accompanied by much unemployment and real poverty, to 756,000 in 1936. A slight rise followed, and then a renewed fall. During World War II about 700,000 were employed. The normal intake of young men almost ceased, and wartime production was maintained by older men, many of whom strained to the utmost for patriotic reasons at ages when they would normally have ceased work. As the war dragged on, the shortage of men became so acute that young men were directed to the mines instead of into the fighting forces, and these so-called "Bevin Boys" helped to maintain output.

After the war patriotic motives did not have the same force. Underground mining held few attractions for young men who had lived an open-air life in the armed forces, and their fathers could not forget the years of unemployment between the wars and no longer encouraged their sons to take up their own old trade. In 1946 the low figure of 697,000 employed was reached, and of these only 626,000 were classed as "effectively" employed. Early in 1947 the National Coal Board introduced a five-day week to stimulate both production and recruitment, but production still lagged and recruitment failed to keep pace with wastage. Later in the year a substantial wage increase reintroduced the economic incentive, and every opportunity was afforded the many European refugees ("displaced persons") in Britain to enter the lines. In particular, this offered a solution to the employment of a considerable number of the 100,000 Poles remaining in Britain. However, Britain still stands in immediate need of 100,000 skilled miners.

Progress in the Industry

Contrary to ideas inculcated by political propaganda, the years between the wars saw marked progress in the coal industry in many directions. The Miners' Welfare Fund, set up with government backing in 1920 and established as a Commission in 1939, was empowered to levy a tax of one penny (2 cents) on every ton of coal raised. The money was used to improve the social conditions of the workers. In particular, the Commission built pit-head baths at the larger collieries. At first, so conservative are the older miners, that there was bitter opposition to what was stigmatized as public washing in place of the tub in the kitchen at home, but this gradually changed to the extent that collieries without pit-head baths had difficulties in getting labor. Later the commission turned its attention to the provision of canteens serving hot meals.

The larger part of the coal production comes from deep, modern collieries, many of them almost completely electrified and employing a thousand men or more, frequently even 5000. Coal-cutting machinery is now in extensive use except where seams are very thin and shattered. The proportion of machine-mined coal increased from 19 per cent in 1924 to 42 per cent in 1933 and 59 per cent in 1938. In some fields where conditions are suitable the percentage is over 80; it was 81 in Northumberland in 1933. In 1938 not only was 59 per cent of the total output cut by machines but 54 per cent was mechanically conveyed. Mechanization advanced rapidly during the war, so that in 1945 these figures were 72 and 71 per cent respectively. The Leicestershire field reported 97 per cent of coal cut by machinery in 1944.

Unfortunately, mechanization has not been reflected in increased output per employee. This figure fell from 301.9 tons in 1939 to 245.2 tons in 1945, and the output per man shift from 1.17 tons in 1937 to 1.00 in 1945 (1.05 tons in 1946). Wages rose from 10s. 7d. per ton of coal disposable commercially in 1938 to 25s. 5d. in 1945—nearly 150 per cent. Explanation of the fall in output per man shift is not simple. There is the increase in the average age of the miners and the continued employment under wartime conditions of many who would normally have already retired from active labor. Further, although an effort is made to supplement the ordinary civilian rations both by canteen meals and by a special allocation, there is no doubt that the large decrease in many important foodstuffs, notably meat and fats, has had a deleterious effect.

The Disposition of Britain's Coal Fields

A brief glance at the geological history of the British coal fields will clarify certain problems of current exploitation.

In early Carboniferous time the present Highlands of Scotland formed part of a great continental mass. Along its southern fringe were deltaic flats, and on them flourished the extensive swamp forests from which coals of Lower Carboniferous age derive. These older coal seams die out southward except for a few in Northumberland. It was not until Upper Carboniferous time that conditions suitable for the growth of coal forests spread over the larger part of England and Wales. At that time, it is believed, a great deltaic flat stretched from the margin of the Scottish land mass to St. George's Land, a low land ridge crossing the Midlands of England. Along the southern fringe of St. George's Land conditions were also suitable for the growth of Coal Measure forests, but farther south (in Devon and Cornwall) rocks of the same age are barren. St. George's Land remained relatively stable during Coal Measure time, whereas the areas to the north and south underwent successive depressions. It would seem that there were thus originally two enormous coal fields of Upper Carboniferous or Coal Measure age, one reaching from the Highlands of Scotland to the Midlands of England, the other lying south of St. George's Land and extending from South Wales across southern England into Kent and on into northern France and Belgium. In the northern area, coal seams traced southward toward the old land bridge are found to get gradually closer together and, in some places, eventually to merge. This is the case with the famous Thick Coal—as much as 36 feet thick—of the Warwickshire or Black Country coal field, and this explains why the coals in some of the famous Midland fields have been virtually worked out. (Fig. 19)

The Armorican or Hercynian earth movements at the end of the Carboniferous period flexed the British Coal Measures into a series of east-west and north-south folds. Where two downfolds cross, an oval basin may be formed, as in the little Forest of Dean coal field. Folding and subsequent denudation of the anticlines resulted in the separation of the British coal deposits into a series of basins. Each basin is geologically a distinct unit and may be said to constitute a coal field. Where the basin is completely surrounded by older rocks, the exact extent of the field is known, and total reserves can be closely calculated. The South Wales and Forest of Dean fields are good examples of such basins; the Scottish fields afford other examples. In other places the Coal Measures may plunge down or be faulted down to such depths that the existence of coal can only be assumed; in any case it is beyond workable depth. Thus between the

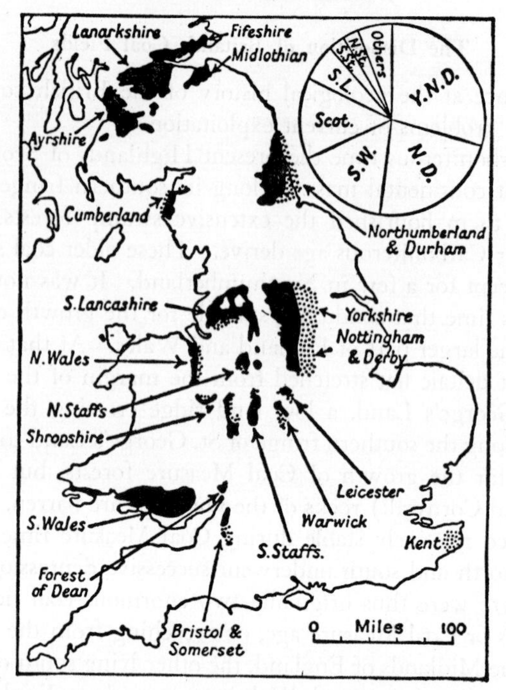

FIGURE 19

The Coalfields of Britain. The dotted areas are the concealed fields; the circle represents the total quantity of coal raised in a year. There are three groups of fields: the fields of the midland Valley of Scotland (some coal here comes from rocks older than the Coal Measures); the fields of northern England and the Midlands; the southern group, including the South Wales, the Forest of Dean, the Bristol, and the East Kent fields (continued under the Strait of Dover into northern France and Belgium). From "Geography for To-Day," edited by L. D. Stamp and L. S. Suggate, London, 1939. (Courtesy of Longmans, Green & Co., Ltd.)

North Wales and Lancashire fields coal probably underlies the whole Cheshire plain, but at depths certainly exceeding 4000 feet. In still other places the Coal Measures plunge beneath younger rocks or the sea, and the precise limits of the field remain unknown. This is the case with the great Yorkshire field.

Unfortunately, different parts of a single geological coal field may be given separate names, and in recent years nomenclature has been further confused by the adoption of regions with new names.

In every field the shift of the foci of production is a well-known phenomenon. The late Professor Ll. Rodwell Jones in his textbook *North England* demonstrated this for the Yorkshire, Nottinghamshire, and Derbyshire coal field, and his method was extended to all the British fields in the first edition of *The British Isles* (Stamp and Beaver). This work has small maps of each of the main fields showing collieries in 1900 and 1931 and distinguishing by dots the number of men employed. The older, shallower parts of the fields are worked by small units, the newer, deeper parts by large units. Gray has recently used the method to show changes in the Yorkshire fields since the seventeenth century.

The extent of the fields as known at present is shown on the official map on the scale of 1:625,000 prepared by the Maps Research Office of the Ministry of Town and Country Planning and published by the Ordnance Survey.

British Coal Reserves and Classification of Coal

No calculations have been made recently of Britain's total coal reserves. . . . When the Coal Act 1938 became law, the ownership of all unworked coal passed from private hands to the nation. Previously, ownership of land had normally included mineral rights, and it is broadly true that the great fortunes made in the industry were those derived from royalties, often accruing to owners who had no active interest in the industry, rather than from profits of exploitation. These owners were compensated by an amount equivalent to the estimated capital value of the coal (as of July 1, 1942) that could reasonably be expected to be raised from the holding in the hundred years 1942–2042.

Thus details were collected of "developed reserves" or total planned output for 1942–2042. The total is 20,500,400,000 long tons, classified for the first time according to type (see table). The Coal Survey officers only in-

CLASSIFICATION OF COALS

This scheme was evolved by the Coal Survey officers to assist the Ministry of Fuel and Power in making a census of fuel consumption. The "code-numbers" are based on content of volatile matter (on the dry ash-free basis) and coking properties.

Low-volatile coals (volatile matter 20 per cent or less)
- 100 Anthracite: noncaking, volatile matter less than 10 per cent
- 200 Low-volatile steam coals (types distinguished as 201, 202, 203, 204, 206)

Medium-volatile coals (volatile matter 20.1–30.0 per cent)
- 300 Scottish medium-volatile, noncaking or weakly caking

301 Coking coals, strongly caking (These are the metallurgical coking coals of Durham and South Wales.)

High-volatile coals (volatile matter over 30.0 per cent) (Each group is divided into 01 and 02, with respectively less and more than 37.0 per cent of volatile matter.)

400 Very strongly caking coals
500 Strongly caking coals
600 Medium caking coals
700 Weakly caking coals
800 Very weakly caking coals
900 Noncaking coals

SUMMARY OF DEVELOPABLE COAL RESERVES IN GREAT BRITAIN [a]
(In millions of long tons)

Type of Coal	*Planned Output 1942–2042* Tons	%	*Proved Additional Reserves* Tons	%	*Output 1938* Tons	%
Anthracite (100)	704.6	3.4	914.3	6.8	6.1	2.7
Steam coals (200, 300; low and medium volatile)	1,861.9	9.1	1,306.6	9.8	20.7	9.1
Coking coals (301, 401; medium volatile)	1,556.2	7.6	1,130.5	8.5	20.7	9.1
Coking-gas and gas coals (400, 500, 600; high volatile)	7,402.3	36.1	3,953.5	29.5	84.0	36.8
Household and industrial coals (700; high volatile weakly caking)	2,894.4	14.1	1,448.0	10.8	34.2	15.0
Household and general coals (800, 900; high volatile noncaking)	5,634.1	27.5	4,623.8	34.6	60.7	26.6
Unclassified	446.9	2.2	......	...	1.8	0.7
	20,500.4	100.0	13,376.7 [b]	100.0	228.2	100.0

[a] Data from "Rapid Survey of Coal Reserves and Production," Fuel Research Board, Dept. of Scientific and Industrial Research, 1946.
[b] Exclusive of at least 2000 million tons unclassified.

cidentally recorded known reserves not scheduled to be worked in the next hundred years, but the additional total was 15 billion long tons. They ignored seams less than 2 feet thick and reserves below 4000 feet (4500 feet in some collieries in Lancashire and northern Staffordshire). During World War II numerous borings made in the search for oil revealed previously unknown extensions of existing coal fields as well as new areas with possibilities for exploitation. Modern developments in deep mining prove that there is no need to regard 4000 feet as a lower limit. On the most conservative estimates Britain has definitely enough coal, proved and capable of being mined economically by existing methods, to last her at the present rate of consumption for at least two hundred years. Indeed, there seems every reason to accept the older estimates that there is probably enough for 750 years, even if we take the old rate of 250 million tons a year rather than the 1947 target of 200 million. Among European countries only Germany (pre-1939 frontiers) is so well served. It must be noted that reserves are not shared equally; in some fields exhaustion is in sight.

Reserve Types of the Fields

The life of the collieries of Northumberland and Durham, as based on reserves and planned outputs, shows a general increase toward the east, so that it is longest—certainly well over a century—in the coastal areas and under the North Sea. West Durham is a dying field, with many abandoned mines and an estimated life of less than 10 years; it is known as a "problem area." The government has constituted the whole coal field a "Development Area"—an area in which the government will encourage industrial development and where the appropriate department of the Board of Trade will invite new industry to settle—but this does not solve the problem whether the old, western part of the field should be allowed to die or whether an attempt should be made to change its economic basis. The change in the physical and chemical characters of any one seam when it is traced entirely across the field is greater than the differences between the various seams in a given locality in the field. The famous medium-volatile coking coals of West Durham (301) pass eastward into coking-gas and gas coals (401, 501, 502) and northward into medium and weakly caking coals (602, 702) marketed chiefly for power stations, general industrial use, and house coal; they are of excellent quality.

The Cumberland coals are all of types 501 and 502, and huge reserves, difficult to prove, are believed to exist under the sea and at great depths northward.

In the West Yorkshire field types 500 and 600 predominate. More than 70 per cent of the production has come from five seams, but there is a noticeable move eastward to the deeper part of the field, and seams with other types of coal are likely to be worked. In South Yorkshire, the Sheffield area, the dominant types are 500, 600, and 700; farther south, in Nottinghamshire, they are 800; and the progressive change continues into the fields of Leicestershire and South Derbyshire, where the coals are mainly noncaking (900), especially in seams of more than five feet thick. In the other Midland fields very weakly caking and noncaking coals (800–900) predominate.

For the Lancashire field (mainly types 600–700) and North Staffordshire (400–800) the future is less clearly foreseeable, because of the extensive faulting and steep dips, but there are undoubtedly very great reserves at depth. In the small Forest of Dean field exhaustion of the chief seam is almost certain to lead to a drop in production.

South Wales coals range from 100 to 400; anthracite predominating in the northwest, dry steam coals (200) in the heart of the field, and medium- or high-volatile coals toward the southeast. In the entirely hidden East Kent field the chief reserves are also of type 200.

Scotland has coals of very varied types. Though anthracite is absent, there are excellent steam coals and a wide range of high-volatile coals.

Opencast Working and Drift Mining

It may seem strange that during the Second World War, after more than a century of essentially deep mining, Britain returned to the quarrying or opencast working of coal to such an extent that from 1944 nearly 10 per cent of the production was obtained in this way; but the reasons are not far to seek. In many of the fields the land surface lies in long dip slopes, paralleling over considerable areas the dip of the underlying Coal Measures, and in steep scarp slopes. The coal seam naturally follows the dip slope but may lie from a dozen to a hundred feet or more below the surface. Although the associated Coal Measure strata vary, the seam is commonly underlain by clays and shales and overlain by shales and sandstones, the sandstones jointed and consequently pervious to water, a frequent cause of flooding and abandonment.

Large-scale mechanical excavators, dragline scrapers, and bulldozers now make it possible to remove greater thicknesses of overburden, and to do it economically. The lowest working costs result when the overburden is left piled in huge ridges, but the resulting "hill and dale" becomes virtually a desert of no economic value. Where, as in parts of South Wales, wild moorland at heights of a thousand feet and more above sea level is involved, the loss is not serious, but it is a very different matter in the rich farmland of Leicestershire and Yorkshire, where every acre is precious. There it is necessary to restore the land for agricultural or other uses, and in some places this has been done so effectively that only one season's crops have been lost. Hotly disputed questions remain: Is it, for example, essential, or at least desirable, to scrape off the topsoil and later to spread it over the restored surface, or are the results incommensurate with the heavy cost? Is working justified over famous parks, gardens, and beauty spots, some of them perhaps now the possession of the nation?

Much of the high cost of opencast coal working in the war years may be attributed to its experimental nature, and on the whole costs now compare reasonably with those of deep mining. It was feared that the coal might be weathered and consequently poor, but this fear has been shown in many instances to be groundless. Opencast mining eases the labor position, since skilled miners are not needed and many semiskilled workers are content with a surface job who would not go underground. However, although temporarily important, opencast working is not likely to continue for long to make a significant contribution to Britain's output. Drift mining is a still later development and has been encouraged by the fact that such local enterprises have not been nationalized.

The British Coal Trade

In the present century coal has been the one primary commodity of which Britain has had a large exportable surplus. In addition to a large coastwise movement, which is the cause of much of the activity of the ports in the coal-producing areas, shipments of coal destined for consumption outside the country may be divided into two categories: true exports to be unloaded at foreign ports and bunker coal for consumption by vessels en route. . . . In 1913, the year of peak production, no less than 94.4 million long tons, or nearly one-third of the total output, was exported. During World War I exports dropped sharply, reaching the low figure of 40.5 million tons in 1918, the year when the German submarine campaign was at its height. When the war ended, Britain's coal markets were completely changed. Polish "reparation" coal has often been blamed for the troubles, but a comparison of the 1913 and 1920 customers for British coal shows that the loss in markets was world-wide and that it was fairly small in the countries receiving reparation coal. Between 35 and 40 per cent of the exports came from South Wales—mainly hard steam coals for bunkers and for the coaling stations of the world. Two changes, however, had taken place during the war: many ships had been coverted to oil burning; and the more distant coaling stations—Panama, Cristóbal, Port

Classified Export of Coal from Britain (Excluding Bunker Coal)
(In thousands of long tons)

	1923	1929	1932	1936	1938	1946
Anthracite	3,182	4,217	3,903	3,321	3,562	963
Steam	58,944	40,805	26,053	24,276	23,812	2,184
Gas	9,103	7,317	4,213	2,994	3,842	53
Household	1,448	1,855	1,408	1,493	1,512	62
Other	6,733	6,072	3,322	2,436	3,128	1,193
TOTAL	79,460	60,267	38,899	34,520	35,856	4,455

Said, Suez, Aden, Colombo, and Singapore—had come to rely on other, usually more local, supplies. Countries that had formerly depended on British coal for their factories had not only developed home resources or turned to other supplies but had also developed hydroelectric power. The rise in exports in the "boom years" 1922 and 1923—reaching the all-time maximum of 97.6 million long tons in 1923—was due largely to the European demand for general-purpose coals, and thus South Wales had a smaller proportion of the trade. The disastrous strikes of 1926 lost Britain other markets, never fully regained, with the result that exports in the 1930's remained almost steady around the 50-million mark but dropped from 25 per cent to 20 per cent of the output. The export of 46.5 million long tons in 1939 was almost exactly 20 per cent of the output.

World War II killed the export trade. The small figures for the years after 1940 are mainly bunker coal. Thus in 1944 the true export was only 1.6 million tons. In 1946 and 1947 the position was entirely different. In a world hungry for coal—especially the devastated countries of Europe and such customers as Denmark and Sweden, able and willing to send much-needed foodstuffs and raw materials in exchange—Britain has a market waiting for at least 50 million tons a year but remains unable to produce enough for even minimum home needs because of the shortage of skilled manpower and equipment. In the very severe winter of 1946–1947 the British froze in their homes and offices, factories went on short time, no outdoor display lighting was allowed, and precious dollars were spent on imports of coal—with a 200 years' supply waiting to be mined.

53. *Petroleum in the Soviet Union: An Appraisal of a Recent German Study* *

Valid information as to current conditions of the petroleum industry in the Soviet Union is generally lacking. The inadequacy of U.S.S.R. statistics naturally causes a great deal of speculation. The fact that her most productive fields are located near her southern borders, on the flanks of the Caucasus, has been given considerable publicity as a strategic weakness. New fields are being developed, however, and the fact remains that the Soviet Union possesses a

* Sherman R. Abrahamson, "Petroleum in the Soviet Union," quoted from *Economic Geography,* Vol. 29, 1953, pp. 267–276.

The author is Economic Geographer, Petroleum and Natural Gas Branch, United States Bureau of Mines. His major interests are climatology, biogeography, and economic geography.

greater area of favorable or possible oil-bearing rock strata than any other nation. Abrahamson adds to our knowledge of this critical resource in a significant area by reviewing a recent book published in Germany.

Perhaps at no other time in the history of the world have the magnitude of a nation's petroleum resources and the productivity of a nation's petroleum industry so dominated international policy discussions as do those of the Soviet Union today. And rightly so—experiences of two world wars have demonstrated that the future of a nation as a world power depends to a very large degree on its possession of, or accessibility to, large reserves of petroleum.

The current atmosphere of tension between East and West gives appraisal of the petroleum situation in the Soviet Union an uncommon timeliness. To assess the Soviet petroleum industry's success in rehabilitating war-damaged producing fields and refineries and in supplying growing domestic demands of manufacturing, agriculture, and commerce, as well as the Soviet war machine and its ancillary activities in Korea, is indeed a lofty purpose. It is also a huge task. Such assessment is made more difficult by lack of authentic information for many phases of the industry. No official statistics with absolute figures have been made public by the Soviet Union since 1938. The practice of reporting all production results in percentages of the production quotas set up within Five-Year Plans has prevailed since 1938.

Despite the difficulties imposed by the immensity of the task and the limitations of source material, Dr. Hassmann * has attempted to correlate the various phases of the Soviet petroleum industry and project them against a background of world-wide political and economic conditions. In the preface he explains the necessity for "going beyond the narrow economic boundaries" to understand the entire Soviet petroleum situation. Soviet petroleum policy has been shaped, in large part, by the fact that on the southwest the Soviet Union is bordered by the Middle East, which contains over half of the world's petroleum reserves. "Only from the background of the entire general world economic and political situation can the peculiarities and special significance of the Soviet petroleum industry be shown."

General Elements of Soviet Industry

Dr. Hassmann has divided his thesis into four parts, which gives the book a very satisfactory arrangement. The first is a treatment of the

* Heinrich Hassmann: "Erdol in der Sowjetunion." 176 pp.; maps, tables. Industrieverleg von Hernhaussen K.G., Hamburg, 1951. DM 5.80. 8 x 5½ inches.

general elements of Soviet industry, including geography, history, population, government, and economic theory. It concludes with a discussion of Soviet industrial accomplishments, in which the author lists, according to their geographic location, the following ten industrial regions:

1. The industrial region of the European northwest, with the main emphasis on Leningrad.

2. The central Russian industrial region, within a wide radius around Moscow, its natural gravitation point. It is based on the brown-coal mines in the Moscow Basin.

3. The south Russian industrial region in the Donets and Dnieper Basins, based upon the anthracite deposits of the Donets region and the iron-ore deposits of Krivoi Rog.

4. The industrial region of the middle Volga, extending from Kazan in the north to Stalingrad in the south. It contains important petroleum and natural gas deposits.

5. The industrial region of the Urals, the most important centers of which are Nishni Tagil, Sverdlovsk, Chelyabinsk, and Magnitogorsk with their rich ore and potash deposits.

6. The industrial region of the Caucasus between Novorossisk in the northwest and Baku in the southeast, where the important element is the rich petroleum deposits.

7. The Kuznetsk region, which lies between the cities of Novosibirsk, Barnaul, Stalinsk, and Tomsk and has important coal mines.

8. The industrial region on Lake Baikal, which owes its existence to coal deposits and has Irkutsk as its central point.

9. The industrial region of the Far East, which is situated astride the Amur River and has two important centers—Khabarovsk and Komsomolsk.

10. The Central Asiatic industrial region between Tashkent and Alma-Ata, important for its rich coal, iron, and petroleum deposits.

These ten regions are shown on a double-page map, along with the principal petroleum regions, natural gas fields, oil-shale deposits, and railroads. Following the regional divisions is a table reviewing Soviet industrial production as follows:

Year	*Coal*	*Pig Iron*	*Steel*	*Petroleum*	*Electricity* (Billions of kilowatt-hours)
	(In millions of tons)				
1913	29	4.2	4.2	8.7	2.0
1938	133	14.6	18.0	28.2	39.4
1949	237	17.2	21.0	33.2	74.2
1950	261	19.5	27.0	37.6	90.0
1960 (Plan)	500	50.0	60.0	60.0	. . .

Development of the Petroleum Industry

The second part of the book begins with a résumé of the historical development of the Russian petroleum industry from 1860 to 1917. Discussed are such topics as the relationship between the industry and the Czarist State, the various methods (rental, 1821–72; auction, 1872–96; and combined auction and tax system 1896–1917) by which individual operators could acquire drilling rights, the formation of the three major petroleum-industry groups that decisively influenced pre-World War I development of the Russian petroleum industry, and the refining, transporting, domestic consumption, and exportation of Russian petroleum in Czarist times.

Fully two-thirds (33 pages) of Part II is devoted to the development of the country's petroleum industry under the Soviets. At present, control of the industry is vested in the Minister of the Petroleum Industry. The individual petroleum fields and installations are organized as trusts, and the trusts are brought together in larger associations. The trusts are subordinate to the associations, which, in turn, are subordinate to the Minister of the Petroleum Industry, who is responsible for all petroleum operations in the Soviet Union.

Under the Soviet regime geological surveys, which had been carried on even before World War I, were intensified in 1927, approximately coincidental with establishment of the First Five-Year Plan. The "Geological Committee," which had existed since 1882 but employed only 70 or 80 geologists before World War I, was reorganized in 1929 into the "Main Administration for Geology and Geodesy in the Supreme Council of the Political Economy of the U.S.S.R." In 1946 this organization became the Ministry of Geology. As a result of the planned co-operation of the State, industry, and science, 75 per cent of the entire area of the U.S.S.R. had been geologically explored by 1947.

In the field of geophysics Soviet scientists have readily adopted methods commonly used by the petroleum industry in the United States as soon as they recognized their practical value. Gravimetric, electric log, magnetometer, seismic, and geochemical methods are being used in the search for petroleum deposits. If there are weaknesses in Soviet petroleum technology, however, they are to be found in the field of drilling techniques, but improvement along these lines has been made. In the Baku region, for example, wells have been drilled deeper than 5000 meters, and a 4000-meter well has been drilled by one rig in one month, records that compare rather favorably with drilling achievements in the United States.

When the Soviet Government took over the petroleum industry, production had dropped to its lowest level since 1889. Under the New

Economic Policy (NEP), which was announced by Lenin in 1922, petroleum production began an upward surge. Ten years after the October Revolution the country's production exceeded its output in 1900, when Russia was the world's leading petroleum producer.

Planned development of the Soviet petroleum industry coincided with the beginning of the State-planned economy. During the first Five-Year Plan (1928–32), no less than 1.6 billion rubles was invested in the petroleum industry, and production increased from 11.8 to 21.6 million tons. Under the Second Five-Year Plan (1933–37), 2.5 billion rubles was placed at the disposal of the industry, and production plans called for 68.1 million tons by 1937. Actual output in 1937 was, however, only 27.1 million tons. The Third Five-Year Plan (1938–42) called for an output of 47.7 million tons by 1942. Interrupted by World War II, production in 1942 was only 31.8 million tons.

World War II caused a general decline in petroleum production, but by 1947 the downward trend had been arrested. The Fourth Five-Year Plan (1946–50), which called for an output of 35.4 million tons, was a great contrast to the high expectancies of the Second and Third Five-Year Plans and appears to have been based on a soberly realistic estimate of the country's petroleum possibilities. The planned production for 1950 was not only achieved, but actual production of 37.6 million tons exceeded the goal by more than 6 per cent. Although it is not possible to give the individual results with absolute certainty, there is a reasonable basis for assuming that the following figures come close to reality:

PETROLEUM PRODUCTION IN 1950

Petroleum Regions	*Output* (Tons)	*Per Cent of Total*
Baku	17,000,000	45.2
Grozny	1,800,000	4.8
Maikop	1,500,000	4.0
Dagestan	500,000	1.3
Georgia	120,000	0.3
Turkmen	1,250,000	3.3
Ukraine	330,000	0.9
Second Baku (Molotov, Ufa, Kuibyshev)	10,600,000	28.2
Emba	1,300,000	3.5
Ukhta-Pechora	800,000	2.1
Central Asia (Fergana Valley)	1,200,000	3.2
Sakhalin	1,200,000	3.2
TOTAL	37,600,000	100.0

These data show that the strategically vulnerable petroleum fields of the Caucasus still have superiority in the Soviet petroleum industry and are not purposely being neglected, as has been asserted by some commentators.

The rank of a petroleum industry is determined not only by its production capacity; the capacity of its refineries is also of great importance, since crude petroleum cannot be used as it is taken from the well. Complex refining processes are necessary to obtain the end products which modern industry demands.

The refineries that the Soviets took over from the Czarist regime were in part obsolete and in part rendered unusuable as a result of the war and the revolution. During the First Five-Year Plan refineries were obtained from abroad, particularly from the United States. Greater efforts were made to expand refinery capacity during the Second Five-Year Plan—new refineries with a total capacity of 7.7 million tons (about 54,000,000 barrels) a year were constructed. At the beginning of the Third Five-Year Plan about 77 per cent of the entire refining capacity was concentrated in the Baku region; 12 per cent was in Grozny, whose refineries also processed crude petroleum from Baku (the Grozny deposits having been greatly overestimated); and 5 per cent was in the Maikop region. In the course of the Third Five-Year Plan refining capacity again was greatly increased. With progressive development of petroleum production in the Second Baku, the Caucasus lost its former unequivocal superiority; new, modern refineries were built in Saratov, Syzran, Sterlitamak, Ishimbai, Tuimazy, Molotov, and Buguruslan. In addition, refineries were also constructed in the centers of petroleum consumption, that is, in Rostov, Stalingrad, Moscow, and Leningrad. By 1951 the Soviet Union had at least 66 refineries of various capacities. The total capacity of all plants is assumed to have been between 33 and 35 million tons (680,000 to 720,000 barrels per day).

Within the total refining capacity and of great importance in the Soviet Union is cracking capacity. Soviet crudes, excepting some from the northern Caucasus, yield under normal distillation only a small percentage of gasoline, generally between 5 and 10 per cent. To achieve a higher gasoline yield, construction of cracking facilities was begun in 1928, and by 1937 the cracking capacity is supposed to have been 9.25 million tons. In 1951 the country's cracking capacity is assumed to have been between 13 and 14 million tons.

A country's petroleum consumption has today become an infallible measure of the technical position of its political economy; from the level of the country's petroleum consumption, and especially from its consumption of fuel oil and lubricants, can be deduced the capacity of industry and the intensity of commerce. The low level of petroleum consumption during the Czarist regime reflected the low level of technical development of the Russian political economy. During the early stages of the Soviet regime, petroleum consumption remained low, while production steadily increased, which gave rise to petroleum exports. Under the First Five-Year Plan petroleum exports grew and reached a maximum in 1932, when more than 6 million tons was shipped out of the country. With the Second Five-Year Plan, however, a basic change took place; a conscious drive developed toward industrialization, motorization, and mechanization, which stimulated the growth of domestic consumption and necessarily brought about a decrease in petroleum exports. Domestic consumption has grown to a point today where it is barely covered by domestic production; for 1950 consumption of petroleum products may be considered to have been between 30 and 32 million tons.

Petroleum-Producing Regions

Part III, which reviews the individual petroleum-producing regions, begins with a discussion of petroleum, natural gas, and oil-shale reserves. On February 14, 1941, the Soviets introduced five classes of petroleum reserves, which range from those "determined with absolute certainty" to "possible supplies." Hassmann excludes several of these classes because they are too conjectural and concludes that Soviet petroleum reserves (presumably comparable to proved reserves in the United States) total about one billion tons. Natural gas reserves have been estimated by individual Soviet geologists at 700 to 800 billion cubic meters, which should be viewed with a certain amount of caution; but oil-shale reserves of 55 billion tons place the country in a class with the United States, Canada, Australia, and Manchuria as one of the most important oil-shale countries in the world.

The descriptions of each of the individual producing regions generally follow the same pattern—the location and a short history of the region; the controlling trust or association; a listing of the producing fields, with a brief reference to geological features; refineries; pipelines; major features of production; and the transportation facilities. Included are 14 small maps showing fields, refineries, and major pipelines in each of the producing regions.

Problems of the Soviet Petroleum Industry

In Part IV various problems of the Soviet petroleum industry are discussed. The author believes that the problem confronting the over-all world petroleum industry—whether petroleum production can match rapidly growing petroleum requirements—also confronts the Soviets. He finds it manifestly difficult, however, to determine the petroleum requirements of the U.S.S.R. The validity of comparing petroleum requirements of other countries, especially the United States, with those of the U.S.S.R. is questioned, because of different economic systems and ways of life. Moreover, a greater part of the Soviet Union's energy demands, which in other countries are satisfied by petroleum, is supplied by coal and electricity. Hassmann claims that, if the increase of world petroleum supply and the increase of world petroleum needs were compared systematically with the performance and requirements of the Soviet petroleum industry without cognizance of the special Soviet economic, political, and sociological relations, a false conclusion would be reached.

The author's determination of Soviet petroleum requirements is predicated on the principle that the petroleum needs in any domestic economy are based on the same factors in all countries, the only difference being the relative importance of each factor. Analyzed are the size of the economic sphere, the number of people, the level of the nation's technology, and finally the nature of the economy. Despite the constriction of civilian requirements, the current mineral-oil needs of commerce, agriculture, industry, and the Soviet army have passed the 40-million-ton mark. To maintain the pace of the aggressive development of its economic policy, the U.S.S.R. must increase its production of petroleum to 60 million tons by 1960, which may be taken to represent the administration's conception of the minimum requirements of the Soviet economy in the next 10 years.

The quantity of petroleum the U.S.S.R. had at its disposal in 1950 totaled about 44 million tons. The separate items are as follows (to facilitate the summary there has been no differentiation between crude petroleum and refined products):

	(Tons)
Soviet production	
Petroleum	37,600,000
Shale oil	400,000
Synthetics	1,000,000
Total	39,000,000
Soviet imports	
Petroleum	4,000,000
Synthetics	1,000,000
Total	5,000,000
GRAND TOTAL	44,000,000

A careful evaluation indicates that these quantities have been disposed of in the following manner:

Soviet consumption	(Tons)
Industry	12,000,000
Commerce	10,000,000
Agriculture	9,000,000
Household uses	1,000,000
Soviet army	8,000,000
Total	40,000,000
Exports to China and Korea	4,000,000
GRAND TOTAL	44,000,000

It may be assumed that the main petroleum demands of Soviet industry have been generally satisfied, but if the tempo of its industrial development is to increase—there is no doubt that the Eastern Block has a variety of raw materials as well as an unsaturated market for them—its future petroleum requirements must be calculated to increase significantly. It should be kept in mind that Soviet industrial production, in relation to the world's industrial production, has sextupled in the last 40 years—from 2.3 per cent in 1913 to 14.2 per cent in 1950. If this upward development continues and if Soviet industry cannot satisfy its energy needs from other sources, the question of an adequate petroleum supply soon becomes the gravest of problems.

In the western world today the Soviet army is frequently referred to as being "super-motorized"; it is rumored that its petroleum needs, even in peace, can no longer be satisfied. Hassmann claims that such a conclusion has no basis in fact. Of the 175 divisions comprising the Soviet army in 1950, only about 50 were motorized. Because of its extraordinarily long boundaries the U.S.S.R. has divided its land armies into six autonomous groups, which have their headquarters in Leningrad, Minsk, Odessa, Tiflis, Tashkent, and Khabarovsk. Each of these army groups is to carry on independent operations in case of necessity. For such an arrangement to be effective, each must establish a self-sustaining economic basis, and certainly a self-sustaining petroleum basis, if each army group is to be really independent in its supply. If nearly one-fourth of the 1950 total petroleum production had been placed at the disposal of the Soviet army, such a quantity probably would have contributed significantly to the army's stockpile. With stabilization of world peace, it is very possible that the Soviet army could manage with much less.

Space does not permit individual discussion of each of the Soviet petroleum industry's problems as seen by Hassmann, but a listing of the problems indicates the scope of Part IV:

1. The mineral-oil requirements of the Soviet Union.
2. Can the mineral-oil requirements of the Soviet Union be readily compared with those of other countries?

3. Could the mineral-oil requirements of the Soviet Union be constricted without economic-political damages?
4. Meeting the mineral-oil requirements of the Soviet Union.
5. Is the petroleum industry aided or hindered by the Soviet economic system?
6. Do Soviet geological conditions and the personnel situation favor an increase in its petroleum industry?
7. Is the steel supply of the Soviet petroleum industry assured?
8. Can synthetic oil production make a substantial contribution to the mineral-oil supply?
9. To what extent can the Soviet mineral-oil requirements be covered through imports?

The Soviet Union and the Middle East

The book concludes with a short epilogue entitled "The Soviet Union and the Middle East," wherein the volume of Middle East petroleum reserves is discussed in relation to United States, European, and Soviet interests. Soviet control of this rich petroleum region, which lies directly before the door of the Soviet Union and is currently under Anglo-American control, would solve and settle forever all supply difficulties and petroleum bottlenecks in the Soviet Union. With these considerations in mind, the current troubles in Iran assume an extraordinarily realistic meaning. The Soviets have long attempted unsuccessfully to gain binding petroleum concessions in Iran and consider it to be in the interests of the Soviet Union "to eliminate the Anglo-American sphere of interest in the Middle East." Inasmuch as the Soviet Union is empowered, on the basis of an Iranian-Soviet agreement, to send troops into the country to protect Iran "as soon as a third power threatens Persian independence," serious entanglements could easily result from these overlapping interests. If the petroleum production of the Middle East is someday added to the Soviet petroleum production, it would result in such an increase in Soviet industrial power that the political future of the world would thereby be changed.

Evaluation and Criticisms

To evaluate the reliability of this work is, in some ways, nearly as difficult as was its original preparation. Since 1938 no truly reliable data that could be used for comparison and reference have been released. In all fairness, any treatment of a national petroleum industry from its historical foundations to its current problems of such a magnitude as that of the U.S.S.R. would probably touch certain aspects of the industry too lightly to be wholly satisfactory for all readers. Nevertheless, Hassmann's subject is so important that a judgment must be made.

A weighty point neglected by Hassmann is the decreasing importance of petroleum relative to coal in the Soviet Union's Fourth Five-Year Plan. According to the Soviet figures, petroleum production in 1950 was 37.6 million tons and coal production 261 million tons, or 0.144 ton of petroleum per ton of coal. By 1960 petroleum production was to increase to 60 million tons, while coal output was to reach 500 million tons. If these plans had materialized, the ratio of petroleum production to coal output would have been 0.120 ton of petroleum per ton of coal. In other words, the importance of petroleum in the Soviet economy relative to coal would have decreased 16.7 per cent, a trend that is just the reverse of what has been taking place in the world energy picture over the past several decades and what appears to be the trend in the present decade.

These data immediately pose the question of why Soviet economic and industrial planners chose to de-emphasize petroleum relative to coal in the nation's future energy consumption pattern. Answers to such a question are admittedly speculative, but there are numerous reports that the situation in the petroleum industry is troubled. This relative de-emphasis might be due to shortages of such steel goods as drill, casing, and line pipe; to supply adequately the steel requirements of the petroleum industry in the process of rapid expansion may have been considered by the planners as secondary to meeting armament needs. Another possibility is that the Soviet Minister of Petroleum is somewhat reluctant to undertake an increased exploratory drilling program. In any country the increasing of exploratory drilling by itself does not guarantee increased production. The possibility of failure and the disastrous effects on responsible personnel may have led the planners to take a less optimistic position toward petroleum than toward coal, the very nature of which involves less risk in development plans. Moreover, under the Soviet economic system there does not appear to be any provision analogous to risk capital in the United States which has played such an important role in the development of the United States petroleum industry Nor should the possibility be overlooked altogether that the U.S.S.R. does not have such abundant petroleum reserves as reported so frequently in both Soviet and western geological circles. It should be noted that most of the western evaluations of Soviet petroleum reserves have been based on data obtained from regional geologic studies made before 1938, and very little on data obtained from geophysical work.

Of particular interest is the Soviet Fifth Five-Year Plan (1951–55), which was released during the second half of 1952. By 1955 crude petroleum production is to be 70 million tons, but the 1960 goal for coal production remained unchanged at 500 million tons. Under this plan the position of petroleum relative to coal has been altered markedly and is now more comformable with the world energy pattern. Again, one can only speculate on the reasons for the change. Whether the new planned output of 70 million tons of crude petroleum a year by 1955 has been based on a realistic evaluation of petroleum resources and the ability of the industry to achieve this level, prescribed as a target toward which the industry should aim, or published as propaganda for home consumption, cannot be ascertained. What can be stated, however, is that a much higher production level than that reached in 1950 is imperative if many other parts of the Fifth Five-Year Plan are to be achieved.

For a more balanced appraisal of the ability of the Soviet petroleum industry to meet the requirements of the country, more attention should have been given to the refining problems stemming from the chemical composition of some of the crudes from Second Baku and other eastern fields. Such problems extend into the important question of aviation-gasoline manufacture and supply. Related to these problems are the petrochemical industries, which in the United States are expanding rapidly not only in volume of output but also into the production of vital components for modern warfare. According to J. C. Tolpin of the Standard Oil Company (Indiana), enough information is available on some of these problems to make possible a more balanced treatment.

Among the minor shortcomings of the book is the petroleum supply and disposal balance drawn up for the year 1950. In making this summary Hassmann readily admits no differentiation between crude petroleum and refined products. Sacrificed for the sake of convenience in the summary are the quantities of petroleum used for such purposes as field operations, fuel in pipeline pump stations, and refining operations. In addition are such losses as evaporation losses from storage tanks and those inherent in refining operations. In the United States, where close attention is given to efficiency and economy of operations, such uses and losses normally represent about 6.5 per cent of the year's total production. Balance sheets of the year's operations made up for the entire petroleum industry by the Bureau of Mines, United States Department of the Interior, and the American Petroleum Institute carefully account for these quantities, so that demand or disposal can be calculated with a minimum of error. In view of the numerous reports of Soviet operational inefficiencies and their difficulties in controlling losses both in storing and transporting petroleum, the uses and losses that account for 6.5 per cent of United States annual production may be estimated conservatively at 10 per cent for the U.S.S.R. Soviet consumption and exports to China and Korea total, in Hassmann's summary, 44 million tons, or precisely the same as total supply. Since crude petroleum for domestic, industrial, and military uses is not consumed as such but in the form of refined products, the supply and disposal balance as drawn up is impossible.

On at least one point the reviewer believes the author to be incorrect. In Part IV Hassmann discusses the steel requirements of the Soviet petroleum industry and arrives at an average steel requirement of one ton of steel for each 32 tons of crude petroleum produced. In calculating this figure he used the total inland requirements of the United States petroleum industry prepared in 1950 by the National Petroleum Council. The figures appearing in the text are as follows:

STEEL REQUIREMENTS OF THE UNITED STATES PETROLEUM INDUSTRY IN 1950

Uses	*Million Tons*	*Per Cent*
Production	2.8	33.0
Transport	1.4	17.0
Refining	0.5	6.0
Distribution	1.8	21.0
Natural gas production	2.0	23.0
TOTAL	8.5	100.0

Dividing the total United States petroleum production for 1950 (about 270 million tons in round figures) by the total steel requirements (8.5 million tons) Hassmann arrives at one ton of steel for 32 tons of crude petroleum. Included in the 8.5 million tons of steel, however, is 2 million tons for natural gas production, but no corresponding adjustment for natural gas production was made in the crude production total. In the above figures steel requirements for petroleum alone in 1950 were 6.5 million tons. The proper ratio of steel requirements to crude petroleum is, therefore, one ton of steel for 41.5 tons of crude petroleum. Hassmann then calculates 1950 steel requirements for the Soviet petroleum industry, basing the calculation on the 1:32 ratio and a production of 39 million tons of crude petroleum, shale oil, and synthetic liquid fuels. He arrives at a total steel requirement of 1,250,000 tons. Actual steel requirements are suggested to have been somewhat higher, since the industry was undertaking much new construction. As a maximum limit he suggests 2,000,000 tons of steel, which appears to be overly generous in view of the method of calculation. Nevertheless, his conclusion that the Soviet petroleum industry takes a smaller share of the national steel production than the United States petroleum industry takes of the United States total steel production appears to be sound.

Hassmann's work is considered to be a valuable contribution to the meager literature on Soviet industry. With respect to Soviet petroleum, this work is the most complete presentation of its geography and economics known to the reviewer. It should not, however, be inferred that these remarks constitute an unqualified endorsement of the book, for it has limitations, some of which have been pointed out. It is to be hoped that others studying various phases of Soviet industry, particularly the petroleum industry, will examine critically all performance claims before accepting them as accomplishments.

54. *Useless Marshlands Yield Rich Louisiana Sulphur* *

Minerals must be exploited at the place where they occur; this fact often results in the development of mining communities in odd and remote corners of the earth. After his utilization and depletion of richer and better located mineral deposits, man is often forced into more adverse areas. Technology has made possible the exploitation of many of these deposits. Sparkman describes conditions in a new sulphur area in the coastal swamps of southern Louisiana, an excellent example of a mineral boom. Frequently such communities are ephemeral but are characteristic of much mineral exploitation—a nonrenewable resource.

Sulphur is the magic word in Louisiana today, focusing new attention to Louisiana's sea-level swamplands, an area opulent in minerals, farms, furs and sea food.

Here, downriver from New Orleans, marshes of muck dropped long ago by a tail-swishing Mississippi are entwined into islets by water hyacinths, saw grass, and cane. The biggest increase in sulphur mining in 20 years is reaching completion. New mines, built at a cost of $25,000,000, are just now achieving full output to feed a growing world demand for versatile sulphur. Keyed to a nationwide industrial growth, this increase is reflected locally in a prodigious boom in all commerce and industry.

New concepts in mining are taking shape here—where coppery skies, torrential downpours, and the silt of the "Father of Waters" guarantee plant food for millions of muskrats, thousands of otters, possums, minks, weasels, crayfish, eels, snakes, bass, oysters, shrimps, and crabs. Mining

* James K. Sparkman, "Useless Marshlands Yield Rich Louisiana Sulphur," *Christian Science Monitor,* Tuesday, May 18, 1954, p. 9.
The author is a staff correspondent for the *Christian Science Monitor.*

techniques now carry ashore the most usable elements of Gulf of Mexico waters, and push "land" out into the brilliant-surfaced, sandy-green Gulf to help man garner mineral wealth for global use.

Few other spots on earth would once have been picked by engineers, company executives or workmen (or their wives) as less desirable for driving down the foundations of an economic empire.

Forbidding Landscape

Few landscapes appear more forbidding. Here men sink waist-deep into what should be solid ground. Piling timbers sink half their length by their own weight before a pile driver can move up to strike them a single blow. Silt marshes, ready to swallow machinery by rust or suction, seem to contain only the colonies of fur animals that have made this the No. 1 pelt state. Here, too, invisible mosquitoes make the night alive with their humming wings, and, in motionless pools that make subdivisions of the bogs, a bass flashes silvery in the moonlight as it slides upward toward an insect hovering in the night.

Yet this, man has found, is one of nature's richest storehouses. Below hundreds of feet of quicksand bogs, bubbling here and there with pockets of lethal, explosive fumes, lie salt domes, each potentially rich in oil, sulphur, and gas, each a future wealth of mineral salts when world demand warrants mining them.

Add to this flat, grassy scene the genie of cheap, abundant, energy from nearby Texas gas wells. Add the ingenuity of modern prospectors armed with sonic and electronic tools to probe silty depths beyond reach of pick or shovel. Sketch in the skill of drillers, pipe fitters, welders, piling experts, and barge skinners.

The result: A vigorous industry in salt for chemical industries; an industry in oil for homes, highways, sea lanes, and skyways; and golden sulphur pure enough as it flows from the mine for all but the most exacting users.

Spurred by Necessity

Dollarwise, Louisiana is first an oil state (though third in United States oil production) known today as the spot where petroleum miners, spurred by necessity, pushed beyond the marshes into hurricane-belt Gulf waters in their quest for "black gold." Spending millions in experiments to reproduce inland drilling conditions with spider-legged ocean platforms, drillers now sink mile-long pipes through 50 feet of salt water before entering the ocean floor.

The Pelican State, once synonymous with cotton, depends today on agriculture as well as mineral wealth, on steaming fields of sugar cane, marshland rice, and yams. The state has gained fame for its fish, shrimp, oysters, and, naturally, for its table recipes, a happy blend of French, Spanish, southern "cracker," and "old mammy" styles.

Sulphur miners must carry whole factories with them to drilling sites. Wresting out sulphur requires a village of people, too. So TV, frozen foods, schools, and livable homes are on the march southward.

Each year, this land, at the tips of roads and rails snaking south from New Orleans, serves as a better model of how industry and comforts can move farther into the bogs. Each season sees further attacks into the bog-bottomed, wave-topped Gulf.

Here in Port Sulphur, the news is not that a bright, clean community has been built by dredging up seven feet of sand, but that this town is now the headquarters for a ponderous push into new sulphur regions, with floating and land-based mines built on spots where watery bogs blend into muddy water.

Sulphur Sky Line

Port Sulphur is a Freeport Sulphur Company town, where a $3,000,000 block of solid sulphur dominates the skyline much like a great pyramid towering above a desert. Since brownish-yellow sulphur is odorless, this stockpile is not objectionable.

From Port Sulphur, workmen and mining engineers leave green-lawned, white homes daily to ride diesel cruisers down a broad canal to work at Grand Ecaille. From Port Sulphur, too, speed cruisers carrying mining men down to the company's newest plant below Pilot Town below the end of the highway and the rough-track railroad line. By air, engineers leave Port Sulphur westward to the company's floating plant at Bay Ste. Elaine, or toward its unfinished diggings in a cypress swamp near Chacahoula.

Sulphur was not always plentiful in America, nor was it always, as now, one of the cheapest chemicals—still only a cent a pound (by the ton) despite inflation and war demands. For in America, sulphur like oil, lies below bogs impossible to shaft mine. Discovered in 1867 clinging to oil-drilling bits, the sulphur defied miners for a quarter century.

Today, even the newest mines still use the basic method invented in 1894 by Dr. Herman Frasch, a method that has made the United States so independent in sulphur that the vital chemical remained unrationed and plentiful even in World War II. Dr. Frasch's suggestion was simple: mine sulphur not as a solid, but as a liquid.

Tribute to Genius

Tribute today to his genius are the chimneys here and there along the Texas-Louisiana coast showing where natural gas is burned to heat water under pressure to a temperature above its normal boiling point. Flames, too, generate electric power to pump the superheated water, and compressed air, down into concentric pipes pushed deep into the salt-dome sulphur beds. Melted into a brown liquid by the heat, the heavy sulphur seeps from lime rock downward to collecting points and is pressure pumped to the surface. A thousand feet above, on the surface, sinking soil spots show where the sulphur has been removed.

Tribute also are the acre-square blocks of solid sulphur, golden landmarks of sulphur mining when seen from the air. While cooling into these blocks, the liquid sulphur frees gaseous impurities absorbed underground.

Blasted and shoveled from these piles, sulphur (usually made into sulphuric acid by burning sulphur inside tanks) goes into fertilizers, insect sprays, plastics, paper making, and almost every type of industry. Thousand-ton Thermos-bottle type barges bring liquid sulphur from distant wells to rebuild stockpiles as crushed sulphur is shipped away in gondolas, barges, and ocean-going steamers. From nearby wells snake the insulated pipes to the stockpile yards—yards themselves built up of solid sulphur in turn supported by 75,000 pilings. ("Sulphur is cheaper than concrete," a Freeport manager explained.)

In both Garden Island Bay and Bay Ste. Elaine mines, Freeport has made use of all the latest tricks of mining. Narrow, dredged waterway "roads," when seen from the air, show where drill rigs are now floated, not rolled, to new drill sites. Though expensive, this method is far cheaper than building roads over the half-water swamps, say Freeport engineers. Oil drillers do the same; from each drill-barge "street" spiral telltale tracks made by the pontoon-tired "swamp buggies" that carried prospectors over land, muck, and water to pick out the best drill site.

Off-shore Mining Nears

Two factors are bringing off-shore sulphur mining closer. Sulphur domes under solid ground now are ever harder to find and usually, when found, have less of the yellow mineral than did early finds. Also, Gulf waves are steadily etching away the bogs and marshes, since the Mississippi is no longer free to lash its tail from Alabama to Texas as evidence shows it did in early years, depositing rich beds of new silt in the process. Upstream damming and soil-conservation measures may be cutting its flow, as well, while engineering freezes its course.

For the subdelta region, movement to the swamp and tidelands means increasing revenues and hints of greater prosperity ahead.

With the state changing rapidly, its temper and ways of living spurred by regional migrations of cattle, cotton, and population, mineral wealth bids largely to serve as a foundation for other, equally prosperous ventures: boosted truck farming, increased citrus raising, perhaps, new ranges for hot-weather cattle, and a new chemical industry keyed to export trade.

Hints of this are as solid as the optimism visible in New Orleans—land prices here are at record levels. They equal those in many blue-ribbon agricultural regions of the nation. Growing interest is shown in southbound bridges and highways into the area, and there is an eager search by industry for choice river-bank spots south of New Orleans.

All this focuses the forces that have kept the Mississippi mouth important since the earliest days of American growth. Louisiana, the outlet of mid-continent commerce and now a gateway to South America, has found its crossroads swamps rich in minerals. In making fullest use of and dovetailing all its advantages, the state, and other Gulf areas, now have an opportunity for growth to world prominence.

55. *The Witwatersrand* *

Gold mining seems to have an irresistible attraction for man. The lure of gold often has been responsible for the development of mining communities in remote and inhospitable parts of the world. If no other means of livelihood is present many of these communities become "ghost towns" after the gold is exhausted. The famous Witwatersrand of South Africa is a major exception. Petterson examines the nature of this mining district and its impact upon the economy, land use, and population of the area.

Among the great gold fields of the world, the Witwatersrand of South Africa stands out for its uniqueness. Here the discovery of gold has so

* Donald R. Petterson, "The Witwatersrand," quoted with omissions from *Economic Geography,* Vol. 27, 1951, pp. 209–221.

The author is an Assistant Professor of Geography, Northwestern University. His primary interests are economic geography and Africa, and he has made two research trips to South Africa.

changed the economic geography that where once roamed a handful of semi-nomadic cattlemen there is now a vigorously growing industrial and manufacturing community. No other discovery of gold has wrought such a change. Other gold rushes have attracted settlers and helped to populate otherwise empty areas, such as California, Siberia, or Australia. But in none of these has the influence of gold mining been so forceful or lasting as to affect the entire nation. In every other gold mining area the mines have sooner or later declined in both relative and absolute importance.

In South Africa, however, the nation's economic life has aligned itself towards the site of the gold mines. An infertile range of hills dividing the waters of the Vaal from the Limpopo River in a sub-humid portion of the country has become the national center of industry, manufacturing, transportation, and finance. The purpose of this paper is both to examine the Witwatersrand in comparison with other gold producing areas in the world and to discuss the changes it has wrought upon the surrounding area and the nation. . . .

Before the Discovery of Gold

Three groups of people, the Bantu, the Boer, and the British, have successively occupied the region of the Witwatersrand. Only the British, however, mined the gold, and in so doing they changed the area from one of pastoralism to one of urban industry. The Bantu, the original settler, and the Boer, his conqueror, wandered freely about the broad and treeless High Veld in search of pasture. To these people the Witwatersrand (Ridge of the White Waters) was but a barren, wind-swept ridge of low hills rising above the veld grasslands. As such it was little desired and little sought.

The Witwatersrand is located in the northern portion of the High Veld about 800 miles northeast of Capetown. The gently rolling surrounding country, known as the High Veld, varies in elevation from four to six thousand feet above sea level. At the northern edge of the High Veld is the Witwatersrand, extending like an inverted "S" for about 60 miles from Randfontein on the west to Springs on the east. The ridge varies in width from two to seven miles, except the eastern edge which spreads out in a wedge-shaped fashion to a width of 18 miles. Towards the south of the Witwatersrand the streams drain into the Atlantic Ocean via the Vaal and Orange Rivers, while to the north streams empty into the Indian Ocean by way of the Crocodile and Limpopo Rivers. Most of the streams immediately adjacent to the Witwatersrand are intermittent (dry during the winter) making them poor sources of water. . . .

The original Bantu inhabitants and their successors, the Boer settlers, found the High Veld around the Witwatersrand covered with grass which extended from the Karoo Desert on the south to the lower and warmer savannas of the north. The prairie and chernozem soil groups which developed on the High Veld in response to the climate and vegetation were potentially productive. Here in a grassland comparable to the Argentine Pampas, the American Great Plains, or the Siberian Steppes, roamed the Bantu and later the Boer, with their great herds of cattle and sheep, ever in search of better pasture.

The Discovery of Gold

When the first Boer settlers came to the Witwatersrand shortly after 1836, they paid scant heed to the prospect of finding gold, seeking instead pasture land. But in 1867 diamonds were discovered in Kimberley, about 250 miles southwest of the Witwatersrand, and professional prospectors and miners immigrated here from all over the world. By 1886 Cecil Rhodes had begun consolidating the diamond holdings into a single company, setting free numerous prospectors and miners to wander elsewhere around the High Veld in search of mineral wealth.

The Main Reef of the Witwatersrand gold-bearing conglomerate was discovered in March, 1886, by George Walker. Further prospecting was rapid, and within the next few months the outcrop of conglomerate beds was found to be continuous for about 60 miles, except for breaks at Witpoortje and Boksburg Gaps. This main gold reef was defined as a bed of conglomerate gold-bearing pyrite ore, varying in thickness but with a maximum width of between six and eight inches, and dipping south at an angle of about 30 degrees.

The Witwatersrand gold reef is unlike any other great gold mining region. There are no glittering nuggets as in Australia, nor the meteoric bursts of the Yukon placers. Instead, this gold reef is a conglomerate composed of rounded quartz pebbles embedded in a fine grained, hard quartzitic matrix. Within the matrix are found the gold particles, usually closely associated with grains of pyrites. This gold reef is remarkably uniform throughout the extent of the Witwatersrand. Other mining regions have flourished, only to become derelict ghost towns when the veins, once heavy with gold, abruptly ended. On the Witwatersrand, however, the uniformity and extent of the gold-bearing ore have insured both a great and an enduring mining industry.

At present the number of tons of gold-bearing ore on the Witwatersrand is yet to be calculated and these mines rank as the richest in the world. On the other hand, however, the Witwatersrand deposits might be classed as the poorest in the world because the average gold content per ton of ore mined is low. In 1946, 4.02 pennyweight of gold was produced per ton of ore mined. In the United States the average richness of gold ore is from three to six times as great. But rich gold-bearing ores are actually rare throughout the world and the poor, but uniform, ores of the Witwatersrand yield tremendous outputs of gold. Thus the problem on the Witwatersrand is not to find the rich gold-bearing ore, but to make the mining of the poor ore profitable.

The Development of Gold Mining

The Witwatersrand discoveries occurred at a fortunate time in history. They were accessible immediately to the capital amassed in Kimberley; the world demand for gold was critically exceeding the supply; and technology had developed to the point where these low grade ores could profitably be mined. Consequently, the development of gold mining was both rapid and extensive.

• • • • •

A low rate of increase of temperature with depth, averaging 1° Fahrenheit for each 200 feet, contributed to economic mining at levels as far as 10,000 feet beneath the surface. Coal was quickly discovered at Boksburg on the Witwatersrand and later, in 1910, at Witbank, 70 miles northeast, which assured the gold mines of a cheap, available power supply. Hence, Witwatersrand mining soon came under the professional guidance of engineers and technicians and the lone prospector from California or Australia quickly vanished.

Urban Development on the Witwatersrand

Just as the goddess Athena sprang fully formed from the head of her father Zeus, so it might be said that the several urban communities of the Witwatersrand developed almost instantaneously. Here was no orderly measured growth of communities from village to town to city. Instead, several thousand miners encamped on the Witwatersrand before an official proclamation declared the existence of town sites. It was from these camps that the present Witwatersrand communities developed into the several municipalities which are all closely integrated by their primary interest in gold mining and tied together by common transportation, communication, and power and water supply systems. (Fig. 20)

In no other country in the world have the gold mines been centralized within a single area such as the Witwatersrand. The advantages of this centralization have had a direct bearing upon the development of gold mining here on a large scale. Little effort is wasted in diffused and decentralized control spread over long distances. Instead, both management and capital can be centralized in Johannesburg where are found the head offices of the mining companies, the banks, and the stock exchange. Similarly, the several Witwatersrand communities enjoy the advantages of centralization as witnessed by their joint efforts in supplying water and power, transportation, and communications.

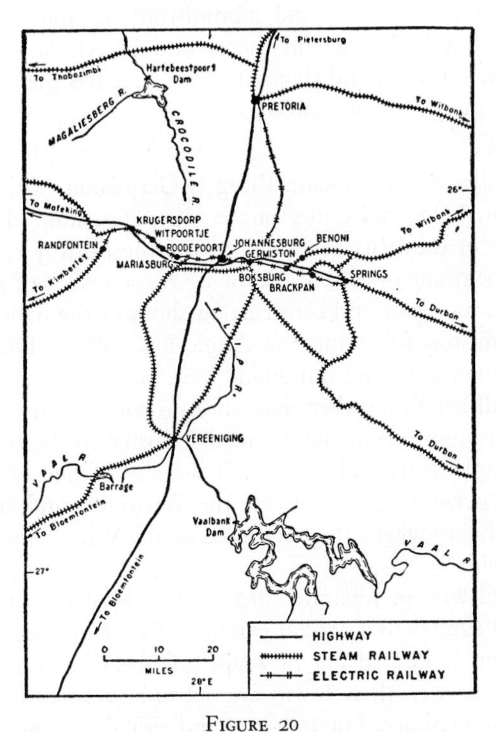

FIGURE 20
The towns of the Witwatersrand in relation to surrounding country.

Gold appears to be the sole reason for the existence of the Witwatersrand urban community. Few natural advantages exist which might offset some of the more obvious disadvantages. For example, the Witwatersrand itself is part of the watershed between the Vaal and Limpopo Rivers which makes the problem of an adequate water supply acute. Furthermore, this gold mining community is not located in the center of any significant agricultural district. On the other hand, the Witwatersrand is easily accessible by highway or railroad. Its situation, moreover, near the border between the High and Low Veld gives it the advantage of serving both regions. Finally, the Witwatersrand enjoys a warm climate, neither excessively hot nor extremely cold. None of these features created the Witwatersrand community, but they certainly fostered its development and growth.

The largest of the Witwatersrand communities is Johannesburg, located approximately in the center of the area. Here is the "nerve-center" of the Witwatersrand and of the gold industry. Here are found such functions as commerce, banking, and administration. Johannesburg is the largest city in South Africa and the second in Africa. With its high buildings, street railways, and shopping district, it has the external aspects of an American city of comparable size.

. . . . .

About six miles east of Johannesburg is Germiston, with a population of 131,197 in 1946, the rail center of the Witwatersrand. Here the principal rail route of the Witwatersrand crosses the railway connecting Pretoria with Bloemfontein and Capetown. As a result of this juncture, the largest railway repair and construction shops of the nation were established in Germiston following the Anglo-Boer War. During the first World War, small arms and munitions were manufactured in Germiston. From this small beginning there has since grown a manufacturing center in Germiston ranging from the garment industry to the manufacture of agricultural implements. Here, also, is the site of one of the principal electric power generating stations for the Witwatersrand, as well as the Rand Gold Refinery where all gold mined on the Witwatersrand is refined before being sold.

Both east and west of Johannesburg are the smaller towns of the Witwatersrand, all similar to a certain extent in size, function, and situation. Since each town is located on the main gold-bearing reef, with mining as its principal activity, these towns are not to be regarded as commuting suburbs of Johannesburg, but rather as individual communities centered upon a particular mine or group of mines, and joined with other communities by a closely knit system of transportation and public utilities.

. . . . .

Effects upon South African Economy

Gradually in the past 50 years the Witwatersrand community has made itself felt upon the surrounding regions, the nation, and the continent. Rail transportation has centered upon the Witwatersrand, heavy heat and power industries have been attracted to the area, and South Africa has changed from a pastoral into an increasingly industrial nation.

Beginning during the first World War and accentuated by the last War, there has been a tendency for gold no longer to dominate the entire industrial economy of South Africa. It is natural that the beginning of the heavy heat and power industries should be in response to the markets created on the Witwatersrand and that these industries be originally located close to the gold mines. Recently, however, the heat and power industries near the Witwatersrand have begun to serve a national market as well as the Witwatersrand. This would seem to indicate the continued growth of an industrial nucleus in South Africa centering about the Witwatersrand.

Thirty miles south of the Witwatersrand on the banks of the Vaal River is the industrial city of Vereeniging. Here extensive coal measures combined with a constant water supply from the river permit electricity to be generated from steam in one of the nation's largest electrical power stations. Some of this electricity is used locally by the two Vereeniging plants producing steel from scrap, most of which comes from the railway shops at Germiston, on the Witwatersrand. The steel is now being marketed not only on the Witwatersrand, but throughout the Union as well. In 1945 several Vereeniging residents pointed out to the author that in the future the heavy heat and power industry of South Africa would be located there because of the abundant coal supply, proximity to the Witwatersrand market, and the good rail connections with the rest of the country as well as with the British colonies in the north. Plans are now under way for the establishment of a carefully organized industrial community in Vereeniging.

Another industrial nucleus is established 40 miles north of the Witwatersrand at Pretoria, the administrative capital of the Union. Here the South African Iron and Steel Corporation, Ltd., began steel production in 1934. The iron ore comes from the extensive hematite deposits of Thabazimbi (mountain of iron), 157 miles northwest of Pretoria, the limestone comes from the Pretoria quarries, and coke is made locally from coal mined at Witbank, 50 miles to the east. At present, most of the Pretoria steel is consumed on the Witwatersrand by either the Germiston railway shops or the gold mines. During the second World War, however, small arms and munitions were manufactured in Pretoria, and, following the War, Pretoria steel is gradually being marketed throughout the nation.

Effects upon Agricultural Land Use

The development of the Witwatersrand has wrought an equally profound change upon the use of the agricultural land of the adjacent High Veld. No longer is this grassland area used by the inhabitants for the production of cattle. This has been superseded by truck gardening and maize (corn) production. Though agriculture on the High Veld has not been able completely to supply the demands of the Witwatersrand market for these products, changes in the use of the land have been profound.

Two irrigation districts have been created in the vicinity of the Witwatersrand, primarily to supply fresh vegetables. The Vaal River valley, 30 miles south, has been the site of a truck gardening area since the end of the first World War when a system of barrages and dams was begun. The other truck gardening area serving the Witwatersrand is located 40 miles north, in the Magaliesberg Valley. Here the Union Government inaugurated an elaborate settlement scheme in 1924, following the construction of the Hartebeestepoort Dam.

Though attempts were made throughout the entire High Veld to change from a pastoral to a commercial agricultural land use, much of the region was found due to insufficient rainfall to be unsuitable for crop cultivation. Only in the "Maize Triangle" of the Prairie Soil Group between Mafeking, Carolina, and Ladybrand is commercial agriculture practiced over any considerable area. Nevertheless, only 15 per cent of the total land is under cultivation so there is little similarity to the American Corn Belt. In the latter region the average output is over 20 bags (each of 200 pounds) of corn per acre, whereas the South African Maize Triangle production averages between four and five bags per acre. A winter wheat crop, however, adds considerably to the total cereal production here. . . .

The change in the agricultural land use wrought by the Witwatersrand markets, the accessibility to world markets via the railway, and the stimulus from Government agricultural subsidies has also had serious effects on the arable land. Soil erosion has begun and the most lasting and valuable of the national resources is fast wasting away. In 1944, Hugh H. Bennett of the United States Soil Conservation Service cautioned the Union against this rapid loss of the soil and advised stringent measures of control. Until such action is taken and the High Veld arable land is used extensively rather than intensively, the soil will continue to erode.

Effects on the Population Pattern

The great industrial structure of the Witwatersrand has acted as a magnet, drawing rural population from all of southern Africa towards the mines. Few European children remain on the farms where they were born, turning instead towards the Witwatersrand and mining. Among the Bantu population the problem is even more acute, for the majority of Bantu males leave their native village at least once during their life to serve an 18-month term in the mines. Many of the vices and few of the virtues of urbanization are thus brought back to the Bantu villages and local tribal life is rapidly becoming disorganized and broken. Thus the population of South Africa is shifting and tending to center around the Witwatersrand, resulting in the "Native" and "Poor White" problems.

Of these two problems, the former is perhaps the more serious in its ramifications. The gold mines, in order to operate on the small margin of profit allowed by the low grade gold-bearing ore, must have a constant supply of cheap, unskilled labor. To insure a constant source of Bantu labor, a system of direct taxation has been inaugurated whereby every Bantu who has reached 18 years of age must pay a personal tax, known as the General Tax, of one pound per year. Thus the Bantu labor complement required by the gold mines is assured.

At the Witwatersrand gold mines "almost all of the manual work is performed by Natives (Bantu) under the supervision of white men (Europeans)." Furthermore, Bantu wages are limited by law, for only thus is the labor cost per ton of ore mined kept within the narrow margins of profit. Such a labor structure in gold mining is without parallel today. The ancient mines were based on forced labor, as were the gold mining activities of the Spanish Conquistadores. But the more recent gold mining industries of California, Australia, and the Yukon have all had a free labor policy. On the Witwatersrand, however, a caste system has evolved, and the Bantu is born to serve and the European to direct.

From this rigid caste system there has also arisen the "Poor White Problem." Since the time of Paul Kruger the great Boer farms have rapidly dwindled in size as they have been divided among succeeding generations. Consequently, the grandchildren of the Transvaal Republic Burghers found themselves on farms too small and too poor to gain a reasonable livelihood. The dispossessed European might desire to become an unskilled laborer, but is prevented from doing so by custom and law. The labor caste system developed with the Witwatersrand gold mines, wherein the European directs and the Bantu serves, does not allow for poor Europeans or unskilled Europeans. The "Poor White Problem" grows increasingly serious with time.

Summary

In the early settlement of South Africa the coastal ports of Capetown, Durban, Port Elizabeth, and East London were the chief focal points and population centers. In 1836 the Great Trek northward occurred and Pretoria of the Transvaal and Bloemfontein of the Orange Free State became the centers of Boer life. By 1870 Kimberley assumed importance as the diamond capital of the world. But the gold fields of the Witwatersrand, opened in 1886, rapidly outgrew all the preceding centers and the economic, commercial, industrial, and transportation activities of South Africa focused upon this site.

Such an evolution has been without parallel in the history of gold mining throughout the world. Ancient gold mining often became transitory when primitive techniques could not wrest further gold from a given site. The great Spanish search for gold in the new world left havoc and destruction in its wake. Gold rushes to California, Australia, and Alaska all opened new regions for settlement, but, in the history of each of these places, gold mining soon gave way to other economic pursuits. Only in South Africa has gold mining dominated the national life for a long period or been of sufficient influence to markedly change the relationship between man and his environment.

CHAPTER EIGHT

Manufacturing

SINCE THE ADVENT of man on the earth, manufacturing or processing has taken place. At first manufacturing was primitive and largely self-subsistent in nature. Given impetus by the inventions and new sources of power that led to the Industrial Revolution, manufacturing is now highly specialized and is the principal basis of livelihood in many sections of the world.

Manufacturing is highly dependent upon the juxtaposition of a number of cultural and physical factors in an area. A variety of raw materials must be drawn together; therefore an efficient transportation net is essential. A source of power, an abundant and skilled labor supply, adequate capital for investment, access to market, and technical "know-how" are other factors necessary for the successful development of manufacturing. These latter factors are generally associated with a relatively dense population and high standards of living. Other factors, such as the type of political climate, can also influence the nature and distribution of manufacturing.

Modern complex manufacturing reaches its greatest development in North America and Europe. Some manufacturing, usually on a small scale, is found in Southeast Asia and other areas scattered over the world. Even in the areas of maximum concentration, the intensity of development is very uneven. Most of Europe's manufacturing, for example, is in the west-central portion within which the Ruhr of Germany and the Midlands of England, occupying little space, are extremely significant. Even in these areas, much space is devoted to agriculture as well as to industry.

Manufacturing represents the epitome of specialized resource use. Technological change and invention are constantly changing the resultant products and, in many instances, the way of living on the earth's surface. The apparent goal of most world areas is to industrialize; however, all areas are not equally endowed. Geographic study analyzes and aids in explaining the present distribution of manufacturing in relation to available resources. The selections in this chapter discuss the principles of manufacturing, areas of industrial concentration, and specialized industries and and their problems as developed in various parts of the world.

---

56. *Principles and Laws of Economic Geography* *

The manufacturing industries of the world utilize a wide variety of raw materials from diverse areas. Some regions are engaged in the production of only certain kinds of raw materials, others combine production of raw material with manufacturing, and still others specialize only in manufacturing. The total orderly productive pattern on the earth's surface has a logical physical and cultural geographic basis. One of the major objectives of introductory geography is to provide the background necessary to an understanding of these world distributional patterns. George Renner in this reading presents some principles and laws of economic geography based on geographic knowledge and reasoning.

Economic geography, or *geonomics* as it is sometimes called, obtained its start during the latter part of the eighteenth century when Immanuel Kant in Germany pointed out the existence of a field of geography which he termed "Mercantile Geography." At about that same time, Adam Smith in England was publishing his *Wealth of Nations.*

From that time on, economics grew vigorously, but economic geography was relatively neglected for nearly a century. Then, beginning with George G. Chisholm in Britain and J. Russell Smith in the United States, economic geography developed rapidly. Today, in America at least, it is the dominant aspect of geography.

* George T. Renner, "Some Principles and Laws of Economic Geography," *Journal of Geography,* Vol. 49, No. 1, January, 1950, pp. 14–22. By permission of the *Journal of Geography,* official publication of the National Council of Geography Teachers.

The author (1900) is Professor of Geography, Teachers College, Columbia University. Among the positions he has held are Associate Professor, State University of Washington; Geographer, Iowa Forest Survey; Senior Economist, United States National Resources Planning Board. His books include *Human Geography in the Air Age, Conservation of National Resources,* and, as joint author, *Global Geography, Human Geography* and *World Economic Geography.* He has written numerous articles for periodicals.

Descriptive and Factual Studies

During the past four decades, a wide variety of specific studies, as well as a considerable number of textbooks and other general works on economic geography, have appeared. Today, altho there is in existence a large volume of geonomic literature, the works composing this literature consist predominantly of either description or exposition, and they generally lack any clear statement of theory and principle. Indeed, some economic geographers appear to have regarded their field as lacking in basic principles and laws, implying that altho economics exhibits many valid generalizations, economic geography is, per se, largely descriptive and factual. This implication is probably the result of the relative immaturity of the latter subject.

Generalizations

Economic geography has, however, evolved to the point where at least a tentative statement of its basic generalizations can be made. Some of these are principles or underlying tendencies which would seem to be valid under all conditions. Some of them, however, are laws which would seem either to operate quantitatively or to involve cause-and-effect relations under specific conditions within the framework of one or another of these principles.

At the outset, it should be noted that there are four basic principles, as follows:

The Principle of Geonomic Relationship
The Principle of Optimum Location
The Principle of Regional Specialization
The Principle of Geonomic Succession

In the paragraphs which follow, each of these is discussed, together with the several laws which would appear to operate under each.

The Principle of Geonomic Relationship

It is a truism that the two considerations in economic geography are man and his technology on the one hand and the natural elements (i.e. the natural forces, processes, and resources) on the other hand. These latter combine in an endless variety of ways to create the natural environment which everywhere constitutes both a foundation for and a limitation upon human society—offering encouragement here, hindrance there. To the quality and peculiar character of this natural environment, man locally and regionally adapts his patterns of industries, economic constructions, and business institutions. Out of this fact, arises the most fundamental phenomenon in economic geography, namely *geonomic relationship.*

Industries, that is productive economic activities, are the foundation of human society. Mankind is able to exist only because it has learned to produce economic goods via these industries. Production is, however, only a more or less complicated process in which man uses the natural environment to obtain the necessaries of life. Each different kind of industry, therefore, represents man's establishing relations to specific natural processes and resources selected from the natural environment. Thus, all of man's occupations and economic institutions have arisen out of human adjustments to Nature.

These, however, do not arise arbitrarily or haphazardly, but instead tend to follow the general Principle of Geonomic Relationship, as follows:

> Every industry represents the capitalization by man of some element or combination of elements in the natural environment. The choice of industry and the success with which it is prosecuted depends upon the quality of the local resources balanced against the level and effectiveness of the available technology.

The Law of Primacy in Resource Use

Economic production is not a simple matter of establishing indiscriminate use relations between man and natural resources. The value of the latter are highly variable. Consequently, what lands are brought under cultivation, what pieces of forest are cut, or what mineral deposits are mined is decided by a very complicated process of choosing and rejecting by man.

Any natural resource possesses value because of two qualities, richness and location. The amount of really rich grades of any natural resource is decidedly limited, a circumstance which is reflected in the order in which man selects the various grades of it for utilization. Indeed, this may be stated formally as the so-called Law of Maximum Productivity or the Law of Primacy in Resource Use. This is as follows:

> In all primitive economies, and in present day local economies not yet fully invaded by modern means of transportation, those resources possessing the greatest richness of fertility tend to be exploited first.

The Law of Accessibility

Improvements in transportation have, however, caused the rapid spread of competitive exchange economy. Under the stress of such an economy, the spread of a power-and-machine technology has also been rapid. Improved transportation has made available many natural resources which were formerly inaccessible, but it has also made available fertilizer, selective breeding, more efficient smelting, improved marketing and all such forms of capital, also. Under their onslaught, the Law of Primacy in Resources Use is being weakened and what might be called the Law of Accessibility is tending to supplant it. This is:

Under an exchange economy, lower-grade resources, if readily accessible to a large market can be utilized profitably, while richer grades of resources, less accessible, remain unexploited.

The Principle of Optimum Location

Quite apart from the question of the selective exploitation of natural resources is the problem of what localizes industries and, in many instances, locates them on specific sites. Every industry (productive economic activity) requires for its prosection some six ingredients or component elements: capital, labor, market, power, raw materials, and transportation. Obviously, it is an advantage for the industry to be as near to these as possible.

This advantage is expressed in the Principle of Optimum Location.

Any industry tends to locate upon a site which provides optimum access to its ingredient elements. If all these elements occur close together, the location of the industry is pre-determined. If, however, they occur widely separated, the industry will be so placed as to be most accessible to that element which would be most expensive or most difficult to transport, and which becomes, therefore, the locative factor for the industry in question.

The Law of Location for Extractive Industries

There are in general four great classes of industry, of which the extractive class is geonomically the simplest. The law governing the localization of such activities is as follows:

The extractive industries are, and must continue to be located by the occurrence of their raw materials.

As a corollary, it may be said that in connection with most industries of this kind, the Law of Accessibility dictates that raw materials nearer to market will be exploited before those lying farther away, and that large areas of forest, grassland, and wild game shelter will be destroyed and replaced by more productive land uses.

The Law of Location for Reproductive Industries

Agricultural and other reproductive industries fall into two groups, those which produce staples, and those which produce perishable commodities. The law governing their localization is:

Reproductive industries which produce staple commodities are localized by raw-material factors, i.e. by nature-made conditions operating under the Law of Comparative Advantage. Those which produce perishable commodities tend to locate close to their markets even under the handicap of increased costs.

The Law of Location for Facilitative Industries

The facilitative industries include transporting, financing, and the "services." Their localization may be expressed in the following terms:

The facilitative industries tend to be located almost entirely by the distribution of markets for their services or utilities.

The Law of Location for Manufactural Industry

The law governing the localization of the fabricative activities is most complex of all. Briefly it may be stated as follows:

Any manufactural industry tends to locate at a point which provides optimum access to its ingredient elements. It will, therefore, seek a site near to—

(a) *raw materials,* if it uses perishable or highly condensable raw substances,

(b) *market,* where the processing adds fragility, perishability, weight, or bulk to the raw materials, or where its products are subject to rapid changes in style, design or technological character, or

(c) *power,* where mechanical energy costs of processing are the chief item in the total cost of fabrication, or

(d) *labor,* where the wages paid to skilled artisans are a large item in the total cost of fabrication.

To this, one might add that *capital* and *labor of management* are locative only during industrial youth of a region, and *transportation* facilities are locative only during economic old age of a region—and then only for miscellaneous industries.

The Principle of Regional Specialization

The elements of the natural environment are not evenly distributed over the earth's surface. In different sections, they are arranged in very different combinations. This means that the earth's surface and even the surface of a country such as the United States is a mosaic of unlike natural regions. Since these regions differ, man must perforce follow different patterns in adjusting his living to the natural environment in these unlike regions. Eventually, the patterns of human construction and business which he establishes, differ markedly from one region to another. As a result of this process of differentiation, economic activity in one region is often quite different from that in other regions.

This may be expressed in the following generalization:

As commercial competition increases, any region will, unless prevented from doing so by political controls, tend to specialize in the production of those commodities for which it possesses a natural or technological advantage.

The Law of Comparative Advantage

The development of means for transporting products widely, together with the creation of a fairly constant market for a great variety of commodities, has largely destroyed the need for regional self-sufficiency. If a region can produce on a large scale, one item for which there is a general demand over the earth, and if it can get that item to market, it can with the resulting income, purchase everything else which it needs. There is, then, a general tendency among all advanced regions to move increasingly toward an economy of specialization. Each region tends in the direction of producing one or several commodities for which it possesses natural or technological aptitudes. This process of regional specialization tends to obey what has been called the Law of Comparative Advantage:

Wherever there are several alternative uses for land or other natural resources, that use which is most advantageous or productive will be selected.

The Four Laws of Trade

It is obvious that the further the Principle of Regional Specialization is extended, the greater will be the necessity for specialized regions to increase their trade with one another. Trade is not haphazard nor whimsical, however, but tends to obey the following four laws of trade.

First Law of Trade (Law of Trade Origin)

Trade is created by the existence of surpluses of different commodities. Differences in commodities are, in turn occasioned by

(a) differences in culture,
(b) differences in natural resources, and
(c) differences in the geonomic stage of development.

The greater are the differences in commodities, the more impelling the inducement to trade.

Second Law of Trade (Law of Trade Change)

As population increases and economic development progresses, geonomic readjustments are made within a region, and the character of the commodities which are exported changes.

Third Law of Trade (Law of Trade Direction)

As commercial relations are extended, trade based upon cultural and economic-geographic differences tends to decline whereas trade resting upon resource differences tends to become accentuated. Consequently, predominantly east-west flows of trade tend to become predominantly north-south flows.

Fourth Law of Trade (Law of Trade Volume)

The volume of commerce moving over any trade route varies directly with the size of the surpluses of goods and inversely with the physical barriers and the political restrictions.

The Principle of Geonomic Succession

The end result of the operation of the Law of Comparative Advantage is to produce what has often been termed the *geographical division of labor*. This has already progressed to where a large amount of regional specialization has occurred and a huge growth of trade has followed.

Any geographical division of labor is, however, a very fragile arrangement and is very susceptible to change. Indeed, it is a general truth that the economic value of any particular area is subject to change in response to population increase, technological advancement, or the discovery or depletion of natural resources.

When the population of a tribe of primitive food gatherers increases to a point where hunting cannot provide an adequate food supply, the more resourceful members of the tribe will capture wild animals, breed them in captivity, and establish ownership over water holes and range grass. Eventually, the tribe shifts its geographic relations from the biota, to water holes and grassland thru the medium of domesticated animals. If human numbers continue to increase, another geonomic readjustment will be made. This time, relations to soil, climate, and landforms may be established and an agricultural adjustment made. This kind of adjustment and readjustment has been made often enough in history to suggest the operation of an underlying principle. It is often referred to as the Principle of Geonomic Succession.

Stated as briefly as possible this is:

As population increases, any human society tends to shift its geonomic dependence from one set of environmental elements to a more productive set of elements.

Conversely, where population decreases, human society tends to shift its geonomic dependence to a less productive set of elements.

The Malthusian Law

The population of any country, region or locality is the most important factor in the economic life of that area. Moreover, because population has a tendency to grow in numbers, it tends also to exert an increasing pressure upon the natural resources of the area which it inhabits. The ratio of human numbers to the quantity of resources at man's disposal, or as it is usually called, the man-land ratio, has long been the subject of widespread interest.

The law governing the man-land ratio, i.e. the Law of Biostatic Pressure, or as it is more often called, the Malthusian Law reveals that:

Human numbers tend to increase by geometrical progression whereas the means of subsistence tend to increase by arithmetical pregression; and therefore the population (unless checked voluntarily) will outrun the food supply to the point where further increase will be prevented by malnutrition, starvation, or pestilence.

The Law of Diminishing Returns

Even without the profound effects of major inventions or of resource discoveries and depletions, the weight of swelling numbers within an area is sufficient to compel a more intensive exploitation of those resources which the inhabitants are utilizing for their support. This involves additional applications of labor and capital to the resources in question.

For each successive application of labor or capital, an enhanced production of goods is obtained. The increase in production, however, after a time gets smaller and smaller until finally a point is reached where the increase is worth less than the additional labor or capital applied. From that point on, more production can be obtained, but only at the expense of a net loss. Stated formally, this Law of Diminishing Returns is:

There is a point in the application of labor and capital to the exploitation of natural resources, beyond which further application yields less than a proportionate increase in production.

Conclusion

The seventeen principles and laws which have been discussed in the foregoing pages, are admittedly an incomplete list of the generalizations of economic geography. Two of them, the Malthusian Law and the Law of Diminishing Returns, are already well known from economic literature. Most of the remaining fifteen have appeared in one form or another, either explicitly or by implication, in the literature of geonomics. The writer has here attempted to formulate some of them and to restate and amplify others. A very large amount of additional mental labor on the part of many geographers will be necessary before all of the geonomic principles and laws can be formulated and stated in final form.

Meanwhile, this tentative statement of the simpler generalizations should prove valuable to teachers by providing them with the means for directing and sharpening their teaching of economic geography.

---

57. *Benchmark* *

The United States has become, in the present century, the major industrial nation of the world. Of fundamental importance to this country is the "uneven geographical intensity" of the industry. In this reading Vinge portrays graphically the postwar distribution of our major industrial centers. Despite war changes in location, the Northeast remains industrially outstanding, while vast areas of the United States still lack industrialization.

The 1947 Census of Manufactures now being made available is the first one taken since 1939. This gap between 1939 and 1947 represents the longest one without an accurate industrial inventory during this century; it was also the eight-year period in which the greatest changes took place. Because no comprehensive fact-gathering was done during the war, the 1939 Census of Manufacturers had to serve as a point of orientation and departure for those who needed to judge what was happening in this important segment of our economy. Although the new census is not yet available in its entirety, some of the data already released lead to interpretations at variance with notions we have become accustomed to hold.

Of facts so far made public, perhaps the most important are those that show changes in geographical intensity of industry from prewar to postwar. What were the major industrial districts in 1939? What are they now? How do they compare? What areas grew most, percentage-wise? In absolute quantities? Was there marked migration to the South and West Coast? Did the heavily industrialized Northeast suffer out-migration? But let us get on to a look at the facts.

The map (Fig. 21) tells most of the story. It shows the uneven arrangement of industry over the land. Fine stipple at the base of bars indicates areal extent of major industrial districts. The measure of industrial intensity (lengths of bars) is based on number of factory workers

* Clarence L. Vinge, "Benchmark," *Scientific Monthly*, Vol. 70, No. 1, 1950, pp. 66–67. The author (1915) is Professor of Geography, Michigan State College. His special fields of interest are economic geography and Anglo America. He is the author of several articles on various phases of geography.

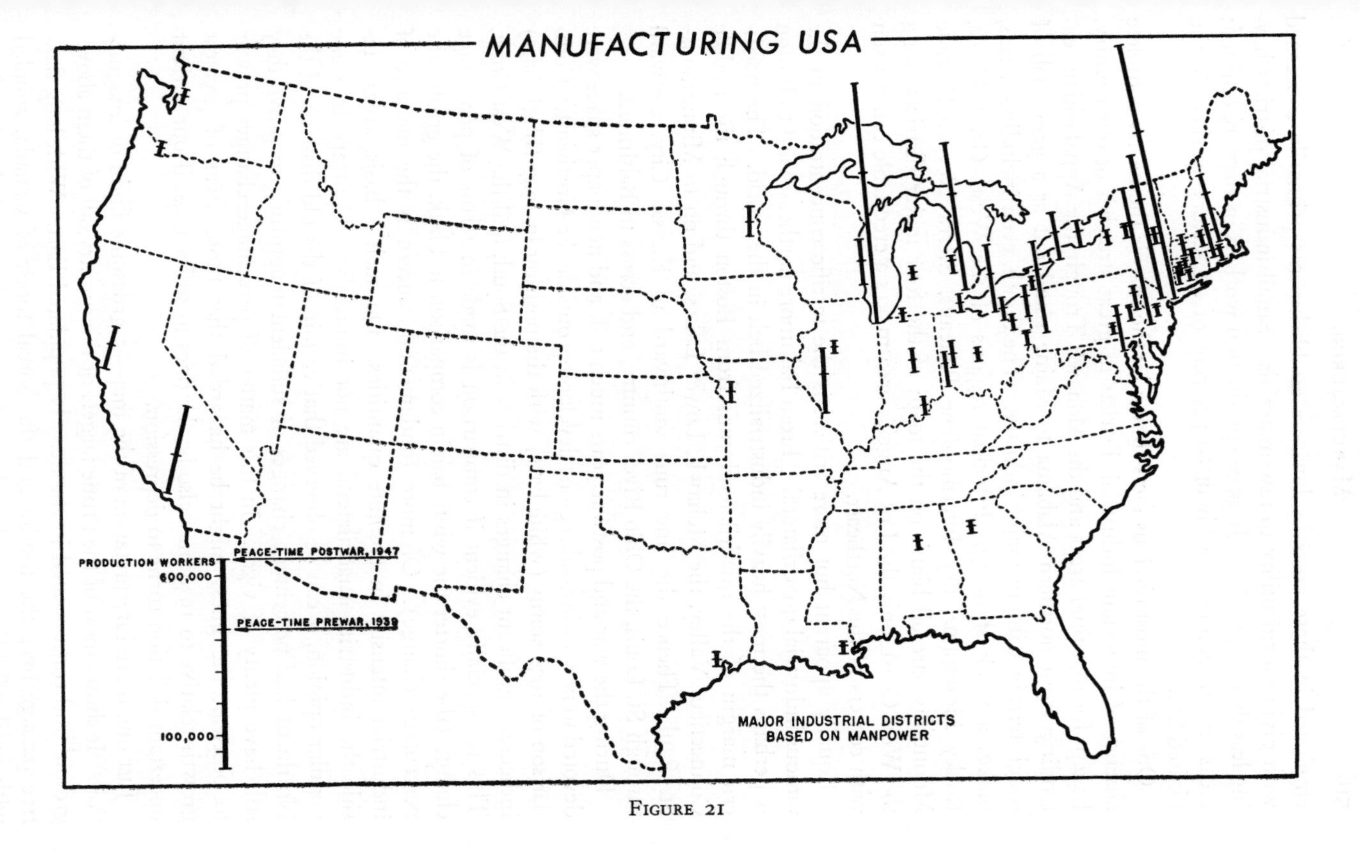
MANUFACTURING USA
PEACE-TIME POSTWAR, 1947
PRODUCTION WORKERS
600,000
PEACE-TIME PREWAR, 1939
100,000
MAJOR INDUSTRIAL DISTRICTS
BASED ON MANPOWER

FIGURE 21

employed in these areas by business establishments primarily concerned with giving form utility to raw materials. Small industrial districts having less than approximately 35,000 production workers in 1947 are omitted; areas shown account for about 60 per cent of all factory workers in the United States.

One of the most obvious facts shown by the map is the nearly complete absence of important industrial districts in great stretches of our country. Except for marginal areas and the Mohawk Trough, the Appalachians extending from northern Alabama to Maine stand out as a great slab of rough terrain without major industry. The South, even including Texas, makes a weak showing. Principal regions of the West—Great Plains, Rocky Mountains, dry Intermontane Plateaus, Sierra Nevada–Cascade Mountains—are all blank on the map; of the four major districts along the West Coast, only the Los Angeles area makes a creditable comparison with centers of the Northeast.

Equally apparent but more critical is the terrific concentration in the famous industrial quadrilateral. From Baltimore northeastward to Boston is perhaps the most heavily industrialized belt in the world. The northern margin of the quadrilateral runs from Boston through the middle Connecticut Valley, the Mohawk, Lower Lakes, and on to Minneapolis–St. Paul. Thence the line runs southward to Kansas City, eastward through St. Louis, the Ohio River country, and across to Baltimore.

During the war and postwar years much talk and newspaper space were devoted to new industrial regions developing outside the Northeast. Comparison of 1939 status (white bars) with the position in 1947 (black bars) indicates significant changes in districts in the South and the West Coast. This is especially evident if comparison is made in terms of percentage change (the shorter the white bar in comparison to black, the greater the percentage change). Of more fundamental concern is the measure of industrial intensity in absolute quantities. On such a basis, areas outside the industrial quadrilateral are not impressive. Contrary to some popular opinion, it can be observed that certain of the old districts of the Northeast had percentage changes of sufficient magnitude to prove they still have plenty of vigor. In this matter of percentage changes prewar to postwar, the guess might be hazarded that those areas of greatest growth relative to 1939 may also be the ones to suffer most if our current uncertain deflation turns to depression.

Just one more interpretation of the map—a gruesome flight of imagination. It shows most of the prime targets of the country, all of them aboveground and concentrated in the densely populated East. With long flak-free passage over the tundra and the boreal forest of Canada, coupled with similar flak-free corridors down the great prongs of Lakes Michigan and Huron, what would prevent at least a few enemy bombers from breaking through our fighter interception?

58. *The Chemical Century* *

Perhaps we are about to pass from the "iron and steel age" to the "chemical age." The phenomenal growth and present importance of the chemical industries is indicated by the following quotation from this *Fortune* magazine article: "If all its [chemistry's] basic and process industry ramifications were rolled into one, they would account for at least 20 per cent of the total national product. Chemistry, in fact, is a great, yeasty force at the center of the economy, creating new industries and recreating old ones, and working changes on all sides." A great variety of synthetic products from the chemistry laboratory and factory are replacing products or raw materials coming from other sources. Such changes have a great impact on the structure and distribution of industry in this country, as well as on the economy of areas that formerly produced such raw materials as natural rubber and silk. The chemical industry provides a good example of the dynamic nature of manufacturing.

Chemicals must now be considered the premier industry of the U.S. Its rise has been recent, precipitous, and largely unnoticed. For most of the first half of the century the title was held by the automobile industry, which is now leveling off on a high plateau of maturity. For the rest of the century the title is likely to be sharply contested by that loose federation of industries pivoting upon the electrical-electronic-nucleonic sciences, which also has had an enormous growth whose ends cannot yet be foreseen. But as of now, the chemical industry cannot be matched by any other in dynamics, growth, earnings, and potential for the future. A few facts:

Since 1937, when *Fortune* last looked at the industry, total sales have risen from some $700 million to well over $3 billion. For reasons that will be seen later, it is hard to say exactly how big the postwar industry is.

In 1937 only seven companies had sales over $25 million; by 1948 nineteen companies were well over that mark. The 1948 sales of one company alone (Union Carbide) were almost equal to the industry's in 1937.

* Reprinted from the March 1950 issue of *Fortune* by Special Permission of the Editors.

From 1939 to 1949, while earnings on net sales for twenty-three companies declined under mounting costs and taxes from 15 per cent to some 11 per cent, net operating income on sales rose from 17.7 to close to 19 per cent.

From 1939 to 1949, the chemical industry more than doubled in plant. In four years following the war, capital expenditures hit a rate of over $1.5 billion a year.

In the same period chemical stocks on the Exchange soared to third place in market value, just behind the utilities and oils. Current value: over $10 billion.

Some 40 per cent of sales in bigger companies is accounted for by products undeveloped fifteen years ago. Big companies introduce ten to twenty-five new products a year.

Plastics now total more in pounds—some 1.5 billion a year—than any nonferrous metal, including aluminum.

Since 1941 chemicals has been outproducing all industry. Against an industrial production index of 191 (1935–39 equals 100), chemicals has been steaming along at 253.

More chemists are now employed outside the industry proper (limited to basic chemical producers) than in it—indicating this industry's underground penetration of other industries. From 1936 to 1949, membership in the American Chemical Society rose from 18,000 to 63,000, making it the second biggest professional group of its kind in the world.

Some visionaries predict that most industry will eventually be absorbed into the chemical industry, and at the rate chemicals is going this may not be farfetched. Whether it is or not, many an industry might learn much, as some already have, from a closer study of the chemical group's growth and motive power. Government might well study it, too. There's nothing mysterious in it, and the industry is neither superhuman nor without fault, but more than any other it has found the power to create for itself and for men everywhere illimitable frontiers.

The Growth of Plant

From being only a small inorganic chemical industry at the turn of the century, far outstripped by Germany's organic industry through World War I, U. S. chemicals must now be reckoned among the great industrial forces of our times. By World War II it had grown so strong that it was ready to beat the Germans at their own game. How soundly it had built was shown by the fact that the war itself, despite its scope, did not add greatly to chemicals' basic capacity.

This is not well understood. The war brought a vast expansion of plant in such special lines as explosives, synthetic rubber, and fixed nitrogen. But the industry's role here was largely to supply the managerial talent to build and run some $3 billion in government war plants. The peak of that program was the creation of a $1-billion synthetic-rubber industry out of almost nothing in two years flat. The industry also supplied much of the indispensable talent for building or operating another $1 billion or so of atomic-energy plants. The magnitude of its contributions here, overshadowed by the glamour of the new physics, has never been fully appreciated.

Beyond that, the industry opened its own plant valves wide and in four years poured into the war economy some $20 billion in basic chemicals, intermediates, dyes, solvents, drugs, resins, plastics, coatings, fibers, filaments, and the hundreds of other chemical products that now permeate all industrial life. Most of this output was gained by devoting full capacity to purposes of war, halting all expansion in consumer lines. From 1943 through 1945, with most of the war plants built, chemical construction hit its lowest ebb in years. As a measure of these curtailments, most chemicals showed up short in the immediate postwar market, despite the fact that there was no lag in production. When the war ended, the industry simply turned back most of the specialized plants to government, flipped its chemical stream back to peacetime channels, and moved to catch up. Its big expansion came only then.

The postwar explosion, largely completed last year, may now be viewed in the round. It entailed so huge an outlay that for the first time in years most major companies, including du Pont, and many of the minors were forced to secure large chunks of new equity capital or loans. Less than a quarter of the expansion money came from these sources, however; the rest came from the industry's traditional, self-generating springs of earnings and reserves.

By 1948, with new capacity flooding in, the stupendous ten-year record (based on twenty-three companies) stood at: a 111 per cent rise in total assets to about $3.3 billion; a 234 per cent jump in net sales; and a 125 per cent increase in net profits. This last was accomplished on prices averaging only 25 per cent above 1939, while all wholesale prices soared some 115 per cent above—a feat achieved by good sense, technical efficiency, and sheer volume of production. Early last year this tremendous production, running into suddenly full inventories and the general business slump, ran chemicals into a decline, but, with only a slight lag in earnings, the industry managed to pull the year up just under 1948. The industry is now at the stage of consolidating and digesting one of the most rapid expansions of physical plant in history.

Such statistics cannot frame the whole bulging picture. They refer only to those primary producers that, in the main, supply basic chemicals and intermediates to industry. These include some fifty companies, led by du Pont, Union Carbide, and the others. . . . Du Pont is still the giant, nearly doubling in size since 1937, and alone accounting for about a quarter of total sales. Others, however, have had an even sharper rise. Dow Chemical, breaking all records, has grown about seven and a half times in assets in the same period, Monsanto about four, and all well-managed companies, great and small, have had proportionately spectacular growth.

The Growth of Area

But in addition to these, and unaccounted for in industry totals, are large and growing chemical divisions in the so-called process industries, which normally convert basic materials from the above companies into rayon, glass, rubber, film, paint, fertilizer, and other finished products. Such companies as Eastman Kodak, Sherwin-Williams, Glidden, Libbey-Owens-Ford, Pittsburgh Plate Glass, and Goodrich Rubber now produce many basic chemicals for themselves and for others. Spurred by the vast postwar shortages, this movement has been enormously accelerated. Celanese Corp., for instance, the biggest factor in acetate rayon, has made a $25-million entry into basic chemicals from petroleum. Most major fertilizer companies have been busy reaching back for basic production and diversifying their products. And even such big food processors as Swift, Armour, General Mills, and Corn Products Refining are now importantly in basic chemicals from some fraction of their natural products.

To add to the confusion, most primary producers have been spreading out just as lustily into more and more semi-finished or consumer products, in which profit margins are fatter. Du Pont's big stake in rayon, nylon, fabric coatings, paints, antifreezes, and the like is a good example. And since the war there has been a major rise in the formation of joint companies, in which a primary chemical producer joins with a process company, usually on a fifty-fifty basis, to exploit some new area from basic chemicals to finished product. Dow, for instance, teamed with Corning Glass to form Dow-Corning Corp. for the production of silicone materials. Monsanto recently teamed with American Viscose to develop new synthetic fibers. American Cyanamid teamed with Texas Co. to form the $12-million Jefferson Chemical Co., Inc., for both basic chemicals and such end products as glycol antifreeze. The proliferation of such cross ties has woven a new pattern. The fact is that the distinction between primary-chemical and process industries is fading. Both groups are fast merging, and must soon be considered as one.

On top of all this, there is the major postwar expansion of the oil industry into basic chemical production, a phenomenon so portentous as to require separate examination later on. None of this booming petrochemical production is included in chemical-industry figures, just as none or only part of the process industries' and joint-company production is included. Nor is this an end to inconsistencies. Not included is the $1-billion pharmaceutical industry, though it is more and more chemical in base, and such basic producers as Cyanamid, Monsanto, and Dow include large pharmaceutical lines. Also not included are all light metals, though Alcoa has a growing chemical division based on aluminum and fluorine compounds, and the basic chemical group includes much metallurgy—Carbide being the country's largest producer of ferroalloys, Dow the sole source of magnesium, and du Pont having recently taken on titanium metal. Finally, there is a sprouting of chemicals in such wildly unclassifiable companies as General Electric, National Distillers, Minnesota Mining & Manufacturing, and Food Machinery Corp.

The industry is still arbitrarily limited to the basic chemical group for the convenience of economists and Wall Streeters who can't keep up with chemistry. But this prewar viewpoint badly needs overhauling. The chemical industry is larger than any of its largest statistics. It now feeds all sixty-eight industrial divisions of the U. S. Department of Commerce. If all its basic and process-industry ramifications were rolled into one, they would account for at least 20 per cent of the total national product. Chemistry, in fact, is a great, yeasty force at the center of the economy, creating new industries and re-creating old ones, and working changes on all sides.

The Growth of Power

From birth the chemical industry exhibited a strange, new leverage upon economics, never before seen. The derivation of a violet aniline dye from coal tar by Sir William Henry Perkin in 1856—the very foundation of the modern synthetic-organic industry—set in motion a force that in a few decades wiped out the ancient madder-plant (red dye) industry of France, the still more ancient indigo industry of India, and the Tyrian purple coming down from immemorial time. As chemists slowly mastered their materials, the pace increased. Within the last ten years this power of chemistry to upset, take over, and change natural markets has reached new and increasing heights. A list of major conquests will show chemicals' mercurial operations in the markets of the world, as well as review some of the recent, notable growths of chemical synthesis.

Synthetic nitrates, based on *synthetic ammonia* by the famed Haber-

Bosch process, have completely undercut Chilean saltpeter, once the world's only major source for vital fertilizers, explosives, and other compounds. In the great postwar shortage, quantities of Chilean nitrate came in duty-free, but at a price *above* the synthetic, indicating its inability to meet competition except by Chilean government subsidy, which was prevalent through the thirties. In ten years the U.S. has quintupled synthetic-ammonia output to over 1,500,000 tons a year—most of it from ten huge government-built war plants, costing $250 million, working largely from natural gas. This tremendous increase in capacity, over half of which was later acquired by private firms, is feeding a great boom in fertilizers. One feature is the tripling in two years of *synthetic urea* production, a further synthesis from ammonia, as a new concentrated source of nitrogen.

Synthetic alcohol (*ethanol*)—straight alcohol that never saw a fermenter—now has nearly 50 per cent of the industrial-alcohol market, once ruled by fermentation from molasses. Carbide & Carbon first synthesized it commercially from natural gas in 1930, and three other producers, working from natural gas and petroleum hydrocarbons, now swell the 190-million-gallon volume of this universal solvent and base for many other organics. The fermentation product can still whip the market around. Late in 1948 Publicker Alcohol negotiated a fast deal with Cuba for all its remaining molasses at a price tied to alcohol's selling price. In a few weeks alcohol was cut from 75 cents a gallon to 20 cents, driving Cuba's molasses down to 4 cents. But such gyrations only speed the movement to the more stable synthetic market. U. S. Industrial Chemicals, one of the biggest fermentation producers, which took about a $2,400,000 loss in the first half of 1949, has a deal with Shell Chemical to absorb part of its synthetic production from petroleum and another tying into the biggest plant addition to synthetic ethanol in 1950.

Synthetic wood alcohol (*methanol*)—that never saw wood—has pushed the wood distillate out of all but a fraction of 1 per cent of the market. Prewar, methanol averaged only a third of ethanol's volume, but with a great postwar spurt, taking over much of the latter's market as a cheap antifreeze, it is now close behind ethanol. It is also a widely used solvent, and a major ingredient in heavy-duty, heavy-volume phenolic plastics. Most of it is synthesized from carbon monoxide by hydrogenation, a growing stream coming as coproduct, by one of those double plays common in chemistry, from ammonia-synthesis plants.

Synthetic rubber, the chemical war baby, has changed at a stroke the whole economy of Indonesia. The U.S. could now produce its full needs (one million long tons a year) economically via butadiene and styrene out of petroleum and from other bases; only the world crisis and national policy force us to continue securing over half of requirements from natural rubber. With the 1947 development of "cold rubber"—a synthetic formed at lower temperatures—tire treads superior to natural in heat and abrasion resistance have finally been achieved. Synthetic capacity is moving over at the rate of 200,000 long tons a year to the improved product. Typical of chemistry's chain reactions at home as well as abroad, the synthetic tire knocked out the use of cotton cord, one of the South's biggest markets, and forced the use of stronger, heat-resistant rayon, swelling that already super-expanding cellulose-chemical market. Recently nylon cord has entered the field, too.

Synthetic fibers now run some 19 per cent of the whole textile field, from a prewar 10 per cent, and are still going higher. The over-all growth of textiles hides just how big the synthetics' bite is: from 459 million to 1.2 billion pounds in ten years. Star of that decade is du Pont's nylon, the first major all-synthetic U. S. fiber. Held back by war, nylon has tripled capacity since 1945, displaced silk in nearly all full-fashioned hose, closed up the future of Japan's silk industry, and is moving swiftly into other forms, fabrics, and dress goods. With these markets only scratched, du Pont last year pulled out of the same basic research a new product called Orlon, which as a continuous filament is more silk-like than nylon and as a staple is much like wool. A $15-million plant will begin turning out the filament later this year. Most major chemical firms have fibers coming along, chief among them Union Carbide's Vinyon, a filament being joined this year by a new staple form called dynel, and Dow's Saran yarn, now in its first major production. The big volume growth, however, is still in semi-synthetic rayon—94 per cent of the synthetic market, more than doubling production in the decade. When the many new chemicals that modify or improve natural fibers are added to all this, textiles form chemicals' single biggest growth area, and one in which they are profoundly changing the whole ecology of human dress.

Synthetic soaps, a postwar phenomenon, are up from small volume in the thirties to some 700 million pounds a year. This is about 20 per cent of all detergents—not all directly competitive with or displacing soap—but in hard-water areas synthetics have taken over half the market. They have largely powered the automatic-home-washer boom. Brought in by high prices and shortages in fats and oils, the new detergents are made from special coal-tar or petroleum derivatives or from fatty alcohols supplied by such companies as Allied, du Pont, Monsanto, Cyanamid, Swift, and the oil majors. No one can say where soapless soaps are going. Over a billion pounds by 1952 is a conservative guess, and new cheap petroleum sources may blow that sky-high. As a classic example of chemistry's ability to work both sides of a street, another postwar growth, small but useful, is in *synthetic antifoaming agents* for industry, which trade on their ability to do the exact opposite of synthetic detergents. Even more striking is the fact that the continuing growth of synthetic detergents could threaten the supply of glycerin, a byproduct of soap, but for Shell Chemical's notable new process for making *synthetic glycerin.*

Synthetic insecticides, led by DDT, are another major postwar growth, now running to 25 million pounds a year. They are moving into a host of special developments, such as Cyanamid's Parathion, U. S. Industrial's piperonyls, and Hercules' toxaphene, a remarkable new specific against grasshopper plagues and the boll weevil. And only last year U. S. Department of Agriculture chemists announced *synthetic pyrethrum,* long derived from a tropical flower, and long sought as the best knockdown insecticide nontoxic to mammals. A number of companies are adapting its eighteen-step synthesis to production—Carbide, for one, found itself already producing seven of its nine ingredients—and worried pyrethrum growers in central Africa, the world's main source, are trying to tie U. S. customers to two-year contracts. But even if this plantation industry is eventually wiped out, it will be by an agent that, in its growing chemical power, is remaking agriculture and may well make the tropics more habitable to broader human development.

Synthetics, given impetus by the disruptions of war, are everywhere and are here to stay. *Synthetic camphor* has displaced camphor from the Far East. *Synthetic toluene,* one of the big wartime expansions for TNT, out of petroleum, undercuts the coke-oven byproduct. *Synthetic cinnamon* and *oil of wintergreen* retain most of their war markets. *Synthetic acetic acid* long ago overtook the natural product. *Synthetic musk* outruns the little musk deer of Tibet as base and fixative for perfumes. And *synthetic gems*—sapphires, emeralds, and rubies equal to the natural stones, and a synthetic called rutile, with a higher infractive index than diamonds—are giving jewelers trouble, and man a foretaste of the disruption in values when atomic chemistry gets around to the economic transmutation of base metals into gold.

In all this is a force that orthodox free-trade economists have been reluctant to recognize, an inherent drive toward what may be called continental self-sufficiency. It is by no means complete; only in the last decade has it reached unmistakable strength and portent. The chemical attrition of colonial raw-material empires goes on apace. Foreign policy is now forced to take this new power into account, and political economists will be wrestling with its mounting effects through the rest of the century.

The Growth Factor

The engine that develops this power is essentially simple. It is, briefly, the science of the transformation of matter. In the great burst of human curiosity that opened the age of experimental science three centuries ago, men began to delve back into the basic materials that make up the world. With the elements classified and a growing idea of how their atoms joined to form molecules, or basic blocks of complex matter, the chemist started to imitate nature. Using elemental substances, he began building up simple molecules in a new way, called synthesis. This structural exercise usually began by approximating a natural substance, such as indigo, then exactly reproducing it, and finally going beyond nature to produce a blaze and range of fast dyes unobtainable by natural means from any animal, vegetable, or mineral matter.

Perhaps the deftest example of this process lies in the recent synthetic detergents. Inquiring into the working structure of soap, chemists discovered that the soap molecule is a rod-shaped affair, composed of a short, water-soluble, acidic segment at one end and a long oil-soluble, fatty segment at the other. In solution these rods rush to the sticky, oily film surrounding most dirt particles, and, energetically trying to keep their water-soluble tails in water and their fatty heads in oil, break up the film and allow the dirt to be flushed away. With this as a model, chemists soon put together a host of water-and-oil-soluble substances, many of them more energetic than soap, and some with special detergent properties no soap possesses.

Most of the big developments of the last decade, however, have come from a further elaboration of structure called polymerization, in which simple molecules are linked repetitively in long chains or massive rings to form giant molecules or polymers. Du Pont derived its nylon and neoprene rubber from brilliant fundamental research in big-molecule chemistry by the late Wallace Carrothers of Harvard, who in 1928 came to du Pont's new basic research laboratory to round out a body of work upon which du Pont is still drawing. Polymerization is also responsible for other synthetic rubbers and fibers, vinyl coatings and plastics, and a great range of other new plastics, resins, and materials never before seen in nature. Plastics, indeed, form the single biggest product classification in chemicals. If paints and protective coatings are linked in—most of them have been shifted to synthetic resins and other plastic-like materials—plastics add up to about a third of the industry's dollar volume.

All the spectacular growth has been in the so-called organic division, the reactive and widely distributed carbon-based compounds, providing the chemist with endless building blocks. The older inorganics, comprising such heavy chemicals as sulfur, sulfuric acid, chlorine, and caustic soda, have merely paralleled industrial growth. Starting with coal tar, the carbon base most readily available to the nineteenth century's coal economy, and moving to other hydrocarbons, the chemist has poured his basic materials into reactors and, by the application of heat, pressure, and catalysts in endless combination, has drawn out a stream of compounds now totaling over 500,000, only a small part of which have so far found use.

It is this profligate creation, coupled with the enterprise to develop it, that points the way for all advanced countries to move from an economy based on distant sources of isolated raw materials to an economy based on local materials chemically converted to protean forms. This is another industrial revolution of which man has seen only the beginning.

To move at all in this area requires great and continuous research and development. The chemical industry regularly expends in this line about 2 per cent of sales, which at the going rate is some $80 million or more a year. Since the war most of the bigger companies have erected new, multimillion-dollar laboratories, in which the trend is toward more basic research to replenish the stocks exhausted in war, when most basic research was necessarily halted.

The Growth of Petrochemicals

The largest new factor in this expanding chemical economy is oil. Chemically, the derivation of materials from petroleum's hydrocarbons isn't new to the chemical industry. Carbide & Carbon founded itself some twenty years ago on high-pressure synthesis from natural gas, swiftly expanded its base to refinery gas, and almost singlehanded created a whole new branch of organic chemicals, called the aliphatic, from nothing but gas. In the last decade du Pont, Dow, Monsanto, Cyanamid, Celanese, and other members of the industry moved into the great Golden Bend on the Gulf Coast, where investment in new chemical plants now totals some $600 million, to tap the rich stream of natural and petroleum gases.

Nor are chemicals from petroleum exactly new to the oil industry. Among the earliest to get into them, in the early thirties, was Shell, whose chemical division is now Shell Chemical Corp., perhaps the most aggressive and diversified of all petrochemicals. And even earlier Jersey Standard moved in. But since the war the rush of oil companies into chemicals has been phenomenal. Standard Oil (Indiana), Standard of California, Texas Co., Socony-Vacuum, Phillips, Atlantic Refining, Sun, Cities Service, Union, McCarthy, Lion Oil, and others—in one way or another all are in. Neither against the oil industry's total sales nor against the chemical industry's are petrochemicals of any staggering volume as yet. In Jersey

Standard they are not much over 1 per cent of sales, in Shell about 5, and in up-and-coming Lion they run about 22 per cent. But even 1 per cent of Jersey's sales is still about $33 million, and all fractions are steadily growing. Altogether, on the Gulf Coast alone, the investment in chemical plants based on petroleum is now equal to more than 30 per cent of oil's investment in refineries. The real portent of oil in chemicals, however, is to be found in a giant, new, multimillion-dollar combination synthetic oil and chemical plant at Brownsville, Texas, which was due to go on stream early this year.

This plant is a symbol of things to come. A string of such plants, based on coal or natural gas, was proposed by the U.S. in the big oil-shortage scare of 1948. The rivers of chemicals that would have flowed from these plants gave the chemical industry a scare, too, which passed with the easing of the oil shortage. The Brownsville project went ahead, however, financed by eight private companies and the RFC, and it is being closely watched by both the oil and chemical industries. For this is a gigantic continuous-flow process that is something new for chemicals and that can link oil more heavily into chemicals than ever before. Oil's growing interest in chemicals is based simply on the growth of some organics into tonnage items, and the new plant is a heavy-tonnage, dual-purpose tool. The chemical industry views this with some equanimity, seeing oil finding its place as supplier of heavy organics at lower price to chemical compounders. But this is basic new competition, and it must propel the basic chemical companies even faster toward diversification and development of end products.

. . . . .

The Growth of the Future

It is hackneyed to say that the chemical industry is still only at the beginning, but that is where it is, a swift glance at the future will plainly show.

By linking inorganics into organic compounds the older branch of chemistry is being pulled into the mainstream of organic growth. These new hybrids are not likely to be so numerous as the organics themselves, but they are of unknown size and portent. The largest and oldest products in this line are chlorinated compounds of wide variety. The newest and fastest growing are: the organosilicons, or silicone plastics, linking silicon (from sand) into carbon compounds for high heat-resistant fluids, greases, resins, and rubber-like materials; and the fluorocarbons, linking in fluorine for a range of similar substances, including the most stable plastics known. Both are in the early, high-cost stages of development but foreshadow a great range of new substances.

The direct synthesis of a new family of organic compounds from coal by hydrogenation, Fischer-Tropsch, or other processes—bringing the industry full circle from its early coal-tar base, which has been steadily dwindling in relation to hydrocarbon gas synthesis—promises an enormous new frontier in organic chemistry. This differs from coal-tar chemistry in that it will build, either from the simplest hydrocarbon molecules to be fractionated out of coal or from a whole new conformation of larger molecules out of coal, a great range of entirely new chemicals. It is being worked on from two ends, by the oil industry as an ace-in-the-hole for gasoline, and by the chemical industry, mainly Union Carbide, as a main source of new chemicals. If any bets are to be placed, they should be put on Union Carbide, for its incentives to open new chemical sources are stronger than the oil companies' immediate need for a new base for oil products.

The building of still more complex molecules beyond the scale of polymerization—which itself is a field so far only scratched—opens another large structural area to future exploitation. This moves up into protein chemistry—the largest and most complex molecules—and out into the whole broad, fast moving field of biochemistry, with the unlocking of the mystery of photosynthesis perhaps the biggest event just around the corner. Another growing province here is enzyme chemistry, bringing in a whole new range of natural catalysts. All this applies with revolutionary force to food processing, food supplies, pharmaceuticals, and another full range of new chemicals.

And on the borderland, still nebulous and hard to assay, is the development of nuclear chemistry out of atomic research. Such companies as Monsanto and Union Carbide are moving in this field, and it is too early to expect anything tangible. But the chemical industry, founded on discovered laws governing the formation and transformation of molecules, is bound to be affected by discoveries pointing to the transformation at will of the atoms making up those molecules. This is, perhaps, the most tremendous frontier of all.

The movement of research in all these directions, and the finding of markets to support it, is recognized by the progressive units of the industry as the hardest and most immediate task. For this the industry has a self-made tool called product development—literally the creation of new markets—which is now being sharpened to a new edge. It cuts in two directions: throwing a new chemical into a broad-scale search for market applications, and tailoring a new chemical to meet a market's specific request. Some examples are Carbide's glyoxal, derivative of its ethylene glycol, which moved out to find uses in thirty different products, the chief one being as a shrink-resistant agent in rayon fabrics; and Monsanto's development for Douglas Aircraft of a superior, flame-resistant synthetic hydraulic fluid for big aircraft landing systems; and Hercules' discovery of a new water-soluble cellulose (CMC) now used in ulcer tablets among other things; and du Pont's promotion of its notable Freon refrigerants as propellents in the booming new aerosol-bomb business; and so on and on. This is the chemical industry, a great and democratic ferment, from the tremendous to the trivial.

The pressure for new markets is creating a new business breed—the chemist-salesman-developer—whose day is at hand. More and more of chemicals' top executive timber is likely to be drawn from this training ground. Meanwhile the chemical fraternity, a group of matter-of-fact gentlemen in plain business suits, busily administer the dreams of the alchemists, which are dreams no longer.

59. *The New Metals Age* *

Light metals, largely developed in chemical research laboratories, are rapidly coming to the fore in the United States. Some are partially replacing the base metals; others, with new uses of their own, are changing rapidly from chemical unknowns to vital metals. The "Jet" and "Atomic" ages call for metals with a much higher resistance to heat than any previously known. Lessing calls this the "New Metals Age," with its tremendous metal consumption, imbalances, temporary shortages, sharply rising costs, and multiplicity of metals. The development, properties, and uses of these new metals will have deep repercussions on the nature and distribution of many types of manufacturing.

Something of a tremendous order is happening in the metals. Histories of civilization have been written in terms of the slow clash and thunder of metals down the centuries, but this new explosion in metals is happening within a single life span, here and now. In fact, the major detonation may be placed exactly in the last decade in the U.S. The main facts are these:

In tonnage alone, U. S. metals consumption increased by nearly two-thirds between 1940 and 1952 to 113 million tons a year, about equal to the rest of

* By Lawrence P. Lessing. Reprinted from the January 1953 issue of *Fortune* by Special Permission of the Editors. Copyright Time Inc.

The author (1908) is a journalist specializing in research, writing, and editing of technical and scientific articles. He also writes on political economy, business, and industrial management. He has been associate editor of *Fortune* magazine (1938–41) and member of the board of editors (1941–52). Since 1953 he has been a member of the board of editors of *Scientific American.*

the world's combined. By the end of 1953, however, the $23-billion primary-metals industry will have built in three years new capacity equal to all new plants built in the preceding ten years.

But tonnage is only part of the story, overweighted as it is by steel's current, massive 105 million tons, a quantity so huge as to hide all significant detail. If steel and the major light metals are plotted on a more realistic basis by volume, as shown in the key chart above, then a much more significant factor appears. In the last decade the light metals have moved up from a small to a ponderable percentage of steel's volume and, since they are growing at a much faster rate, they are going on, by projection through 1975, to challenge the primacy of steel itself.

But volume, too, is only part of the story, for the most significant aspect of the last decade's explosion in metals is the variety of new metals coming up, small in volume but vital to a host of new industries and technologies. . . . How fast they have grown is shown by one fact. In 1941 the number of metals on the U. S. list of scarce and strategic materials was twelve; in 1951 the number was well over thirty.

In other words, we are at the real turning point of a great revolution. War and defense have had much to do with its speed, but its advance is implicit in the whole, complex technical civilization being built on this continent. While metals, starting from a much older and broader base, cannot show the phenomenal short-term growth of chemicals, they are exhibiting some of the same dynamics, the ability to create, or re-create, industries, new markets, new competition, new relationships in endless profusion. Since metals are, indeed, basic, this revolution is economic, political, and social, as well as technological, and its import is seen clearest in the perspective of history.

The Ages of Metals

From remotest time to the sixteenth century, men worked with but seven metals: gold, silver, copper, tin, iron, lead, and mercury. The next three centuries added seven more, antimony, zinc, bismuth, arsenic, nickel, cobalt, and manganese, of which two (bismuth, arsenic) were hardly considered metals at all. Up to 1900, with chromium and tungsten just coming into use, that was about the lot. About half a dozen major metals carried the wealth and weight of the world. Yet, in the next fifty years, the number of different metals known to commerce tripled, and not merely tripled, for with the development of high-alloy steels and super-alloys a broad stream of new materials became available. What caused this unprecedented upsurge and why was it so late in coming? The answers are important.

The old metals industry grew up in the fixed world of the ancients, secretive, prescientific. There were the noble metals and base metals of antiquity—those found closest to a pure state—and no more. Workable ore bodies were few. The great metal and banking houses of the Middle Ages, such as the Fuggers of Augsburg, sat upon these first natural monopolies, wresting a few metals from the earth with ax and fire, and dispensing them to society with monopolistic complacence. Techniques advanced but in the slow tempo of an artisan industry, in which most of the artisans died young from the fumes and burdens. The metal lords patronized alchemists, not for a rational investigation of nature or processes, but in pursuit of the witless dream of transmuting base metals into gold. Ironically, the alchemists' probings, more rational than their employers knew, laid the foundations of chemistry and fed the growth of experimental science in the seventeenth and eighteenth centuries, in which many of the metals now hailed as new were discovered and isolated as chemical elements. But the practical metal barons weren't interested in chemical elements.

Some of this medieval air clung to the old metals industry even in the industrial revolution. The obsession and monopolistic growth then centered on iron and steel. Other men picked up chemistry and found hidden in its few non-metallic elements the endless, readily reactive compounds still being elaborated into the giant organic-chemical industry. But the less reactive metallic elements, by reason of some of the very properties that make them important—hardness, strength, stability—were more refractory to development. And the old metals industry didn't try. Dim in social outlook, it was even dimmer in scientific foresight. It wouldn't think of poking into the table of elements, the atom, or the molecule for new products or markets. Even now only 3 per cent of all U. S. industrial research is done by the primary-metals industry. The chemical industry, as yet only a fourth as big in dollar volume, carries 20 per cent.

The Chemical Revolution in Metals

Hence, almost none of the new metals have been introduced to commerce by the industry that might have been expected to know most about metals. Nearly all the upsurge in new metals is the product of the chemical industry, which, having enormously developed its organic compounds, is circling back to develop the inorganics. Not far behind is the electrical industry, also mixed up in chemicals, particularly such huge aggregations as General Electric, Westinghouse, and Bell Laboratories, which, to develop power plants, the incandescent lamp, electronic tube, and other newer devices, found that they had to develop a whole range of new metals and alloys. Thus the alchemists, cast out when they failed to turn lead to gold, return in modern guise to throw the ancient metals industry into entirely new patterns of growth.

Elements Endlessly Flowing

Consider the stages since 1900. First aluminum, freed from clay by the electrochemist, Charles Martin Hall, and breaking out of its early monopoly pattern into growth as a dynamic chemical operation. Then magnesium, won from brine and sea water by Dow Chemical. Then titanium, newest of the structural light metals, first offered for sale by E. I. du Pont de Nemours & Co. less than five years ago. And even more recently, germanium, developed by Bell Laboratories for the newest of electronic devices, transistors. Even the major alloy steels, rising only since 1900, have had their basic development largely in the laboratories and pilot plants of big chemical-metallurgical producers. The Electro Metallurgical division of Union Carbide & Carbon Corp., for instance, the biggest and broadest supplier of ferroalloys, had a major role in the development of stainless steels in the U.S. And International Nickel Co., in one of the earliest research laboratories, developed in collaboration with the industry a prodigious line of nickel steels.

Approximately a century, therefore, after Mendelyeev's periodic law brought atomic order to the elements, the seemingly simple but arduous linking of science to industry is beginning to release the immense power and store of materials residing in the table of elements. Of the 100 elements now known, over three-fourths can be classed as metals.* Yet this large group has been the slowest to emerge. Of the eighty-three known metals, only about a third so far are of important tonnage or value, about a third are still of minor importance or just coming into use, and a third are practically unknown metals waiting future development. Thus nearly two-thirds of the area is still frontier. When it comes to putting a name to the era in which this frontier is being sweepingly entered, the familiar "Light Metals Age" won't do. It is more than light metals, it is a plethoric mixture of metals. For want of a better term, and provisionally, it is the New Metals Age.

The Amazing Metals Mix

The new age has three leading characteristics. It is consuming metals, old and new, at a rate never before known in history. As the report of the

* The non-metals: hydrogen, helium, carbon, nitrogen, oxygen, fluorine, neon, phosphorus, sulfur, chlorine, argon, bromine, krypton, iodine, xenon, astatine, and radon.

President's Materials Policy Commission underlined, the U.S. alone since World War I has used most metals in quantities exceeding the total used throughout the entire world in all history preceding 1914. It is an age that, under this driving consumption and a second round of armament in a decade, is running into imbalances, temporary shortages, and sharply rising costs, particularly in the older, strategic metals. And, finally, it is the age of a multiplicity of metals, which in the long run offers the best solution to the supply difficulties.

Under all these pressures, and with technology moving up to relieve them, steel, copper, and most of the older metals continue to grow bigger—steel embarking on a $500-million, low-grade-taconite-ore program to hold its stake in the thinning Mesabi, while throwing out giant new supply lines to high-grade iron deposits in Labrador and Venezuela. It is plain that the time-tested older metals are neither going to disappear nor much diminish for a long time to come. But the new metals grow faster. And while each metal has its own character, and many are irreplaceable in certain uses, the sheer variety of new metals introduces an explosive new freedom of choice and action.

It is this power of technology to create new materials and techniques on an ever widening scale that injects a new element into twentieth-century economics, confounding both Marx and Manchester. Reasoning from the still fairly static materials of nineteenth-century industrialism, it was easy to foresee a concentration of power in monopolies, oppressive or shining, depending on the viewpoint. But, while the concentrations of power have taken place, technology is now constantly creating new situations, shifts in power, and a new kind of competition that make old monopolistic concepts less and less operative. This is nowhere more clear than in the metals, where, in the upthrust of new materials, markets are in the greatest flux in history.

The real force of this new order may be seen in a development that, in three years, has made a new material out of the oldest of all ferrous products, dormant and declining for a century—cast iron. International Nickel's laboratories, searching for improvements in nickel-alloy cast irons, developed a method for making brittle cast iron as strong and tough as ordinary steel by small additions of magnesium. Called ductile or spheroidal graphite iron, it was an entirely new material—strong, ductile, wear-resistant, heat-resistant—combining the casting economy of iron with many of the advantages of steel.

Few metal developments have moved so quickly as ductile iron. Opened to licensing in 1949, the process now has over 200 licensees in eighteen foreign countries and the U.S., operating in over 600 foundries. It is replacing gray iron, cast steel, wrought steel, bronze, and even aluminum in big diesel and automotive crankshafts, gears, bearings, plowshares, pistons, compressor heads, valves, pipes, and fittings. And, through precision casting by the shell-molding process, it is opening up for foundries a whole new low-cost field of precision-parts manufacture. It is, in fact, putting the foundry industry, with over 3,000 small, dispersed units, back in competition with big steel and big steel fabricators. Since 1949 the tonnage in ductile iron has jumped from nothing to 100,000 tons, and in a few years it may go to five million tons to become the third-biggest metal in the economy.

The Shifting Mix

Across the board, the metals shift and strain as developments rise and the pressures vary. Aluminum takes an increasingly substantial bite into copper's wire and cable markets, and bites steadily into other copper uses. The can industry pushes coatings on steel to replace perennially critical tin in 80 per cent of its production, while a new aluminum solder moves in to displace tin alloy in smoothing automobile bodies. And the Malayan tin industry fights back with increased research and assurances of ample supply. Union Carbide's Electromet division makes a notable development of manganese-containing stainless steel to cut in half the content of critical nickel, urgently needed elsewhere. Titanium alloys begin to displace stainless steel in aircraft. And continuous casting and hot extrusion of stainless bring it within range of competing with aluminum for other markets. General Motors develops an aluminum dip for coating steel to replace zinc, which is also being squeezed out of increasing numbers of automotive parts by aluminum die castings. And moving up behind aluminum are magnesium die castings, propelled by the economics of getting more parts per pound from a metal lighter than aluminum.

No small part of the flux is economic, in which regard the older metals industry is increasingly vulnerable as it is forced to thinner ores, deeper mining, more distant ore bodies, with costs mounting all along the way. Over a 1939 base, zinc prices have soared 280 per cent, lead 275 per cent, pig iron 145 per cent, copper 118 per cent, while the higher-priced newer metals as a whole have been held to the well-managed price levels of the chemical industry, 25 per cent above 1939, with aluminum actually 5 per cent below 1939. Unless the older metals companies attack their costs, diversify, and more aggressively develop new markets, the competitive gap between old and new will close tighter. And not only under the squeeze of new metals, for the chemical industry is ambidextrous and catholic in developing new meterials. Polystyrene plastics already have ousted some 9,000 tons a year of aluminum and 2,000 tons of stainless steel in making refrigerators. And polyester-glass-fiber laminates are coming up fast as a remarkable new engineering material, this year making its bow in all-plastic, stock, sports-car bodies. For the next quarter of a century at least, this amazing materials mix will be precipitating a new industrial structure.

The Light Metals

To see some of the major directions in which this structure is building, it is necessary to review the new metals by groups and functions. The first group in point of size, dynamics, and growth is the structural light metals, in which the signal fact is the rapid rise to tonnage proportions.

The alloy steels have nearly doubled in tonnage since 1940. These are the high-strength, high-heat and corrosion-resistant steels—with high strength-weight ratios—that tool, equip, and enter into the power, chemical, oil, electrical, aircraft, armament, and other high-technology industries. Now about 10 per cent of total steel, or roughly 10 million tons, they are expected to hold that percentage in steel's current expansion, and eventually outrun it. Heavy defense needs, along with stockpiling of critical alloying metals, have pushed alloy-metal expansion much higher and faster than the steels themselves. Supply goals for 1954–55 have been successively bumped up: ferrochrome to about double its 1950 level; cobalt to 10,000 tons, or exactly double 1950; nickel nearly double to 190,000 tons; and so on, through silicon, manganese, vanadium, molybdenum, tungsten, columbium, and others. To meet this, Carbide's Electromet is upping capacity with a $100-million new plant at Marietta, Ohio, probably the world's largest, with two radically new mass-production processes for low-carbon ferrochrome and electrolytic chrome and manganese. Expanding in scale below Electromet is a tight, competitive group of less-diversified alloy suppliers, including Pittsburgh Metallurgical, Ohio Ferro-Alloys, Vanadium Corp. of America, and Climax Molybdenum.

Aluminum is now running at five times its 1940 rate of production, and by the end of 1953 it will be up to nearly eight times. In less than three years the industry will have doubled its pre-Korea capacity to over 1,500,000 tons. On top of this, the government last year pushed forward still another round of expansion, totaling 200,000 tons, which will carry U. S. supplies, imports and secondary production included, to 2,400,000 tons by 1955. Yet the industry consensus is that aluminum has only begun to realize its potential, so far primarily based on aircraft and transportation, but beginning to exploit the building, construction, electrical, automotive, appliance, and air-conditioning industries. Versatile, still developing alloys (Alcoa has just announced two new ones with equal strength at half the weight of older alloys) will open still other fields. Only since 1945 the number of aluminum fabricators has jumped from 5,500 to nearly 20,000.

On the present expansion through 1953, total primary ingot capacity will divide thus: Alcoa, which alone is spending $350 million on new plant, 40 per cent (down from 50 per cent in 1950); Reynolds Aluminum, 28 per cent (down from 32); Kaiser Aluminum, 27 per cent (up from 18); and, a newcomer, Anaconda Copper, 5 per cent, from a new $45-million plant in Montana. Opening the new round of expansion late last fall, the departing Administration, following its policy of deliberately creating competition, brought still another basic producer into the program. This was Olin Industries, which, adding to its diverse interests in gunpowder, manufacturing, and chemicals, will build a $170-million, 110,000-ton-a-year aluminum plant. Also interested in getting in on the expansion are Kennecott Copper (some 40 per cent of copper's market is vulnerable to aluminum), Wheland Co., a big gray-iron foundry at Chattanooga, Tennessee, and Apex Smelting Co., which is building the first aluminum-from-clay plant at Springfield, Oregon. To top all this, Alcoa last fall proposed a mammoth hydroelectric-power and aluminum development in Alaska to deliver 200,000 tons of capacity by 1957, costing initially $400 million and eventually $700 million. These are figures to rival steel's capital investments, and indicative of aluminum's humming potential.

Magnesium is moving at more than twenty times 1940 production. Its output is six times the pre-Korean rate, and is scheduled to reach 130,000 tons by early 1953. The lightest of structural metals, magnesium had the disadvantage of following closely on aluminum in time and end uses, with some peculiarly tough fabricating and corrosion problems of its own. But in 1951 magnesium registered a significant growth stage when its wrought products passed castings in volume; and increasing markets in the automotive, trailer-truck, materials-handling, machinery, and appliance fields, as well as in aircraft and ordnance, indicate that the metal has reached a major turning point. The main deterrent to faster growth now is that there is still only one private producer, Dow—which itself would welcome some competition. All current increased capacity is from government standby plants, operated by Dow, National Lead, Kaiser Aluminum, Diamond Alkali, Nelco Metals, and Pacific Northwest Alloys. One or another of these, besides Dow, may stay in the business, but it isn't certain. In the long view, however, magnesium's limitless availability, lightness, and strength in evolving alloys must lead it to parallel aluminum.

Titanium, almost non-existent as a pure metal four years ago, is on the most spectacular growth curve of all, up from nothing to 1,200 tons last year. Defense goals for 1955, or earlier, have been hiked twice in twelve months, first to 10,000 tons, then to 22,000, with another revision probable in mid-1953. In contrast to aluminum's or magnesium's quarter-century struggle to reach like tonnages, this is the fastest development in history of an entirely new metal. It is the more phenomenal in that the problems besetting titanium make those of the older light metals pale. A highly reactive metal in the molten state, ductile titanium is wrested from ilmenite and rutile-ore sands only by the most laborious means. The only commercial methods thus far are based on the U. S. Bureau of Mines' cumbersome Kroll process, by which the metal is batch-handled in inert helium atmospheres and vacuum-arc furnaces, producing a mill-finished product at $15 to $30 a pound. Yet titanium has such a combination of high strength, light weight, and good heat and corrosion resistance—bridging the gap between aluminum and stainless steel—that even at the price it is a natural for high-speed aircraft, naval construction, and ordnance.

Getting the new metal into production, while simultaneously solving its multiple alloying and fabricating problems, has generated a scramble unlike any previously known in the metals. There are three basic producers so far: du Pont, which is tripling production to 13,500 tons by 1956 in a government-financed, $14,700,000 expansion; National Lead, which was the first to get to ton-a-day production and is now moving toward ten tons a day; and Crane Co., the most recent and smallest. But du Pont early assigned the ingot-melting and fabricating part of the job to its subsidiary, Remington Arms, which in turn formed a joint company with Crucible Steel (Rem-Cru Titanium, Inc.) to draw in heavy fabricating experience. And National Lead formed a fifty-fifty company with Allegheny Ludlum Steel (Titanium Metals Corp.) to do the same. And P. R. Mallory & Co., Inc., with a pilot plant going, joined with Sharon Steel in Mallory-Sharon Titanium Corp. Meanwhile, nearly everyone has going a research project to outflank the Kroll process, including Union Carbide, Monsanto, Dow, National Research, Horizons, Inc., Glidden, Kennecott Copper, New Jersey Zinc. To encourage the market and build experience, the Air Force has now specified titanium sheet and parts in two advanced jet planes. Originally over-glamorized as a metal to withstand high jet-engine heats, titanium is now more soberly seen as a major addition to the structural metals, important not only to the military but to many prospective industrial users. If the problems of a continuous process can be solved soon, prognosticators do not blink at 500,000 tons by 1960.

The Rare Metals

Ranging far below the light metals in volume, but wider in variety of use and outlook is a growing group of materials that might be called the rare metals. Except for such older items as platinum, palladium, and indium, these are, for the most part, rising new metals of specialized uses that may grow to considerable poundage but never perform more than small, critical functions in advancing technologies. A few, however, may someday soar out of the rare category on some turn of events, for this group forms part of the metals frontier.

Perhaps the member of this group closest to the light metals is titanium's sister metal in ductile form, zirconium, which has many of the same properties as titanium, is obtained by the Kroll process, but is more difficult and expensive to get into pure ingot form. Thus far its only outstanding property is high permeability to slow neutrons, a factor useful in nuclear-reactor construction, hence the Atomic Energy Commission has been pushing production. Only two producers have made zirconium in pure bar form, Foote Mineral Co. and Westinghouse, working up a laboratory process to industrial scale to produce metal to the fantastic purity of 99.7 per cent. The program for more basic production now includes a new $2,400,000 plant that Carborundum Metals Co. is building and will operate for the AEC at Akron, New York, to supply seventy-five tons a year of sponge zirconium and hafnium, a metal closely associated with zirconium in its ores and in its properties. Until secondary or civilian uses appear for the metal, however, private producers are reluctant to risk their own money on zirconium metal. Less pure or alloying forms have been made for some time by Carbide's Electromet, National Lead, and others, for deoxidizing high-alloy steels and for creating a growing number of nonferrous alloys. A new zirconium-cerium alloy of magnesium so raises strength and stability at medium temperatures that it has put magnesium castings into some jet-engine parts. More aggressive development of high-purity zirconium alloys will probably produce special, high-corrosion-resistant materials and a possible replacement for scarce tantalum.

The work on titanium and zirconium has stimulated much work on getting other metals into highly pure forms, for with titanium it was discovered that small impurities could change the entire character of a metal. Inclusions of oxygen and nitrogen beyond 0.2 per cent, along with other slight contaminations of carbon, silicon, aluminum, or iron, made all the difference between getting ductile metal or a useless, brittle composition. Union Carbide, Climax Molybdenum, Foote Mineral, Battelle, and others have been working in turn on ultrapure chromium, vanadium, molybdenum, columbium, tungsten, silicon, calcium, manganese, lithium, boron, and hafnium. In pure form these are to be classed as rare metals, with characteristics quite different from previously known forms. They are just beginning to develop uses and are likely to lead to a whole range of new alloys.

The Range of the Rare

The range of rising new metals is bewildering. There is germanium, the semiconductor or electronic-transistor metal, which is moving so fast that dozens of small manufacturers, trained by Bell Labs and others, are springing up to meet demand, and West Virginia's coal beds are being ransacked for germanium-bearing seams to extend the supply. Zinc concentrates are the only U. S. source thus far, and Eagle-Picher Co. is the main supplier. But there are also other developing semiconductors: silicon metal, selenium, tellurium, gray tin, and a new cadmium sulfide crystal that may equal germanium in efficiency.

And there is silicon metal itself, which is going into the big growth of silicone plastics, and moving into the rising field of intermetallic coatings on metal. And lithium, the lightest metal known, but reactive with air and water, which goes into lithium-silicone high-temperature greases, new magnesium alloys, aluminum welding and brazing compositions, and which may, if the hydrogen bomb comes off, become the main source of tritium, or heavy hydrogen. Lithium compounds are in expansion, mainly by Lithium Corp. and Foote Mineral, to 10 million pounds or more by 1955. Then there is gallium, a metal that melts in the hand, and expands like water on freezing, whose unusual properties are being explored on the basis of a few hundred pounds' production by Eagle-Picher and Alcoa. And there is a weird, important, new combination of bismuth and manganese called Bismanol, developed by powder metallurgy in the Naval Ordnance Laboratory. This material, though both constituents are nonmagnetic, forms a permanent magnet with the highest coercive force known, aimed to supplant high-nickel-cobalt Alnico magnets in many uses.

Finally, just about to come into much wider exploitation are the rare-earth metals, a group of fifteen or so metals with fantastic names, which are neither very rare nor earths, but which are so closely mixed in their ores that most of them until recently have resisted separation in any quantity. Cerium, the best known of the group, has been available for a long time in a mixture of rare earths more properly known as misch metal, which makes lighter flints, and is growing as an alloy in magnesium and in stainless and other steels, where it adds workability. But development under the AEC of ion-exchange extraction and a new liquid-to-liquid industrial separation process is now bringing out in kilogram amounts for the first time relatively pure rare earths: in order, lanthanum, cerium, praseodymium, neodymium, promethium, samarium, europium, gadolinium, terbium, yttrium, dysprosium, holmium, erbium, thulium ytterbium, lutecium. And discovery of large, new rare-earth ore bodies in the West has increased activity. This is a vast area of unknown properties and uses to be explored. But one of the metals, gadolinium, has the highest known absorption of slow neutrons, which makes it potential atomic-reactor material, and there is likely to be found in the group a range of entirely new light-metal alloys and additives to steel and super-alloys.

The Hot Metals

The next large group, the refractory metals, embraces the most pressing and intense area of development on the metals frontier. The salient point of this frontier is the bladed turbine wheel of the aircraft gas-turbine or jet engine. Under the blasting hot temperatures and centrifugal loads and stresses at which these blades must operate, they are pressing the ultimate limits of presently known metals. The thin turbine blades must maintain their strength, curvature, shock resistance, and dimensional stability in the red-hot range of 1,300° to 1,600° Fahrenheit and beyond. Steel in this whirling inferno would burn out like paper. Titanium, whose high melting point (3,300°F) had built high hopes for a great heat-resistant metal, has so far developed no alloy that does not begin to lose strength sharply around 1,000°F. Stainless steel, a ranking high-temperature metal, starts to lose its grip rapidly at 1,300°F. Yet the jet engineer, to gain the efficiencies inherent in the thermodynamics of his engine, is pressing for metals or materials to break the heat barrier at 1,600° to 2,000°F.

So far the only working metals approaching this barrier are a group of complex nickel-chrome-cobalt-molybdenum-columbium-tungsten super-alloys, containing little or no iron. These are related to or descended from the old Stellite cutting-tool alloys developed by Haynes Stellite Co., another division of Union Carbide, which underlies most of U. S. metallurgy, and which is the major supplier of super-alloys to the hottest spots in jet aircraft. Also within the super-alloy range, but in limited use in this country, is a British group of nickel-chrome alloys, minus cobalt, called the Nimonic series, which bears the brunt of British jet production. The newest Haynes cobalt-base, high-temperature alloy, however, has reached an operational level of 1,600° Fahrenheit, and for short intervals, 1,800°, which is the ultimate thus far.

The working and shaping of such refractory metals has the banging, brawny air of a frontier. Only the oldest, heaviest type of mills can work these red-hot hard metals, which give forth deep groans and crunching protests in the working. The critical turbine blades are either forged or cast, and a big producer like Thompson Products does both. Haynes Stellite has adapted to bucket-blade mass production the "lost wax" of investment-molding method of precision casting, ancient to the jewelry and dental arts, and some idea of its scope may be gained by the fact that this one department alone has shot up to some 2,000 employees, and will shortly be duplicated in a second plant.

The Outer Frontier

To withstand the temperatures the jet engineer is striving for, entirely different materials will probably have to be developed. Spurring the effort is the critical factor of supply, for the super-alloys take such huge amounts of the most strategic metals—some run as high as 78 per cent nickel or 67 per cent cobalt—that in an all-out war, production or quality might be crippled. Much work is going into new powder-metallurgical hybrids of metals and ceramics, generally called "cermets." Carbide's Electromet is working on aluminum oxide with chromium and other binders. Tiny Kennametal, Inc., has started production on a series of new titanium carbide and nickel cermets, which have worked in experimental bucket blades at temperatures up to 2,200°F. And mixed carbides of hafnium and tantalum have been reported to have the highest melting point recorded for any substance. But one property common to all discontinuous ceramic-metal structures thus far is a tendency to brittleness, fatal in high-stress turbine blades.

In the search for a tough metal to do the job, there is high interest in Climax Molybdenum's development, since 1945, of larger and larger ingots of pure molybdenum. This ductile metal, with a melting point of 4,750° Fahrenheit, could be the most available of all high-temperature metals. The drawback is that molybdenum oxidizes rapidly at high temperatures. To overcome this, a multiplicity of metallic coatings (e.g., silicon) and bonded ceramic coatings (e.g., chromium-glass frit) are being worked on, which also have a tendency to brittleness but which have allowed moly to function for many hours at 3,000° Fahrenheit and are promising of future development.

In Labyrinthian Progress

When and if a new high-temperature composition for turbine blades is achieved, however, then the whole range of jet-engine operating temperatures and the materials to fit them will also have to be stepped up. Titanium alloys can move up in places where aluminum, magnesium, and some stainless steels are now functioning, but super-alloys will probably have to take over a greater part of the hotter regions now served by lesser alloys. Thus there is a kind of labyrinth in the heat-barrier problem, with no end to the pressure on metals.

Yet this problem not only defines the outer frontiers of jet engines and metals, but the future of the whole industrial civilization massed behind it. The full realization of atomic power for peaceful, industrial uses cannot be gained without metals and materials to withstand even higher temperatures than in jet aircraft. And, behind that, the progress and increased productivity of the power, chemical, petroleum, electronic and other advanced industries are dependent to a critical extent on raising operating temperatures and pressures to new heights. And, in turn, the chemical and electrical industries are now joined in storming those heights with the protean development of new metals, materials, and markets, moving steadily toward clean, continuous processes, tapping ever more abundant sources of metals in sea water, alumina clay, and ilmenite sand. These are the characteristic marks of the new age in progress.

60. Recent Trends in the Pattern of European Manufacturing *

Since the beginning of the Industrial Revolution in England and its subsequent spread to neighboring countries, Western Europe has been the leading manufacturing center of the world. The technical ability developed there has, however, lagged behind industrialization developed on other continents. Twice in the last 35 years the industries of Europe have faced the problem of recovery from physical war destruction and disruption of labor supply and markets. In this reading Miller discusses Europe's most recent recovery efforts, the progress that has been made, and current problems facing Europe's principal industries.

At the conclusion of hostilities in 1945, a large portion of Europe's industrial capacity had either been destroyed or was not functioning at the time. The transportation system, always a primary target for enemy bombs, was severely damaged in many regions. Trade had essentially ceased to exist. Everywhere machinery was worn and obsolete. Since

* E. Willard Miller, "Recent Trends in the Pattern of European Manufacturing," *Journal of Geography,* Vol. 53, No. 5, May 1954, pp. 185–196. By permission of the *Journal of Geography,* official publication of the National Council of Geography Teachers.

The author (1915) is Professor of Geography and Chief, Division of Geography, The Pennsylvania State College. His primary interest is economic geography, and he has published a number of articles in geographical journals on mineral resources and manufacturing.

Europe had one of the great industrial economies prior to World War II, it was imperative for the welfare of millions of people that industrial productive capacity be restored as quickly as possible.

Bottlenecks to European Industrial Recovery

Because of the chaotic condition in the early postwar economy there were many bottlenecks that had to be overcome before manufacturing could resume. Of the early basic problems none were more critical than that of securing necessary fuels and steel as a raw material. It is said that in 1945 and 1946 Europe's need for fuel was second only to its need for additional food. The shortage of coal was one of the greatest limiting factors in the early postwar industrial recovery. While coal supplies were allocated to the most strategic industries, supplies were insufficient for even such critical industries as steel, fertilizer, gas and electric plants. This great shortage was due to the low output of coal in Germany. Consequently the other coal producing nations of Europe took strong measures to increase their production. These actions included improving productivity, development of rehabilitation and reconstruction programs underground as well as on the surface, additional manpower was secured in some countries, absenteeism was discouraged, transportation of coal to consuming points improved, output of metallurgical coals was emphasized, and a start was made to adjust burning equipment and practices to the use of available types of solid fuels. As a result coal production rose in Europe from about 408 million tons in 1946 to 460,000,000 in 1948 and to nearly 550 million tons in 1950. However, this output was still between 20 and 30 million tons below prewar coal production.

In the postwar period France and Poland had the largest increases. United Kingdom and Belgium were still below their output of the 1930's, and Germany's coal production in 1950 was barely two-thirds that of the prewar period. It is, thus, evident that while coal production was rising in certain countries other sources of energy were needed if industrial recovery were to be achieved.

The development of hydro and thermo electric power and the growing use of petroleum are important developments in the substitution of other fuels for coal in postwar Europe. The increase in the use of electric power since 1938 is common to all European countries. Striking developments have occurred in United Kingdom, Sweden, The Netherlands, Czechoslovakia, Austria, Yugoslavia and Spain, where capacity has been enlarged by more than 50 per cent. Electricity now provides half of Sweden's total consumption of energy and an even greater proportion in Italy, Switzerland, Norway and Finland. From 1938 to 1950 the annual electrical power production in Europe increased from 180 to nearly 300 billion kilowatt hours.

There has likewise been a great increase in the use of petroleum since World War II. Compared with prewar, there has been a rise of more than 50 per cent in the consumption of petroleum products. The most important general reasons for the large increase in European petroleum consumption since the war have been the substantial expansion of truck transportation and the substitution of fuel oil for coal in merchant shipping and in industry. France and Great Britain have had the largest refinery expansion programs but significant increases have also occurred in Italy, Austria, Belgium and Sweden.

As a result of these expansion programs the total consumption of energy has increased considerably since the prewar period. If all energy is converted to equivalent tons of coal, consumption rose from 715 million tons in 1938 to 718 million in 1948, and reached 800 million tons in 1950. Greatest increases in total energy consumption per capita occurred in Norway, Sweden, Poland and Czechoslovakia. Moderate increases in energy consumption on a per capita basis are shown for the United Kingdom, The Netherlands, Denmark, Switzerland and Austria.

At the conclusion of hostilities all European countries attempted to expand their engineering industries, so that steel was one of the basic raw materials immediately in great demand. However, in the first postwar year output in Europe was but two-thirds the production of 1938. The most significant factor in this decline was the low level of production in Germany which in 1946 was barely 16 per cent of prewar output. Since Germany could no longer supply steel to Europe, many countries increased their steel capacity to supply their own needs and export to deficient areas.

Altho there were many fundamental problems to be solved such as inadequate supplies of coke, iron ore and scrap metal, and difficult means of increasing capacity, steel production has risen by 10 to 30 per cent each year over the preceding year. The low point in production was 1945 when less than 19,000,000 tons of steel were produced. This was essentially 30,000,000 tons below the 1938 level of production. The most important feature of European industrial history in 1948 was a rise in steel production of 10.5 million tons or 28 per cent over 1947. The consumption of finished steel which is the best single indication of the activity of the engineering industries—was in 1948, outside Germany, 42 per cent above prewar levels. The critical steel shortage was, thus, essentially eliminated.

Output has, however, continued to rise from the 45,500,000 tons produced in 1948 to over 59,000,000 tons in 1950. Significant increases have occurred in the United Kingdom, Luxembourg, Poland and Sweden. By 1950 Germany was the only steel producing country that had not exceeded its prewar output; however, production was increasing rapidly.

Trends of Major Industries

Textiles

Before the war, the European textile industry occupied a prominent place, not only in the economic activity of Europe, but also in the world textile industry. Altho the European textile industry declined during the 1930's depression, it is estimated that in 1938 this industry employed 3.6 million workers and produced 35 per cent of the world's textiles. World War II had a strong adverse effect on the industry in partially dispersing its labor force, by preventing the replacement of worn out equipment, securing necessary raw materials and by cutting off markets which in the postwar period have been difficult to regain owing to newly developed competition.

At the conclusion of the war the rehabilitation of the textile industry was necessary because of the size of the labor force it employed, the basic human requirement which it provided for, its economic significance and the volume of its international trade. Of the basic textiles the cotton industry has shown a substantial recovery in the postwar period and many countries have surpassed their prewar level of production. A lag in recovery is most noticeable in two of the traditional textile producing nations—United Kingdom and France. The greatest growth has occurred in the smaller nations where output had been limited prior to World War II.

Of more significance has been the notable change in the type of textiles produced in the postwar period. There has been a general displacement of cotton by wool and, particularly, rayon. The increase in cotton goods in 1950 was only six per cent over 1935, compared with 75 per cent by rayon and 27 per cent by wool. Significant advances have been made in rayon production in the United Kingdom, France, Belgium, The Netherlands, Norway, Sweden, Czechoslovakia, Austria and Switzerland. Italy, the major producer in 1938, however, had not attained her prewar level by 1950. Emphasis has been placed on the synthetic fibers because of available raw materials and the demand for this type of cloth.

. . . The 1951 output was substantially above the 1938 level in essentially all countries. Since 1946, the smaller countries such as Ireland, Norway, Sweden, Finland, Denmark, The Netherlands, Belgium, Poland, Hungary and Greece have increased their textile production by 50 per cent or more. However, production in the major producing countries such as the United Kingdom, Western Germany, France and Italy, have had a much smaller expansion. As a result there has been a greater change in the pattern of the postwar textile production than in any of the other major industries of Europe.

By 1950 a crisis was growing in the textile industry and by 1951 it had spread throughout the whole of western Europe. Of manufactured products, textiles were first to be in excess supply in postwar Europe. Retail sales dropped to a low level and supplies increased nearly everywhere. Some observers felt that it was a temporary decline, but most believed that the difficulties were the beginning of a long period of depression in textiles due to overexpansion after the war.

The situation was most acute in the new, smaller producing countries. In nearly all of these countries, textile production is based exclusively on sales to the home market. For several years after the war this expanded output was easily absorbed by a domestic market. However, by 1950, this pent-up demand was largely satisfied and the larger countries had gained the export markets so that the level of textile production in most of the smaller countries seems to be quite out of line with changes in their real national income and consumption patterns. It seems extremely unlikely that these countries will develop textile exports on a large scale and major structural changes appear unavoidable in the years to come. This prospect carries with it the danger of a revival of textile protectionism in the smaller countries, which in turn would make the great European textile producers still more dependent on exports overseas. The solution of the western European textile crisis is, therefore, closely connected with the outlook for world trade in textiles and with Europe's competitive position in the world market.

Engineering Industries

Because of great destruction and inability to replace worn-out machinery during the war years, there has been a heavy demand in the postwar years for products of the engineering industries. Consequently, production in the engineering industries has risen more rapidly than industrial production in general. Germany and Italy are the only nations where these industries lagged greatly during the early postwar recovery. By 1948, with the exception of Germany, the engineering industries of Europe were some 30 per cent above their postwar level of production. However, Western Germany's engineering industry rose rapidly after 1949 and by the end of 1951 was approximately one-fifth larger than in 1938.

Many branches of the engineering industries have shown a remarkable growth. One of the spectacular increases over prewar levels of production has been achieved in the agricultural machinery industries. In 1950 tractor production was six times as great as in 1938 with the result that there were four times as many tractors on European farms as there had been in the prewar period. The United Kingdom provided nearly half of the total output until 1950, but in recent years tractor production has increased rapidly in Germany. With the increased farm mechanization there arose the need for new types of farm implements. As a result production of agricultural machinery has risen so that Europe in 1950 produced about 25 per cent of the world's total in contrast to 15 per cent prior to World War II.

Output of motor vehicles has also had a considerable rise over the prewar period. In the early postwar years commercial vehicles had the greatest expansion, but since 1949 passenger cars have experienced the largest gains. In 1950, passenger car production was 45 per cent above the 1938 level and the stock of commercial vehicles was more than 40 per cent greater than in 1938. In most countries the market price of used cars has continually exceeded the list price of new cars. The limits to European output have been set by capacity to produce and not by demand. In most countries vehicle sales have been restricted in order that there can be a large export trade, particularly, in passenger cars.

Production in other engineering industries has also shown a strong upward trend. The shipyards of Europe, with the exception of Germany and Italy, whose output was restricted, have essentially worked at full capacity. The United Kingdom has produced about one-half of the total output, a proportion somewhat higher than before the war, when German production was considerable. German shipyards began their revival in 1949 and are once again competing with other European shipbuilders. Finally, output of industrial machinery was more than one-third higher in 1950 than in 1938.

In conclusion, let us consider the total trends in engineering production. First, by 1951 all countries of Europe had a higher output in the engineering industries than before World War II. The greatest increases since 1946 occurred in Poland, Austria, Denmark, The Netherlands, Hungary and the United Kingdom. It is to be noted, however, that increases in many of the older industrial nations such as France, Italy, Belgium, Switzerland and Germany were moderate.

Chemical Industries

In the chemical industries the most striking feature of the immediate postwar period was the elimination of Germany as an exporter of chemical products from the world market in which she formerly held first place. Because of the dollar shortage combined with war destruction and the general lack of coal and power, there was an alarming deficiency of chemical products and fertilizers in most countries.

Simultaneously with the collapse of European production, demand rose above that of the prewar period. In the case of fertilizers, this was the result of the impoverishment of the soil during the war and of the effort made in most countries for increasing agricultural production to cope with the shortage of foodstuffs. In the case of other chemical products, the greater demand came as a result of technical progress which has greatly increased the various methods of application.

In order to overcome the deficiencies there have been large expansion programs initiated in all of the fertilizer industries. Most remarkable has been the increases in super phosphate production in Spain, the United Kingdom, Belgium, The Netherlands, Sweden and Finland. By 1950 Germany and France were the only countries that had not surpassed their prewar production, and total European output had risen from 6,900,000 to 8,600,000 tons.

The basic chemical industry has also experienced a rapid expansion. For example, production of sulphuric acid has shown significant increases in Spain, the United Kingdom, Sweden, Finland, Poland and Czechoslovakia. By 1950 total European production was about 15 per cent above the 1938 output. Again, Germany was one of the few countries where output was below prewar levels, but rapid expansion was occurring.

. . . The replacement of Germany by other European countries in supplying their own needs is shown by the fact that in 1947 total European output had nearly reached its prewar level. In each of the postwar years production has increased by 10 to 20 per cent over the preceding year. By 1951 an index figure of 165 was attained when compared with the 1938 output. Greatest gains were experienced by Austria, Finland, Greece, Italy, The Netherlands, Poland, Sweden and the United Kingdom. By 1951 Germany had also exceeded its prewar chemical output. Thus, all European countries had risen above their 1938 level of production.

Present Pattern of Industrial Production

While industrial production was on a low level at the conclusion of hostilities in 1945, output has had a generally steady rise in the postwar period (Fig. 22). By 1947 European industrial production was still but 85 per cent of its prewar level. Since then, however, output has risen rapidly so that by 1948 the prewar level of production had been surpassed, and in 1951 the index number of European industrial production was 140 compared with a 1938 value of 100.

The rate of recovery, however, varied considerably with the individual countries. Of the European nations, the greatest relative gains have been achieved by the United Kingdom, Denmark, Norway, Sweden, Finland, Austria and Yugoslavia. The striking industrial growth in such countries

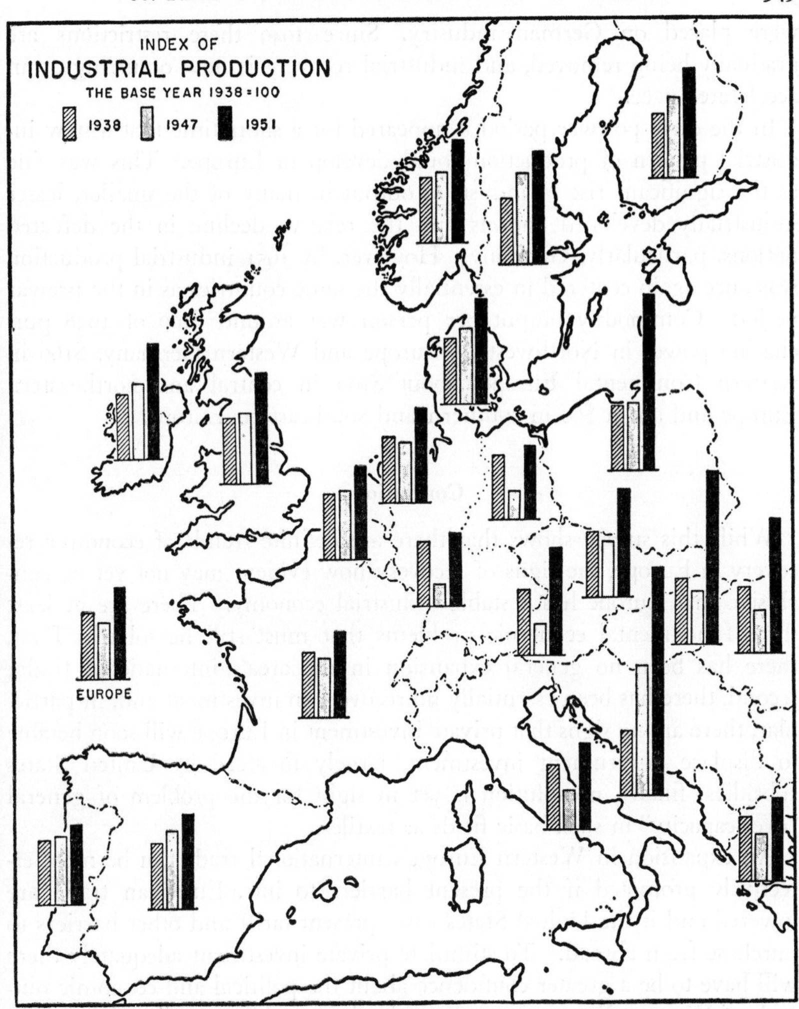

Figure 22

By 1951 all European countries had surpassed their 1938 level of industrial production. This illustrates a remarkable recovery from the effects of World War II.

as Bulgaria, Hungary and Rumania appear significant largely due to their low industrial output prior to World War II, and in Poland, the acquisition of Silesia has greatly strengthened her industrial position. Countries that have experienced moderate expansion include France, Belgium, The Netherlands, Italy and Spain. One of the striking features in the postwar period was the long industrial collapse of Germany where recovery lagged greatly until 1949. In the early postwar years heavy restrictions were placed on German industry. Since 1949 these restrictions are gradually being removed, and industrial recovery is now occurring at an accelerated pace.

In the early postwar period it appeared for a short time that a new industrial pattern of production could develop in Europe. This was due to the significant rise of industrial output in many of the smaller, lesser industrially developed nations and the relative decline in the defeated nations, particularly, Germany. However, by 1951 industrial production was once again centered in essentially the same countries as in the prewar period. Commodity output per person was around $200 of 1938 purchasing power in Northwestern Europe and Western Germany, $160 in western Continental Europe, about $100 in central and northeastern Europe and about $60 in southern and southeastern Europe.

Conclusions

While this survey shows that there are definite trends of economic recovery in Europe, the signs of recovery now evident may not yet be conclusive that Europe has a stable industrial economy. There are at least three fundamental economic problems that must still be solved. First, there has been no general expansion in the area's international trade; second, there has been essentially no recovery in investment and, in particular, there are no signs that private investment in Europe will soon be able to displace government investment, largely financed by United States subsidies; finally, no solution is yet in sight for the problem of general "over-capacity" in such basic fields as textiles.

An expansion in Western Europe's international trade can be most effectively promoted if the present barriers to intra-European trade are lowered and if the United States eases present tariff and other barriers to purchase from abroad. To stimulate private investment adequately there will have to be a greater confidence about the political and economic outlook of Western Europe, as well as the free world generally. The problem of chronic excess capacity in textiles would vanish if Europe's workers and farmers could enjoy higher real earnings, an improvement which in turn depends upon higher productivity. The general conclusion would seem to be that fundamental improvements of Europe's economy depends upon changes in both the economic and political structures, not only in that area, but also in the rest of the world. The cyclical upswing in Europe's production now evident is indicative, however, of continued economic vitality there, even in the face of the fundamental difficulties.

61. The Ruhr *

An example of one of the most intensely industrialized districts in Western Europe—if not in the world—is the Ruhr Valley of Germany. Pounds points out the productive and strategic importance of this relatively small region. The example of the Ruhr illustrates the significance of access to good-quality coal in the development of modern industry.

The Ruhr is a very small area to have figured so prominently in the news. At most it is only about 50 miles from west to east and even less from south to north. Yet within this area there are more than 6 million inhabitants, who are almost wholly dependent on its industries. There is a steel-producing capacity almost as great as that of the United Kingdom, and coal mines capable of yielding 120 million tons of coal a year.

This small area is of the greatest significance, because it has been the arsenal from which the Germany of the Kaiser and of Hitler equipped and supplied its armies and navies, and it may again produce munitions for use either for or against the West. For this reason it is important that we should know how this complex industrial area operates, what geographical problems it presents, and how their solution will further or hinder the cause of the Western democracies. In any future conflict the Ruhr may well serve to tip the balance.

[The Ruhr is] in northwest Germany, close to the Belgian and Dutch frontiers. In the south the Ruhr is hilly, and large areas are forested. In the north it is low and rolling; movement is easy, and much of the land that has not been built upon is agricultural. Most of the cities and towns lie on the northern plain. They are separated by "green belts," which are larger and more numerous than in most other European industrial areas.

Across the western edge of the Ruhr flows the Rhine, a great highway of trade between South Germany and the Netherlands. The industrial area is drained by the Ruhr, Emscher, and Lippe Rivers. . . . The courses of these rivers lie parallel to one another and also parallel to the edge of the hills to the south. Canals have been built along the Emscher and

* Norman J. G. Pounds, "The Ruhr," *Focus*, Vol. 1, No. 3, December 15, 1950, pp. 1–4. Reprinted from *Focus*, American Geographical Society.

The author (1912) is an Associate Professor of Geography, Indiana University. Born and educated in England, with a Ph.D. from London University, he came to the United States after World War II. His research centers on the political and historical geography of Europe. He is author of *A Historical and Political Geography of Europe*, *Europe and the Mediterranean*, and *The Ruhr*.

Lippe valleys and at their east ends are joined to the Dortmund-Ems Canal, by which they are linked with the German North Sea ports of Emden and Bremen.

The Ruhr industrial area has grown up within the last 100 years. Its origins lay in the primitive iron refining carried on in the hills, where there were small deposits of iron ore, as well as charcoal for the furnaces and running streams to power the machines and the hammers. It was not until after 1850 that industry spread on any considerable scale from this early center into the area that we now call the Ruhr. It was attracted by the beds of coal, much of which was suitable for coking and thus for the iron furnace. In the years 1850 to 1870 many steelworks were built. Local supplies of ore were soon exhausted and the Ruhr came to depend more and more on imports from foreign countries.

As industry developed in this area, so the cities grew in size and importance. There are today three cities each with more than half a million inhabitants: Essen, Dortmund, and Düsseldorf. There are 14 cities with more than 100,000 inhabitants.

But without the coal field there would be no Ruhr as we know it today. The coal seams reach the surface along the valley of the Ruhr (as may be seen in Figure 23), and dip northward beneath the North German Plain. Mining began along the southern edge, but for more than a hundred years

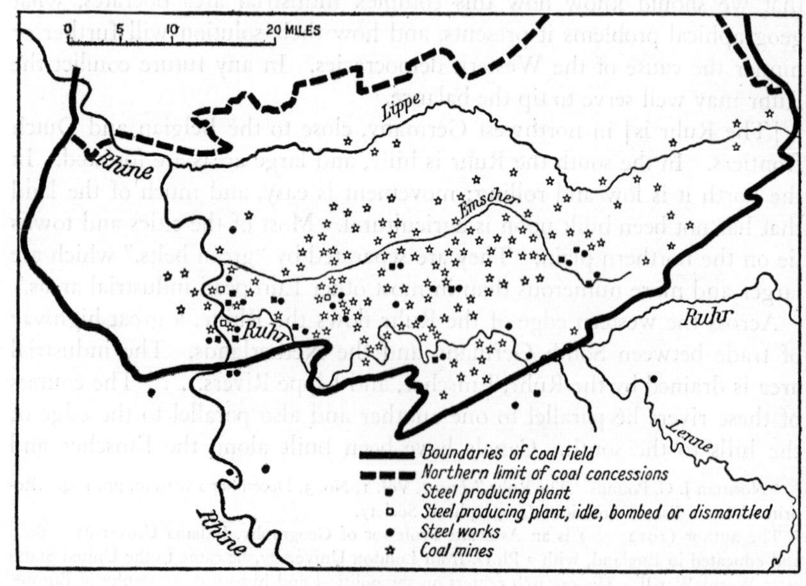

FIGURE 23

Coal mines and steel works of the Ruhr.

it has been spreading slowly northward, with the opening of mines of ever-increasing depth. The oldest mines are in the Ruhr Valley, which has thus given its name to the region; the newer are in the valleys of the Emscher and the Lippe. There seems to be no limit to this northward expansion except that set by the increasing depth and cost of mining.

The coal varies in quality. The lowermost seams, which come to the surface in the south, are anthracitic. Above them are, in order, coking, gas, and flame coals. Of these the coking coals, which are mined in the Emscher Valley, are of the greatest industrial importance.

Between the two wars the Germans concentrated production in a reduced number of larger mines. At many of these, coking furnaces were erected. Here the coal is pulverized, blended, and coked. The coke is sent to the blast-furnaces, and the gas from the retorts is used for various heating purposes in the steelworks; the exhaust gases from the furnaces go to fire the retorts in the cokeries. Coal mining and steel working have thus been integrated geographically, not merely in the balance sheets of the operating companies.

The abundance of coal has led to the erection of synthetic-fuel plants, whose production of fuel oil from coal was of vital importance to the German military machine during the last war.

Before the Second World War, nearly 40 per cent of the coal mined was used within the Ruhr, about 30 per cent was sent to other parts of Germany, and about 30 per cent was exported. Exports went chiefly to France, Italy, the Netherlands, Belgium, Luxembourg, Scandinavia, and Switzerland, countries with small or inadequate coal reserves of their own. These countries have come to rely heavily on German exports, and one of the problems facing the Allied administration in Germany today has been to revive the former export trade.

The second great industry of the Ruhr is the manufacture of iron and steel. Germany has little iron ore, and the Ruhr relies to the extent of three-quarters of its requirements on imports from Sweden, France, Spain, North Africa, and elsewhere. Some comes in through the German North Sea ports, but most through the Dutch ports, whose prosperity depends greatly on the trade of the Ruhr. Most of the steelworks are well placed on the Rhine or its neighboring canals for the import of ore.

The smelting industry is carried on in about 15 separate works, all on the plain between the Rhine in the west and Dortmund in the east. At all of them the steel is rolled into sheets, bars, and girders. Steel-using industries, especially those making castings, boilers, tubes, and wire, lie not only in the neighborhood of the steel plant but also scattered throughout the Ruhr area.

South of the area of large towns and heavy industries, in the hills where the ancient craft of smelting was carried on, there are many metallurgical industries which call for refinement and skill rather than for large quantities of metal and fuel: the manufacture of screws, nuts, springs, and locks, of high-quality alloy steels, of cutting and machine tools. Here industry is carried on in small workshops, and handwork and skill count for more than mass production. The towns of Remscheid and Solingen are centers of this branch of the metal industry.

In terms of war potential, the northern plain, with its huge factories and large cities, produces armor plate, guns, and heavy castings; the hilly area to the south, the motors, machines, precision instruments, and fuses.

Although the coal mining and steel industries dominate the manufactures of the Ruhr, chemicals and textiles are also of some importance. Chemicals are made in several of the larger cities, notably Duisburg, Leverkusen, and Düsseldorf. The textile manufactures are now concentrated in just two areas: the Wupper Valley, in which lies the great cloth-making city of Wuppertal, and the cities west of the Rhine of München-Gladbach, Rheydt, and Krefeld-Uerdingen.

The Ruhr thus has a varied industrial development, but the coal and steel industries stand supreme. The area accounted for five-sixths of German coal production before 1939, and more than two-thirds of German steel.

In the hands of a military-minded government the Ruhr would assume a truly frightening importance. In 1923 the French and Belgians occupied the Ruhr, hoping in this way to control its use and influence German policy. Germany has twice within a generation broken the peace of Europe. In 1945 the victorious powers held that control of the Ruhr was at least one way of preventing German rearmament and aggression. This control is now being achieved by a close supervision of the Ruhr industries through an organization known as the Ruhr Authority. Industrial plant thought to have mainly a military purpose has been dismantled, and the cartels and trusts that formerly controlled the industrial machine and harnessed it to Hitler's war effort have been broken up.

This policy has aroused antagonism among many Germans and, locally at least, has created a serious unemployment problem where large works have been closed down. At the same time, it has not altogether satisfied the anxieties of France, which fears the prospect of a rearmed Germany, even now when greater dangers threaten.

To many it seems illogical to destroy steel plants in the Ruhr when both within Europe and outside there is an urgent need for more heavy equipment, or to break up into small firms the complex and integrated industrial concerns at a time when the Schuman Plan is trying to bring some unity to the industry of Europe. We forget too often that, although some may fear a prosperous Germany, there are many outside Germany who depend for their own prosperity on the vigor of German industry and German trade. Without the trade of the Ruhr the docks of Rotterdam, Amsterdam and Antwerp would be less busy. Iron miners would be idle in Sweden and France, and the light industries of Switzerland and Italy would suffer from a shortage of materials.

EXPORTS OF COAL,[a] COKE AND BRIQUETTES FROM THE BRITISH ZONE TO SOME EUROPEAN RECOVERY PROGRAM COUNTRIES [b]
(In thousand metric tons [c])

	1936	*1948*
Austria	302	2,398
France and French North Africa	5,792	4,657
Belgium	3,705	1,172
Netherlands	6,108	1,755
Denmark	687	635
Norway	110	244
Luxembourg	1,987	2,315
Italy	5,640	1,517
Switzerland	1,191	305
Sweden	1,182	714
Coal production (Ruhr)	107,478	103,237 [c]
Coke " "	27,368	18,920
Pig iron " "	10,900	7,140 [c]
Crude Steel " "	13,356	7,156 [c]

[a] Bituminous and anthracite; excluding lignite and brown coal.
[b] The Ruhr accounts for 93 percent of total coal production in the British Zone.
[c] Western Germany 1949.

For the time being a compromise has been achieved. The controlling authorities have set a top limit, 11 million tons, to the amount of steel the Ruhr may be permitted to produce. But a compromise is not a solution, and as the events of the last few months have clearly shown, a solution of the Ruhr problem is an urgent necessity. For it is no longer a problem of controlling the area in the interest of European peace but rather of developing it for the protection of the West. The greater part of its industrial capacity remains undamaged. The decision has to be made whether to guard it, assist it, and use its resources in the common struggle, or to allow its sores to fester, with the grave danger that it may be lost to the West. And what the West loses the East is likely to gain.

62. *Steel and the Schuman Plan* *

Economic difficulties brought on by two world wars, difficulties in trade, and the loss of colonies by Western European powers have resulted in their consideration of economic unions and the combining of certain key resources. The Schuman Plan, effective February 10, 1953, calls for the pooling of steel and coal in six Western European nations. It is an attempt to offset the disadvantages of small size and international boundaries interfering with the most economic utilization of coal, iron, labor, capital equipment, and communications in the manufacture of steel. There is some hope that this will prove to be the first step in the unification of Europe. Coker discusses in this reading the plan, its advantages and problems.

In August, 1948, an Italian football player was transferred to a neighboring club for a fee of 800 tons of iron. Fortunately for our pockets checkbooks remain generally more popular, but the incident indicates the crucial importance of iron and steel in postwar Europe. It was in the hope of accelerating its production that M. Schuman advanced the plan which bears his name, and his advocacy of its merits has been so far successful that six countries have signed the draft agreement.† The advantages so clearly demonstrated on paper have yet to be tested in practice, and the absence of Britain and Sweden may minimize the benefits to which M. Schuman looked forward. But if the plan does become a reality and the economies of cooperation are forthcoming, then not only Britain and Sweden but also the United States must ultimately prepare for keen competition in world markets. In spite of proposals for closer European cooperation from many quarters, the prospect of working internationalism is a novelty, and it may help us to gauge the potential strength of the Schuman community if we survey the prewar steel industry of western Europe and see how different it would have looked had the Schuman plan been operating.

* J. A. Coker, "Steel and the Schuman Plan," quoted with omissions from *Economic Geography,* Vol. 28, 1952, pp. 283–294.

The author (1925   ) is Assistant Lecturer, Queen Mary College, London. His special research interests include the economic and industrial geography of Europe, the British Isles, and America.

† The countries concerned are France, the West German Federal Republic, Belgium, The Netherlands, Luxembourg, and Italy. Italy is excluded as being of less importance, and the term "Schuman" is applied throughout to the first five countries.

Prewar Position

At that time output of the group both in raw materials and finished goods was impressive. Collective iron ore output was comparable with that of the United States, and Germany alone had tonnage figures almost equal to those of Britain or Sweden.* Imported ore amounted to less than 15 per cent of total needs, most of this being German imports from Sweden. Coal and coke were also available on a large scale. While it is true that Britain supplied France with a great amount of coal the shipments were not very significant over the group as a whole. Less than 7 per cent of total coal needs came from outside sources in 1937. Moreover the corresponding figure for coke was only 0.8 per cent, and it is the latter which gives a truer measure of dependence on outside sources of fuel for steel production. In the long run the Schuman group should have no insuperable raw material problems. Production of iron and steel amounted to nearly a third of the world total.

The combined effort in world trade was even more striking. As an entity the group would have dominated the crude steel market. In Africa each country had its own well-defined territory and so there was no clash with Britain and the United States, but things were very different in the rest of the world. Schuman countries strongly challenged the United States and easily outclassed Britain in the Far East, while in South America their exports were more than those of Britain and the United States combined. In Europe they had almost a clear field. Only in the much smaller markets of Australasia and the Near East was Britain supreme.

The geographical features of the steel industry are of vital importance in evaluating the Schuman plan (Fig. 24). By far the greater part of the coal, iron ore, pig iron, and steel plants, and the finishing industries which form the immediate markets lie in a relatively compact triangle, the sides of which are about 200 miles long. Superimposed on the United States it covers an area only slightly larger than a triangle between New York, Boston, and Utica. The Ardennes form a central barrier, but no more so than the northern Appalachians between Pittsburgh and Philadelphia. No manipulation of prices, wages, investment, or freight rates could have achieved the unity implicit in this simple geographical arrangement. Had the industry not been so concentrated the advantages of the plan would be much less apparent. For if trade frontiers disappear then the industries of France and Germany cease to be marginal to a national unit, and become facets of an international unity. This triangle coincides with the population center of western Europe. Unrestricted trade within it will

* Swedish ore is of much higher grade than German or British, and thus consumes less fuel per ton of pig iron produced.

bring the Rhine effectively nearer to Belgium and France, and France will also benefit from the proximity of the Belgian and Dutch seaports. In other words, the attractions of the location become at one stroke far more potent. At the same time smaller producing areas may suffer. The strategic considerations which encouraged France and Germany to develop industry away from the frontier lose their point. These less important areas all have some geographical basis, but given complete trading freedom within the Schuman area, the overwhelming advantages of the main region will outweigh those of less ideally situated plants. The possibility of surplus plant and labor in outlying parts of Germany and France must be faced, and Italy in particular may get very little out of the plan.

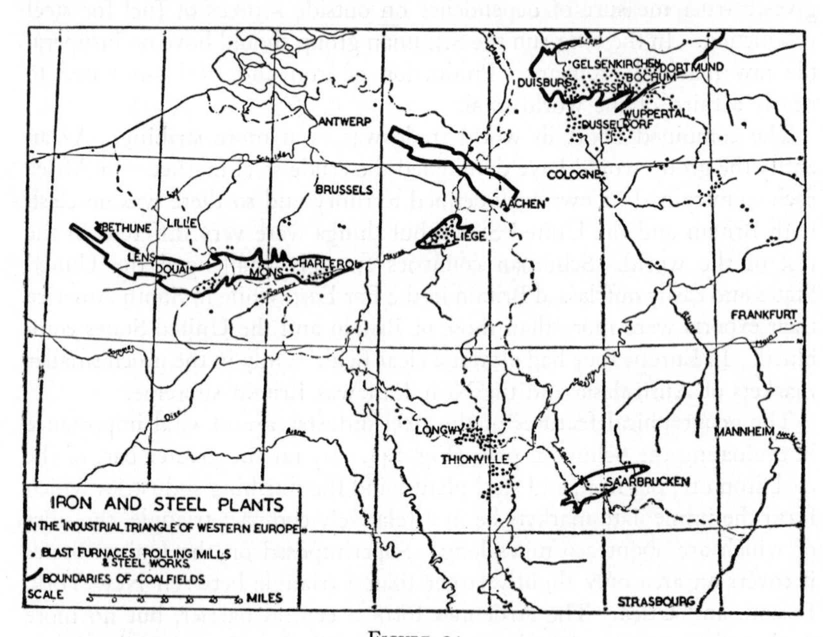

FIGURE 24

The "Industrial Triangle" showing iron and steel plants.

Germany

The existence of frontiers clearly prevented the unity of this industrial triangle before the war, especially in the thirties when the Nazi regime pursued its policy of economic nationalism. It hindered most of all the exchange of raw materials, and it was during this period that the traditional link between Ruhr coal and coke, and Lorraine ore was finally severed. Excluding the Saar, which has always depended largely on

France for ore, the proportion of German iron ore needs supplied by Lorraine dropped from 14 per cent in 1929 to 1.5 per cent in 1937. The difference was made up by Swedish and German ore. The latter was costly to mine, the scattered German deposits being neither so continuous nor so easy to work as those of Lorraine, and the stimulation of German mining to the detriment of Lorraine exports naturally embittered French opinion. But in its full perspective German policy had some economic justification. Against the background of depression and unemployment no government, Nazi or otherwise, could have afforded not to expand production in the mines. Average iron content is as high as that of the Jurassic ores of Britain which were being increasingly mined at the same period under a free economy. Furthermore the trend away from French ore was manifest as early as 1918 when Germany lost Alsace-Lorraine to France. As for Swedish ore, the Germans were not alone in finding it expedient to use as much of this high grade ore as possible. The French hope that under the Schuman plan the trend can be reversed may therefore be too sanguine. Reorganization of Ruhr plant to utilize French ore will be a slow process, even if Germany agrees to close down some of her mines. Swedish ore remains attractive, and with coal so short the incentive to use it will for many years to come be as powerful as before the war.

Increased home ore supplies as well as strategy influenced the dispersal of the German steel industry. Conforming to a world trend it took the form of transferring capacity from the coalfields to the ironfields, and was justifiable economically on the grounds of diminishing iron ore quality and technical developments in fuel saving. The Ruhr, the Siegerland, and the Saar retained their supremacy, but other areas were forging ahead, notably Salgitter and Peine in the north, the Oberpfalz group in northeast Bavaria, the Saxony group around Pirna, and a further twenty or so plants throughout the country. Without preferential treatment some of these plants might not have survived. Those on orefields may soon find the ore economically unworkable, and transporting coal from the Ruhr is bound to remain an expensive proposition. Their continued existence may be questioned by the Schuman authority once European steel is able to meet home and export calls.

France

We have already noted that larger sales of ore to Germany would have been a welcome source of foreign exchange to France, as well as a solution to chronic under-production in French ore mines. But French steel has other problems. There were labor difficulties in the mines only partly solved by importing Polish and Italian miners. France never created a selling organization for steel the equal of the German Stahlverksverband, or the Belgian Cosibel, which played such a large part in the success of those countries in export trade. Neither were French steel companies so highly integrated as the Ruhr "big six." In the nature of things vertical integration is less easy in France. Whereas in the Ruhr ore imported cheaply via the Rhine can be taken through all the stages to finished steel on the same spot, in France ore and coal are widely separated without a connecting water route. Consequently Alsace-Lorraine concentrates on pig iron and the Northern district on steel, and this division cannot be eliminated by the signing of any pact. Rather it is being widened by the ever-growing use of scrap. For the Basic-Bessemer (Thomas) process is retained almost exclusively in Alsace-Lorraine owing to the abundance of pig-iron, the dearth of scrap, and the absence of coke. In the north on the other hand most furnaces are Basic Open-Hearth (Martin) since fuel and scrap are both plentiful. The effect of the Schuman plan will be to accentuate rather than eliminate such regional specializations within the industrial triangle. One further French specialization is relevant. We have noted that in Germany, outlying plants may suffer in free trade conditions; in France the smaller districts of the Massif Central, the Alps, and the Pyrenees still produce the bulk of the electric steel, partly because they have plentiful electric power, and partly because of the ready market for such steel in the Massif Central. With these advantages they will more effectively resist the pull of the industrial triangle than will the smaller areas of Germany. Normandy is an exception, but has the advantage of near-by sea transport.

Belgium

Belgium provides more interesting speculations. The Belgian industry is concentrated largely on the Sambre-Meuse coalfield, and has less obvious geographical foundations than those of France or Germany. For the original coal measure iron ores were long ago exhausted, and while coal is plentiful, coke is not. Nearly a third of Belgian coking needs came from the Ruhr, and the expense of the long journey through Antwerp led to proposals for a direct Rhine-Meuse canal. Ore, too, involved expensive haulage. Ore costs could have been reduced by building more Martin furnaces and using scrap, but this would have required more coke, since the Thomas furnaces need less fuel. The dilemma was not resolved during re-equipment after the first world war. Few Martin furnaces were introduced, and Belgium remained incapable of using to the full her own large scrap resources. Her success as a large iron and steel producer and even more as an exporter is both a tribute to the efficiency of Belgian production methods, and a comment on the compactness of the industrial triangle. For assembly costs of raw materials were not so great but that they could not be overcome by economies in manufacture.

Holland

In Holland integration of the Ijmuiden plant was completed in 1939, and its site at the seaward end of the North Sea Canal is significant. Taking advantage of water transport it was found more profitable to import Spanish and Swedish iron ore than to use overland routes from Lorraine. This plant is geographically the Sparrow's Point of Europe and unique in that respect.

The War

There are two points to be noted concerning wartime conditions. German iron ore output fell steadily in all years after the peak of 1940 until the end of the war. If in wartime Germany could not maintain production and found it better to ship ore from France, then the same tendency is likely to recur in free trade conditions, and to this extent French hopes are justified. Another pointer to postwar events was the inability of the countries concerned to absorb all the scrap provided in war. In 1943 the consumption of scrap on the continent was less than that of Britain who was producing less steel and possessed less scrap. Most of the open-hearth furnaces were in the Ruhr or northern France, and their destruction aggravated the problem.

Postwar Recovery Problems

It is sufficient comment on 1945 that steel output of the group fell from nearly 23,000,000 tons to just over 4,000,000. For the group to have reached five years later no less than 85 per cent of their 1937 production is a very great achievement indeed. Quite apart from physical damage they have had to contend with financial and political problems of no small magnitude.

Iron Ore

Iron ore supplies have been the least troublesome. The proportion coming from outside remains at about 15 per cent, suggesting that this is a semipermanent feature, and one not easily set aside. But imports have been unduly high owing to the fuel shortage, and would have been still higher but for currency difficulties. The most striking effects on ore trading of the coal shortage come from Belgium. Before the war Swedish ore accounted for only 1 per cent of consumption; in 1949 it represented

28 per cent, and even in 1950, 13 per cent. An instance of "taking coals to Newcastle" was the Luxembourg import of Swedish ore in 1948 to save coke. Germany has perforce cut down on Swedish ore and prefers to supplement her needs by extra home production, rather than by importing from France. German ore output is indeed up to prewar levels, but the increase comes almost entirely from the Wiehengebirge, Osnabruck, and Harz districts. The Siegerland, Salzgitter, and Peine-Lengende fields remain in much the same position, while North Bavaria and the Taunus-Hunsruck are clearly practically exhausted. In France, ore fields remain in the same relative position to each other as before the war, and this stable regional balance is a French characteristic, being repeated in steel. Luxembourg has been in a worse position than France. In no year since the war has her total exceeded 53 per cent of 1937, and in 1950 it was only 49 per cent, compared with a French output very nearly equal to that of 1937.

But comparisons between the three countries cannot be taken at their face value since they do not reflect true costs of production. German ore production has been encouraged by grants of preferential freight rates to distant producers, and other producers have consequently been affected by a drop in demand. In 1949 the rail cost of moving Lorraine ore was 0.8 cents per ton/km; but ore could be brought from Salzgitter for only .025 cents per ton/km; while ore from Baden was only 0.20 cents per ton/km. To rationalize such charges will be no easy matter, and it is to the credit of M. Schuman that as a result of early discussions on the plan this disparity was reduced. It has not yet been eradicated, however, and while it exists French producers are clearly at a disadvantage.

Coal

The coal shortage has been persistent. The great strides made by France have not sufficed to offset the decline in the Ruhr, and in 1948 the combined resources of the group were only 90,000,000 tons short of 1937, so that even without the loss of British supplies the position would have been serious. If the shortage is not overcome within the group, Swedish ore will continue to be in great demand, and French output correspondingly depressed, for the resumption of British coal exports seems highly improbable. Coal may ultimately be saved by the expansion of hydroelectric power in France and elsewhere, but electric power creates new demand as well as supplying the old, and it does not replace coal of coking grade. This is crucial, for the coke position, where relief could not be expected from Britain in any case, is far worse. Prices and transport charges have played their part in aggravating the situation. Belgian coal prices are more than double those in Britain, and in 1949 it was estimated that France could have bought Ruhr coke at a price 20 per cent lower than that of French coke had excessive duties been removed. Many alternative sources of coal have been tapped: Holland has brought coal from the Union of South Africa, and even Germany imported a small quantity of Swedish coke in 1950. The United States has come to the rescue, but only at the cost of dollars which might have been better spent.

Steel

In spite of these and other problems steel production has risen steadily, and superficially there seems to be no insuperable obstacle between the Schuman group and prewar levels of output. But the over-all rise in 1950 was so small as to be negligible, and individual countries are not faring so well. Belgium was the first to encounter setbacks. In 1948 she became the first to pass her 1937 total; in both subsequent years production has fallen. The whole of the decline has curiously taken place in the Liege area. Hainaut and Brabant have continued to go ahead, and this disparity between the two main areas gives point to Belgian enthusiasm for the Rhine-Meuse canal which would terminate near Liege. Belgian worries are not confined to assembly costs and manufacture. Her emphasis on exports has meant a depression in output after the immediate postwar boom, despite larger home demands. The Korean war and general rearmament have once again set production on the upward path, but merely serve to mask the real problem of Belgian assembly costs.

Holland has gone rapidly ahead, and when in 1949 steel production passed that of pig iron, she may be said to have "arrived" as a full, if diminutive partner in the Schuman plan. Imports of steel are still considerable, but Sweden, not Holland, is now Europe's largest steel importer.

Fluctuations in France are less disturbing than in Belgium. Like that country France has been unable to take full advantage of German scrap supplies, and as the North has recovered more slowly the proportion of Thomas steel to Martin has actually increased. But France has shown greater initiative than the other partners in expanding capacity. The Northern district and Alsace-Lorraine have made up leeway in electric steel, and new continuous strip mills at Denain and Hayange will help to overcome a chronic shortage of steel sheet. The integrated plant at Mondeville, near Caen, has now been rebuilt completely, and there are many new furnaces, and sheet and tinplate mills in operation, including some at Strasbourg. Financial developments will also help expansion: one merger has formed the new Usinor company, now the largest concern in France. The Saar is still below prewar levels of production in both iron and steel.

In Germany the whole position has been complicated by the conflicting claims of dismantling and civilian demand, and more recently by western defense calls. Recovery has been astonishingly swift. Excluding the Saar and eastern Germany, and taking the 1929 figure rather than that of 1937 which was boosted by armaments, the normal prewar civilian steel production of western Germany can be put at about 14,000,000 tons. 1950 saw a figure of over 12,000,000 tons, larger than the limit set earlier in the year by the occupying authorities. The Ruhr accounts for 85 per cent of this compared with 89 per cent before the war, Saxony and Bavaria having slightly increased their importance. Exports have not been so successful, and much of the tonnage has been in pig iron or crude steel rather than in finished products. Nevertheless, the 1950 figure of 1,800,000 tons exported compared with 3,100,000 tons in 1937 must be accounted a considerable achievement.

Summary

The geographical facts of location demand a closer working unity such as is envisaged in the Schuman plan, whatever legal form the organization takes. Nowhere else in the world do labor, capital equipment, raw materials, communications, and finishing industries coincide in such a small compass. France has the ore, Germany the coke, and Holland and Belgium the ports. The Schuman community has therefore a potential strength greater than the aggregate of the individual countries. It is a case of two and two making five. On the economic side their output is sufficient materially to affect world supplies of steel; with low assembly costs their prices may establish world levels. In addition the next few years will see the group with a high proportion of modern plants.

On the other hand the Schuman plan as a first experiment in working federalism in Europe still has to prove itself even if it is ratified. The stresses and strains involved in submerging national interests in favor of general benefits may be too strong for the combination to withstand. While gaining much, each country will lose something, and previous experience of private international agreements shows that disrupting sectional forces often have the last word. For the sake of Europe it is to be hoped that this will not be the case, and in the meantime the western world can be thankful that recovery has been so swift.

63. *Linen Industry of Northern Ireland* *

Is there a logical explanation for the location or concentration of a particular industry in a specific place? Any of a number of physical factors (such as topography, climate, or accessible raw materials) or economic factors (such as transportation, abundant and skilled labor, or capital) may be responsible. In other cases, accident or the impetus of an early start may be primarily responsible for the location of an industry. Dohrs analyzes in this reading the locational factors in the development and decline of the linen industry of Northern Ireland. This selection also provides a good illustration of the way in which technological change in the textile industry has resulted in strong competition from the better and cheaper synthetic fibers.

The linen industry of Northern Ireland has shown a remarkable development from its humble beginnings in subsistence spinning and weaving of home grown flax in the cottages of the Irish peasants more than three centuries ago. To-day it stands as the leading manufacturing industry of the country, and is, next to agriculture, the most important industry.

The various factors of location which have exerted influence on the development of the linen industry have changed considerably during the growth of the industry, and certain of these factors have contributed in varying degree to the industry's decline.

No single factor, or in fact, no simple grouping of the locational factors at a given time or place can be cited specifically as the critical determining influence on any particular locational situation or adjustment which has developed during the growth and maturing of the industry. However, throughout this study it has been apparent that during various stages of development, and in the contemporary scene, and in the different sections of the industry, that certain locational factors and considerations are of greater significance than others.

1. The linen industry of Northern Ireland was initially oriented toward the raw material and labour supply available on the small farms of Ireland. At that time flax was raised successfully in many parts of the country, but

* Fred E. Dohrs, "The Linen Industry of Northern Ireland," *Textile Quarterly,* Vol. 2, No. 2, pp. 153–157. Summary of a series of articles by Dr. Fred E. Dohrs which was published in *The Textile Quarterly,* Belfast, Vols. 1 and 2.

The author (1917) is an Assistant Professor of Geography, Wayne University. His special interests include the geography of Europe, political geography, and photography. His Ph.D. thesis "The Linen Industry of Northern Ireland" was published in full in *The Textile Quarterly.* He has traveled widely and done considerable field work in Western Europe.

the land tenure policies in Ulster allowed a growth of the industry beyond the mere subsistence level.

2. As the industry continued to grow, the orientation toward domestic raw materials and labour continued, but entrepreneurial ability was an important factor in the growth of capitalism in the industry. The settlement of many Huguenot families in the Lagan valley near Belfast brought a group of people with experience, advanced technical skills and capital, and the large scale industry grew from this nucleus.

3. Two principal factors, mechanization of the industry with steam power, and the increased use of imported flax, influenced the rise of Belfast as an industrial centre and port where raw materials and coal for power were most accessible. The labour supply of the industry, formerly widespread and independent, adapted itself to the new industrial structure, and increasing urbanization was the result. During this period the serious famines in Ireland accelerated this adjustment and movement.

4. Markets and sources of raw materials are important factors in the concentration of the contemporary industry in Belfast and vicinity. This two way orientation is evidenced by the fact that 80 per cent. of the flax used is imported, and about 60 per cent. of the output leaves the United Kingdom and much of the balance is sold in Great Britain. These two alignments have the same locational influence—the concentration of the industry in and around the port of Belfast. The earlier orientation toward power in the form of imported coal remains, but with the wide-spread use of electric power with its flexibility of transmission, access to coal is no longer as significant a locational factor as formerly.

5. Approximately one half of the productive capacity of the industry is located in Belfast. Another 25 per cent. is immediately adjacent to the city extending along the main communication lines. The other mills, factories and works comprising the industry are in villages and towns, only two of which are located at distances greater than 35 miles from Belfast. Each section of the industry shows locational factors peculiar to that phase of production.

(a) In the spinning section the orientation is toward raw materials, yet the water required in the process has been in some cases a limiting factor on mill location. The three spinning mills located more than 30 miles from Belfast are in areas which formerly were great flax producing areas, and even today continue to grow large quantities of flax.

(b) The location of the weaving factories, most of which are outside of Belfast, shows a carryover from the earlier days of the independent hand weavers who worked on their own farms. As this was the last phase of the industry to be mechanized, the former centres of hand weaving in the outlying districts are today the villages and towns which have many of the weaving factories.

(c) The bleaching and finishing works are chiefly oriented toward the weaving factories which supply them with most of their work, usually on a contract basis. Other locational factors have been land for grass bleaching, a process which is unimportant today, and soft water for processing. Many of these works also do large amounts of cotton bleaching and finishing for English firms. For this latter function, the port locations of some of these works is advantageous.

(d) The making-up phase of the industry, in common with this phase in other textile industries, is concentrated chiefly in many small units in and around the commercial core of the industry in Belfast. This concentration shows a distinct point of transhipment since most of the output is exported from Belfast. More important, the concentration of this phase of the industry shows a gregarious, clustering characteristic of many textile making-up centres.

(e) Almost without exception, the commercial functions of the industry are located in Belfast, and concentrated within a small part of the commercial core of the city. The commercial functions include the activities of the flax, yarn, cloth and other merchants as well as the offices, salesrooms and warehouses of the firms whose mills and factories are located elsewhere in the city or in the outlying districts. This commercial concentration illustrates the entrepot nature of Belfast as well as the entrepot character of the linen industry, where imports of flax are transformed in a short time and then exported to markets.

6. The connection of the linen industry with local agriculture is very slight, as only about 20 per cent. of the flax used by the industry is raised in Northern Ireland. Flax production occupies less than 3 per cent. of the arable land and is concentrated in very few areas. In the vicinity of the outlying linen mills and factories however, which include about 50 per cent. of the industry, the rural population comprises an important part of the labour force.

7. The cost of flax amounts to between 70 and 75 per cent. of the cost of the finished product and therefore, the fluctuations in the price of flax have a major effect on the productivity of the industry. Low flax prices mean lower prices for finished products, resulting in a greater demand and therefore also means greater production and higher employment. Since the industry depends on imported flax, the output of the industry is subject in a major way to the vagaries and variations which arise not only from general price fluctuations on the world market, but also as a result

of national policy, notably that of the Soviet Union. Two world wars have accentuated the problem of dependence on foreign flax sources. Attempts to produce more flax in Northern Ireland, even under highly subsidised schemes, have been virtually complete failures, and since it appears impossible to grow sufficient flax locally, the industry must continue to be dependent upon imported flax.

8. One alternative solution to the problem of recurring flax shortages and the high cost of flax has been an increasing use of rayon which can be spun and woven on linen textile machinery. Although this provides a means for maintaining production with machinery which might otherwise be idle, the large scale adoption of rayon as a raw material for the linen industry raises serious questions as to the desirability of such a change and the long run competitive position of the industry as a producer of rayon fabrics. While Northern Ireland has certain unique advantages in the production of linen, involving a long history in the industry, a labour force highly skilled in the production of high quality linens, and capital equipment designed for the production of fine textiles, there are no special locational advantages for Northern Ireland in the production of rayon, other than general textile know-how common to all textile industries. Although rayon goods of competitive quality can be produced on the existing linen textile machinery, the production of the finest rayon fabrics requires specialized machinery. Finally, although Irish linen has established its reputation as the highest quality linen textile in the world market, there is little reason to suppose that Irish rayons could occupy a similar place in the market, particularly in countries such as the United States where the rayon and other synthetic fibre industries are already well developed.

9. During the last 25 years the linen industry has shown a secular decline in all productive factors, including quantity of flax used, number of workers and amount of capital equipment operating, with the result that gross volume of output has declined correspondingly. This overall decline contrasts greatly with the price averages of flax and finished linens, both of which have increased more than 200 per cent. during the same period. Although the total *value* of production is at present higher than ever before, the *quantity* of production, which is the factor on which the long term prosperity of the industry is based, was lower in 1947 and 1948 than in any year during the period from 1922 to 1940. The high dollar volume of the immediate postwar exports is a short run inflationary boom derived from pent up demand of the war years. Experts in 1948 showed that this boom had reached a peak and demand was falling.

A general explanation of the secular decline in the industry is the tendency for demand to shift away from the high quality but also high cost linen goods to cheaper substitutes, both cotton and synthetic. For some types of textiles, the substitutes, particularly the newer synthetic fibres such as nylon, have superior properties for specialized uses.

These trends in the markets coupled with the clearly defined general decline in the industry and the continuing high cost of raw materials indicate long run problems of a very serious nature. The short run boom now reaching its end may well bring special problems of unemployment over and above the general problems of the industry. For employment in the industry has been bolstered by the postwar boom and serious unemployment may result when it ends.

10. The linen industry cannot hope to regain all of the export markets lost during the war, particularly in areas where local textile industries have developed recently. Some of the old markets may be regained and possibly enlarged through better marketing methods and merchandising. It is apparent that the potential market in the United States has never been measured or thoroughly exploited. Furthermore, the higher prices of linens in general make it appear unlikely that in the future, even the lower grades of linen can compete with lower priced substitutes, particularly in the export markets.

11. The long run decline in the linen industry may have a wide-spread and marked effect on the internal structure of the industry as well as on the social structure and total economy of Northern Ireland. Within the industry the major effect may be an increase of vertical integration to eliminate marginal mills and factories and as a means of bringing about more efficient production. This is a long run prospect viewed as desirable and essential by the Committee for Postwar Planning in the Linen Industry. However, the marginal firms are not necessarily the firms most remotely located, for this study has shown that distance as such is not necessarily critical in determining locational advantage.

Decline in the margin of profit and curtailment of the production of the linen industry cannot help but cause unemployment. Present indications show that diversification in the textile industries of Northern Ireland, which is currently taking place, can absorb a part of the labour released from the linen industry. The problem of unemployment among linen textile workers reaches a critical stage in the outlying districts where a whole village or town may be completely dependent upon the local mill or factory for a livelihood. In instances such as this the closing of a marginal plant has a far more serious significance than mere production at lowest cost. Such situations are a part of the long run problem of the industry, but as they are of such local importance, they must be considered separately from the general problems of the industry.

12. Diversification of industry in Northern Ireland, not only in the production of other textiles but in all products appears to be a solution for the long run decline of the linen industry. Hence the policy of the Government of Northern Ireland since the war has been to encourage industrial diversification. In fact, during the war, several linen mills were completely converted to various kinds of non-linen war production. The availability of a labour supply trained in the factory method if not specifically trained for a special type of manufacture in a new factory, as well as a political atmosphere favouring and partly subsidizing private industrial development and diversification have aided in the establishment of a wide variety of small industrial establishments throughout Northern Ireland. There is no doubt but that these new industries, if their development continues, can absorb a major part of the labour rendered surplus by the declining linen industry.

13. Assuming, therefore, a continuation of the long run decline in the linen industry, there are related locational factors involved which merit consideration.

(a) It is not industrial *dis*-location which has brought on this decline in the industry. Higher costs of raw materials have not changed the locational situation with reference to them, for efforts to raise sufficient flax in Northern Ireland have resulted in an equally high cost but inferior product. The locational advantages which influenced the growth of the industry in Northern Ireland remain as advantages. Insofar as the industry continues to operate these factors remain.

(b) Technological changes resulting in the production of new textile fabrics have shifted consumer demand away from linen. No locational factors are involved directly in this change. New fibres as well as older ones such as cotton have become relatively cheaper than flax. Improvement of techniques has resulted in textiles which have in some cases better qualities than linen. The linen industry reached a stage of maturity prior to the wide-spread development and use of synthetic fibres. This does not imply that the industry was or is now badly located, except in the broadest sense of not possessing locally either the best equipment or techniques for producing the new textiles.

(c) Finally it should be re-emphasized that the linen industry of Northern Ireland developed because of a variety of major locational advantages. The industry remains productive, but is facing a declining demand. Despite the slackening of demand, the locational advantages within Northern Ireland preclude the likelihood of any important locational changes of the industry. Despite downward trends in volume of demand, the linen industry in all probability will maintain a moderate level of production and tend to stabilize on this level. This will mean a continued sale throughout the world of the highest quality linens for which the Northern Ireland linen industry has a world wide reputation.

64. *Significance of Industrialization in Latin America* *

Industrialization seems to be the eventual goal of most nations. Some, such as Britain and the United States, have already achieved a high degree of industrialization, while others are still largely raw-material-producing or agricultural nations. Many Latin American countries, however, are in the process of transition toward industrialization, as are other parts of the world. The stage of progress varies from country to country, but all of them face "growing" problems and it is to those problems that Preston James devotes a large part of the following article.

The transformation of a pre-industrial agrarian society to an urban-industrial society is a fundamental cause of conflict in present-day Latin America. Underneath the political, economic, and social frictions which take a somewhat different form in each country, there is a basic change taking place in the ways of living.

Industrialization, which had its beginnings around the shores of the North Sea nearly two centuries ago, has spread in ever widening circles from that nuclear area. To some countries it came easily; to others, especially those in which industrial and agrarian areas were geographically separate as in Spain and the United States, the conflict even developed into civil war. But in any case, the change from a rural society consisting of a small minority of wealthy landowners and a great majority of illiterate agriculturists, to one consisting of a small group of owners of capital and literate wage workers necessitated basic revisions of long-established institutions and habits of thought. In Latin America the development of the industrial way of living is today going forward at such a rapid pace that the old way of life of the story books and the movies has already disap-

* Preston E. James, "The Significance of Industrialization in Latin America," quoted from *Economic Geography,* Vol. 26, 1950, pp. 159–161.

The author (1899) is Professor and Chairman, Department of Geography, Syracuse University and is leading United States authority on the geography of Latin America. He is the author of *Latin America, Outline of Geography, Geography of Man,* and co-editor of *American Geography, Inventory and Prospect.*

peared in many places. The flavor of the traditional pre-industrial Latin America with its picturesque people, its gauchos and guitars, is to be found today only in remote places difficult of access from the outside world.

As usual, however, over-all statistics of industrial growth obscure the very significant differences in the rate and degree of development. The outstanding centers of manufacturing industry are São Paulo, Buenos Aires, Rio de Janeiro, Mexico City, and Santiago, with several of the smaller cities of Chile, Colombia, and Mexico not far behind. The largest single industrial area is around São Paulo and Rio de Janeiro in Brazil, supported now by Volta Redonda between the two cities. But the country which has gone farthest in transforming its way of living is Chile. Argentina, with the largest per capita income of all the Latin American countries, bases its prosperity in part on the great agricultural and pastoral productivity of the Humid Pampa, and to a lesser extent on industry.

Statistics Obscure the Significant Facts

The statistics of industrialization commonly available are poor indicators of the growth of the industrial way of living. This is due to the fact that all industrial establishments are counted, and there is no distinction made between the large-scale, low-cost per unit factory, employing many workers and involving a large capital investment, and the small-scale, high-cost per unit factory or workshop, in which only a few workers are employed and in which the capital investment is small. In Colombia, for example, more than 70 per cent of all the establishments listed as industrial about 1940 had a capital investment of less than $5,500. The average number of employees per plant in Colombia was only about eight; in Argentina and Brazil about 16; and in Chile about 27. In comparison the average number of workers per plant in the United States was about 42. In other words only a small fraction of the plants listed in Latin American countries ought to be considered as large-scale operations. The workshop is characteristic of the traditional pre-industrial society; the large-scale factory is the symbol of the industrial society.

Handicaps to Industrialization

Industrialization in Latin America faces four major difficulties. The first is the prevailing poverty and widespread illiteracy of the people. This handicaps the successful operation of an industrial plant in two ways. It restricts the market for manufactured products because only a small proportion of the people have enough income to purchase such goods even if they should want to do so. In fact, the advertising of an attractive gadget in a city where less than 10 per cent of the people can afford to buy the gadget might be one of the most effective ways to develop the atmosphere of revolution. And poverty and illiteracy also reduce the supply of skilled workers needed in the factories. This condition is remedied over a period of years, however, because the presence of opportunities for employment brings people together in cities where the children can be educated, where there are better health conditions and better diet than in rural areas, and where workers can be trained.

The second major handicap to the progress of industrialization is the traditional attitude of the well-to-do people. In the pre-industrial society prestige is gained by the ownership of land. To invest surplus funds, even in agricultural enterprises, for the purpose of increasing production or of lowering costs is not the usual way of using such funds. In the major urban centers of Latin America, and in such unusual agricultural areas as Cuba and São Paulo state, many Latin Americans have already changed their attitude toward investments, and prestige is now actually derived from the ownership of capital. For many years to come, however, industrialization must depend to a considerable degree on foreign investors; and under present world conditions this means chiefly individuals in the United States who are willing to risk investments abroad for the sake of the large returns they bring.

The third handicap is the prevalence of a concept inherited from the pre-industrial society—the concept of national self-sufficiency. Industrial plants can produce things people want at low enough cost per unit so that the material well-being of the people is greatly increased. But this can only be done if large quantities of goods are produced, and if the raw materials are brought to the plant from the lowest-cost sources. The idea that every country must make use of its own raw materials even at high cost, or that every country must have its own steel plant as the basis for industrialization, is an idea which could eventually destroy the capitalist system if it is not overcome in time. Argentina, for example, has a world advantage in the manufacture of things from wool, hides, meats, grains, and the other special products she can supply at low cost. But to use government subsidies to build and protect a steel industry based entirely on imported raw materials can only mean high-cost goods, and eventual economic disaster. There are only two alternatives: to accept international interdependence and give up the concept of national self-sufficiency, or to accept the idea that all labor is for the good of the state and to give up the hope of decreasing costs. At present too many persons in Latin America are inclined toward the second alternative.

And finally, the fourth handicap to industrialization is the generally inadequate development of the means of transportation. The isolated pattern of clusters which characterizes the geography of man in Latin America is still a principal characteristic. With certain notable exceptions, the railroad lines are so cheaply built and so poorly integrated with the pattern of settlement that the movement of goods is still very costly. All-weather highways are also rare, and in many cases where they appear to provide access to a wide extent of country, a close examination shows that the weakness of certain key bridges make their use for heavy loads impossible. With high costs of transportation the small, high-cost workshops are effectively protected from the competition of low-cost goods from the large-scale factories.

Yet the progress of industrialization is something to watch. Already it makes Chile something quite different from the "land and society" described by McBride in the 1930's. It underlies the political conflicts, such as those which produced Perón. To understand present-day Latin America a much more penetrating study of the geography of large-scale industries is needed than has yet appeared.

65. *Regionalism in Factory Industry in India–Pakistan* *

Southeast Asia is a traditionally rural area; it is estimated that over 90 per cent of the people make their living directly or indirectly from the soil. In this area, only Japan is advanced in its industrial development. In India, for instance, less than 1 per cent of the total population is permanently employed in large-scale manufacturing. A large number of small factories, many of the home or family type, are in existence, but statistics as to their number and production are unavailable. Though India's industry is not comparable in volume and type to the industrial development found in west central Europe and east central North America, the trend toward increasing industrialization in India

* Glenn T. Trewartha and James L. Verber, "Regionalism in Factory Industry in India-Pakistan," quoted with omissions from *Economic Geography*, Vol. 27, 1951, pp. 283–286.

Glenn T. Trewartha (1896) is Professor of Geography, University of Wisconsin. He has taught at Wisconsin since 1926 and was chairman of the department, 1945–50. In 1926–27 he was Senior Guggenheim Fellow for geographical research in the Far East; several subsequent trips and further research have made him a recognized authority on the geography of the Far East. He is author of *A Reconnaissance Geography of Japan, Elements of Geography* (with V. C. Finch), *Introduction to Weather and Climate,* and *Japan: A Physical, Cultural and Regional Geography.*

James L. Verber received his Master's degree in geography from the University of Wisconsin and is now employed at Franz Theodore Stone Institute of Hydro-biology at Put-in-Bay, Ohio.

is significant. Trewartha and Verber in this selection describe the types and regional distribution of industry in India and Pakistan.

A particularly valuable source for studying the regional patterns of Indian manufacturing is the official government publication, Large Industrial Establishments of India, put out biennially by the Department of Commercial Intelligence and Statistics, Delhi. The latest issue of the above publication, dated 1948, which contains employment statistics for Indian industry as of late 1943 or early 1944, is sufficiently recent to reflect some of the changes resulting from World War II. In the above publication each factory employing 20 or more workers is listed by name and precise location, and the total number of workers is indicated. No information on output is furnished. Even with this wealth of detail, however, the picture of Indian industry is still incomplete since there is omitted the host of ubiquitous, small household and craft industries which continue to be so important in the Orient.

As of about the beginning of 1944 there were slightly over 2,800,000 employed in "large industrial establishments" in the India-Pakistan region. For a country of over 400,000,000 people this is an abnormally small proportion. Moreover, some 13 per cent of the 2.8 million factory workers in India are employed in seasonal plants which regularly operate only a portion of the year. Thus the perennial factories employ only six-tenths of one per cent of the total population. Only the perennial factories are considered within the scope of this paper.

India-Pakistan has no industrial belt or belts such as exist in some highly industrialized countries. Factories are widely scattered and exist chiefly as clusters in widely separated towns. Thus the four cities of Calcutta, Bombay, Ahmedabad and Cawnpore employ nearly one-half (47 per cent) of all the factory workers in India-Pakistan. Only 29 cities have as many as 10,000 workers in perennial factory industries, and these 29 urban centers account for 65 per cent of the total so employed.

But although an industrial belt is lacking, there is, nevertheless, a recognizable pattern in the distribution of factory industry. Figure 25, showing the distribution of industrial wage earners in India-Pakistan, reveals that there are three general regions in which factory industry is more concentrated than in others. Within these three regions of concentration there are employed nearly nine-tenths of the factory workers.

The Northern Region

This includes chiefly the Indo-Gangetic lowland as far west as West Punjab in what is at present Pakistan. The principal states included are:

West Bengal, Bihar, United Provinces, East Punjab, and West Punjab. In general this northern industrial region is fairly coincident with the belt of dense population extending west and northwest from the Bay of Bengal, a population which provides the market for the output from the factories of the region. Of the three industrial subdivisions the northern one is the most important, for its factories employ 44 per cent of the total workers in large perennial industries. As is true for the whole of India-Pakistan, the specialization of this subdivision is in the light industries, more especially textiles. In the western part of the Northern Region, especially in the United Provinces and Punjab, the textile specialization is in cotton. In the Calcutta area at the eastern end of the Northern Region, on the other hand, over 50 per cent of the industrial workers are employed in jute mills of large size. Within this eastern part, also, about 150 miles west and northwest of Calcutta, is located almost the whole of India's pig iron and steel production. At Kulti and Asansol in westernmost West Bengal, and at Jamshedpur and Tatanagar in eastern Bihar over 95 per cent of the country's pig iron and steel are processed.

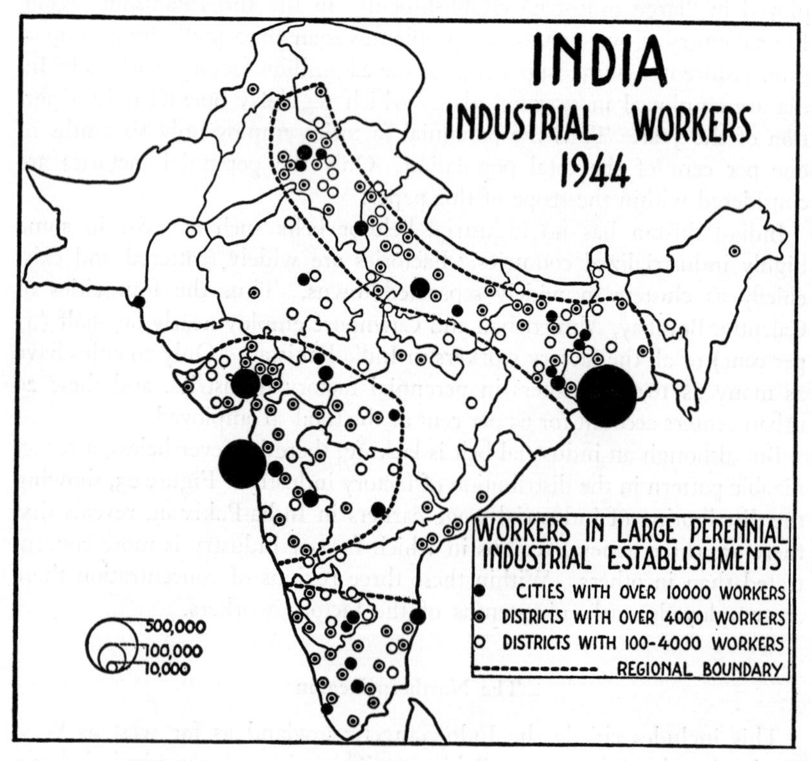

FIGURE 25

The Western Region

This subdivision includes chiefly the narrow coastal plain at the foot of the western Ghats in Bombay State, and a considerable part of the Deccan Lava Plateau east of the Ghats. In industrial importance it ranks after the Northern Region with about 33 per cent of the industrial workers as compared with 44 per cent for the latter. Although the Northern Region had only one primate industrial city, this Western Region has two: Bombay on the coast and Ahmedabad, an inland city on the more extensive plain at the northern end of Bombay State. These two cities account for some 65 per cent of the factory workers in the whole region. The preponderance of cotton textiles is striking, with 60 per cent of the region's factory workers employed in this specialization. This Western Region leads not only in cotton textiles but likewise in chemicals and in the wood-stone-glass industries. While Bombay city is a greater cotton textile center than is Ahmedabad, the latter is more specialized, having 75 per cent of its workers in textile mills. Other than Bombay city and Ahmedabad, additional textile cities are: Sholapur, Ujjain, Baroda, Indore, and Nagpur.

The Southern Region

The Southern Industrial Region is largely included within the political subdivisions of Mysore, Madras, and Travancore. Much less important than the other two, the southern subdivision contains only 12 per cent of the factory workers. This is only one-quarter the number of the Northern Region and one-third that of the Western Region. As in the other two, cotton textiles greatly predominate, supporting approximately 50 per cent of the factory workers. There is no great primate industrial city in the region, although Madras, Coimbatore, Madura, and Bangalore, all textile cities, are of second rank. To a somewhat greater extent than in the other two industrial regions, factory industry seems to be concentrated in the smaller towns of the districts rather than in a few larger centers.

66. *The Economic Geography of Atomic Energy* *

The feasibility of harnessing atomic power for peaceful uses is a very speculative topic. It has sometimes been stated that atomic energy is the panacea for areas lacking other conventional forms of power and for those located in such presently inaccessible regions as the Amazon Basin. Considerable information has been published on the economic possibilities of this new source of power. Jones summarizes in this review the major points brought forth in ten articles and books on this subject, and adds some interpretations of his own.

In a statement to the editors Jones comments as follows: "Since this review was written, much has been learned about the technology of industrial atomic energy. Most of the general principles of the application to economic geography, as here discussed, remain valid, however."

Even to speculate about the economic possibilities of atomic energy may seem pointless in this time of international tension. But paradoxically the war emergency, with its great demands for power, may speed the industrial use of atomic energy, especially if it proves possible for the same reactor to serve both military and industrial purposes. However and whenever they may come about, it is the possible changes in the location of industry that may result that most interest the economic geographer.

Some Technological Problems

Before there can be any atomic power at all, some technological problems must be solved. Before atomic power can be widely used, the solutions of these problems must, as Etherington says, be transferred from the realm of physics to that of engineering. A nuclear reactor for industrial purposes must operate at much higher temperatures than those built during World War II. Temperatures at least as high as those now employed in conventional steam plants must be attained—perhaps 1050°, Fahrenheit. Actually, atomic energy may make possible much higher temperatures. No oxygen is involved in atomic fission, so that gases heated by nuclear energy will be less corrosive than those produced by combus-

* Stephen B. Jones, "The Economic Geography of Atomic Energy," quoted with omissions from *Economic Geography*, Vol. 27, 1951, pp. 268–274.

The author (1903) is Professor and Chairman, Department of Geography, Yale University. He has held positions with Oregon College of Education, the University of Hawaii, and the Department of State. His primary interest is political geography, and he is a frequent contributor to professional periodicals.

tion, if used in a gas turbine. Within the reactor itself, however, deterioration of materials may be an important item of expense. Repairs and replacements within the reactor will have to be made by remote control.

Natural uranium does not contain enough of the fissionable U-235 to make feasible the economical operation of a reactor at industrial temperatures. A fissionable concentrate must be added. This concentrate may cost a thousand times as much as natural uranium. (Even so, it is comparable in terms of energy to medium-priced coal.) Once the reaction is established, fissionable materials will breed within the reactor, perhaps in quantities more than sufficient to sustain the desired temperature. Successful "net gain breeding" of fissionable materials in industrial reactors, as ordinary uranium and thorium are consumed, will mean that (in the cautious words of Dunning) "an appreciable fraction" of the uranium and thorium of the earth may be utilized for atomic fuel.

One of the question marks of atomic technology, as far as public information goes at the time of writing, is the extent to which a nuclear reactor can serve multiple purposes. Schurr and Marschak wonder whether the high temperatures desired for industrial purposes will prove the best for net gain breeding. Cockroft says that breeder piles "present difficult technical problems and may take a considerable time to develop into reliable power units." The solution of these problems will be an important milestone, for if an efficient industrial reactor can produce a surplus of fissionable materials, a profitable tie between military and non-military use may result. On the other hand, if industrial reactors require replenishment with fissionable concentrates they will be in competition with military needs. In an article in *Time,* C. A. Thomas, of the Monsanto Chemical Company, is stated to believe it possible to generate heat for industrial use and at the same time realize a revenue from the sale of plutonium bred within the reactor. Since Thomas has been on the conservative side in his estimates of the cost of atomic energy, this statement is significant.

The removal of fission products from the nuclear fuel is a delicate mechanical and chemical operation. Dunning suggests the possibility of using the fuel in a fluid suspension, permitting circulation and processing. The disposal of dangerous radioactive wastes he regards as a problem that may be solved "with full safety and without excessive costs," since the quantity might be only a pound or so a day even from a very large power station.

The technological problems of developing atomic energy will limit the first installations to the industrially advanced nations. As long as international relations remain tense, the specialized apparatus and "know-how" are not likely to be freely exported, especially if the breeding process makes every industrial reactor a source of extra plutonium. If this means that each nation must develop its own atomic technology or do without, many small or backward nations must do without. "Unto him that hath shall be given"—a common principle in economic geography—may thus operate in the atomic field.

Fuel Supply and Costs

It is now well known that uranium and thorium are relatively abundant and widespread. Moreover, even at a hundred times its present price, uranium would be very cheap in terms of energy. This is a far cry from saying that granite will become an ore of uranium, but it does indicate that atomic fuels for industry can be drawn from other sources than the few high-grade deposits now known. Net gain breeding of the much more valuable fissionable products might even turn the fuel cost into a profit.

Schurr and Marschak describe uranium as "an amazing fuel, which could absorb enormous increases in the cost of prying it from the earth and refining it and still remain cheaper than the cheapest coal." This low, perhaps negligible, and possibly negative fuel cost (depending upon the success of net gain breeding) should not be given undue prominence. One well-known source of power has no fuel cost. This is hydro-electricity. The unique property of atomic fuels is their great transportability. This is the line on which the ultra-enthusiastic believers in atomic energy make their last stand. Pushed to admit that atomic energy will be far from free and, even if free, would not greatly reduce the production costs of many industries, they point out that the fuel for a nuclear reactor could be flown to the South Pole if need be. The rejoinder is a question: Does it need to be?

Even though uranium and thorium are relatively widespread, the geography of their ores is by no means unimportant. It would depart from all previous experience with the minor metals if their occurrence showed a nice congruence with the industrial or military requirements of nations. Possession of, or reliable access to, the more easily mined deposits will certainly be highly desired. The great powers will probably seek to control the international movement of these ores. Possession of an important deposit will give a small country a valuable diplomatic lever. The "economic geography" of atomic energy may thus reflect political geography as much as it does strictly economic forces.

Costs of Atomic Power Plants

No way is now foreseen to use directly the energy of atomic fission. All the proposed methods involve the transfer of the resulting heat by liquids, molten metals, or gases. Because of radiation hazards, the schemes diagrammed by Dunning employ a second heat transfer (in spite of the inevitable loss) between the reactor and the driven machinery. The nuclear reactor is therefore really a new type of fire-box rather than a complete power plant.

Estimates of the cost of atomic energy have been made on the assumption that the heat will be converted into electricity by conventional means. This may not be true for all purposes. Hot gases may be used directly in kilns or furnaces. Following the customary analysis, however, we note that much of the apparatus for generating electricity will be identical with that of a conventional steam plant. Therefore, there is little reason to expect that atomic power plants will be cheaper than conventional ones. At least in the early years of their development, they are likely to cost more. Control systems will be elaborate, with remote-control apparatus for repairs, and facilities for removing the radioactive "ash" from the fuel will be needed. This last may be very expensive, but it has been suggested that a central processing plant might serve a number of power stations. The lowest estimates of cost for atomic and conventional plants of equal capacity are about the same. On the high side, Sporn cites estimates for atomic plants that run to seven times the cost of conventional plants of the same size. The unreliability of all the estimates is stressed by Isard and Whitney and is crisply stated by Hafstad who says that accurate cost figures ". . . do not exist even within the Atomic Energy Commission. If they did exist, they could not be released for security reasons. If they did exist and if they could be released, I wouldn't believe them anyway."

By postulating large economies with increasing size, it is possible to imagine an atomic power plant that is cheaper per kilowatt of capacity than a conventional steam plant. But if we think in terms of "atomic Niagaras" we greatly limit the possible applications. There must be a large market, in existence or highly probable, within transmission range. Only well-heeled governments or very large corporations could pay the initial costs.

Schurr and Marschak, while fully realizing the difficulties, make estimates (in 1946 prices) of the cost of electricity generated from atomic energy in a 75,000 kilowatt plant at 50 per cent of capacity. They class their results as minimum (4.0–4.3 mills per KWH), intermediate (6.6–7.0 mills) and maximum (10.2 mills). Two things are noteworthy about their estimates. One is that 80 per cent of the cost of atomic electricity is charged to fixed costs. Others agree that capital investment may play a very important part in the cost structure. Isard and Whitney estimate that a 3 per cent increase in interest rates means a 2.5 mill increase in cost per kilowatt-hour. (They point out, also, that interest rates are lowest in the most advanced countries.) Secondly, the cost estimates of Schurr and Marschak are of the same general order of magnitude as the cost of electricity generated in conventional thermal plants and are considerably higher than low-cost hydroelectricity. This point is well brought out by an interesting world map of electricity generating costs. Current (no pun intended) thought, then, is that atomic energy may be competitive with coal. This is a far cry from "a world set free" by unlimited, virtually cost-free energy. It makes atomic energy not really revolutionary (in an economic sense) but rather one more possible source of power that an engineer must consider in a given case. Whether he chooses it or a conventional fuel for a given location and purpose will not be answerable with confidence until practical experience with nuclear power plants has been gained.

Atomic Power in Selected Industries

Among the most interesting parts, to a geographer, of the Schurr and Marschak book are the discussions of the possibility of using atomic power in specific industries. Isard and Whitney give a briefer treatment of the same theme. Both publications make it clear that the impact of even free energy upon the location of industry would be far from uniform. Energy costs range from an almost negligible fraction of total costs in some industries to as much as one-fifth in a power-hungry process like aluminum refining. (A proposed electrical process for manufacturing phosphate fertilizer would spend one-third of its total costs on energy.) Since atomic energy actually will be little, if any, cheaper than energy from conventional sources, the savings (again, if any) would be only a fraction of a fraction, though even a tiny saving per kilowatt-hour can be important in an industry with heavy power demands.

There are, however, two other routes to possible savings through the use of atomic energy. One results from the easy transportability of atomic fuels. This makes possible the relocation of some industrial processes so as to effect savings in the transportation of raw materials or finished products, even though there is little or no economy in energy costs. One such possibility is the refining of aluminum at the mine instead of shipping the bulky ore. The second possible route to savings is to introduce new processes, perhaps combined with locational changes that would reduce transportation costs. Schurr and Marschak suggest that the sponge-iron process, using hydrogen as the reducing agent and atomic energy for the production of the hydrogen and the required heat, might permit the smelting of iron at the mine, thus eliminating the shipment of both ore and coal. (Their computations, however, lead them to conclude that the economic feasibility of such a step is highly speculative.) The most fruitful applications of atomic energy, if it is possible to use it in economic rather than politically-determined ways, may lie along such lines. As Schurr and Marschak say, "If really revolutionary results occur they will probably come about through the invention of entirely new applications of atomic energy rather than simply through lessening the cost of electricity."

Regional Redistribution of Industry

Part Three of Schurr and Marschak's book, dealing with *Atomic Power and Economic Development,* and pages 46–50 of Isard and Whitney's paper would be well worth reading by geographers (who shy away from the more theoretical work of economists) even if they had no interest in atomic energy. Without jargon or the use of symbols, these readings show the economist at work with his sharp tool, the study of costs. That the cost of atomic energy is not accurately known does not vitiate the arguments. It merely makes the results algebraic, so to speak, rather than arithmetical. But both these readings end with a deferential bow to political factors, which may localize the supplies of atomic energy without reference to costs.

To follow out first the arguments based on cost: Isard and Whitney point out that the use of atomic energy may tend to reinforce existing patterns of industry rather than to alter them. The economies of large plants will favor their construction near large markets. On the other hand, a number of the underdeveloped areas have unused energy sources at hand. "In Rhodesia, for example, where there are excellent coal deposits and where excellent hydro sources are within reach, economic backwardness is not due to lack of power resources. In the case of such countries it seems foolish to think that the introduction of a new power source will bring about any transformation."

Isard and Whitney argue further that cheap atomic energy might favor the concentration rather than the dispersal of industry, though perhaps a concentration at new sites. Those industries, like aluminum refining, that are attracted to power are also strongly affected by small differentials in the cost of power. Electricity generated by atomic energy will not be of the same cost everywhere. It will be cheapest near very large installations, in countries of advanced technology and low interest rates. Cheap atomic electricity might draw aluminum refining, for example, to the mine or to the market, but in either case there might be concentration about a few large power plants rather than dispersion about many small ones.

Schurr and Marschak are more hopeful about the role of atomic energy in the industrialization of underdeveloped lands, although they point out the need for capital (roughly $1000 for each new worker), skills, and raw materials as well as power. They estimate that four to eight tons of coal, or its equivalent in other forms of energy, are needed for each new worker employed in industry. This energy is available in conventional forms in some underdeveloped areas and can be transported to most of them. But investments in railroads, rolling stock, and mines, in the case of coal, and in dams and transmission lines, in the case of water-power, may add very substantially to the costs. In terms of total investment, atomic power might prove cheaper in some cases.

Schurr and Marschak also discuss the underdeveloped countries "which propose to industrialize by plan—and many backward countries do." Planning may lead to the location of industries for social, political, or military reasons, without strict regard to costs. In such conditions, the use of atomic energy may be indicated if there are no local supplies of energy in conventional forms and if imported supplies are expensive. Schurr and Marschak conclude: "There are not many areas of the world that meet all these criteria, but among them are several of real importance: Pakistan, central and southern India, and the east coast of South America, particularly Argentina." Important though they be, they are a rather small residue from the underdeveloped world. One can only guess whether these lands can bargain or make their own ways into the coterie of nations having atomic energy.

Political Factors

We have already seen repeatedly that political considerations may play an important and perhaps determining role in deciding if, how, when, and where atomic energy is used for industrial purposes. The importance of atomic energy in world politics was so clear that the strongly capitalistic Congress of the United States placed the whole atomic development program under a government commission with little hesitation. There is no likelihood of the program as a whole being de-nationalized. Use of fissionable materials for energy development by private enterprise is not only possible but likely, but certainly it will be under the license and ultimate control of the Atomic Energy Commission. Not even in a World State does it seem likely that atomic energy could be turned over completely to private hands, for a World State would have to be on guard against rebellions, and a rebellious province with atomic bombs would be formidable indeed.

Government participation introduces an element of unpredictability into almost every phase of atomic power development. Government determines how much effort is put into the necessary research. Government determines how much fissionable material will be released to industry. Costs may be lowered by government subsidies or through government purchases of the products of net gain breeding. The location of reactors may be determined by the convenience of government rather than that of industry. The need to counter communism might push government towards the export of atomic materials and equipment, but the fear of giving atomic explosives to possible enemies will work in the opposite direction. All in all, it looks unlikely that those who read these lines will ever see a geography of atomic energy that is truly an economic geography.

Solar Energy

By stretching the common usage of the term, solar heat may be called a form of atomic energy. Efforts to use solar heat are much older than even the knowledge that atoms contained energy, but they appear to be farther from practical success than are methods of using nuclear reactors. The direct use of solar heat for generating steam appears to be uneconomic. An acre of mirrors provides little more power than a large outboard motor. Use of solar heat for house heating may be practical, but this review focusses (again, no pun intended) on industrial applications. The amount of solar energy falling on the United States exceeds the country's energy requirements two thousandfold but how to harness this energy for industry is an unsolved problem.

Thermoelectricity, thermochemistry, or photochemistry may be the fields in which to find the philosopher's stone that will transmute sunshine into industrial energy. Currently, much thought is being given to photosynthesis. Even if this cannot be used directly to produce usable energy, it may be possible to grow vegetable fuels or vegetable sources of inflammable liquids. Under controlled conditions, as in a greenhouse, it is possible greatly to improve on nature's records. A theoretical yield of 200 tons per year is possible, as against a few tons for even the most prolific field crop. But out of doors, taking the sun and the rain and the carbon dioxide as they come, nature is a closer competitor to science. Food yields can be increased substantially and profitably, but the chances of raising fuel in fields, at going prices, are slim. Daniels concludes his survey hopefully but soberly, "Practical atomic and solar energy will come slowly, but both have considerable promise."

The economic geography of solar energy presumably would show some relation to the map of solar radiation received at the earth's surface. But energy is only one factor in industry, and often only a minor factor. There would be no reason to speculate in industrial sites in Saharan oases. For one thing, water is a requirement of most industries and is less mobile than is energy. We might expect, however, the successful harnessing of solar energy to reinforce the southward spread of industry that has been going on in this country and to assist the industrialization of the Mediterranean lands.

The industrial use of solar energy might differ in one important respect from the industrial use of atomic energy. If, as seems reasonable, solar energy has no special military value, there would be no political obstacles to the spread of its use. If the technology is not excessively complex and if the installations need not be of great size, it may be of greater significance to underdeveloped tropical and subtropical countries than atomic energy. There is surely reason to hope that, if solar energy can be harnessed economically at all, the means may be little or no trickier than those needed for conventional sources of power.

Bibliography

Cockcroft, Sir John, "The Development and Future of Atomic Energy," *Bulletin of the Atomic Scientists,* Vol. 6, Nov., 1950, pp. 325–331.

Daniels, Farrington, "Atomic and Solar Energy," *American Scientist,* Vol. 38, Oct., 1950, pp. 521–548.

Dunning, J. R., "The Future of Atomic Energy," *American Scientist,* Vol. 38, Jan., 1950, pp. 60–84.

Etherington, H., "Atomic Power for Industry," Chapter 5 of "Constructive Uses of Atomic Energy," edited by S. C. Rothmann, Harper and Brothers, 1949.

Hafstad, Lawrence R., "Reactor Program of the Atomic Energy Commission," *U. S. Atomic Energy Commission Press Release,* Nov. 15, 1950, 14 pp., mimeographed.

Isard, Walter, and Whitney, Vincent, "Atomic Power and the Location of Industry," *Harvard Business Review,* Vol. 28, March, 1950, pp. 45–54.

Schurr, Sam H., and Marschak, Jacob, "Economic Aspects of Atomic Power," Princeton University Press, 1950, 287 pp.

Sporn, Philip, "Prospects in Industrial Application of Atomic Energy," *Bulletin of the Atomic Scientists,* Vol. 6, Oct., 1950, pp. 303–306.

Time, Vol. 57, Feb. 19, 1951, pp. 90–91.

CHAPTER NINE

Trade and Transportation

No PRESENT-DAY NATION is completely self-sufficient. The degree of a nation's dependence on exchange with other parts of the world varies considerably and can be largely accounted for by geographic differences that exist from place to place. In Selection 56, the following Law of Trade Origin was given: "Trade is created by the existence of surpluses of different commodities. Differences in commodities, in turn, are occasioned by: (1) differences in culture; (2) differences in natural resources; and (3) differences in the economic-geographic stage of development. The greater are the differences in commodities, the greater the inducement to trade."

The diversity of the earth's surface, its peoples and products, is reflected in the tremendous variety of goods found in the channels of domestic and international trade. As the population and utilization of a region change, so do the commodities of exchange. The Eskimos of northern Canada and the Lapps of Scandinavia are nearly self-sufficient, whereas the people of New York City are completely dependent on trade for their existence.

In order to carry out trade, peoples or areas must be connected by some means of transportation. In early history transportation was by human beings, beasts of burden, or crude sailing vessels. Trading areas were limited in distance and the products necessarily had to be of high value per unit weight. Increasingly efficient means of transport have enlarged trade areas and trade products to include the entire world and all types of commodities. As a result, countries or regions have been able to specialize largely in one type of agriculture or industry and supply their remaining needs from other areas. Thus local, regional, and world trade is vital to the maintenance of most economies at these levels.

The following readings indicate the significance of world trade to the world and to specific countries such as Canada, and show the part geography plays in the development of that trade. Studies of representative land, water, and air transportation follow the readings dealing with trade.

---

67. *Crisis in World Trade* *

"If trade does not cross international boundaries, armies will" is a statement that lies behind many of the world's past and present troubles. Nations have often attempted to obtain resources by force rather than trade. "In world trade the whole is balanced but not the parts." The inequality of distribution of people and resources means that peaceful exchange of goods is desirable if the continuing needs of world societies are to be satisfied. Free world trade tends to decrease international friction. Colby contends in this selection that geography plays a major part in the "understanding of the laws, principles and implications of pattern in the world order."

The world has not recovered from World War II as rapidly as most people hoped. We expected that after the war the nations would work together to attain a long period of peace and prosperity. At present, however, the international political situation is most unsatisfactory. We have only the pretense of one world order in which all the nations play a part, and the actuality of two worlds separated by the Iron Curtain. We anticipated some measure of international good will and, instead, find that suspicion and mistrust make international relations difficult, to say the least. We thought that production of food, coal and other essentials would increase rapidly as the economy of Europe and other areas recovered from war-time dislocations. We visualized, most of all, a rapid recovery of world trade and the establishment of an international credit system which would make it possible for any and all nations to participate in world trade. None of these expectations materialized. The lack of recovery in

* Charles C. Colby, "Crisis in World Trade," *Journal of Geography,* Vol. 48, No. 3, March 1949, pp. 89–99. By permission of the *Journal of Geography,* official publication of the National Council of Geography Teachers.

The author (1884) is Professor Emeritus of Geography, University of Chicago. He is currently a lecturing Professor of Geography at Southern Illinois University. He has been Consultant, Division of Land Planning and Housing, Tennessee Valley Authority (1935–38); member, National Research Planning Board (1938–42); member, National Research Council (1940–42); and adviser, War Shipping Administration (1942). Colby is a recognized leader in American geography with interests in Canada and the United States, and in the fields of economic and regional planning. He is the author of *Area Analysis—A Method of Public Works Planning* (with V. Roterus) and *Economic Geography* (with A. Foster).

one phase of international relations has blocked or retarded recovery in the others. This is true particularly in the case of world trade. Its recovery awaits better political, economic, and social relations among the nations, and conversely the sluggish nature of world trade increases international friction.

As the present crisis in world trade mirrors the difficulties in the present world order, I invite your attention to the nature of the crisis and to the basic considerations which underlie it. Altho the crisis is revealed by commercial statistics, its magnitude as an international problem grows out of misconceptions as to the function of trade in the world order.

Recent Gain in World Trade

Substantial gains in world trade were made in 1947. The actual volume was from 10 per cent to 20 per cent greater than that of 1946 and slightly above the level of 1938. In world terms, however, the increase was more apparent than real, for practically all the gains were in the western hemisphere where the volume of trade more than doubled prewar figures. In the eastern hemisphere, gains were made in 1947 as compared with the previous year, but the volume was about 35 per cent less than the prewar level. In this connection it should be remembered that the large prewar trade of Germany and Japan virtually disappeared after the war. In view of the key position of Germany in Europe and of Japan in the Far East, it is difficult to visualize a recovery of trade in the old world without active participation on the part of Germany and Japan. This contention highlights the significance of viewing the world trade, or for that matter any aspect of the world order, in terms of the key areas in the international scene.

According to Britannica Book of the Year, production in half the countries of Europe by the end of 1947 had exceeded prewar levels. Imports from non-European countries still were heavy to replace plant and equipment, and to supplement local production of coal, fertilizers and foods. Thus the inability of these European countries to produce surpluses of their traditional export commodities is an important reason for the slow recovery of world trade.

Many conditions, political, social and economic have a bearing on Europe's slow recovery, but none is more fundamental than the shortage in coal. This shortage has been in the making since 1913. At that time the coal trade of Europe was organized on a rational basis. Germany, for example, imported into its coastal areas 18 million tons of coal largely from England. The coal moved at low cost from England's seaboard mines. On the other hand, Germany exported 44 million tons of coal across its borders to supply the needs of continental countries with little or no coal. This trade was society's mechanism by which resource deficiencies in some areas were supplied by surpluses in others. Since 1913, under the impact of two wars and a depression, the mechanism has never functioned adequately.

Shortage of Coal Retards Recovery

The crisis in trade is tied to and illustrated by the extremely difficult situation in Britain—the traditional heart of world trade. Since the war, Britain has been unable to export enough goods to pay for the imports of raw materials and food desperately needed for the nation's recovery. Loans from the United States and large shipments of food have alleviated the symptoms but have not cured the patient. Purchases from abroad have been restricted to essentials and plans were made by the government to increase "exports in 1947 to 140 per cent of the 1938 level." Shortages of coal and raw materials defeated the program. Why should Britain be short of coal while it still has abundant reserves? The answer is that the production of coal has steadily declined since 1940. In fact, instead of exporting 74,000,000 tons of coal as was done in 1913, Britain since the last war has not mined enough coal to meet its own demands. This inability to export coal on the part of Britain and Germany is the crux of the European situation because the outflow of coal from these countries in their decades of prosperity before the first world war helped to balance the inflow of raw materials for their industries. Coal means energy and thus Britain, for example, traditionally exported energy to the coast of Europe, to Italy, to the east coast of South America, and to many lesser areas. This energy was utilized to operate the physical plant without which the coal importing countries could not have produced the foods and raw materials needed by Britain and other countries of Western Europe.

In the brief compass of this paper I cannot go into the causes of Britain's decline in coal production. I am convinced, however, that it is closely tied to the impact of postwar social legislation and perhaps since January, 1947, to ineffective operation of the mines by the National Coal Board, a government agency. Possibly the social and political changes were needed but the timing in terms of Britain's econoomy and trade has been tragic. This difficulty in Britain epitomizes the world situation where increasingly the economy of nation after nation is being affected wisely or unwisely by the impact of social reform and political programs. In many cases the result is a lowering of the level of living and a decline in the national income. Mind you, I am not arguing against social and political changes, but I do argue that such changes will not improve the lot of the common man, unless and until they are so projected as not to destroy trade and other mechanism by which society utilizes resources to supply wants.

Role of Trade in World Order

To meet the present crisis in world trade, society needs a clearer understanding of the role of trade in the world order. When such understanding is adequately disseminated, better international policies should be forthcoming.

Foreign trade consists of a series of transactions between the people of two or more countries and of the financial accommodations behind those transactions. To the men who handle the business, foreign trade is a matter of profit. To the nations involved, trade means the presence of commodities and services essential to the welfare and standard of living of their nationals. World trade implies that all nations participate and this means trade between nations and among the nations. In this connection it is well to remember Sargent's statement of many years standing, that in world trade, the whole is balanced but not the parts. At present, as has been said, we have only the pretense of one world, and the actuality of two. Thus under existing conditions there can be no trade in world dimensions, no balancing of the whole, for the parts are not cooperating. Can there be a satisfactory substitute? That is, can the maritime nations facing the Atlantic and Pacific oceans develop satisfactory trade without the participation of the vast continental area under the flag of the Soviet Union? To advance our thought, I shall attempt to formulate two fundamental laws of economic geography and then suggest their bearing on the present international crisis.

Trade, either domestic or foreign, is a functional adjustment to two laws, namely, the law of continuity of human wants and the law of irregularity in resource patterns. Or in other words, trade is a means of bringing the irregular distribution of resources into harmony with the continuing needs of society.

Law of Continuity of Wants

The law of continuity of wants pervades every phase of modern life. Human wants are ever with us. The wants of today repeat the wants of yesterday and forecast the wants of tomorrow. In satisfying these never-ending wants, society has built a complex physical plant into and upon the natural landscape, has developed the whole range of modern techniques and methods, and has come into possession of numerous customs, social attitudes and legal measures: all these must integrate into a functioning whole if the wants even of a single commodity are to be met. For example, the gas for your car is the end result of a long and complex series of installations and services organized and directed by corporate administrations, and protected by the agencies of local, state and federal governments. As oil resources are not spaced evenly in this country or in the world, trade and the associated transportation facilities are essential parts of the whole structure. They adjust the dynamic phenomena of wants to the more nearly static phenomena of pattern.

Law of Irregular Spacing of Natural Resources

The law of irregular spacing of natural resources is a law of nature. Resources are where they are and if man wants them he must come and get them. These facts are axiomatic in geographic thought. We take them seriously and are perplexed, and at times disheartened when they are given little or no attention by framers of administration or legislative measures. We argue that if governmental or other policies interfere with the utilization of resources and the trade by which the products of resources are distributed, the policies should be changed.

Interaction of the Two Laws

Britain's apple supply in normal times illustrates the interaction of the two laws under discussion. Apples are sold in Britain's food shops every month of the year. This illustrates the law of continuity of wants. To make this possible, apples are drawn according to ripening season from producing districts in England, France, Canada, the United States, Australia, Tasmania and other countries. Conditions suitable for commercial apple culture are highly localized and the producing districts are widely and irregularly spaced. This illustrates the law of irregularity of resource patterns. As the fruit of these districts come into harvest at different seasons, the agencies of trade and transportation can deliver apples in England from month to month thruout the year.

Apple culture in any district is undertaken by orchardists who on the one hand believe that their sites possess the conditions essential for commercial apple production, and on the other are convinced that the demand for apples will continue for the 15 or more years before the trees begin to bear, and for the 20 to 50 years that the trees may produce after they come into bearing.

As the apples ripen in any district, one of two things must happen. If the apples are not picked, eventually they will fall to the ground under the law of gravity. Or in response to the law of continuity of wants the fruit may be picked, graded, packed and shipped to market. It moves from the producing areas to the consumer by means of the agencies of trade and transportation, or in geographic terms, by the integrated series of adjustments by means of which the desired end for society is attained.

Trade and International Boundaries

In view of the continuing wants of modern life, the irregular distribution of earth conditions and earth resources, and the existing pattern of national units, it is clear that some trade must cross international lines. The commodities in demand and the resources from which they are produced, in many cases, are not on the same side of an international boundary. No nation is in possession of all the resources and all the technology required to supply the continuing wants of its people. Either the wants go unsatisfied or trade crosses the frontiers. As has been said elsewhere, if trade does not cross international boundaries, armies will.

Under the present emphasis on extreme nationalism with its accompanying high tariffs, quotas, and other controls, the flow of trade across international boundaries is so channeled and restricted that it does not accomplish its true function of organizing widely distributed resources to help supply the wants of the world's population. At present, as has been said, international trade largely is between nations rather than among all the nations. Thus the whole cannot be in balance because the parts are not functioning. If this principle were widely understood, policies might be forthcoming under which international boundaries would become pumping stations to accelerate the flow of international trade, rather than retarding dams or barriers as they are today.

If the Iron Curtain continues to divide the world into two operating units, which unit has the best promise of succeeding under the laws of economic geography? In terms of restrictions on the flow of trade within its sphere of operation, the U.S.S.R. with its all-powerful central government might have the best of it. Presumably, within the Soviet territory, trade is not retarded by political lines. Apparently, however, it is profoundly influenced by government action. One may argue that the law of continuity of wants, as applied to the needs of all the people, is disregarded. In terms of favoring natural conditions, most of the Soviet territory lies north of the latitude of the northern boundary of the United States. This means that either the Soviet people must go without tropical and lower middle latitude products, or they must resort to trade to get them. Modern technological developments in the U.S.S.R. are limited to a relatively few areas and thus only a few parts of the country are ready to function as parts of a national property geared to twentieth century needs. Confined within their national frontiers the Soviet level of living, individually and collectively, will be lower than if they relied on international trade to supplement and enrich their domestic production and trade.

The world outside the Iron Curtain on the one hand has the disadvantage of numerous and zealously regarded national boundaries and on the other the advantage of greater and more diversified resources of land and men. Most modern technology is confined to Western Europe and the United States. It's one thing to be ambitious for modern technology and quite another to have it already installed and in operation. If the United States and Western Europe find a satisfactory plan of procedure, they will command most of the world's largest technological developments.

In terms of natural resources and earth conditions which promote the utilization of resources, the countries outside the Iron Curtain have a distinct advantage. For example, probably 75 per cent of the world's mineral resources are controlled from New York and London. In amount and variety of timber, in arable land, in fisheries, in grazing lands and in natural accessibility the maritime countries have superior assets. The same holds true for their position in science, engineering, education and religion. The one great need, therefore, is an international program to which the western nations can adhere with confidence and profit. Is there sufficient understanding of fundamentals, sufficient international tolerance, and sufficient determination to make possible the development of such a program? That is the $64 question, the supreme issue of our time.

International Issues of the First Order of Importance

In considering the question of international relations of the Atlantic and Pacific nations, I am convinced that a wise way to begin would be to concentrate on issues that are truly international in character. Ocean trade and air transportation concern all the nations and thus are international matters of the first order of importance. International credit, trans-oceanic communication, and international law are in the same category. Perhaps most important of all is the international action which will be required if religious freedom and individual liberty are to be preserved. If the Soviet program had succeeded in Italy, what would have become of the time-honored seat of the Catholic division of Christianity? If the coastal low lands, enlivened and enriched by the Reformation, come into Soviet jurisdiction, what will be the fate of the Protestant Church in Europe? These questions are international issues of the first order and are squarely before the world today.

Under my thesis, a program to promote world trade would help solve many of the current international problems. It is a logical line of attack. Because of the influence now exercised by the United States, and the United Kingdom, these countries are the logical areas from which to launch the attack. Because geography is one of the fields of learning which leads to understanding of the areas and issues involved in world trade and other international matters, it should contribute notably in the formulation of the desired program and policy.

Slow Appearance of Effective Foreign Policies in America

If you become impatient at the slow appearance of effective American foreign policies, please remember that the people of the United States are not internationally minded. We have not learned that relations with other nations may have a decisive bearing on our welfare. As yet, we may not agree with the assertion of the editor of *Barron's National Business and Financial Weekly* that "every nation in the world, past and present, has had to learn at one point or another in its history of the supremacy of foreign over domestic affairs." He argues that "it is foreign policy that makes history" and that "the difference between bad and good foreign policy is often the difference between disaster and happiness, death and survival."

In the early period of our national life, that is before the Congress of Vienna in 1815 initiated a century of world peace, our leaders and our people in general were much concerned with foreign affairs. This knowledge was of immense value from 1776 to 1815 when the young nation struggled to maintain an existence during Napoleon's attempts to gain control of Europe. Our idea, as voiced by Washington, of keeping free of European entanglements, was a wise policy for a young country during troubled times.

In the world order of the 19th century, the United States gave primary attention to domestic problems, more especially to consolidating its territory, to the settling of its vast area, and to the development of its resources. The resulting production of cotton, grain and raw materials created a huge surplus for export. The nation had a continental or domestic emphasis, and developed no major foreign policy except the doctrine enunciated by Monroe. Altho this regional bid for peace in the New World affronted the diplomats of Europe, it was in harmony with the British policy of world trade and both nations profited accordingly.

During the 19th century, Americans made discovery after discovery in the technologies of agriculture, industry, and engineering. Our record of invention is unique in the history of civilization. As other nations bought our products, largely financed our international transactions, and transported our foreign trade, we gave little or no thought to international relations. The geography of that time concerned itself briefly and brilliantly with western surveys and exploration, but until the turn of the century, economic geography and other aspects of modern geography almost were unknown.

Then came 1914. After a century of peace, Germany felt strong enough to challenge the world order. The United States moved rapidly thru World War I, a postwar boom, a great depression, and World War II. We learned in tragic fashion of the impact of foreign affairs on our national life. We tried to improvise a workable foreign policy but the understanding on which such a policy should have been based was conspicuous by its absence. After the first war we retreated into normalcy and provincialism. Since the second war we have squandered money and effort in honest attempts to bring order out of chaos in Europe and the Far East, areas so complex that no American or group of Americans can claim to understand them. Progress has been made, but not enough. The wants continue, the resources of men and land are available, but the human intelligence to organize the one to serve the other is lacking. This is the real reason for the present crisis in world trade, and for that matter, for the other crises in international relations.

Our foreign policies and our foreign relations will improve with experience. As in Washington's time, our leaders and our people are awake to the issues. But we also must learn thru education. If knowledge is power, then we need infinitely more knowledge. We need the right rather than the wrong system of education. We must have more truth and less propaganda in our curriculum. The Social Sciences are diffusing their energies in fruitless attempts to study and teach all knowledge at once. Some seem to want knowledge put up like candy bars in chocolate coated parcels. What we need in facing the grave national and international problems of our time is better disciplined minds. We must move on to a system of functional education under which minds will be trained to reason and to follow reason and thus gain understanding. Even understanding is not enough. We must learn how to implement understanding, that is to utilize understanding in the solution of problems and the development of policies.

Geography Breeds Understanding of World Trade Problems

What has geography to offer in a functional system of education which will breed intelligence and understanding of world problems? The answer is clear, it can offer one of the major understandings, that is the understanding of the laws, principles and implications of pattern in the world order. Such understanding makes clear that just as self-preservation is the first law of life for the individual, the organization of natural and human resources to meet the continuing wants of mankind, is the major problem of society at present and probably in the future.

Geography has made amazing progress since the turn of the century. As a discipline, however, it has not come of age. We need specialists on any and all parts of the world, specialists who can speak with the authority of deep understanding of the interaction of men and land in the areas they represent. We need to develop the systematic aspects of geography. Physical geography needs a complete overhauling in competent geographic hands. Historical geography offers challenging opportunities and problems. Political geography at long last has competent leadership but needs time, money and brains in large quantities. It is hardly necessary to tell this audience that educational geography cries for attention and expert cultivation. Furthermore, economic geography needs new definition and new emphasis. For example, we have tried to show here that world trade is an essential part of the organization of resources and that an understanding of world trade, the organization of resources, and the continuity of wants are gained by studying geography, especially economic geography.

In conclusion may I repeat, that geography has made great progress but not enough. The demand for geographic talent has outrun the supply. The value of geographic thought, geographic teaching and geographic research is widely and increasingly recognized. We need apologize to no man or no discipline. However, we need to learn how to recruit students who have the spark of talent for geographic thinking. We must have more research and better teaching. We must be ready to utiilize our knowledge and understanding in the solution of the problems of our time. Just as at present there is a crisis in world trade, there also is a crisis in geography, a crisis calling for rapid and effective improvement. Each of us can help with better thinking, better study, and better teaching.

68. What Foreign Trade Means to Indiana *

Though this study was undertaken by a Representative to determine whether high tariffs would hurt or help his voters, it represents a unique

* Carroll Kilpatrick, "What Foreign Trade Means to Indiana," *Harper's,* Vol. 208, No. 1245, Feb. 1954, pp. 61–64.

The author (1913   ) is a newspaper editorial writer. He was a correspondent for

opportunity to observe the impact of foreign trade upon a relatively small political area. The results of exports and imports filter down and are of significance to the small farmer or independent industrialist as well as large concerns. Very often in our complicated system of buying and selling the whole pattern of trade implications is not understood.

A few months ago a freshman Republican Congressman from Indiana decided to try to find out what, if any, effect foreign trade has on his District. From the day he arrived in Washington for the opening of the 83rd Congress, D. Bailey Merrill of Evansville had been buffeted by pleas of free traders on one hand and high-tariff advocates on the other. Lobbyists representing every point of view had begun knocking on his door almost before he could take his oath of office.

After some weeks of this, and after listening to the impassioned debate on extension of the Reciprocal Trade Agreements Act, Merrill appealed to the Library of Congress. Two staff men from the Library's Legislative Reference Service—Howard S. Piquet and Harold T. Lamar—were assigned to his project.

As a result, we now have a detailed case study showing exactly what foreign trade means in one fairly typical Midwestern constituency. It is the *only* comprehensive study of its kind and it will be invaluable when the great national debate on trade policy erupts again after the Randall Commission makes its recommendations for a new foreign economic policy.

The seventeen-man Randall Commission has been wrestling with trade and currency issues since last fall and has already held debates throughout the country. But these have been mostly between people speaking either purely theoretically or on the basis of only their own personal business experience. The Merrill study is something else.

The Eighth Indiana, the subject of the study, is an eleven-county district of 393,000 people in the southernmost part of the state. It has 225,000 city dwellers and a rural population of 168,000. Like almost any other area in the country, it has among these people determined free traders and stubborn protectionists. A leading furniture manufacturer in the district, for example, recently argued for a high tariff wall against all countries except those "that are founded on a true and absolute democracy." Another furniture maker from the same area, arguing for low tariffs, replied that trade with all nations should be on an equal basis. "When one nation is out of balance in relation to the others," he said, "the people suffer."

---

various newspapers (1940–51) and Assistant chief, State Department press section (1951–52). Since 1952 he has been an editorial writer for the *Washington Post*.

Both Indiana's Senators—Republicans Homer E. Capehart and William E. Jenner—are conservative protectionists of the old school. But Congressman Merrill's study shows clearly that if they were successful in erecting a high tariff wall around the United States, there would be immediate unemployment on the farms and in the factories of the Eighth District of Indiana. In fact, a severe depression could easily follow.

The Farmer's Stake

Take agriculture first. Almost one-fifth of the District's population lives on farms, and 12 per cent of the labor force works on them. The farmers produced corn, soybeans, tobacco, and other field crops that were worth $15,169,000 in 1949, the last year for which detailed statistics are available. Livestock production the same year brought them $31,420,000.

"Most of the major agricultural commodities produced in the Eighth District are important export commodities," the Library of Congress report said. "Such products as corn, small grains (including wheat, oats, barley, and rye), soybeans, tobacco, milk and cream, eggs, and hogs not only account for the major portion of the District's agricultural production, but are among the most important agricultural commodities exported by the United States."

The District's wheat crop in 1949 brought $2,780,000—and 33.5 per cent of all United States wheat produced in 1949 was exported. Soybean production brought District farmers $3,013,000 in 1949—and 25.1 per cent of the nation's soybean production was sold overseas. Eighth District farmers produced $954,000 worth of tobacco in 1949—and 25.1 per cent of the United States tobacco production was exported. The corn crop in the District was worth $5,272,000—and 3.5 per cent of the nation's corn was exported. (Actually, a much larger percentage of the corn found its way abroad in the form of meat products, for most corn is fed to livestock.)

It is not possible to give exact figures on dairy exports because of inadequate statistics. While most of the District's dairy products were undoubtedly sold locally, in 1949–51 more than half the dried whole milk produced in this country was exported, as were 13.5 per cent of the condensed milk, 7.1 per cent of the evaporated milk, and 6.3 per cent of the cheese. So it is clear that District dairymen too have a stake in foreign trade. So do the hog producers, who took in $10,680,000 in 1949. Their precise stake is also uncertain because of inadequate statistics, but one per cent of the pork and 22 per cent of the lard produced by American farmers are sold abroad. Egg production brought Eighth District farmers $3,526,000 in 1949—and 2.7 per cent of domestic egg production was exported.

The effect of foreign trade on District minerals is not so clear as it is on agriculture. About 3,300 men in the District (2 per cent of the labor force) are employed in the production of minerals; two-thirds of them in coal mining. They have been producing 5.5 million tons of bituminous annually at a time when 10 per cent of America's soft coal has been exported.

Petroleum production brings about $15,000,000 annually to the District. Coal and oil producers elsewhere in the country have complained bitterly that they are subjected to severe competition from imports of crude and fuel oil. The Library of Congress study found, however, that the Eighth District is not materially affected either by exports or imports of coal and oil, and it concluded that on balance producers seem to share to a greater extent in coal exports than in the competitive impact of fuel oil.

Jobs for Factory Workers

Manufacturing is the most important economic activity in the Eighth District. The value of manufactures in 1947, when the last Census of Manufactures was taken, was about $250,000,000. The following table shows the 1950 breakdown of employment:

Industry	*Number of employees*
Machinery	15,896
Furniture and lumber	8,955
Foods and related products	5,277
Motor vehicles	2,073
Chemicals	2,473
Fabricated metals	2,179
Apparel and related products	2,105
TOTAL	39,959

Evansville, the largest city in the District, is the world's largest refrigeration center. The significant fact for this industry is that 13 per cent of all refrigerators produced in the United States in 1952 were exported. Servel, Inc., of Evansville, which employs more than 10,000 refrigerator workers, reported that every type of refrigeration equipment it manufactures is exported.

Furniture and lumber producers export some of their products, but of the four District companies that expressed concern over imports, three were in this field. (The fourth, a small cement manufacturer, said he had had trouble from import competition before World War II but none since.) The three lumber and furniture men said that competition is not serious now, but they were worried about the future. One of them, a manufacturer of single-ply face veneers, said imports "will eventually become serious." Another, a manufacturer of fancy veneer, said he faced the possibility of competition from imported mahogany veneers; and the third, a plywood manufacturer, said imports of thin plywood, while not directly competitive with his product, had forced some other thin plywood manufacturers "to go after our customers for relief."

In the food products field, the Mead Johnson Company, which employs 1,100 workers to make baby-formula products, vitamins, and nutritious foods, reported that at least 10 per cent of its sales are for export.

The 3,073 auto workers, chiefly in assembly plants of Chrysler, Briggs Manufacturing Company, and the Hercules Body Corporation, know that about 5 per cent of American passenger cars are exported. Also in this group are farm-machinery manufacturers, 12 per cent of whose output is exported. The Bucyrus-Erie Company of Evansville, manufacturers of road-building and heavy construction equipment, reported that between 40 and 50 per cent of its production is for export.

In chemicals, the Colgate-Palmolive-Peet Company plant in Clarksville reported that they counted little on exports, but depended heavily on the import of such items as coconut oil, palm oil, olive oil, talcum, and crude glycerine.

A leading wholesale druggist in the District explained that though he does not import directly, he sells imported merchandise. "We feel quite strongly," he added, "on the free trade side of the question."

"Among the products manufactured in the District," the researchers concluded, "there are no conspicuous instances where imports are injurious to domestic producers." Or, if there are, the Library team was unable to find them.

On the contrary, it found "other manufacturers in the District who, while not producing directly for export markets, are vitally affected by exports. For example, the expansion of the refrigeration industry has influenced the growth of a number of metal working industries in Evansville, including metal stamping and fabricating plants, furnishing parts and fittings for refrigerator cabinets, along with a variety of other metal parts and supplies for other kinds of manufacturing and assembly plants. . . .

"Such establishments as railway companies, motor transport concerns, warehouses, banks, and insurance companies all profit from foreign trade. Several hundred in nonmanufacturing enterprises are directly dependent upon foreign trade for their livelihood. These include railroad engineers, brakemen, switchmen, and mechanics, truck drivers, office workers, and warehouse employees."

Facts vs. Prejudice

Expansion of foreign trade would inevitably mean "increased development and economic growth for the Eighth District," the Library of Congress researchers concluded. By the same token, contraction of foreign trade would mean the reverse. It would not only injure those industries that depend upon exports, it would fail to give substantial aid to the few producers who want protection—for some of these are high-cost manufacturers who suffer as much from more efficient domestic industries in related fields as they do from foreign competition.

Moreover, more workers in the Eighth District are employed in the manufacture of refrigeration products alone than in all the industries that might benefit from tariff protection together.* If there were layoffs in the refrigerator, automobile, and construction-machinery industries, and lower farm prices, as a result of the loss of export markets, the consumption of coal, oil, and gas would be cut.

Perhaps the most significant thing about the Eighth District study is its substantial refutation of the popular argument that only the mammoth corporations of the country benefit from foreign trade. Clearly, most of the industries in the Eighth District that are dependent upon exports for their margin of profit are small companies.

The consumer's interest was not considered in the study, but he is the one who should benefit most from competitive international trade. Neither was the security interest of the United States. But the expansion of the market for American industry means a consequent increase in the economic and military strength of the nation. The interests of our allies were not considered, but the development of the widest possible area of economic freedom clearly would strengthen the nations on whom we must rely in any future conflict.

Another study somewhat similar to this one but on a less intensive scale was completed a short time ago in the Eighteenth District of Pennsylvania. The Pennsylvania study, conducted by the United States Council of the International Chamber of Commerce, was an attempt to find out whether Representative Richard M. Simpson (R), the Eighteenth District Congressman, actually was representing the best interests of his constituents in his crusade for protectionism. It found that he was not; that if he had his way, he would do his District more harm than good.

Many detailed studies like these are needed to fortify Senators and Representatives against the special pleas of producers who want protection without regard to the effect on the community as a whole. During the recent

* There are 13,000 refrigerator workers and 12,000 workers in the coal mines, the oil fields, and the furniture and lumber industries.

Congressional recess Representative Merrill continued his study, interviewing scores of persons and double-checking the experts' findings. Now he is convinced that a "mutually profitable world commerce is essential for world peace" and for the welfare of the Eighth District. Unlike many of his fellow Congressmen, he is able to speak on the basis of knowledge rather than from prejudice or what might have been true half a century ago.

69. *Trade and Geography* *

This selection provides an excellent contrast to Kilpatrick's "What Foreign Trade Means to Indiana." Canada is a large nation with a great diversity of physical resources. Climate and relative position restrict major development of the country to an area approximately 100 miles north of the United States border. Because of its abundance of natural resources and relatively small population, Canada is one of the major trading nations. Master in this reading shows how the geography of Canada is basic to the nature and development of her foreign trade.

Why Canada is a Trading Nation

Canadians are so used to being told that Canada is one of the world's three or four greatest trading countries that we may have reached the stage where such statements have become stale and overdone.

Granted that Canada is a great trading country, what of it? Surely our particular rank or position in the line is not of any major importance in itself. What are the factors that account for it? What does it signify?

Why are Canadians, as a people, such large international traders? Have we some special gift for commerce? Have we a stronger bent toward trade than most other peoples have? How does it come that we carry on a greater volume and value of foreign commerce than countries with two or three times our population, such as France and Brazil, or such countries as India and China and Russia with many times our numbers? And why, on a per capita basis, do we transact far more trade with other

* Oliver Master, "Trade and Geography," reprinted from *Canadian Geographical Journal,* Vol. 48, No. 1, January 1954, pp. 3–14.

The author is Assistant Deputy Minister of Trade and Commerce for Canada. He has given many years of service to the Canadian Geographical Society, having been a member of the Editorial Committee since the publication of its first journal in 1930.

nations than the Americans or the British, or the Dutch, or the Germans? How is it that in the whole world there are hardly half a dozen countries that do as much international trade, either per person or in the aggregate, as we do?

One series of questions leads to another. If we do so much trade with other peoples, is that a good position to be in, or is it not too good? Is it something that is growing on us, or does it tend to become less pronounced? Should we encourage it still further, or try to lessen it? Is it a condition that we could change materially if we wished, or something that we have to live with? Some of these questions can be answered readily and simply, others neither so readily nor very simply.

As a people Canadians can claim no unique bent towards commerce. We are no more talented, certainly no more experienced, than the British or the Dutch, the Swedes, the Swiss, the Belgians, or many others. We have neither more nor less affinity for international commerce than the peoples of many other lands. Nor do we purposely go in for foreign trade on such a heavy scale because the wealth or the welfare of nations is always to be measured by the amount of international commerce they carry on. That assumption is not a valid or reliable one.

The Basic Answer

The broad fact that answers most of our questions is this: that it is the geography of Canada that accounts chiefly for our position as a trading country. When we stop to study our trade figures, we are looking into a mirror that reflects the kind of land we live in. Our trade and our trade records are produced not only by our people but by our soil, our forest cover, our below-the-surface resources, our inland and coastal waters, by our rainfall, hours of sunshine, frost-free seasons, and other climatic features. All these are parts of our geography. Another and very important part of it is Canada's situation on the globe in relation to other countries. These are the factors that basically determine the nature of our trade, its size, and its main directions. Our commerce is cast in the mould of our national geography.

Having said that, one must hasten to add that countless factors, other than geography, together play a vital and manifold role in shaping the commercial pattern of any country. The character of its people conditions everything—not simply their general level of physical and mental vigour but especially their technical ability. To achieve commercial eminence they must be capable of developing the diverse types of industry that enable them to make good use of all the resources they have at hand.

They must be capable also of competing with the most progressive peoples in other lands both as primary producers and as manufacturers, merchants and bankers. Commercial policies, too, are immensely important. The trade of any nation may be fostered or frustrated by its own commercial policies, as well as by those of other countries.

In Canada, as in other countries, these and many other influences may not be overlooked or discounted. But when all is said and done, the fact remains that Canadian commerce is basically the product of the physical setting in which the Canadian people live and work. Whether we look at the size and nature of our exports, or at the composition of our imports, or at the main directions of our trade with other countries—wherever we look the effects of geography stare us in the face.

Canada as an Exporter

Consider, first, the export side of Canada's trade. In 1952 Canada stood third among all countries in total value of exports; only the United States and the United Kingdom stood higher. In value of exports per capita, Canada stood second and was exceeded only by New Zealand. While the geographic factor may seem at first sight to have no bearing on these facts, the strength of its influence becomes apparent as soon as one starts to examine why our exports are so high. Little more than a glance at the character of our export trade is needed to show how obviously the whole picture is coloured by the hand of geography.

Indeed, the list of Canada's twenty principal exports in 1952 could be made the theme of an extremely interesting series of lessons in commercial geography. These twenty commodities accounted for about 70 per cent of our total exports and they are very largely the products of basic resources of three or four different forms—arable and pasture lands, softwood forests, coastal and inland fisheries, and mineral deposits of many kinds, especially base metals. The foundations of our export trade rest in great degree upon these resources. The trade owes its size as well as its other features, first, to the fact that our national geography includes such natural assets on such a generous scale and, secondly, to the fact that the demands from other countries enable us to push our production of food, mineral and forest products far beyond the rising but still modest needs of our domestic market.

There are few countries where, to such a degree as in Canada, external markets have been the mainspring of internal development. By the same token there are few countries where new internal development has produced such immediate and large results in the form of expansion of exports. In Canada these two elements or phases of national growth have gone hand-in-hand. Here again the reasons are to be found mainly in the geographic background.

Whenever we look at a table or a chart of Canada's major exports, we should see much more than a neat diagram or an interesting set of figures. We should see something of the real substance of Canada. We should catch a breath of fresh air from the diverse and far-reaching regions where the farmers, fishermen, lumberjacks, miners, and millmen are at work—from the black soil expanse of the prairies, from the blue waters of the Atlantic and Pacific, and from the green bush and the grey rock country. These are the sources that give Canada its towering rank in international trade, whether expressed in dollars, or in volume terms for such exports as wheat, lumber, paper, or nickel, cattle, fish or furs—not to mention scores of others.

Well-balanced Trade

Canada's prominence in international commerce is not due solely to high rank as an exporter. Our standing as an importer is almost as high. In 1952, besides ranking third in exports, we stood third also in total imports, and fourth, in per capita imports. Only the United States and the United Kingdom exceeded Canada in total imports, although France crowded us rather closely for third place. Iceland, New Zealand and Hong Kong were the three countries whose imports, on the per capita basis, were greater than those of Canada.

The reasons why Canada holds such an advanced position in sales of goods to other countries are probably better known than the reasons why we buy so much from other lands. Nearly everyone is familiar with the fact that we have to find markets abroad for our huge surpluses of grain and grain products, lumber, pulp and paper, cattle and fish and furs, and mineral products of many kinds. It is not so generally known that we usually import nearly as much as we sell to other countries, and frequently more.

Indeed, over the past few years the margin between the total value of our exports and that of our imports has been very slim. For the period 1948 to 1952, as a whole, the excess of exports over imports was less than 6 per cent. On a total volume of business approaching 35 billion dollars, the trade could hardly have been more closely balanced. If two or three of the other leading commercial countries in the world could reach a similar position, the entire structure of international trade would gain immeasurably in strength and stability.

Broadly speaking, foreign trade is the means by which the peoples of different countries are enabled to exchange the surplus goods which they produce. The commerce between nations follows literally thousands of well-travelled trade routes on land and sea and in the air. Beneath the whole flow-sheet of world trade lies the panorama of global geography. And it is this underlying geographic pattern which to a very great extent governs the cargo movements from one country or continent to another—wheat from Canada to Britain, coal from Britain to Argentina, hides from Argentina to the United States, cotton from the United States to Canada. International trade matches the surpluses and the needs or deficits of scores of countries.

A major part of this trade, it is true, arises less from the geographic differences between one country and another than from disparities in the industrial experience and skill of their peoples. Nevertheless, world commerce owes its basic shape and features to the movement of staples such as wool, wheat, iron and steel, cotton, coffee, copper, coal, sugar, meat, fish, oil, lumber and paper. These are commodities that move in immense volume from the more to the less favourable areas of production. Trade in food products and raw materials is the trade that must go on in good times and bad. It may run into periods of slow and sluggish movement but it is far less subject to sudden and almost complete stoppages than the trade in many classes of highly manufactured goods that are so often caught in the meshes of customs restrictions devised to permit the entry of "essentials" and to shut out the "nonessentials."

The Variety of Our Imports

The reasons why Canada stands so high as an importing country—both in total imports and in imports per capita—become obvious as soon as one examines the list of principal commodities we buy from other countries. Such a list reveals very clearly most of the more glaring gaps in the physical and economic geography of Canada which compel us to look elsewhere for many products that are vital to the economy of a nation which has reached both a high standard of living and an advanced stage of industrial development. Some of the products which we find necessary to purchase abroad cannot be grown at all, or not to any great extent, in the Canadian climate, e.g., cotton, jute, cocoa, tea and coffee, citrus fruits. Sugar and early season vegetables exemplify the problem of comparative costs. Other major imports—notably petroleum and coal—reflect our geographical deficiencies of another type. We have immense domestic coal deposits but their wider use involves the difficulties of competition with the nearby sources of United States coal. Again, while oil developments in Canada have been making rapid headway, imports of petroleum and petroleum products still account for several of the very large items among our purchases south of the border.

To any one examining the list of principal Canadian imports it may seem at first sight that the geographic factor has little or no bearing upon certain items for which we have to meet some of our most expensive bills abroad. Our whole foreign shopping list is weighted very heavily in favour of products that represent foreign manufacturing skill as distinct from those that reflect weaknesses in Canada's basic resources. Machinery of many kinds, electrical apparatus, rolling mill products, automobiles, tractors, engines, refrigerators, etc.—these, in the aggregate, account in great measure for the size of our annual import bill. Even in the case of such purchases as these, however, the geographic influence is far from negligible. Actually it is the key to the whole picture.

Much the greater part of Canada's imports of manufactured and semi-manufactured goods comes from the United States. There is no more potent influence affecting both the size and the nature of our import trade than the geographic fact that our country lies immediately next door to the nation which possesses both a larger and a more diversified industrial structure than any other country in the world. In the final analysis it might well be found to be true that both the make-up and the extent of our imports are influenced even more by our geographic location vis-à-vis the United States than by the obvious shortcomings of our climatic or other geographic features which compel us to depend on other lands for supplies of tin, cotton, coffee, tropical fruits, and a long list of other requirements.

Exports Beget Imports

It is plainly evident how and why geography so largely determines the nature of our imports, and where we get them. But it is by no means so readily apparent that geography has very much bearing upon the actual amount of our purchases from other countries. Nevertheless, it is not an overstatement to say that geographic factors exert almost as great an influence upon the volume and value of our imports as upon their character and their origin. Here we come back to the basic fact that the economy of Canada is so distinctly that of an exporting country.

Our national growth has been traditionally tied into our success in finding external markets for the products of the new resources we have been able to open up during a long series of consecutive periods. From these new developments, over many years, we have had vast cumulative increases in the volume and in the value of our total exports. Closely coupled with these export increases have come corresponding increases or changes in countless other aspects of the Canadian economy—in its size and diversity, population, purchasing power, and in its consumption of foreign as well as domestic products. Our import trade—which services this whole economy —has had a long record of expansion which not only reflects but also anticipates the scale of export growth. Thus the geographic factors which furnish the basis for our high standing as an exporting country have had a dual effect in making Canada equally prominent among importing countries. The two positions go hand-in-hand, although the influence of the geographical factor is more direct and more obvious in the one case than in the other.

Distribution of Trade

Strongly marked as the imprint of geography is, on both the selling and the buying side of our foreign commerce, the full force of its influence is seen still more clearly when we look at the distribution of our trade among the many different countries with which we do business. While there are scores of countries with which we carry on a more or less regular trade, about 90 per cent of our total foreign commerce in 1952 was transacted with fifteen countries. But, most significant of all, 63 per cent of the total (in value) was accounted for by the immense volume of business passing across the border between Canada and the United States. By all odds the most important factor affecting the direction of our foreign trade, both buying and selling, is our proximity to the United States. That country alone, in 1952, bought more than half of our exports, and supplied nearly three-quarters of our imports.

Two distinct factors contribute in a special way to the force of the commercial influence which this proximity exerts.

First, the United States embraces within its own borders a unique combination of basic resources and of developed industries. With the possible exception of Russia, no other country is so well equipped in respect to the variety of natural products it can produce on a huge scale. And no other nation whatever possesses an industrial structure which, in either size or diversity, even approaches that of the United States. In these circumstances, it is small wonder that 70 per cent or more of our imports come from our nearest neighbour.

Whether we require food products or raw materials, or whether we require goods that are mainly the product of highly specialized industrial skill, the United States holds a matchless array of competitive advantages in the Canadian market. Not all of them are due to the proximity of the two countries—but many of them are. A common language, similar habits and standards of living, ease of travel across the border, transport systems that link up with each other, the various media that carry the full effect of American advertising into Canadian homes and offices—these are among the factors that explain why the trend toward greater domination of our import market by the United States has been perhaps the most persistent of all the long-term trends associated with the growth of Canada's foreign commerce.

Secondly, these effects of proximity—of geography—operate also in the reverse direction. The selling pressure which the United States exerts in our market has so far been stronger—and certainly much more in evidence clear across the board—than the tendency for American business to look to Canada as a source of supply. Nevertheless, in more recent years the United States has become incomparably the greatest buyer of Canadian exports.

Despite the natural wealth which the United States itself embraces, there are certain fields in which the rapid rise of consumption has already outrun that country's capacity to meet its own needs. The vast volume of Canadian exports of paper and other forest products furnishes the star illustration of a gigantic American demand being turned in Canada's direction. In other fields many similar trends on a smaller scale seem to be well under way. All told, a very wide range of other Canadian exports —farm and fisheries products, metallic and non-metallic minerals—are mainly underwritten by the needs of the American market. Relatively speaking, Canada is less of an overseas trader and more of a North American trader than was the case as recently as, say, fifteen years ago. The extent of the change in that respect may not be very widely realized. It is traceable partly but not solely to changes in world conditions. In no small measure it is also the result of the more forceful assertion of geographical influences.

Our Overseas Commerce

With 63 per cent of our total foreign trade in 1952 being done with the United States, the remaining 37 per cent comprises our commerce with overseas countries in every part of the globe. However, it is perhaps a little confusing to speak in terms of '*total foreign trade*.' We get a more accurate picture by saying that nearly half of our exports went to overseas countries, and that those countries, in turn, supplied slightly more than one-quarter of our imports.

The United Kingdom is the great sheet anchor of our overseas business. Britain has lost some of her early pre-eminence as a market for Canadian exports and as a source of our imports, but on both counts she is still far in front of any other overseas country. In 1952 our ten other main overseas markets together purchased less from Canada than the United Kingdom alone. Again, as a supplier of our own needs, Britain's supremacy among the overseas countries is still unchallenged, although it is rather less marked than her margin of leadership as a customer for our products. While British-Canadian trade rests on firm geographical footings, the influence of geography is in this instance interwoven to a unique degree with that of many other factors, such as the close political link and the strong racial ties between the two nations, and the countless ways in which the drive-belt of Britain's mature metropolitan economy has, over a long series of years, helped to turn the wheels of growth in the younger Canadian economy.

The distribution of our overseas trade exhibits another rather notable feature. Both our export and our import commerce are widely diffused but, with the sole exception of Great Britain, each of the overseas countries with which we do business accounts for only a very small percentage of our total trade. It is perhaps rather surprising to find that in 1952 Venezuela figured so prominently—chiefly because of our heavy purchases of petroleum from that country. It is interesting to observe, too, that very few overseas markets take as much as 2 per cent of our total exports, and that still fewer countries supply as much as 1 per cent of our imports. Our "world" commerce is subdivided among dozens of countries, and even such populous nations as France, Western Germany, Italy, Japan, India and Brazil do not loom up comparatively in a very large way. Although the trade with single countries is in every instance of high importance to us, it accounts for a sizeable portion of our entire commerce only in the case of, first, the United States, and, secondly, the United Kingdom.

Geography and Trade Balanced

Nothing illustrates better than the criss-cross currents of our commerce with more than a hundred overseas countries that "many a mickle makes a muckle." Limited as our trade is in many directions, virtually every country in the world produces something that we want—and needs something that we can provide. Very seldom does it happen that our exchange of goods with any one country can be closely balanced in money value. Most countries need from us either much more or much less than we need from them. The economic geography of the world is largely responsible for that fact. Closely balanced bilateral trade is neither a normal nor a natural feature of the world in which we live. Resources of climate and of terrain would require to be distributed over the various parts of the globe in a much more uniform way before given pairs of countries could trade with each other on a basis that would make it possible for them to keep the values of their respective purchases and sales in near balance. For nearly every country, including Canada, it is both natural and necessary to carry on trade that results in a marked excess of purchases with many countries and in a substantial excess of sales with many others. Bilateral trade could be more neatly managed and balanced, and the basic necessity for multilateral trade might largely disappear, only if our commercial and political world were compressed within a few huge national units, each possessing such a large share of the world's surface that it would contain all or most of the essentials of self-sufficiency. And in that event the elimination of smaller nations would mean the elimination, as well, of most of our present international trade.

Under conditions as they are, we have several scores of nations living and seeking higher standards of living in a world with a more or less rigid pattern of economic geography. For each of them, but much more so for some than for others, international commerce provides the pathway to their objective. Nature has willed it that Canada belongs to the "much more so" group. We must seek far and near for the markets and the products that are essential to our national growth and strength and well-being.

Conceivably the economic progress of Canada may in future be less closely linked with the expansion of foreign trade than it has been during the past half-century or more. A new national "growth-pattern" may bring a diminishing degree of dependence upon either exports or imports. Whether that be so or not, the influence of geography upon Canadian trade will remain as one of the major forces affecting its volume as well as its principal directions. Moreover, it is difficult to see how, in our geographic circumstances, the destiny of the Canadian people within any measureable period can be other than that of one of the world's most prominent and most versatile trading nations.

70. *The Civilizing Rails* *

Perhaps one of the best indicators of the stage of economic development of an area is its rail network. During the past century the "ribbons of steel" have penetrated many sections of the world. In this

* Mark Jefferson, "The Civilizing Rails," quoted with omissions from *Economic Geography,* Vol. 4, 1928, pp. 217–231.

The author (1863–1949) was a Professor of Geography and head of the department at Michi-

classic study, Mark Jefferson defines various degrees of density, such as railweb, railnet, railway tentacle, and river link, as they exist on various continents. A few changes in the railnet have been made in Australia, Asia, Africa, and South America since this article was written, but the basic pattern is still very much the same. The railway-accessibility maps, when compared to physical and economic resources, reveal a great deal of the geography of the world.

Northwest Europe is indubitably one of the regions of highest culture in the world. It is white on the accompanying map revealing England, Holland, Belgium, Denmark, Germany, Czechoslovakia, and Hungary as having no points farther than ten miles from a railway. And there are none in much the greater part of France, Switzerland, and Austria, and the southern half of Sweden. That means that every field, every factory, every forest, every mine, every village, and every home in all this region is within easy reach of railway transportation, the agency that for the century past has done more than any other single one of man's inventions to transform human life, especially in the way of pushing backward people forward and lifting submerged classes. The old-fashioned peasant, clinging closely to the ways of his fathers, and accepting a status of inferiority, has disappeared here before the whistle of the locomotive and the rustle of the newspaper. Local costumes and customs have had to yield here to the garments and manners of wider areas. The rural dweller here is familiar with the ways of the townsfolk. The movement of persons and goods over the region is very great. It would have been stupendous but for the ingenuity governing classes have used in devising a dozen customs and other barriers and in cherishing the form of love of country which consists of suspicion and hatred of neighbor nations, sentiments which duly blossomed into the terrible war that has just involved so much of this cultured area. (Fig. 26)

To have advantage from a railway, we do not need to live beside it. We prefer to be somewhat away but in easy reach. How wide is the useful neighborhood of the line? Of course, it varies with the viability of the country between. Five miles of swamp or lofty mountain ridges may be a complete barrier in practice. On fine, hard roads, twenty miles is no great distance. In this study, the author calls it arbitrarily everywhere ten miles on each side of the rails. Each line then provides a twenty-mile-wide

---

gan State Normal College from 1901–39. He went on American Geographical Society expeditions to Chile, Argentina, and Brazil and was chief cartographer, American Peace Commission, Paris, in 1920. He received various awards for his work in geography; his contributions to the field included studies on the nature, growth, and distribution of cities, on climate, on the distribution of population, and on numerous other phases of geography. He is the author of *Man and Climate, Principles of Geography, Man in Europe,* and *Peopling the Argentine Pampa.*

band of mobility. The author leaves white all places within ten miles of the railway.

Mobility transforms and ennobles peoples. It has always been so. Mobility along the Nile made old Egypt significant. Mobility on the sea distinguished in turn Phoenicians, Venetians, Norsemen, Dutch, and English. Sea-mobile Carthage compelled sedentary Rome to take to the Mediterranean and greatness. In Rome as in mediaeval Europe a class of

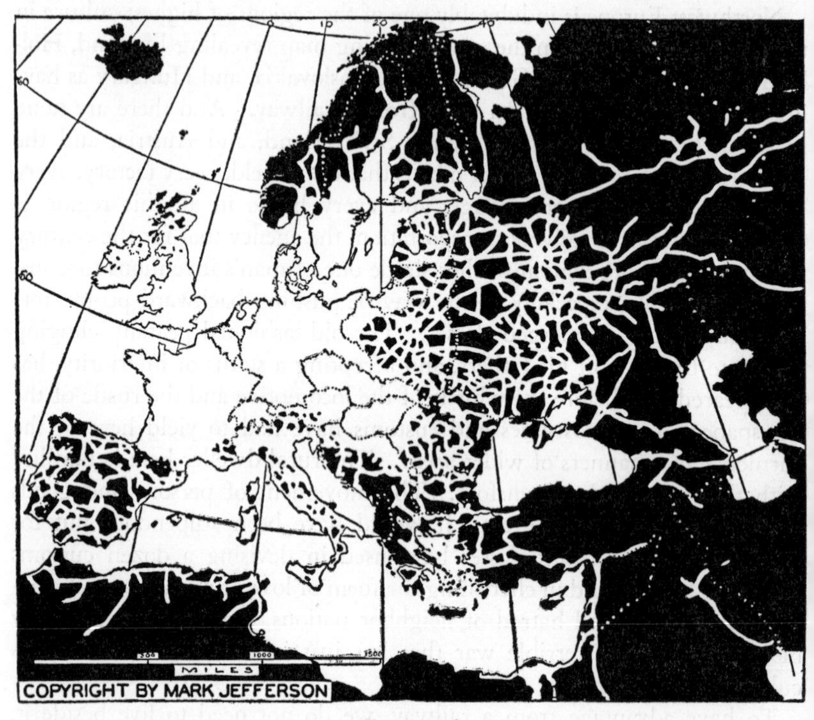

FIGURE 26

Europe within ten miles of a railway is white. Black regions are farther from the rails. The continuous white area is called a *railweb,* the network of lines as in Spain and Russia a *railnet.*

horse owners came early into prominence, and the name of their element of mobility—the horse—still lingers in their titles chevalier, and marshal. The common Spanish word for gentleman, *caballero,* once meant a horseman just as peasant, *peon,* meant once a man on foot. Not merely is the *caballero* a gentleman today, although he has not the horse which made his forbears gentle, but the Argentine workman, though he may now possess one or more horses, is *peon* because he is of the working class. And it is noticed that this Argentine horse-owning and horse-using peon is rendered wonderfully independent and dignified thereby, far superior in his bearing to his horseless blood cousins, the *roto* of Chile and the *chulo* of Peru. Sea-mobility distinguished the early Scandinavians, making them dominate in France and England. The British Empire was founded on British mobility on the sea, and rests today on its maintenance. We forget at times the pains Britain has been at to ensure and safeguard this mobility. What was the Beagle doing there in the Chilean archipelago when Darwin made his famous voyage in her? Charting the channels for all the world to find their way. Theirs are the only charts available for most of those waters and many another out-of-the-way sea path to this day.

Now the Romans, having become masters of the Mediterranean, built roads to extend their mastery from the shore inland. Just so, the Britain which mastered Napoleon and asserted world empire by controlling the seas soon after developed the iron horse and its rail path that have made much of the land surface of the globe as viable as the path of the ocean.

From the Alps to the uplands of Scandinavia in west Europe neighboring bands of twenty-mile width along the railways overlap so perfectly that if the band be white on the map all western Europe is white. There are no interstices. One is always in reach of the rails. The lines and threads of communication are lost in one great fabric of easy transportation, extended and continuous, a very *web* of transportation. This west European *railweb* covers three quarters of a million square miles and is inhabited by some two hundred millions of people. As a work of men's hands, it is most imposing, but its greatest significance is as an implement for spreading culture among men. When it picks up and transports men's bodies, it makes an inevitable impression on their attention. They never fail to take to it with enthusiasm. We may see this in remote regions, negroes "riding the cyars" in Mississippi, to squander pay-day wealth; Hindoos in India or Arabs in Algeria hanging in swarms from the steps of British or French trains. These colored brothers, all jealous to keep their ancient ways of thought untouched by the ideas of Europe, yield their persons eagerly to the white man's vehicle. There is no people so backward that it does not want to "go." This is a beginning of acceptance of the white man's civilization, an acceptance of the idea of white superiority, not as a slave who accepts power that is too painful to deny, but as a learner who recognizes that his teacher can do things that he cannot and does not yet know how to do.

To move things across the possible ten miles within the railweb here are the best roads in the world. All means of transport here are best. These people are "sold on the proposition" of spending much labor to secure easy transportation.

It may seem arbitrary to select ten miles as the critical distance of easy access to a railway. But the distance selected appears to matter less than one would suppose. To test this, three different widths have been mapped for Great Britain and Ireland. In either case, little of Britain is remote from the rails. This is civilized country. It has few back-woods corners.

The railweb of western Europe is remarkable for the abruptness with which it ends at the Spanish and old Russian frontiers. There is no transition at all. Change of gauge is sufficient reason. "The official gauge of the principal Spanish railways has hitherto, for strategical reasons, been purposely kept different from that of France, and in consequence of this passengers are obliged to change trains at the frontier stations." The Russian roads, too, used a strategic change of gauge to ward off invasion by rail from Germany. This has left Poland, reconstructed from fragments of Russia, Germany, and Austria, with a difficult situation. The edge of the railweb ran squarely across her territory, which was partly within and partly without the web. This is no doubt the reason Poland has built 2,000 miles of railway since 1919. The lined areas on the map show what significant areas this new building has cut out of the former backwoods along the old frontier.

The type of railway communication characteristic of Spain, Portugal, Russia, and the Balkan countries is the net of separate bands of railway movement, the *railnet*. Its feature is the separateness of the individual lines and the distinctness of the back-woods spaces between, spaces often twenty to fifty miles across in which are people who do not travel. Some of them have never left their home region, have never seen a locomotive. Here live true peasants, with peasant costumes and peasant ways. Those who live within reach of the road are town dwellers. Those of the backwoods are country folk. Through their mobility the railway users grow rapidly away from the rural folks. Modern cities are all on the line of the railway.

Mediaeval towns built walls to keep their enemies out and for the most part failed. We have now learned to build the best possible road out to our city limits and put up the sign there "Welcome." We cannot keep people out, it appears, and it is very much more to our advantage to have them come in. In the railnet of Europe are Portugal, Spain, Russia, and the Baltic and Balkan countries, as well as the European strip of North Africa.

The Russian region is marked by the distinct pattern of the strands, a cobweb effect centering about Moscow, Warsaw, the Baltic states, and Finland, as well as on the Donetz coal basin, just north of the Sea of Azov, but not much about Leningrad or Odessa. The pattern results from the facility of construction on a plain in any direction, together with the planning by central authorities in whom lay all the power of decision. It is the pattern of autocratic rule. In the Balkans and Iberia rough ground locates the lines on the easiest passages and makes the net irregular.

But south of the railweb and in northern Britain occurs a transition region, intermediate between web and net. It is as nearly a web as the great ruggedness of the relief will allow. Alpine masses can be pierced here and there by a tunnel, the cost forbidding their multiplication, but considerable areas will never be approached by the rails. Still it happens that these wild regions are rarely as wide as the belts of mobility along the tracks so that the distinct bands of white across a black background which characterize the railnet are not here apparent, rather splatterings of black in a field of white. It is an *interrupted* railweb.

Beyond the railnets occurs the third type of railway development. This is the railway *tentacle,* such as thrust out eastward toward Asia, four of them; the Trans-Siberian in the north, the line from Samara north of the Caspian to Samarcand and Tashkent, the Trans-Caspian from Krasnoyarsk to Merv and Khiva, and the uncompleted line from Constantinople to Baghdad from which Germany hoped so much. These lines represent the attempts of Russians and Germans to carry their culture into Asia. Shorter but more numerous tentacles thrust from the North African railnet toward the Sahara, offering it the culture of France.

The lines from the Russian net to Archangel on the White Sea and to Muransk on the Arctic are merely crossing space to reach the ocean. So are the lines across the Norwegian uplands. They are not carrying the light of Europe into a benighted Norway. Bergen and Trondhjem on the Norse coast awakened from the darkness of the middle ages before it dawned in central Europe, thanks to their possession of the seaways while most men were still bound to the paths of the land. Those were the days when colonies were planted in Iceland, the land that is all black today when it is constructing its first railway. But Iceland is not out of the world. It knows what the world is doing, and has acquired autonomy in the general urge of the smaller people for national existence. But vast barren areas are unlikely ever to carry people enough for much development of railways.

A *river link,* the last of our types of railway construction, occurs between Tura and Tavda, two tributaries of the river Ob in the northeast of Europe. The links are characteristic of underdeveloped regions where rivers must be used for travel, not because they are good means of communication but because people in those countries have none better. In Russia more than in any other country in Europe rivers are used. So the railways there often terminate on a river to which they deliver their freights. The first road east of the Archangel road terminates at Kotlas on the Dwina and in the wide black mesh next south of the Kotlas-road four of the five points terminate on the Volga, the greatest of Russian rivers. It is quite characteristic that even in so poorly developed a country as Russia the railroads twenty years ago were reported carrying 55 million tons of freight, while the rivers together carried but 9 million.

The railweb of North America is rather similar in shape to that of Europe, but somewhat smaller, having an area of less than 550,000 square miles. The people within its borders are hardly a third as many as the Europeans. From the Atlantic in Massachusetts it stretches through Connecticut, New Jersey, Pennsylvania, Ohio, Indiana, Illinois, and Iowa into Kansas and Nebraska and the Dakotas, crossing parts of Ontario, Michigan, Wisconsin, and Minnesota. The area penetrates Canada in Peninsular Ontario, freely crossed by the New York Central, and again in Manitoba and Saskatchewan. It is familiar that the rails here have supplanted for most purposes the water traffic of the Lakes, which was so important in pioneer and immigrant days. Scrutiny of the railway map at the northern and southern border of the United States shows no sign that man has imposed obstacles to the expansion of the rails. From the Atlantic it extends westward mostly across fertile plains to end in the west at an aridity barrier, the 100th meridian. In Europe the equivalent rainfall occurs about the 30th meridian east and the railweb stops short of it as if it were inhibited by the Russian defensive change of gauge.

Though the people of the American railweb are so much less numerous than their European cousins, and have been so short a time in occupation of their continent, the extent to which they have utilized their railweb has been enormously increased by some happy circumstances, two of which have been easy acquisition of land by all classes of the people and a constitutional prohibition of tariffs within the national area, which other circumstances increased to more than fourfold its original amount.

As a result, according to a competent French observer, in 1910 American railroads carried four times as many ton-miles of freight per capita of the population as did French and German roads at half the cost per ton-mile, and transported the average American citizen 31 per cent further than French roads carried their nationals, and 3 per cent further than German roads carried theirs at about twice as great cost per passenger-mile.

"In Europe," says Mr. Colson, "civilization developed before the period of easy transport, so that production had to be organized in such a way that each district should, as far as possible, supply itself; while in America farming and industries started nearly everywhere simultaneously with the railroad. Each district could devote itself to producing those articles for which its soil, its subsoil and its climate rendered it most suitable, the facility of long-distance exchanges thus making it possible to subdivide the work among the different parts of the territory."

Concerning this the American observer has to comment that what Europeans regard as civilization includes a lot of inhibitions on farming, industry, and the long-distance exchange of commodities. Further, that it is by no merit of intelligence on the part of present-day Americans that our civilization is free from some of those inhibitions, yet it is a very happy form of civilization and we are grateful to our ancestors for handing it to us.

It is interesting to see the same good fortune of the United States cropping out—without any reference to railways—in the comment in 1927 of the Managing Director of the German General Electric Company, Privy Counselor Deutsch, after a tour in America. "While the German General Electric Company is compelled to produce thousands of articles of special design to suit the wishes of its customers at home and in other European markets, its parent firm in America deals with a clientele familiar with the same business practices and having identical tastes. . . . A vast public that wears collars of the same pattern, cravats of the same color, and garments of the same cut naturally calls for the same kind of electrical appliances." (*The Living Age,* Jan. 1, 1928, page 11.) Mr. Deutsch exaggerates, it seems, but we get his point.

On the northern Great Lakes and throughout the South occur interruptions of the railweb, at barren or mountain lands that resist development or transit. Little backwoods occur every here and there in these regions where one can get far from the railway and old fashions prevail. (Fig. 27)

Toward the west a transition of streaming parallel lines leads to a great railnet in Canada, the United States, and Mexico throughout the plateau country. The backwoods are large, rough mountain masses, most difficult to cross. In four favored basins, the Valley of California, Salt Lake, southern Idaho, and eastern Washington, little railwebs are beginning to develop, but for the most part the railnet is typical and fairly uniform. The towns occur, of course, on the railways. I believe there is now no town of ten thousand people that is off the line, but the interspaces are not so much of backward people as regions without inhabitants.

Cuba has a net of her own.

Railway tentacles are flung from the North American railnet into the Peace river country and Alaska (beginning at the sea). The very straight-flung tentacle from Manitoba toward Port Nelson, like the shorter one from Cochrane near James Bay, seeks to take out the prairie grain in the short open season by Hudson Strait. Within the western railnet many a short tentacle invades a little valley.

In Alaska and again in Central America and Mexico, traffic is from the sea inland. The appearance of transportation down from Arizona through Mexico into Central America is illusory. Traffic that way lacks interchangeable wares, but if it existed it would compel the closing (it is

FIGURE 27
North America within ten miles of a railway.

now closed, June, 1928) of the gap between Tepic and Guadalajara at once, as it is represented closed on many inaccurate maps, notably the great European atlases. It is beside the only bay on the west Mexican coast. Similar gaps occur along the west coasts of Central America. In all these regions traffic is from the sea inland. What appear to be longitudinal and main lines are merely minor connections between these lines from the coast.

South America has a railweb on the Argentine Pampa of about a hundred thousand square miles area, extending across a fertile plain from the Atlantic to a boundary of aridity in the west. Three widths of gauge have undoubtedly hindered its greater expansion. Two incipient webs occur at São Paulo and Rio in Brazil. Half of the Pampa, still cattle country, has only a net of rails and most of the country about Rio and São Paulo is covered by a railnet. Tentacle lines reach into the interior in many directions, notably from São Paulo to Corumbá just north of Paraguay and from the Atlantic coast of the Argentine westward across Patagonia toward the Andes, lower there for a passage to Chile and with well-watered lands at their eastern foot. Brazil has a dozen such tentacles from the coast, not often penetrating deeply. So has almost every country in the continent. Internal commerce they largely lack. They exchange their raw products with factory wares from Europe or North America and their railways respond to this need. In some cases the tentacles from the sea have been connected up. Thus the through connection between Montevideo and Rio de Janeiro consists really of links between the ends of these tentacles from the sea. Through bookings of either passengers or freight are the exception. (Fig. 28)

It looks from such a map as this as if one could buy a ticket in Buenos Aires for Cuzco, Peru, but this is not the case. The Argentine has a railway from the sea to Jujuy and this has been extended to and beyond La Quiaca into Bolivia. Bolivia has two lines from the Pacific with ports at Arica in the bend of the west coast and Antofagasta further south, both now in Chile. Though these two are connected together they carry mainly traffic between the Pacific and the Bolivian interior. So the main line of Southern Peru is from Mollendo by Arequipa to Puno and Cuzco. It is the tentacular part of the lines from the sea inwards that always carries the bulk of the goods. Northern Peru has nothing but tentacles, without connections between, and there is little demand for connections. Chile has what appears to be a superb development of longitudinal railway the length of the country, but quite illusory. It looks as if you could travel from Iquique to Puerto Montt, but you cannot buy a ticket for Puerto Montt even at Santiago except in the tourist season of January and February. To the northward through travel hardly exists. One goes to a point up the coast by steamer and inland by rail, as the products of the country go out to the sea by rail.

River links are represented by the Railway around the falls of the Madeira, just north of Bolivia, bridging from the water traffic of the upper to the lower Madeira. The Amazonian wilderness is served almost exclusively by its rivers. Colombia has its links from Bogotá to the Magdalena and from the Magdalena to the Cauca, eastern Brazil a link between Theresina on the Parnahyba and Caxias on the Itapicurú, in the province of Maranháo, and one around the falls of Paulo Affonso on the São Francisco in Alagoas and Pernambuco, both near the northeastern corner of the continent.

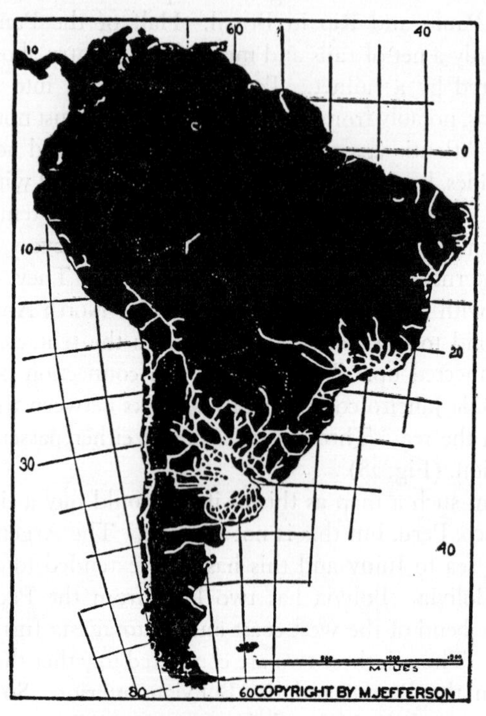

FIGURE 28
South America within ten miles of a railway.
Note the *riverlinks* of Colombia and Brazil.

There is much room for more railway building in this continent. If the Amazonian country is to be exploited from its uplands rather than from its river banks as Roy Nash predicts, it will be served by tentacle lines from eastern Brazil.

Africa has railnets in the Atlas and in the Union of South Africa. In most of the country the development is tentacular, seeking to penetrate the hinterlands from the sea and getting above the falls that isolate the upper river navigation. The Congo has three or four rivers links just south of the middle of the continent. There is certain to be much new building in this continent, but some of the plans for lines across the desert may find the motor car a better solution of their need. (Fig. 29)

Australia is better supplied. A well-developed railnet in the southeast serves South Australia, Victoria, and New South Wales, with beginnings of railweb in the country north of Melbourne. A smaller railnet in West Australia is connected to the east by the Transcontinental line across the desert. For the rest the scheme is tentacular as in all new lands. The lines have already penetrated well into the desert on many sides. Possibly motor transportation will serve most further needs in that direction. The

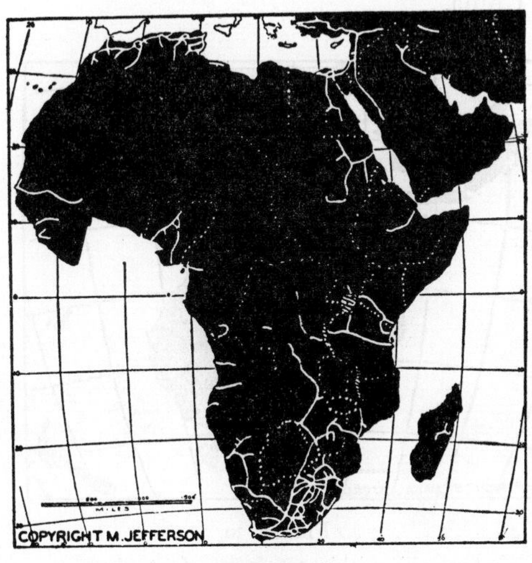

Figure 29

Africa within ten miles of a railway.

humid part of the island is fairly well supplied with rails. New Zealand to the southeast and Java to the northwest have each a well-developed railnet corresponding to their high development, while the great tropical islands—Papua, Celebes, Borneo, and Sumatra—as yet have almost no rails. The Malay peninsula has a considerable development. It is likely that the large islands will yet see much railway built. (Fig. 30)

Asia, as the greatest unbroken land mass, has greatest need of land transportation, offered in part from time older than history by its great rivers. The two great accomplishments of the continent are the railnets of India built by England, and that of Japan by herself, the only oriental country that has put her shoulders to self-development on the most approved occidental lines. There are still two backwoods of Asia greater than any others in the world except the Saharan. Nothing could put England's contribution to the civilizing of India in a clearer light than this map of the Indian railnet with its thickening in the valley of the Ganges. (Fig. 31)

The entry of Russian culture into the continent is evident in the three great tentacles from the northwest, reaching down toward the Hindoo Koosh on the one hand and closely margining the Chinese domain on the north, with tentacles aimed at it in various points. The connection with the South Manchurian Railway, which is in the hands of Japan, with a bridge of lines through Korea, suggests willingness on the part of Japan to supply the culture that shall develop the railnet already incipient on the plains of eastern China.

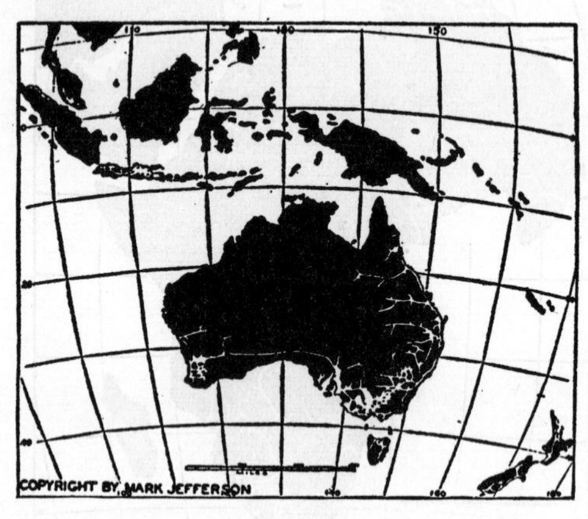

FIGURE 30

Australia within ten miles of a railway.

Though Afghanistan has no railways the Transcaspian from Krasnoyarsk has a branch from Merv ready at the frontier to push into Herat and another from Khiva ready to advance the longer distance to Kabul, while the English, skirting Afghan territory just as closely on the south, have a branch from Quetta on the Baloochistan line flung out to the frontier towards Kandahar and another from Peshawar on the side of Kabul, all with an air of readiness to go when wanted.

Persia is entered by the Baloochistan line as far as Duzdab, and by a Russian line from the Caucasus as far as Tabriz, west of the Caspian Sea, and has its own little line from Bushire on the Persian Gulf to Borazjan, tentacular all. Besides these is the railhead from Baghdad on the side of Iraq, which fails of connecting with Europe by the gap from Nisibin to well south of Mosul, the line along which Imperial Germany was pushing toward the east when war came. The long tentacle from Anatolia into Arabia to Medina, built by the Turkish faithful as a religious pilgrim route from the domain of the Sultan who claimed the headship of the Moslem world to its holy city Mecca, fails at both ends, and its middle part, far withdrawn from the sea to be out of the reach of British warships, is now in British hands in Transjordania.

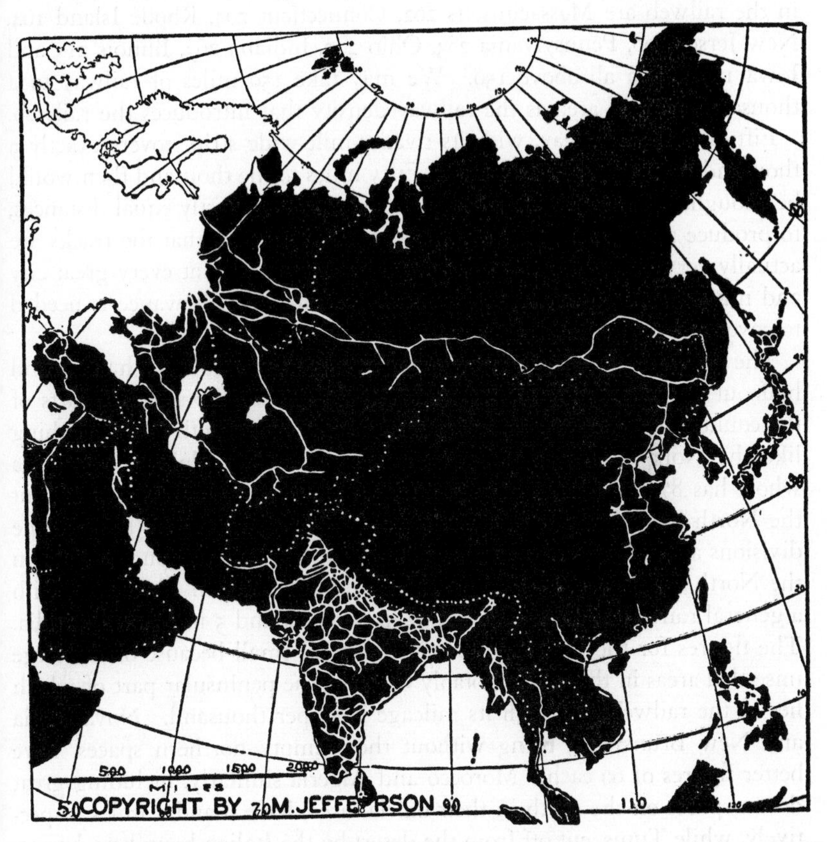

Figure 31

Asia within ten miles of a railway. The most suitable situation for a *railweb* is in China, where as yet only a beginning of a *railnet* has been made and this based apparently on Japan.

River links are in evidence in China, connecting Nanchang with Kiukiang on the Yangtse and south of Omsk in Siberia where one connects Kamenong Kopi with the nearest point on the Irtish, for in this most backward continent, river travel is all impotrant.

It is of some interest to compare statistics of railway mileage with these maps of nearness to the rails. For comparison between countries the author takes the mileage for each thousand miles of area, using the data for

1925 from the Statesman's Yearbook of 1927. The countries of the European railweb have the following mileages per thousand miles area: Britain 290, Belgium 263, Holland 191, Denmark 190, Germany 220, Czechoslovakia 160, Hungary 150, all over 150. Turning to the United States the states in the railweb are Massachusetts 262, Connecticut 204, Rhode Island 164, New Jersey 308, Pennsylvania 283, Ohio 207, Indiana 263, Illinois 215 and Iowa 177, again all above 150. We may take 150 miles of railway to a thousand miles of area as the railway density that introduces the railweb.

Fifty miles of railway, with its twenty-mile-wide strip, covers exactly a thousand square miles of country. Fifty miles to the thousand then would be enough, if the tracks were everywhere spaced at exactly equal distances, to produce a railweb. That we really need 150 means that the tracks are actually very irregularly spaced, with a great crowding at every great city and much thinning out in the country. A threefold allowance is needed to cover this irregularity.

The Swedish figure, 58, is a proper average for a country half in and half out of the railweb. If we could get figures for the separate parts of the country we should doubtless get over 150 for the south and something like the Norwegian figure for the north. Thus the United States as a whole has 87 miles of railway to the thousand square miles of area, but the North alone has 137, the South 91, and the West 37. Or taking nine divisions as the United States Census does, we find a variation from 221 in the North Atlantic states to 29 in the Mountain division. Australia, with a general railway density of 9, has 53 in Victoria and 5 in West Australia. The figures for the Canadian provinces are all small because of the large unsettled areas in the north, notably Ontario, the peninsular part of which lies in the railweb, although its mileage is 21 per thousand. Nova Scotia and New Brunswick, being without these empty northern spaces, have better figures of 69 each. Morocco and Algeria similarly, including great desert spaces on the south in their official area, have 6 and 2 miles respectively, while Tunis, cut off from the desert by the Italian boundary, has 33. The same thing is illustrated in every part of the world. For this reason a real comparison of the provision with railways of the settled part of any country should be rated by the settled, not the total, area.

Italy has 85 for its figure, much like Tennessee, Arkansas, Mississippi, and Alabama. The author has put the *interrupted* railweb at 75 miles to the thousand, an insufficient excess over the 50 miles that would just fill out the territory with 20-mile-wide white bands, if the roads were spaced with geometrical evenness. Hence the spattering with little backwoods.

The Spanish and Portuguese figures, 53 and 51, the Russian at 22, and the Balkan ones at from 16 to 64, like Mexico with 17 and the North American West, ranging from 20 to 75, suggest a lower limit for the railnet of fifteen miles per thousand miles of area. A symmetrical network of rail-bands twenty miles wide, if there were 15 miles of rails to a thousand square miles of area, would enclose interstices seventy miles on an edge. At fifty miles, as has been stated, there would be no gaps between the lines unless they were uneven.

Americans are naturally concerned to know the future of railways in the United States. The United States has been aptly called a railway-created country (Herbert Quick). Railways here enable men to carry civilization, a civilization that was undoubtedly European, into what had been a trackless wilderness and create there that widespread prosperity which has recently been revealed to Europe to arouse astonishment—and other sentiments! It is not that the railways happened to come along just as the country was being settled. The country did get settled then because the railway was available to do the work. Without the rails there would be no such country today. Settlement would have crept slowly along the rivers; numbers would still be small and wealth far less. Canals would be more numerous and fewer of those once built would have fallen into decay. All the waterways would be in use but the total movement would be by our present lights insignificant. The railways made the United States and the present generation has its whole life tied up with the effects of railways. The present is the moment to survey the geographic aspects of railway development for the reason that signs abound that a new epoch is about to dawn or has already come.

The presence of more than twenty million automobiles on surfaced roads, already half as extensive as our railway mileage, cannot but impress the observer with the fact that great masses of passengers and freight are now definitely moving without much regard to the railways. The Class I railways of the United States carried a peak traffic in 1920 of 46.8 billion passenger-miles. In 1926 it had fallen to 35.6 billion. Freight, it is true, showed no decrease. It was 410.3 billion ton-miles in 1920 and 443.9 ton-miles in 1926. The increase, however, is only a fourth as rapid as in the previous six years. Before the great war we had been building railways in the United States at the rate of four or five thousand miles a year. Our maximum mileage was 254,000 miles in 1916 and it is believed to be four thousand less in 1925, that is of road actually in use. These figures accord too well with what we see going on all about to be in doubt. Had we summer figures, when the automobile goes farthest afield, we should see greater differences, at least as far as passenger traffic is concerned.

What will the outcome be? In undeveloped countries railways can in many cases render service at less expense than it costs to maintain passable roads. This is especially true in humid regions. In desert or semi-desert regions motor transport appears to have points of great advantage over the railway. In Spain in 1927 motors carried passengers in every direction across the "backwoods." In this connection, it is worth noting that the United States had about 46 per cent of the world's total mileage of railways in 1890, 43 per cent in 1900, the same in 1910 and 38 per cent in 1920. As Europe's mileage too has fallen from 34 per cent of the total in 1905 to 31 per cent in 1925, it appears evident that the remaining third of the world's railways, the railways of the less developed regions, are now increasing mileage more rapidly than are those of Europe or the United States. In populous countries, as more roads are built and more motors manufactured, more people and more goods will take to the roads. The railways will presently have to content themselves with carrying freight which is from its nature unfitted for transport in small units, and passengers under conditions so much more agreeable than the railroads offer today that some who could travel by car would actually prefer to travel by train. It is quite possible that future new building of railways in the United States and Europe may be in good part offset by taking up unprofitable lines, and that in densely peopled regions, where highway building is not beyond the means of the inhabitants, there may yet be a considerable shrinking of present railway mileage.

71. Trade and Navigation on the Rhine *

Rivers and canals play a much greater role in the transportation network of Europe than they do in the United States or other parts of the world. Waterways developed prior to railroads and, in some European areas, the rail lines are only supplementary or "feeders" to the waterway network. Inland waterways specialize in bulk cargo. The Rhine has long been the major link in the navigable waterways of northwestern Europe; it is essential to the economic health of the Ruhr Valley of Germany as well as to the whole valley from Switzerland to the Netherlands. Though its role was disrupted by World War II and its aftereffects, the Rhine is playing a significant part in the recovery of Europe. Bashkin indicates the nature, traffic, and problems of this great river—an excellent example of an inland waterway.

* Henry S. Bashkin, "Trade and Navigation on the Rhine," *Foreign Commerce Weekly*, Bureau of Foreign Commerce, U.S. Dept. of Commerce, Vol. 38, No. 6, 1950, pp. 3–6.

The author (1918) is Program Officer, Strategic Controls Division, Bureau of Foreign Commerce, U.S. Department of Commerce. From 1947 to 1950 he was a metals economist and foreign transportation analyst and from 1950 to 1953 was with the National Production Authority. He is author of transportation articles on France and Africa of the Sahara.

European economic cooperation and the lowering of national barriers to trade have been very much to the fore in recent American thinking. It may be useful, now, to survey and appraise an example of such cooperation that has already worked successfully for many years.

To many Americans the words "Rhine River" evoke thoughts either of pillboxes and tank traps or of centuries-old castles lending their surroundings an air of unreality and legend. The Rhine, however, is much more than a line of demarcation or a tourist attraction. It is a basic economic resource, and serves the industry and commerce of five major Western European countries.

The economic development of the Rhine Basin is in part due to the usefulness of the local rivers as transportation media; the cost of moving materials plays a vital role in determining their economic utility. Modern civilization requires the moving of vast quantities of low-unit-value nonperishable goods, and it is from the movement of such goods that the Rhine and its tributaries take their importance. Petroleum products, iron ore, grain, and other raw materials are distributed from the ports of the Netherlands and Belgium to the interior of Germany, France, and Switzerland via Rhine shipping, while a good part of the coal, steel, lumber, and potash produced in France and Germany also moves toward the ultimate consumer via the Rhine and its confluent rivers and canals.

In general, canals and rivers play a very important role in inland transportation in Europe. The Rhine, however, carries more freight than any other European river, and has usually accounted for at least one-sixth as much traffic as the German railways.

By the end of World War II the movement of goods on the Rhine had stopped completely. Dozens of bridges and hundreds of ships and port installations had been destroyed or badly damaged. The results of Allied bombardment were compounded by demolitions carried out by the Germans themselves, so that no sector escaped without heavy damage.

But the restoration of inland transportation received a high priority in postwar Europe, and by the end of 1946 traffic was once more moving through the entire Rhine system, albeit slowly and carefully. Since that date the utilization of the Rhine has depended less upon physical factors than upon a solution of administrative difficulties and the general level of Rhineland production and trade.

Under the rules established by the Convention of Mannheim in 1868, the Rhine became a great international trade route. This regime began to collapse in 1936 under the impact of German nationalism and, of course, ceased to function altogether at the outbreak of the war. The *future* of Rhine navigation is clouded by the many changes that have occurred in the European economy and by the still unresolved political questions. But strenuous efforts are being made to restore the freedom of international navigation that contributed so heavily to the economic welfare of the Rhine Basin in the past and can easily do so again.

FREIGHT TRAFFIC ON THE RHINE [a] AND ON THE GERMAN RAILWAYS,[b] IN SELECTED YEARS 1913–49
(In thousand metric tons [c])

Year	*Rhine*	*Railways*
1913	54,563	399,000
1925	57,664	373,009
1926	69,521	381,868
1927	76,159	434,063
1928	71,553	432,300
1929	74,934	485,900
1930	30,782	199,500
1931	59,952	325,600
1932	48,613	280,400
1933	51,387	308,100
1934	62,382	366,000
1935	66,034	408,000
1936	70,714	452,400
1937	85,821	499,047
1938	86,148	n.a.
1939–45	n.a.	n.a.
1946	15,090	n.a.
1947	n.a.	n.a.
1948	42,910	n.a.

[a] Sources: 1913–37 from Annual Report, Central Rhine Commission, 1937 and 1946; 1948, estimated.

[b] Sources: 1913, 1928–31 from Foreign Commerce Yearbook, 1935; 1925–27 from Report No. 7, Commissioner for the German Railways; 1932–37 from Foreign Commerce Yearbook, 1939.

[c] One metric ton = approximately 1.1 short tons.

n. a. = Not available.

Rhine System's Significance

The Rhine waterway system may be briefly described as follows: The *Rhine River* is navigable by 2,000-ton barges from its outlets on the North Sea to Basel, a distance of approximately 520 miles; barges of over 4,000 tons can travel upsteam as far as Cologne. The permissible draft at mean low water is 1.75 meters from Basel to Mannheim; 2 meters from Mannheim to Bingen; 2.5 meters from Bingen to Bonn; and 3 meters from Bonn to the sea. Pilots are generally required only during periods of low water, except in the sections St. Goar-Bingen and Mannheim-Strasbourg, which are marked by swift current and a narrow channel.

The Rhine has the least amount of icing of any important German stream.

Shipping is affected by ice on an average of only 17 days per year, usually between December 23 and February 10. Low water, on the other hand, is much more of a hindrance to navigation, and may prevent passage of some part of the river for as many as 50 days per year. In general, low water reduces loadings by an average of 10 percent of capacity for 1 month out of the year, below Duisburg, and from 10 to 40 percent for 3 months out of the year between Duisburg and Basel.

The Rhine is linked with the internal transportation systems of France, Germany, and Switzerland, and with Dutch, German, and Belgian seaports by the following rivers and canals:

The *Rhone-Rhine canal,* which forms part of the link between the coal fields of the Saar, the iron mines of Lorraine, and the Rhone Valley, parallels the Rhine from Strasbourg to Mulhouse, from which point a branch canal goes to Basel. The Rhine between Basel and Strasbourg is subject to frequent periods of low water, and the Rhone-Rhine canal makes it possible to bypass this section of the river when necessary. A major disadvantage of the canal is that it cannot accommodate Rhine barges, which must load or unload to canal ships at Strasbourg. Nevertheless, in recent years the canal has carried about one-third of the total traffic between Basel and Strasbourg.

The French have begun work on another canal to connect these two cities. Named the "Grand Canal d'Alsace," it would provide not only a large-capacity waterway but also a considerable amount of electric power generated at eight stations along the canal.

The *Rhine-Marne canal,* which extends from the Marne at Vitry-le-François to Strasbourg, is one of the most useful canals in France. It puts the Saar and Lorraine industrial districts into contact with Paris and northeastern France, on the one hand, and with the Rhine and Germany, on the other.

The Neckar River joins the Rhine at Mannheim. It is navigable for craft up to 1,200 tons as far east as Heilbronn, although some progress has been made in extending the navigable channel to Plochingen. This is part of a project to construct a large-capacity waterway between the Rhine and the Danube—a scheme that has been talked of and worked on spasmodically for many years.

Another large river, the *Main,* flows into the Rhine at the city of Mainz (Mayence). The Main River is the basis for another scheme to connect the Rhine and the Danube, one that is centuries old. Work on this project was begun in the eighth century under the orders of Charlemagne, and it was finally completed in 1846 by King Ludwig of Bavaria. The Ludwigs canal, however, can accommodate barges of only 100 tons and is therefore of only local use.

The present plan visualizes the construction of a waterway that will carry 1,500-ton barges from the North Sea to the Black Sea through the center of Europe. Much of the preliminary work has been done, and a number of power stations have been erected in conjunction with this project which, it is hoped, will help to pay for it.

Work on the upper Main is now in progress, and the completion of the entire project is being sought by 1959. The lowering of the "Iron Curtain" at the western Hungarian border may, however, postpone fulfillment of this plan indefinitely.

From Basel to Strasbourg the Rhine flows almost due north. At Strasbourg the river curves to the northeast, and flows in a gentle arc whose easternmost point is near Mannheim at the confluence of the Rhine with the Neckar, from which point it curves northwest as far as Mainz.

At Mainz the Rhine turns west to the town of Bingen. This is the most difficult stretch to navigate. Its swift current, narrow channel, and shallowness require the use of a pilot at all times.

At Bingen the Rhine makes another sharp turn and resumes its northwestern course, cointinuing in this direction past the well-known cities of Coblenz, Bonn, Cologne, Dusseldorf, and Duisburg-Ruhrort.

There is only one tributary of commercial importance between Bingen and Duisberg. This is the *Moselle River,* which joins the Rhine at Coblenz. Although the Moselle seems ideally placed to provide a short water route between the Ruhr, the Saar, and Lorraine, it has been only scantily developed. Improvement of navigation on the Moselle and the concurrent development of a considerable amount of power are now subjects of debate in both France and Germany. The upper Moselle has been used for navigation for many years, while some hydroelectric installations have already been made in the Germany sector of the river.

Whether the Moselle will ever be fully developed is still uncertain, for there is by no means agreement that such development would be economically sound.

Importance of Ruhr District

The most important patron of Rhine transportation is the Ruhr district of Germany. Passage from the Rhine to the Ruhr is provided by a number of short canals, all of which are based on natural water courses. The *Rhine-Herne* canal, which goes from Ruhrort to the Dortmund-Ems canal and the *Wesel-Datteln* canal, which goes from Wesel to the Dortmund-Ems canal, traverse the Ruhr from east to west about 5 miles apart, while the *Ruhr River* provides a waterway from the Rhine to the city of Mulheim.

The *Dormund-Ems* canal extends north through the Ruhr from Dortmund to the deep-water port of Emden, a distance of 160 miles. It cannot handle craft large enough to compete with the lower Rhine for the Ruhr-"Benelux" traffic, but serves to link the Rhine with the German waterways based on the Weser, Elbe, and Oder Rivers via the Midland Canal.

The Rhine continues northwestward below Ruhrort. It crosses the Dutch border at Emmerich and shortly thereafter divides into two arms—the *Waal* and the *Nieder Rhine.* A smaller branch leaves the Nieder Rhine near Nijmegen and flows north to the Ijssel Sea, while the Waal and the Nieder Rhine (also called the Lek) flow due west to the sea a few miles apart.

These three branches of the Rhine, together with the Maas (Meuse) River form the basis of the Dutch waterway system. In conjunction with a number of large canals they make possible the movement of large vessels between the ports of Rotterdam, Amsterdam, and the Ruhr, and have thus played a vital role in the development of the Netherlands as a shipping center.

Navigation on the Nieder Rhine is hampered by shallowness and the number of locks that must be traversed. However, a new canal is being constructed to remedy this situation. This canal will branch off from the Merwede Canal at Utrecht and join the Waal at Tiel, thus bypassing most of the Nieder Rhine. When completed it will reduce travel time between Amsterdam and the German border from 40 to 20 hours. Completion of this canal is anticipated in 1952, at a total cost of $33,000,000 for the new sections.

There is at present no direct connection between the Belgian waterways and the Rhine, and Belgian Rhine traffic takes place via either the Dutch waterways or the North Sea. Nevertheless, the Belgian port of Antwerp is one of the largest handlers of Rhine traffic. The construction of a canal from Liege, the present terminus of the Albert Canal, to Dusseldorf has been projected, and Belgian interests especially are hopeful that this canal will one day be brought into being.

Character of Ships in Rhine Trade

The great majority of ships built for the Rhine trade are between 800 and 1,500 tons burden, while relatively few are built smaller than 500 or larger than 2,000 tons. (The largest ship in the Rhine trade is the Dutch *Grotius,* a vessel of 4,300 tons.) One of the most popular types of towed barges, the so-called Rhine-Herne barge, has a capacity of 1,350 tons. These barges can navigate the full length of the Rhine, Main, and Neckar Rivers, and the Rhine-Herne Canal. Although they are primarily coal carriers, they are also well suited for carrying ores, grain, crushed stone, and other common types of cargo.

Their dimensions are: Length, 80 meters; breadth, 9.5 meters; draft loaded, 2.5 meters; and draft empty, 0.5 meters. In contrast to this, a common type of all-purpose barge on inland waterways in the United States has a capacity of 815 tons; length of 53.3 meters; breadth, 7.9 meters; and draft loaded of 2.3 meters. The proportion of special-purpose, large-size barges in use on American rivers is much higher than on the Rhine, however; and there is also a great difference in the composition of tows. An average convoy on the Rhine will have a load of from 6,000 to 7,000 tons below Duisburg; 5,000 tons between Duisburg and Mannheim; 2,000 tons between Mannheim and Strasbourg; and only 1,200 to 1,500 tons between Strasbourg and Basel. The convoy might thus consist of from 1 to 5 barges.

In contrast to this, it is not unusual to have a convoy of from 6 to 18 barges on American rivers, while on the Mississippi there are giant tows such as 1 tug pushing 35 assorted barges with 15,000 tons of cargo, or 1 tug pushing a fleet of 15 specially designed tankers carrying 23,000 tons of oil.

Lest this seem to reduce the significance of Rhine shipping, it may be well to mention that even one bargeload of 1,200 tons is the equivalent of a train of 40 railway freight cars.

At times of low water, when the Rhine barges cannot carry their full capacity, numerous canal barges enter into the Rhine trade. These barges are designed primarily for use on the French and Belgian waterways and do not exceed 350 tons in capacity, the average being 200 to 250 tons. Barges of this size are also employed on the Strasbourg-Basel section of the Rhone-Rhine canal.

The development of the Diesel motor caused a vast increase in the proportion of self-propelled to towed barges—a movement that was significantly speeded by the spate of new construction after World War II. Self-propelled barges can give faster and more reliable service than can towed barges, and thus in part reduce the competitive advantage of the railways. . . . The rather shallow water of the Rhine and the fact that the stretches of lowest water also have the swiftest current have called for the exercise of considerable ingenuity in tug design. One result of the necessity for keeping draft to the minimum was the widespread use of paddle-wheel drives. During the past few years, however, the paddle-wheel steamer has been largely superseded by multiple-propeller, Diesel-motored craft.

The power rating of Rhine tugs on the lower Rhine is only 400 to 500 horsepower. On the middle and upper Rhine, however, units of 1,200 to

2,000 horsepower are common, while a four-propeller, 4,000-horsepower tug was put in service at Basel in April 1949.

RHINE FLEET BY COUNTRY OF REGISTRY,[a] 1939, 1946, AND 1948

Country	*January 1, 1939*		*January 1, 1946*		*January 1, 1948*	
	Number	Tonnage	Number	Tonnage	Number	Tonnage
Netherlands	7,180	3,752,118	2,600	1,800,000	4,502	2,852,000
Germany	3,461	2,199,382	867 [b]	554,853 [b]	2,089	1,543,998 [b]
Belgium	1,530	864,679	924	503,570	1,441	810,738
France	401	364,674	116	106,432	417	410,790
Switzerland	172	125,182	134	83,769	225	175,000
TOTAL	12,744	7,306,035	4,641	3,048,624	8,674	5,792,526

[a] It should be noted that the above table gives country of registry, which does not necessarily coincide with ownership. The flag of the vessel determines, as a rule, the country that earns the freight charges.

[b] British-U. S. Zones only.

Flags Flown by Rhine Shipping

Before the war the greatest tonnage of Rhine shipping flew the Dutch flag, with Germany taking second place and Belgium third. This ranking is still unchanged, despite wartime losses and the transfer of some shipping from Germany to the other countries as reparations. The German fleet, however, is now less modern than the fleets of the other countries, which have been strengthened by the addition of many new vessels.

The altered pattern of traffic brought about by the war has caused a change in the distribution of traffic by country. This is particularly true of the Dutch and Belgian fleets. Before the war practically all of these ships were employed on the lower Rhine, between the Ruhr and the seaports. The decline in German industrial activity has so reduced total Rhine traffic, however, and especially the traffic on the lower Rhine, that Dutch and Belgian shipping are now competing actively for business along the whole length of the river.

The utilization of water transportation is dependent to a large degree on the development of complementary facilities. Materials-handling equipment, storage space, connections with other forms of transportation, and, it goes without saying, the presence of large-scale consumers or suppliers of commodities amenable to movement by water—all these play a major role in determining whether or not exploitation of navigable waterways is profitable. And, conversely, the potentiality of extensive water traffic will soon bring about the establishment of port facilities and commercial centers to handle it.

From this point of view, the high stage of development which water transportation has reached in the Rhine Basin is readily apparent. None of the cities or towns that dot the banks of the river are without port facilities of some kind. In addition, the Rhine and its feeders are the site of a significant number of Europe's most important manufacturing and commercial centers, among which the regions cited in succeeding paragraphs may be especially noted.

Many Centers Served

The upper terminus of Rhine shipping is the city of *Basel,* Switzerland's second largest city and its leading commercial center, handling more than 50 percent of total Swiss imports and from one-fifth to one-third of total Swiss foreign trade. The development of Basel as a port began in 1904. Since then the original few hundred meters of wharfage have been multiplied more than nine times over, and the annual capacity of the port increased to the figure of 4,500,000 to 5,000,000 tons.

The importance of Rhine shipping to the Swiss economy is threefold. It reduces the cost of imported materials such as coal, cellulose, sugar, and timber. It makes possible the exploitation of low-grade ores and industrial byproducts that would otherwise be valueless. And it enhances the value of Switzerland as a transshipment center.

It has been estimated that in 1938 there was a saving of 3 francs per ton on imported freight and 5 francs per ton on exported freight as compared with the cost of shipping by rail, in addition to the probability that the existence of waterway competition had a depressing influence on the general level of railway charges.

Below Basel, the Rhine forms the border between France and Germany for 184 kilometers. There is only one major port in this sector, the city of *Strasbourg*. Strasbourg, the only French Rhine port, is situated at the junction of the River Ill, the Marne-Rhone Canal and the Rhone-Rhine Canal. Commodities handled by the harbor of Strasbourg consist mainly of potash, coal, petroleum products, grain, metal products, and iron ore. The city is the site of important light and heavy metal-manufacturing industries, of large-scale flour milling, and of thermal power stations operated with water-borne coal, as well as a major transshipping point for both the French and the German railway systems.

The cities of *Ludwigshafen* and *Mannheim* were the upper termini of Rhine shipping for many years. Located at the confluence of the Rhine and Neckar Rivers, they are still important distributing points to the German interior, although their significance has decreased since the improvement of navigation on the upper Rhine. A very substantial part of their port facilities was destroyed during the war, and their complete restoration will take many years.

Whether this will actually be accomplished in large measure on railway rate policy, which may cause the diversion of traffic from the waterways (Rhine-Benelux route) to the railways (rail-North German port route) and upon the recovery of the chemical manufacturing industries of which these cities are the center. Statistics indicate, however, that there has already been a significant improvement over the postwar low.

The general economic characteristics of the Ruhr are too well known to require description here. Coal, coke, and metal products form the bulk of exports from the Ruhr, while iron ore, lumber, and grain are the chief imports. The major port for Ruhr-Rhine traffic is the twin city of *Duisburg-Ruhrort,* which handled about 30 percent of total Rhine traffic before World War II. Located at the junction of the Rhine and the Rhine-Herne Canal, and served by a dense net of railways and highways as well, it is the traffic center for the entire lower Rhine and the Rhenian-Westphalian industrial area. Water-borne traffic amounted to more than 23,000,000 tons in 1937, but is now averaging considerably less. Harbor facilities, which have been largely repaired since the end of the war, could handle three times the 1948 volume.

Water traffic in Duisburg-Ruhrort, for three cited years, has been: 1937, 23,236,000 metric tons; 1947, 4,288,000 metric tons; 1948, 7,990,000 metric tons.

RHINE TRAFFIC IN THE PORT OF ROTTERDAM, 1938 1946, AND 1947
(In thousand metric tons)

Year	*Downstream to Rotterdam*	*Upstream from Rotterdam*	*Total*
1938	14,150	17,760	31,910
1946	1,868	1,097	2,965
1947	1,591	1,681	3,272

One of the largest ports in Europe is the city of *Rotterdam.* Rotterdam is located on the Rhine estuary, a position that makes it a natural trans-shipping point for trade between Germany, Switzerland, and the rest of the world. In 1938 it handled 57 percent of total Rhine traffic, consisting mainly of imports of ores and grain and exports of coal and metal products. It is expected that the vast amount of reconstruction made necessary by war damage will be finished in 1950; the port is already sufficiently restored so that the diminution of traffic as compared with its prewar size leaves considerable idle capacity.

In addition to the above-described ports, the Rhine system also serves such well-known centers of trade and industry as Karlsruhe, Frankfurt, Mainz, Dusseldorf, and Antwerp.

Broad Measures Arising From Political Considerations

As might be expected in a region marked by conflicting national interests and periodic warfare, navigation on the Rhine has not been completely free of political interference. The importance of establishing a modus vivendi for Rhine shipping was early realized, however. The first step toward establishing the principle of free navigation of international rivers was taken in 1815 at the Congress of Vienna, while the basic agreement upon which modern Rhine navigation rests was signed at Mannheim in 1868 by France, the Netherlands and the German riparian States. An international commission with administrative, judicial, and quasi-legislative functions was established. The recommendations of this commission were generally accepted by the member governments, and the Rhine became a truly international waterway except for the tidal reaches, which remained subject to Dutch control.

The Convention of Mannheim was revised by the Versailles Treaty, and membership in the Central Rhine Commission was broadened to include all countries with an interest in Rhine shipping. Germany withdrew from this Commission in 1936, but navigation of the German Rhine was still permitted on a reciprocal basis and, by and large, Rhine navigation was free of political hindrance during the interwar period. With the outbreak of the war, of course, non-German use of the Rhine practically ceased.

The resumption of international administration of the Rhine became the object of Allied attention shortly after the war ended. A general survey of Rhine shipping was made by the European Central Inland Transport Organization (ECITO) in November 1945, and soon thereafter a Rhine Interim Working Committee was created by the Western Zone occupation authorities in conjunction with the Governments of the Netherlands, Belgium, and Switzerland. The Central Rhine Commission was also reactivated in December 1945, with a membership consisting of all nations bordering the Rhine or having an immediate interest in Rhine navigation. The United States at that time became a member as one of the Occupying Powers. There is as yet no German representation except through the Occupying Powers.

The Act of Mannheim is still accepted as the basic document governing use of the Rhine, although it is not yet settled whether the withdrawal of Germany from the Central Rhine Commission in 1936 represented a valid denunciation of this agreement. For several years after the war the application of this act was sharply circumscribed. But most of the qualifications made necessary by special postwar conditions have been removed, and the Rhine is once more open on equal terms to the shipping of all nations. There are at present seven flags in regular commercial service on the river —German, Dutch, French, Belgian, Swiss, Luxembourg and British—in addition to an occasional visit by vessels of other countries such as Czechoslovakia.

Questions of Competition

The existence of an international regime, however, should not give the impression that there were no serious conflicts of interest. Even during the periods of greatest activity there was not enough business to satisfy the entire Rhine fleet plus the competing railways, the Benelux ports, the German ports, and the many ports on the Rhine itself. The Mannheim Convention precluded the use of open discrimination, but various other devices were used during the interwar period in the battle for a greater share of the Rhineland freight traffic.

The Dortmund-Ems Canal, which has been described above, was a product of this competition. It was meant to divert the Ruhr-Rhine traffic to the North German ports, but did not prove successful. The German railways, however, by quoting special rates to these ports, did succeed in capturing a substantial amount of traffic that would otherwise have gone via the Rhine, and thus were instrumental in benefiting the German over the Benelux ports.

The French railways also competed with Rhine shipping to some extent, but the keenest French competition was for port traffic—a struggle that was maintained over many years by the French, Belgian, and Dutch Governments.

France for many years had a special import tax on commodities imported from third countries through other than French ports. This tax did not apply to goods shipped via Antwerp and the Rhine, an exception that naturally worked to the disadvantage of Rotterdam. Belgium further improved the position of Antwerp vis-à-vis Rotterdam by paying premiums to offset the difference between the Antwerp-Strasbourg and the Rotterdam-Strasbourg shipping rates.

These moves were partially countered by the Dutch through the reduction of Rotterdam port charges.

Some agreement as to the division of traffic was finally reached in 1939. In April of that year France, Belgium, and the Netherlands agreed to repeal or adjust their special taxes, premiums, and port charges so as to effect a predetermined division of business among the ports concerned. The following month, the railways and Rhine shipping companies which served the port of Basel also established an agreement concerning rates and the division of traffic among themselves. The basic principles of this agreement were that certain bulk goods, such as solid fuels, grain, and fodder, in quantities of 10 metric tons or more, were to be transported only by Rhine shipping, while all goods in quantities under 10 metric tons as well as certain goods without limitation of quantity were reserved to the railways.

Although many conferences were held on the subject, the problem of uneconomic competition between Rhine shipping and the German railways was never satisfactorily settled.

High Postwar Priority for Rebuilding of Rhine Facilities

The war, of course, caused the almost complete cessation of Rhine shipping. As elsewhere, however, transportation facilities in the Rhine basin received high priority in reconstruction. The railways, ports, and river fleet soon rebounded to near their prewar capacity. The output of German mines and factories, however, and their raw-material requirements remained well below the prewar level, thus greatly reducing the volume of freight traffic. The problem of obtaining an adequate amount of traffic was thus in evidence again by the beginning of 1948.

There were also numerous administrative questions hampering the resumption of Rhine navigation. Relief supplies were routed to the North German rather than the Benelux ports, because of the desire to minimize dollar costs, even though the Rhine route was cheaper. The widespread use of rationing made the provisioning of foreign crews difficult—a problem that was accentuated by the difficulty of converting the German mark into other European currencies. It was impossible for a boat to buy supplies or to effect repairs outside its own zone, while ship registrations, visas for crews, and many other details had to be "ironed out" between the makeshift German government and the other Rhine States.

One by one, these latter difficulties have been resolved.

Main Difficulty: Insufficient Traffic

The basic problem of insufficient traffic still remains, however. This problem has been accentuated by the augmentation of the Rhine fleet with vessels from the East German waterways, vessels that could no longer find employment in their home waters because of the reduction in East-West trade. At one time in June 1949, there were more than 500 German Rhine ships alone awaiting loads.

This does not mean that there have not been times since the war when there was a shortage of barge space. The water level has been unusually low, and was a result it sometimes took three barges to carry what would normally have been a load for just one. From the viewpoint of the shipowners and ports, however, operations have been far from satisfactory. In addition to long periods of idleness, railway competition prevented the raising of rates that is customary during periods of low water because of increased operating costs.

The intensity of competition has been somewhat relieved by a number of agreements. Belgium and the Netherlands have agreed to share traffic between their Rhine ports and Germany on a proportional basis—an agreement that is administered through a joint body known as the Rhine Central Booking Office. The 1939 agreement between the carriers serving Basel has been revived, while its provisions were revised somewhat in favor of water carriage.

But the major problem, competition from the German railways, is still unsolved. Its solution is dependent upon an increase in total traffic, and must therefore await the settlement of the broad issue of German industrial participation in the European economy. As a step toward cooperation, however, a representative of the water transportation industry was admitted to membership on the German Railways Tariff Committee, in order to assist in the re-evaluation of railway and waterway rates. A railway representative will also participate in all future sessions of water-transport rate boards.

"Tremendous Vitality"

Despite the fact that it has never been, and is not now, a prosperous industry, the Rhine shipping industry has a tremendous amount of vitality. The extension of navigability on the upper Rhine to Lake Constance, and the canalization of the Main and Neckar Rivers to the Danube is being vigorously agitated, as is a proposal to establish a Rhine Developmnt Corporation patterned on the Tennessee Valley Authority, to develop to the full the Rhine potential for transportation and power production. Many new, fast boats have been placed in service since the war, and the best units of the German barge fleet are rapidly being fitted with engines in order to increase their ability to compete with ships flying other flags, as well as with the railways.

Industrial production in 1948 in the Bizone, the mainstay of Rhine traffic, was 60 percent of the 1936 level. . . .

Production in all fields in the U. S.-U. K. Zones rose swiftly after the currency reform of June 1948. This upward trend is continuing, especially for coal, which is one of the few industries in which the level of permitted production is above the 1936 figure. The production of stones and earth and other construction materials can also be expected to accelerate as the tempo of reconstruction increases along with general economic recovery.

Resuming Traditional Role

With regard to those industries especially suited to the use of water transportation, therefore, the outlook is favorable. As described in foregoing paragraphs, many of the administrative difficulties resulting from the war have been resolved, and navigation on the Rhine is therefore able once more to resume its traditional role as an international artery of commerce serving the heart of Europe.

With a history of more than a century and a quarter of international cooperation, and the subordination (not complete, but substantial) of short-range national interests in favor of the long-run benefits of collaborative effort, free navigation on the Rhine is proof that such international cooperation is not only possible but profitable. Commerce in the Rhine Basin has benefited and will continue to benefit from a truly competitive transportation system, and perhaps other parts of the European economy can profit from this example.

72. *Air Transportation—World Coverage* *

In the last 35 years air lines have developed a world network. The density of this coverage and the part it plays in the economy of regions or countries varies considerably. Certain continents or sections of continents that a few years ago had only antiquated means of transportation now have air service; therefore, they may never develop a dense land transport network. The Belgian Congo and the Amazon Basin are examples of areas that have partially skipped the intervening stages of road and rail development. Pearcy discusses here the present role of air travel throughout the world, especially in the so-called backward areas.

* G. Etzel Pearcy, "Air Transportation—World Coverage," *Journal of Geography,* Vol. 48, No. 3, 1949, pp. 105–112. By permission of the *Journal of Geography,* official publication of the National Council of Geography Teachers.

The author (1905) is Geographic Attache, American Embassy, Paris, France. He was formerly System Geographer for Trans World Airline. His major interests are transportation and political geography, and he is co-editor of *World Political Geography.*

The present world coverage of commercial air routes is far greater than most of us suppose. At thousands of airports on the six habitable continents planes are landing and taking off and changing the face of the earth. In the terminology of aviation folks, the skies are full of passenger-miles and ton-miles—billions of them—as people, mail, and goods move rapidly from one spot on the world's surface to another. And without suffering the physical handicaps presented by barriers on that surface to any great extent. These "run-of-the-mill" services, performed every hour of every day in all parts of the world are the potent forces behind what we may call the "Air Age."

The pattern of postwar flying is taking shape, or, in many cases, has already been established. Therefore, we are in a position to re-evaluate some of our ideas of the Air Age, and to discard some of the misconceptions built up in the past:

1. Some air age enthusiasts have been inclined to exaggerate the importance of over-the-pole flying. Granted the shortest route between Washington and Chungking tops the North Pole. But to fly such an itinerary would, from an economic standpoint, be highly illogical. It is rather well accepted among commercial aviation people that air routes will follow established traffic arteries for a good while to come, altho total route distances may add up to hundreds, or even thousands, of additional miles.

2. The "ocean-of-the-air" concept has been overworked. While the airplane can easily surmount barriers of the physical landscape, it is not economically feasible to fly long distances (as from one continent to another) except from certain selected international termini. Thus, the various nations of the world have and will continue to have relatively few points within their borders, usually only one, from which most international flights originate and terminate.

3. The mere fact that airplanes can rapidly go from one country to another does not mean that we will automatically have an ideally unified world and universal peace. Suspicion, distrust, and strong nationalistic feelings may travel the airways as well as goodwill and understanding. Our objective, then, must be to gradually break down the prejudices between peoples by a million international passengers, by a million pieces of mail with cancelled stamps from another country, and by a million commodities sent via air cargo.

4. The modern Air Age is not to be found in the Sunday Supplement. It does not lie in rockets to the moon, in milk delivery by helicopters, or 300-passenger ships flying at supersonic speeds. Such marvels may well come to pass at a future date, but for the moment they are impractical. More symbolic of the true Air Age is the fellow in white coveralls handing packages up into the cargo compartment of a plane; the flashing of a beacon which lights the way of Flight 63 on its nocturnal way to Indianapolis; the slick black limousine packed with business men, slithering its way between a downtown hotel and the airport; or the maintenance man on his rounds checking the landing strips at Singapore.

Perhaps if we look at the development of commercial air transportation as it is taking place around the globe we can better appreciate the resultant economic, political, and social changes among the population. Too often we do not look beyond the borders of our own country for such changes. Most of us are more or less aware of the extent to which airplanes come and go in the United States, but fail to recognize the tremendous activity taking place in many other parts of the world—oftentimes in areas we thoughtlessly classify as primitive and backward.

At the moment there are around 240 commercial airlines in the world offering regularly scheduled service. Aircraft of these organizations represent the flags of more than seventy-five different countries and possessions. Among the conglomeration of airlines are some which are world wide in their scope, such as Trans World Airline with a route pattern extending from San Francisco eastward to Bombay. At the other end of the scale small regional carriers may feed traffic into important termini or make accessible remote spots poorly served by means of surface transportation. For example, Leavens Brothers Air Services in Ontario connects two termini only twenty-two miles apart, one on a small island in Lake Erie. But large or small, these 240 air carriers all go to form the gigantic mosaic of global air routes that now span the continents and cross the oceans of the world.

Political Philosophy and Airlines

The political philosophy of a country frequently determines the air pattern and aviation policy for both internal and international flying. Some of the more important countries of the world have a dozen or more individual airlines; others have but one. The United States and most of the other nations of the Western Hemisphere advocate free enterprise in air transportation; consequently the routes of a great number of different airlines criss-cross thru their airways. On the other hand, if air transportation in a country is government owned, government operated, or government controlled it is likely that the flag carriers will be monopolies, or "chosen instruments." Most European countries have a single airline representing national interests. Air France, Sabena (Belgium), KLM (The Netherlands), Iberia (Spain), and Swissair are examples of important airlines without competition except that from air carriers representing flags other than their own. Great Britain has three major airlines, but each is allotted its own geographical sphere of influence in which to operate.

A number of the airlines in the global system of routes represent political entities far removed from the important capitals of the world.

Nevertheless, they fill vital gaps in the overall transportation pattern, oftentimes having come into being where surface transportation was slow and cumbersome, or virtually nonexistent. In Iceland the Flugfelag Islands Airline fans out from Reykjavik to settlements rimming the coast of the North Atlantic island. Altogether Iceland has a population no greater than Wilmington, Delaware, but over it has been developed a full fledged air transportation system. Far to the south in the same ocean the Bahamas Airways snugly ties together the more important islands of that archipelago. In the midst of the Mediterranean Sea the tiny island of Malta is now closely in touch with the mainland, both north and south, by means of the airline, Air Malta. Routes extend from this insular possession of Britain to Rome, Palermo, and Catania in Italy and to Tunis in Tunisia. Even the new dominion of Pakistan already has its own air route, tying its two principal cities, Lahore and Karachi, to Delhi, capital of neighboring India.

Australia

Looking to Australia one can see that the air transportation pattern of that continent is remolding the whole economy of the country. With but seven million people in an area as large as the United States, the country has long suffered because of great distances in relation to its industrial and commercial development. Now, a total of sixteen Australian airlines span the continent and form a network of routes which take in virtually every habitable area. Three of the airlines are transcontinental, and the remainder are regional. The latter permit a group, or "circuit" of cities with similar interests to more closely integrate their energies in the creation of stronger regional ties.

Key cities in Australia, such as Melbourne, Sydney, Brisbane, Canberra, Adelaide, and Perth are linked together with multiple schedules daily. Frequency of service between Melbourne and Sydney is not unlike that between two major American cities. But beyond this type of flight, scores of small communities now have a regular and dependable means of transportation to replace remoteness and isolation. In the desert heart of Australia the leading center of Alice Springs lies on the most important north-south transcontinental route in the interior of the country. To the south a railroad carries three trains weekly into Adelaide; to the north only a highway leads into Darwin. But from Alice Springs air routes extend in all directions and tie dozens of tiny desert communities into a regional pattern. In turn, Alice Springs itself is tied in with the larger Australian cities, thereby giving the most out-of-the-way desert dweller convenient access to his choice of commercial, financial, political, or cultural centers.

Africa

If one were to examine an air route map of Africa he would find around a score of cities, the names of which do not appear on the National Geographic map of Africa, in the large Encyclopedia Brittanica Atlas, in the large Rand McNally's Commercial Atlas, or in the Oxford Advanced Atlas. And yet these cities have regularly scheduled air service, much like Peoria and Paducah in our own country. If one were to travel in Africa he would find new cities springing up or old ones being developed along remarkably modern lines. To stand on the African plateau in the middle of a city of fifteen or twenty thousand population is a revelation—one would have no difficulty in believing he were in an American city of the same size. Thus, Africa is not only experiencing the Air Age, but experiencing it in a more startling fashion than is the average American, who, in theory at least, is supposed to be accustomed to technical advancement.

For many years European airlines have penetrated African territory, tying colonial areas with the national capitals of the home country. But more recently local airlines have supplemented these intercontinental trunk line services. The case of Ethiopian Air Lines will serve to illustrate this type of development. Less than three years ago Addis Ababa was tied to Cairo on the north and Nairobi on the south by the new American-inspired airline. In addition, spur lines were extended out from the capital city to a number of small Ethopian cities, such as Gimma, Gondar, Gore, and Debra Marcos. Internal surface transportation in the country is of the poorest sort, and travel is slow or sometimes nearly impossible. A hundred mile trip by road might take days or even weeks for it could demand the rebuilding of bridges to get across streams or pulling animals or vehicles thru deep mud. But now residents of these small air termini may, and do, climb into a plane and in a few minutes be up and away to places previously considered far distant. As likely as not the passengers will be barefooted, and with them they probably take small livestock or items of produce (the interiors of these locally used planes are not finished in cushioned upholstery, but carry bucket seats). Despite the high cost of air transportation in Ethiopia this type of travel is going on with the obvious result that the inhabitants are depending more and more on the airplane.

Africa also furnishes many other evidences of advancement in air transportation. The Belgian Congo was once a region so hard to traverse that it awed men by its mystery—here was the darkest part of the Dark Continent. As it was opened up the rivers and streams—not railroads and highways—became the leading arteries of commerce. But now both European and regional air routes form a network over the area. Cities such as Stanleyville, Elizabethville, Leopoldville, Albertville, and Coquilhatville are not merely air stops, they are nodal points from which routes extend in several directions in the overall pattern.

The French have long since stopped trying to push a railroad across the Sahara. Nine different airlines now traverse this huge barren expanse, their parallel north-south routes lying between the Atlantic Coastal zone and the Nile River valley. A few hours after a southbound passenger gets his last look at the Mediterranean he can sight the green of the Niger country in French West Africa. Conforming to the same viewpoint the British no longer actively promote their great Cairo-to-Capetown rail project. It is far easier to lay out an airway across Africa than it is to build a railroad with its interminable series of grades, bridges, tunnels, sidings, stations, water tanks, supply depots, and other attendant items.

South America

Many stirring examples of air transportation in a wild country springs from the mountains, tropical rainforest, and savanna lands of South America. In the West Coast countries are mining communities almost solely dependent upon the airplane. The necessity of a week of tedious travel between Colombia's chief seaport (Barranquilla) and its capital (Bogota) has been supplanted by two or three comfortable hours in the air.

Brazil, with its limited rail and highway facilities fringing the coast, now has a pattern of air routes tapping cities thruout the huge country. Surprisingly enough, the eastern part of Brazil has a density of routes about equal to eastern United States (tho the frequency of flights over them may be considerably lower).

The great cities of the east coast of South America, especially Rio de Janeiro, Montevideo, and Buenos Aires, are closely tied by air to capitals of western Europe. At present the planes of ten nations (Great Britain, Spain, Italy, Netherlands, France, Sweden, Norway, Denmark, Brazil, and Argentine) provide these links by flying across the Atlantic between the bulge of Africa and Northeast Brazil. In each direction there are seventeen flights per week, about the same number as across the Pacific connecting North America with Eastern Hemisphere lands.

Soviet Union

In the Soviet Union there is but one major airline. Known as Aeroflot, it forms a huge system, covering not only European Russia and Siberia, but extending into the periphery zone between Soviet territory proper and the Iron Curtain. A few examples from the Aeroflot network should serve to show how air transportation in the U.S.S.R. follows that of the United States and Canada, other large countries with which we are more familiar. Every day from Moscow two flights leave for Kharbarovsk, four thousand miles distant, in maritime Siberia on the slopes of the Pacific.

Moscow, and also Leningrad, are tied in closely with all of the major industrial areas of the country, especially those in southern European Russia and in the Ural district. Likewise, Archangel, Murmansk, and other northern cities lie on direct routes from Moscow and Leningrad. Soviet Central Asia, with Tashkent as the central air terminal, is a focal point for routes. There is even a route thru the Kamchatka area, terminating at Petropavlosk. In addition, trunk routes extend from Moscow to the national capitals of Soviet dominated territory, that is, Bucharest, Sofia, Tirana, Budapest, Warsaw, Berlin, Prague, and Helsinki. Beyond the Iron Curtain Aeroflot does not extend as do the international airlines of the Western democracies.

Island Groups

Air transportation is particularly important in island groups and over narrow seas. Here the superior speed of the aircraft over surface means of travel is further enhanced by no need for a break in the journey in passing from land to water or water to land. Between London and Paris the fastest train-boat-train journey requires seven and one-half hours; the plane trip one and one-half hours. The Hawaiian Islands, Philippines, East Indies, West Indies, and other archipelagoes have well developed route systems which bring the major islands within each group close to one another in travel time. Before the airplane came to the West Indies passenger travel between Cuba and Hispaniola was largely limited to irregular sailings of freighters on which might be available accommodations. Now, airplanes flit between the two islands, permitting travel at frequent intervals. In many instances small islands are tied to mainland areas by air routes: Norfolk and Lord Howe islands off the east coast of Australia, the Scilly Islands off the southwest coast of England, Ceylon off the southern tip of India, and others. Instead of an occasional steamer to bring people, mail, and supplies, the inhabitants of such offshore islands now have the advantage of knowing they are in close touch with the mainland, and benefit accordingly.

Summary

In the short span of thirty years was developed the pattern of world air route coverage indicated above. At first, the operational phases of aircraft performance—the ability of man to successfully take-off, fly, and land—primarily determined the extent of commercial aviation. Next, with technological progress, the economic aspects were the limiting factors. Men had difficulty in justifying air traffic at premium costs. Now that the airplane is capable, or nearly capable, of paying its own way a traffic pattern to cover the world can be systematically planned in accordance with the commercial needs of an economically active earth. Only international friction stands as a major stumbling block in the realization of an efficient global air route pattern. At the present time international boundaries, landing rights, and a multitude of restrictive regulations on the part of a country toward aircraft of all other countries alter and distort the route structure from what it would be were the carrying of traffic the prime consideration. Gradually, the impact of the heavy international traffic that does exist, plus the volume of domestic traffic within the various countries, should break down those restrictions which impede a free flow of people and goods thru channels best suited to an interregional economy.

CHAPTER TEN

Population and Settlement

PEOPLE ARE the most significant element in the study of geography. Factors of population that are of significance include numbers of people and their distribution on the earth's surface. Many qualitative factors are also involved in a geographical study of population.

Significant also is the fact that some areas have too many people, whereas others—relatively small in extent—have too few. This population disequilibrium increases tensions between peoples, nations, and areas.

The pattern and nature of man's habitations constitutes the core of a study of settlement. The city certainly is the most complex of the various types of remarkably diverse settlements throughout the world.

Rural settlement forms reveal significant differences in the nonurban areas of the world, which include, of course, the greatest extent of land surface. While urban settlement is characteristic of the United States and Western Europe, it is by no means characteristic of the world, for the majority of the world's population is rural in character.

---

73. *Land for 2.4 Billion Neighbors* *

The problems of population are very closely related to the problems of the land, and the increasing population makes the problem of the

* George B. Cressey, "Land for 2.4 Billion Neighbors," reprinted from *Economic Geography*, Vol. 29, 1953, pp. 1–9.

The author (1896   ) is Professor of Geography at Syracuse University. He has traveled extensively in the Soviet Union and the Far East. His most recent book is *How Strong is the Soviet Union?*

land from which the inhabitants are to obtain their food even more critical. It is obvious that there can be no ready answer to this problem. Part of the answer lies in the productivity of the land, part lies in intelligent control of births, an approach only recently undertaken as a policy of the government of India. The study of population by the geographer must of necessity consider man in relation to the productive resources of the earth. Cressey presents here a summary statement of the population potentials and limits as well as an analysis of the actual land use and possible production limits of the world.

Each of us has nearly two and a half billion neighbors. Every hour the total increases by 3000; each day by 70,000 people. By the end of the century the world's population may approach four billion. Where can these people live and in what comfort? Each year adds about one per cent. In the history of the earth few figures are more dramatic than this increase of population. In three centuries the numbers of mankind have increased fivefold; from 470 million in 1650 to 2,400 million in 1950.

Geography is concerned with people; it is equally concerned with land. Where is our good land, how much do we have, and how much more remains unused? For the earth as a whole there are some 42 people per square mile, but in terms of arable land the figure rises to 500. It is immediately obvious that some areas are better than others. One square mile of Manhattan Island supports a daytime population of a million people, and they are among the most prosperous on earth. But the entire population of a million square miles in Siberia or the Sahara numbers only a few thousand. The world differs enormously in its agricultural potential, in its mineral resources, and in the desirability of its locations.

Geographers are interested in population but so are demographers; we are concerned with food but agriculturists have the last word. No one else is more competent to evaluate the totality of land. This includes all of its environmental characters. Land is not an absolute, since soil may be depleted and climate fluctuates, but it is more of a constant than food production with its new seeds and techniques, or man with his changing standards. The function of the geographer is to locate and evaluate land of various qualities; what man does with it is another matter. Geography cannot set an absolute limit to population, but it can inventory our resources.

Present Land Use

The best data on present world land use are those of the Food and Agricultural Organization, presented in its annual Yearbook. These figures are based on information supplied by 158 political units, with estimates for other areas. This gives a world total of "arable land including fallow, plus orchards" (in French: "terres labourables et vergers"), as 1,230,000,000 hectares. This amounts to 4,747,000 square miles, or 8 per cent of the land surface. No data are supplied for the area actually plowed and harvested in any one year, but allowing for orchards, fallow, and crop failure the cultivated area proper may be but two-thirds of this figure. Pasture and meadows cover 2,187,000,000 hectares, or 15 per cent. In per capita terms, these figures provide but 1.3 and 2.4 acres respectively.

Lautensach believes that 18 per cent of the land is cultivated, which seems quite high, 29 per cent is in forest, 21 per cent is steppe, and 25 per cent is wasteland.

For the area actually cultivated in comparison with that merely arable, we may turn to the 1941–46 Yearbook of the former International Institute of Agriculture, which gives a total, without the Soviet Union, of 1,621,879 square miles. To this may be added 583,152 square miles for the U.S.S.R., or a world total of 2,205,031 square miles. This is equal to 4 per cent of the continents.

Another figure is that of Pearson and Harper who report a total food crop area of 1,529,000,000 acres, 2,390,000 square miles, or 4 per cent.

Agricultural Limitations

In order to evaluate land use potentials, let us look at limitations in terms of climate, soil, natural vegetation, and land form. All of these are variables in time and space. No place has too much light or warmth, but some have too little. Only fortunate areas always have the proper rainfall. Soil is more than mere dirt, and it is not a constant. Some lands are too dry, some have too short a growing season, some are too steep, some are too infertile. Too much of the earth is too limited by nature.

In terms of climatic regions, Thornthwaite finds that areas of permanent frost, tundra, and boreal forest occupy 16,881,000 square miles. Almost all of this is too cold for crops. Desert and steppe account for 16,996,000 square miles, which is largely too dry. Each of these covers 30 per cent of the land area, with no overlap. Some possibilities do exist for crops or grazing in these areas; but the total is very limited. Not all of the remaining 40 per cent is usable due to steep slopes, infertile soils, or poor drainage. Some areas are too wet, others are so hot that evaporation is excessive. On the basis of Thornthwaite's map, at least 60 per cent of the continents appear climatically unsuited for agricultural use. Another climatic estimate is supplied by Pearson and Harper, who report that in terms of adequate and reliable rainfall and suitable temperature, 68 per cent of the land area is not adapted to food production.

WORLD LAND USE *
(In hectares; 000,000 omitted)

Continent	Total Area	*Arable Land (incl. fallow and orchards)*	*Permanent Pasture and Meadows*	*Forest and Woodlands*	*Unused but Potentially Productive* [a]	*Built on and Wasteland*
Africa	3,042	187	579	918	80	1,278
Asia	2,684	346	257	472	92	1,517
Europe	493	147	96	128	10	112
Oceania	856	19	368	76	12	381
North America	2,428	241	421	764	107	895
South America	1,779	64	343	746	66	560
U.S.S.R.	2,227	225	124	920	12	946
TOTAL	13,509 [b]	1,230 (2,838 acres)	2,187 (5,402 acres)	4,024 (9,139 acres)	379 (936 acres)	5,689 (14,052 acres)

* Food and Agricultural Organization, Yearbook, 1950, Table I.
[a] Incomplete data. World totals may be twice this figure.
[b] This total omits Antarctica; including Antarctica the total land area of the earth is 59,407,786 square miles, or 38,020,983,000 acres.

The world wide extent of various soil types is given by Praslov. Desert, mountain, and tundra soils, plus permanent snow and ice, take up 48 per cent of the continents. These areas have virtually no food producing value. Chernozems and grassland soils, gray and brown forest soils, and alluvium occupy 24 per cent, and for the most part are available for agriculture, although rainfall is locally precarious and topography is not always favorable. This leaves 28 per cent in a marginal category; podzolic soils in cold areas of short summer, or red and lateritic soils in hot, tropical areas. While each of these has agricultural possibility, its fertility is low. Passably good land in cold or hot areas is more than counterbalanced by inferior patches within otherwise usable areas. On Praslov's data and for the continents as a whole, poor soils eliminate at least half of the land from significant food production, with another quarter of debatable value. Pearson and Harper find 52 per cent of the land unavailable due to soil restrictions.

In terms of natural vegetation as it relates to crop land, H. L. Shantz finds that the extent of vegetation types in cool areas theoretically adapted to food production amounts to 11,778,000 square miles. Similar warm weather vegetation areas amount to 12,730,000, a total of 24,508,000 square miles or 43 per cent of the total land surface. This implies that 57 per cent of the land is probably unavailable for agriculture.

The usability of land for crops or pasture is further restricted by land form. Spectacular terracing reaches into the hills of the Orient, but only at the cost of excessive human labor. The tragic result of soil erosion on even gentle slope lands in the United States is a warning of the danger of plowing slopes that are subject to rapid erosion. Mere altitude is not a barrier except as it affects climate. Although most of the earth is mapped as to elevation, we have no proper maps of land *form*. Here is one of the major needs in geography. About a quarter of the earth is mountainous or hilly. Plateaus cover a third, but include many level areas. Plains occupy two-fifths, but this includes snow surfaces in Antarctica, rolling deserts in many continents, and other areas climatically impractical for cultivation. Allowing for level or rolling land in each category, Pearson and Harper estimate that 36 per cent of the land surface has topography unfavorable for agriculture.

Geography is concerned with land in all its qualities. Whether man uses this land wisely is his responsibility. The engineer may reclaim the desert, if we wish to pay the price. Land which appears marginal or undesirable in one economy may prove usable under another. Geography per se can set no limits on maximum areas of land use, but it can properly inventory and evaluate the physical base. No statistics as to the ultimate extent of crop land or food supply can be absolute. Each generation must answer its own problems.

Available Arable Land

Figures for the total of so-called arable land still unused vary widely. They also depend on estimates as to minimum requirements of frost-free days, rainfall, or soil fertility. A new variety of wheat which would mature in, for example, 80 days would extend the cultivable area many miles poleward; while wheat which would grow with 10 inches of rain would push cultivation into the deserts. Unfortunately, localities with these conditions have weather which fluctuates widely from year to year. Crop failures are chronic.

The 1950 Yearbook of the Food and Agricultural Organization includes "unused but potentially productive" land (in French: "susceptible d'utilisation"). Data have been supplied by only 57 political units and no attempt has been made to fill in figures elsewhere. China, Australia, and important areas in Africa are omitted, nor are the figures compiled on any comparable basis. This preliminary total amounts to 379,000,000 hectares (1,500,000 square miles). If data were supplied by all countries, this total might be doubled. The limited value of these estimates as to potentials is indicated by the variation between Canada, 83,652,000 hectares, and the Soviet Union which reports but 12,000,000 hectares undeveloped. Brazil and the French Cameroons list 29,296,000 and 64,000,000 hectares respectively.

O. E. Baker takes the area of tropical and subtropical lands as 23,000,000 square miles, of which he estimates that 8,000,000 are too arid for use. Of the remaining 15,000,000 with suitable rainfall, Baker assumes that about one-third might some day be usable. Cultivated land now amounts to 1,200,000 and pasture 600,000 square miles. This leaves 3,200,000 square miles as "potentially arable, not used for crops or pasture" in warm lands. In the temperate zones, Baker finds a land area of 29,000,000 square miles of which 7,600,000 are too dry and 6,400,000 square miles are too cold. This leaves 15,000,000 square miles with satisfactory growing season and rainfall. Again, assuming that one-third ought to be usable, and deducting the 2,500,000 now cultivated and the 1,500,000 square miles now in pasture, Baker believes that 1,000,000 square miles are potentially available for crops or pasture. This gives a world total of 4,200,000 square miles, or 2,688,000,000 acres, of now unused agricultural land. Obviously, such figures are meaningful only in terms of his one-third assumption.

Another estimate has been made by Robert M. Salter. He uses Praslov's areas for soils, cited above, and concludes that there may be available for cultivation 900,000,000 acres in Africa and South America, and an additional 100,000,000 acres in Madagascar, Sumatra, Borneo, and New Guinea. This is a total of some 1,000,000,000 acres or 1,500,000 square miles, in the tropical red soil areas. An additional 300,000,000 acres or 500,000 square miles, may be developed in the cool podzol areas. These totals are a third of Baker's figures.

Charles B. Fawcett believes that areas too dry for agriculture total 40 per cent, while those too cold and hilly account for 30 per cent. This leaves 30 per cent of the land surfaces as potentially arable, some 17,000,000 square miles. From this is to be subtracted 108,000,000 hectares which Fawcett states are now arable, leaving 7,801,000 acres still available.

The most specific analysis of the land possibilities is that of Pearson and Harper. On the basis of map studies, they find that 17 per cent of the land is too cold, 66 per cent too dry, 36 per cent too steep, and 54 per cent too infertile. Allowing for overlaps, the remaining area suitable for cultivation is thought to cover 7 per cent of the land. This is actually less than the 8 per cent shown as now arable by the Food and Agricultural Organization.

A further figure is that of Carl Alsberg, who states that there are 5.5 to 6 million square miles now cultivated or in pasture, and a total of 10 million which would be used if necessary. This would leave 2,560 to 2,880 million acres still available. L. Dudley Stamp believes that cultivable land totals 10 billion acres, of which 3 to 4 billion are now in use. Just where this unused land may be, or what its characteristics are, few of the above writers indicate. . . .

Undeveloped land unquestionably exists in many parts of the world;

it is the extent and quality which is in dispute. Abandoned hillsides in the northeastern United States might again be cultivated, but the economic return would be small. It might be possible to increase the present 370 million acres of crop land to 450 million if costs were not important. Heath land in Britain could be cleared and plowed. Once-cultivated fields outside the Great Wall of China which were abandoned because of drought might be reused with better machinery and dry farming techniques. The Amazon and Congo may some day produce large crops, but soils are so infertile that expensive enrichment will be necessary. Java is the one equatorial area where food has become available for a dense population. This illustrates the difference between the continental and maritime tropics. There will never be another Columbus; pioneers can never again find good land free for the asking.

There are few limits to the maximum area which may be cultivated, given labor and capital. Even parts of the tundra may grow specialized vegetables, and some of the desert has a limited agricultural potential. None of these are now attractive in terms of costs or returns. The problem of maximum land use is one of agricultural techniques and of economics. Geographers can only inventory and evaluate the resources. Land of marginal quality will remain inferior in yields. Handicaps of cold and of drought, and of sterile soils, will continue to hold back pioneer settlement on the frontiers.

There will always be a pioneer fringe, but it seems probable that the major increase of food will come within existing farm areas. Improved seeds and more efficient methods will produce larger yields in the more advantageous areas. This is noticeably true within the Soviet Union, where most of the area brought into production since the Revolution has been within the established agricultural triangle rather than on its fringes. It is quite proper that we examine pioneering possibilities, but there is more unexploited pay dirt in Illinois than Wyoming, or in Honan than in Kansu, or in France than in Finland.

Our expanding population will certainly call for more food. The easiest source is through increased yields on existing farm land. It is doubtful whether much food can soon or economically come from new land. Agricultural Australia has about reached its limit. Homesteading has essentially ended in the United States. The Peace River Country of Canada offers little more attractive farm land. Siberia has nearly plowed its last virgin prairie. Irrigation projects in the dry parts of the Soviet Union are ambitious but questionable.

If the Amazon and Congo or the Arctic have crop potentials of large extent, their exploitation lies well in the future. Meanwhile erosion and soil exhaustion result in the abandonment of impressive acreages.

Marginal land cannot compete with more favorable areas. Photographs of erosion in the loess country of China are tragic scenes from a moving picture of land abandonment. So too are views in the American Piedmont. Despite the pressure for food the world around, the United States is abandoning land about as fast as it is adding to it.

Until we conquer the arctic and the tropics, it is quite possible that the world is near the peak of total cultivated acreage. We may have already passed it. World population increases at the rate of one per cent a year, or more. Cultivated acreage is or may soon be on the decline. This need not mean diminished food, for we may secure greater yields through more intensive development of our better land. The point is this: if more food is needed, and that is obvious, geography cannot offer new land of much value. The good earth is essentially all in use, and the major map boundaries of cultivated land have become stabilized. This must be emphasized, for there are no longer empty areas worth developing. Idle land does exist, but it is of very unattractive quality. If added millions are to be fed, the geographer has no new Iowa or Murray Valley or Siberian steppe. The map cannot be stretched much more.

On the other hand, some competent geographers take a different point of view and write of "millions of square miles of potential farm land," and state that "There is then, for the present, ample room in the world; and there is no purely *areal* reason why every man should not have enough land and to spare on which to feed himself and his family." All would agree, however, that the first requisite is to find the facts. One should not confuse space with opportunity.

This study was initiated in the hope that it might be possible to draw precise maps; first, of existing crop land; and second, of potential areas; each with appropriate gradations and evaluation. That this is impractical is due not so much to the absence of surveys as to the inherent nature of land itself. We may map a farm and measure its wheat fields, but what we call a wheat field is only partly occupied by wheat, half the ground is bare. Furthermore, some fields yield two or three times as much per acre as others even nearby. Land as a resource is not a matter of square miles, it is qualitative and relative. We surely need comprehensive surveys and maps, but critical estimates as to potentials must await better data than are now available. Every time we measure land, we need a fresh yardstick to fit the changing requirements of man's technology.

Food Possibilities

There have been many estimates as to future food supply—some pessimistic, others glowingly optimistic. At one moment, we are alarmed by

Malthusian possibilities; the next day we are assured that food from the sea or through new fertilizers will provide nourishment for all. Whereas Malthus predicted an unequal race between a rabbit (population) and a tortoise (food), the contest proceeds neck and neck. The rabbit shows no signs of slowing down and the turtle is a mechanical marvel which can run as fast as necessary to keep pace.

How much food can our land supply under reasonable improvements? At the moment, half of the world's population lives in a permanent state of hunger. Salter estimates that, if all present crop land were brought up to possible yields, in general 20 per cent above present returns, the world could meet most of its food needs by 1960. This would eliminate famine and malnutrition. The cost in money and organization would be large. In addition, if there are a billion acres of potential farm land in the tropics which prove usable and could be developed to yield at the Philippine average, and if there are 300 million acres of cool soils possibly available for crops which could be cultivated to produce at Finnish levels, then the world might more than double its output of cereals, triple its supply of fruits and vegetables, and increase its meat supplies by half.

The world's population now exceeds 2.4 billion. Estimates as to the maximum population which the earth might support depend on the standard of living and many other unpredictables. Salter's figures of maximum food supply indicate a possible doubling of our population. Fawcett suggests three times the present, say 6 or 7 billion. Albert Penck once proposed 13.5 billion. Kuczynski believes that more than 11 billion is impossible. "The maximum population . . . can, of course, only be attained with the freest possible migration. The United States . . . would have to accept her due share of the 10 or 11 billions, say 800,000,000."

A more conservative estimate is that of Pearson and Harper. Since grains supply about three-fourths of man's diet, they estimate that if everyone lived on Asiatic standards of living, the present world production might support nearly three billion people. If all the world had European food standards, we would have only enough food for our present population, while on American standards of living and the present total food supply, the population which could be supported would be less than a billion, or 40 per cent of the present total. Pearson and Harper also estimate that 4 per cent of the land is now cultivated, and only 7 per cent capable of crop production. The additional 3 per cent is of marginal value, and its capacity to support added population is limited.

On the basis of geographic evidence, it seems probable to the author that our food potential is adequate for all the population likely to inhabit the earth during the present century. Unfortunately, the areas where production can be increased do not correspond with the present areas of excess people. Unlimited migration and a free movement of food are essential if the expected population is to be fed. It is doubtful whether we shall soon cultivate the Amazon and Congo basins or northern Canada and Siberia; but if we do, the crowded areas of China, India, and Europe will demand access to this food.

What does all this mean to a geographer? Variations in land capability are obvious. Unfortunately, we do not yet know what all the earth is like. We have no world inventory of land or its potentials. Soil surveys are incomplete, so are data on agricultural climatology. We do not even know how much of the earth is level. In fact, large areas are without basic maps. Geographers are concerned with inventory, with how much of what is where. This is the beginning of all wise planning. Before anyone can predict the potential extent of arable land, or of food supply, or of world population, we must greatly extend our fundamental knowledge of land itself.

Man has lived on the earth for a long time, and we have learned much. But we have been living off the cream with little appreciation of what comes next. Peace and normal living require economic well-being, and this requires a wise understanding of our resources. To all this, geography offers an essential preface.

74. *The Nature of Cities* *

As a settlement form, the city is remarkably diverse both in function and structure. Every city has a *raison d'être,* although the original locating factor may have long since been replaced by newer functions. The physical structure of the city is a more stable form, and a number of basic patterns have been identified. Harris and Ullman in this reading identify a number of functions and patterns that may be discerned in virtually any city.

Cities are the local points in the occupation and utilization of the earth by man. Both a product of and an influence on surrounding regions,

* C. D. Harris and E. L. Ullman, "The Nature of Cities," *The Annals* of the American Academy of Political and Social Science, Vol. 242, 1945, pp. 7–17.

Chauncy D. Harris (1914   ) is Professor of Geography at the University of Chicago. He has done considerable work on urban geography in the United States and Europe.

Edward L. Ullman (1912   ) is Professor of Geography at the University of Washington. His research has been in the fields of industrial location and commercial aspects of urban development.

they develop in definite patterns in response to economic and social needs.

Cities are also paradoxes. Their rapid growth and large size testify to their superiority as a technique for the exploitation of the earth, yet by their very success and consequent large size they often provide a poor local environment for man. The problem is to build the future city in such a manner that the advantages of urban concentration can be preserved for the benefit of man and the disadvantages minimized.

Each city is unique in detail but resembles others in function and pattern. What is learned about one helps in studying another. Location types and internal structure are repeated so often that broad and suggestive generalizations are valid, especially if limited to cities of similar size, function, and regional setting. This paper will be limited to a discussion of two basic aspects of the nature of cities—their support and their internal structure. Such important topics as the rise and extent of urbanism, urban sites, culture of cities, social and economic characteristics of the urban population, and critical problems will receive only passing mention.

The Support of Cities

As one approaches a city and notices its tall buildings rising above the surrounding land and as one continues into the city and observes the crowds of people hurrying to and fro past stores, theaters, banks, and other establishments, one naturally is struck by the contrast with the rural countryside. What supports this phenomenon? What do the people of the city do for a living?

The support of a city depends on the services it performs not for itself but for a tributary area. Many activities serve merely the population of the city itself. Barbers, dry cleaners, shoe repairers, grocerymen, bakers, and movie operators serve others who are engaged in the principal activity of the city, which may be mining, manufacturing, trade, or some other activity.

The service by which the city earns its livelihood depends on the nature of the economy and of the hinterland. Cities are small or rare in areas either of primitive, self-sufficient economy or of meager resources. As Adam Smith stated, the land must produce a surplus in order to support cities. This does not mean that all cities must be surrounded by productive land, since strategic location with reference to cheap ocean highways may enable a city to support itself on the specialized surplus of distant lands. Nor does it mean that cities are parasites living off the land. Modern mechanization, transport, and a complex interdependent economy enable much of the economic activity of mankind to be centered in cities.

Many of the people engaged even in food production are actually in cities in the manufacture of agricultural machinery.

The support of cities as suppliers of urban services for the earth can be summarized in three categories, each of which presents a factor of urban causation:

1. Cities as central places performing comprehensive services for a surrounding area. Such cities tend to be evenly spaced throughout productive territory. For the moment this may be considered the "norm" subject to variation primarily in response to the ensuing factors.

2. Transport cities performing break-of-bulk and allied services along transport routes, supported by areas which may be remote in distance but close in connection because of the city's strategic location on transport channels. Such cities tend to be arranged in linear patterns along rail lines or at coasts.

3. Specialized-function cities performing one service such as mining, manufacturing, or recreation for large areas, including the general tributary areas of hosts of other cities. Since the principal localizing factor is often a particular resource such as coal, water power, or a beach, such cities may occur singly or in clusters.

Most cities represent a combination of the three factors, the relative importance of each varying from city to city.

Cities as Central Places

Cities as central places serve as trade and social centers for a tributary area. If the land base is homogeneous these centers are uniformly spaced, as in many parts of the agricultural Middle West. In areas of uneven resource distribution, the distribution of cities is uneven. The centers are of varying sizes, ranging from small hamlets closely spaced with one or two stores serving a local tributary area, through larger villages, towns, and cities more widely spaced with more special services for larger tributary areas, up to the great metropolis such as New York or Chicago offering many specialized services for a large tributary area composed of a whole hierarchy of tributary areas of smaller places. Such a net of tributary areas and centers forms a pattern somewhat like a fish net spread over a beach, the network regular and symmetrical where the sand is smooth, but warped and distorted where the net is caught in rocks.

The central-place type of city or town is widespread throughout the world, particularly in nonindustrial regions. In the United States it is best represented by the numerous retail and wholesale trade centers of the agricultural Middle West, Southwest, and West. Such cities have imposing shopping centers or wholesale districts in proportion to their size; the stores are supported by the trade of the surrounding area. This contrasts with many cities of the industrial East, where the centers are so close together that each has little trade support beyond its own population.

Not only trade but social and religious functions may support central places. In some instances these other functions may be the main support of the town. In parts of Latin America, for example, where there is little trade, settlements are scattered at relatively uniform intervals through the land as social and religious centers. In contrast to most cities, their busiest day is Sunday, when the surrounding populace attend church and engage in holiday recreation, thus giving rise to the name "Sunday town."

Most large central cities and towns are also political centers. The county seat is an example. London and Paris are the political as well as trade centers of their countries. In the United States, however, Washington and many state capitals are specialized political centers. In many of these cases the political capital was initially chosen as a centrally located point in the political area and was deliberately separated from the major urban center.

Cities as Transport Foci and Break-of-Bulk Points

All cities are dependent on transportation in order to utilize the surplus of the land for their support. This dependence on transportation destroys the symmetry of the central-place arrangement, inasmuch as cities develop at foci or breaks of transportation, and transport routes are distributed unevenly over the land because of relief or other limitation. City organizations recognize the importance of efficient transportation, as witness their constant concern with freight-rate regulation and with the construction of new higways, port facilities, airfields, and the like.

Mere focusing of transport routes does not produce a city, but according to Cooley, if break of bulk occurs, the focus becomes a good place to process goods. Where the form of transport changes, as transferring from water to rail, break of bulk is inevitable. Ports originating merely to transship cargo tend to develop auxiliary services such as repackaging, storing, and sorting. An example of simple break-of-bulk and storage ports is Port Arthur-Fort William, the twin port and wheat-storage cities at the head of Lake Superior; surrounded by unproductive land, they have arisen at the break-of-bulk points on the cheapest route from the wheat-producing Prairie Provinces to the markets of the East. Some ports develop as entrepôts, such as Hong Kong and Copenhagen, supported by transshipment of goods from small to large boats or vice versa. Servicing points or minor changes in transport tend to encourage growth of cities as establishment of division points for changing locomotives on American railroads.

Transport centers can be centrally located places or can serve as gateways between contrasting regions with contrasting needs. Kansas City, Omaha, and Minneapolis-St. Paul serve as gateways to the West as well as central places for productive agricultural regions, and are important wholesale centers. The ports of New Orleans, Mobile, Savannah, Charleston, Norfolk, and others served as traditional gateways to the Cotton Belt with its specialized production. Likewise, northern border metropolises such as Baltimore, Washington, Cincinnati, and Louisville served as gateways to the South, with St. Louis a gateway to the Southwest. In recent years the South has been developing its own central places, supplanting some of the monopoly once held by the border gateways. Atlanta, Memphis, and Dallas are examples of the new southern central places and transport foci.

Changes in transportation are reflected in the pattern of city distribution. Thus the development of railroads resulted in a railroad alignment of cities which still persists. The rapid growth of automobiles and widespread development of highways in recent decades, however, has changed the trend toward a more even distribution of towns. Studies in such diverse localities as New York and Louisiana have shown a shift of centers away from exclusive alignment along rail routes. Airways may reinforce this trend or stimulate still different patterns of distribution for the future city.

Cities as Concentration Points for Specialized Services

A specialized city or cluster of cities performing a specialized function for a large area may develop at a highly localized resource. The resort city of Miami, for example, developed in response to a favorable climate and beach. Scranton, Wilkes-Barre, and dozens of nearby towns are specialized coal-mining centers developed on anthracite coal deposits to serve a large segment of the northeastern United States. Pittsburgh and its suburbs and satellites form a nationally significant iron-and-steel manufacturing cluster favored by good location for the assembly of coal and iron ore and for the sale of steel to industries on the coal fields.

Equally important with physical resources in many cities are the advantages of mass production and ancillary services. Once started, a specialized city acts as a nucleus for similar or related activities, and functions tend to pyramid, whether the city is a seaside resort such as Miami or Atlantic City, or, more important, a manufacturing center such as Pittsburgh or Detroit. Concentration of industry in a city means that there will be a concentration of satellite services and industries—supply houses, machine shops, expert consultants, other industries using local industrial by-products or waste, still other industries making specialized parts for other plants in the city, marketing channels, specialized transport facilities, skilled labor, and a host of other facilities; either directly or indirectly, these benefit industry and cause it to expand in size and numbers in a concentrated place or district. Local personnel with the know-how in a given industry also may decide to start a new plant producing similar or like products in the same city. Furthermore, the advantages of mass production itself often ten to concentrate production in a few large factories and cities. Examples of localization of specific manufacturing industries are clothing in New York City, furniture in Grand Rapids, automobiles in the Detroit area, pottery in Stoke-on-Trent in England, and even such a specialty as tennis rackets in Pawtucket, Rhode Island.

Such concentration continues until opposing forces of high labor costs and congestion balance the concentrating forces. Labor costs may be lower in small towns and in industrially new districts; thus some factories are moving from the great metropolises to small towns; much of the cotton textile industry has moved from the old industrial areas of New England to the newer areas of the Carolinas in the South. The tremendous concentration of population and structures in large cities exacts a high cost in the form of congestion, high land costs, high taxes, and restrictive legislation.

Not all industries tend to concentrate in specialized industrial cities; many types of manufacturing partake more of central-place characteristics. These types are those that are tied to the market because the manufacturing process results in an increase in bulk or perishability. Bakeries, ice cream establishments, ice houses, breweries, soft-drink plants, and various types of assembly plants are examples. Even such industries, however, tend to be more developed in the manufacturing belt because the density of population and hence the market is greater there.

The greatest concentration of industrial cities in America is in the manufacturing belt of northeastern United States and contiguous Canada, north of the Ohio and east of the Mississippi. Some factors in this concentration are: large reserves of fuel and power (particularly coal), raw materials such as iron ore via the Great Lakes, cheap ocean transportation on the eastern seaboard, productive agriculture (particularly in the west), early settlement, later immigration concentrated in its cities, and an early start with consequent development of skilled labor, industrial know-how, transportation facilities and prestige.

The interdependent nature of most of the industries acts as a powerful force to maintain this area as the primary home of industrial cities in the United States. Before the war, the typical industrial city outside the main manufacturing belt had only a single industry of the raw-material type, such as lumber mills, food canneries, or smelters (Longview, Washington; San Jose, California; Anaconda, Montana). Because of the need for producing huge quantities of ships and airplanes for a two-ocean war, however, many cities along the Gulf and Pacific coasts have grown rapidly during recent years as centers of industry.

Application of the Three Types of Urban Support

Although examples can be cited illustrating each of the three types of urban support, most American cities partake in varying proportions of all three types. New York City, for example, as the greatest American port is a break-of-bulk point; as the principal center of wholesaling and retailing it is a central-place type; and as the major American center of manufacturing it is a specialized type. The actual distribution and functional classification of cities in the United States, more complex than the simple sum of the three types, has been mapped and described elsewhere in different terms.

The three basic types therefore should not be considered as a rigid framework excluding all accidental establishment, although even fortuitous development of a city becomes part of the general urban-supporting environment. Nor should the urban setting be regarded as static; cities are constantly changing, and exhibit characteristic lag in adjusting to new conditions.

Ample opportunity exists for use of initiative in strengthening the supporting base of the future city, particularly if account is taken of the basic factors of urban support. Thus a city should examine: (1) its surrounding area to take advantage of changes such as newly discovered resources or crops, (2) its transport in order to adjust properly to new or changed facilities, and (3) its industries in order to benefit from technological advances.

Internal Structure of Cities

Any effective plans for the improvement or rearrangement of the future city must take account of the present pattern of land use within the city, of the factors which have produced this pattern, and of the facilities required by activities localized within particular districts.

Although the internal pattern of each city is unique in its particular combination of details, most American cities have business, industrial, and residential districts. The forces underlying the pattern of land use can be appreciated if attention is focused on three generalizations of arrangement—by concentric zones, sectors, and multiple nuclei.

Concentric Zones

According to the concentric-zone theory, the pattern of growth of the city can best be understood in terms of five concentric zones.

1. *The central business district.* This is the focus of commercial, social, and civic life, and of transportation. In it is the downtown retail district with its department stores, smart shops, office buildings, clubs, banks, hotels, theaters, museums, and organization headquarters. Encircling the downtown retail district is the wholesale business district.

2. *The zone in transition.* Encircling the downtown area is a zone of residential deterioration. Business and light manufacturing encroach on residential areas characterized particularly by rooming houses. In this zone are the principal slums, with their submerged regions of poverty, degradation, and disease, and their underworlds of vice. In many American cities it has been inhabited largely by colonies of recent immigrants.

3. *The zone of independent workingmen's homes.* This is inhabited by industrial workers who have escaped from the zone in transition but who desire to live within easy access of their work. In many American cities second-generation immigrants are important segments of the population in this area.

4. *The zone of better residences.* This is made up of single-family dwellings, of exclusive "restricted districts," and of high-class apartment buildings.

5. *The commuters' zone.* Often beyond the city limits in suburban areas or in satellite cities, this is a zone of spotty development of high-class residences along lines of rapid travel.

Sectors

The theory of axial development, according to which growth takes place along main transportation routes or along lines of least resistance to form a star-shaped city, is refined by Homer Hoyt in his sectory theory, which states that growth along a particular axis of transportation usually consists of similar types of land use. The entire city is considered as a circle and the various areas as sectors radiating out from the center of that circle; similar types of land use originate near the center of the circle and migrate outward toward the periphery. Thus a high-rent residential area in the eastern quadrant of the city would tend to migrate outward, keeping always in the eastern quadrant. A low-quality housing area, if located in the southern quadrant, would tend to extend outward to the very margin of the city in that sector. The migration of high-class residential areas outward along established lines of travel is particularly pronounced on high ground, toward open country, to homes of community leaders, along lines of fastest transportation, and to existing nuclei of buildings or trading centers.

Multiple Nuclei

In many cities the land-use pattern is built not around a single center but around several discrete nuclei. In some cities these nuclei have existed from the very origins of the city; in others they have developed as the growth of the city stimulated migration and specialization. An example of the first type is Metropolitan London, in which "The City" and Westminster originated as separate points separated by open country, one as the center of finance and commerce, the other as the center of political life. An example of the second type is Chicago, in which heavy industry, at first localized along the Chicago River in the heart of the city, migrated to the Calumet District, where it acted as a nucleus for extensive new urban development.

The initial nucleus of the city may be the retail district in a central-place city, the port or rail facilities in a break-of-bulk city, or the factory, mine, or beach in a specialized-function city.

The rise of separate nuclei and differentiated districts reflects a combination of the following four factors:

1. Certain activities require specialized facilities. The retail district, for example, is attached to the point of greatest intracity accessibility, the port district to suitable water front, manufacturing districts to large blocks of land and water or rail connection, and so on.

2. Certain like activities group together because they profit from cohesion. The clustering of industrial cities has already been noted above under "Cities as concentration points for specialized services." Retail districts benefit from grouping which increases the concentration of potential customers and makes possible comparison shopping. Financial and office-building districts depend upon facility of communication among offices within the district. The Merchandise Mart of Chicago is an example of wholesale clustering.

3. Certain unlike activities are detrimental to each other. The antagonism between factory development and high-class residential development is well known. The heavy concentrations of pedestrians, automobiles, and streetcars in the retail district are antagonistic both to the railroad facilities and the street loading required in the wholesale district and to the rail facilities and space needed by large industrial districts, and vice versa.

4. Certain activities are unable to afford the high rents of the most desirable sites. This factor works in conjunction with the foregoing. Examples are bulk wholesaling and storage activities requiring much room, or low-class housing unable to afford the luxury of high land with a view.

The number of nuclei which result from historical development and the operation of localization forces varies greatly from city to city. The larger the city, the more numerous and specialized are the nuclei. The following districts, however, have developed around nuclei in most large American cities.

The Central business district. This district is at the focus of intracity transportation facilities by sidewalk, private car, bus, streetcar, subway, and elevated. Because of asymmetrical growth of most large cities, it is generally not now in the areal center of the city but actually near one edge, as in the case of lake-front, riverside, or even inland cities examples are Chicago, St. Louis, and Salt Lake City. Because established internal transportation lines converge on it, however, it is the point of most convenient access from all parts of the city, and the point of highest land values. The retail district, at the point of maximum accessibility, is attached to the sidewalk; only pedestrian or mass-transportation movement can concentrate the large numbers of customers necessary to support department stores, variety stores, and clothing shops, which are characteristic of the district. In small cities financial institutions and office buildings are intermingled with retail shops, but in large cities the financial district is separate, near but not at the point of greatest intracity facility. Its point of attachment is the elevator, which permits three-dimensional access among offices, whose most important locational factor is accessibility to other offices rather than to the city as a whole. Government buildings also are commonly near but not in the center of the retail district. In most cities a separate "automobile row" has arisen on the edge of the central business district, in cheaper rent areas along one or more major highways; its attachment is to the highway itself.

The wholesale and light-manufacturing district. This district is conveniently within the city but near the focus of extra city transportation facilities. Wholesale houses, while deriving some support from the city itself, serve principally a tributary region reached by railroad and motor truck. They are, therefore, concentrated along railroad lines, usually adjacent to (but not surrounding) the central business district. Many types of light manufacturing which do not require specialized buildings are attracted by the facilities of this district or similar districts: good rail and road transportation, available loft buildings, and proximity to the markets and labor of the city itself.

The heavy industrial district. This is near the present or former outer edge of the city. Heavy industries require large tracts of space, often beyond any available in sections already subdivided into blocks and streets. They also require good transportation, either rail or water. With the development of belt lines and switching yards, sites on the edge of the city may have better transportation service than those near the center. In

Chicago about a hundred industries are in a belt three miles long, adjacent to the clearing freight yards on the southwestern edge of the city. Furthermore, the noise of boiler works, the odors of stockyards, the waste disposal problems of smelters and iron and steel mills, the fire hazards of petroleum refineries, and the space and transportation needs which interrupt streets and accessibility—all these favor the growth of heavy industry away from the main center of the large city. The Calumet District of Chicago, the New Jersey marshes near New York City, the Lea marshes near London, and the St. Denis district of Paris are examples of such districts. The stockyards of Chicago, in spite of their odors and size, have been engulfed by urban growth and are now far from the edge of the city. They form a nucleus of heavy industry within the city but not near the center, which has blighted the adjacent residential area, the "back-of-the-yards" district.

The residential district. In general, high-class districts are likely to be on well-drained, high land and away from nuisances such as noise, odors, smoke, and railroad lines. Low-class districts are likely to arise near factories and railroad districts, wherever located in the city. Because of the obsolescence of structures, the older inner margins of residential districts are fertile fields for invasion by groups unable to pay high rents. Residential neighborhoods have some measure of cohesiveness. Extreme cases are the ethnically segregated groups, which cluster together although including members in many economic groups; Harlem is an example.

Minor nuclei. These include cultural centers, parks, outlying business districts, and small industrial centers. A university may form a nucleus for a quasi-independent community; examples are the University of Chicago, the University of California, and Harvard University. Parks and recreation areas occupying former wasteland too rugged or wet for housing may form nuclei for high-class residential areas; examples are Rock Creek Park in Washington and Hyde Park in London. Outlying business districts may in time become major centers. Many small institutions and individual light manufacturing plants, such as bakeries, dispersed throughout the city may never become nuclei of differentiated districts.

Suburb and satellite. Suburbs, either residential or industrial, are characteristic of most of the larger American cities. The rise of the automobile and the improvement of certain suburban commuter rail lines in a few of the largest cities have stimulated suburbanization. Satellites differ from suburbs in that they are separated from the central city by many miles and in general have little daily commuting to or from the central city, although economic activities of the satellite are closely geared to those of the central city. Thus Gary may be considered a suburb but Elgin and Joliet are satellites of Chicago.

Appraisal of Land-Use Patterns

Most cities exhibit not only a combination of the three types of urban support, but also aspects of the three generalizations of the land-use pattern. An understanding of both is useful in appraising the future prospects of the whole city and the arrangement of its parts.

As a general picture subject to modification because of topography, transportation, and previous land use, the concentric-zone aspect has merit. It is not a rigid pattern, inasmuch as growth or arrangement often reflects expansion within sectors or development around separate nuclei.

The sector aspect has been applied particularly to the outward movement of residential districts. Both the concentric-zone theory and the sector theory emphasize the general tendency of central residential areas to decline in value as new construction takes place on the outer edges; the sector theory is, however, more discriminating in its analysis of that movement.

Both the concentric zone, as a general pattern, and the sector aspect, as applied primarily to residential patterns, assume (although not explicitly) that there is but a single urban core around which land use is arranged symmetrically in either concentric or radial patterns. In broad theoretical terms such an assumption may be valid, inasmuch as the handicap of distance alone would favor as much concentration as possible in a small central core. Because of the actual physical impossibility of such concentration and the existence of separating factors, however, separate nuclei arise. The specific separating factors are not only high rent in the core, which can be afforded by few activities, but also the natural attachment of certain activities to extra-urban transport, space, or other facilities, and the advantages of the separation of unlike activities and the concentration of like functions.

The constantly changing pattern of land use poses many problems. Near the core, land is kept vacant or retained in antisocial slum structures in anticipation of expansion of higher-rent activities. The hidden costs of slums to the city in poor environment for future citizens and excessive police, fire, and sanitary protection underlie the argument for a subsidy to remove the blight. The transition zone is not everywhere a zone of deterioration with slums, however, as witness the rise of high-class apartment development near the urban core in the Gold Coast of Chicago or Park Avenue in New York City. On the fringe of the city, overambitious subdividing results in unused land to be crossed by urban services such as sewers and transportation. Separate political status of many suburbs results in a lack of civic responsibility for the problems and expenses of the city in which the suburbanites work.

75. *Here Is New York* *

Among all the cities of the world, New York is unique. This, of course, may be said of any city, for like all of the other phenomena of geography, each urban agglomeration differs from all others. But if anything can be "more unique" or "most unique," New York is that among cities. It cannot be compared with any of the other great cities of the world, and probably defies geographic description and analysis more effectively than any section of land anywhere. Perhaps for this reason an artist, the writer E. B. White, has achieved here the most geographic description of the city. For in this article are not only the space and dimension of the city, here also are the flavor, the spirit, the good and bad, the sublime and the ridiculous in urban life.

On any person who desires such queer prizes, New York will bestow the gift of loneliness and the gift of privacy. It is this largess that accounts for the presence within the city's walls of a considerable section of the population; for the residents of Manhattan are to a large extent strangers who have pulled up stakes somewhere and come to town, seeking sanctuary or fulfillment or some greater or lesser grail. The capacity to make such dubious gifts is a mysterious quality of New York. It can destroy an individual, or it can fulfill him, depending a good deal on luck. No one should come to New York to live unless he is willing to be lucky.

New York is the concentrate of art and commerce and sport and religion and entertainment and finance, bringing to a single compact arena the gladiator, the evangelist, the promoter, the actor, the trader and the merchant. It carries on its lapel the unexpungeable odor of the long past, so that no matter where you sit in New York you feel the vibrations of great times and tall deeds, of queer people and events and undertakings. I am sitting at the moment in a stifling hotel room in 90-degree heat, halfway down an air shaft, in midtown. No air moves in or out of the room, yet I am curiously affected by emanations from the immediate surroundings. I am twenty-two blocks from where Rudolph Valentino lay in state, eight blocks from where Nathan Hale was executed, five blocks from the publisher's office where Ernest Hemingway hit Max Eastman on the nose, four miles from where Walt Whitman sat sweating out edi-

* E. B. White, *Here Is New York* (New York: Harper & Brothers), copyright, 1949, by The Curtis Publishing Company.

The author (1899) is an editorial writer and contributor to the *New Yorker*, for which he wrote "Talk of the Town" columns for eleven years.

torials for the Brooklyn Eagle, thirty-four blocks from the street Willa Cather lived in when she came to New York to write books about Nebraska, one block from where Marceline used to clown on the boards of the Hippodrome, thirty-six blocks from the spot where the historian Joe Gould kicked a radio to pieces in full view of the public, thirteen blocks from where Harry Thaw shot Stanford White, five blocks from where I used to usher at the Metropolitan Opera and only a hundred and twelve blocks from the spot where Clarence Day the Elder was washed of his sins in the Church of the Epiphany (I could continue this list indefinitely); and for that matter I am probably occupying the very room that any number of exalted and somewise memorable characters sat in, some of them on hot, breathless afternoons, lonely and private and full of their own sense of emanations from without.

When I went down to lunch a few minutes ago I noticed that the man sitting next to me (about eighteen inches away along the wall) was Fred Stone. The eighteen inches were both the connection and the separation that New York provides for its inhabitants. My only connection with Fred Stone was that I saw him in *The Wizard of Oz* around the beginning of the century. But our waiter felt the same stimulus from being close to a man from Oz, and after Mr. Stone left the room the waiter told me that when he (the waiter) was a young man just arrived in this country and before he could understand a word of English, he had taken his girl for their first theater date to *The Wizard of Oz*. It was a wonderful show, the waiter recalled—a man of straw, a man of tin. Wonderful! (And still only eighteen inches away.) "Mr. Stone is a very hearty eater," said the waiter thoughtfully, content with this fragile participation in destiny, this link with Oz.

Side-Line Citizens

New York blends the gift of privacy with the excitement of participation; and better than most dense communities it succeeds in insulating the individual (if he wants it, and almost everybody wants or needs it) against all enormous and violent and wonderful events that are taking place every minute. Since I have been sitting in this miasmic air shaft, a good many rather splashy events that occurred in town. A man shot and killed his wife in a fit of jealousy. It caused no stir outside his block and got only small mention in the papers. I did not attend. Since my arrival, the greatest air show ever staged in all the world took place in town. I didn't attend and neither did most of the eight million other inhabitants, although they say there was quite a crowd. I didn't even hear any planes except a couple of westbound commercial airliners that habitually use this air shaft to fly over. The biggest ocean-going ships on the North Atlantic arrived and departed. I didn't notice them and neither did most other New Yorkers. I am told this is the greatest seaport in the world, with six hundred and fifty miles of water front, and ships calling here from many exotic lands, but the only boat I've happened to notice since my arrival was a small sloop tacking out of the East River night before last on the ebb tide when I was walking across the Brooklyn Bridge. I heard the *Queen Mary* blow one midnight, though, and the sound carried the whole history of departure and longing and loss. The Lions have been in convention. I've seen not one Lion. A friend of mine saw one and told me about him. (He was lame, and was wearing a bolero.) At the ballgrounds and horse parks the greatest sporting spectacles have been enacted. I saw no ballplayer, no race horse. The governor came to town. I heard the siren scream, but that was all there was to that—an eighteen-inch margin again. A man was killed by a falling cornice. I was not a party to the tragedy, and again the inches counted heavily.

I mention these merely to show that New York is peculiarly constructed to absorb almost anything that comes along (whether a thousand-foot liner out of the East or a twenty-thousand-man convention out of the West) without inflicting the event on its inhabitants; so that every event is, in a sense, optional, and the inhabitant is in the happy position of being able to choose his spectacle and so conserve his soul. In most metropolises, small and large, the choice is not often with the individual at all. He is thrown to the Lions. The Lions are overwhelming; the event is unavoidable. A cornice falls, and it hits every citizen on the head, every last man in town. I sometimes think that the only event that hits every New Yorker on the head is the annual St. Patrick's Day parade, which is fairly penetrating—the Irish are a hard race to tune out, there are 500,000 of them in residence, and they have the police force right in the family.

The quality in New York that insulates its inhabitants from life may simply weaken them as individuals. Perhaps it is healthier to live in a community where, when a cornice falls, you feel the blow; where, when the governor passes, you see at any rate his hat.

I am not defending New York in this regard. Many of its settlers are probably here merely to escape, not face, reality. But whatever it means, it is a rather rare gift, and I believe it has a positive effect on the creative capacities of New Yorkers—for creation is in part merely the business of forgoing the great and small distractions.

The Three New Yorks

Although New York often imparts a feeling of great forlornness or forsakenness, it seldom seems dead or unresourceful, and you always feel that either by shifting your location ten blocks or by reducing your fortune by five dollars you can experience rejuvenation. Many people who have no real independence of spirit depend on the city's tremendous variety and sources of excitement for spiritual sustenance and maintenance of morale. In the country there are a few chances of sudden rejuvenation—a shift in weather, perhaps, or something arriving in the mail. But in New York the chances are endless. I think that although many persons are here for some excess of spirit (which caused them to break away from their small town), some, too, are here from a deficiency of spirit, who find in New York a protection, or an easy substitution.

There are roughly three New Yorks. There is, first, the New York of the man or woman who was born here, who takes the city for granted and accepts its size and its turbulence as natural and inevitable. Second, there is the New York of the commuter—the city that is devoured by locusts each day and spat out each night. Third, there is the New York of the person who was born somewhere else and came to New York in quest of something. Of these three trembling cities the greatest is the last—the city of final destination, the city that is a goal. It is this third city that accounts for New York's high-strung disposition, its poetical deportment, its dedication to the arts, and its incomparable achievements. Commuters give the city its tidal restlessness; natives give it solidity and continuity; but the settlers give it passion. And whether it is a farmer arriving from Italy to set up a small grocery store in a slum, or a young girl arriving from a small town in Mississippi to escape the indignity of being observed by her neighbors, or a boy arriving from the Corn Belt with a manuscript in his suitcase and a pain in his heart, it makes no difference: each embraces New York with the intense excitement of first love, each absorbs New York with the fresh eyes of an adventurer, each generates heat and light to dwarf the Consolidated Edison Company.

Slaves of the Timetable

The commuter is the queerest bird of all. The suburb he inhabits has no essential vitality of its own and is a mere roost where he comes at day's end to go to sleep. Except in rare cases, the man who lives in Mamaroneck or Little Neck or Teaneck, and works in New York, discovers nothing much about the city except the time of arrival and departure of trains and buses, and the path to a quick lunch. He is desk-bound, and has never, idly roaming in the gloaming, stumbled suddenly on Belvedere Tower in the Park, seen the ramparts rise sheer from the water of the pond, and the boys along the shore fishing for minnows, girls stretched out negligently on the shelves of the rocks; he has never come suddenly on anything at all in New York as a loiterer, because he has had no time between trains. He has fished in Manhattan's wallet and dug out coins, but has never listened to Manhattan's breathing, never awakened to its morning, never dropped off to sleep in its night. About 400,000 men and women come charging onto the Island each week-day morning, out of the mouths of tubes and tunnels. Not many among them have ever spent a drowsy afternoon in the great rustling oaken silence of the reading room of the Public Library, with the book elevator (like an old water wheel) spewing out books onto the trays. They tend their furnaces in Westchester and in Jersey, but they have never seen the furnaces of the Bowery, the fires that burn in oil drums on zero winter nights. They may work in the financial district downtown and never see the extravagant plantings of Rockefeller Center—the daffodils and grape hyacinths and birches and the flags trimmed to the wind on a fine morning in spring. Or they may work in a mid-town office and may let a whole year swing round without sighting Governors Island from the sea wall. The commuter dies with tremendous mileage to his credit, but he is no rover. His entrances and exits are more devious than those in a prairie-dog village; and he calmly plays bridge while buried in the mud at the bottom of the East River. The Long Island Rail Road alone carried forty million commuters last year; but many of them were the same fellow retracing his steps.

The terrain of New York is such that a resident sometimes travels farther, in the end, than a commuter. Irving Berlin's journey from Cherry Street in the lower East Side to an apartment uptown was through an alley and was only three or four miles in length; but it was like going three times around the world.

A poem compresses much in a small space and adds music, thus heightening its meaning. The city is like poetry: it compresses all life, all races and breeds, into a small island and adds music and the accompaniment of internal engines. The island of Manhattan is without any doubt the greatest human concentrate on earth, the poem whose magic is comprehensible to millions of permanent residents but whose full meaning will always remain illusive. At the feet of the tallest and plushiest offices lie the crummiest slums. The genteel mysteries housed in the Riverside Church are only a few blocks from the voodoo charms of Harlem. The merchant princes, riding to Wall Street in their limousines down the East River

Drive, pass within a few hundred yards of the gypsy kings; but the princes do not know they are passing kings, and the kings are not up yet anyway—they live a more leisurely life than the princes and get drunk more consistently.

New York is nothing like Paris; it is nothing like London; and it is not Spokane multiplied by sixty, or Detroit multiplied by four. It is by all odds the loftiest of cities. It even managed to reach the highest point in the sky at the lowest moment of the depression. The Empire State Building shot 1250 feet into the air when it was madness to put out as much as six inches of new growth. (The building has a mooring mast that no dirigible has ever tied to; it employs a man to flush toilets in slack times; it has been hit by an airplane in a fog, struck countless times by lightning, and been jumped off of by so many unhappy people that pedestrians instinctively quicken step when passing Fifth Avenue and 34th Street.)

The Perpendicular City

Manhattan has been compelled to expand skyward because of the absence of any other direction in which to grow. This, more than any other thing, is responsible for its physical majesty. It is to the nation what the white church spire is to the village—the visible symbol of aspiration and faith, the white plume saying that the way is up. The summer traveler swings in over Hell Gate Bridge and from the window of his sleeping car as it glides above the pigeon lofts and back yards of Queens looks southwest to where the morning light first strikes the steel peaks of midtown, and he sees its upward thrust unmistakable: the great walls and towers rising, the smoke rising, the heat not yet rising, the hopes and ferments of so many awakening millions rising—this vigorous spear that presses heaven hard.

It is a miracle that New York works at all. The whole thing is implausible. Every time the residents brush their teeth, millions of gallons of water must be drawn from the Catskills and the hills of Westchester. When a young man in Manhattan writes a letter to his girl in Brooklyn, the love message gets blown to her through a pneumatic tube—*pfft*—just like that. The subterranean system of telephone cables, power lines, steam pipes, gas mains and sewer pipes is reason enough to abandon the island to the gods and the weevils. Every time an incision is made in the pavement, the noisy surgeons expose ganglia that are tangled beyond belief. By rights New York should have destroyed itself long ago, from panic or fire or rioting or failure of some vital supply line in its circulatory system or from some deep labyrinthine short circuit. Long ago the city should have experienced an insoluble traffic snarl at some impossible bottleneck. It should have perished of hunger when food lines failed for a few days. It should have been wiped out by a plague starting in its slums or carried in by ships' rats. It should have been overwhelmed by the sea that licks at it on every side. The workers in its myriad cells should have succumbed to nerves, from the fearful pall of smoke-fog that drifts over every few days from Jersey, blotting out all light at noon and leaving the high offices suspended, men groping and depressed, and the sense of world's end. It should have been touched in the head by the August heat and gone off its rocker.

Manhattan Microcosm

Mass hysteria is a terrible force, yet New Yorkers seem always to escape it by some tiny margin: they sit in stalled subways without claustrophobia, they extricate themselves from panic situations by some lucky wisecrack, they meet confusion and congestion with patience and grit—a sort of pereptual muddling through. Every facility is inadequate—the hospitals and schools and playgrounds are overcrowded, the express highways are feverish, the unimproved highways and bridges are bottlenecks; there is not enough air and not enough light, and there is usually either too much heat or too little. But the city makes up for its hazards and its deficiencies by supplying its citizens with massive doses of a supplementary vitamin—the sense of belonging to something unique, cosmopolitan, mighty and unparalleled.

To an outlander a stay in New York can be and often is a series of small embarrassments and discomforts and disappointments: not understanding the waiter, not being able to distinguish between a sucker joint and a friendly saloon, riding the wrong subway, being slapped down by a bus driver for asking an innocent question, enduring sleepless nights when the street noises fill the bedroom. Tourists make for New York, particularly in summertime—they swarm all over the Statue of Liberty (where many a resident of the town has never set foot), they invade the Automat, visit radio studios, St. Patrick's Cathedral, and they window shop. Mostly they have a pretty good time. But sometimes in New York you run across the disillusioned—a young couple who are obviously visitors, newlyweds perhaps, for whom the bright dream has vanished. The place has been too much for them; they sit languishing in a cheap restaurant over a speechless meal.

The oft-quoted thumbnail sketch of New York is, of course: "It's a wonderful place, but I'd hate to live there." I have an idea that people from villages and small towns, people accustomed to the convenience and the friendliness of neighborhood over-the-fence living, are unaware that life in New York follows the neighborhood pattern. The city is literally a composite of tens of thousands of tiny neighborhood units. There are, of course, the big districts and big units: Chelsea and Murray Hill and Gramercy (which are residential units), Harlem (a racial unit), Greenwich Village (a unit dedicated to the arts and other matters), and there is Radio City (a commercial development), Peter Cooper Village (a housing unit), the Medical Center (a sickness unit) and many other sections each of which has some distinguishing characteristic. But the curious thing about New York is that each large geographical unit is composed of countless small neighborhoods. Each neighborhood is virtually self-sufficient. Usually it is no more than two or three blocks long and a couple of blocks wide. Each area is a city within a city within a city. Thus, no matter where you live in New York, you will find within a block or two a grocery store, a barbershop, a newsstand and shoeshine shack, an ice-coal-and-wood cellar (where you write your order on a pad outside as you walk by), a dry cleaner, a laundry, a delicatessen (beer and sandwiches delivered at any hour to your door), a flower shop, an undertaker's parlor, a movie house, a radio-repair shop, a stationer, a haberdasher, a tailor, a drugstore, a garage, a tearoom, a saloon, a hardware store, a liquor store, a shoe-repair shop. Every block or two, in most residential sections of New York, is a little main street. A man starts for work in the morning and before he has gone two hundred yards he has completed half a dozen missions: bought a paper, left a pair of shoes to be soled, picked up a pack of cigarettes, ordered a bottle of whisky to be dispatched in the opposite direction against his home-coming, written a message to the unseen forces of the wood cellar, and notified the dry cleaner that a pair of trousers awaits call. Homeward bound eight hours later, he buys a bunch of pussy willows, a Mazda bulb, a drink, a shine—all between the corner where he steps off the bus and his apartment. So complete is each neighborhood, and so strong the sense of neighborhood, that many a New Yorker spends a lifetime within the confines of an area smaller than a country village. Let him walk two blocks from his corner and he is in a strange land and will feel uneasy till he gets back.

The Small-Town Touch

Storekeepers are particularly conscious of neighborhood boundary lines. A woman friend of mine moved recently from one apartment to another, a distance of three blocks. When she turned up, the day after the move, at the same grocer's that she had patronized for years, the proprietor was in ecstasy—almost in tears—at seeing her. "I was afraid," he said, "now that you've moved away I wouldn't be seeing you any more." To him, *away* was three blocks, or about seven hundred and fifty feet.

I am, at the moment of writing this, living not as a neighborhood man in New York but as a transient, or vagrant, in from the country for a few days. Summertime is a good time to re-examine New York and to receive again the gift of privacy, the jewel of loneliness. In summer the city contains (except for tourists) only die-hards and authentic characters. No casual, spotty dwellers are around, only the real article. And the town has a somewhat relaxed air, and one can lie in a loincloth, gasping and remembering things.

I've been remembering what it felt like as a young man to live in the same town with giants. When I first arrived in New York my personal giants were a dozen or so columnists and critics and poets whose names appeared regularly in the papers. I burned with a low steady fever just because I was on the same island with Don Marquis, Heywood Broun, Christopher Morley, Franklin P. Adams, Robert C. Benchley, Frank Sullivan, Dorothy Parker, Alexander Woollcott, Ring Lardner and Stephen Vincent Benét. I would hang around the corner of Chambers Street and Broadway, thinking: "Somewhere in that building is the typewriter that Archy the cockroach jumps on at night." New York hardly gave me a living at that period, but it sustained me. I used to walk quickly past the house in West 13th Street between Sixth and Seventh where F.P.A. lived, and the block seemed to tremble under my feet—the way Park Avenue trembles when a train leaves Grand Central. This excitation (nearness of giants) is a continuing thing. The city is always full of young worshipful beginners—young actors, young aspiring poets, ballerinas, painters, reporters, singers—each depending on his own brand of tonic to stay alive, each with his own stable of giants.

New York provides not only a continuing excitation but also a spectacle that is continuing. I wander around, re-examining this spectacle, hoping that I can put it on paper. It is Saturday, toward the end of the afternoon. I turn through West 48th Street. From the open windows of the drum and saxophone parlors come the listless sounds of musical instruction, monstrous insect noises in the brooding field of summer. The Cort Theater is disgorging its matinee audience. Suddenly the whole block is filled with the mighty voice of a street singer. He approaches, looking for an audience, a large, cheerful Negro with grand-opera contours, strolling with head thrown back, filling the canyon with uninhibited song. He carries a long cane as his sole prop, and is tidily but casually dressed—slacks, seersucker jacket, a book showing in his pocket.

This is perfect artistic timing; the audience from the Cort, where *The*

Respectful Prostitute is playing, has just received a lesson in race relations and is in a mood to improve the condition of the black race as speedily as possible. Coins (mostly quarters) rattle to the street, and a few minutes of minstrelsy improves the condition of one Negro by about eight dollars. If he does as well as this at every performance, he has a living right there. New York is the city of opportunity, they say. Even the mounted cop, clumping along on his nag a few minutes later, scans the gutter carefully for dropped silver, like a bird watching for spilt grain.

The Inner Man

It is seven o'clock and I re-examine an ex-speakeasy in East 53rd Street, with dinner in mind. A thin crowd, a summer-night buzz of fans interrupted by an occasional drink being shaken at the small bar. It is dark in here (the proprietor sees no reason for boosting his light bill just because liquor laws have changed). How dark, how pleasing; and how miraculously beautiful the murals showing Italian lake scenes—probably executed by a cousin of the owner. The owner himself mixes. The fans intone the prayer for cool salvation. From the next booth drifts the conversation of radio executives; from the green salad comes the little taste of garlic. Behind me (eighteen inches again) a young intellectual is trying to persuade a girl to come live with him and be his love. She has her guard up, but he is extremely reasonable, careful not to overplay his hand. A combination of intellectual companionship and sexuality is what they have to offer each other, he feels. In the mirror over the bar I can see the ritual of the second drink. Then he has to go to the men's room and she has to go to the ladies' room, and when they return, the argument has lost its tone. And the fan takes over again, and the heat and the relaxed air and the memory of so many good little dinners in so many good little illegal places, with the theme of love, the sound of ventilation, the brief medicinal illusion of gin.

In the Night

Another hot night I stop off at the Goldman Band concert in the Mall in Central Park. The people seated on the benches fanned out in front of the band shell are attentive, appreciative. In the trees the night wind stirs, bringing the leaves to life, endowing them with speech; the electric lights illuminate the green branches from the under side, translating them into a new language. Overhead a plane passes dreamily, its running lights winking. On the bench directly in front of me, a boy sits with his arm around his girl; they are proud of each other and are swathed in music.

The cornetist steps forward for a solo, begins, "Drink to me only with thine eyes. . . ." In the wide, warm night the horn is startlingly pure and magical. Then from the North River another horn solo begins—the *Queen Mary* announcing her intentions. She is not on key; she is a half tone off. The trumpeter in the bandstand never flinches. The horns quarrel savagely, but no one minds having the intimation of travel injected into the pledge of love. "I leave," sobs Mary. "And I will pledge with mine," sighs the trumpeter. Along the asphalt paths strollers pass to and fro; they behave considerately, respecting the musical atmosphere. Popsicles are moving well. In the warm grass beyond the fence, forms wriggle in the shadows, and the skirts of the girls approaching on the Mall are ballooned by the breeze, and their bare shoulders catch the lamplight. "Drink to me only with thine eyes." It is a magical occasion, and it's all free.

On week ends in summer the town empties. I visit my office on a Saturday afternoon. No phone rings, no one feeds the hungry *in*-baskets, no one disturbs the papers; it is a building of the dead, a time of awesome suspension. The whole city is honeycombed with abandoned cells—a jail that has been effectively broken. Occasionally from somewhere in the building a night bell rings, summoning the elevator—a special fire-alarm ring. This is the pit of loneliness, in an office on a summer Saturday. I stand at the window and look down at the batteries and batteries of offices across the way, recalling how the thing looks in winter twilight when everything is going full blast, every cell lighted, and how you can see in pantomime the puppets fumbling with their slips of paper (but you don't hear the rustle), see them pick up their phone (but you don't hear the ring), see the noiseless, ceaseless moving about of so many passers of pieces of paper: New York, the capital of memoranda, in touch with Calcutta, in touch with Reykjavik, and always fooling with something.

In the café of the Lafayette, the regulars sit and talk. It is busy yet peaceful. Nursing a drink, I stare through the west windows at the Manufacturers Trust Company and at the red brick fronts on the north side of Ninth Street, watching the red turning slowly to purple as the light dwindles. Brick buildings have a way of turning color at the end of the day, the way a red rose turns bluish as it wilts. The café is a sanctuary. The waiters are ageless and they change not. Nothing has been modernized. Notre Dame stands guard in its travel poster. The coffee is strong and full of chicory, and good.

Walk the Bowery under the El at night and all you feel is a sort of cold guilt. Touched for a dime, you try to drop the coin and not touch the hand, because the hand is dirty; you try to avoid the glance, because the glance accuses. This is not so much personal menace as universal—the cold menace of unresolved human suffering and poverty and the advanced stages of the disease alcoholism. On a summer night the drunks sleep in the open. The sidewalk is a free bed, and there are no lice. Pedestrians step along and over and around the still forms as though walking on a battlefield among the dead. In doorways, on the steps of the savings bank, the bums lie sleeping it off. Standing sentinel at each sleeper's head is the empty bottle from which he drained his release. Wedged in the crook of his arm is the paper bag containing his things. The glib barker on the sight-seeing bus tells his passengers that this is the "street of lost souls," but the Bowery does not think of itself as lost; it meets its peculiar problem in its own way—plenty of gin mills, plenty of flophouses, plenty of indifference, and always, at the end of the line, Bellevue.

East Side Garden Party

A block or two east and the atmosphere changes sharply. In the slums are poverty and bad housing, but with them the reassuring sobriety and safety of family life. I head east along Rivington. All is cheerful and filthy and crowded. Small shops overflow onto the sidewalk, leaving only half the normal width for passers-by. In the unshaded lights gleam watermelons and lingerie. Families have fled the hot rooms upstairs and have found relief on the pavement. They sit on orange crates, smoking, relaxed, congenial. This is the nightly garden party of the vast Lower East Side—and on the whole they are more agreeable-looking hot-weather groups than some you see in bright canvas deck chairs on green lawns in country circumstances. It is folksy here with the smell of warm flesh and squashed fruit and fly-bitten filth in the gutter, and cooking.

At the corner of Lewis, in the playground behind the wire fence, an open-air dance is going on—some sort of neighborhood affair, probably designed to combat delinquency. Women push baby carriages in and out among the dancers, as though to exhibit what dancing leads to at last. Overhead, like banners decorating a cotillion hall, stream the pants and bras from the pulley lines. The music stops, and a beautiful Italian girl takes a brush from her handbag and stands under the street light brushing her long blue-black hair till it shines. The cop in the patrol car watches sullenly.

The Consolidated Edison Company says there are eight million people in the five boroughs of New York, and the company is in a position to know. As in every dense community, virtually all races, all religions, all nationalities are represented. Population figures are shifty—they change almost as fast as one can break them down. It is safe to say that about two million of New York's eight million, are Jews—roughly one in four. Among this two million who are Jewish are, of course, a great many nationalities—Russian, German, Rumanian, Austrian, and so forth.

The Urban League of Greater New York estimates that the number of Negroes in New York is about 700,000. Of these, about 500,000 live in Harlem, a district that extends northward from 110th Street. The Negro population has increased rapidly in the last few years. There are half again as many Negroes in New York today as there were in 1940. There are about 230,000 Puerto Ricans living in New York. There are half a million Irish, half a million Germans. There are 900,000 Russians, 150,000 English, 400,000 Poles, and there are quantities of Finns and Czechs and Swedes and Danes and Norwegians and Latvians and Belgians and Welsh and Greeks, and even Dutch, who have been here from away back. It is very hard to say how many Chinese there are. Officially there are 12,000, but there are many Chinese who are in New York illegally and who don't like census takers.

The collision and the intermingling of these millions of foreign-born people representing so many races, creeds, and nationalities make New York a permanent exhibit of the phenomenon of one world. The citizens of New York are tolerant not only from disposition but from necessity. The city has to be tolerant, otherwise it would explode in a radioactive cloud of hate and rancor and bigotry. If the people were to depart even briefly from the peace of cosmopolitan intercourse, the town would blow up higher than a kite. In New York smolders every race problem there is, but the noticeable thing is not the problem but the inviolate truce. Harlem is a city in itself, and being a city Harlem symbolizes segregation; yet Negro life in New York lacks the more conspicuous elements of Jim Crowism. Negroes ride subways and buses on terms of equality with whites, but they have not yet found that same equality in hotels and restaurants. Professionally, Negroes get on well in the theater, in music, in art and in literature; but in many fields of employment the going is tough. The Jim Crow principle lives chiefly in the housing rules and customs. Private owners of dwellings legally can, and do, exclude Negroes. Under a recent city ordinance, however, apartment buildings that are financed with public moneys or that receive any tax exemption must accept tenants without regard to race, color or religion.

To a New Yorker the city is both changeless and changing. In many respects it neither looks nor feels the way it did twenty-five years ago. The elevated railways have been pulled down, all but the Third Avenue. An old-timer walking up Sixth past the Jefferson Market jail misses the railroad, misses its sound, its spotted shade, its little aerial stations, and the tremor of the thing. Broadway has changed in aspect. It used to have a discernible bony structure beneath its loud bright surface; but the signs are so enormous now, the buildings and shops and hotels have largely disappeared under the neon lights and letters and the frozen-custard façade. Broadway is a custard street with no frame supporting it. In Greenwich Village the light is thinning: big apartments have come in, bordering the Square, and the bars are mirrored and chromed. But there are still in the Village the lingering traces of poesy, Mexican glass, hammered brass, batik, lamps made of whisky bottles, first novels made of fresh memories—the old Village with its alleys and ratty one-room rents catering to the erratic needs of those whose hearts are young and gay.

The Passing of the Mansion

Grand Central has become honky-tonk, with its extradimensional advertising displays and its tendency to adopt the tactics of a travel broker. I practically lived in Grand Central Terminal at one period (it has all the conveniences and I had no other place to stay) and the great hall always seemed to me one of the more inspiring interiors in New York, until Lastex and Coca-Cola got into the temple.

All over town the great mansions are in decline. Schwab's house facing the Hudson on Riverside is gone. Gould's house on Fifth Avenue is an antique shop. Morgan's house on Madison Avenue is a church administration office. What was once the Fahnestock house is now Random House. Rich men nowadays don't live in houses; they live in the attics of big apartment buildings and plant trees on the setbacks, hundreds of feet above the street.

There are fewer newspapers than there used to be, thanks somewhat to the late Frank Munsey. One misses the *Globe,* the *Mail,* the *Herald;* and to many a New Yorker life has never seemed the same since the *World* took the count.

Sky Acreage

Police now ride in radio prowl cars instead of gumshoeing around the block swinging their sticks. A ride in the subway costs ten cents, and the seats are apt to be dark green instead of straw yellow. Men go to saloons to gaze at televised events instead of to think long thoughts. It is all very disconcerting. Even parades have changed some. The last triumphal military procession in Manhattan simply filled the city with an ominous and terrible rumble of heavy tanks.

The slums are gradually giving way to the lofty housing projects—high in stature, high in purpose, low in rent. There are a couple of dozens of these new developments scattered around; each is a city in itself (one of them in the Bronx accommodates 12,000 families), sky acreage hitherto untilled, lifting people far above the street, standardizing their sanitary life, giving them some place to sit other than an orange crate. Federal money, state money, city money and private money have flowed into these projects. Banks and insurance companies are in back of some of them. Architects have turned the buildings slightly on their bases to catch more light. In some of them, rents are as low as eight dollars a room. Thousands of new units are still needed and will eventually be built, but New York never quite catches up with itself, is never in equilibrium. In flush times the population mushrooms and the new dwellings sprout from the rock. Come bad times and the population scatters and the lofts are abandoned and the landlord withers and dies.

New York has changed in tempo and in temper during the years I have known it. There is greater tension, increased irritability. You encounter it in many places, in many faces. The normal frustrations of modern life are here multiplied and amplified—a single run of a crosstown bus contains, for the driver, enough frustration and annoyance to carry him over the edge of sanity: the light that changes always an instant too soon, the passenger that bangs on the shut door, the truck that blocks the opening, the coin that slips to the floor, the question asked at the wrong moment. There is greater tension and there is greater speed. Taxis roll faster than they rolled ten years ago—and they were rolling fast then. Hackmen used to drive with verve; now they sometimes seem to drive with desperation, toward the ultimate tip. On the West Side Highway, approaching the city, the motorist is swept along in a trance—a sort of fever of inescapable motion, goaded from behind, hemmed in on either side, a mere chip in a millrace.

The city has never been so uncomfortable, so crowded, so tense. Money has been plentiful and New York has responded. Restaurants are hard to get into; businessmen stand in line for a Schrafft's luncheon as meekly as idle men used to stand in soup lines. (Prosperity creates its bread lines, the same as depression.) The lunch hour in Manhattan has been shoved ahead half an hour, to 12:00 or 12:30, in the hopes of beating the crowd to a table. Everyone is a little emptier at quitting time than he used to be. Apartments are festooned with No Vacancy signs. There is standing-room-only in Fifth Avenue buses, which once reserved a seat for every paying guest. The old double-deckers are disappearing—people don't ride just for the fun of it any more.

At certain hours on certain days it is almost impossible to find an empty taxi and there is a great deal of chasing around after them. You grab a handle and open the door, and find that some other citizen is entering from the other side. Doormen grow rich blowing their whistles for cabs; and some doormen belong to no door at all—merely wander about through the streets, opening cabs for people as they happen to find them. By comparison with other less hectic days, the city is uncomfortable and inconvenient; but New Yorkers temperamentally do not crave comfort and convenience—if they did they would live elsewhere.

The subtlest change in New York is something people don't speak much about but that is in everyone's mind. The city, for the first time in its long history, is destructible. A single flight of planes no bigger than a wedge of geese can quickly end this island fantasy, burn the towers, crumble the bridges, turn the underground passages into lethal chambers, cremate the millions. The intimation of mortality is part of New York now: in the sound of jets overhead, in the black headlines of the latest edition.

All dwellers in cities must live with the stubborn fact of annihilation; in New York the fact is somewhat more concentrated because of the concentration of the city itself, and because, of all targets, New York has a certain clear priority. In the mind of whatever perverted dreamer might loose the lightning, New York must hold a steady, irresistible charm.

Twin Billing

It used to be that the Statue of Liberty was the signpost that proclaimed New York and translated it for all the world. Today Liberty shares the role with Death. Along the East River, from the razed slaughterhouses of Turtle Bay, as though in a race with the spectral flight of planes, men are carving out the permanent headquarters of the United Nations—the greatest housing project of them all. In its stride, New York takes on one more interior city, to shelter, this time, all governments, and to clear the slum called war. New York is not a capital city—it is not a national capital or a state capital. But it is by way of becoming the capital of the world. The buildings, as conceived by architects, will be cigar boxes set on end. Traffic will flow in a new tunnel under First Avenue. Forty-seventh Street will be widened (and if my guess is any good, trucks will appear late at night to plant tall trees surreptitiously, their roots to mingle with the intestines of the town). Once again the city will absorb, almost without showing any sign of it, a congress of visitors. It has already shown itself capable of stashing away the United Nations—a great many of the delegates have been around town during the past couple of years, and the citizenry has hardly caught a glimpse of their coattails or their black Homburgs.

This race—this race between the destroying planes and the struggling Parliament of Man—it sticks in all our heads. The city at last perfectly illustrates both the universal dilemma and the general solution, this riddle in steel and stone is at once the perfect target and the perfect demonstration of nonviolence, of racial brotherhood, this lofty target scraping the skies and meeting the destroying planes halfway, home of all people and all nations, capital of everything, housing the deliberations by which the planes are to be stayed and their errand forestalled.

A block or two west of the new City of Man in Turtle Bay there is an old willow tree that presides over an interior garden. It is a battered tree, long suffering and much climbed, held together by strands of wire but beloved of those who know it. In a way it symbolizes the city: life under difficulties, growth against odds, sap-rise in the midst of concrete, and the steady reaching for the sun. Whenever I look at it nowadays, and feel the cold shadow of the planes, I think: "This must be saved, this particular thing, this very tree." If it were to go, all would go—this city, this mischievous and marvelous monument which not to look upon would be like death.

76. *Grip, a Populated Skerry of Norway* *

If New York City is the largest urban settlement (and Londoners to the contrary notwithstanding, it is), Grip must come very close to being the smallest. Here is a tiny settlement in one of the most inhospitable places in the world, a settlement so located because of the proximity to a very valuable resource—fish. Between these two urban types, Grip and New York, lies the vast gamut of urban settlements—villages, towns, and cities—that follow the theoretical patterns of urban development more closely. But geography is not concerned only with the typical. Through the study of the unique, it may be possible to determine patterns and characteristics not readily observable in the more representative examples.

It is estimated that approximately 150,000 islands occur along the extensive coast line of Norway. Only 2,141 of these are populated; they contain about one seventh of the people of Norway. This paper deals with one of the populated islands, Grip.

There is tremendous diversity among the Norwegian islands. Some of

* Lawrence M. Sommers, "Grip, A Populated Skerry of Norway," reprinted from *Papers of the Michigan Academy of Science, Arts, and Letters*, Vol. XXXVII (Ann Arbor: U. of Michigan Press, 1952), pp. 227, 232.

The author (1919) is Professor of Geography and Head of the Department of Geography at Michigan State University. He has done extensive field work in Scandinavia and has published several articles on this area.

the islands barely protrude above the water level, while others thrust their rocky heights far above the sea. Many are so aligned as to form a barrier against the open sea, the skerry guard, and thus protect ships plying the inland passage along the mainland. A considerable number of the islands are fortunate in having a sufficient soil cover for limited agricultural activity. Numerous others have been completely denuded of soil by glacial or wave action (Fig. 32).

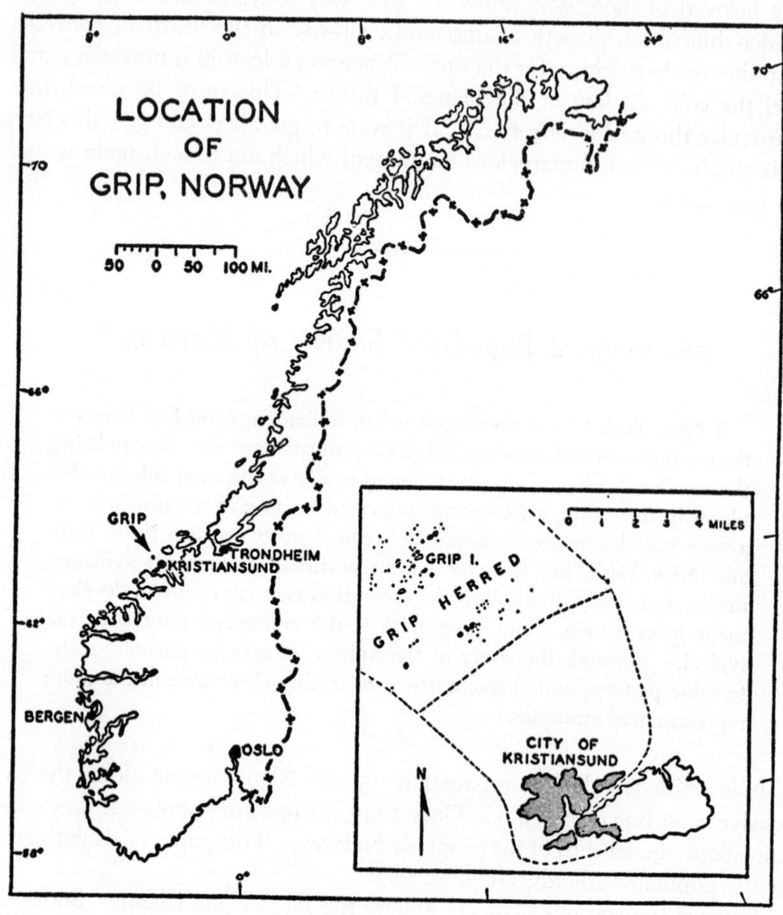

Figure 32

Yet a few of these rock-bound islands have managed to support a dense population. As a matter of fact, they have some of the highest population densities found anywhere in Norway. The answer to this anomaly, in most instances, appears to be the occupation of fishing. Though the islands themselves may be poor in resources, the surrounding waters abound in valuable species of fish.

An illustration of this unusual development is found on the island of Grip. It is one of a group of eighty-two islands and islets comprising a *herred,* which is also named Grip (Fig. 32). A herred, the smallest administrative unit in Norway, is similar in function to a United States township.

The islands of Grip Herred are scattered widely in an expanse of open sea approximately ten miles northwest of the important fishing center of Kristiansund. The total land area of the entire herred, however, is only 119 acres—less than one fifth of a square mile. The island of Grip, our primary concern, is less than two average city blocks in size. Yet this tiny rock, the only populated island in the herred, listed 224 inhabitants in the 1946 census. Thus the island not only has a remarkably high population density for Norway, but also compares favorably with population densities of major urban areas of the world. If the population density of Grip were given in terms of a square mile, the figure would be slightly less than that for New York City, which has an average density of 25,000 persons per square mile.

Throughout the history of Grip the nature and the location of the island has limited the means of livelihood of its occupants almost exclusively to fishing. It has long been a leading *fiskevaer* ("fishing station"). Prior to 1897, however, the community lacked local administrative authority. Ownership and control of the island had changed frequently. In early times Grip belonged to the archbishop of Trondheim. In the nineteenth century it was purchased by a group of businessmen from nearby Kristiansund. During this latter period the fishermen were subservient to the owner-merchants, who strictly controlled their activities. For example, the fishermen were forced to sell their fish only to the owners of the island. In addition, they were pledged to house designated fishermen during the fishing season. Thus spare rooms were not available to fish buyers and friends from other areas. The attainment of herred status by Grip in 1897 was a major accomplishment. The inhabitants enjoyed, for the first time in the history of the island, such privileges as protection by communal laws, the right to vote, and payment of local taxes. The herred government purchased the fishing station from the Kristiansund merchants. Fishing continued to be the chief occupation of the islanders.

A detailed inspection of the island reveals the inhospitable environment it offers to its inhabitants. Glaciation and the ocean waves have scoured all usable soil from the island. The islanders even lack sufficient earth in which to bury their dead. In rare favored spots near a few of the houses blades of grass and a lone flower or two can be seen, but bushes and trees are entirely lacking. Even if soil were available, the constant exposure to cold, damp winds and the salt air and spray would retard plant growth. The Norwegians use a word meaning "sour" (*sur*) to describe the prevalent winds of such exposed areas.

The ubiquitous rock does have some utility, however. Cisterns hollowed out of solid rock are made alongside the houses for storage of rain water. The rocks also serve as surfaces on which salted codfish are spread and sundried to make the traditional Norwegian product, *klipfisk*, a type of codfish which Norway markets in large quantities in Portugal, Spain, Cuba, Mexico, Brazil, and Argentina.

Although the rocky island of Grip provides a solid foundation for the construction of houses, any site selected is precarious. Like a town of the Middle Ages the island's forty-five houses are huddled together on the slightly higher central portion for safety. The houses surround, and all but conceal, a small wooden red church dating back to 1580, which lies in the very center of the settlement. In addition to the services held by a Kristiansund pastor about every fifth Sunday, this little church is also a refuge for prayer and a protection for the islanders when severe storms or the monthly spring tides threaten to sweep their homes into the sea. This small island, rising only a few feet above sea level, is always at the mercy of stormy waters.

POPULATION OF GRIP BY OCCUPATIONAL GROUPS, DECEMBER 3, 1946[a]

Occupational Group	*No. of Persons*
Hunting and fishing	135
Industry and handicraft	24
Communication	23
Trade	11
Housework for wages	4
Public office and other professional work	2
Occupations not listed and other means of livelihood such as income from property, public care, and pension	25
TOTAL	224

[a] Data from preliminary unpublished statistics, 1946 Census, Statistisk Sentralbyraa, Oslo, 1948.

Living space on the island is at a premium. Its only thoroughfare is a narrow cement walk, almost too narrow for two people to pass, which winds among the houses.

Though the sea may at times be an enemy, it provides Grip with a livelihood. Slightly over 60 per cent of the inhabitants depend directly, and most of the remainder indirectly, upon fishing (see table). Fish, especially codfish and coalfish, are abundant and have been exploited for centuries. With the motorizing of the fishing fleet Grip has lost some of its former importance as a fishing station. The tiny artificial harbor accommodates only the smallest fishing vessels. All large vessels owned by Grip fishermen have to be kept in nearby Kristiansund. This situation will be somewhat alleviated by the state-financed project of deepening and improving the present harbor. Grip fishermen often are lured away from the home island for part of the year by fisheries in other areas, either operating their own boats or working as hands on those of others.

The people of Grip rely upon the outside world for all daily necessities other than fresh fish. All supplies, including building materials and fuel, are transported by ships from Kristiansund (Fig. 32). Groceries and tobacco may be obtained in a general store on the island, but most other articles, such as clothing, are purchased in Kristiansund by the inhabitants. One vessel plies between Kristiansund and Grip thrice weekly carrying passengers and a cargo. Because of the present shallowness of the harbor, it anchors a few hundred yards off the island and the passengers and cargo are transferred to small rowboats to complete the journey. In stormy weather the mission of the supply vessel is often frustrated by rough seas, which prevent the rowboats from traversing the last few hundred yards. With the completion of the harbor improvements the transportation service will be much more reliable and efficient.

With such infrequent contact with the outside world the residents of Grip naturally lead a simple life. Social and religious activity centers in the one Lutheran church, to which the majority of the people belong. Elementary education is available on the island, but for secondary and higher education the student must go to Kristiansund or even farther. Those in need of medical care must either travel to Kristiansund or call a doctor from there, since none live on the island. Postal and radiotelephone services are available. Dependence upon Kristiansund for all needs except the simple ones provided on the island is almost complete.

In such an inhospitable environment the inhabitants of Grip carry on their isolated existence. Despite the severe economic, social, and educational limitations, the people cling doggedly to their precarious rocky homeland. The Norwegian government has attempted to resettle the people in more favored areas, but these efforts have been in vain. Though some inhabitants have migrated to the mainland, the majority of the people are content to stay and battle the sea for their livelihood and for possession of their island. With such idomitable tenacity, it seems logical to predict that Grip will continue to be one of Norway's most densely populated skerries.

77. The Distribution of Rural Settlements *

As agriculture differs markedly from place to place, so also do the settlement forms established by the rural peoples of the world. Today, despite the great increase in urbanization during the last century, most of the people of the world live in rural areas. There is a basic correlation between the rural activity, chiefly agriculture, and the structure of the settlement, as Fawcett points out in this reading. Similar to urban settlements, some of the rural settlement forms have changed their function, but the continuity of settlement structure remains.

The International Geographical Union has had in being for the last twenty years an active committee on rural habitat, which has stimulated research in many countries. The results have appeared in its reports to the last five congresses, and in many journals. Those presented to the last two congresses occupy respectively 142 and 168 pages of the transactions of the section on human geography. Besides these numerous articles there is the volume 'L'habitat rural en Belgique' by Mlle M. A. Lefévre (1926), which is both a notable contribution to the study and a source of inspiration for many subsequent workers, and some earlier works, in particular that of Meitzen. At the Warsaw Congress, Z. Góralówna summarized a bibliography of works on rural habitat published up to the end of 1933; the total was then 748, and many more have appeared and been recorded, either in full, in abstract, or by reference, in the publications of the Congress or elsewhere. Of this total of about a thousand studies half have been made within the last twenty years, and the bibliography is probably not exhaustive.

The most widespread evidence of the human occupation of the earth is the modification of the surface of the land made by past and present generations of rural workers in agriculture, in pastoral husbandry, and in tree culture and exploitation for both fruits and forest products. The marks of these essentially rural occupations form by far the greater part of the cultural landscape of human geography, which man has superposed on the natural landscape of physical geography. More or less prominent among the visible and relatively permanent facts of the rural landscape are the building, or buildings, of the farmsteads, housing the population, forming

* C. B. Fawcett, "The Distribution of Rural Settlements," *Geographical Journal,* 1939, pp. 152–155. By permission of the *Geographical Journal* of the Royal Geographical Society, London.

The late author was Professor of Geography at the University of London. He has published numerous articles on rural settlement and rural sociology and geography in Europe and Asia.

storeplaces for materials and tools, and often sheltering the animals. This rural habitat is much more than the residence of the farmer and his family; it is also a chief tool of his trade, which has been developed in relation to his work and adapted to the existing type of rural economy. Hence it and its distribution have been the principal topic of research. M. A. Demangeon, a leading worker in this field and an inspirer of many students, has termed this habitat "un outil adapté au travail du paysan." This concept had led to studies of the form and arrangement of the buildings as well as of their distribution; but the basic contributions are those which describe and map the actual distribution of the rural habitat in specific areas, and show that distribution both as a fact in itself and in its areal relations to other geographical facts, such as relief and altitude, water supply and drainage, soils and underlying rocks, dominant crops and types of cultivation, roads and other means of communication, density and distribution of population in the area, and, sometimes, political boundaries. In some cases it has been possible to do this for past periods, as in the mapping of the Doomsday Survey in England and of the prehistoric settlements in Sardinia. Though records of past distributions are almost always incomplete, where they are available it may be possible to trace some stages in the evolution of the rural settlement in the area.

In the actual distribution of rural habitat two characteristic types, with many intermediate stages, can be discerned. In many areas the habitats are all, or nearly all, grouped into compact villages or large hamlets; so that the rural settlement is concentrated or agglomerated. At the other extreme are areas in which the majority of the farmers or peasants dwell on their own lands, scattered over the township or commune. In such a township there may be no village, and only very few buildings clustered together where the church and school, the inn, and a general shop or store stand near a convenient road focus. This is the scattered or dispersed habitat. But these extreme types are rare to-day, and more commonly the township contains a village and a varying number of scattered habitations, some of which may be grouped into hamlets. In such an intermediate type of settlement the relative proportions of concentrated and dispersed population may vary widely. It may result from either a spread outwards over its area of colonists from the concentrated nucleus or the partial clustering round a central focus of a formerly scattered population. It could also result from the settlement of immigrants among an already established rural population. There is some evidence of all three of these developments.

In one of the earliest of the well-known works on this topic, Meitzen, as his title indicates, ascribed the different types of rural settlement, both in distribution of habitat and in characteristic plan of village, to racial or ethnic factors. He found Germanic, Keltic, and Slavic settlement types. Later work has completely destroyed this hypothetical explanation of the differences which exist. Scattered settlement, or dispersed habitat, is not confined to people of any one racial type; it is found among peoples of all the chief racial types known in Europe. It is clear that the plan of a village, or the distribution of farm lands and buildings, is not a function of race; nor are these things associated with linguistic distributions. Contrasting types are frequently to be found in the same country.

In semi-arid regions, as in southern Tunis, permanent settlement clearly depends on water supply; and the population generally dwells in compact villages or small towns whose site is determined by the accessibility of reliable supplies of water. But in humid lands it is usually possible for the peasant to obtain sufficient water for man and beast almost anywhere. Hence in lands of adequate rainfall the local water supply is not often the decisive fact in the siting of the habitations. It appears to be true that a large and well-distributed rainfall, as in Ireland and Brittany, is often associated with dispersed habitat; but the connection is probably through the type of rural economy rather than direct.

In areas where there is only a small proportion of cultivable land, chiefly in scattered patches, agricultural settlements are necessarily limited to the good lands, and are thus dispersed. This dispersion is characteristic of some mountainous lands, such as Norway and the Alps; and also of some morainic belts in drift-covered lowlands. Yet it seems that it is only in these marginal cases of poverty of water or of cultivable land that such purely natural factors are decisive in rural distributions. Over most of the inhabited lands rural distribution shows little or no direct dependence on such factors.

Instances of change of distribution in a given area are well established. Archaeological survey, based on air photography, has established the fact that there was a widespread agriculture on the chalklands of southern England, probably lasting from late Neolithic to early Iron Age times, which divided the land into compact enclosed fields. But the agricultural land of medieval England was worked on the openfield system, in which the land of a village was held in common and the arable was redistributed among the peasants at short intervals, usually annually, while the whole was used as common pasture from harvest to spring. The openfield was associated with concentrated habitat, for the peasants lived in a compact village. These openfields disappeared in the enclosures from the sixteenth to the nineteenth centuries, and the rural landscape changed to our present familiar one of compact fields enclosed by hedges and hedgerow trees, with scattered farmsteads, each in its own land. This is in its turn now giving way in some areas to a more open scene of large fields, suitable to mechanized agriculture; and there the traditional character of our landscape of the last two or three centuries is again disappearing.

Similar changes have taken place in northern France and parts of central Europe. But it seems significant that in France the openfield system, with its strip cultivation and common pasture, did not become so dominant in the southern and western parts of the country. It is suggested that the difference may have been due largely to simpler cereal cultivation—a rotation of wheat, barley or oats, and fallow—combined with pastoral husbandry, in these lands during the Middle Ages. In the south tree culture was much more prominent in the ordinary rural work; in particular the edible chestnut supplied a large part of the food of both men and animals; and tree culture is not easily adaptable to a frequent redistribution of the cultivated land. A dependence on long-lived plants is usually associated with a system of permanent holdings.

The choice of annuals or perennials as the staple crops of cultivation is undoubtedly influenced by climatic facts which limit the possible range of any plant. It is also affected by the degree of social security, and by the level of skill in agriculture. In turn the dominant crop influences the work and organization of the people and their land tenure, and so the form and distribution of the rural habitat. The destruction of a crop of wheat affects only one season; when the destroyer has passed the peasant can prepare for a harvest next year. But the destruction of an orchard or a chestnut grove cannot be repaired in less than ten or twenty years, or of an olive grove in fifty. Hence one effect of a period of insecurity, such as that which followed on the collapse of the Roman Empire, was to increase the area and importance of the annual plants on which the relatively simple economy of the openfield system depended, at the expense of the more varied and elaborate cultivation of a wider ange of plants. The change led to an impoverishment of the regions, with a decline in the numbers and prosperity of their peoples. The openfield system also facilitated the grouping of the rural population into compact villages, where they were more fully under the control of the lord to whom they looked for protection. It is probable that the openfield system, with its scattered strip cultivation and periodic redistribution of the arable land among the peasants, its common pasture, and its concentrated habitat, which long dominated, and still influences, the pattern of rural settlement over much of Europe, is the product of a particular type of social organization and its associated rural economy rather of any specific racial or physical facts.

An article on Sardinia, by M. Lannou, records a very marked change in that island from the dispersed settlement of later prehistoric time—from five thousand to six thousand such settlements are known from existing remains of their stone buildings, the *nuraghi*—to the concentrated habitat of the present day, with only some 350 compact and generally large villages. In the period from the fall of Rome to the thirteenth century there was here a system of communal agriculture with compulsory rotations, like that of the openfield system of Europe north of the Alps; though such a system is not well suited to the more characteristic crops of a Mediterranean climate. For many centuries the search for security was the dominating fact in the life of the people, and it determined their modes of habitat, of land distribution, and of agriculture.

In North America the settlement of the lands west of the Appalachians in the later decades of the nineteenth century was mostly carried out under the homestead system, which virtually imposed the dispersed type of habitat, since each homesteader must build on his farm. But in Latin America the hacienda is often a compact settlement where all the workers of a large estate, comparable with a township, live near to one another. Here a different social system and different land laws have produced the alternative concentrated rural habitat.

Several writers draw attention to a widespread tendency towards the loosening out of the compact settlement. This is often associated with the distribution of the cultivated land into many small parcels, either held permanently or redistributed at every year or few years. Such a fragmentation of the land is wasteful in many ways. It still exists in many parts of Europe; but most European Governments have, during the present century, pursued a policy of consolidation of such scattered holdings. The expropriation of great landlords and the distribution of the land among the peasants, which followed the establishment of new States east of the Baltic and the break-up of the Austrian Empire, were accompanied by such a consolidation; so that the peasant ceased to be a tenant cultivating several fragments and became the owner of a small compact farm. In such cases there has been a gradual move towards dispersed settlement. On the other hand the extreme dispersion of habitat on the prairies of North America has caused a lack of centres of social life and organization which has led to a movement for the development of community centres there, often focusing round the school, an indication of a slight reversal of the trend towards extreme dispersion.

Some explanation suggested (*e.g.* by Meitzen) on the base of a narrower range of studies and *a priori* reasoning have been proved wide of the truth by the work of these later investigators. As the result of their studies it may be said that while physical facts, such as those of climate, relief, and soil, set limits to the extension and character of the rural landscape, these limits are usually wide; and within them the differences are determined by man himself. Within the limits of the physically possible the type and distribution of habitat is mainly dependent on the type of rural economy and the stage of its development.

---

78. *The Indian Village* *

Whereas towns and cities are characteristic of the United States, more than 80 per cent of the population of India lives in farm villages with less than 5000 inhabitants, and most of the people are in much smaller settlements. Yet this is one of the most densely populated areas of the world, a land overpopulated and existing at a level of subsistence below the comprehension of most Americans. The student should bear in mind, as he reads this selection, that the composite picture of Indian villages presented here is characteristic of the living conditions and surroundings of nearly a half-billion people. This fact is not particularly pleasant to contemplate, but it must be considered, for this kind of living aggravates the tensions between peoples and nations in the world today.

The Village in General

The phrase "a land of villages," so frequently applied to India, is true but pointless; any mainly agrarian country is a land of villages. There is some point, however, in noting the actual size of population units. Of the 658,595 inhabited localities of India in 1941, some 654,000 had under 5,000 people and no fewer than 450,902 under 500. Settlements of under 5,000 held 315,000,000 souls—80% of the total population.

The great majority of the country folk, then, live in small or large nucleated settlements, and areas of dispersed habitations are few: the Himalayan zone, and by no means all of that, is perhaps the only extensive area where there is much true dispersal of the type found in European highlands. But elsewhere in the hills, and in many parts of the Himalayas themselves, the unit is the small hamlet rather than the homestead.

In the arid west this is enforced partly by the paucity of waterpoints, partly

* O. H. K. Spate, with a contribution by C. D. Deshpande, "The Indian Village," *Geography*, Vol. 37 (1952), pp. 142–152. This material also appears in O. H. K. Spate, *India and Pakistan: A General and Regional Geography* (London and New York: Methuen and Dutton, 1954), pp. 171–181. Reprinted by permission of Methuen and Co. Ltd., London.

O. H. K. Spate (1911) is Professor of Geography at the Australian National University. His work has been largely on population problems and settlement forms in southeast Asia and the Pacific area.

C. D. Deshpande (1912) is Professor of Geography, Karnataka University, India.

by the needs of defence—needs still visibly attested by the watch-towers of Pathan villages. Among the tribes of the Assam-Burma border defence is also an important factor; villages are on hilltops or spurs, often stockaded; but it must be remembered also that the valleys of the wet jungly hills are extremely malarial, and that communication is easiest along the relatively open ridgeways.

Bengal—especially the eastern delta—is *sui generis:* there is, indeed, much setlement that is not nucleated, but "dispersal" seems an exceedingly inappropriate term for the dense stipple of separate homesteads, hardly isolated except in the most literal sense of the word when, during the rains, each is an island on its little earthen plinth, which in turn has been built up from the individual tank. From the air this is a landscape of the most delicate beauty, compounded of all shades of green from the almost luminescent young paddy to the dark mangoes, and diversified by the clumps of bamboo clustered round the tanks.

Other areas of more or less dispersed settlement are those of recent or temporary reclamation, by squatters in the Assam jungle—the last reasonably easy farming frontier of India, or by farmers in the great floodplains where they use the rich *khadar* (newer alluvium) for high-value crops after the rains. But in both groups the very small hamlet of, say, six to twelve huts is the rule, rather than true dispersal, and in the second case the huts are often only temporary; inhabited during the dry weather by people normally residing in big villages on the bluffs above.

These, however, are anomalies: in the great homogeneous plains nucleation is almost invariable, and the spacing of settlements remarkably uniform; there are large areas where Christaller's hexagons fit to perfection. In the past defence played its part in enforcing close grouping, and in areas which were open to almost constant warfare (e.g. the Sutlej-Jumna and Jumna-Ganges doabs, Rohilkhand, the fringes of central India, the Raichur [Kistna-Tungabhadra] doab) villages are often grouped around a petty fort; even to-day the close-packed houses, with blank outer walls and low doorways, massed into a ring with few entrances, present a markedly defensive aspect. Often there is not much in the way of site selection; one place is as good as another, and the village rises are as often as not their own creation, the rubbish of generations. But any discontinuity, any break in the almost imperceptible slope, produces linear settlement patterns; especially notable are the bluffs above floodplains and the margins of abandoned river-courses. Bluff villages tend to be larger than those on the drier interfluves; they have the advantage of two types of terrain, the upland doab and the valley-bottom with the excellent silts of its *chars* or *diaras*—the floodplain islands—submerged in the rains and liable to disappear completely during floods, but always cropping up again sooner or later. Cultivation here is risky but rewarding; these alluviated areas are often given over to cash crops of high value, and near large towns to market gardens easily irrigated from wells in the high water-table.

Settlement lines tend to occur also at the marked break of slope where steep residual hills grade into a fan, which has usually a fairly high water-table and is possibly enriched by soil-wash. There are suggestions of a similar line along the flanks of the Salt Range. Lateritic shelves along deltaic margins are also important building sites, poor land in themselves but offering rough grazing and scrubby woodland (supplier of a great range of minor needs from timber and thatch to illicit alcohol), and providing space for dry crops, the flats below being entirely under paddy. These shelves form, as it were, neutral ground between the jungly hills and the water-logged paddy plain. Here not only the general arrangement of settlements but the village itself in markedly linear; islands of lateritic and older alluvium in the deltas are often completely ringed with houses. Linear settlement is also, of course, prominent in the deltas and wider flood-plains themselves, strung out along embankments or natural levées, and in places (e.g. Malabar and the Contai area of south-west Bengal) along old beach-ridges. Very often such sites are the only dry-points in the rains and the only water-points in the hot weather.

There is in general very little that looks like a "plan," other than that dictated by such site factors as alignment along bluffs or levées grouping around a fort or tank; but within the seemingly chaotic agglomeration there is, as a rule, a strong internal differentiation, that of the separate quarters for the various castes. An exception to the lack of planning is afforded by the strictly rectangular villages of the Punjab Canal Colonies, reminiscent of a Roman *castrum* and a complete contrast to the villages of the older-settled strip along the great piedmont route of the northern Punjab. Here, as Darling remarks, is the real India, "hot and prickly but above all warm-hearted"; the Canal villages are alien and severe in many cases, officially numbered, not named. But even in the Colonies untidiness creeps in.

A Village in Detail

These points are best brought out by a close view of a specific village, not indeed "typical" (no single village could be that) but certainly the most random of samples. Our exemplar is from the Deccan, more precisely the Bombay Karnatak.

Aminbhavi lies seven miles north-northeast of Dharwar, an old settlement, going back at least 13 centuries, originally walled and moated. Essentially its site is governed by the junction of the Dharwar rocks, forming poor red soils around the mosque-crowned hill to the west, with the crystallines which have weathered into a deep black cotton soil to the east. It is a typical agricultural village on the black soils, with a rainfall of about 24 inches, devoted mainly to dry crops (cotton, jowar, wheat, pulses, safflower, in that order); it is tending to become a satellite of Dharwar, the market for its dairy and agricultural produce. On the poorer land to the west is rough grazing, supporting a few shepherds, and immediately west of the village is the common or *gauthana,* an essential part of its economy, the centre of all harvesting.

Caste and community largely govern the lay-out. Of its 4,106 inhabitants, Lingayats, the sturdy agricultural caste of the Karnatak, number some 2,650. Next come 550 Muslims, an unusually high proportion, but the place was of some importance in the days of the Sultans of Bijapur (16th–17th centuries) and the first element of its name is indeed that of some forgotten Muslim notable (Aminbhavi = roughly Amin's Well). But the culturally dominant groups are the Jains (250) and the Brahmins (75). This is an *Inam* (landlord) village, most of it belonging to the Desai (Jain) and Deshpande (Brahmin) families, whose *wadas* (more or less equivalent to manor houses) stand within large compounds on the best sites. The Desais provide the *patel* or village headman. For the rest, each caste tends to occupy a solid block of contiguous houses in a lane named from the caste; where, as with the Lingayats, several lanes are occupied, each is named from the leading family residing in it. Besides the groups mentioned, there are 300 Talwars (domestic servants and agricultural labourers), 200 Harijans ("untouchables"), and smaller groups of other low castes—Wadars (quarrymen), Shikalgars (backward semi-nomadic casual labourers), washermen, and so on. These groups live on the circumference of the village, or even beyond the old moat.

Occupations likewise are still mainly on a caste basis: the Lingayats provide the bulk of the tenant-farmers, Talwars and Harijans landless agricultural labour; carpenters, smiths, cobblers, washermen, barbers are all separate castes. Apart from these crafts and agriculture, there is some handloom cotton weaving, a subsidiary occupation of the Lingayats.

Except among the Jains and Brahmins, houses are generally built on to each other, or at least the mud walls of the compounds are continuous. The house lay-out is as standard as in any English working-class street. In front is a verandah or open porch (*katte*), used for drying agricultural produce, as a formal reception "room," as "a place of female gossip when the master of the house is out," and above all as a sleeping place in the stifling summer nights. Behind this is the main room, some 25 feet square, part of which is a cattle pen at threshold level; the remainder, raised some two or three feet, is the general living-room, for sleeping, eating, more intimate entertainment of guests, and perhaps for handicrafts. The most prominent object is the pile of grain stored in gunny bags, sadly depleted towards the end of the agricultural year. Behind is a separate kitchen (with a corner for the bath) and the backyard with a manure-pit and straw-stacks. This is the standard pattern; construction is similar in all groups (except the lowest), differences in economic status being reflected merely in size, except that the well-to-do have more separate single-purpose rooms. The Jains and Brahmins do not live so tightly-packed as the rest, either in the spacing of their houses or within them.

The poorest castes live in wretched one-room mud or wattle-and-daub huts with thatched roofs. Apart from these all houses have walls of mud-brick, one or two feet thick with few (and high) or, more likely, no windows: Indians in general have a doubtless well-founded burglar-phobia. The flat roof is supported by wooden posts and made of mud on a frame-work of crude beams and babul (acacia) branches; it has rounded mud parapets and clay pipes to take off rain-water.

As for services, these are mostly grouped around the main village lane: marketplace for the weekly bazaar, eight shops (four grocery, two cloth, one tailor, one miscellaneous) and a number of booths selling tea and *bidis,* the cheap crude "cigarettes" of the Indian masses. Near the marketplace is the village *panchayat* or caste council, an ancient institution which fell into desuetude under the impact of the tightly-organised British bureaucracy, but now being fostered as the first step in local self-government. Associated with this tiny "urban core" are the government establishments—police station, post office, grain warehouse. There are three mosques, one giving its name to the Idgah Hill west of the village, and eight temples, including that of the Deshpandes, as well as the Lingayat *math,* a centre of religious fellowship and charitable assistance to castemen. The professions are represented by an Ayurvedic (indigenous) dispensary, an Urdu school for the Muslims, and separate schools for boys and girls. The boys' school is the most modern building in Aminbhavi, its stone walls and red-tiled roof standing in sharp contrast to the monotony of mud walls. There are also, of course, the ubiquitous *banias*—traders, grainbrokers, and money-lenders.

Finally we may note the large masonry-lined public well, now open to Harijans; it is no mean excavation, an apt reminder of the all-importance of water-supply in Indian life.

Once more, no one village can be typical of the whole sub-continent; but many of the features detailed above can be paralleled over and over again in most parts of India. Our random sample is at least very representative.

The Village: Its Aspect and Life

The aspect of the village varies not only with the general regional setting, with building materials and house-types, but with social factors. In southern India, the generally greater emphasis on caste takes social fragmentation allied with spatial separation to the extreme, segregating the untouchables in outlying *cheris* or sub-villages, sometimes located several hundred yards from the main villages of which they are service-components. This is indeed the climax of geographical differentiation: *apartheid*. A typical *cheri* may consist of two rows of huts with a narrow central street; in the middle this widens to make room for a tiny temple.* The huts have thick mud walls, roofed with palmyra thatch, and low mud porches scrupulously swept. To enter, one must bend double; the only light comes from the door and from under the eaves, and the furniture consists of a few pots and pans, a couple of wooden chests, and the essential paddy-bin, four to six feet high and three to four in diameter, built up of hoops of mud and raised from the ground to escape the rats. Poor as they are, these dwellings are yet homes, and obviously loved as such: their cleanliness, the surrounding mangoes, coconut and palmyra palms, redeem them from utter squalor. The naidir is reached in the *bustees* of Calcutta—shacks jammed so close together that the internal structure of a *bustee* area can only be photographed when half of it has been burnt in a communal riot—and in the revolting camps of casual tribal labourers on the outskirts of the larger towns: shelters (they cannot be called even huts) of matting, of rags, of petrol tins beaten flat, on waste spaces open to the sun and reeking with filth.

A geographical study of Indian house-types would be a work vast in scope and rich in instruction. Social factors are no less important than environmental, at least once we go beyond the fundamental antithesis between the south-west Asian flat-roofed type found in the dry north-west and the thatched gables of the more humid areas, and beyond the elementary dictates of availability of stone, wood, brick, or mud. Not only the site and lay-out of the village, but "the geography of the house" often reflects age-old religious and magical traditions: the round Telugu huts, with bold vertical stripes of white and rusty red, are clearly culturally rather than geographically influenced. At the other extreme from the rude massive stone huts of Bundelkhand we have the elaborate courtyard house of the richer farmer of Uttar Pradesh (United Provinces), with some pretensions to elegance—the survival of decayed traditions—in doorways and arcading. Some Indian domestic building indeed reaches a very high standard of artistry:

* Often put up by the pre-war Congress provincial governments as a concession; in 1943 one such had been decorated by the children with ARP signs.

the carved timber of the Kumaoni Himalayas or of the small towns of the Konkan, the restrained but excellent brick details and the very pleasant white bungalow-type houses, with low gables of semi-cylindrical tiles, found in the Maratha country.

Environmental influences are well seen in the flat-roofed blank-walled boxes standard in the Punjab and western Uttar Pradesh; thick-walled and dark, designed to trap and keep what coolness is possible. These are strongly reminiscent of arid south-west Asia, and fit well into the four-square planned villages of the Canal Colonies. Against these may be set the Bengal house, walled with bamboo matting, which lets plenty of draught through in the hot weather and in the rains swells to stop up the cracks; the thatched gables are pitched high to shed the rain, and ingeniously designed to take the strain of cyclonic gales, while in well-to-do houses the gable may be in two stages with a clear space between. Such construction is admirably suited to hot humid conditions; for mere comfort (neglecting the obvious risks of vermin and fire) the writer would sooner live in a "bamboo basha" than in a European-style bungalow any day, though better than either are the few survivals of old Portuguese building, with stone walls two to four feet thick and cool marble floors.

In Madras "we see flat-roofed stone houses in the Ceded Districts (Deccan), so constructed as to protect the dwellers from the severe heat of the sun, the rocks and slabs locally available being used. In contrast we find in Malabar timber entering into the construction. Here the buildings are on high ground and have sloping roofs, both necessitated by the high rainfall . . . In the Tamilnad we have tiled brick houses with open courtyards, reflecting an equable climate and moderate rainfall." It must be added that corrugated iron spreads wherever there is easy access to a railway; it has the great merits of being fire-proof and being less fostering to vermin than is thatch, but is about as unsuited to the climate as it is possible to be. Its use is largely a matter of prestige, a symbol of wealth; in some areas a good compromise between the climatic comfort of thatch and the lessened fire-risk is obtained by putting a roof of corrugated iron or of tiles over thatch.

As for what life in the Indian village is really like, who knows save the Indian villager?—a few officials like M. L. Darling, whose Punjab rural rides compare with Cobbett's, a few devoted social workers, Indian and European, Christian and otherwise. But even then there is the difference between living in the village from cradle to grave and living in the village with one's territorial—and social and psychological—base outside. The alien may perhaps glean something from that rich harvest of salty rural proverbs (a comparative regional anthology of them would be fascinating) which are as vital a part of India's cultural heritage as the lyrical and metaphysical visions of her sages. Not that this latter strain of culture is wanting from the village: the great epics *Ramayana* and *Mahabharata* pass from lip to lip in folk-versions: to some extent at least every man is still his own poet, improvising as he walks to his work or sits in the cool of the evening; and not a few of the noblest figures in India's predominantly devotional literature have sprung from the villages rather than the schools—Kabir the Weaver, Tukaram. It is significant that the Communist Party has found its most effective translation of its modernising propaganda in the traditional media of song and dance. The things that strike the outsider, then, are perhaps not ultimately the most important: the flies and the sores, the shrill clamour of gaunt pi-dogs, the primitive implements, the utter lack of sanitation.

At its worst the Indian village is infinitely depressing: in the great alluvial plains where so much ground is cultivated that the scanty village site cannot grow with its growing population, or where a few miserable huts cling to shadeless stony rises in the drier parts of central India or the Archaean Deccan. Yet cheerfulness keeps breaking in, despite the most adverse circumstances; fatalist as he is and must be, the peasant often displays an astonishing resilience, and some particularly hard-pressed areas apart, refuses to be broken by his often bitterly hard physical and social environment. And over much of the land the villages have their amenities, their beauties even: in the plains and deltas they rise out of the sea of arable, emerald or gold or drab stubble-grey according to season, like dark green islands, shaded in mango or orange trees, tamarinds, bamboos, palms. The tank or the well, the shade of the great banyan or the porch of the headman's hut, are essentially free clubs for the women and the menfolk respectively.

Though the substratum of life—the gruelling round of the seasons—remains and will ever remain the same, though a miserable livelihood exacts an exhorbitant price in endless toil, there have been great changes since Edwin Montagu, Secretary of State for India in 1917–19, spoke of the "pathetic contentment" of the Indian village. Pathetic it still too often is; contented, less and less; which is as it should be. "These idyllic village communities confined the human mind within the narrowest possible compass." This is overstated; there *were* the epics and the proverbs; but the horizons were far too narrow for a full life. Now new motifs are changing the tempo of life in the larger villages; perhaps a communal radio, perhaps a mobile film unit, more and more frequently a school. The mass movements launched by Congress were not always amenable to a thus-far-and-no-farther policy; the peasant had other enemies than British imperialism, and Congress taught him organisation: it is no great step from a no-tax to a no-rent movement. Then, as in Tsarist Russia and in

Africa or New Guinea to-day, there are those powerful catalysts of social change, the factory worker retaining his links with the village, the soldier from the wars returning. All are helping to break down the isolation and the lack of information which rendered the villager so helpless a prey to the moneylender, the shopkeeper, and the grainbroker—often all three being one and the same person. Perhaps the most powerful agent of change is the battered ramshackle motor-bus, packed to the running-board and coughing its way through clouds of dust along the unmetalled roads to the nearest town.

There may be, there probably is, loss as well as gain in all this. But it is idle to bewail the break-up of integrated codes of life—codes too often integrated by religious, social, and economic sanctions which were a complete denial of human dignity. In any case the disintegration set in long ago, with the advent of the new all-embracing (and to the peasant generally restrictive) administrative standards of the British Raj and with the impact of the world market.* It is high time that new horizons should be opened, that the villager should see whence the forces that have subverted his old life have their origins, and what of good they may bring.

* "These small stereotype forms of organisation . . . are disappearing, not so much through the brutal interference of the British tax-gatherer and the British soldier, as the working of English steam and English free trade." K. Marx, *loc. cit.* This brilliant analysis—the whole is well worth reading—was written just over a century ago (1853).

CHAPTER ELEVEN

Political Geography and Geopolitics

"MAN IS NOT born free, he is born national." The national state system as it exists throughout the world is one of the great geographic realities. The state occupies space—usually carefully defined and protected space—on the surface of the earth. Nearly all of the wars of the last centuries have had as underlying causes differences between national states. These differences were not only in physical characteristics such as size and resources, or in population, but were also differences in attitudes, ideologies, and desires. A study of the differences that exist both within a national state and between national states constitute the core of political geography and its somewhat more dynamic associate, geopolitics.

"Political Geography views the state from the standpoint of space, while Geopolitics views space from the standpoint of the state." While controversy may continue about the works of the writer of these words, Major General Doktor Professor Karl Haushofer, who subverted scholarship and fact to Nazi party ideology, his statement defines precisely the nature and limits of these subjects.

Most introductory geography textbooks do not include material on political geography. For this reason only three selections are included here. In a world deeply torn by conflict between nations it is essential that every student and every citizen become acquainted with the geographic realities underlying the affairs of nations.

---

79. The Geographical Pivot of History *

Although this article was first published in 1904, it remains of great interest and significance, because it embodies one of the twentieth century's most thought-provoking views of the world—a view that has exercised profound influence on foreign affairs and on history. In this article, Mackinder shattered the old comfortable picture of the relations of the continents as well as complacent notions of the relations of sea power and land power. His British countrymen paid little heed, but German strategists pondered carefully what he had disclosed, and Hitler came close to bringing sea power to destruction by capturing the land bases on which it rested. Despite the use of the third dimension of space through air power, statesmen, generals, seamen, and airmen everywhere today see the round world through Mackinder's eyes. They also see the Soviet Union in control of what he describes as the "Heartland."

When historians in the remote future come to look back on the group of centuries through which we are now passing, and see them foreshortened, as we to-day see the Egyptian dynasties, it may well be that they will describe the last 400 years as the Columbian epoch, and will say that it ended soon after the year 1900. Of late it has been a commonplace to speak of geographical exploration as nearly over, and it is recognized that geography must be diverted to the purpose of intensive survey and philosophic synthesis. In 400 years the outline of the map of the world has been completed with approximate accuracy, and even in the polar regions the voyages of Nansen and Scott have very narrowly reduced the last possibility of dramatic discoveries. But the opening of the twentieth century is appropriate as the end of a great historic epoch, not merely on account of this achievement, great though it be. The missionary, the conqueror, the farmer, the miner, and, of late, the engineer, have followed so closely in the traveller's footsteps that the world, in its remoter borders, has hardly been revealed before we must chronicle its virtually complete political appropriation. In Europe, North America, South America, Africa, and Australasia there is scarcely a region left for the pegging out of a claim of owner-

* Halford J. Mackinder, "The Geographical Pivot of History," *Geographical Journal,* Vol. 23, 1904, pp. 421 ff. By permission of the *Geographical Journal* of the Royal Geographical Society, London.

The author (1861–1947) has probably had a more far-reaching influence than any other geographer. Two of his books, *Britain and the British Seas* and *Democratic Ideals and Reality* are classics of regional and political geography.

ship, unless as the result of a war between civilized or half-civilized powers. Even in Asia we are probably witnessing the last moves of the game first played by the horsemen of Yermak the Cossack and the shipmen of Vasco da Gama. Broadly speaking, we may contrast the Columbian epoch with the age which preceded it, by describing its essential characteristic as the expansion of Europe against almost negligible resistances, whereas mediæval Christendom was pent into a narrow region and threatened by external barbarism. From the present time forth, in the post-Columbian age, we shall again have to deal with a closed political system, and none the less that it will be one of world-wide scope. Every explosion of social forces, instead of being dissipated in a surrounding circuit of unknown space and barbaric chaos, will be sharply re-echoed from the far side of the globe, and weak elements in the political and economic organism of the world will be shattered in consequence. There is a vast difference of effect in the fall of a shell into an earthwork and its fall amid the closed spaces and rigid structures of a great building or ship. Probably some half-consciousness of this fact is at last diverting much of the attention of statesmen in all parts of the world from territorial expansion to the struggle for relative efficiency.

In appears to me, therefore, that in the present decade we are for the first time in a position to attempt, with some degree of completeness, a correlation between the larger geographical and the larger historical generalizations. For the first time we can perceive something of the real proportion of features and events on the stage of the whole world, and may seek a formula which shall express certain aspects, at any rate, of geographical causation in universal history. If we are fortunate, that formula should have a practical value as setting into perspective some of the competing forces in current international politics. The familiar phrase about the westward march of empire is an empirical and fragmentary attempt of the kind. I propose this evening describing those physical features of the world which I believe to have been most coercive of human action, and presenting some of the chief phases of history as organically connected with them, even in the ages when they were unknown to geography. My aim will not be to discuss the influence of this or that kind of feature, or yet to make a study in regional geography, but rather to exhibit human history as part of the life of the world organism. I recognize that I can only arrive at one aspect of the truth, and I have no wish to stray into excessive materialism. Man and not nature initiates, but nature in large measure controls. My concern is with the general physical control, rather than the causes of universal history. It is obvious that only a first approximation to truth can be hoped for. I shall be humble to my critics.

. . . . .

The most remarkable contrast in the political map of modern Europe is that presented by the vast area of Russia occupying half the Continent and the group of smaller territories tenanted by the Western Powers. From a physical point of view, there is, of course, a like contrast between the unbroken lowland of the east and the rich complex of mountains and valleys, islands and peninsulas, which together form the remainder of this part of the world. At first sight it would appear that in these familiar facts we have a correlation between natural environment and political organization so obvious as hardly to be worthy of description, especially when we note that throughout the Russian plain a cold winter is opposed to a hot summer, and the conditions of human existence thus rendered additionally uniform. . . . As a consequence of this climatic *régime,* the north and north-west were forest broken only by marshes, whereas the south and south-east were a boundless grassy steppe, with trees only along the rivers. The line separating the two regions ran diagonally north-eastward from the northern end of the Carpathians to a point in the Ural range nearer to its southern than to its northern extremity. Moscow lies a little to north of this line, or, in other words, on the forest side of it. Outside Russia the boundary of the great forest ran westward almost exactly through the centre of the European isthmus, which is 800 miles across between the Baltic and the Black seas. Beyond this, in Peninsular Europe, the woods spread on through the plains of Germany in the north, while the steppe lands in the south turned the great Transylvanian bastion of the Carpathians, and extended up the Danube, through what are now the cornfields of Roumania, to the Iron Gates. A detached area of steppes, known locally as Pusstas, now largely cultivated, occupied the plain of Hungary, ingirt by the forested rim of Carpathian and Alpine mountains. In all the west of Russia, save in the far north, the clearing of the forests, the drainage of the marshes, and the tillage of the steppes have recently averaged the character of the landscape, and in large measure obliterated a distinction which was formerly very coercive of humanity.

The earlier Russia and Poland were established wholly in the glades of the forest. Through the steppe on the other hand there came from the unknown recesses of Asia, by the gateway between the Ural mountains and the Caspian sea, in all the centuries from the fifth to the sixteenth, a remarkable succession of Turanian nomadic peoples—Huns, Avars, Bulgarians, Magyars, Khazars, Patzinaks, Cumans, Mongols, Kalmuks. Under Attila the Huns established themselves in the midst of the Pusstas, in the uttermost Danubian outlier of the steppes, and thence dealt blows northward, westward, and southward against the settled peoples of Europe. A large part of modern history might be written as a commentary upon the changes directly or indirectly ensuing from these raids. The Angles and Saxons, it is quite possible, were then driven to cross the seas to found England in Britain. The Franks, the Goths, and the Roman provincials were compelled, for the first time, to stand shoulder to shoulder on the battlefield of Chalons, making common cause against the Asiatics, who were unconsciously welding together modern France. Venice was founded from the destruction of Aquileia and Padua; and even the Papacy owed a decisive prestige to the successful mediation of Pope Leo with Attila at Milan. Such was the harvest of results produced by a cloud of ruthless and idealess horsemen sweeping over the unimpeded plain—a blow, as it were, from the great Asiatic hammer striking freely through the vacant space. The Huns were followed by the Avars. It was for a marchland against these that Austria was founded, and Vienna fortified, as the result of the campaigns of Charlemagne. The Magyar came next, and by incessant raiding from his steppe base in Hungary increased the significance of the Austrian outpost, so drawing the political focus of Germany eastward to the margin of the realm. The Bulgarian established a ruling caste south of the Danube, and has left his name upon the map, although his language has yielded to that of his Slavonic subjects. Perhaps the longest and most effective occupation of the Russian steppe proper was that of the Khazars, who were contemporaries of the great Saracen movement: the Arab geographers knew the Caspian as the Khazar sea. In the end, however, new hordes arrived from Mongolia, and for two centuries Russia in the northern forest was held tributary to the Mongol Khans of Kipchak, or "the Steppe," and Russian development was thus delayed and biassed at a time when the remainder of Europe was rapidly advancing.

It should be noted that the rivers running from the Forest to the Black and Caspian seas cross the whole breadth of the steppe-land path of the nomads, and that from time to time there were transient movements along their courses at right angles to the movement of the horsemen. Thus the missionaries of Greek Christianity ascended the Dnieper to Kief, just as beforehand the Norse Varangians had descended the same river on their way to Constantinople. Still earlier, the Teutonic Goths appear for a moment upon the Dniester, having crossed Europe from the shores of the Baltic in the same south-eastward direction. But these are passing episodes which do not invalidate the broader generalization. For a thousand years a series of horse-riding peoples emerged from Asia through the broad interval between the Ural mountains and the Caspian sea, rode through the open spaces of southern Russia, and struck home into Hungary in the very heart of the European peninsula, shaping by the necessity of opposing them the history of each of the great peoples around—the Russians, the Germans, the French, the Italians, and the Byzantine Greeks. That they stimulated healthy and powerful reaction, instead of crushing opposition under a widespread despotism, was due to the fact that the mobility of their power was conditioned by the steppes, and necessarily ceased in the surrounding forests and mountains.

A rival mobility of power was that of the Vikings in their boats. Descending from Scandinavia both upon the northern and the southern shores of Europe, they penetrated inland by the river ways. But the scope of their action was limited, for, broadly speaking, their power was effective only in the neighbourhood of the water. Thus the settled peoples of Europe lay gripped between two pressures—that of the Asiatic nomads from the east, and on the other three sides that of the pirates from the sea. From its very nature neither pressure was overwhelming, and both therefore were stimulative. It is noteworthy that the formative influence of the Scandinavians was second only in significance to that of the nomads, for under their attack both England and France made long moves towards unity, while the unity of Italy was broken by them. In earlier times, Rome had mobilized the power of her settled peoples by means of her roads, but the Roman roads had fallen into decay, and were not replaced until the eighteenth century.

• • • • •

The full meaning of the Asiatic influence upon Europe is not, however, discernible until we come to the Mongol invasions of the fifteenth century; but before we analyze the essential facts concerning these, it is desirable to shift our geographical view-point from Europe, so that we may consider the Old World in its entirety. It is obvious that, since the rainfall is derived from the sea, the heart of the greatest land-mass is likely to be relatively dry. We are not, therefore, surprised to find that two-thirds of all the world's population is concentrated in relatively small areas along the margins of the great continent—in Europe, beside the Atlantic ocean; in the Indies and China, beside the Indian and Pacific oceans. A vast belt of almost uninhabited, because practically rainless, land extends as the Sahara completely across Northern Africa into Arabia. Central and Southern Africa were almost as completely severed from Europe and Asia throughout the greater part of history as were the Americas and Australia. In fact, the southern boundary of Europe was and is the Sahara rather than the Mediterranean, for it is the desert which divides the black man from the white. The continuous land-mass of Euro-Asia thus included between the ocean and the desert measures 21,000,000 square miles, or half of all the land on the globe, if we exclude from reckoning the deserts of Sahara and Arabia. There are many detached deserts scattered through Asia, from Syria and Persia north-eastward to Manchuria, but no such continuous vacancy as to be comparable with the Sahara. On the other hand, Euro-Asia is characterized by a very remarkable distribution of river drainage. Throughout an immense portion of the centre and north, the rivers have been practically useless for purposes of human communication with the outer world. The Volga, the Oxus, and the Jaxartes drain into salt lakes; the Obi, the Yenesei, and the Lena into the frozen ocean of the north. These are six of the greatest rivers in the world. There are many smaller but still considerable streams in the same area, such as the Tarim and the Helmund, which similarly fail to reach the ocean. Thus the core of Euro-Asia, although mottled with desert patches, is on the whole a steppe-land supplying a wide-spread if often scanty pasture, and there are not a few river-fed oases in it, but it is wholly unpenetrated by waterways from the ocean. In other words, we have in this immense area all the conditions for the maintenance of a sparse, but in the aggregate considerable, population of horse-riding and camel-riding nomads. Their realm is limited northward by a broad belt of sub-arctic forest and marsh, wherein the climate is too rigorous, except at the eastern and western extremities, for the development of agricultural settlements. In the east the forests extend southward to the Pacific coast in the Amur land and Manchuria. Similarly in the west, in prehistoric Europe, forest was the predominant vegetation. Thus framed in to the north-east, north, and north-west, the steppes spread continuously for 4000 miles from the Pusstas of Hungary to the Little Gobi of Manchuria, and, except in their westernmost extremity, they are untraversed by rivers draining to an accessible ocean, for we may neglect the very recent efforts to trade to the mouths of the Obi and Yenisei. In Europe, Western Siberia, and Western Turkestan the steppe lands lie low, in some places below the level of the sea. Further to east, in Mongolia, they extend over plateaux; but the passage from the one level to the other, over the naked, unscarped lower ranges of the arid heart-land, presents little difficulty.

The hordes which ultimately fell upon Europe in the middle of the fourteenth century gathered their first force 3000 miles away on the high steppes of Mongolia. The havoc wrought for a few years in Poland, Silesia, Moravia, Hungary, Croatia, and Servia was, however, but the remotest and the most transient result of the great stirring of the nomads of the East associated with the name of Ghenghiz Khan. While the Golden Horde occupied the steppe of Kipchak, from the Sea of Aral, through the interval between the Ural range and the Caspian, to the foot of the Carpathians, another horde, descending south-westward between the Caspian sea and the Hindu Kush into Persia, Mesopotamia, and even into Syria, founded the domain of the Ilkhan. A third subsequently struck into Northern China, conquering Cathay. India and Mangi, or Southern China, were for a time sheltered by the incomparable barrier of Tibet, to whose efficacy there is, perhaps, nothing similar in the world, unless it be the Sahara desert and the polar ice. But at a later time, in the days of

Marco Polo in the case of Mangi, in those of Tamerlane in the case of India, the obstacle was circumvented. Thus it happened that in this typical and well-recorded instance, all the settled margins of the Old World sooner or later felt the expansive force of mobile power originating in the steppe. Russia, Persia, India, and China were either made tributary, or received Mongol dynasties. Even the incipient power of the Turks in Asia Minor was struck down for half a century.

. . . . .

The conception of Euro-Asia to which we thus attain is that of a continuous land, ice-girt in the north, water-girt elsewhere, measuring 21 million square miles, or more than three times the area of North America, whose centre and north, measuring some 9 million square miles, or more than twice the area of Europe, have no available water-ways to the ocean, but, on the other hand, except in the subarctic forest, are very generally favourable to the mobility of horsemen and camelmen. To east, south, and west of this heart-land are marginal regions, ranged in a vast crescent, accessible to shipmen. According to physical conformation, these regions are four in number, and it is not a little remarkable that in a general way they respectively coincide with the spheres of the four great religions—Buddhism, Brahminism, Mahometanism, and Christianity. The first two are the monsoon lands, turned the one towards the Pacific, and the other towards the Indian ocean. The fourth is Europe, watered by the Atlantic rains from the west. These three together, measuring less than 7 million square miles, have more than 1000 million people, or two-thirds of the world population. The third, coinciding with the land of the Five Seas, or, as it is more often described, the Nearer East, is in large measure deprived of moisture by the proximity of Africa, and except in the oases, is therefore thinly peopled. In some degree it partakes of the characteristics both of the marginal belt and of the central area of Euro-Asia. It is mainly devoid of forest, is patched with desert, and is therefore suitable for the operations of the nomad. Dominantly, however, it is marginal, for sea-gulfs and oceanic rivers lay it open to sea-power, and permit of the exercise of such power from it. As a consequence, periodically throughout history, we have here had empires belonging essentially to the marginal series, based on the agricultural populations of the great oases of Babylonia and Egypt, and in free water-communication with the civilized worlds of the Mediterranean and the Indies. But, as we should expect, these empires have been subject to an unparalleled series of revolutions, some due to Scythian, Turkish, and Mongol raids from Central Asia, others to the effort of the Mediterranean peoples to conquer the overland ways from the western to the eastern ocean. Here is the weakest spot in the girdle of early civilizations, for the isthmus of Suez divided sea-power into Eastern and Western, and the arid wastes of Persia advancing from Central Asia to the Persian gulf gave constant opportunity for nomad-power to strike home to the ocean edge, dividing India, and China on the one hand, from the Mediterranean world on the other. Whenever the Babylonian, the Syrian, and the Egyptian oases were weakly held, the steppe-peoples could treat the open tablelands of Iran and Asia Minor as forward posts whence to strike through the Punjab into India, through Syria into Egypt, and over the broken bridge of the Bosporus and Dardanelles into Hungary. Vienna stood in the gateway of Inner Europe, withstanding the nomadic raids, both those which came by the direct road through the Russian steppe, and those which came by the loop way to south of the Black and Caspian seas.

Here we have illustrated the essential difference between the Saracen and the Turkish controls of the Nearer East. The Saracens were a branch of the Semitic race, essentially peoples of the Euphrates and Nile and of the smaller oases of Lower Asia. They created a great empire by availing themselves of the mobilities permitted by their land—that of the horse and camel on the one hand, that of the ship on the other. At different times their fleets controlled both the Mediterranean as far as Spain, and the Indian ocean to the Malay islands. From their strategically central position between the eastern and western oceans, they attempted the conquest of all the marginal lands of the Old World, imitating Alexander and anticipating Napoleon. They could even threaten the steppe land. Wholly distinct from Arabia as from Europe, India, and China were the Turanian pagans from the closed heart of Asia, the Turks who destroyed the Saracen civilization.

Mobility upon the ocean is the natural rival of horse and camel mobility in the heart of the continent. It was upon navigation of oceanic rivers that was based the Potamic stage of civilization, that of China on the Yangtse, that of India on the Ganges, that of Babylonia on the Euphrates, that of Egypt on the Nile. It was essentially upon the navigation of the Mediterranean that was based what has been described as the Thalassic stage of civilization, that of the Greeks and Romans. The Saracens and the Vikings held sway by navigation of the oceanic coasts.

The all-important result of the discovery of the Cape road to the Indies was to connect the western and eastern coastal navigations of Euro-Asia, even though by a circuitous route, and thus in some measure to neutralize the strategical advantage of the central position of the steppe-nomads by pressing upon them in rear. The revolution commenced by the great mariners of the Columbian generation endowed Christendom with the widest possible mobility of power, short of a winged mobility. The one and continuous ocean enveloping the divided insular lands is, of course, the geographical condition of ultimate unity in the command of the sea, and of the whole theory of modern naval strategy and policy as expounded by such writers as Captain Mahan and Mr. Spencer Wilkinson. The broad political effect was to reverse the relations of Europe and Asia, for whereas in the Middle Ages Europe was caged between an impassable desert to south, an unknown ocean to west, and icy or forested wastes to north and north-east, and in the east and south-east was constantly threatened by the superior mobility of the horsemen and camelmen, she now emerged upon the world, multiplying more than thirty-fold the sea surface and coastal lands to which she had access, and wrapping her influence round the Euro-Asiatic land-power which had hitherto threatened her very existence. New Europes were created in the vacant lands discovered in the midst of the waters, and what Britain and Scandinavia were to Europe in the earlier time, that have America and Australia, and in some measure even Trans-Saharan Africa, now become to Euro-Asia. Britain, Canada, the United States, South Africa, Australia, and Japan are now a ring of outer and insular bases for sea-power and commerce, inaccessible to the land-power of Euro-Asia (Fig. 33).

But the land power still remains, and recent events have again increased its significance. While the maritime peoples of Western Europe have covered the ocean with their fleets, settled the outer continents, and in varying degree made tributary the oceanic margins of Asia, Russia has organized the Cossacks, and, emerging from her northern forests, has policed the steppe by setting her own nomads to meet the Tartar nomads. The Tudor century, which saw the expansion of Western Europe over the sea, also saw Russian power carried from Moscow through Siberia. The eastward swoop of the horsemen across Asia was an event almost as pregnant with political consequences as was the rounding of the Cape, although the two movements long remained apart.

It is probably one of the most striking coincidences of history that the seaward and the landward expansion of Europe should, in a sense, continue the ancient opposition between Roman and Greek. Few great failures have had more far-reaching consequences than the failure of Rome to Latinize the Greek. The Teuton was civilized and Christianized by the Roman, the Slav in the main by the Greek. It is the Romano-Teuton who in later times embarked upon the ocean; it was the Graeco-Slav who rode over the steppes, conquering the Turanian. Thus the modern land-power differs from the sea-power no less in the source of its ideals than in the material conditions of its mobility.

In the wake of the Cossack, Russia has safely emerged from her former seclusion in the northern forests. Perhaps the change of greatest intrinsic importance which took place in Europe in the last century was the southward migration of the Russian peasants, so that, whereas agricultural settlements formerly ended at the forest boundary, the centre of the population of all European Russia now lies to south of that boundary, in the midst of the wheat-fields which have replaced the more western steppes. Odessa has here risen to importance with the rapidity of an American city.

A generation ago steam and the Suez canal appeared to have increased the mobility of sea-power relatively to land-power. Railways acted chiefly as feeders to ocean-going commerce. But trans-continental railways are now transmuting the conditions of land-power, and nowhere can they have such effect as in the closed heart-land of Euro-Asia, in vast areas of which neither timber nor accessible stone was available for road-making. Railways work the greater wonders in the steppe, because they directly replace horse and camel mobility, the road stage of development having here been omitted.

. . . . .

The Russian railways have a clear run of 6000 miles from Wirballen in the west to Vladivostok in the east. The Russian army in Manchuria is as significant evidence of mobile land-power as the British army in South Africa was of sea-power. True, that the Trans-Siberian railway is still a single and precarious line of communication, but the century will not be old before all Asia is covered with railways. The spaces within the Russian Empire and Mongolia are so vast, and their potentialities in population, wheat, cotton, fuel, and metals so incalculably great, that it is inevitable that a vast economic world, more or less apart, will there develop inaccessible to oceanic commerce.

As we consider this rapid review of the broader currents of history, does not a certain persistence of geographical relationship become evident? Is not the pivot region of the world's politics that vast area of Euro-Asia which is inaccessible to ships, but in antiquity lay open to the horse-riding nomads, and is to-day about to be covered with a network of railways? There have been and are here the conditions of a mobility of military and economic power of a far-reaching and yet limited character. Russia replaces the Mongol Empire. Her pressure on Finland, on Scandinavia, on Poland, on Turkey, on Persia, on India, and on China, replaces the centrifugal raids of the steppemen. In the world at large she occupies the central strategical position held by Germany in Europe. She can strike on all sides and be struck from all sides, save the north. The full development of her modern railway mobility is merely a matter of time. Nor is it likely that any possible social revolution will alter her essential relations to the great geographical limits of her existence. Wisely recognizing the funda-

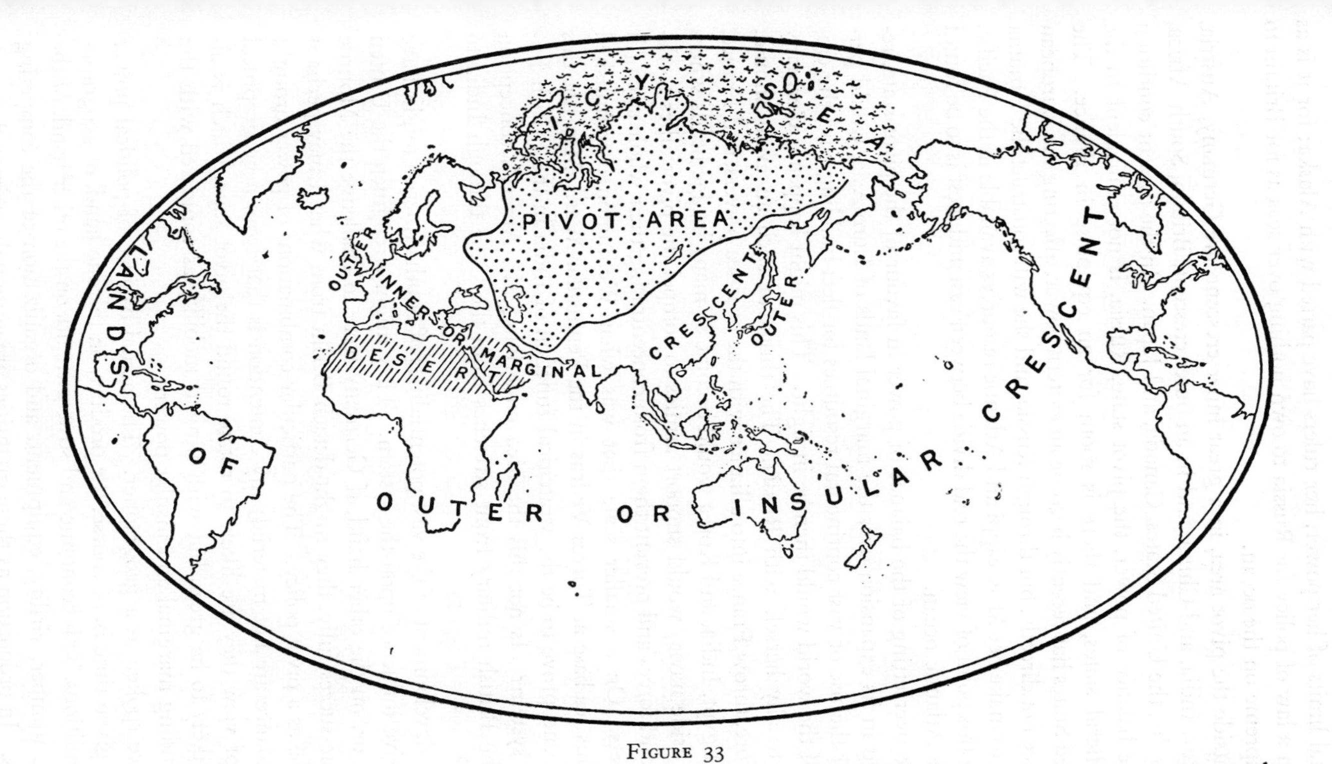

FIGURE 33

The Natural Seats of Power. Pivot area—wholly continental. Outer crescent—wholly oceanic. Inner crescent—partly continental, partly oceanic.

mental limits of her power, her rulers have parted with Alaska; for it is as much a law of policy for Russia to own nothing over seas as for Britain to be supreme on the ocean.

Outside the pivot area, in a great inner crescent, are Germany, Austria, Turkey, India, and China, and in an outer crescent, Britain, South Africa, Australia, the United States, Canada, and Japan. In the present condition of the balance of power, the pivot state, Russia, is not equivalent to the peripheral states, and there is room for an equipoise in France. The United States has recently become an eastern power, affecting the European balance not directly, but through Russia, and she will construct the Panama canal to make her Mississippi and Atlantic resources available in the Pacific. From this point of view the real divide between east and west is to be found in the Atlantic ocean.

The oversetting of the balance of power in favour of the pivot state, resulting in its expansion over the marginal lands of Euro-Asia, would permit of the use of vast continental resources for fleet-building, and the empire of the world would then be in sight. This might happen if Germany were to ally herself with Russia. The threat of such an event should, therefore, throw France into alliance with the over-sea powers, and France, Italy, Egypt, India, and Korea would become so many bridge heads where the outside navies would support armies to compel the pivot allies to deploy land forces and prevent them from concentrating their whole strength on fleets. On a smaller scale that was what Wellington accomplished from his sea-base at Torres Vedras in the Peninsular War. May not this in the end prove to be the strategical function of India in the British Imperial system? Is not this the idea underlying Mr. Amery's conception that the British military front stretches from the Cape through India to Japan?

The development of the vast potentialities of South America might have a decisive influence upon the system. They might strengthen the United States, or, on the other hand, if Germany were to challenge the Monroe doctrine successfully, they might detach Berlin from what I may perhaps describe as a pivot policy. The particular combinations of power brought into balance are not material; my contention is that from a geographical point of view they are likely to rotate round the pivot state, which is always likely to be great, but with limited mobility as compared with the surrounding marginal and insular powers.

I have spoken as a geographer. The actual balance of political power at any given time is, of course, the product, on the one hand, of geographical conditions, both economic and strategic, and, on the other hand, of the relative number, virility, equipment, and organization of the competing peoples. In proportion as these quantities are accurately estimated are we likely to adjust differences without the crude resort to arms. And the geographical quantities in the calculation are more measurable and more nearly constant than the human. Hence we should expect to find our formula apply equally to past history and to present politics. The social movements of all times have played around essentially the same physical features, for I doubt whether the progressive desiccation of Asia and Africa, even if proved, has in historical times vitally altered the human environment. The westward march of empire appears to me to have been a short rotation of marginal power round the south-western and western edge of the pivotal area. The Nearer, Middle, and Far Eastern questions relate to the unstable equilibrium of inner and outer powers in those parts of the marginal crescent where local power is, at present more or less negligible.

In conclusion, it may be well expressly to point out that the substitution of some new control of the inland area for that of Russia would not tend to reduce the geographical significance of the pivot position. Were the Chinese, for instance, organized by the Japanese, to overthrow the Russian Empire and conquer its territory, they might constitute the yellow peril to the world's freedom just because they would add an oceanic frontage to the resources of the great continent, an advantage as yet denied to the Russian tenant of the pivot region.

80. *The Geographical Situation of the United States in Relation to World Politics* *

"What an astonishing thing it would have been some twenty-five years ago to find the United States interested in Azerbaijan or in Trieste or in Korea or in any of the matters and places taken for granted to a great extent by American opinion today" is a 1948 statement by Lord Halifax, British ambassador to the United States. This indicates the foreign policy revolution that the United States has undergone in the present century. Especially since Pearl Harbor we have been forced "to think in global terms and we were nationally unprepared for such thinking." Our relatively new role as a world leader means that an understanding of the areas with which we have political dealings is absolutely essential. Geographical study, with its goal of world areal

* Isaiah Bowman, "The Geographical Situation of the United States in Relation to World Policies," *Geographical Journal,* Vol. 112, 1948, pp. 139–145. By permission of the *Geographical Journal* of the Royal Geographical Society, London. (For a brief biographical sketch of Dr. Bowman, see Selection 2 on page 11.)

differentiation, is vital to obtaining this understanding that United States citizens, as well as diplomats, need. All of our foreign policy is based to some degree upon geographical fact. Bowman, a leading United States political geographer and advisor to two presidents, analyzes in this selection some of these geographical factors that underly our relations and policy in regard to other world areas.

On the higher levels of strategy and statesmanship, two critical themes emerge that bear directly upon our well-being and survival. For what high ends we use power is one centre of effort, and how we make use of geography is the other. . . . Like the United Kingdom and certain members of the British Commonwealth of Nations, America has undertaken to share responsibility within the wide circle of the United Nations. The grand principle that permeates the Charter of the United Nations is that agreements respecting the solution of international problems shall be reached and executed on the basis of collective opinion determined by majority vote. For reasons only too well known, the application of that principle has been tragically delayed by the breaching of an interpretation, agreed to by the Great Powers at San Francisco, that the restricted and special device of the veto would be used but rarely. In consequence, the fear of war again overshadows the world. It is natural, therefore, that men should return to the idea of a balance of power, once so roundly denounced, and look closely at the world in terms of economic and military advantages.

In the effort to attain a balance of forces in world politics two disturbing questions arise. First, is such a balance possible? And second, can a balance or equilibrium be attained by international agreement? A biologist suggests that nature abhors an equilibrium. We should not dismiss as mere analogy this interesting idea when applied to human organization and effort. For example, the tendency toward disequilibrium is the root of the difficulty in devising any scheme of power control in the United Nations. As geological exploration and scientific discovery proceed and new resources of astounding potential are discovered, power disequilibrium comes into play concurrently. The present feverish search for sources of uranium cannot end in a nice balance of access and use. With vast oil deposits, two otherwise weak countries, Saudi Arabia and Venezuela, suddenly rank high in the power field. It is often said that geography does not change. In truth geography changes as rapidly as ideas and technologies change; that is, the *meaning* of geographical conditions changes. No first-class power can overlook the new geographical significances that come to light daily as the great international experiment proceeds. Every major technical and power development must be followed by a resurvey of world geography, region by region and indeed point by point.

The fleeting condition known as balance of power can be elevated to dangerous heights in national thought and come to be accepted as a dominant "principle," with resulting waste of vital resources. It is really an unattainable goal. Instead of fixing our hopes on so unreal but comfortable and reassuring an objective, it would be better to accept the idea that nature, including human nature, abhors an equilibrium. The forces of life are not equally nourished over the wide earth. The differences in birth rates and population structures country by country are a case in point. The basis of a numerical voting scheme in a world assembly for to-day is destroyed tomorrow by rapidly changing rates or amounts of population growth.

Ideas are even more potent in their unbalancing effect than continuing discoveries of resources. Strive as they may for a balance of power, the nations of the world cannot agree upon a mode of attaining it. To-day the clash of social ideas behind the effort keeps the whole world structure in unbalance. It is the great merit of the United Nations that it attempts, not the unattainable but an attainable goal. It is a way of reaching *working agreements,* not an agreement to attain a balance of power. Geography, like history and politics, is a discipline by which we can better understand "power," that vast network of changing forces that both enclose and condition two groups of human societies that are now contending on a world scale with fateful consequences. If we are wise we shall focus our attention on the unending process of readjustment among the many, rather than on a temporary condition of balance among the few. The process of adjustment of men's claims and rights must be as continuous as life itself. Confronted by the eternal difficulties of world politics, minds that wish to escape from reality prefer an heroic solution, hence the popularity and appeal of "world government" and peace by force. Heroic solutions solve few problems and always create a crop of new ones for all rest essentially on force without prior agreement on how to use it in unpredictable circumstances.

Power is not a matter of resources only. National confidence is a single, often neglected, psychological factor among many. When a distinctive cultural group gains a place of acknowledged power it becomes self-confident, indeed too confident for the comfort of its neighbours. The makers of its political theories and structure are likely to think that they have found the key to permanent success. Conceit leads them to assert that they have solved at last the complex art of governing men. The Soviet Union now has vast territory and resources, a vigorous people and, to weak or frustrated souls, a bewitching theory. The confidence of Soviet leaders, after enjoying thirty years of power unqualified by a free and popular referendum, enhances our present danger. In the United States we know the mood of confidence. We know how easily it acquires a mystic quality. Not long ago the American phrase for it was "manifest destiny." Both Russia's "urge to the sea" and America's urge to the Pacific are old stories; now for both peoples come the consequences. They meet in the East as in the West; two totally unlike stocks with different historical and cultural backgrounds, Slav on the one hand, and on the other that mixture known as American with basically Anglo-Saxon institutions.

The self-dependence of the American pioneer entailed political independence; and the impulse and opportunity of growth and the sense of destiny stimulated a spread of population and sovereignty that spanned a broad and richly diversified continent from sea to sea. America at all stages had the feeling of great days ahead. The rapid expansion of a culture eventually so well equipped technologically did indeed create a sense of destiny and of providential success which was carried over into easy assurance about the good life and its attainability by all mankind. Woodrow Wilson, a powerful advocate of American political ideals, frequently employed the phrase "all men everywhere" as if the diverse peoples of sixty nations in their widely different environments and unequal stages of cultural and political advancement (or retrogression) were all waiting eagerly to receive the demonstrated blessings of Jeffersonian democracy.

America was fortunate in the inheritance of political ideals and theories that kept its national compass needle fairly steady. Whatever the deviations, American political leaders did obtain true bearings by which to correct the national course. Our constitution and legal system, our adherence to the World Court, our Good Neighbour Policy, our willingness twice in a quarter of a century to stand, however tardily, beside the democracies of Western Europe, were neither materialist nor imperial in origin. They reflected a deep conviction about values, and if it was a slow-grown conviction it was also deliberate, and therein lies its chief assurance. If isolationism did not die at Pearl Harbour, the virtual destruction of our Pacific Fleet at least permanently disabled this mistaken policy. Our economy, the so-called "American system," believed to be impregnable in the 1920's, took a plunge in the 30's—a humiliating experience. It was the final cure for our century and a half of over-confidence. We learned that pulsing, unpredictable life is above system, that our defence and our destiny alike grow out of wide comprehension and virility joined to ideals and sophistication, and that without these our vaunted "system" will in time be one with Nineveh and Tyre.

The economic crash of 1929 ended the era of over-confidence. The long train of dismal consequences, world-wide in scope, taught us that we had to be sensitive to the realities of the whole globe if our American system was to have any meaning or stability. There is no doubt that the depression contributed to that new cycle of power politics and dictatorship in which we became rapidly involved. In the end we were compelled to remove our rose-coloured spectacles as we looked at the geographical stage and historical background of other men's dreams as well as our own. It was no longer enough to recognize an advantage here or a disadvantage there; not Greenland only, or Guam or the Panama Canal had become important but also the northernmost stretches of Alaska, the vulnerability of the Amazon, the happenings in Outer Mongolia and Sinkiang, and the forces that contend along the 38th parallel in Korea. Whatever the inconsistencies and vagaries of current politics, the United Nations is now a definite part of the American system and ideal. In this we occupy no unique position. Such is the theory and intent of the Charter that, in a sense, the territorial base of every sovereign state that signed it is now the world.

On the instant of Pearl Harbour we had to think in global terms and we were nationally unprepared for such thinking. Perhaps 95 per cent. of our people "finish" geography in the seventh grade of elementary school. As in England before the era of Mackinder and his professional contemporaries, we were "parochial" in thought, to use Lord Morley's term for British thinking in 1910. Distant countries were words and pictures in a book, not land and field and culture systems and irreducible human diversities. They were strange and far away, of no significance to the United States except as sources of trade or as fields of Christian missionary endeavour. To-day it is universally recognized that geographical realities play a significant rôle in major cultural advances and also in that slow-growing process that holds the most substantial promise for human dignity and freedom, namely, the consolidation of power in countries outside the orbit of Soviet Russia.

America has confidence still but it is a new and higher confidence based upon deep conviction, upon tested foundations and, however we may regret to include it, upon material power and the national will to use it when confronted by acts of aggression collectively defined. To my mind nothing symbolizes the contrast between the Soviet and the non-Soviet world so sharply as the different conceptions they hold respecting the use of power. To-day the choice is clearly presented between the contrasting values and systems of Eastern and Western Europe, and the contrasting ends towards which they direct their policies and powers. For America the choice is clear because our object is liberty. Turn liberty any way you please, and acknowledge the too-frequent betrayal and corruption of some of its advocates, yet peoples provided with an opportunity to do so move instinctively towards it.

In the renewed world struggle between freedom and the arbitrary use of power, we cannot risk public misunderstanding of the foundation of our faith in democratic institutions. The free flow of criticism, and a high degree of self-criticism supply the indispensable conditions of flexibility and experimentation that keep men productively hopeful and willingly united. The contrast between democratic flexibility and the brittle structures reared by force and arbitrary command was never better demonstrated than in the period 1933 to 1945. Again we see the contrast taking shape in the divided world of to-day. Again we see the fundamental error emerging, an error that I would state as follows: if a spontaneous human organization exists, arbitrary power, whether secret police or military, assumes the right to command it, and *when arbitrary assumes command it begins by depreciating and ends by despising the men it commands.*

• • • •

Relations Within the Western Hemisphere

To what extent are the resources of the United States supplemented by the resources of Latin America? Does the western hemisphere form a self-contained economic system? It there a natural solidarity of ideas and interests? What is at the root of Pan-American effort, political, economic and strategic? How one answers each of these questions depends upon the political weather. At all times Latin America has certain resources that we urgently desire to exchange for some of our own. War increases our need, and enhances that unpredictable variability of trade and policy that puzzles the European observer and at times upsets the calculations of some of the governments of Latin America. Some see in our western hemisphere policy a turning to isolationism, forgetting that we have the fixed policy, now of long standing, to assist democratic states in time of crisis, partly on political theory and partly because such a course increases our defensive strength. Hemisphere policy is not the policy of withdrawing into a shell. The ocean routes to most of South America are far longer than those to Europe. Ships and 'planes, not the isthmus of Panama, unite the two *economic* Americas.

Before drawing the conclusion that the policy of the United States is volatile and unpredictable, we should ask how much, if any, of the rest of the world is stable and predictable. Neither world production nor world export are closely calculable things. Every nation at times miscalculates—Brazil on coffee, the United States on cotton, Russia on rainfall, and all the world on oil. Industrially powerful, the United States is now in the position, long familiar to British government and business, that our business barograph feels the effect of every change in pressure anywhere in the world. All this gives added importance to areas of possible though relative stabilization. It is in this light that we view our trade and political relations with Latin America. It is natural that in time of general disturbance we should strive for hemisphere strength. As late as the spring of 1941 there was a strong sentiment, shared for a time by President Roosevelt, that hemisphere defence was practicable. When he invited me to express an opinion on the idea I stated that the setting of hemispherical limits to military defence was not practicable. A paragraph from that opinion follows:

> Since the foundation of the Republic it has been our settled policy to uphold the right of Americans freely to go and come upon the seven seas in pursuit of peaceful trade. . . . At times, however, we have deliberately and voluntarily restricted the sphere of our trade in the interests of neutrality and peace. At the outbreak of the present war, in accordance with Acts of Congress, American shipping was barred from war zones as defined by the President. Such a restriction was not imposed upon us by international law; it was based upon our desire to avoid entanglements that might lead to war. No foreign power has a right to request that such voluntary restriction of our trade be maintained, much less to request that we still further restrict it in the interest of totalitarian conquest.

A "free sea" position cannot be taken on paper only. A nation adopting that point of view must face the military implications, which are world-wide. Nevertheless, the American public has played with the idea of hemispheric self-sufficiency time and again. We shall therefore look in some detail at the weakness of that position. The firmest and most spontaneous international association in America is between Canada and the United States. By contrast the bonds between Latin America and the English-speaking portion of the hemisphere, outside trade, are largely artificial. We do little about our natural Canadian-American friendship, while we are forever tending with anxiety our cultural and political ties with Spanish-speaking neighbours and Brazil. No amount of hemisphere talk quite stabilizes the bridge between us. Trade has not done it. Cultural embassies create extremely pleasant personal relations but leave the general situation untouched.

The cause of our division is to be found chiefly in our contrasting cultural inheritances and our different geographical environments. Geographical obstacles tended to keep the peoples of Latin America apart even among themselves. Each nation of to-day represents an earlier colony walled off by desert or mountain or distance from its neighbours. In origin, each nation was a geographically separated group. Even the major divisions of territory within a country suffered a like compartmentation; the histories of Mexico, Bolivia and Argentina afford many examples right down to our time. For a whole century, revolution was easy in every Latin-American country because the several communities within each nation were neither contiguous nor effectively interlocked. Local differences are known in all countries. In Latin America the political expression of internal cohesion has been most difficult to attain and impossible to hold for long.

Contributing to the same end was the marked (and still existent) regionalism and cultural contrasts in Spain and Spanish history for at least a millennium. The cultural capital of early colonial Chile or Peru or Mexico was not Madrid but some provincial Spanish town. The provinces of Spain are no less distinctive than the colonial groups that formed in Spain's vice-royalties. The Spanish system of fleets and fairs, established in 1561, continued almost down to the time of the American Revolution. Only as late as 1774 was the prohibition removed on direct trade between New Spain, Peru, Guatemala and New Granada. And it was not until 1778 that the port of Buenos Aires and the ports of Chile and Peru were open to direct trade with Spain. Fragmentation, both natural and enforced, was deemed a principle of imperial control and lasted for nearly three hundred years.

With weak internal cohesion, each new government that emerged from the Wars of Liberation was preoccupied with merely holding on, and only a few individuals, among whom Bolivar was foremost, thought in terms of western hemisphere trade and political union. Unaccustomed to constitutional forms, the first national groups of little more than a hundred years ago found themselves in possession of a simple *theory* about rights, and confronted with the complex *duty* of operating a democratic government without any established tradition of compromise. Lacking the patience to run that ponderous and at times baffling machinery, and without sufficient respect for majority vote on the part of a small electorate, control became an affair of families rather than proven political leadership, while office became a privilege and too often a badge of unwarranted prestige. The national economy became a medley of forces little understood. Wealth was in land and minerals and livestock. Native populations and mixed blood groups constituted the masses from Mexico to Bolivia who long had little or no representation in elections or office. The pack mule, the trail, the simple exchange of goods at weekly, monthly or annual fairs, the dependence on foreign capital, foreign reduction-plant, and foreign demand and consumption of mineral and other raw materials, were the enduring marks of a primitive economy whose controls lay outside Latin America.

The nervous relation of Latin America to the United States to-day depends in part upon these contrasts in cultural backgrounds and traditions and in part upon a disparity of military and economic power. The feeling is accented by differences in political and social philosophy. A poet sums up one such contrast, no less true of Latin America than of Spain, when he writes: "God bless those who labour and we who guide them." To the traditional ruling class it is nonsense to claim that the peon knows what is good for him in government or society. "Look at him," it will be said, "the answer is in his face and bearing." The official will add that few are those who understand complex public policies and those few have acquired their abilities over the centuries. The heroic supplies an ingredient to the composition of Spanish rulership that has not lost its flavour and should not be undervalued, for some of its essence sifts down in variant forms through all classes of Latin America. Nobleman and priest stood together on many a critical battlefield where the cross overwhelmed the crescent in Spain's historical yesterday.

Underneath the veneer of popular government in the new Latin sovereignties of a hundred years ago were institutions that supported, if they did not create, a new political élite. The bride changed her name but not her initial. The Spanish officials were gone but the land baron remained in possession of estates derived in many instances from original *encomiendas* or their subdivisions. The institution of the *hacienda* was continued as naturally as if it were divinely ordained, for it had a powerful economic and social base. Land was the commonest and most reliable form of wealth. Grants of land were the coveted rewards of valour in the days of the Conquest and were consolidated by marriage or transferred and perpetuated, some of them down to our day. With the land and water went rights to a part of the labour of those, chiefly Indian or mixed breeds, who lived by sufferance upon it.

Labour, whether on the land or in the towns, is the core of the present-day internal difficulties of Latin America. Those who wrote the constitutions that were the sequel of successive revolutions never forgot the resounding phrases of the vice-regal grants made as rewards for loyalties kept, services rendered and risks endured. Until the Mexican revolution less than forty years ago it was never intended that a new constitution should effect land titles or eliminate special privileges. A new government meant a change of masters, not a change in the economic or land-tenure systems. If reforms were promised, they met the same fate as the ideals respecting native labour and fair dealing in the famous "Recopilación de Leyes" of the Indies of colonial times, ideals expressed in faultless rhetoric and a noble humanity but with little ensuing effect.

The rôle of land in Latin-American economy is not generally understood in the United States, where the "homesteads for freemen" principle has affected policy with varying success since Benton's day, for over 125 years. To many minds the answer to the tough problem of refugees and displaced persons is, "there is plenty of land in South America." To reach that confident answer one merely divides a number representing the population by a number representing square mileage and one sees how relatively empty South America appears to be! In 1938 the Banco Agricola del Peru in Lima distributed a paper by R. A. Ferrero significantly entitled, "The scarcity of cultivated land in Peru," meaning arable land with a tolerable climate and with some prospect of having or getting transport without which a remote production system in a far valley had no hope of success. There are a number of Latin-American regions, upland Brazil being the largest, where arable land is available but burdened with troublesome problems of transport and markets. Always excepting the upland interior of Brazil, it is a hard fact that the total of undeveloped arable land in Latin America is small. Its development will be slow because most of the land is marginal. The population of Latin America is growing rapidly, even alarmingly. At the present rate it may double in a century; it will push out to the potential limit of land development, but it will not change greatly the land-occupation map. Its further strength and fortune will be built upon industry added to land. It will not be based upon a new generation of land-seeking pioneers. The land is not there. The best of it is already cultivated.

The large Indian population of parts of Latin America creates a special problem and, in places, presents an impenetrable iron curtain to the white overlords, as among the Aymará of the Central Andes. It is idle to talk of universal suffrage and democratic majority procedures to an Indian group ignorant of political theory, incapable of choice and walled off by centuries of deep-seated hostility towards whites. Out of a total population of seven millions in Peru, two and a half millions are upland Indians who do not speak Spanish. Ability to speak and write Spanish being a requirement for the citizen desiring to vote, the electorate probably does not exceed 800,000 or 10 per cent. of the population. Arca-Parró's work on the census of 1940 is a landmark in the analysis of the population structure of Peru. In the United States we have no such masses of indigenous population to bring so far forward. Our Indian population of 400,000 is a minor though still grossly neglected problem. The white citizens of Guatemala face white-Indian ratios of 9 to 13. For the United States the equivalent would be an Indian population of ninety millions! We are not prepared, therefore, either to criticize the policies of Latin-American states or to display examples of better conduct. The irreducible fact is that in half the Latin-American countries colour and race and wide economic inequalities introduce strains and risks that frighten foreign capital. A country that cannot reduce the risk is penalized by high rates of return on capital. The economy pays double—once for domestic dislocation, and again for using outside money to develop its resources or finance its trade. The foreigner is alternately courted and disliked in Latin America. To-day national sovereignty means more than flag and sentiment. It means also economic handicaps, irreducible native problems, a lack of cohesion even in the top layers of society where opposing groups strive for the privileges of government rather than for its use as an instrument of national improvement and solidarity. Unity and stability are not there.

How shall we weigh the Latin-American nations in the scales of western hemisphere interests? What strength do they contribute to a unified hemisphere or a world policy of peace and defence? In World War Two we found them cooperative, understanding the vital issues. We needed their products and they needed, as never before, our markets. Transport was chiefly at our cost and the ships lost to submarines were chiefly our ships. To oil, coffee, tropical fruit, copper and tin among leading Latin-American imports, were added cotton, maganese, industrial diamonds and quartz crystal, to mention only a few products; and through all this there ran a great deal of preclusive buying. Argentina had exports, mainly livestock, of 700,000,000 pesos in 1940 and of 1,350,000,000 in 1944. All benefited marvellously considering the times. Yet all knew that a day of reckoning was coming. Where would they find themselves in the crisis of post-war reconstruction?

A new cloud of anxiety darkened the Latin-American sky as the discussion of a world charter proceeded at San Francisco in 1945. Communism threatened both Church and State in these Catholic countries. As in old Spain, common cause was made by the representatives of the existing different governments against the possibly extreme positions of the rising and politically immature lower middle class and the third estate. What part would Soviet Russia play in the expected revolutions? When the difficult question of the admission of Argentina arose in the United Nations there was presented an opportunity to give positive expression to the fear of communism by opposing the Soviet position. Astonishingly enough, security was sought by Latin-American representatives in a hemisphere agreement, with United States leadership implied in matters political and military. Hemisphere interests were considered to be ahead of world interests. The Act of Chapultepec carried a provision for a future military agreement on hemisphere defence. The representatives of the United States agreed to meet the representatives of Latin-American countries in 1946 to forge an instrument of closer collaboration. It was impossible to keep this pledge because of preoccupation with European problems and delays arising from Soviet intractability. The Bogotá conference was held two years too late. The riots there, and in Cartagena and Barranquilla, only underscored what was long well known, that no guarantee of stability appears on the political horizon; and every revolution is marked by attacks upon the large property owners and upon the position and profits of the foreign investor and producer.

Thus is the soil prepared for the Communist sowing, as it was for the Nazi sowing. A solution based on force is fatally attractive where there is weak internal unity. Only the files of the intelligence services could disclose the wartime scale of Nazi divisive influence in more than half the countries of Latin America—in the commercial companies, in the army, among the "citizens" of foreign origin, among office holders and members of national congresses. The joining of American and Soviet interests for war purposes gave Communism for a time a field day in Latin America. The fantastic and costly wartime expansion of Soviet embassies in Latin America was not done in a fun-loving or peace-making spirit. The flaming torches of Bogotá were a demonstration that there is much fuel at hand. It could happen in twenty other South American cities. We do not know and shall not know, until a cycle of profound change has been completed, what the long pull ahead of us will disclose. We believe that we cannot make and keep friends, even though both sides recognize the artificial quality of our friendship, unless we keep our political and social aims in parallel. To do this, all the resources of science, diplomacy, goodwill, economic improvement and steadfastness will be required, and above all resolution and patience.

. . . . .

The Long-range View

It is clear that while we may talk of the geographical situation of the United States in relation to world policies, we cannot think in geographical terms alone even though we may emphasize geography because it has been so long neglected. We must think in terms of the whole plexus of circumstances that surround us. This is a hard intellectual exercise. Our chief difficulty in the democracies is to get men thoughtfully engaged in the exercise. It is so much easier to deal in simplicities and broad generalizations, or search for salvation in a single idea, or think ourselves secure because of a recent military victory. All must realize that the boundary between war and peace can be smudged with resulting disorder and danger. Events and ideas are now involved in a vast turbulence which statesmen must direct into strong and positive currents.

The great design for peace has yet to be forged. I say this, in spite of constant personal devotion to the United Nations, because the world has not yet demonstrated that steady will for peace that is the first condition of it. The dangerous over-confidence of Russia, its exuberant faith in a distorted and cruel system, is the mainspring of our troubles to-day. I have faith that we shall surmount these troubles as we have done before. I am encouraged by examples in our past history. A quotation entitled "The lesson of the day" forms a fitting conclusion to this review:

> It is a gloomy moment in history. Not for many years—not in the life time of most men who read this paper—has there been so much grave and deep apprehension; never has the future seemed so incalculable as at this time. . . . In France the political caldron seethes and bubbles with uncertainty; Russia hangs as usual, like a cloud, dark and silent upon the horizon of Europe; while all the energies, resources, and influences of the British Empire are sorely tried, and are yet to be tried more sorely. . . . Of our troubles no man can see the end. . . . These are the things that make the profound interest of the moment, besides others whose roots are spreading underground, out of sight. It is no time for idleness or trifling, for forgetfulness or selfishness. The complexion of every country, and of the world, rests at last upon the character of the individuals. . . .

This quotation from *Harper's Weekly* for 10 October 1857 describes a situation that seems overdrawn, as we look back upon it. Perhaps it is no more overdrawn than the American view to-day of British and European difficulties.

81. *Geography and War Strategy* *

Von Clausewitz, the brilliant student of warfare, has said that "warfare is the continuation of diplomacy by other means." At the opposite end of the military scale, every infantry private is acutely aware of the advantages of irregular surfaces as cover from enemy fire. Wars are fought between the armies of nations or groups of nations, and at all

* Cyril Falls, "Geography and War Strategy," *Geographical Journal,* Vol. 112, 1948, pp. 4–18. By permission of the *Geographical Journal* of the Royal Geographical Society, London. The author is Chichele Professor of Military History at Oxford University, and military analyst for the *London Times.* Field Marshal Montgomery has said, "I always do what Cyril Falls tells me."

levels of military operation the importance of the factors of geography are pre-eminent. The grand strategy of World War II, as described by Falls, an outstanding military analyst, shows the direct relationship between warfare and geography. The comments by Field Marshal Montgomery that follow the article regarding its content and geography in the strategy of World War II are particularly illuminating.

When I came to examine the subject set me by this Society I saw at once that it might be treated in two different ways. Both geography and strategy are imprecise words with elastic meanings. They may be concerned with the world at large, the land and water masses, the globe itself with all its resources. They may be concerned with narrower but no less important considerations: the characteristics of a coast, a country, a province, a mountain chain or a river valley. I could therefore have dealt with my subject on the broad lines of the illuminating address delivered by Professor E. G. R. Taylor to the British Association in 1947, or I could have confined myself to studying past and possible future campaigns in the light of their local geographical features and the approaches to their theatres by land and sea. I was bold enough to decide to do both, that is, to look first upon the world as a whole and then upon theatres of war. That seemed the most interesting method. But when I set to work I found that within the compass of a lecture it was not possible for me to be thorough along those lines. The result is that I cannot promise more than a few suggestions and reflections, something to think about, disconnected ideas upon the subject. I hope it will be worth while and that you will not grumble if you find yourself rather abruptly switched from one aspect to another.

To-day more than ever the strategist, like the economist, has to look upon the world as a whole. I do not mean by this that distance has been abolished; that is a cant phrase which may lead to absurdities. It would be absurd, for instance, to say that modern weapons and means of communication have made New Zealand as vulnerable as the British Isles. Common sense tells us that it is not. But the modern conqueror who succeeds in dominating the main land masses of the world will have everything else speedily added unto him. New Zealand will not long elude his clutches. Strategically as well as geographically the earth is a whole. And the earth is something about which we know surprisingly little. Even its precise shape is not quite clear, and it seems to be subject to changes in shape of which we know nothing. We make maps, that is projections on paper which are of course conventional, and the projection which the public knows best is the most uninformative and even deceptive —I mean of course Mercator's. We compile lists of the times and levels of tides; but they go out of date without our noticing it. Only a very small proportion of the earth have we covered by instrumental survey, and wonderful as modern methods of photographic survey are, they have not yet replaced instrumental survey on the ground.

The more we study the world, the more we feel the gaps in our knowledge of it. Professor Taylor, about whose address I spoke just now, suggests that the exact size and shape of the earth may be elevated to the rank of "top secret" and that for a country to be ill-mapped might provide a species of camouflage. Both may well be the case. When working on Russian maps during the war I was told that railways might be plotted several miles off their true course, and if the most recent Russian surveys are allowed to pass west of the Iron Curtain I shall be most astonished. Bad mapping is indeed camouflage to-day—and not only to-day. When Sir Arthur Chichester was carrying out the Plantation of Ulster in the reign of James I he had a survey made by Sir Josias Bodley and William Parsons; and though the country was then quiet these prudent men took a guard with them. Sir John Davies, the Attorney-General, wrote home: "Our geographers do not forget what entertainment the Irish of Tyrconnell gave to a map-maker about the end of the late rebellion; for, one Barkeley being appointed by the late Earl of Devonshire to draw a true and perfect map of the north part of Ulster (the old map of Tyrconnell being false and defective), when he came into Tyrconnell the inhabitants took off his head, because they would not have their country discovered." From their point of view they acted wisely.

And if it be objected that the modern system of stereoscopic survey from the air, though not the equal of ground triangulation with astronomical observation, will still render it possible for every part of the globe to be relatively well mapped, infinitely better than it has ever been before, I agree; but this is nevertheless the sort of intelligence which it may be difficult to obtain, especially in time of peace. And even in war it would be hard for photographic aircraft to penetrate deeply into a territory of vast extent so as to cover more than a fraction on the outskirts. Here the little country may be handicapped in comparison with the big one, because a little country may be much more easily photographed against its will. And here also the democratic nation may be handicapped as against the totalitarian, because a democratic nation does not conceal its geographical surveys. Yet even in democratic countries in these troubled days I can well conceive certain features being omitted from the maps of the future.

World geography should be a subject of study for the commander and staff officer. They can get from it not only concrete information but also general ideas which may be of high value to them in their profession. Another subject which will not only give them concrete information but will be fruitful in general ideas is historical geography as taught by the modernists such as the late Sir Halford Mackinder. His brilliant expositions of the growth of states and cities under the influence of geographical features made a deeper impression abroad than at home. He became in a sense the father of the German school of geopolitics. As developed by the Nazis, geopolitics is a bogus science. It was used as a justification for absurd racial theories, for naked aggression, for the notorious doctrine of *Lebensraum*. Yet it has within it a core of scientific truth. The features of a country, its mineral and agricultural wealth, its situation with regard to world communications and their junctions, do in fact go far towards determining that country's destiny.

The qualification of a great power to-day depends largely upon its minerals, above all coal, iron ore and oil, though many others may be added, some of which have a special application to its actual armaments for war. But it must also possess the basis for a great and vigorous population, and this implies big stretches of lowland, reasonably well watered, with soils suited to certain grain crops and to cattle. Adverse political and social conditions, or an undesirable location in regard to the most advanced forms of civilization, may retard a nation's rise to power as they did to a striking extent in the case of Russia and even more so in the case of Japan. But if it has the qualifications it will sooner or later enter into the ranks of the great nations; and then its rise may be very rapid. As world time is measured, it was rapid in the case of Russia and astounding in the case of Japan. A nation need not be altogether self-sufficing, but if not it must possess natural communications with outside sources of wealth or secure them for itself by sea power. One can think of various other attributes of power. Falling water is one of the chief of them, and this is an age of great power dams. A moderate and equable climate is another, but not a necessity. Russia has an extreme climate which condemns its agricultural population to long spells of inactivity, yet this has not prevented the development of great agricultural wealth. But to a certain extent climate and race are linked. It seems to be the mixed climates which produce the highest human energy, even when they go to extremes.

Not long ago the American airman General Spaatz pointed out that the qualifications of great powers to-day were to be found only in the northern hemisphere. They were to be found above all in his own North American continent, in Northern and Central Europe and perhaps in a block of territory comprising Japan, Korea, Manchuria and adjacent parts of China and Far Eastern Russia, all in the northern hemisphere. The northern hemisphere is a land hemisphere, the southern a water hemisphere. Apart from these European and Asiatic blocks, nowhere else in the world were there regions which could constitute a peril to the United States within measurable time. This factor, he said, must greatly modify

United States military policy in an age of long-range weapons. And he pointed out an entirely new feature in the strategic situation of North America, the fact that the northern fringes of Europe and Asia, from North Cape in Norway to East Cape on the Bering Strait, formed a rough semi-circle of the Old World facing another semi-circle of the New World formed by the north coast of Greenland, the arctic islands north of Canada, and Alaska; while Alaska itself, looking westward, almost touched Far Eastern Russia. He thought it possible that some long-range weapons might be projected across the polar region into the North American continent. And I need not add that this consideration—which is new because these intensely cold areas had no strategic significance whatever in the past—accounts for the fact that Canada and the United States now look north as well as in other directions, and accounts for the defence measures taken in concert by the two states to cover approaches from this hitherto disregarded direction.

What General Spaatz said about the impossibility of a great world power appearing within measurable time anywhere outside the northern hemisphere was perfectly true; but there are land masses in the southern hemisphere, small by comparison with those of the northern but in many respects richly dowered and capable of exerting great strategic influence and perhaps of swinging over the balance of power one way or the other, according to the direction in which they lean. One is Australia with New Zealand and the East India Islands, the last lying mainly south of the equator. Here we have the only white population in the Pacific, and immense wealth of raw materials. Australia and neighbouring territories have not the full qualifications of a world power for as far ahead as we can see, but they are potentially a power of the second order and, as I have said, may exert great strategic influence.

The second is of course South America, prosperous, still expanding, one of the world's great food depôts as well as rich in other respects. South America is mainly in the southern hemisphere, the equator running north of the Amazon. And this continent lies much closer than does the United States itself to the Panama Canal which is of such vital importance to United States strategy. There we see in the recent Treaty of Rio, fathered by the United States but not imposed, not signed under duress, that it is possible in these days of what are called power politics for the greatest power in the world to gain legitimate ends without threats or bullying. One must admire the combined prudence and moderation of the dealings of the United States with South America. At the same time one must realize, from the great pains bestowed by the President and the Secretary of State upon the question of American unity against aggression, how highly they rate its importance.

And then there is Africa; for though only about a quarter, anyhow less than one-third, of African territory lies in the southern hemisphere, this fraction contains a larger proportion of its actual and potential wealth. South of the equator there are to be found huge resources virtually untapped until this generation and capable of being almost indefinitely expanded. And they are, so to speak, tucked away behind the immense barrier of the Sahara. Africa might become a storehouse from which the present shortages of Europe could be largely supplied. But it would take time, money and organization. At present it is only in the Union of South Africa and perhaps in Southern Rhodesia that there exist administrations able to tackle the possibilities which face them.

In Africa too there is an alliance between economic and strategic possibilities. Its northern shore fringes the Mediterranean, its eastern the Red Sea and the Arabian Sea, great traffic routes of the world. And to put matters in a concerte form, for I see no reason to be afraid of doing so, the continent flanks a possible Russian drive across Western Europe and may thus be considered as a base for a counter-offensive. It is not possible to imagine Africa as a great power in itself, at all events not in this century nor perhaps in the next; but in a very much shorter space of time it might become a great adjunct of power.

I warned you that I should be able only to look at geography in relation to global strategy for a brief moment. Now I am going to increase the map scale so as to picture a smaller area. I cannot better picture in terms of geography what has been throughout history one of the vital problems of European strategy than by quoting a passage from the writings of General de Gaulle:

> Supposing one has forced a passage of the Rhine and entered Germanic territory. The soil, in all its accidents, fights against the invader. If he should take the southern route, a score of *massifs,* that of Baden, the Hessian, Westphalian, Swabian, Franconian, Thuringian, Saxon, facing in all directions, combine to disperse him. But if he would march by the north, how many rivers cut across his route, how many bogs, heaths of sand, areas of ponds, spreading out indefinitely, use up his forces and his courage! It is the old story of Varus, of Soubise, of Moreau; it recalls the supreme hesitation of Foch.
>
> In his five hours' flight in an aircraft from Berlin to Paris the traveller sees marked on the ground German security and French weakness. On leaving the banks of the Spree he can in the long leisure at his disposal until he reaches our Meuse, over one hundred and twenty-five leagues, discern the moats, the Elbe, the Aller, the Leine, the Weser, the Rhine, contemplate the fortresses, the Harz, the Hessian Mountains, the Rothaargebirge, the Eifel, whose nature pays homage to the Germans. Then suddenly the ground is smoothed out, becomes softer, is humanized. No more mountains, no more ravines, no more escarpments. It is France! Hardly are we clear of the frontier when this land in form of a basin

which dips towards its centre, these rivers, these railways, these routes converging in the same direction, this suburban air which the country rapidly assumes make us feel that Paris is quite near. And there it is already, a monument, a mart, a workshop, collecting a thousand arteries, ill guarded by its mediocre hills, fringed by easily permeable woods, lacking an acropolis, a prey so close, so fine and so easy.

Surely in those words we find the key to half the history of Western Europe. They explain much more than that France has stood for century upon century in deadly danger from the east. They explain, for example, why France, which might have been the greatest seafaring and naval and colonizing race of the world, has never reached that position. She could not afford to. And they explain diplomatic history and military history over a long period. As Napoleon said, the policy of a state is in its geography. The two forms in which policy is expressed are diplomacy and war. And in both France has constantly sought a remedy for the protection which geography has denied to her. The attempts to establish a military frontier on the Rhine, the alliances with Protestant Sweden and Muhammadan Turkey, the alliance of the Radical Republic with Tsarist Russia, pacts as with Czechoslovakia, patronage of the Little Entente, concessions to Mussolini, flirtations with Soviet Russia, carefully cultivated friendship with Switzerland which bars the entries into Burgundy and the valley of the Rhône—all these can be traced to the geographical facts which General de Gaulle describes as unrolling before the eyes of the traveller flying from Berlin to Paris.

Now I take a smaller area again, and on a larger scale. In military books you sometimes find a quotation from the Archduke Charles that the Danube is the strategic key to southern Germany and that the result of wars there is always decided upon the Danube. I suspect that a large proportion of those who read these words are vague in their minds about what the writer means. I own I was until I had studied his works and his actual campaigns more closely. His meaning is that there is a long stretch of the Danube, from Ulm to Regensburg, where there were in his day—and the general conditions have not enormously changed—a dozen good crossing-places with bridges. Farther downstream, from the Isar to the Inn, there was only a single crossing, that at Passau, and no road along the left bank. But from Ulm to Regensburg there were these twelve crossing-places and excellent communications.

And he certainly exemplified his meaning by his brilliant conduct of the campaign of 1796. The French, in superior numbers, had driven him back from the Rhine. They then advanced with two separate armies, Moreau on the north bank of the Danube, faced by the Archduke himself, Jourdan on the highway through Nürnberg, pushing in front of him the Austrian force which the Archduke had detached to contain him. At Neresheim the Archduke struck a blow at Moreau. Then he fell back quickly and crossed to the south bank of the Danube, drawing Moreau after him. Leaving another detachment to hold Moreau there, the Archduke then recrossed in secret to the north bank with a small force and hurried north to assist the detachment which was facing Jourdan on the Naab. He came in on Jourdan's flank, beat him in two battles, and swiftly drove him back over the Rhine in confusion. Then he marched up the right bank of the Rhine, came in on the flank of Moreau who was retreating through the Black Forest after learning the fate of his colleague, and drove him also back over the Rhine. And the basis of this brilliant campaign was, as the Archduke himself points out, this stretch of the Danube with its excellent communications. Without it he would have been unable to execute his manoeuvre. The formation of double bridgeheads in this reach of the Danube was of inestimable benefit to those who knew how to make use of them. Ten years later the Austrians were commanded by a man who did not, and everyone remembers what happened to General Mack in the double bridgehead of Ulm.

The next geographical study of a theatre of war I want to make—though perhaps I am going so fast that I should say I am glancing at it rather than studying it—is that of the Burmese theatre of war. I need not remind you that the campaigns in Burma were fought in the most disadvantageous way from our point of view. The first look we take at an orographical map shows us that the natural way in which to fight a campaign in Burma from a base or bases in India is through Rangoon, and therefore that the natural way in which to open it would have been to retake Rangoon first of all. It is all very well to say that the Indian Government in the years before the war ought to have improved the land communications with Burma. Perhaps they ought to have. We all of us leave undone things we ought to have done. But I feel sure that if you or I had been responsible in those years and had had to pick the objects on which to spend a limited amount of money we should have put a road or roads from India into Burma on a relatively low priority. After all we were a naval nation, not what Mr. Churchill calls a "land animal." If we lost command of the sea all calculations would be upset. To envisage inability to maintain the sea routes between Calcutta or Colombo and Rangoon we had to presuppose not only a simultaneous war with Germany and Japan but also the complete overthrow of France; for it was that which brought the Japanese into French Indo-China and Siam. We had to presuppose a disaster such as the sinking of the *Prince of Wales* and *Repulse* without their having inflicted damage on the Japanese fleet. We had to go even further and presuppose such prior calls from the European theatre of war that we should not be able to allot coastwise craft to Burma even when there was a possibility of using them. As early as the winter of 1942–43 there was a possibility of using such craft to secure Akyab; but at the last moment Field Marshal Wavell was informed that they were not available, being required for the landings in the Mediterranean theatre. So the capture of Akyab was attempted by an advance down the Arakan, which failed after heavy fighting.

Not until the very end was the naval material forthcoming in sufficient strength for the capture of Rangoon by sea, though a little was produced earlier on the Arakan coast. And when it was produced to take Rangoon it arrived too late for practical purposes. We did land at Rangoon, but to find it empty. General Slim had by this time already won the campaign on overland communications and air supply and transportation, and I do not think the Rangoon landing can be said to have made any great difference in the long run.

And so the campaign of General Slim and of the American-directed Chinese forces which started from the Hukawng valley had to be conducted in the most difficult of all ways. There were no roads leading from Assam across the huge jungle-clad ridges which barred the way to the valleys of the Chindwin and the Irrawaddy. Everything had to be improvised. But none of the extraordinary work accomplished, such as that of the American railway battalions on the Bengal-Assam railway, would have sufficed to provide a basis for a successful campaign entirely over land communications. It could not have been done. To atone for the weakness of the land communications, inventive minds set themselves to work out revolutionary methods of air transport. These were produced under the pressure of sheer necessity. I yield to none in my admiration for the planning and organization or for the boldness and determination of the pilots who flew under abominable conditions in the monsoon, but I am certain that the stimulant was a necessity and that their minds would not have worked on those lines if there had been any hope of developing the administration on more traditional lines. A division which was enveloped by the enemy or which was advancing through country in which it could not maintain a line of communication was supplied by air not as a matter of emergency but as a matter of course. A whole division could be picked up and transported from one sector to another over the heads of intervening Japanese forces. Reinforcements in thousands could be flown in to a hard-pressed garrison, and administrative troops who had temporarily become an embarrassment to the defence could be flown out.

The tactics of the campaign were influenced as well as the strategy. Thus a division marching along a valley would not necessarily have to seal it off behind as in normal circumstances. The divisional commander did not have to waste troops by stringing them out along his line of march. So long as he had a strong rearguard, it did not much matter to him if the Japanese flowed into the valley in his wake. And this new conception of administration, which may have so important an effect upon warfare of the future, was created by the terrain itself, by those gigantic offshoots of the Himalayas which are called the Lushai hills, the Naga hills, the Patkai hills, and farther south the Arakan Yoma and Pegu Yoma which overhang the basin of the Irrawaddy; and created also by the difficulties of operating in the natural way over sea communications.

Now I look back again to Europe for a moment and to ground which has been familiar to British or English forces for centuries. The Rhine can be outflanked in Holland, but the nation which has always up to the present century, and to some extent in the present century, desired to force a passage of the Rhine from west to east has been France, and France could only turn the Rhine barrier if she possessed control over Holland, which was not often. Prior to this century, when we went into Holland it was not generally for the purpose of forcing the Rhine barrier but in order to keep the French out of the Low Countries. On the two occasions in this century when we fought as allies of the French, we were unable to gain possession of north Holland and so could not outflank the Rhine barrier. The country is in any case not very suitable for operations because it is so easily inundated by a defender. In the First World War Holland's neutrality was respected, so that the question never arose. In the Second World War, Holland's neutrality having been early violated by Germany, it did arise. As the 21st Army Group's spearhead was thrust northward into Holland there seemed every chance that the task of outflanking the Rhine barrier might this time be accomplished. If it had been it would have had a very important effect upon the future of the campaign, because there are no obstacles of any importance, except those of the soil itself, in passing round the elbow of the Rhine until the Ems is reached; the Ijjsel cannot be called a serious barrier.

But there were three factors which fought against us. First of all, the number of water obstacles. The Rhine divides into two channels, the southern called the Waal, the northern the Lek or, higher up opposite Arnhem, the Neder Rhin. Farther south the Maas or Meuse for a short distance follows a parallel course, forming another great water obstacle. And as if nature had not done enough to make things difficult, man has thrown in two parallel canals, the first known as the Meuse-Escaut or Maas-Scheldt, the second the Albert Canal. The second factor was the nature of the soil, particularly north of the Maas where it is spongy even for Holland. The third was the bad weather, especially disadvantageous when allied with this sponginess of the soil, which practically confined the advancing column to the main road. I do not say that the bad weather should have come as a complete surprise to us, because rain in September is common enough in Holland. And so, despite the skill in mounting a triple airborne operation and the gallantry with which it was carried out, especially at Arnhem, the 21st Army Group leapt four barriers, the two canals, the Maas and the Waal, but failed to maintain its footing beyond the last. I think I am right in supposing that this failure modified not only the Group's strategy but the whole of the Allied strategy in the west until the passage of the Rhine had been effected. Everybody knows something of the story of Arnhem, but I fancy there must be a great number of people who fail to grasp the significance of the episode because they do not connect first of all the motive involved, the turning of the line of the Rhine, and secondly its fate, with the nature of the country, in fact with the local geography.

I could enlarge on this subject almost indefinitely. I might have dealt with the drainage system in the Ypres sector, which in 1917 we, the attackers, dislocated and smashed up by our own artillery fire, thereby handicapping ourselves and providing defences for the enemy. I might have spoken of the situation in the main theatre of the American Civil War, where the proximity of the Federal and Confederate capitals, Washington and Richmond, so markedly influenced the whole course of operations. I might have talked about Norway in strategy; the malign influence of German possession of its coast and its numerous fjords in the Second World War and its extraordinary significance to-day, the vital issue being whether it can be preserved from Russian domination which would be at least as disastrous from our point of view as was German domination. I might have considered the situation of Italy, so wonderfully shielded from aggression by land by reason of the Alps and the cover afforded by Switzerland but with a portal open at Trieste to a potentially hostile state. As it is I have time only to glance at these things in passing.

I will end with a story told me by General Laycock in 1944, soon after the allied landing in lower Normandy, because I think it illustrates a point I want finally to leave in your minds. At an early stage in the planning he put three small teams, which were not to communicate with each other until they had their results ready, on to the problem of deciding where the landing ought to be made. They all produced the same answer —the bay of the Seine. That appeared to him not only striking but actually perturbing. By this time he knew that the Planning Staff had actually plumped for the bay of the Seine though his teams did not know it, and he thought that if there was such extraordinary unanimity on the subject on our side the German intelligence would certainly have come to the same conclusion. In fact, it does not seem to have done so.

The point I want to make is that to the mind which has been specially trained to work along such lines geography will constantly hold out a key to strategic problems. But it requires intense application and a most diligent accumulation of facts before the problem can be answered with as much certainty and unanimity as it was here. We had got down to it quite steadily; the landing took place in 1944, and I think it was in 1940, after the fall of France, that the Admiralty said it would like to look at my seaside photographs which, curiously enough, included some of the beaches of Hermanville and Lion-sur-Mer. Obviously you will never get either all that application or all that information in time of peace. But we can in time of peace train the minds and the eyes of men so that if ever they are called to walk these paths the way will be familiar to them. I do not know that we do this now in our military educational establishments. We teach topography of course, but that is a narrower subject and, odd though this may sound, the standard of map-reading in a generation of fighting men which has passed through a great war is one of its greatest weaknesses. The unimpeachable authority who told me this the other day said that he thought, where the Army was concerned, this might be due to the wealth of air photographs with which the Army was supplied and the abundance of road signs. Possibly much of our geographical teaching in all fields wants shaking up. The opportunity was never so great and the subject was never so interesting. I am only an amateur in that field, but it seems to me that for those who are experts modern geography may sketch not only the world's past and present but also perhaps its future.

• • • • •

Discussion

The PRESIDENT: You have heard Professor Falls range over a subject as great as the earth and as wide as the mind of man. He has spoken of things that are very near some of those here to-night and among them Field Marshal Montgomery, whom I am going to ask if he will comment on what Professor Falls has said.

Field Marshal LORD MONTGOMERY (Chief of the Imperial General Staff): I must, Mr. President, refuse your invitation to comment on what Professor Falls has said. I should like to say I hardly recognize him by the name of "Professor Falls"; I know him as Cyril Falls. Any comment from me on what he has said would not be right. I have listened to a really supreme exposition of this business of geography and war strategy, and I would say that amongst those who know about it Cyril Falls stands proudly in the front rank. We soldiers deal with a great many military writers and gentlemen of the press at various times; we have complete trust in Cyril Falls.

There are in the world, sir, historians and soldiers, and if it were not for the soldiers the historians would have nothing to write about! They seize on our victories, such as they are, they examine them and explain how much better it would have been if they had been gained in another way; and they cash in on our failures and on the whole they have a very good time. I suppose we provide Cyril Falls with a certain amount of his income, but I do not grudge him one penny of it; he deserves it all and more.

You have asked me, Mr. President, to comment on the lecture and I have refused to do that. I would however like to take up the story and try to link geography to my own profession. I am one of those who believe that what matters in war is the battle, and that the war is won by victories in battle. That needs to be remembered by statesmen in wartime when they are weighing up the military and political considerations and deciding which should carry the most weight. I often used to feel during the war that it was not always realized that political considerations which are going to end in failure are no good; they do not advance the cause of a war. Victories in battle win wars. That being the case, I feel the making of war resolves itself into very simple issues, and the simplest in my view is: what is possible, and what is not possible? In trying to discover what is possible and what is not possible, I would say that three things matter most. I am assuming, of course, that the weapon is a sharp weapon and not a blunt one; that is to say, that you have good armies and so on. I am assuming that you have a good command set up to wield the weapon; and finally that the Allied solidarity is complete. Assuming all that, what is possible will depend firstly on geography, secondly on transportation in its widest sense, and thirdly on administration. Really very simple issues, but geography I think comes first.

. . . . .

I would offer historians this thought: that their great argument for years to come will centre round the development of the Allied strategy after crossing the Seine, that is, after the Normandy battles had been won.

As you know, there were two schools of thought. There was one which wanted to exploit the situation at once and deal a blow which would make quick recovery for the Germans impossible. That school of thought wanted to see a bridgehead over the Rhine, the great Rhine barrier which Cyril Falls mentioned, and wanted to get firmly established on the other side of the Rhine before the bad weather of the winter set in. That bridgehead over the Rhine must give access to the North German plain because it was in that plain that, from the geographical point of view, the promise of decisive results existed. And the object of that school of thought was to shorten the war. It also held that there were possibilities of bringing the war to an end in Europe with a political balance very much more favourable to an early and stable peace than that which we now have. You know the other school of thought; it planned an advance on a broad front, and that school of thought was adopted. Once that broad-front plan was adopted there was no question of finishing the war in 1944; it was obvious that the war must go on into 1945.

After the Falaise battle I do not think I personally had any doubt whatever about our ability to cross the Seine. I cannot remember; I must ask the chief of my Intelligence whom I see here, but I do not think I had any doubt at all. My eyes, and I think the eyes of us all, were fixed on this great geographical barrier of the Rhine. Could we get over the Rhine and get access to that great plain of North Germany? As Cyril Falls explained, we finally went to outflank it in the north.

Another factor—I do not think this has ever been said before—another factor which took us to Nijmegen and Arnhem, instead of farther south down the Rhine, was the V2 attack going on in England. We had settled by the V1 by cutting across the back of the Pas de Calais. I well remember receiving a telegram from London: could we bring relief to England from the V2 menace? That, plus the need to outflank the vital barrier by the northern route, took us up to Nijmegen, Arnhem and so on. You know what happened. We got over every obstacle, every single one, including the Neder Rhin; but the weather went bad on us and we were too weak on the ground, because of this broad front, to offset the bad weather and supply our troops by road. The point really is that even if we had got over the last barrier, we could not have brought the thing to fruition and finished the war because we were not strong enough; and so the war had to go on into the next year.

I would like to say that I agree with practically everything Cyril Falls has said. I do everything he tells me to do; I consider the world as a whole, definitely I obey orders in this respect. In my business as a soldier —I used to be a soldier and I suppose I am still—as I sit in my office I have in front of me a great Map of the World, and all day long I consider that world map as he told us we should do. My own experience is, and I am sure it will be the same for many soldiers in this room, and Lord Chetwode will agree with this, that every single operation that confronts one in battle is in itself unique and it is impossible to consider it in any other way. I was recently reading Winston Churchill's 'Marlborough, his life and times' and I came across this passage: "There is no surer way to disaster than to copy the plans of bygone heroes and to fit them to novel situations." I agree very much with that.

But there is one statement of Cyril Falls with which I do not agree: that the officers of the Army were always dependent on road signs and cannot read maps. I personally travelled over 2000 miles of desert in Africa and I never saw a single road sign. I believe that the officers of the Eighth Army learned a very great deal of geography in the desert. I certainly did. And I learned during the recent war that every situation has to be tackled as a wholly new problem to which there is a wholly new answer. I believe in that very firmly indeed, particularly in the geographical approach and the link between geography and the making of war. Cyril Falls has put that to us to-night extremely clearly.

CHAPTER TWELVE

The Regional Concept

THE DIVERSITY of opinion among geographers concerning the regional concept is perhaps greater than for any other idea in the field of geography. Of the numerous definitions of a region, ranging from "homogeneity of heterogeneous phenomena" to "a generalization about space," all have one underlying idea in common: that a region involves a high degree of similarity and integration in space.

Whether regional or systematic geography is of greater importance is a subject of philosophic discussion among professional geographers, but there is little doubt that regions do exist in an intangible way, and the establishment of effective regional patterns and boundaries makes for a better understanding of the interaction of natural and cultural phenomena.

Regional geography, therefore, provides, if nothing else, convenient areal units for study and analysis. The geographic region is often compared to the "period" of history—the historian delimits time into periods of similarity and integration, while the geographer divides space into regions.

This chapter has been kept as brief as possible, because throughout the book are many types of regional studies that effectively demonstrate the nature of the regional concept as applied in different areas.

82. *Toward a Further Understanding of the Regional Concept* *

Most geographers hold the view that the core of geography is to be found in the regional concept. James is no exception, and this reading shows definitively how the idea of region develops the variety of areal expression found in regions, and the real significance of the concept for students of geography.

The regional concept constitutes the core of geography. This concept holds that the face of the earth can be marked off into areas of distinctive character; and that the complex patterns and associations of phenomena in particular places possess a legible meaning as an ensemble, which, added to the meanings derived from a study of all the parts and processes separately, provides additional perspective and additional depth of understanding. This focus of attention on particular places for the purpose of seeking a more complete understanding of the face of the earth has been the continuous, unbroken theme of geographic study through the ages.

. . . . .

The things geographers deal with on the face of the earth are not uniformly distributed over it. As Hartshorne points out geographers have long selected for study those things which are not uniformly distributed and have rejected as lacking geographical interest those things which are uniformly distributed. There are things which are present in some places, absent from others; or which vary in intensity or motion from place to place. They may be referred to as phenomena which result from the operation of processes. A process, as we understand the term, refers to a sequence of changes systematically related as in a chain of cause and effect. A phenomenon is an observable fact or event which represents the embodiment at any one time of the intellectually-conceived sequence we describe as a process. A geographical phenomenon is any fact or event not uniformly distributed over the face of the earth.

The phenomena which are irregularly distributed over the earth are also irregularly associated with other phenomena in particular parts of the earth. Those phenomena which are systematically related because they

* Preston E. James, "Toward a Further Understanding of the Regional Concept," reprinted from *Annals of the Association of American Geographers,* Vol. 42, Sept. 1952, pp. 195 ff. By permission. (For a brief biographical sketch of Professor James, see Selection 64 on page 571.)

are produced by one kind of process are associated on the face of the earth with other phenomena produced by quite different processes. This is what William Morris Davis means when he writes of "natural but unsystematic groupings." The phenomena associated in a particular place are unsystematically related because they are produced by different processes.

. . . . .

Obviously no one person could embrace the whole field of geography, any more than one person could embrace the whole of the field of history. A geographer must become especially competent in some restricted part of the field: in the study of a selected group of related processes as they operate in a few specific parts of the world. As Ackerman recognizes, the geographer must specialize both topically and regionally, or topically within regions. He cannot possibly develop a real competence in the study of all possible processes that are at work in even a restricted part of the earth, nor can he possibly understand all the modifications imposed, in all parts of the world, on those processes in the study of which he is competent. Topical and regional specialization are not separable. It does seem true, however, that knowledge of process is more important than knowledge of place for persons working at the extreme physical end of geography, especially in climatology; whereas knowledge of place is more important than knowledge of process at the opposite end where human behavior is involved.

It is important to understand that no two spots on the face of the earth are identical. Yet one does not have to receive professional training in geography to perceive that there are areas on the earth throughout which a more or less homogeneous association of characteristics exists. The sense of regional uniformities is what we call regionality; regionality is a part of the lay vocabulary and is reflected in many aspects of life, even where a sophisticated definition of boundaries cannot be achieved.

There are, then, areas on the earth which are homogeneous with respect to this or that phenomenon or combination of phenomena. But even the smallest of these homogeneous areas could be subdivided. There is no such thing as a "unit area," an indivisible entity completely uniform in character. Nevertheless, if we are to bring the complexity of the face of the earth into manageable units for the purpose of examining the causes and consequences of area differentiations, it is obviously not possible to examine each minute point separately. The anthropologist defines general classes into which the diverse individuals of a society are grouped; the historian defines certain spans of years as periods each with certain distinctive characteristics; the geologist defines categories of rock in each of which a certain range of characteristics is permitted: this is the method of all science—to define categories in terms of selected criteria.

The region is a geographic generalization. A generalization of the characteristics of area is accomplished by defining categories of area difference in terms of selected criteria. The criteria which are selected must be in terms of a stated objective or problem. For the purposes of a specific problem, it is possible to define and identify areas which are homogeneous in terms of relevant criteria, disregarding, as all generalizations do, conditions which are not homogeneous but which are considered to be irrelevant. A homogeneous area, so defined by announced criteria, must be evaluated, as all generalizations are evaluated, in terms of the purpose for which they are made. A system of regional differences is justified if it illuminates the factors or elements of a problem: it is not justified if it obscures the factors of a problem. Such a generalization of area is based on a selection of parts of a whole for the purpose of clarifying our understanding of a situation which otherwise would remain less clearly understood. Whether, or to what degree, it accomplishes this purpose must be the basis of judgment or critical appraisal. There can be no such thing as a correct system of regions, or a system of "true regions;" no one system of regions is right and all others, wrong: there are as many regional systems as there are problems worth studying.

• • • • •

Areas can be differentiated on the basis of two kinds of conditions. There are the static conditions, the patterns and associations of phenomena which at any one moment of time are fixed and immobile. Static conditions have most commonly been used in the definition of regional systems. It is also possible to define area differences on the basis of the pattern of movement at any one period of time, and these might be designated as kinetic regions. Kinetic regions might be based on such phenomena as traffic flow, commuter movement, or tourist travel.

The phenomena which produce likenesses and differences between places on the face of the earth, whether static or kinetic, form four different kinds of patterns. There are patterns of lines, patterns of points, patterns of areas, and patterns of volumes. Because of the importance of the map as a device for the analysis and presentation of geographic phenomena, these different kinds of patterns are commonly shown as areas, with lines forming the underlying base data. Nevertheless on the face of the earth the patterns are distinctive, and there are many cases when it is important to distinguish between them. Lines are illustrated among the natural features by drainage lines; many of the phenomena produced by man himself are arranged in linear patterns, such as roads, fences, and political boundaries or property lines. The movements characteristic of kinetic regions are usually linear. The nodal region, defined by Whittlesey as being organized around a focus, usually, but not necessarily always, consists of a pattern of lines. We must realize that a line, such as a road, can be transformed into an elongated area by enlarging the scale; on the other hand some lines, such as boundaries, which have the property common to all geometric lines of possessing length but no breadth, remain lines regardless of change of scale. Many settlement forms are arranged in patterns of points, as are also mines, manufacturing establishments, and other human phenomena. Like lines, many kinds of points become discrete areas upon enlargement; but the points used in geodesy remain points at all scales.

Some phenomena form patterns of areas or patterns of volumes. For example, soil types cover areas, as do also many of the forms of land use and forest cover, or the national territories of politically organized units. Air masses and climates are actually volumes, although mapping techniques usually require that they appear as areas.

. . . . .

When we attempt to go beyond the logical definition of the regional concept and to indicate what must be done, operationally, to identify meaningful regional patterns, we come at once to the problem of scale, or degree of generalization. Some degree of generalization is required if we are to define a homogeneous area no matter how small, for we must keep in mind that no two points on the face of the earth are identical. There is no such thing as a "unit area" which is truly and completely uniform in all its components. Sometimes we are inclined to think of such a feature as a single field of corn as constituting a unit which is not further divisible. The fact is, however, that in many corn fields less than half of the area of the field has corn on it. The field of corn is a generalization, defined by the presence of corn (which is relevant to a problem involving agricultural land use) and disregarding those parts of the area not used for corn (which are considered irrelevant to the problem). Even the smallest area, examined more closely, would obviously be further divisible into more minute parts.

When we view the earth more broadly the degree of generalization necessary for the identification of homogeneous areas becomes greater, and the scale of the maps we use becomes smaller. What factors determine the degree of generalization most appropriate for a particular kind of problem? What is it that determines the smallest degree of generalization that we consider worth making?

. . . . .

The regional concept involves the idea that there are associations of phenomena to be observed on the earth; that these associations, and the patterns of their individual elements, are significant of the interacting processes at work on the earth; and that these associations give character to particular places. For some purposes the synthetic approach to the definition of area associations may be justified: especially for pedagogical purposes the simplicity of a synthetic region, like the basin floor cleared for farming, and the steep, rocky, uncleared slopes, may offer a compelling reason supporting this kind of approach. Some geographers, however, will prefer to develop their more highly generalized regional systems on the basis of the cartographic analysis of component parts, building up by analysis rather than asserting by an initial synthesis.

By these various methods, however, geographers are seeking accordant relationships, and having discovered them to demonstrate the causal connections through the study of the processes involved. Simply to define and map a system of regions without investigation of underlying processes operating through time, and without showing clearly the relevance of the regional system to the underlying purpose, comes perilously close to what Kimble calls "doodling." The regional concept, as presented here, involves the time perspective as an integral part.

Geographical study based on the regional concept recognizes the need for focusing attention on place rather than on isolated process. It accepts from other fields the illumination cast by knowledge of process as it operates in an isolated system, and clearly recognizes the extraordinarily fruitful methodology of process study. But the geographical field also can make distinct contributions. It contributes to an understanding of the meaning of area differentiation, and of the operation of processes in particular places. It focuses attention on the modifications in the operation of processes by the other things that are not equal, by noting the actual operation of processes in particular places modified by the presence of the other things unsystematically associated there.

Individual scholars do not attempt to cover this whole broad, complex field. Rather they specialize in small parts of it, topically in certain groups of related processes, and regionally in certain limited areas where conditions are similar. Competence in geography is not easily gained, and even for a limited sector requires a lifetime of devotion. The geographers, whatever their specialties, are united by the concept which underlies all their investigations, and by the cartographic field methods and methods of analysis which lead to a deeper understanding of the meaning of area difference. The concept, to which we have attempted to give both a logical and an operational definition, is the concept of area differentiation based on patterns and associations of phenomena and meaningful in terms of continuing processes of change. This, the common denominator of geographical study, is what we know as the regional concept.

---

83. *The United States—A Study of Unity in Diversity* *

The United States is a political region wherein the underlying unifying concept is that of allegiance of the people to a political ideal; this ideal may be expressed as a belief in freedom and the worth of the individual. Within the territory of the United States, great physical and cultural diversity exist. If these factors were considered separately they might be indications of disunity. Fleure points out regions within the country that reflect interdependence, despite a high degree of integration within each region. This study also shows that penetrating analysis is often achieved more effectively by a foreign than by a native geographer.

It is particularly important at the present time that American and British people should know all they can of one another, and, on both sides, should realise that there are manifold diversities among the people of U.S.A. as among those of Great Britain, indeed specially deep ones conditioned by the vast spaces of U.S.A. and the backgrounds of the diverse groups of immigrants. Nearly 3,000,000 square miles formed of 48 states gives an average size for a state as twice that of Scotland. A few of the original states, it is true, are small, however important they may be; some of the nineteenth-century additions, on the other hand, are very large, Texas being more than twice the size of the whole of the British Isles. The name United States of America was given by the famous thinker Tom Paine, who rendered such great, if at times a little erratic, service to the Founding Fathers. Those fathers included three very different groups. There were, in New England, the descendants of the immigrants of the *Mayflower,* the *Arabella* and other ships of Puritans seeking the opportunity to found communities, usually of strict Calvinists inclined to ostracise, expel, or punish those who did not agree with them. In Pennsylvania,

* Herbert J. Fleure, "The United States—A Study of Unity in Diversity," reprinted from *The Scottish Geographical Magazine,* 1946, Vol. 62, pp. 1–7, by courtesy of the author and of the editor.

The author (1877), Emeritus Professor at the University of Manchester, England, has a long and distinguished record of research and publication in the field of human geography.

there were Quaker groups inspired by William Penn, the aristocratic Englishman whose idealism saw visions centuries ahead of his time. To Maryland and Virginia, North and South Carolina came scions of the British landed gentry, the Washington family being a most notable instance. These families developed estates worked by African slaves in Virginia and farther south, and, with their larger resources, they were able to travel to Europe to be in contact with the critical movements leading to the French Revolution, in which indeed Thomas Jefferson and Tom Paine played their parts.

In New England, the colonists of the *Mayflower* in December 1620 faced the bitter cold of winters with snow on the ground from three to four months and temperatures sometimes falling to 60 or 70 degrees of frost (Fahrenheit). They found it difficult to grow wheat because of rust disease; they saw as the snow melted that rock surfaces (planed by old ice sheets) limited the arable area; they faced vast forests with wild animals and Indians. Nathaniel Hawthorne's *Scarlet Letter* gives a telling account of the superstitions bred by the mystery and danger of the forest, as well as of the rigidity of the Puritan outlook which was not in the least disposed towards freedom of conscience. But with all this went a stern determination, a faith in the future that made them overcome obstacles. Food came through maize planting learned from Indians, and by and by from potatoes and other vegetables, some of which the Pilgrim Fathers brought with them. They cut timber and built clapboard houses with stone hearths and chimneys, and gradually gathered strength and founded villages and towns which were inspired by the gracious traditions of the better building in England of the eighteenth century, traditions that have made many a little New England town a heritage of beauty. "Queen Anne" and "Georgian" houses may have a handsome fanlight over the dignified doorway, often a gambrel or a mansard roof, sometimes a cupola lookout on the middle of the roof-ridge, especially if they are houses of sea captains. The houses often rise from broad unfenced grass verges, sometimes edged with low cut barberry, and they stand in individual dignity, or semi-detached, along tree-lined avenues. And the trees are maples, yellowish crimson in spring, a rich green in summer, and wonderfully aflame in October, or they may be oaks (*Quercus rubra*) with large leaves that take on a deep wine red colour as the maple colours pass away. Their deep red is followed in its turn by the bright red of the dying barberry leaves and the barberry fruits.

The settlers looked to England not only for their house types, but also for their churches, and the influence of Sir Christopher Wren is to be seen all over New England, unfortunately replaced or supplemented here and there by the weakest features of the nineteenth-century Gothic revival.

Generally, however, the white-painted, wood-built village church with its Wren spire is a decorative feature; and it is of special interest to note that in both Old and New England it is the style of the parish church, but, while that parish church in Old England is of the Anglican Communion, in New England it belongs to the Independents (Congregationalists) or some other Puritan group. The Puritans set their stamp on New England, and, on the original hill of Boston, they built rows of fine houses along Beacon Street, Chestnut Street, Mount Vernon Street and around Louisburg Square, making a neighbourhood that would be the pride of any English town if it were lucky enough to possess such a collection.

After the Ice Ages, the rise of sea level flooded the lower ends of the broad rivers of New England and gave endless opportunities for fishing and seamanship, with the great forests to supply timber for shipbuilding which became a highly skilled industry in the first half of the nineteenth century. The schooner-rigged three-masters, sometimes four-masters, sailed the seven seas, and the captains and officers often took their wives with them, so that New England gossip went on around the Horn, and Chinese silks and pots came to New England houses bought sometimes with taste, sometimes without. When iron ships became common, the old industry declined and the old seamanship was lost save in the greater ports, mostly outside New England with the exceptions of Boston and Portland, but even these were outdistanced by New York as the railways and the interior were opened up. Nevertheless, Boston and the surrounding settlements have grown together to form an agglomeration of over two million people, comparable with Philadelphia, Detroit and the San Francisco group, if no longer with New York and Chicago.

Not only did the end of the Ice Ages flood the estuaries, it obstructed the valleys with morainic bars of boulder clay so that, as the rivers re-established themselves, they often found new courses, sometimes leaping down steep slopes that gave water power for textile mills. Irish immigrants, followed later by Italians, French Canadians and others, were drawn into the factory towns that grew in the nineteenth century, and the large families of the operatives came to be contrasted with the small families of the older settlers who directed the industry. So New England has changed, and is changing, from its older Puritan tradition to a newer order in which Roman Catholicism plays a very large part. The Puritan tradition, too, has changed of itself largely through late eighteenth- and nineteenth-century contacts with European movements. The old Calvinism has often transformed itself into Unitarianism or something akin to this, and "The King's Chapel," as it is still called in Boston because it was the official place of worship of the Governor of Massachusetts in

Colonial days, uses a revision of the Anglican Book of Common Prayer edited to remove features to which Unitarian thinkers took exception.

The opening up of the interior not only gave New York its supreme position in the life of the U.S.A., it led New England farmers to leave the pockets of poor soil in order to occupy the fertile lands that became the state of Ohio. So it has come about that decayed farms and decayed shipbuilding, and beautiful little towns with memories of a more active past, are features of New England. Yet, these north-eastern states maintain themselves on skilled industries, among which those of Waltham and Waterbury watches are widely known, and on commerce and science, which last has become vastly important at Harvard University in Cambridge, now effectively a part of the Boston agglomerate, and at the Massachusetts Institute of Technology (M.I.T.) in Boston as well as at Harvard's slightly younger competitor, Yale, in New Haven, Connecticut. These are but the more famous of a number of centres of learning, among which geographers in particular well know Clark University, Worcester, Mass., where our subject receives special attention.

New York, the New Amsterdam of Dutch settlers of the seventeenth century, on the splendid Hudson, grew especially when the Hudson-Mohawk gap became available for communication, particularly by rail. By this time the original Dutch element had become outnumbered by Irish, British, Germans, and Jews from several central European countries. It is therefore all the more interesting that the old Dutch contribution has become prominent—for example, in the Roosevelt family, to name only one among several. The magnificence of the streets, the Central Park, the skyscrapers (better called towers) of Manhattan, the wonderful spaciousness of the harbour, the riches of the museums, and the degradation of the coloured quarter of Harlem are too well known to need discussion. It may, however, be useful to point out that only to a slight extent in Greenwich Village, downtown, does New York have anything comparable with the historic quarter of Boston. Boston has its old State House of 1710, its South Meeting from which the citizens went to throw the tea into the harbour, its Faneuil Hall, one of the chief cradles of the Revolution. New York has little remaining even from the early years of the nineteenth century. Its unique and rapid growth has transformed it; and it has been said, with only very fractional truth, that Boston's future is in the past and New York's past in the future. Actually there is scope for both, and Boston's tradition is being handed on to the immigrants of many nationalities, whatever may be the fate of its old families.

Independence Hall and the American Philosophical Society, in Philadelphia, are inheritances from the Revolution and Benjamin Franklin, while Bryn Mawr College for women with its high academic reputation springs from the Quaker tradition of the city and the state. The city, a centre of varied industry, commerce and finance, though long since outpaced by New York and Chicago, is still the third in the U.S.A., or the fourth if we consider the Boston agglomerate as the real unit in place of the officially delimited city. The interior of the state has numbers of what are called "Pennsylvania Dutch," the word Dutch being a corruption of Deutsch. These people are German Lutherans long settled in the U.S.A. but still clinging to linguistic and religious associations brought from Europe.

Were this article an attempt to describe the U.S.A., it would be most important to enlarge upon Washington in which the great republic has tried to express its unity, but we are concerned rather with the diversity of elements of tradition that are interweaving themselves into American life, so we may pass on. Maryland and its great city of Baltimore give notice, in their flowers and in their people, that we are nearing the south, and, once in Virginia, there is no doubt that we are among the successors of plantation owners and the children of the slaves.

Of the first five of the Presidents of the U.S.A. only the second, Adams, belonged to Boston. Washington, Jefferson, Madison, and Monroe belonged to Virginia. But since then Virginia has given only one Vice-President, who became President because the elected President died. Some old family names are still found in the south, but the old order has changed. Mansions with pillared fronts, which Jefferson's prestige as an amateur architect helped to spread, may now be inhabited by hirelings or may have fallen still lower. Coloured labour is everywhere, and only germs of a real effort to lift that element to a level of dignity and responsibility are apparent. The U.S.A. is here faced with an insoluble problem, to be softened by goodwill, time and compromise and, especially, a humane as well as a technological education. The problem is made no easier by the losses of the cotton planters through the boll weevil, by their neglect of the education of the coloured folk to better cultivation, and by the outbursts of prejudice and violence that all serious Americans deplore. The situation is such that unprincipled agitators have more than once caused crises and gained political power for a time, and there still linger old hatreds from the days of the Civil War. Lincoln was murdered, and his immediate successors were incompetent to work out ideals he had for both the south and the north. Among the monuments of Virginia is its University at Charlotteville, planned academically and architecturally by Jefferson after he retired from the Presidency of the U.S.A. at the age of 69. Like everything else coming from that mind, the University is original in style and arrangement of its buildings, probably the most artistic buildings of the days before the twentieth century in North America.

The wide spaces between the Appalachians and the Rockies, with only a few local fragments of very moderate highland, vary from the almost Scandinavian Minnesota to the still somewhat French-flavoured Louisiana, with a decrease of the coloured element as we go north, but not such a marked decrease as of old because the coloured folk are moving bit by bit to the greater opportunities of the north and away from the increasingly felt inhibitions of the deep south.

Apple and other orchards south of the great lakes, corn (*i.e.* maize), spring wheat, winter wheat, and cotton characterise the farming until we reach the drier cattle-lands towards the Rockies, into which cultivation spread too far in the war of 1914–18 and gave rise to the dustbowls of the dry years of the early 'thirties. A population ready to move on west is less careful of its soil than a long settled peasantry, and still less thoughtful about the forests which, where they existed towards the Appalachians, should have been preserved as sponges to hold up the water and so prevent the floods of the Ohio which have brought so much destruction from time to time. Industry has added itself to cultivation and Pittsburgh's smoke pall is perhaps worse than any we have in Britain. Cleveland on Lake Erie smelts iron from the south-west of Lake Superior with coal brought down to the lakeside from Pittsburgh. And Chicago, with its stockyards, its mills, its meat, its splendid lakeside drive and its crowded streets still darkened by the overhead railways that New York has almost discarded, has hoped to become the great city of the U.S.A. It still has much to do before it rivals New York but it has risen to second place, and Detroit may be about fifth or sixth.

The express train takes about nine hours to traverse the plains of Kansas with widely spaced homesteads lost in the level immensity. Isolation, save for radio and automobile, is written over the face of many a great stretch of the Middle West. In these great areas groups of immigrants from several European countries are able to cling to the language and religious ceremonies of their old homes and so to delay complete absorption into the unity of the republic of which they are usually loyal and industrious citizens. The immense Mississippi basin is full of economic possibilities as well as of political problems for the United States. Soil conservation, care of forests, reduction of isolation are all prime needs that the isolated farmer often does not realise. Unfortunately the situation has sometimes given opportunities to political "bosses" and their nominees, as is only too easy to understand.

The deserts of the south-west, from the Grand Canyon to the Mexican border, impress the visitor with their great long rock-scarps, fantastically worn, rising out of the desert plain that may be covered with sage brush and cacti of many kinds. Scrub cattle mysteriously find food in these dry lands, and drink from irrigation ditches which also refresh patches of cultivation near the occasional towns. But there is the danger of too much evaporation and a resulting deposition of salt, and the dams of the irrigation reservoirs are apt to accumulate salt. Here again, then, careful administration will be needed to maintain economic utilisation. It is characteristic of the U.S.A. that a great motor road, beautifully surfaced, streaks across the wastes right-away to California.

In California we see not only the wonderful beauty of the Sierra Nevada, the Yosemite, the fruit groves of the Santa Clara Valley, the rich colours of the giant redwoods, but also the achievements of a hundred years of work on a basis provided by the older Spanish missions. San Francisco, with Oakland, Berkeley, and other settlements around its bay, looks forward to becoming the premier city of the U.S.A.—perhaps, say some citizens, of the Pacific, or even, they may add with characteristic enthusiasm, of the world. The summer fog-belt near the Golden Gate was long a trouble, but hopes are entertained that Radar will get over this and ensure San Francisco's superiority over its hastily developing rivals, Los Angeles, already well over the million mark, and San Diego. In San Francisco, Chinatown is not only a picturesque attraction for visitors, it is a sign of racial problems, different it is true from those accompanying the children of the slaves in the southern states, but a basis of prejudice against people of Chinese, and especially of Japanese, ancestry, though they may be well established Americans even of the second or third generation. California has to think of forest conservation, of irrigation control to avoid salting, of the future exhaustion of mineral oils, of the care of her soil, but for the time being she seems to prosper and to look forward to a great future.

In north-western U.S.A., Portland (Oregon) and Seattle (Washington) have become large commercial centres and ports for a country with a magnificent supply of fine timber. The great pines of the hillsides may cluster round some high and lonely volcanic peak projecting above the snow line. But even here the main lines of development seem to be laid down.

This look and fragmentary survey has taken us around some larger regions of the U.S.A. and should enable us to draw the inference that there is no longer an open and unknown west to absorb those who cannot quite find a suitable means of livelihood in their homes, either in Europe or in Atlantic America. It may even be suggested that the open west of the nineteenth century was a more important factor of the evolution of *laissez faire* and liberal democracy than has sometimes been realised. At any rate, the great republic has to face new adjustments and policies to avoid unemployment and social disintegration. The economic systems of America, Britain, and Europe have to depend more on controls and conservation even if Britain still has something of the open frontier in parts of the Dominions. Broadly, there are growing analogies between the problems of the U.S.A. and of the British Commonwealth, analogies which are gradually replacing earlier contrasts when Britain itself, with its dependence on industry and commerce, loomed larger in our Commonwealth life. We, in Britain, have spent almost our all in defence of ourselves and of the U.S.A., as the American Chief of Staff, General Marshall, so generously said. We are as little accustomed to being debtors as our American friends are to being creditors, after many years in which they had to have an export surplus to cover the interest on bonds held in Britain as mortgages on American railroads. In the last quarter of the nineteenth century the railroad bonds and shares of the U.S.A. were a major feature of our London Stock Exchange activities. Now they are not dealt in enough to make them worth quoting on the finance page of most of our London dailies.

From this it follows that, along with growing analogies in the matter of economic controls, employment policy, social security and international relations, there goes an increasing commercial diversity. We cannot import as freely as of old; we now lack the wherewithal to pay for luxuries we used to enjoy. Our American friends, on the other hand, will need to adjust themselves to increased imports if they are to receive any interest from their numerous debtors.

In both America and Britain the great experiment goes on, aiming at the freest possible choice of persons to exercise government over us and to change our government without violence or proscription. In both, the new conditions of economic activity of governments make these ideals more difficult without making them impossible. Long British experience and American freshness can supplement one another if there be a reasonable realisation of one another's problems as well as of one's own opportunities for service. It has been the aim of this short summary of a lecture to promote that realisation on our part, a realisation which is one of the most urgent needs of the world today.

84. *Economic Regionalization of the Soviet Union* *

The economic regions of the Soviet Union are of particular interest because they represent, in part, a planned organization of space. That the evolution of the regional pattern is strikingly similar to that found in the United States is evidence of the important role played by historical evolution and the existing distributions of minerals and other physical environmental factors. This article further effectively demonstrates that use of the regional concept provides a framework for analysis of large and diverse areas.

Despite the profound historical and politico-economic differences between the United States and the Soviet Union, the trends in the economic regionalization of the two countries have been surprisingly similar. Both have had a stable core area that has persisted in importance. In both, increasing economic decentralization, reduction of regional inequalities, and displacement of economic activity from agricultural to mineral producing areas have been significant. Differential rates of displacement for various economic factors have been evident in both. The primary difference has been in the speed of regional economic displacment and readjustment; that is, speed relative to the rate of over-all economic growth. This has been greater in the United States than in the Soviet Union.

Over the past 25 years the pattern of Russia's economic geography has been twice recast, and a third reformation is under way. The earliest pattern, characterized by the concentration of economic development west of the Volga and the Caspian Sea, was inherited from pre-Revolutionary Russia; in its formation, mining and allied heavy manufacturing had been less influential than other factors, especially preindustrial demography. The second pattern was the fruit of the First Five-Year Plan; it was dominated, to an extraordinary degree, by the attempt to maximize the output of mining and allied heavy manufacturing while minimizing over-all investment, and it resulted in an efficient but rigid economic layout.

The third pattern, which exists today, reflects, above all, the impact of World War II, postwar territorial acquisitions, and economic rehabilitation on the economic-geographical structure inherited from the First Five-

* Demitri B. Shimkin, "Economic Regionalization in the Soviet Union," from *Geographical Review,* Vol. 42, 1952, pp. 591–614; published by the American Geographical Society, New York.

The author (1917) is a Research Associate in the Russian Research Center, Harvard University. He is engaged almost exclusively in research on the Soviet Union and has published several articles on Soviet economy.

Year Plan. Adjustments of the growing conflicts between the consequences of that plan and the increasing strategic and economic needs for a more nearly balanced development have been far less important.

The objective of the present study is threefold. First, it seeks to determine the impact of industrialization, from 1926 to 1950, on the patterning of Soviet regional development. Second, it attempts to assess the possible effects of current Soviet plans and of the greater utilization of underdeveloped human and physical resources on the future economic geography of the country. Third, it compares the patterns, processes, and rates of regional economic development evident in the U.S.S.R. between 1926 and 1950 with those characterizing the United States during a period of comparable *relative* growth, 1900–1950.

Regional Development Before 1926

Before the Revolution the economic geography of the Russian Empire largely reflected, on the one hand, preindustrial demographic distributions and historic trade routes, and on the other the rapid expansion of foreign trade, of the rail network, and of agricultural lands. The oases of Central Asia, the valleys of the Transcaucasus, the plains of Crimea, the Western Ukraine, and Central Russia had been densely populated long before the twentieth century. With few exceptions, such as Khar'kov and Baku, the great cities of Imperial Russia lay on the tracks of ancient trade routes: Tashkent-Astrakhan-Saratov-Kazan'-Nizhne Novogorod (Gor'kii)-Moscow-St. Petersburg (Leningrad); the Black Sea-Kiev, thence west via L'vov to Cracow or north to the Gulf of Finland or Riga.

During the nineteenth century the political and economic geography of the Russian Empire changed profoundly. Finland, Bessarabia, the Transcaucasus, Central Asia, and the Far East south of the Amur all came under Russian rule. The Ukraine, peaceful at last, developed rapidly as an exporting agricultural region; this led, among other consequences, to the rise of Odessa. The construction of railroads connecting the Ukraine with Central and Northwest Russia expanded the domestic grain market and accelerated thereby a transition, in the latter areas, from marginal agriculture combined with cottage industry to urban employment. The rise of textile manufacturing, largely working American cotton and domestic flax, was especially important. Toward the turn of the century a great influx of foreign capital further speeded railroad construction, and also the development of export industries—petroleum and manganese in the Transcaucasus, grain and coal in the Ukraine, dairy products in the Baltic States, and timber in North Russia. St. Petersburg and the Baltic States became heavy importers of foreign products, both manufactures and raw materials. Finally, the unending demands of the railroads stimulated the growth of heavy industry in the Donets Basin. This region, accessible to superb resources of iron ore, coal, and refractories, well located with respect to food supplies and a developing system of transportation, rapidly relegated the old metallurgical establishments of the Urals and Central Russia to insignificance. A parallel development, centered on the Dombrova coal fields, took place in Poland.

In Asiatic Russia, basically important rail lines were completed between the 1880's and the Russo-Japanese War, particularly the Transsiberian (by way of Manchuria) and the Volga-Tashkent-Caspian loop. These, in turn, set the scene for major agricultural changes: large-scale settlement in Western Siberia; and in Central Asia, an ever-hastening shift from subsistence farming and livestock raising to cotton for Central Russian mills.

At the end of the Revolution and Civil War, the Soviet Union inherited a setting for rapid industrialization. The loss of Polish coal and manufacturing capacity intensified the need for quick increases in the Ukraine to supply Northwest Russia. The achievement of direct rule in Central Asia, replacing the protectorates of Tsarist times, also expanded markets and strengthened the need for industrial growth in the Urals. Only in the Far East, increasingly cut off from Manchurian trade, and lacking a significant substitute base in human or physical resources, was the situation unfavorable for development.

In general, the economic geography of the Soviet Union in the late 1920's may be summarized as follows. Central Russia and the Ukraine together held almost half of the country's population, total and urban, and 46 per cent of the sown area. They generated 51 per cent of the electricity, produced 42 per cent of the mineral output. Their significance for a series of mineral nonintensive industries was enormous: 96.5 per cent of the sugar, 89.4 per cent of the cotton cloth, 53.9 per cent of the shoes, and 49.6 per cent of the flour manufactured in the U.S.S.R. came from these two regions. Within them originated or terminated 54 per cent of the nation's freight traffic.

Northwest Russia, though poor in cultivated land and mineral output, had exceptionally important processing industries based on imported raw materials. About a quarter of the nation's output of machines, including 44.8 per cent of the electrical equipment, came from Leningrad. Among the mineral nonintensive manufactures, rubber (75 per cent of the country's total production), paper, shoes, and tobacco were especially significant. In all, Northwest Russia was by far the most urbanized part of the Soviet Union, with the greatest per capita supply of electric power, a fact making for high labor productivity. With less than 4 per cent of the country's population, this region had almost 13 per cent of the large-city folk, 23 per cent of the electric power.

Other regions remained undeveloped. North Russia's sole important enterprise was lumber and paper production. The Caucasus specialized in petroleum production and refining but were otherwise almost wholly devoted to agriculture and handicrafts. The eastern regions—Volga, Urals, Siberia, and Turkestan—were overwhelmingly agricultural. In them lived a third of the total population; their sown areas aggregated 38 per cent of the country's whole. In large-city population, in rail-freight movement, in mining, and, especially, in electric-power production, their shares were disproportionately small. The east did not hold a single one of the six manufacturing centers with a gross output above $100,000,000 (1937 United States prices): Leningrad, Moscow, Yaroslavl-Ivanovo (largely textiles), the Donets Basin (steel), Odessa (flour milling), and Baku (petroleum).

The First Five-Year Plan and Its Consequences

In 1928 the Soviet Union launched its first program of intensified industrialization. This plan envisaged devoting 82 per cent of investments to mining and mineral-intensive industries. The geographical aspects of the First Five-Year Plan, probably influenced in their formulation by the earlier experiences of the United States, emphasized the cardinal importance of regional specialization and nation-wide economic interchange. They delineated four types of economic regions: industrial (both actual and potential), agricultural, mixed, and timber-producing. Industrial regions fell into two groups. The first, Leningrad Oblast and the Central Industrial Region, were already important as centers of medium and light industries. Their critical development needs before conversion into centers of heavy, mineral-intensive manufacturing were cheap, high-capacity transportation from mineral—and food—surplus areas, and, to a smaller extent, an augmented local fuel production. In the second category of industrial regions were those with large, but incompletely balanced, mineral resources —above all, coking coal or iron ore. Two such regions, the Ukraine and the Urals, were already partly developed; the third, chosen from a considerable range of possibilities, was the Kuznetsk Basin of Western Siberia. In all, somewhat more than 60 per cent of the total Five-Year Plan investment fell to a few favored regions and their interconnections. The axes Leningrad–Moscow–Eastern Ukraine and Moscow–Urals–Kuznetsk Basin were to be developed as the nation's industrial core; subsidiary specialization in agricultural, lumber, petroleum, or other raw-materials production was the lot of the other economic regions. Even in the low-priority sector of mineral nonintensive industries, 50 per cent of the planned investment fell to Central Russia, the Ukraine, and Northwest Russia.

Unbalanced investment led to unbalanced growth. The extreme concentration of light industry in Central Russia, the Ukraine, and Northwest Russia continued: in 1935 these three regions were still producing 96 per cent of the nation's cotton cloth, 94 per cent of its sugar, 75 per cent of its shoes, and 74 per cent of its paper. Their proportion of the national mineral output increased from 43 per cent to 45 per cent; otherwise their significance remained stable or declined very slightly. Thus, in the mid-1930's, they still accounted for 64 per cent of the country's electric-power output, 60 per cent of its rail freight originated and terminated, 58 per cent of its large-city population, 51 per cent of its total population, and 45 per cent of its sown acreage.

Elsewhere in the Soviet Union, extremely rapid gains were made by the Urals and Western Siberia. Their electric-power output soared from some 3 per cent of the national aggregate to 16 per cent; their mineral output, from 12 per cent to almost 20 per cent. Rail traffic increased from 10 to 15 per cent; urban population, from 7 to 11 per cent. The relative growths in total population and sown acreage were much smaller—respectively from 12 to 14 per cent and from 13 to 16 per cent of the U.S.S.R. totals.

Natural increases in Turkestan and net immigration in Eastern Siberia and the Soviet Far East caused rapid population growth in these other regions of Asiatic Russia. Their share of the total Soviet population rose from 10 per cent in 1926 to 14 per cent in 1939. On the other hand, neither sown acreage nor electric output increased more rapidly than the all-Union average. The sharp upswing in mining, which reached 6.8 per cent of the Soviet total in 1937, was probably the dynamic for moderate gains in rail traffic and urban population.

Finally, the development of the secondary economic regions of European Russia—North Russia, Byelorussia (the Baltic region), the Volga, the North Caucasus, and the Transcaucasus—lagged in every way. The relative contributions of these regions to the nation's large-city population, rail freight, electric-power output, and mineral production declined rapidly.

The concentration of economic growth in a small number of widely separated yet intimately related centers of heavy industry produced extreme congestion on their intercommunications, since the Soviets begrudged the construction of new rail lines. In 1928, for example, less than 5 per cent of the Soviet trackage carried two to three times the average freight loading, 1.21 million metric ton-miles per mile; less than 15 per cent carried less than half the average loading. By 1937, however, more than 14 per cent of the trackage was carrying two to *six* times the average (now, 4.18 million metric ton-miles per mile); nearly 39 per cent, less than half the average. As a matter of fact, 70 per cent of the freight loaded in 1937 originated in only 12.5 per cent of the stations; two-thirds of the unloadings, in 9 per cent of the stations.

In general, the great, the overwhelming, role of mineral production and the mineral-intensive industries in the capital development program of the Soviet Union is clear from many lines of evidence. For example, 13 out of the 16 industrial areas developed since 1926 have been primarily either mineral-processing or metal-fabricating centers. Only Kiev, Novosibirsk, and Tashkent are significant essentially for food processing, textiles, or other light industries (Fig. 34). The pace of railroad construction between 1928 and World War II was far slower than in pre-Revolutionary days. Of the new lines, furthermore, the great bulk were designed to carry minerals and had little significance for agricultural development and settlement. Notable illustrations are found in Turkestan (Kandagach-Guryev, for petroleum; Petropavlovsk-Karaganda to Lake Balkhash and Dzhezhazgan, for coal and copper; Akmolinsk-Kartaly, for coal shipments to Magnitogorsk), Western Siberia (the Kuznetsk Basin network), the Urals (Chelyabinsk to Magnitogorsk, and to Orsk-Chkalov; the Serov network), and North Russia (Konosha-Kotlas-Vorkuta, for coal). The lines opening up new agricultural areas or markets have been few: the Turkestan-Siberian railroad, connecting Central Asia with Western Siberia; the Tatarsk-Pavlodar line, also running into Turkestan; and the Kazan'-Sverdlovsk railroad about sum up the list.

Changes and Continuities to 1950

By the middle 1930's the economic and strategic inadequacies of the pattern laid out by the First Five-Year Plan, and continued in the Second, had become obvious to the Soviet government. As a result, the Third Five-Year Plan, covering the years 1938 through 1942, embodied a radically altered theory of regional development. Its fundamental emphasis was the reverse of the earlier one; that is, it sought a maximum of regional self-sufficiency rather than interdependence, homogeneous development rather than specialization. To attain this goal, it devised new, larger economic regions, to be ultimately capable of both agricultural and industrial development. These regions have, with minor alterations, survived up to the present time.

It was hoped, though often on inadequate evidence, that these new regions might achieve substantial autonomy in fuel, cement, gypsum, mineral fertilizer, glass, food, and consumers' goods. New industrial development was to be concentrated near sources of raw materials and fuel;

the plan prohibited further industrial expansion in the crowded cities of Moscow, Leningrad, Kiev, Khar'kov, Rostov, Gor'kii, and Sverdlovsk. In general, new construction was to take place in the eastern regions; for example, three-quarters of all the new blast furnaces were to be located there. In particular, the plan contemplated rapid development of the Soviet Far East, which was to acquire by 1942 a capacity of 680,000 metric tons of pig iron and 890,000 metric tons of steel, as well as a truck-manufacturing plant and many other establishments. Eastern Siberia was also to be developed as a significant center of ferrous metallurgy. Although the plan anticipated that the predominance of Central Russia and the Ukraine in light industry would continue, the share of Western Siberia and Turkestan in cotton spinning was to rise from 2.4 per cent of the national total to 10 per cent.

During these years the Soviets were also building up plans for the continued development of the country in 1942 to 1947. These programs stressed uniform development but put far greater weight on intensified use of the water resources than in earlier Soviet experience. The largest undertaking, outlined for completion by 1947, was the Volga Basin plan, which had been admittedly influenced in its formulation by American experience. The Volga plan was revived in 1950 and will be described below. Here it is pertinent to state only that the plan hoped to industrialize the Volga Region and also to integrate economically the vast area extending from Central Russia to the Urals.

Despite these plans, the increasing diversion of Soviet resources directly to armaments permitted little progress up to the German invasion in 1941. Only in the development of local fuel production did the Soviets have much success. But the disastrous German break-through in the Ukraine in August, 1941, forced the Soviets to a new, desperate policy of economic displacement. In the fall and winter of 1941 the Russians evacuated to the east 1360 large plants, producing a wide variety of important manufactures, a quarter of them from Moscow and Leningrad. Of these factories, 455 were installed in the Urals, 250 in Turkestan, 210 in western Siberia, and 200 in the Volga Region; the fates of the others have not been stated. Most of Leningrad's vital electronics industry moved to western Siberia, and also a considerable fraction of the Ukrainian sugar-refining capacity, though the Ukrainian shoe factories were shipped to Central Asia. In general, the war forced the development of certain regions and certain parts of the economy at rates completely unforeseen in earlier Soviet planning. For example, the Urals were exceeding before the end of the war the aluminum production envisaged for them for 1947. Similar frenzied growth took place in Central Russian lignite production and in the Pechora coal field. In contrast, there was not only the destruction of industry in the war-

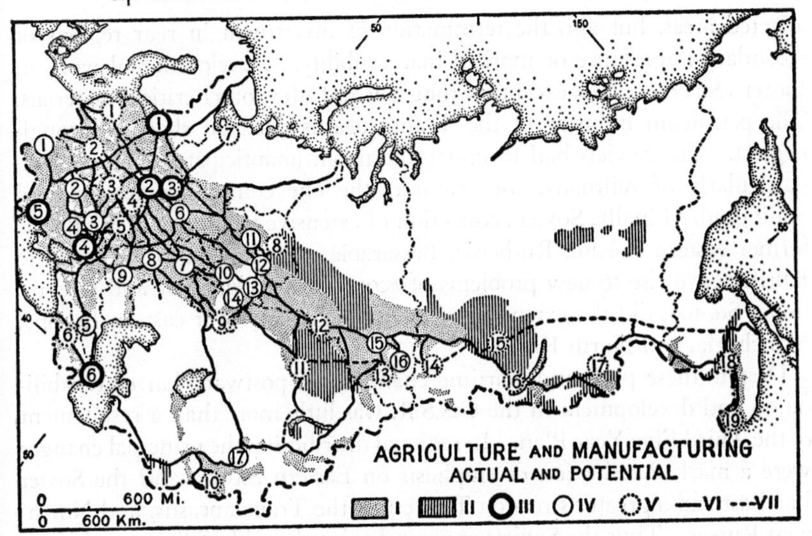

FIGURE 34

Agricultural and manufacturing areas, actual and potential. Numerals refer to legend below.

I. Agricultural areas substantially occupied in 1935.

II. Potential agricultural areas (with deciduous, forest-steppe, and grassland vegetation) undeveloped in 1935.

III. Manufacturing centers with estimated annual output exceeding $100,000,000 in 1926 (U. S. 1937 prices):

1. Leningrad
2. Moscow
3. Yaroslavl-Ivanovo
4. Donets Basin
5. Odessa
6. Baku

IV. Manufacturing centers with estimated annual output exceeding $100,000,000, developed or acquired since 1926:

1. L'vov
2. Kiev
3. Khar'kov
4. Dnepr Complex
5. Grozny
6. Gor'kii
7. Kuibyshev
8. Saratov
9. Stalingrad
10. Ufa
11. Molotov-Berezniki
12. Nizhni Tagil-Sverdlovsk
13. Chelyabinsk-Zlatoust
14. Magnitogorsk
15. Novosibirsk
16. Kuznetsk Basin Complex
17. Tashkent

V. Locations favorable to developing manufacturing centers:

1. Riga
2. Minsk
3. Bryansk
4. Tula
5. Voronezh
6. Tbilisi
7. Arkhangel'sk-Molotovsk
8. Serov Complex
9. Orsk
10. Stalinabad-Termez
11. Karaganda-Akmolinsk
12. Omsk
13. Barnaul-Biysk
14. Minusinsk
15. Bratsk
16. Irkutsk
17. Sretensk-Bukachacha
18. Khabarovsk
19. Vladivostok-Voroshilov

VI. Railroads carrying more than four million metric tons in 1949.

VII. Major railroads planned or under construction.

affected areas, but also the termination of investment in rear regions of secondary importance or marked inaccessibility. Developmental work in Eastern Siberia ceased, except for tungsten and a few other critical materials. The petroleum industry of the Transcaucasus declined sharply through neglect. The Soviets had to undertake much unanticipated construction, particularly of railroads; for example, the one connecting Kazan' and Stalingrad. Finally, Soviet acquisition of extensive territories in the Baltic, former eastern Poland, Ruthenia, Bessarabia, southern Sakhalin, and the Kuriles gave rise to new problems of economic development and integration. So, too, did the extension of Soviet hegemony over eastern Europe, Manchuria, and North Korea.

Despite these profound wartime changes, the postwar plan of rehabilitation and development in the U.S.S.R. was little more than a restatement of the Third Five-Year Plan. In regional distribution the principal changes were a marked reduction of emphasis on Eastern Siberia and the Soviet Far East and a greater stress on Turkestan, the Transcaucasus, and Northwest Russia. Thus the Soviets apparently abandoned building up pig-iron and steel capacity in Eastern Siberia, and early completion of the Baikal-Amur Railroad. On the other hand, they laid great emphasis on a radical improvement of rail communications in Turkestan, with new lines connecting Karaganda to the Kuznetsk Basin, and to the Tashkent area. They stressed intensive geological exploration to lay the foundations for a steel plant near Karaganda. They planned to establish a large fertilizer industry in Central Asia and to revive the program of expanded textile output there. The Transcaucasus was to receive a steel mill, a truck factory, and other important installations. For Northwest Russia the Soviets contemplated replacing Leningrad's war-destroyed steel industry with a new plant at Cherepovets, fantastically designed to be supplied with coal from Pechora and low-grade iron ore from the Kola Peninsula. Other war-damaged areas were in essence to be restored to prewar levels of output. The Ukraine, for instance, was to be again, in 1950, the source of some 70 per cent of Russia's sugar. Estonian textile output was to be rehabilitated.

In the Fourth Five-Year Plan, as in the Third, an unexpectedly heavy load of armaments exercised a profound effect on Russia's investment program. In general, the Soviets succeeded, between 1946 and 1950, in rehabilitating the heavy industry damaged by the war. But with few exceptions, such as the development of fertilizer capacity in Turkestan, their program of new construction had barely been started by the end of 1950. None of the railroads or the steel plants mentioned earlier were finished.

In all, the effects of 25 years of intense, though disrupted, economic growth on the regional structure of Russia appear to be the following. Important continuities are evident. Central Russia and the Ukraine are still the economic heart of the Soviet Union, accounting in 1950 as in 1926 for some 45 per cent of the country's total and urban population and sown acreage, but their significance in rail traffic, in electric-power output, and in mining has declined. North Russia, Eastern Siberia, and the Soviet Far East remain virtually undeveloped, contributing less than 5 per cent each to the nation's total in every major economic sphere. Some regional shifts have taken place, notably the increased significance of the Urals, Western Siberia, and Turkestan and the greatly reduced importance of the Caucasus and Northwest Russia. Yet, so far as the scanty and none too reliable data indicate, economic concentration in the Soviet Union has not changed greatly. For example, in 1926 half the country's mineral output came from the Ukraine and the Transcaucasus; in 1950 the Ukraine and the Urals provided this share. In 1926 the Ukraine and Central Russia produced 60 per cent of the country's electric power; in these regions originated and terminated 55 per cent of the nation's rail freight. These proportions may now be attributed to three regions: the Ukraine, Central Russia, and the Urals.

While economic concentration has—by and large—continued, the foci of mineral output on the one hand, and of population and sown acreage on the other, have shifted respectively eastward and westward. As a result, the significance of regional interdependence and the pressure on Soviet transportation are greater now than ever before.

In 1926 the Urals, Siberia, and Turkestan were underdeveloped areas, important only as producers of agricultural and mineral raw materials. Today the Urals, characterized by the highest per capita mineral and electric-power output of all the economic regions in the Soviet Union, may well lead in productivity. On a per capita basis, the most poverty-stricken part of the Soviet Union now appears to be the Baltic.

Finally, no economic region of the Soviet Union, as defined officially in 1946, is self-sufficient. The closest approach to autarky is found in the Urals, but even they are weak in coking coal and lacking in cotton, deficient in many manufactures such as textiles, rubber, and electronics, and unequipped to fabricate their surpluses of metal ingots. The Ukraine lacks nonferrous metals, and Western Siberia is strong only in coal; the Transcaucasus is strong only in petroleum and manganese. The rest are characterized by modest to very low per capita mineral production. Electric power, a key to fabricating capacity, is exceptionally low in the Baltic, the North Caucasus, Turkestan, Eastern Siberia, and the Far East. Finally, limited acreage per person and serious deficiencies in food production characterize Northwest and North Russia, the Transcaucasus, Eastern Siberia, and the Far East. Central Asia, specializing perforce in cotton, must import food from Western Siberia.

Plans and Possibilities in Regional Development

In the fall of 1950 the Soviet government announced the beginning of a new series of developmental projects, to be completed in 1955–1957, though those outlined in the Fourth Five-Year Plan were still unfinished. These new projects may be divided into three groups: the Volga Basin–Don River program, the South Ukrainian plan, and the Turkmen Canal scheme. Important indications of future trends can be gained by analysis of the probable impacts of the new river-development programs. Successful completion would permit a relatively uniform level of economic activity in the entire area encompassed by the Volga Basin, the eastern Ukraine, the North Caucasus, and the Urals. The controlling force of mineral output and consumption on economic location and transportation therein would be reduced through the differentially great rise of water power.

For other areas of the Soviet Union, broad developmental plans are not currently in evidence. Nevertheless, the abundance of undeveloped human and agricultural resources in the west, of mineral resources in the east, points some possible courses.

As was mentioned earlier, the Volga-Don program was conceived before World War II. In its present version it has eliminated augmentation of the flow of the Volga by water diverted from the Northern Dvina basin and has added a canal eastward from the Volga to the Kamysh-Samar Lakes, and ultimately to the Ural River. The southernmost dam of the Volga system is now to be at Stalingrad, rather than at Kamyshin, somewhat farther north. Otherwise the basic program appears unchanged.

Four parts of the Volga plan have already been completed: the Ivan'kovo, Uglich, and Rybinsk (Shcherbakov) dams and the Moscow-Volga Canal. If all the planned dynamos have been installed, the station at Ivan'kovo Uglich, and Shcherbakov now have capacities of 30,000, 100,000, and 330,000 kilowatts respectively (Fig. 35). Two other dams, one at Chkalovsk, a little above Gor'kii, and the other at Molotov, were also started in 1933, to be completed in 1938–1939 with installed capacities of 400,000 and 500,000 kilowatts respectively; they have not yet been finished. All these dams, except the one at Molotov, are wide but low and raise the natural water level only 35 to 50 feet; the Molotov dam is to be considerably higher, with a head of 115 feet.

Lower on the Volga, two new dams are to be built at Kuibyshev and

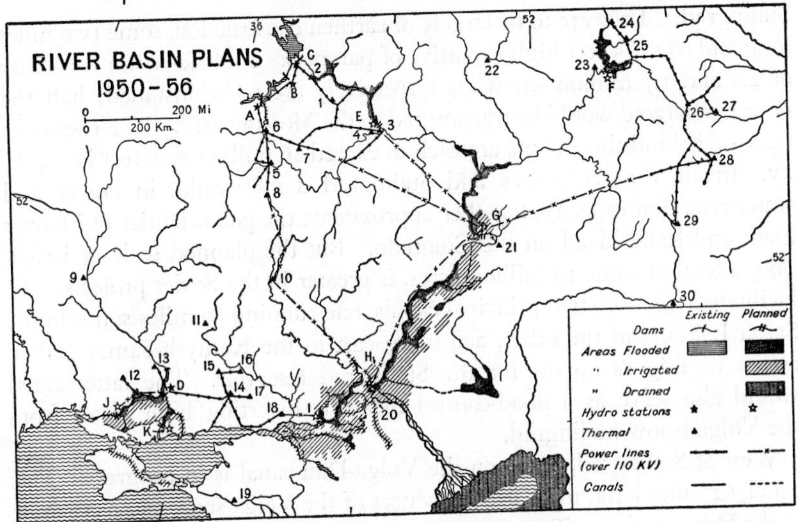

Figure 35

River basin plans of the Volga Basin, Ukraine, and Urals, showing major electric-power stations existing and planned. Numerals and letters refer to legend below. Sources: Bol'shoi Sovietskii Altas Mira, Vol. 1, 1937, Pl. 129–130; Proyekt Vtorogo Pyatiletnogo Plana Razvitiya Narodnogo Khozyaistva SSSR, 2 vols., State Planning Commission, Moscow, 1934; Narodno-Khozyaistvenniyi Plan na 1936 God, Vol. 2, State Planning Commission, Moscow, 1936.

DAMS AND HYDROELECTRIC STATIONS

Existing

A. Ivan'kovo
B. Uglich
C. Shcherbakov
D. Dnepr (Kichkas)

Planned

E. Gor'kii (Chkalovsk)
F. Molotov
G. Kuibyshev
H. Stalingrad

Planned (cont.)

I. Tsymlyanskaya
J. Kakhovka
K. Molochnaya

THERMOELECTRIC STATIONS
(Believed to exceed 50,000 kw. capacity)

1. Ivanovo
2. Yaroslavl
3. Gor'kii (Balakhna-Sormovo) *
4. Dzerzhinsk
5. Kashira
6. Moscow
7. Shatura
8. Stalinogorsk *
9. Kiev
10. Voronezh
11. Khar'kov (Chuguyev)
12. Krivoi Rog
13. Dneprodzerzhinsk
14. Zuyevka *
15. Kramatorsk
16. Lisichansk
17. Krasny Luch
18. Nesvetai-Shakhty
19. Krasnodar
20. Stalingrad
21. Kuibyshev
22. Kirov (Cheptsa)
23. Krasnokamsk
24. Berezniki
25. Gubakha
26. Sverdlovsk
27. Kamensk
28. Chelyabinsk
29. Magnitogorsk
30. Orsk

* Believed to exceed 250,000 Kw. capacity.

Stalingrad. They are to be largely of earthen construction, some two miles long and 66 to 85 feet high exclusive of parapets. Electric-power capacities of 2.0 and 1.7 million kilowatts respectively are to be installed; half the power generated would be transmitted to the Moscow grid. The reservoirs built up behind these dams are each to exceed 16 million acre-feet in capacity. In all, the Kuibyshev and Stalingrad dams would, in power and water-retention capacity, together approximate the potentialities of Hoover Dam and Lake Mead on the Colorado. But the planned scale of irrigation, a total of some 10 million acres, is greater in the Soviet projects. To facilitate irrigation, two principal canals, one running 60 miles south to the Sarpa Lakes, and the other, 200 miles east to the Kamysh-Samar Lakes, are to be dug as outlets for the Stalingrad reservoir. The latter canal would also serve as a flood-control measure, diverting high water from the Volga below Stalingrad.

West of Stalingrad, work on the Volga-Don canal is in progress. This canal, 62 miles long, must lift the waters of the Volga some 250 feet; those of the Don, 125 feet. To accomplish this, thirteen locks and a large pumping system will be needed. Below the canal, at Tsymlyanskaya, the Soviets have constructed a low but extremely long retaining structure consisting of a 500-yard-wide concrete dam and two earthen dikes totaling 13,000 yards in width. The structure will raise the water level of the Don about 85 feet and create a reservoir with a capacity of some 10 million acre-feet. The bulk of the pent-up water is to be diverted to irrigating 1,850,000 acres, largely south of the Don, by new canals aggregating 350 miles in length. Part of the flow is to be released at Tsymlyanskaya, operating turbines with an over-all capacity of 160,000 kilowatts, and maintaining a moderate stream flow on the Don to Rostov.

The South Ukrainian project continues the development of the Dnepr begun in the First Five-Year Plan. To the existing dam and electric-power station, now restored to a capacity of about 550,000 kilowatts, a second dam on the lower Dnepr at Kakhovka is to be added; installed power is to total 250,000 kilowatts. In addition to these principal structures, a diversional canal tapping the floodwaters of the Dnepr is to be dug from the old Dnepr reservoir southward to the Molochnaya River, where a new dam will permit the accumulation of five million acre-feet. The Molochnaya River reservoir will also be connected by canal with the Kakhovka system. In all, 3.7 million acres of land is to be irrigated as a result of this project.

The Turkmen canal scheme envisages the construction of a dam diverting much of the waters of the Amu Darya from the delta and the Aral Sea southwestward, by way of canals and old stream beds, to the Caspian. The main purposes of this project are alleged to be the irrigation of 3.2

million acres and the provision of an industrial water supply to Krasnovodsk and other mining centers.

The paucity of technical and economic data on the new construction plans makes an evaluation of them extremely hazardous. My impression is that, although these projects involve very large undertakings in moving earth and laying concrete, none of them are inherently impossible with present-day technology. However, the degree to which they appear to be serious plans rather than fanciful schemes varies greatly. Technically, the most dubious seem to be the Turkmen project, the Stalingrad–Kamysh-Samar Lakes canal, the Tsymlyanskaya dam, and the Volga-Moscow 400-kilovolt transmission lines. The Amu Darya is still a completely unregulated river, with enormous variations in discharge, carrying an extremely heavy load of silt. The effectiveness of a dam, built just above the delta on unconsolidated sedimentary rock, is thus highly doubtful. In addition, the complete absence of industrial facilities in, and even transportation to, this region would make necessary preliminary investment on a very large scale. As for the Stalingrad canal, not even the route has yet been determined. The Tsymlyanskaya dam, although technically not difficult to build, will face maintenance and seepage problems, since it is being constructed on deep, unconsolidated sands. Finally, the planned transmission line from Kuibyshev and Stalingrad to Moscow would strain Soviet technology to the utmost.

At the same time, it is essential to note that all these projects can be carried out in stages, and that alternative plans are fully possible for the later stages. In general, the first effects of dam construction will be to facilitate local water supplies and navigation; the power facilities can be built up gradually, since the small drop characterizing all the sites will need numerous small generators rather than a few giants. Furthermore, the power developed can be used locally, or transmitted for various distances. In the Volga project, as laid out in 1937, barely 20 per cent of the power from Kuibyshev was to be transmitted to Moscow; most of it was to be used locally for power-intensive industry and irrigation, and the bulk of the remainder was to be transmitted to Kazan', Gor'kii, and Ufa. The prewar variant of the lower Volga project anticipated using nearly all the power for nonferrous metals, fertilizer, synthetic rubber, and other plants to be located near the dam site. The enormous power and water requirements for the manufacture of fissionable or fusionable atomic raw materials are well known; thus it is conceivable that the Volga projects might eventually augment Soviet atomic potential rather than furnish power to Moscow.

If we exclude the Turkmen Canal project as unlikely of completion in the foreseeable future, the long-term effects of the present Soviet investment will probably be the following. The most important potential gain will be in elecrtic power—an increase of 25 to 30 per cent in output without corresponding demands on fuel production. The completion of power lines between the hydroelectric stations and the existing Moscow, Urals, and Ukrainian grids, creating a flexible and economical system, would magnify such a gain. Scarcely less important than power would be the abundant availability of industrial and urban water supplies in the Volga and South Ukrainian regions.

In transportation, both gains and losses may be foreseen. A 9- to 12-foot channel, from Tsymlyanskaya to Moscow and to Molotov in the Urals, would be of great advantage to the Soviet Union, particularly in the movement of coal from the Ukraine, petroleum from North Caucasus pipeline terminals, grain from the Volga, metals and lumber from the Urals, and manufactures from Central Russia. At the same time, it must be remembered that this waterway system would be closed by ice for four to five months a year; consequently, major investments in extra rail capacity or in warehousing facilities, for the winter months, would be indispensable in maximizing the usefulness of these channels. The loss of 15 to 20 per cent of the Volga River discharge because of water diversions and increased evaporation from reservoirs would accelerate the already rapid drying up of the Caspian Sea. The north shore would recede possibly 40 miles in a couple of decades; Kara Bogaz Gulf, already a separate lake, would disappear. Maintenance of transportation on the lower Volga and in the Caspian would be both difficult and costly. The effect on the important Caspian Sea fisheries would be disastrous. Much the same can be said for the prospects of the Don River below Tsymlyanskaya, faced by a loss of some 40 per cent of its present discharge.

The projects envisage irrigation of some 15.5 million acres of land. They do not emphasize, however, that almost a million acres of cultivated land has already been flooded in the creation of the Rybinsk reservoir, and that the new reservoirs on the Volga and the Don would ultimately flood an additional four million acres of developed agricultural land. Thus, even if all the planned acreage is irrigated, the net gain in cultivated land would total barely 3 per cent of the acreage sown in 1950; the net gain in agricultural production, not more than 6 or 7 per cent. Clearly, these plans, though important for limited regions of Russia, provide no long-range solution to the Soviet Union's pressing agricultural problems. The extraordinary difficulty and expense of irrigation in the Volga-Don region must be emphasized. Because the arable land is generally much higher than the rivers, the proposed irrigation of 10 million acres would require 3.5 billion kilowatt-hours of power annually for the pumping stations.

With regard to regional development, the possible effects of these projects would be to add a new major industrial region to the Soviet Union, the Volga; and to integrate the economic regions of Central Russia, the Ukraine, the Volga, the Urals, and, in part, the North Caucasus into an interdependent whole. The Volga region would have potentialities for developing both mineral-intensive and light industry. In the former group, the best possibilities seem to rest in nonferrous metallurgy, using imported ores; in chemistry, using the salt of Baskunchak and the sulphur and gypsum of the Kuibyshev area; and in ferrous metallurgy. Creation of the Tsymlyanskaya reservoir would make economical the conjunction of coal from the eastern wing of the Donets Basin and the hitherto unexploited iron ore from Khoper. In light industry, expanded food and cotton production would provide needed raw materials.

In contrast with these possible gains, the Volga project would, almost certainly, exercise seriously adverse effects on the Transcaucasus.

For long-term potentialities, the developmental challenges of still other regions in the Soviet Union must be considered briefly. Using mineral resources, potential agricultural output, water and timber, labor, transportation, and markets, it is possible to delineate a considerable number of areas favorable to industrialization (Fig. 34). They fall into two basic and several secondary groups. Of the basic groups, the vast area west of the line Leningrad-Moscow-Volga-Khar'kov-Kiev-Odessa is a zone of underdeveloped human and agricultural resources, inhabited by about 57 million persons, more than 80 per cent of whom are rural. It holds 48 towns with more than 50,000 dwellers, of which only three exceed 300,000. Only one center, L'vov, manufactures—so far as available data show—a gross product exceeding $100,000,000 annually, at United States 1937 prices. With this area, Riga, Minsk, Bryansk, Tula, and Voronezh appear especially promising for development of labor, transportation, and market hinterlands.

In the eastern areas mineral-producing potentialities seem to be the most significant base for industrialization. Furthermore, Stalinabad-Termez, Barnaul-Biyisk, Minusinsk, Bratsk, Irkutsk, and Sretensk have good to extraordinary hydroelectric-power resources. Only for the areas of Omsk and Barnaul-Biyisk are the food-producing possibilities excellent; for the other areas they appear to range from fair to modest. Transportation and markets constitute, in my opinion, the major advantages open to the two Far Eastern centers, Khabarovsk and Vladivostok-Voroshilov.

Elsewhere in the Soviet Union, Tbilisi in the Transcaucasus combines abundant labor and moderately large markets with strong mineral and hydroelectric-power potentials. The Arkhangel'sk-Molotovsk area is the natural focus of exports from North Russia. In addition, it appears less fantastic than Cherepovets, near Leningrad, for a combination of Vorkuta coal and Kola iron ore serving shipbuilding, wood manufactures, and fish canning. Its future rests on that of Soviet foreign trade.

To summarize, the Russians in their current plans are still pursuing a policy of differential economic development, strongly favoring the central regions (Central Russia, Ukraine, Volga, and Urals). Within this industrial heartland, hydroelectric power and water transportation would reduce the need for close conjunction between industry and mining. The decision to emphasize the central regions is clearly based on political and strategic considerations, rather than purely economic; for both the western regions of European Russia and Soviet Asia afford major opportunities for industrial growth.

Comparisons with the United States

The relative growth of the economy of the Soviet Union between 1926 and 1950 was roughly comparable to that of the American economy between 1899–1902 and 1947–1950. During these respective periods the urban population of both countries tripled, manufacturing output multiplied about sixfold, and sown acreage increased possibly a quarter. In the United States, however, the gross national material product almost tripled, whereas that of the Soviet Union somewhat more than doubled. American increases in total population were also greater, a doubling as opposed to a rise of less than 40 per cent. On the other hand, Soviet mining output multiplied 7.5 rather than 4.8 times; Soviet increases in the power used in manufacturing also seem to have been greater, though the evidence is obscure.

As has already been mentioned, the patterns of regional development in the two countries over the periods compared have been fairly similar. At the beginning of the twentieth century the dominance of the Middle Atlantic and East North Central regions over the American economy was about as firm as that of Central Russia and the Ukraine over the Soviet. The two American regions accounted for 41 per cent of the total population, and for 65 per cent of the country's mineral output exclusive of gold, 53 per cent of the power in manufacturing, 55 per cent of the light-industry output, and 64 per cent of the urban population. Only in sown acreage, 27 per cent of the national total, were they exceeded by another region, the West North Central. The position of New England, with only some 8 per cent of the country's population and negligible mineral and soil resources, but with 17 per cent of the manufacturing power, 21 per cent of the light industry, and 12 per cent of the urban population, rather resembled that of Northwest Russia. Of the other American regions, the Mountain States were large producers of nonferrous metals and yielded 12 per cent of all mineral output. Otherwise, these and the Pacific Coast States were still a raw frontier with less than 5 per cent each of the national total for all economic factors. The East South Central and West South Central States were but little more developed.

Today the Middle Atlantic and East North Central regions, though diminished in importance, are still primary in many respects. They hold 40 per cent of the country's total population, 52 per cent of its urban population, 48 per cent of its light industry; they produce 48 per cent of the individual income, 44 per cent of the electric power. Their significance in mining and in agriculture has dropped most sharply, to only 30 and 21 per cent respectively.

The most general economic shift has been toward the West South Central, Mountain, and Pacific Coast States. Together, they now account for half the national mineral output, as opposed to a sixth at the turn of the century. Although their share of the national population has grown from 14 per cent to almost 23 per cent, their growth in other respects has been even more rapid: from 15 to 26 per cent in agriculture, from 9 to 22.5 per cent in power, from 7 to 15 per cent in light industry, and from 6.6 to 21 per cent in urban population. Today they produce 21.7 per cent of the country's individual income and 16 per cent of the rail traffic (the latter low figure reflects the relative significance of pipelines and power grids in these regions).

The development of the South Atlantic and East South Central States has been much more uneven. They have actually lost ground in their shares of the country's total population and sown acreage. Most important has been their rise in light industry—from 10 to 19 per cent of the national total. Rises in mineral output, power, and urban population have also been appreciable, averaging 4 per cent of the national aggregates. The large proportion of rail transport, 24 per cent relative to other economic measures, indicates a weak development of pipelines and electrical grids.

The West North Central area has remained extraordinarily specialized in agriculture, with 37 per cent of the country's cultivated acreage. It has remained insignificant in mining, and of slight importance in power and light industry. Its share of the national population has decreased, from 13 per cent to 9 per cent; in urban population it accounts for 7 per cent, as compared with 8 per cent at the turn of the century. Agricultural specialization has been accompanied by low economic vitality.

Finally, New England has remained a negligible mineral and agricultural producer. But it no longer retains a special advantage in urbanization, power, or income, which are closely proportionate to its share of the nation's population, 7 per cent. Its share of output in light industry has fallen from 21 per cent to only 11 per cent.

These shifts indicate an extensive economic decentralization and equalization in the United States. It is noteworthy that every economic region has achieved significant development in two factors or more; for example, the Mountain States in mining and in agriculture. In that respect, progress in this country has been more rapid than in the Soviet Union, in which North Russia, Eastern Siberia, and the Far East are still untamed frontiers. Evidently, free flow of capital and labor has been more effective in achieving regional economic diversification and self-sufficiency than has rigidly centralized, planned investment. The differences in per capita development between the most and the least productive regions have diminished, except for sown acreage, in both countries. However, although these differences were more extreme in the United States in 1900–1902 than in the Soviet Union in 1926, they are less extreme today. This is demonstrable for urbanization and light industry, highly probable for power, rail traffic, and individual income. In both the United States and the Soviet Union, mineral output and electric power have shifted more readily than total population and cultivated land. On the other hand, the mobility of urban concentrations has been greater in this country than in Russia, a phenomenon probably attributable to Soviet attempts to minimize housing and transportation investments. Finally, general economic development appears, in both countries, to have been accelerated or severely inhibited by the presence or absence, respectively, of large-scale mining development.

APPENDIX

Careers in Geography

GEOGRAPHY IS a relatively recent, but presently well-entrenched, college and university subject. The role of geography in the undergraduate curriculum is one of the following: an elective in a liberal arts program, fulfilling a laboratory-science or a social-science requirement, depending on the type of course and the institution, a requirement for majors in elementary or secondary education; a requirement for business administration majors; and a major subject. Unfortunately, geography is taught in too few high schools, and students with only an elementary school background are not prepared for it as a college subject and often do not realize what the discipline encompasses. United States educational practices in this regard are quite contrary to those of Europe where geography is a required principal subject through the secondary school level.

Very few students enter introductory geography courses with the purpose of majoring in the subject. The editors of this book, however, feel that students should be made aware of opportunities for geographically trained people. During World War II great attention was directed to the value of information furnished and methods employed by professional geographers. This interest has continued in the postwar period and, as a result, the field will continue to expand.

Geographically trained people find employment in government service, in teaching at the elementary, secondary, and college levels, in regional and city planning, and in research of various kinds in business and industry. The total number of trained geographers is limited, but is increasing. Many positions utilize geographic knowledge and method but do not carry the title "geographer." Thus many businessmen, especially those dealing with foreign products or markets or with diverse areas within the United States, can benefit by educations that include considerable geography.

The subject also aids greatly in understanding and interpreting current world affairs, whether of an economic, political, or cultural nature.

Teaching is a major outlet for geography majors and minors. Some college courses in geography are absolutely essential for the prospective elementary school teacher. For teaching at the secondary level, geography is often one of several subjects in which a teacher must obtain specialized training. Teaching opportunities at the college level increased tremendously after World War I, and were again intensified during and after World War II. Graduate training with a Masters degree, and preferably a Ph.D. degree, in geography is necessary to obtain a university position. Advanced training and degrees are often desirable or mandatory for other positions for which geographers qualify.

Most colleges and universities in the United States now offer general geography courses and many offer specialized training. Often the undergraduate work lays a foundation for the advanced academic preparation necessary to qualify as a professional geographer. The following readings describe the nature of the work and the training necessary in two of the major career outlets: government service and planning.

A. Opportunities for Geographers in Government Service *

Government service now engages something like 500 geographers and is exceeded only by the long established field of teaching as an employment area. It employs roughly one-fourth of those with professional training in geography. Positions with the Federal Government strongly predominate, but some individuals have important work with international agencies or with state or local governmental units. Some are in the foreign service, some in domestic or field service. A considerable number travel occasionally or frequently, on official business; others live abroad for extended periods. But a large majority work and live in or near Washington, D.C. Hence, by and large, serious consideration of a government

* John K. Rose, "Opportunities for Geographers in Government Service," *The Professional Geographer,* Vol. VI, May 1954, pp. 1–6.

The author (1905) has been Geographer for the Legislative Reference Service, United States Library of Congress since 1946. Before that, he taught geography at various universities, was principal analyst and acting chief, Resources Development Section, Office of Economic Warfare (1942–43), and was head economist and chief, Resources Division, Foreign Economic Administration (1943–45). He is a contributor to several books and periodicals. His interests include statistical geography, climatology, and world resources.

career in geography means, in perhaps nine cases out of ten, weighing and balancing the advantages and disadvantages of working for the Federal Government in Washington, D.C.

The Nature of Geographic Work for the Federal Government

What can a geographer expect to do in Washington? To scientists, the geographer among them, few things are more important than the nature of the work they can anticipate doing if they prepare for and take employment. If a geographer turns to the well established teaching field, he knows rather well the metes and bounds of what he can anticipate and what will be expected of him. Not so in Government work, at least not yet. A first approximation to an answer to the above question involves a look at present employment of geographers in Government. As a guide to the future we can do no better at present than to report some things about geographers now employed. A recent survey for this report indicates that fully 200 are employed by the Department of Defense, most but not all in the Washington area as civilians, a rather small fraction in uniform at domestic bases or overseas. Other Departments and the miscellaneous Independent Offices of the Executive Branch as well as the Legislative Branch employ approximately another two hundred. Relatively large users, employing more than a score each, are the Department of State, the Department of the Interior and the Department of Commerce. Of the rather large number of geographers in the Washington area who did not designate their official connections it is estimated that roughly one hundred are not primarily students, teachers or businessmen, but are employed by the Government, thus bringing the total to approximately 500.

However, a bare statement as to which Departments are employing geographers in considerable numbers falls far short of describing the nature of geographic work in Washington. Unfortunately, there is not much that can be said about some of it. A reasonable estimate is that something like three-fourths of the total are employed primarily in map-making or map information work. It is this sector which appears to have increased sharply since the early post-World War II period, at which time it was estimated that about half of the 200 geographers remaining in Washington were primarily map people. This includes not only those actually making maps, the cartographic work and the editing, etc., but also the map librarians and geographers doing map information or map intelligence work.

Fortunately for those who may be considering a career in geography in Washington, considerably more can be said about some of the geographic employment in Washington, particularly that which we give the broad label of "research."

The Department of Agriculture has long offered opportunities for substantial geographic work and has employed a modest number of geographers, some at high levels, but mostly as dispersed individuals. Numbers have remained relatively constant in recent years. The Soil Survey and the Land Economics portion of the Agricultural Research Administration, the Soil Conservation Service, and the Foreign Agricultural Service have been the usual places of utilization, though some other sectors as, for example, the Forest Service and Crop Insurance, would seem attractive to geographers.

In the Department of Commerce, geographers are employed and geographic work done particularly in the Bureau of the Census and the Area Development Division, but also in the Office of International Trade and the Coast and Geodetic Survey. There are, however, few or none employed in some other sectors of the Department where one might reasonably expect to find them represented as, for example in the Weather Bureau, the Maritime Administration, the Bureau of Public Roads and, perhaps, the Civil Aeronautics Administration.

In the Department of Defense, in addition to those geographers employed primarily for intelligence collection and evaluation in the operating Departments—Army, Navy, and Air Forces—a considerable number of geographers have found employment in recent years in research for development requirements. Among these are the Environmental Protection Branch of the Office of the Quartermaster General, the Corps of Engineers and Ordnance Departments, the Geography Branch of the Earth Sciences Division of the Office of Naval Research, the Air Weather Service and the Research and Development Board. In the Army Map Service alone there are several hundred geographers employed. Most of these are engaged in various phases of the mapping program, and a smaller number in research and analysis for intelligence.

The Division of Geography in the Office of the Secretary of the Department of the Interior, and the Geological Survey, as might be expected, employ most but not all of the geographers in that Department. The Bureau of Reclamation, the Bureau of Land Management, the Bureau of Mines, Trust Territories and the Indian Service apparently offer opportunities.

Geographic work and geographers are now considerably dispersed in the Department of State, including, among others, the Special Advisor on Geography, the Special Assistant for Maps, the Director of South American Affairs and several attaches.

The Library of Congress, in the Legislative Branch, employs some fifteen professional geographers in various capacities.

In much of the rest of Washington, dispersion appears to be the rule, one or two here and there. Archives, Bureau of the Budget, Civil Defense Administration, Foreign Operations Administration, Public Health, even the Department of Justice, among others, employ modest numbers of geographers in Washington.

Qualifying for Government Positions in Geography

How does one qualify for a geography position with the Federal Government? The bare but largely uninstructive answer is, "by training and experience." But *what* training and *what* experience? Actually, the training, at least to date, differs little if any from that of geographers who plan to teach, particularly in colleges or universities, or more rarely, to go into the business world. They are broadly trained in some combination of systematic and regional geography, with varying amounts of training in related fields. That is not to say that there is standardization: The particular combination that any individual may offer will, of course, vary with the interests of the individual, with the requirements of a particular department, and with the professors available during the period when the student was in residence.

Though standards for admission into the profession are far from being as rigid as in law, medicine, and several other fields, the would-be Government geographer should be aware that there are standards of a sort—some written, some unwritten—that there are minimum entrance requirements, and that the minimum requirements are hardly every adequate for major advancement. Even so, there appears to be less emphasis on the Ph.D. degree in setting up a Government job or in later advancement than is the case in university teaching.

The undergraduate degree with a geography major now serves as the minimum basic requirement. At that stage of training it has been possible in some years to take an examination from which the Civil Service register of junior professionals is drawn. Normally, the examination has been given in the spring, with college seniors eligible to take the examination and qualify on later certification of graduation. Purposely it has been timed to attract at least part of the emerging senior class. Actually, the senior with his nearly completed degree has found himself in competition with those who have more training, who hold an M.A. or who are at an even more advanced stage. However, those with graduate degrees are eligible for the higher level unassembled examinations when those are offered; hence, these persons have constituted less actual competition for the junior jobs than would have appeared initially to be the case. Nevertheless, for the intermediate and higher positions in Government service, specialized training, at least equivalent to the M.A. degree, is almost a basic requirement. For most better positions, the Ph.D. degree, although not set as a formal requirement, is nevertheless very likely to be a practical one, since initial and later competition will be largely with those who have such training.

Some come to Washington with the residence work for the Ph.D. degree completed and find it possible in their first few years to complete a thesis while employed. Yet, this is hardly to be recommended save for exceptional cases or because of necessity. If the thesis topic does not tie into Government problems particularly, or if Washington does not offer exceptional facilities for the study of that particular problem, it might be better to come to Washington without a thesis topic definitely selected. The person can work for a year or so, meanwhile exploring vigorously for a really meaningful thesis topic acceptable to the Department, then take leave from the Government job to finish the degree.

It does not appear either desirable or necessary that there should be a major variance in training between those students who anticipate doing geographic work for the Government and those who look forward to the fields of teaching or business. Nor does it appear that training to qualify women differs significantly from that needed by men. What does appear to be desirable in both cases is an early decision by the student as to the kind of geographer he is going to be and what specialization as to area or systematic field is preferred. Then he should pursue that specialization as vigorously as possible during the training period, not only as to its core but as to needed tools and inter-disciplinary fields.

How Do You Get a Job?

It is one thing to be qualified, even admirably qualified, to do geographic work for the Government, and quite another matter to find a job, particularly the right job. Intent and desire on the part of the candidate are important, but are not controlling unless circumstances are otherwise favorable. Suggestions incorporated below may not be applicable to specific individuals, but are the result of general observation in Washington over a period of years.

It is particularly important that the candidate make up his mind what kind of geographic work he wishes to do—even geographic work is becoming more specialized. If the decision is made while completing the undergraduate major or in the early stages of graduate work, so much the better. Having made that decision, and granting that it is in line with one's training, abilities, and ambitions, the next step is to find out as much as possible about those parts of the government where such work is done and the people who do it. In part this can be done by selective survey of publications, in part by discussion with teachers and fellow students. It may be helpful to attend meetings of the Association, and even to make an exploratory trip to Washington during vacation, possibly for thesis material but also to get acquainted with some of those who are actively working on geographic problems of special interest to the future job hunter. Of possible interest during such exploratory periods are the summer projects of the Map Division of the Library of Congress which have employed six to ten graduate students of geography each summer for the past three years.

It is probably wise to take any Civil Service examinations that are offered for which the geographer in training is qualified, either in the major field or in one or more minor fields. Except during unusual times there are not enough calls on the geographer register at the Civil Service Commission for the examination (unassembled) to be offered very frequently. The assembled junior assistant examinations are more likely to be offered frequently. Examinations are open occasionally for economists, economic analysts, social science analysts, climatologists, cartographers and librarians, in one or more of which fields the individual geographer may be adequately qualified to participate, perhaps at a favorable level.

When an examination is taken and a report is received of favorable rating and of placement on a register of eligibility, immediate or even near future appointment should not be expected. Rather, it should be planned to continue graduate work or teaching, or perhaps to take whatever job may be available until the professional position is open and offered. All of this is likely to take more time than is at first anticipated. This is particularly true of positions in which security clearance is required—sometimes a matter of many months. And impatient inquiries are not likely to help. Even the fact that the fiscal year begins on July 1 may play a part in the decision as to when to fill a job.

What next? Primarily it is a matter of finding out, if possible, where the desired jobs are, or are to be, then filing such necessary forms and information as are required by the particular agency. Fully as important is the matter of getting acquainted on a professional basis with those who are in charge of the work and who are likely to make decisions regarding new personnel. They may or may not be geographers; if they are, the annual convention of the Association may afford such an opportunity. Congressional interest or inquiry may be useful in some instances, but should be used sparingly and with the utmost of discrimination. Copies of theses or other publications, and letters from the candidates' major professors should, of course, be available for examination by those who will make the selection. The standard form 57, available from the Civil Service Commission and most government agencies, should be carefully filled out and provided to interested individuals as well as filed with the personnel officer of prospective employing agencies. As with most jobs, personality, adaptability, energy, and luck will be significant factors in the selection.

Satisfactions and Opportunities in Geographic Work for the Government

It may be safely assumed that many, perhaps most, of the geographers now engaged in Government work find such work satisfactory. That it is a challenge to their abilities, a satisfaction to their creative desires, and provides compensation and working conditions at least on a par with opportunities elsewhere, appears to be evidenced by the fact that so many have continued with the Government. It is not so much, perhaps, a survival of the fittest as of the better satisfied. Many Government geographers have had favorable opportunities to return to, or to go into, teaching posts. Such opportunities were most frequent in the early postwar years of booming college and university enrollments expanded by returning veterans. Departments were being established, reorganized, or expanded during that period, and a substantial number of those who had assisted the Government during World War II were happy to return to their former campus posts or to obtain new and better academic positions.

And what are the drawing and holding powers of Government employment?

(a) The rate of pay may well be the most important, in spite of the fact that Government employees have not fared particularly well during this period of inflation. Oddly enough, the pay scale is probably more favorable for younger than older geographers. That is, the recent graduate, or, more particularly, the person with the Ph.D. degree, probably enjoys a wider advantage in government when his salary is compared with university salaries for those of the same age and training. If one has reached the full professorship level, the comparison may be decidedly less of an incentive to Government employment.

The fact that very few geographers are appointed at any level below GS-5, the base pay of which is $3,410, means a favorable starting salary. Contrawise, very few geographers in the Federal service have attained the so-called supergrades, which begin at $12,000 per year. However, fully one-fifth of those employed by the Federal Government are estimated to be in grades GS-12 or above, hence with a base salary of $7,040 or upwards. Women with considerable training appear to break into these levels somewhat more easily than they would attain full professorships on university or college faculties.

(b) Promotion policies also on the whole appear to be more liberal in Government—that is, the beginner can climb more rapidly during the first few years in Government than he could reasonably expect to do on the campus. Even within the same grade, increases are provided periodically for those serving satisfactorily. Of course, opportunities for promotion are more abundant in periods of war and Government expansion. The past two decades, with war and organization of action agencies, may very well prove untypical of promotion rates in Government over a longer period in the future.

(c) For those who have reached the plateau in Government, a level which compares favorably with the full professorship in the university, additional satisfactions are to be found in the nature of the work itself and in travel which may be involved in the work The satisfactions of administering or being a part of some of the vital research or action programs of our period are not insignificant, and opportunities to serve on interesting committees, to attend international conferences, to pursue research in special fields, domestically or in foreign areas, are available to most Government geographers who have reached the GS-12 level or above, as well as to some who are more junior.

On the other hand, it must be admitted that the annual leave is in no wise equivalent to the summer "vacation" of the academic world, and limits on leave accumulation make it particularly difficult to do extended private research in the field.

(d) So, too, some Government geographers have been or have at times felt themselves to be restricted, if not more seriously inhibited, in regard to publication of research. This, of course, is a major restriction during wartime or in "sensitive" positions, but even during more normal times in most positions there is no such incentive nor, in many cases, such freedom to publish, nor, indeed, the institutional urge to do so that is the gadfly pushing at least part of those in universities. Moreover, much of the work published by Government geographers, if not actually anonymous, is likely to be a cooperative study with credit given to two or more persons. Emphasis is on team approach to problems, and credit to the team —hence the earlier mentioned desirability of both specialization and interdisciplinary training.

B. Geographers in City and Regional Planning *

City and regional planning has, in recent years, presented geographers with an increasingly important outlet for the employment of their discipline and approach. The relationships between the geographer and the planner have become very close, and a significant number of persons trained and experienced in both regional and systematic branches of geography have found, and are finding, satisfactory and stimulating employment with official agencies concerned with city and regional planning.

Planning is now recognized as a specialized field, the scope of which has been defined by the American Institute of Planners as "unified development of urban communities and their environs and of states, regions, and the nation, as expressed through determination of the comprehensive arrangement of land uses and occupancy and the regulation thereof."

Since geography is also primarily concerned with regions, with land uses and their inter-relationships, and with the similarities and differences in man's occupance and use of areas, it, too, is a field which synthesizes. Indeed, one prominent planner has termed planning "the geography of the future." Geographers are increasingly concerned with the dynamics of occupance and land use, and the remedial actions which become reflected in public policy with relation to the development and redevelopment of areas.

Within the past two decades, there has been a marked increase in the number of geographers holding responsible positions with city and regional planning agencies as well as with Federal agencies concerned with urban and regional problems. The Chicago Plan Commission has had at least two geographers on its staff at all times since that Commission was reorganized as an official agency in 1939, and over the years at least a score of geographers have served that organization. Geographers have headed research divisions of planning agencies in Philadelphia and in Cincinnati. Others have been, and are, directors or members of city planning staffs, or with similar official organizations such as housing and redevelopment authorities, from Boston to San Diego. Geographers now

* Harold M. Mayer, "Geographers in City and Regional Planning," *The Professional Geographer,* Vol. VI, May 1954, pp. 7–12.

The author (1916) is Assistant Professor of Geography, University of Chicago. He served previously with the Chicago Planning Commission and was Director of Research there from 1948–51. His primary interests include geographic and economic problems relating to city planning and transportation.

head planning agencies in Tennessee and in Puerto Rico, both of which are concerned with urban problems. Among Federal agencies that have used geographers on their planning staffs are the Housing and Home Finance Agency, Department of State, Bureau of the Census, Bureau of the Budget, Tennessee Valley Authority, Bureau of Reclamation, President's Water Resources Commission, and many others.

Geographers, too, have had frequent opportunities to serve on planning boards and commissions directing planning policy while their own full-time professional activities have been outside of, or only partly within, the field of planning. Among communities that have had geographers on their planning commissions are Valparaiso, Indiana; Wellesley, Massachusetts; and University City, Missouri. Geographers also are called upon frequently as consultants both for official and unofficial planning agencies.

There are no cut-and-dried avenues to successful careers for geographers in planning. One of the most challenging facts is that the way is wide open for new ideas and new methods. Here is a real opportunity, but at the same time there are serious obstacles to be encountered at the outset. One stumbling block is tradition. Many employers are unaware of the contributions geography can make and continue to employ many persons trained in engineering and architecture, fields that have furnished the majority of planning personnel in the past. Furthermore, an increasing proportion of planners hold degrees from university departments or schools having definite planning curricula.

In one sense, there is no such person as a professional planner. By its very nature, planning embraces a variety of skills and talents, only a few of which can fall within the competence of any one individual. There is need for the geographer as well as the engineer and the architect, although the geographer may devote a considerable portion of his attention to matters beyond the field of geography and outside the scope of his academic training. He will acquire much needed knowledge and skill on the job, and should be alert to learn from his office colleagues, most of whose training and experience will be very different from his own. Broad training, including other fields as well as geography, will be helpful in all stages of his planning career.

Openings for the Geographer-Planner

There are several organizational frameworks within which the geographer can contribute to planning and within which he can carry on his professional career. First, and probably the most common, is the official planning agency.

Official Planning Agencies

Many cities, some counties, most states, and a few other political entities have more-or-less active planning agencies, some of which employ professional staffs. The largest cities, such as New York, Chicago, Philadelphia, Detroit, and Los Angeles, employ twenty to fifty, or even more, persons on such staffs. Several large metropolitan areas have unofficial or quasi-official agencies with staffs of comparable size. These staffs consist of specialists trained in a number of disciplines, from engineering and architecture on the one hand to economics, sociology, political science, and geography on the other. The Executive Director or Planning Director of such a staff is responsible to a board or commission which in turn reports to the executive, or less commonly to the legislative, branch of the governing body. The director is primarily a coordinator, who, in addition to his usual executive functions, has considerable responsibility for educating the planning commission in ideas and concepts developed by the staff. He may also direct the staff's research studies.

A large planning agency is usually organized into several divisions. Typical subdivisions are long-range comprehensive planning, routine administrative functions such as passing upon zoning changes and approving subdivision plats, and, where the commission is charged with such responsibilities, the preparation of an advisory capital improvements program, which may cover up to six years in advance but is revised annually. One of the great difficulties faced by planning executives is the need to free a portion of the staff from routine recurrent activities in order to carry on the basic task of long-range, comprehensive city planning. Commonly this is assigned to a portion of the staff, which may even then be subject to frequent interruptions and pressures to participate in the more routine day-to-day work.

Preparation and continuous revision of comprehensive plans calls for a wide variety of talents, from basic research in the social sciences to architectural rendering. Commonly the research function is carried on by a subdivision of the planning staff, varying from one to a dozen or more persons, with complementary backgrounds of training and experience. Most geographers in planning have begun as members of such research staffs. Some have advanced to positions as directors of research or analysis branches of the staff, and a few to positions as executive directors. The larger the staff, the more specialized are the problems with which a geographer deals. On the other hand, a member of a small staff is called upon to exercise his competence in a wider variety of disciplines; commonly a geographer is the sole researcher. In such instances, in addition to basic geographic competence, knowledge and skill in statistical and cartographic techniques, in demography, social organization, economics, and other fields may be demanded. Effectiveness in written, verbal, and graphic presentation of his findings to the staff, the commission, and the general public is essential if the young planner-geographer is to advance professionally.

Even the best academic training in geography is not adequate preparation for a career in planning. Additional skills are indispensable. Among the qualities which the geographer-planner will find essential are a broad understanding of governmental processes and the political system, a knowledge of public finance, skill in graphic design, a background in the social sciences and in research techniques including statistics, some knowledge of architectural and engineering principles, a sympathetic tolerance for differing points of view, an even temper, and a high degree of immunity from frustration. Of course, no one person embodies all these skills and qualities; but the effective pursuit of a planning career will be easier for one who has many of them. Furthermore, a knowledge of the outstanding trends and accomplishments of past and contemporary periods in city and regional planning is essential. Thus, a broad general education, specialized geographic training, and some knowledge of the other fields contributing to planning are important educational goals. The degrees awaited are not of special significance in themselves, although an increasing number of persons with Master's degrees in the social sciences, as well as a few with Ph.Ds, are entering the planning profession.

More and more positions with official planning agencies are under local or state civil service regulations and are filled competitively. Often eligibility for the lower positions is confined to local residents, but most technical positions, even in the largest cities, are open to non-residents. Sometimes this has come about only after considerable time and effort on the part of the planning administrator who had to convince the local Civil Service Commission that the positions could not be filled by the same persons as those who staff routine municipal departments. Not uncommonly, top staff positions are filled after nation-wide examinations.

Mobility is an indispensable characteristic of the successful geographer-planner. Because the demand for such persons normally exceeds the supply, advancement in rank, income, and job satisfaction is most rapid as the result of relatively frequent moves from city to city. Furthermore, changing local political situations and varying degrees of support given to city planning programs often dictate frequent changes of locale for the individual practitioner. The average tenure in a planning post is very short—not over two or three years.

The cross-fertilization of planning ideas from city to city, resulting from the migration of planners, gives vitality to the profession. On the other hand, this migratory characteristic of planners has forced them in many instances to make recommendations based upon inadequate first-hand knowledge of the less tangible qualities of the local situation, such as the tempo of the city, its prejudices, its internal balance of political and economic power and its general human climate. The geographer in such a situation must have the ability to inspire confidence on the part of established civic leaders, and as a prerequisite, he must be able to determine who are the actual, as distinguished from the nominal or official, leaders.

Although a number of geographers have had, and are having, successful careers in the larger city and regional planning agencies, few geographers have entered the smaller agencies. In many cities, counties, and regions, the planning agencies are at best able to support a staff of only one or two professional persons. In such a situation, geographers and other social scientists often have had to give way to engineers, architects, and especially to persons trained in the planning curricula of universities. The geographer's typical deficiency in design ability is here a considerable handicap. The larger and more specialized the planning staff, the wider the opportunities for the geographer, providing he is alert to the chances of broadening his knowledge, his skills and understanding, and his circle of intimate professional colleagues.

The opening wedge by which a young geographer can join a planning staff varies from time to time and place to place. Most begin as the result of personal contacts between planners and individual faculty members of universities. It is suggested that geography departments make concerted efforts to establish and maintain such contacts, not only for mutual interchange of ideas and knowledge, but also as an avenue for professional employment of students and alumni.

The geographer who is interested in a possible career in planning must realize at the outset that there is no standard method by which he can enter the field. Typically, his first professional position will involve work within the field of geography only a part of his working time and, as he advances toward administrative positions, even less of his work will be essentially geographic. There is at the present time no official planning position with the words "geographer" or "geographic" in the title. More commonly, the technical posts which might be filled by geographers are entitled Planning Analyst, Research Planner, or Planning Technician. Few planning administrators, and even fewer local civil service examiners, recognize geography as a basic discipline contributing to planning. Even in obtaining his first position, the geographer competes with men trained in a variety of other fields, and such competition will continue throughout his professional career. The advantages of the geographic approach, however, will aid the geographer-planner in successfully meeting the competition.

Consulting Opportunities

A second outlet for the services of the geographer in planning is as a consultant, or as a staff member of a consulting agency. Many communities are too small to maintain permanent planning staffs but wish to avail themselves of the services of professional planners. Other communities, including the largest ones, often wish to supplement the work of their regular agencies and staffs, or to secure independent outside opinions relative to specialized problems. A number of individuals and organizations have built up excellent reputations as either general or specialized planning consultants. Studies of the economic base of cities, transit requirements, housing demand, and the like are frequently made by consultants. Market and site studies for the location of new shopping centers, not only for public agencies but also for merchandising and real estate firms, usually have been made by consultants. Potentially, the geographer can contribute greatly in such specialized studies, either as an individual consultant or as a member of a larger organization engaged in that form of professional activity.

Remuneration

Remuneration for the professional planner is comparable to that in other professions, and is considerably higher than that for academic positions involving a similar level of professional competence. Initial positions at junior staff levels in planning agencies now average about $4000 per year, varying somewhat with city size and section of the country. Advancement is commonly facilitated by moving from city to city. With a Master's degree in geography following adequate academic training in related social sciences, and with two or three years of experience in a planning agency, the young geographer-planner should be earning a salary of $5000 to $6000 a year. With five or more years of experience accompanied by broadening of knowledge and professional contacts, opportunities for positions as executive director or planning director of an agency may arise. Such positions typically involve salaries from about $5000 in the smaller cities to $12,000 to $15,000 in the large metropolitan centers. The latter, however, generally require a minimum experience of ten years.

Even top executive positions in the planning agencies of such large cities as Philadelphia, Detroit, and Los Angeles are filled by nationwide competitive civil service examinations. The position of director involves executive and administrative ability rather than technical skills, and it is clear that the academic training of the geographer-planner is much less important in qualifying him for such a position than his subsequent professional experience and especially his ability to get along with people. Upon being offered such a position, one must consider very carefully whether he wishes to change his emphasis from a professional career to an administrative one. Many persons, at that point, have chosen the former, and have thereafter either stagnated at the top technical staff post, have left the official agencies in favor of practice as a consultant, or have chosen to transfer their activities to universities, putting their years of planning experience to use in research or teaching, sometimes with considerable sacrifice of income.

The remuneration of specialized planning consultants is limited only by their imagination and initiative. Typical fees paid by public agencies are $100 a day or more, plus travel expenses. Geographers making location and other studies for industries, or testifying in court procedures as expert witnesses, may be paid considerably greater fees, out of which overhead and expenses must be met. With the recent curtailment of Federal planning activities and the increasing number of planners entering the field of private consulting, the business is becoming increasingly competitive. The fact that few, if any, geographers are full-time planning consultants offers a unique potential opportunity for the practical application of geographic concepts and techniques.

Conclusion

In summary, the advantages of a planning career include the opportunity to apply geographic concepts in an important and stimulating public service, reasonably satisfactory remuneration, and contacts with people who have a wide variety of interests. In spite of the disadvantages of relatively insecure tenure and frequent involvement in politics, most geographers who are engaged in city and regional planning have very satisfying careers. The field is wide open, and its opportunities offer a challenge to the geographer.

INDEX

Index